EX LIBRIS

McGraw Hill NAME

MATRIX THEORY WITH APPLICATIONS

International Series in Pure and Applied Mathematics

Ahlfors: *Complex analysis*
Bender and Orszag: *Advanced Mathematical Methods for Scientists and Engineers*
Boas: *Invitation to Complex Analysis*
Buck: *Advanced Calculus*
Colton: *Partial Differential Equations*
Conte and deBoor: *Elementary Numerical Analysis: An Algorithmic Approach*
Edelstein-Keshet: *Mathematical Models in Biology*
Goldberg: *Matrix Theory with Applications*
Hill: *Experiments in Computational Matrix Algebra*
Lewin and Lewin: *An Introduction to Mathematical Analysis*
Morash: *Bridge to Abstract Mathematics: Mathematical Proof and Structures*
Parzynski and Zipse: *Introduction to Mathematical Analysis*
Pinter: *A Book of Abstract Algebra*
Ralston and Rabinowitz: *A First Course in Numerical Analysis*
Ritger and Rose: *Differential Equations with Applications*
Rudin: *Functional Analysis*
Rudin: *Principles of Mathematical Analysis*
Rudin: *Real and Complex Analysis*
Simmons: *Differential Equations with Applications and Historical Notes*
Small and Hosack: *Calculus: An Integrated Approach*
Small and Hosack: *Explorations in Calculus with a Computer Algebra System*
Vanden Eynden: *Elementary Number Theory*
Walker: *Introduction to Abstract Algebra*

Churchhill / Brown Series

Complex Variables and Applications
Fourier Series and Boundary Value Problems
Operational Mathematics

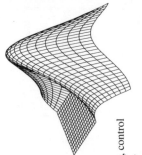

Also Available from McGraw-Hill

Schaum's Outline Series in Mathematics & Statistics

Most outlines include basic theory, definitions, and hundreds of solved problems and supplementary problems with answers.

Titles on the Current List Include:

Advanced Calculus
Advanced Mathematics
Boolean Algebra
Calculus of Finite Differences & Difference Equations
Complex Variables
Differential Equations
Differential Geometry
Discrete Math
Fourier Analysis
General Topology
Group Theory
Laplace Transforms
Linear Algebra, 2d edition
Mathematical Handbook of Formulas & Tables
Matrices
Matrix Operations
Modern Algebra
Modern Introductory Differential Equations
Numerical Analysis, 2d edition
Partial Differential Equations
Probability
Probability & Statistics
Projective Geometry
Real Variables
Set Theory & Related Topics
Statistics, 2d edition
Tensor Calculus
Vector Analysis

Schaum's Solved Problems Books

Each title in this series is a complete and expert source of solved problems containing thousands of problems with worked out solutions.

Titles on the Current List Include:

3000 Solved Problems in Calculus
2500 Solved Problems in College Algebra and Trigonometry
2500 Solved Problems in Differential Equations
3000 Solved Problems in Linear Algebra
2000 Solved Problems in Numerical Analysis
3000 Solved Problems in Precalculus
2000 Solved Problems in Statistics

Available at your College Bookstore. A complete list of Schaum titles may be obtained by writing to: Schaum Division
McGraw-Hill, Inc.
Princeton Road S-1
Hightstown, NJ 08520

MATRIX THEORY WITH APPLICATONS

Jack L. Goldberg

University of Michigan

McGraw-Hill, Inc.

New York St. Louis San Francisco Auckland Bogotá
Caracas Hamburg Lisbon London Madrid Mexico Milan Montreal
New Delhi Paris San Juan São Paulo Singapore Sydney Tokyo Toronto

This book was set in Times Roman by Publication Services.
The editors were Richard Wallis and John M. Morriss;
the production supervisor was Richard Ausburn.
The cover was designed by Joseph Gillians.
Project supervision was done by Publication Services.
R. R. Donnelley & Sons Company was printer and binder.

MATRIX THEORY WITH APPLICATIONS

1 2 3 4 5 6 7 8 9 0 DOC DOC 9 0 9 8 7 6 5 4 3 2 1

ISBN 0-07-557200-1

Library of Congress Cataloging-in-Publication Data

Goldberg, Jack L. (Jack Leonard), (date).
Matrix theory with applications/ Jack L. Goldberg.
p. cm.—(International series in pure and applied mathematics)
Includes index.
ISBN 0-07-557200-1
1. Matrices. I. Title. II. Series.
QA188.G645 1991
512.9'434—dc20 90-41595

ABOUT THE AUTHOR

Jack L. Goldberg is Associate Professor of Mathematics at the University of Michigan in Ann Arbor. He received his B.S. degree from the City College of New York, where he graduated with honors and was elected to Phi Beta Kappa. He then went on to receive his M.S. and Ph.D degrees from the University of Illinois, Champaign-Urbana. As a graduate teaching assistant at the University of Illinois, he received an AMOCO award for excellence in teaching and scholarship. After graduation, Professor Goldberg served two years as a member of the technical staff at Bell Telephone Laboratories and then moved on to accept a position at the University of Michigan. During his tenure there, he has received a Fulbright Grant to lecture in Turkey and an AMOCO Good Teaching Award.

Professor Goldberg is the author of numerous research papers and coauthor of two texts: *Systems of Differential Equations: An Introduction* with Arthur Schwartz, and *Mathematical Methods* with Merle Potter. He is a member of the American Mathematical Society and the Mathematical Association of America.

IN MEMORY OF MY BELOVED WIFE,
Harriet,

whose too brief life
added so much to mine

CONTENTS

PREFACE

This text is a reflection of the "computer revolution" in the teaching of mathematics that began some 25 years ago, when linear algebra entered the standard curriculum for students in engineering and the physical sciences. This audience, encouraged by the success of high-speed digital computing in the solution of numerically intensive problems, demanded increased attention to matrix theory. Textbooks addressing these needs appeared soon thereafter and encouraged further changes in the syllabus.

The next step in this pedagogical evolution was the splitting of linear algebra into two distinct courses: a traditional development emphasizing the structure of vector spaces and linear transformations on them; and by contrast, a course in which matrices are treated as a subject worthy of study independent of its roots in linear algebra. Indeed, this text evolved from notes designed specifically for this latter purpose, in a sequence of two courses in matrix theory offered to juniors and seniors at the University of Michigan.

The first course in this sequence covers much (but not all) of the content of the first six chapters in this text. Its aim is a relatively detailed study of the eigenvalue-eigenvector problem. However, in order to achieve this goal in one semester, I have made a significant compromise. The abstract definition of finite dimensional vector space and its development from first principles is substantially ignored. Instead, vector spaces are presented as sets of n-tuples that are closed under linear combinations. It is my contention that this is the best pedagogical approach to matrix theory for the intended audience, even if time were not a consideration. A natural outgrowth of this compromise is that vector spaces are represented as column (or row) spaces of appropriately selected matrices. Thus, for example, the Gram-Schmidt method for finding an orthonormal basis for the vector space $\mathcal{V}$ becomes, in essence, the **QR** factorization of **A** where **A** is a matrix whose column space is $\mathcal{V}$.

The second course is designed to begin with a review of the material in Chapter 5 and then proceed with the remaining chapters in the text. There is significant freedom in selecting topics for this second course, but in my view Chapters 6–8 and the first six sections of Chapter 9 are essential.

Although there is much here that can be found in the standard texts in matrix theory and applied linear algebra, there are some significant differences, Here are the most prominent:

1. I have assumed that the student has already seen many of the elementary properties of matrices and vectors. Thus, for example, he or she has multiplied matrices, is familiar with the use of vectors to represent forces and velocities in physics, and has solved some simple simultaneous equations by a process resembling Gaussian elimination. These topics are covered in Chapter 0, and therefore Chapter 0 should be used to provide a review of these familiar topics as well as to introduce the notational conventions used in the text.
2. Where appropriate, sections end with an *optional* subsection devoted to the use of MATLAB in the context of the section. Furthermore, many of the book's exercise sets contain problems designed for solution using MATLAB.
3. I have presented as many arguments as possible in algorithmic form. A natural tool for this purpose is elementary row operations, and it is for this reason that the row reduced echelon form plays such a prominent part in Chapters 1–3.
4. Each exercise set is divided into three (and sometimes four) parts. The first group contains routine drill questions. The second group presents relatively straightforward but somewhat more theoretical exercises; often these problems require a simple argument or an example. The third group contains problems that challenge the student's understanding and creativity. Some are designed as extensions of the theory and some require extensive arguments; these problems are meant to be optional. Whenever MATLAB problems appear in an exercise set, they are set aside as a fourth group of problems.
5. I have included rather extensive introductions to topics often relegated to the exercise sets in other undergraduate texts:
   - **a.** Gerschgorin's theorem and its application to the roots of polynomials,
   - **b.** limit theorems for stochastic matrices,
   - **c.** the connections between eigenstructures of **AB** and **BA**,
   - **d.** the theory of systems of linear inequalities,
   - **e.** the theory of invariant subspaces.

It is customary and proper in a preface to acknowledge the many sources of inspiration to which an author is indebted. I do so with pleasure. First of all, I thank Cleve Moler for sharing his insightful views with me on the possibilities of a course in matrix theory. These discussions occurred while he was at the University of Michigan long before the present popularity of such courses made such opinions seem obvious. At approximately the same time, the publication of Ben Noble's *Applied Linear Algebra* confirmed the feasibility of many of Moler's ideas. Besides the debt I owe to these two significant innovators, I am also indebted to Professor Arthur Schwartz for his untiring patience in listening to my ideas and offering his insightful advice.

A special note of thanks is due the many reviewers of this manuscript for their suggestions and insights. Among these I want specifically to thank Professor Robert Moore of the University of Washington for his careful reading of various stages of this text and his imaginative and supportive criticisms and his many constructive ideas. Additional reviewers were Stephen L. Campbell, North Carolina State University; Bruce A. Chartres, University of Virginia; Carl C. Cowen, Jr., Purdue University; Carol G. Crawford, United States Naval Academy; Stephen V. Dragosh, Michigan State University; Michael W. Ecker, Pennsylvania State University; Hans P. Engler, Georgetown University; Jacob K. Goldhaber, University of Maryland; Murli M. Gupta, George Washington University; William A. McWorter, Jr., Ohio State University; J. T. Scheick, Ohio State University; and Bostwick F. Wyman, Ohio State University.

I am also appreciative of the support offered me by the Department of Mathematics at the University of Michigan and to the students who suffered through the many versions of the classroom notes that were to become this text.

Jack L. Goldberg

ON USING THIS TEXT

The following outline can be used for a one semester course whose goal is a study of the eigenvalue-eigenvector problem.

Chapter 0. This chapter is intended as a review and an introduction to the notational conventions used in the text. There is sufficient detail here to provide an introduction for the student with little or no previous study of vectors or matrices. Spend no more than four lectures on this chapter.

Chapter 1. Six lectures on this chapter; Section 1.7 is optional.

Chapter 2. Eight lectures; most of these on linear independence and rank.

Chapter 3. Eight lectures; Section 3.8 is optional.

Chapter 4. Ten lectures; the details in Section 4.7 and Section 4.10 are discussed only briefly.

Chapter 5. Ten lectures for Part 1; use two lectures to outline the ideas in Sections 5.10 and 5.11.

Chapter 6. Depending on the time available, cover as much as possible in this chapter. One can usually reach many of the significant results on Hermitian matrices.

The material for a second course in matrix theory tends to vary widely with the interests of the instructor. If this text is used for such a course, a review of Chapter 5 seems essential because Chapters 6 and 7 depend heavily on the fundamental ideas developed there. Chapters 6–9 provide enough material for the remaining part of the course.

MATRIX THEORY WITH APPLICATIONS

CHAPTER 0

INTRODUCTION AND REVIEW

0.1 INTRODUCTION

The advent of high-speed digital computers in the last half of this century has had a profound, even revolutionary effect on mathematics, an effect that reaches to its most diverse applications. It is no surprise that computers play a major role in engineering, physics, chemistry, astronomy, statistics, and economics. Computation is a vital part of these fields. But, remarkably, computers are also being used in history, sociology, psychology, art, architecture, design, and cryptography. What makes the computer useful in all these areas is its capacity to manipulate vast amounts of data rapidly and accurately. The tool for this manipulation is the modern theory of matrices. It is no coincidence that matrix theory has grown in importance roughly in proportion with the increase in computer capacity and speed. In 1940 a multiplication of two 10-place integers by a mechanical computer took about a second. In 1980 the same computation takes less than a thousandth of a second on a cheap hand-held calculator, and less than a millionth of a second on mainframe computers.

Some examples will illustrate the wide diversity of the applications of matrix theory. Of course, this is no complete catalogue, nor are these necessarily the most important examples; but these illustrations are representative of the many possible applications. All but the first example, *magic squares,* are analyzed in detail later in the text. We have included a discussion of magic squares because of its intrinsic interest and historical significance.

0.1.1 Magic Squares

Among the many symbolic elements in Albrecht Dürer's masterpiece, *Melencolia I* (see Fig. 0.1) is this 4 × 4 matrix of integers:

$$\begin{bmatrix} 16 & 3 & 2 & 13 \\ 5 & 10 & 11 & 8 \\ 9 & 6 & 7 & 12 \\ 4 & 15 & 14 & 1 \end{bmatrix}$$

This matrix is no random array. All 16 integers from 1 to 16 are used, and the sum of each row, column, and the two diagonals is 34. Given how remarkable it is that these constraints can be met, it is no wonder that such arrays were believed to have mystical significance. Indeed, as a measure of the awe in which they were held, these matrices were and are still known as *magic squares*. There are magic squares of every size, except 2 × 2. Clearly the common sum of the rows, columns, and diagonals is a function of n. For $n = 3$, the sum is 15.

FIGURE 0-1
Melencolia I. (Courtesy of Princeton University Press.)

MATLAB[1] returns an $n \times n$ magic square in response to the input magic(n). Here are the outputs magic(3), magic(4), and magic(5), respectively.

$$\begin{bmatrix} 8 & 1 & 6 \\ 3 & 5 & 7 \\ 4 & 9 & 2 \end{bmatrix} \qquad \begin{bmatrix} 16 & 2 & 3 & 13 \\ 5 & 11 & 10 & 8 \\ 9 & 7 & 6 & 12 \\ 4 & 14 & 15 & 1 \end{bmatrix} \qquad \begin{bmatrix} 17 & 24 & 1 & 8 & 15 \\ 23 & 5 & 7 & 14 & 16 \\ 4 & 6 & 13 & 20 & 22 \\ 10 & 12 & 19 & 21 & 3 \\ 11 & 18 & 25 & 2 & 9 \end{bmatrix}$$

Magic(4) differs from the magic square in Dürer's engraving in having its second and third columns interchanged. (So there is more than one magic square of size 4×4! Is there more than one magic square of size 3×3?) The common sum of the rows, columns, and diagonals of magic(5) is 65. What is this sum for magic(6)?

0.1.2 Linear Programming

A brewer brews and bottles three brands of beer: Brand X, Brand X-lite, and Brand Y. The malt and hops used in the fermentation process are grown on the brewer's own farm. Table 0.1 shows how many bushels of each grain are used in the production of one keg of each variety of beer.

TABLE 0.1
Ingredients and profits per keg

Grain	Brand X	Brand X-lite	Brand Y	Availability
Malt	2	1	1	10 bushels/day
Hops	1	0	1	5 bushels/day
Net profit ($/day/keg)	2	3	4	

The brewer wishes to produce a mix of beers using her limited resources of hops and malt so that her profit is maximized. The algebraic formulation of this problem begins with the definition of the variables x, y, and z. Let

x = number of kegs of Brand X produced in one day
y = number of kegs of Brand X-lite produced in one day
z = number of kegs of Brand Y produced in one day

Then the net profit function, read from the third line in Table 0.1, is given by $2x + 3y + 4z$ (in dollars per day), and it is this function that the brewer must maximize. But she cannot simply increase profits by increasing her output of beer because she has limited raw materials. The malt and hops available to her each

[1]MATLAB is a sophisticated computer program designed especially for matrix computations. An introduction to its use is provided in Chapter 1.

day constrain her output by the inequalities $2x + y + z \leq 10$ (= available malt) and $x + z \leq 5$ (= available hops), read from lines one and two of Table 0.1.

This particular *resource allocation problem,* maximize $2x + 3y + 4z$, $x \geq 0$, $y \geq 0$, $z \geq 0$, subject to the constraints

$$\begin{aligned} 2x + y + z &\leq 10 \\ x + z &\leq 5 \end{aligned}$$

can be solved by elementary methods (and incidentally, the brewer's maximum profit is \$35/day, which she gets by producing five kegs of Brands Y and X-lite and stopping all production of Brand X); more realistic problems involving literally hundreds of variables and constraints require sophisticated mathematical techniques and vast computer power. Until the invention of the *simplex method* by G. Dantzig in the 1950s and the availability of high-capacity, high-speed digital computers, these problems were intractable. Our interest in this subject, known as *linear programming,* stems from the fact that the simplex method is an application of the theory of matrices.

0.1.3 Graph Theory

There are many applications of matrix theory in the social sciences. Some of the more accessible illustrations are from sociology, in which kinship relationships, "pecking orders," the flow of rumors, and networks of acquaintances are all amenable to our methods. Consider an example of the latter. In a social setting, two individuals are "acquainted" if they both report that they know each other. Sociologists are interested in the acquaintance patterns that develop in closed communities such as dormitories, nursing homes, and workplaces. Simple and useful means for describing these networks are needed. A commonly used scheme begins with each person being depicted as a point in the plane. If two people are acquainted, a line is drawn between the points representing them. This collection of points and lines is called a *digraph.* Indeed, any (nonempty) finite set of points and (possibly empty) finite set of lines connecting some of these points is a digraph. A few examples of digraphs are shown in Fig. 0.2.

A connection between digraphs and the theory of matrices can be made by labeling the points in a digraph, say P_1 through P_5, as done for the digraph drawn in Fig. 0.3*a*. Then a matrix of zeros and ones is constructed as follows: If a line joins point P_i to point P_j, then 1 is placed in the ith row and jth column and in the jth row and ith column of this matrix. If no line joins these points, 0 is put in these positions. The matrix constructed by this rule is called the *incidence matrix of the digraph.* The incidence matrix of the digraph in Fig. 0.3*a* is given in Fig. 0.3*b*.

Let us call a set of mutually acquainted individuals an "acquaintance set." Within an acquaintance network, an acquaintance set is called a *clique* if it contains at least three members and there is no other acquaintance set containing it. Thus

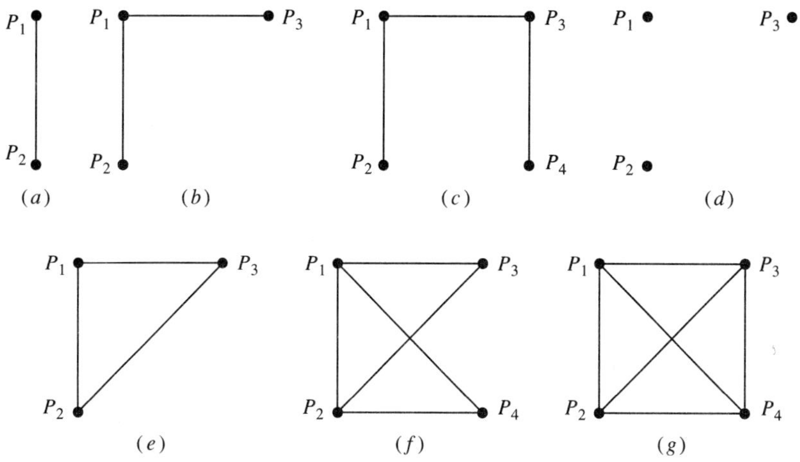

FIGURE 0-2
Seven digraphs.

a clique is a "maximal" acquaintance set in a network. Suppose Fig. 0.3*a* depicts the acquaintance network of some social grouping. Which individuals belong to at least one clique? The digraph shows that P_4 and P_5 do not belong to any clique, but this fact can also be deduced algebraically. We compute the cube of the incidence matrix (see Section 0.5) to obtain

$$\begin{bmatrix} 2 & 3 & 4 & 1 & 1 \\ 3 & 2 & 4 & 1 & 1 \\ 4 & 4 & 2 & 4 & 0 \\ 1 & 1 & 4 & 0 & 2 \\ 1 & 1 & 0 & 2 & 0 \end{bmatrix}$$

The appearance of zero entries in the (4,4) and (5,5) position shows that P_4 and P_5 belong to no clique. The remaining diagonal entries are nonzero, so P_1, P_2, and P_3 all belong to cliques.

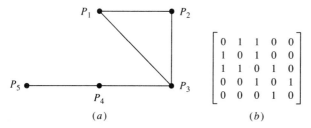

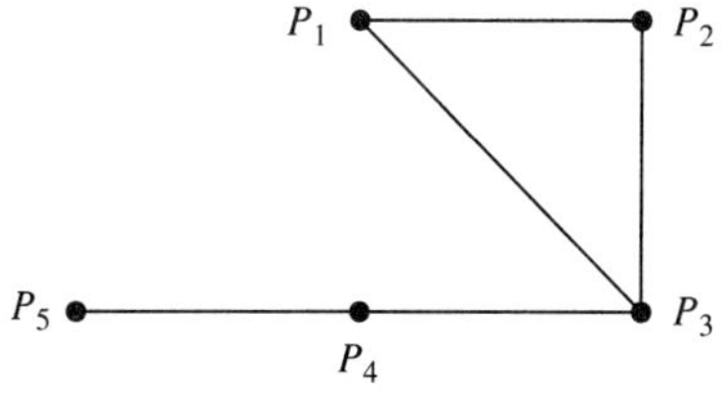

(*a*)

$$\begin{bmatrix} 0 & 1 & 1 & 0 & 0 \\ 1 & 0 & 1 & 0 & 0 \\ 1 & 1 & 0 & 1 & 0 \\ 0 & 0 & 1 & 0 & 1 \\ 0 & 0 & 0 & 1 & 0 \end{bmatrix}$$

(*b*)

FIGURE 0-3
Digraph with 5 points and the associated incidence matrix.

0.1.4 Least Squares

Blood is drawn from volunteers to determine the effects of a new experimental drug designed to lower cholesterol levels. The data presented in Table 0.2 show the results of varying the dosage from 0 units to 1 unit in steps of 0.2. The units for the cholesterol level are milligrams per unit volume of blood. The data suggest that C and D are linearly related. If we assume that this is so, what line "best fits" the data?

TABLE 0.2
Effects of dosage variation

Drug Dosage: D	0.0	0.2	0.4	0.6	0.8	1.0
Cholesterol: C	289	273	254	226	213	189

One possible interpretation of best fit, called least squares, requires that the constants a and b in $C = a + bD$ satisfy

$$\begin{bmatrix} 6 & 3.0 \\ 3 & 2.2 \end{bmatrix} \begin{bmatrix} a \\ b \end{bmatrix} = \begin{bmatrix} 1444.0 \\ 651.2 \end{bmatrix}$$

We find that $C = 291.24 - (101.14)D$ is the line of best fit. The graph of this line and the values of C and D in Table 0.2 are given in Fig. 0.4. (See also Section 4.10 of Chapter 4.)

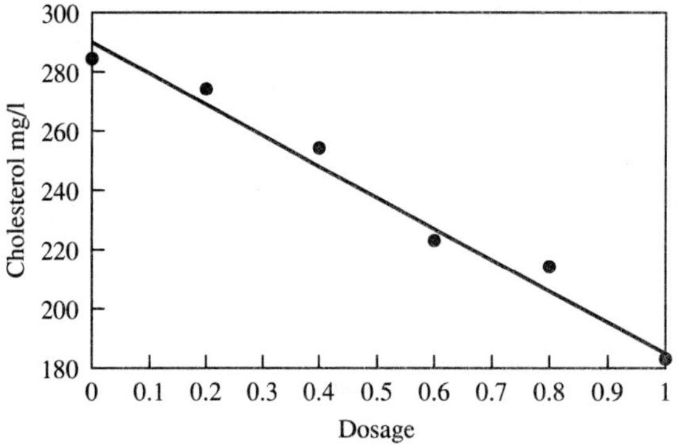

FIGURE 0-4
Cholesterol reduction versus dosage.

0.1.5 Quadratic Forms

An instructive and elementary application of matrix theory in other areas of mathematics occurs in the study of conic sections. Consider the problem of deciding whether the graph of $5x^2 + 4xy + 2y^2 = 1$ is an ellipse or a hyperbola. A solution can be obtained by eliminating the mixed term $4xy$ by a change of variables of the form $x = \alpha X + \beta Y$, $y = \gamma X + \delta Y$. A proper choice of α, β, γ and δ casts the conic into one of the standard forms

$$\pm\frac{X^2}{a^2} + \frac{Y^2}{b^2} = 1 \qquad \frac{X^2}{a^2} \pm \frac{Y^2}{b^2} = 1 \tag{0.1.1}$$

from which the nature of the conic can be easily determined. Although it is possible to find α, β, γ, and δ by elementary means, a more insightful analysis derives from writing $5x^2 + 4xy + 2y^2$ in the form

$$q(x,y) = [x \quad y]\begin{bmatrix} 5 & 2 \\ 2 & 2 \end{bmatrix}\begin{bmatrix} x \\ y \end{bmatrix} = 5x^2 + 4xy + 2y^2 \qquad (0.1.2)$$

The function $q(x,y)$ is an example of a *quadratic form* (in two variables) and the means for eliminating the $4xy$ term is part of a general theory of quadratic forms in n variables presented in Chapter 7. The matrix

$$\mathbf{A} = \begin{bmatrix} 5 & 2 \\ 2 & 2 \end{bmatrix}$$

is called the *matrix of the form*. It turns out that the change of variables

$$\begin{aligned} -.8944X - .4472Y &= x \\ -.4472X + .8944Y &= y \end{aligned} \qquad (0.1.3)$$

results in the expression $6X^2 + Y^2 = 1$. Hence the conic is an ellipse in standard form in the new variables X and Y. (See Fig. 0.5.)

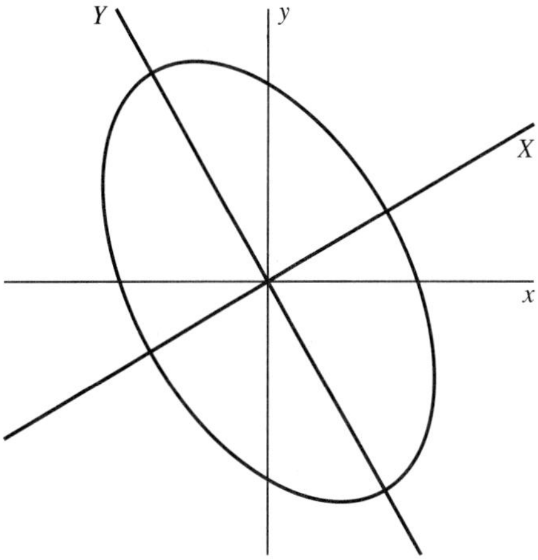

FIGURE 0-5
Ellipse in standard form in new variables X and Y.

The change of variables, Eq. 0.1.3, is derived from a study of the eigenvalues and eigenvectors of the matrix $\mathbf{A}$ of the quadratic form. The eigenvalues and eigenvectors of square matrices constitute such an important topic that we devote all of Chapters 5 and 6 to its study.

0.1.6 Modeling Population Dynamics

Suppose there is a species of beetle with a three-year life span that reproduces only in its second and third years. Suppose, on average, that each female alive in its second year produces four fertile females and that those surviving into their third year produce six fertile females. (We ignore the male beetles except to note that there are sufficiently many to fertilize all reproductively available females.) Mortality in this species is high. Fully one-half of all females die in the first year, and of those that survive to their second year, only one-third live to reproduce in their third year. We study the population growth of this species in an environment in which all the females in the colony were born there and none leave to establish new colonies. Our first census shows 100 females in their first year, 50 in their second, and 25 in their third.

Assuming no changes in fertility or mortality rates, what are the long-term survival prospects for this colony? Will the population stabilize? Will the colony ultimately become extinct? To answer such questions, we construct the initial population distribution vector $\mathbf{p}_0 = [\,100 \quad 50 \quad 25\,]^{\mathrm{T}}$ and a matrix $\mathbf{P}$, which represents the effects of the mortality and fertility assumptions:

$$\mathbf{P} = \begin{bmatrix} 0 & 4 & 6 \\ \frac{1}{2} & 0 & 0 \\ 0 & \frac{1}{3} & 0 \end{bmatrix}$$

The ultimate fate of this species depends on the limit of the sequence, $\mathbf{P}\mathbf{p}_0$, $\mathbf{P}^2\mathbf{p}_0, \ldots, \mathbf{P}^n\mathbf{p}_0$. (See Chapter 5, Section 5.10.) The nth term in this sequence contains the nth power of $\mathbf{P}$ and represents the population vector after n years. A few terms of this sequence are suggestive:

$$\mathbf{P}^5\mathbf{p}_0 = \begin{bmatrix} 1.9000 \\ 0.4750 \\ 0.1333 \end{bmatrix} \times 10^3 \qquad \mathbf{P}^{10}\mathbf{p}_0 = \begin{bmatrix} 1.9350 \\ 0.6100 \\ 0.1217 \end{bmatrix} \times 10^4$$

$$\mathbf{P}^{20}\mathbf{p}_0 = \begin{bmatrix} 2.3981 \\ 0.7411 \\ 0.1526 \end{bmatrix} \times 10^6 \qquad \mathbf{P}^{50}\mathbf{p}_0 = \begin{bmatrix} 4.4619 \\ 1.3788 \\ 0.2841 \end{bmatrix} \times 10^{12}$$

The evidence supports the contention that the population in each age group increases without limit. A more subtle conjecture is that the population distributions among age groups tend to limits. Consider, for example, the ratio of the number of one-year-old beetles to the total population after 5, 10, 20, and 50 years. These ratios are 0.758, 0.726, 0.729, and 0.729. This suggests that the ratio tends to the limit 0.729. The ratio for two-year-old beetles appears to tend to 0.23, and for three-year-old beetles to 0.04.

This example of population growth, called a "deterministic, discrete model," is attributed to H. Bernardelli, P. H. Leslie, and E. G. Leslie.

0.1.7 Discrete Markov Processes

Two airline passengers, A and B, stranded by foul weather decide to play a card game to test a theory proposed by B. Player A guesses that a spade will be drawn from a pack of three cards containing two hearts and one spade. Player A receives one chip from B if a spade is drawn and gives up a chip if a heart is drawn. Each draw of a card is considered a round, and a player wins the game as soon as his opponent loses all his chips, regardless of the number of rounds taken to achieve this. Since the probability of drawing a spade is ⅓, which is half the probability of drawing a heart, B conjectures that the game can be made fair by allotting twice as many chips to A as to B. To test this theory, A starts with four chips and B starts with two. Does each player have the same likelihood of winning?

The analysis of this game has features in common with many other probabilistic models. (These models are called *discrete Markov processes* after the Russian mathematician A. A. Markov; see Section 7.7.) Two ideas permeate the theory. The first notion is that of a "state." Loosely speaking, A's bankroll at each round of play is his state. There are seven states[2] for A:

S_i, the state in which A has i chips, $1 \le i \le 5$
S_6, the state in which A has 0 chips
S_7, the state in which A has 6 chips

Player A begins in S_4. After one round, he is in either S_5 or S_3, depending on whether he has won or lost. The following 7-tuple represents the likelihood that A is in each state after one round:

$$\mathbf{p}_1 = \begin{bmatrix} 0 \\ 0 \\ 2/3 \\ 0 \\ 1/3 \\ 0 \\ 0 \end{bmatrix} \begin{matrix} \\ \\ \leftarrow S_3 \\ \\ \leftarrow S_5 \\ \\ \\ \end{matrix}$$

In other words, A is in state 3 with probability ⅔ and in state 5 with probability ⅓. The vector $\mathbf{p}_1$ is called a probability vector because its entries are probabilities and because all possible cases are listed. Thus the sum of the entries is 1. The initial probability vector $\mathbf{p}_0$, and the vector $\mathbf{p}_2$ that lists the probability that A is in a given state after two rounds, are given by

$$\mathbf{p}_0 = \begin{bmatrix} 0 \\ 0 \\ 0 \\ 1 \\ 0 \\ 0 \\ 0 \end{bmatrix} \begin{matrix} \\ \\ \\ \leftarrow S_4, \\ \\ \\ \\ \end{matrix} \qquad \mathbf{p}_2 = \begin{bmatrix} 0 \\ 4/9 \\ 0 \\ 4/9 \\ 0 \\ 0 \\ 1/9 \end{bmatrix} \begin{matrix} \\ \leftarrow S_2 \\ \\ \leftarrow S_4 \\ \\ \\ \leftarrow S_7 \end{matrix}$$

[2]The states S_6 and S_7 seem out of order. They are labeled this way for reasons that are best ignored for the time being. As it turns out, this ordering leads to a convenient form for the transition matrix.

Note that the seventh entry of $\mathbf{p}_2$ tells us that the probability that A has won in two rounds is $1/9$. This is obvious from elementary probability theory since A can win in exactly two rounds only by winning both rounds.

The game is over whenever either player has no chips left. It is convenient, however, to imagine the fiction that the game is played forever. So if A reaches S_7 in k rounds, he is in S_7 for all further rounds. Hence the seventh entry of the limit of $\mathbf{p}_k$ as $k \to \infty$ gives the probability that A will win, sooner or later. We write this limit as $\mathbf{p}_\infty$.

The second notion common to all discrete Markov processes is the idea of a transition matrix, $\mathbf{T}$, the role of which is to convert $\mathbf{p}_k$ to $\mathbf{p}_{k+1}$. Specifically, a_{ij} is the (conditional) probability that A arrives in S_i given that A is in S_j. The transition matrix for the game described above is given by

$$\mathbf{T} = \begin{bmatrix} 0 & 2/3 & 0 & 0 & 0 & 0 & 0 \\ 1/3 & 0 & 2/3 & 0 & 0 & 0 & 0 \\ 0 & 1/3 & 0 & 2/3 & 0 & 0 & 0 \\ 0 & 0 & 1/3 & 0 & 2/3 & 0 & 0 \\ 0 & 0 & 0 & 1/3 & 0 & 0 & 0 \\ 2/3 & 0 & 0 & 0 & 0 & 1 & 0 \\ 0 & 0 & 0 & 0 & 1/3 & 0 & 1 \end{bmatrix}$$

Let us check the entry a_{43}. If A is in S_3 and in one round goes to S_4, then A has won that particular round. The probability that A wins in any draw is $1/3$, and thus $a_{43} = 1/3$.

If we were to examine each entry of $\mathbf{T}\mathbf{p}_{k-1}$, something we choose not to do here, we would discover that $\mathbf{p}_k = \mathbf{T}\mathbf{p}_{k-1}$ follows easily from the theory of conditional probability. This relationship between consecutive probability vectors can be used to deduce $\mathbf{p}_k = \mathbf{T}^k\mathbf{p}_0$. Hence $\mathbf{p}_\infty = \lim(\mathbf{T}^k)\mathbf{p}_0$. MATLAB was used to compute $\mathbf{T}^{50}$ and $\mathbf{T}^{50}\mathbf{p}_0$. Here are the results rounded to two decimal places:

$$\mathbf{T}^{50}\mathbf{p}_0 = \begin{bmatrix} 0.00 & 0 & 0.00 & 0 & 0.00 & 0 & 0 \\ 0 & 0.00 & 0 & 0.00 & 0 & 0 & 0 \\ 0.00 & 0 & 0.00 & 0 & 0.00 & 0 & 0 \\ 0 & 0.00 & 0 & 0.00 & 0 & 0 & 0 \\ 0.00 & 0 & 0.00 & 0 & 0.00 & 0 & 0 \\ 0.98 & 0.95 & 0.89 & 0.76 & 0.51 & 1 & 0 \\ 0.01 & 0.05 & 0.11 & 0.24 & 0.49 & 0 & 1 \end{bmatrix} \begin{bmatrix} 0 \\ 0 \\ 0 \\ 1 \\ 0 \\ 0 \\ 0 \end{bmatrix} \approx \mathbf{p}_\infty = \begin{bmatrix} 0 \\ 0.00 \\ 0 \\ 0.00 \\ 0 \\ 0.76 \\ 0.24 \end{bmatrix}$$

So A wins only 24 percent of the time, and B has managed a "con." Note that if A had started with five chips (and hence B with one), the game would be almost fair, but B would still retain a slight edge.

Other applications of matrix theory that appear later in the text but are not included in this introduction are systems of linear inequalities (Chapter 9) and systems of linear difference and differential equations with constant coefficients (Chapter 5).

0.2 NOTATION AND TERMINOLOGY

Good mathematical notation has many virtues; it suggests generalizations and analogies and, most importantly, clarifies the underlying mathematical idea. Indeed, poor notation can muddy even the simplest of concepts. The fundamental notational tool in this text is the matrix. This felicitous invention is attributed to one of the founders of our subject, the English mathematician Arthur Cayley. It is a model of good notation.

For the purposes of this work, a *matrix* is a rectangular array of real or complex numbers. The number of rows and columns in the array is the *size* of the matrix. Thus the matrices

$$\begin{bmatrix} 1 & 0 & 1 \\ 2 & 5 & 7 \end{bmatrix}, \qquad [1 \quad 0 \quad i], \qquad \begin{bmatrix} -1 & 2 & 3 \\ 0 & 0 & 0 \\ 1 & 1 & 1 \end{bmatrix}, \qquad \begin{bmatrix} x \\ y \\ z \end{bmatrix} \qquad [0]$$

have sizes 2×3, 1×3, 3×3, 3×1, and 1×1, respectively. The size 2×3 is read "2 by 3." (In many texts "order" or "dimension" is used as a synonym for size.)

In general, the matrix **A**, defined by

$$\mathbf{A} = \begin{bmatrix} a_{11} & a_{12} & \cdots & a_{1n} \\ a_{21} & a_{22} & \cdots & a_{2n} \\ \vdots & \vdots & & \vdots \\ a_{m1} & a_{m2} & \cdots & a_{mn} \end{bmatrix} \tag{0.2.1}$$

has size $m \times n$. The numbers a_{ij} are the *entries,* or *elements,* of **A**; the first subscript defines the row position of a_{ij}, the second its column position.

It is sometimes convenient to subscript **A** to display its size. Thus $\mathbf{A}_{m\times n}$ is a matrix with m rows and n columns, whereas $\mathbf{A}_{n\times n}$ (usually written $\mathbf{A}_n$) has n rows and n columns. The notations $\mathbf{A}_3 = (i^j)$ and $\mathbf{B}_{2\times 4} = (i - j)$ define matrices by the formulas $a_{ij} = i^j$ and $b_{ij} = i - j$. Thus, in expanded form,

$$\mathbf{A}_3 = \begin{bmatrix} 1 & 1 & 1 \\ 2 & 2^2 & 2^3 \\ 3 & 3^2 & 3^3 \end{bmatrix}, \qquad \mathbf{B}_{2\times 4} = \begin{bmatrix} 0 & -1 & -2 & -3 \\ 1 & 0 & -1 & -2 \end{bmatrix} \tag{0.2.2}$$

The system of simultaneous equations,

$$\begin{aligned} 2x_1 - x_2 + x_3 - x_4 &= 1 \\ x_1 \qquad - x_3 \qquad &= 1 \\ x_2 + x_3 + x_4 &= -1 \end{aligned} \tag{0.2.3}$$

has the *coefficient matrix* **A** and *augmented matrix* **B** given by

$$\mathbf{A} = \begin{bmatrix} 2 & -1 & 1 & -1 \\ 1 & 0 & -1 & 0 \\ 0 & 1 & 1 & 1 \end{bmatrix}, \qquad \mathbf{B} = \left[\begin{array}{cccc|c} 2 & -1 & 1 & -1 & 1 \\ 1 & 0 & -1 & 0 & 1 \\ 0 & 1 & 1 & 1 & -1 \end{array}\right] \tag{0.2.4}$$

respectively. Note that the coefficient matrix is obtained from the coefficients of the unknowns in the system of equations. The first row in the coefficient matrix corresponds to the first equation, the second row to the second equation, and so on. The augmented matrix is the coefficient matrix with an extra column containing the right-hand-side constants. The column of right-hand-side constants is often separated from the others by the vertical dotted line, as in Eq. 0.2.4.

The *i*th row of the matrix **A** in Eq. 0.2.1 is often denoted by $\mathbf{A}_{i*}$, the *j*th column by $\mathbf{A}_{*j}$. Thus the rows of **B** are

$$\mathbf{B}_{1*} = [2 \quad -1 \quad 1 \quad -1 \quad 1], \qquad \mathbf{B}_{2*} = [1 \quad 0 \quad -1 \quad 0 \quad 1],$$
$$\mathbf{B}_{3*} = [0 \quad 1 \quad 1 \quad 1 \quad -1]$$

and its columns are

$$\mathbf{B}_{*1} = \begin{bmatrix} 2 \\ 1 \\ 0 \end{bmatrix} \qquad \mathbf{B}_{*2} = \begin{bmatrix} -1 \\ 0 \\ 1 \end{bmatrix} \qquad \mathbf{B}_{*3} = \begin{bmatrix} 1 \\ -1 \\ 1 \end{bmatrix}$$
$$\mathbf{B}_{*4} = \begin{bmatrix} -1 \\ 0 \\ 1 \end{bmatrix} \qquad \mathbf{B}_{*5} = \begin{bmatrix} 1 \\ 1 \\ -1 \end{bmatrix}$$

The *diagonal* entries of $\mathbf{A}_{m\times n}$ are those entries with equal subscripts; those with unequal subscripts (a_{ij}, $i \neq j$) are called the *off-diagonal* entries of $\mathbf{A}_{m\times n}$. By the term "the diagonal of **A**," written diag(**A**), we mean the column matrix

$$\text{diag}(\mathbf{A}) = \begin{bmatrix} a_{11} \\ a_{22} \\ \vdots \\ a_{rr} \end{bmatrix} \tag{0.2.5}$$

where r is the lesser of m and n. For example, if

$$\mathbf{A} = \begin{bmatrix} 2 & 1 & 1 & -1 \\ 1 & 0 & -1 & 0 \\ 0 & 1 & 1 & 1 \end{bmatrix}, \qquad \mathbf{C} = \begin{bmatrix} 2 & -1 \\ 1 & 0 \\ 0 & 1 \end{bmatrix}$$

then

$$\text{diag}(\mathbf{A}) = \begin{bmatrix} 2 \\ 0 \\ 1 \end{bmatrix}, \qquad \text{diag}(\mathbf{C}) = \begin{bmatrix} 2 \\ 0 \end{bmatrix}$$

A *square matrix* is one that has the same number of rows as columns. An *upper trapezoidal* matrix has zero entries below its diagonal entries; that is, $a_{ij} = 0$ if $i > j$. A *lower trapezoidal* matrix has zero entries above its diagonal entries; $a_{ij} = 0$ if $i < j$. The following matrices are examples of these special forms. Here are some upper trapezoidal matrices:

$$\begin{bmatrix} * & * & * & * & * & * \\ 0 & * & * & * & * & * \\ 0 & 0 & * & * & * & * \end{bmatrix}, \qquad \begin{bmatrix} * & * & * & * \\ 0 & * & * & * \\ 0 & 0 & * & * \\ 0 & 0 & 0 & * \\ 0 & 0 & 0 & 0 \end{bmatrix}, \qquad \begin{bmatrix} * & * & * \\ 0 & * & * \\ 0 & 0 & * \end{bmatrix} \tag{0.2.6}$$

(Here and in the following "*" is used to signify that the specific value of the entry is irrelevant. In particular, * may be zero.) Now some lower trapezoidal matrices:

$$\begin{bmatrix} * & 0 & 0 & 0 & 0 & 0 \\ * & * & 0 & 0 & 0 & 0 \\ * & * & * & 0 & 0 & 0 \end{bmatrix}, \quad \begin{bmatrix} * & 0 & 0 & 0 \\ * & * & 0 & 0 \\ * & * & * & 0 \\ * & * & * & * \\ * & * & * & * \end{bmatrix}, \quad \begin{bmatrix} * & 0 & 0 \\ * & * & 0 \\ * & * & * \end{bmatrix} \tag{0.2.7}$$

Square upper trapezoidal matrices are called *upper triangular;* square lower trapezoidal matrices are called *lower triangular*. We use **U** and **L** as generic notations for upper and lower triangular matrices, respectively.

A *diagonal* matrix is a square matrix with off-diagonal entries zero. The following are diagonal matrices:

$$\begin{bmatrix} 1 & 0 \\ 0 & -1 \end{bmatrix}, \quad \begin{bmatrix} 0 & 0 & 0 \\ 0 & 0 & 0 \\ 0 & 0 & 0 \end{bmatrix}, \quad \begin{bmatrix} 1 & 0 & 0 \\ 0 & 2 & 0 \\ 0 & 0 & 3 \end{bmatrix}, \quad [-2] \tag{0.2.8}$$

The *identity* matrix of size $\mathbf{I}_n$, written I_n, is the $n \times n$ diagonal matrix in which $a_{ii} = 1$ for all i. Thus, $\mathbf{I}_1$, $\mathbf{I}_2$, and $\mathbf{I}_3$ are given by

$$\mathbf{I}_1 = [1], \qquad \mathbf{I}_2 = \begin{bmatrix} 1 & 0 \\ 0 & 1 \end{bmatrix}, \qquad \mathbf{I}_3 = \begin{bmatrix} 1 & 0 & 0 \\ 0 & 1 & 0 \\ 0 & 0 & 1 \end{bmatrix} \tag{0.2.9}$$

Diagonal matrices are simultaneously upper and lower triangular; conversely, every matrix which is both upper and lower triangular is diagonal.

The *transpose* of **A**, written $\mathbf{A}^{\mathrm{T}}$, is the matrix obtained from **A** by interchanging its rows and columns; the first row of **A** becomes the first column of $\mathbf{A}^{\mathrm{T}}$, the second row becomes the second column, and so on. For example,

$$\mathbf{A} = \begin{bmatrix} 2 & -1 & 1 & -1 \\ 1 & 0 & -1 & 0 \\ 0 & 1 & 1 & 1 \end{bmatrix}, \qquad \mathbf{A}^{\mathrm{T}} = \begin{bmatrix} 2 & 1 & 0 \\ -1 & 0 & 1 \\ 1 & -1 & 1 \\ -1 & 0 & 1 \end{bmatrix} \tag{0.2.10}$$

If the generic entry in $\mathbf{A}^{\mathrm{T}}$ is denoted by a_{ij}^{T} so that $\mathbf{A}^{\mathrm{T}} = (a_{ij}^{\mathrm{T}})$, then $a_{ij}^{\mathrm{T}} = a_{ji}$ is an equivalent way of describing the operation of transposition. Also, we can view transposing **A** as a reflection of its entries in its diagonal.

Write $\mathbf{A} = \mathbf{B}$ if corresponding entries of each matrix are equal; that is, if $a_{ij} = b_{ij}$ for each i and j. (Implicit in this definition is the assumption that the sizes of **A** and **B** are the same.) Thus, for example, for every **A**, $\mathbf{A} = (\mathbf{A}^{\mathrm{T}})^{\mathrm{T}}$. It follows from the definition of the transpose operation that the transpose of an upper trapezoidal matrix is a lower trapezoidal matrix and that only for square matrices is the size of the transposed matrix the same as the size of the original matrix.

Matrices that are their own transposes are *symmetric*. So **A** is symmetric if $\mathbf{A} = \mathbf{A}^{\mathrm{T}}$ or, in terms of its entries, if $a_{ij} = a_{ji}$, $i \neq j$. Clearly diagonal matrices are symmetric. Another important class of symmetric matrices comprises the $n \times n$ matrix of ones, which is symbolized $\mathbf{J}_n$. In the various notations of this section,

$$\mathbf{J}_{n\times n} = \mathbf{J}_n = (1)_n = \begin{bmatrix} 1 & 1 & \cdots & 1 \\ 1 & 1 & \cdots & 1 \\ \vdots & \vdots & & \vdots \\ 1 & 1 & \cdots & 1 \end{bmatrix}, \qquad \operatorname{diag}(\mathbf{J}_n) = \begin{bmatrix} 1 \\ 1 \\ \vdots \\ 1 \end{bmatrix} \tag{0.2.11}$$

Example 0.2.1. Show that all symmetric matrices are square.

Solution. By definition, $\mathbf{A}$ is symmetric if $\mathbf{A} = \mathbf{A}^{\mathrm{T}}$; that is, if $\mathbf{A}$ and $\mathbf{A}^{\mathrm{T}}$ are identical. But if $\mathbf{A}$ and $\mathbf{A}^{\mathrm{T}}$ are the same matrices, they have the same size. Assume $\mathbf{A}$ is $m \times n$. Then the size of $\mathbf{A}^{\mathrm{T}}$ is $n \times m$ and hence, $m = n$.

A *column vector* is a matrix of size $m \times 1$, and a *row vector* is a matrix of size $1 \times n$. For simplicity, we shall use the term "vector" for column vector; thus a row vector is the transpose of a vector. Vectors play such a central role in our theory that we use a distinctive notation for these special matrices. We symbolize vectors with boldface lowercase letters as in the following:

$$\mathbf{x} = \begin{bmatrix} x \\ y \\ z \end{bmatrix}, \qquad \mathbf{a} = \begin{bmatrix} a_1 \\ a_2 \\ a_3 \\ a_4 \end{bmatrix}, \qquad \mathbf{1}_4 = \begin{bmatrix} 1 \\ 1 \\ 1 \\ 1 \end{bmatrix}, \qquad \mathbf{0}_6 = \begin{bmatrix} 0 \\ 0 \\ 0 \\ 0 \\ 0 \\ 0 \end{bmatrix}$$

The notation $\mathbf{x} \in \mathcal{R}^n$ signals that $\mathbf{x}$ has real entries. If $\mathbf{x}$ may contain complex entries, then the notation $\mathbf{x} \in \mathcal{C}^n$ is used.

Note the special notations for the $n \times 1$ vectors, $\mathbf{1}_n$ and $\mathbf{0}_n$. Other vectors that have their own symbols are the *standard unit* vectors of size $n \times 1$:

$$\mathbf{e}_1 = \begin{bmatrix} 1 \\ 0 \\ 0 \\ \vdots \\ 0 \end{bmatrix}, \qquad \mathbf{e}_2 = \begin{bmatrix} 0 \\ 1 \\ 0 \\ \vdots \\ 0 \end{bmatrix}, \qquad \ldots, \qquad \mathbf{e}_n = \begin{bmatrix} 0 \\ 0 \\ 0 \\ \vdots \\ 1 \end{bmatrix} \tag{0.2.12}$$

The standard unit vectors are the columns of $\mathbf{I}_n$. The subscript indicates where the sole 1 occurs in the vector and is unrelated to the number of entries in the vector. Finally, a *scalar matrix* is a diagonal matrix with all diagonal entries equal. Thus $\mathbf{I}_n$ and $\mathbf{0}_n$ are examples of scalar matrices; the general case is given by

$$\begin{bmatrix} a & 0 & \cdots & 0 \\ 0 & a & \cdots & 0 \\ \vdots & \vdots & & \vdots \\ 0 & 0 & \cdots & a \end{bmatrix}$$

More rarely used are the notations for rectangular matrices of zeros and ones:

$$\mathbf{O}_{m\times n} = (0)_{m\times n} = \begin{bmatrix} 0 & 0 & \cdots & 0 \\ 0 & 0 & \cdots & 0 \\ \vdots & \vdots & & \vdots \\ 0 & 0 & \cdots & 0 \end{bmatrix} \qquad \mathbf{J}_{m\times n} = (1)_{m\times n} = \begin{bmatrix} 1 & 1 & \cdots & 1 \\ 1 & 1 & \cdots & 1 \\ \vdots & \vdots & & \vdots \\ 1 & 1 & \cdots & 1 \end{bmatrix}$$

PROBLEMS

PART 1

Write out the entries for each matrix in Problems 0.2.1–0.2.4.

0.2.1. $\mathbf{A}_{3\times3} = (j^i)$ **0.2.2.** $\mathbf{A}_{2\times4} = (i + j)$ **0.2.3.** $\mathbf{A}_{3\times3} = (i)$

0.2.4. $\mathbf{A}_{3\times3} = (j)$

What are the coefficient and augmented matrices for each of the systems in Problems 0.2.5–0.2.8.

0.2.5. $x_1 = 0$, $x_2 = 0$, $x_3 = 0$ **0.2.6.** $x_1 + x_2 + x_3 = 0$ **0.2.7.** $x_1 = x_2$, $x_2 = x_3$, $x_3 = 1$

$$\begin{aligned} x_1 &= 0 \\ x_2 &= 0 \\ x_3 &= 0 \end{aligned} \qquad x_1 + x_2 + x_3 = 0 \qquad \begin{aligned} x_1 &= x_2 \\ x_2 &= x_3 \\ x_3 &= 1 \end{aligned}$$

0.2.8. $x_1 = 0, x_2 = 1, x_3 = 1$

0.2.9. Explain why a square matrix is diagonal if and only if it is both upper and lower triangular.

0.2.10. Is a 1×1 matrix upper triangular? Lower triangular? Diagonal? A vector? A row vector? A diagonal matrix? A symmetric matrix?

0.2.11. What is the diagonal of $\mathbf{A}_{2\times4} = (i - j)$? Of $(\mathbf{A}_{2\times4})^{\mathrm{T}}$?

0.2.12. Explain why the transpose of an upper (lower) trapezoidal matrix is lower (upper) trapezoidal.

0.2.13. Write an upper trapezoidal column vector. Do the same for a row vector. Do the same for lower trapezoidal column vectors and row vectors.

0.2.14. Identify the entries (*a*) a_{22}, (*b*) a_{32}, (*c*) a_{44}, (*d*) a_{14} for the matrix

$$\mathbf{A} = \begin{bmatrix} 5 & -1 & 0 & -3 \\ 1 & 0 & 0 & 2 \\ 2 & 2 & 2 & -2 \\ 0 & -5 & 3 & -3 \end{bmatrix}$$

PART 2

0.2.15. Clarify the sentence "$\mathbf{A}^{\mathrm{T}}$ is obtained from **A** by rotating the entries of **A** about its diagonal."

0.2.16. If **A** is upper trapezoidal and **B** is formed from **A** by deleting the last *r* columns of **A**, is **B** upper trapezoidal? Suppose the first *r* columns of **A** are deleted? The last *r* rows of **A**? The first *r* rows and columns?

0.2.17. If **A** is not a square matrix, is the diagonal of **A** the same as the diagonal of $\mathbf{A}^{\mathrm{T}}$? Explain. (*Hint:* Discover whether the transposition operation leaves some entries of **A** fixed in position.)

0.3 ADDITION AND SCALAR MULTIPLICATION

Consider the two matrices **A** and **B** given by

$$\mathbf{A} = \begin{bmatrix} a_{11} & a_{12} & \cdots & a_{1n} \\ a_{21} & a_{22} & \cdots & a_{2n} \\ \vdots & \vdots & & \vdots \\ a_{m1} & a_{m2} & \cdots & a_{mn} \end{bmatrix} \qquad \mathbf{B} = \begin{bmatrix} b_{11} & b_{12} & \cdots & b_{1n} \\ b_{21} & b_{22} & \cdots & b_{2n} \\ \vdots & \vdots & & \vdots \\ b_{m1} & b_{m2} & \cdots & b_{mn} \end{bmatrix}$$

We define the sum of **A** and **B**, $\mathbf{C} = \mathbf{A} + \mathbf{B}$, by $\mathbf{C} = (a_{ij} + b_{ij})$. In expanded form,

$$\begin{bmatrix} c_{11} & c_{12} & \cdots & c_{1n} \\ c_{21} & c_{22} & \cdots & c_{2n} \\ \vdots & \vdots & & \vdots \\ c_{m1} & c_{m2} & \cdots & c_{mn} \end{bmatrix} = \begin{bmatrix} a_{11} & a_{12} & \cdots & a_{1n} \\ a_{21} & a_{22} & \cdots & a_{2n} \\ \vdots & \vdots & & \vdots \\ a_{m1} & a_{m2} & \cdots & a_{mn} \end{bmatrix} + \begin{bmatrix} b_{11} & b_{12} & \cdots & b_{1n} \\ b_{21} & b_{22} & \cdots & b_{2n} \\ \vdots & \vdots & & \vdots \\ b_{m1} & b_{m2} & \cdots & b_{mn} \end{bmatrix}$$

$$= \begin{bmatrix} a_{11} + b_{11} & a_{12} + b_{12} & \cdots & a_{1n} + b_{1n} \\ a_{21} + b_{21} & a_{22} + b_{22} & \cdots & a_{2n} + b_{2n} \\ \vdots & \vdots & & \vdots \\ a_{m1} + b_{m1} & a_{m2} + b_{m2} & \cdots & a_{mn} + b_{mn} \end{bmatrix} \tag{0.3.1}$$

We use the words *scalar* and *number* synonymously. The product of a number and a matrix, called *scalar multiplication* and written $k\mathbf{A}$, is defined by (ka_{ij}). In expanded form,

$$k\mathbf{A} = \begin{bmatrix} ka_{11} & ka_{12} & \cdots & ka_{1n} \\ ka_{21} & ka_{22} & \cdots & ka_{2n} \\ \vdots & \vdots & & \vdots \\ ka_{m1} & ka_{m2} & \cdots & ka_{mn} \end{bmatrix} \tag{0.3.2}$$

For a positive integer k, Eq. 0.3.2 reduces to the familiar algebraic identities, $\mathbf{A} + \mathbf{A} = 2\mathbf{A}$, $\mathbf{A} + \mathbf{A} + \mathbf{A} = 3\mathbf{A}$, and so on. Likewise, $0\mathbf{A}_n = \mathbf{O}_n$. The following theorem lists some of the variety of other algebraic relationships that follow from these definitions.

Theorem 0.3.1. *Assume that all the sums listed below are defined. Then, for all matrices* **A**, **B**, *and* **C** *and all scalars h and k,*

(*a*) $\mathbf{A} + \mathbf{B} = \mathbf{B} + \mathbf{A}$	(*b*) $\mathbf{A} + \mathbf{O} = \mathbf{A}$
(*c*) $\mathbf{A} + (\mathbf{B} + \mathbf{C}) = (\mathbf{A} + \mathbf{B}) + \mathbf{C}$	(*d*) $\mathbf{A} + (-1)\mathbf{A} = \mathbf{O}$
(*e*) $0\mathbf{A} = \mathbf{O}$	(*f*) $h(k\mathbf{A}) = (hk)\mathbf{A}$
(*g*) $(h + k)\mathbf{A} = h\mathbf{A} + k\mathbf{A}$	(*h*) $k(\mathbf{A} + \mathbf{B}) = k\mathbf{A} + k\mathbf{B}$
(*i*) $(\mathbf{A} + \mathbf{B})^{\mathrm{T}} = \mathbf{A}^{\mathrm{T}} + \mathbf{B}^{\mathrm{T}}$	(*j*) $(k\mathbf{A})^{\mathrm{T}} = k\mathbf{A}^{\mathrm{T}}$

Proof. Here is the proof for (g). If $\mathbf{A} = (a_{ij})$, then

$$\begin{aligned}(h+k)\mathbf{A} &= \big((h+k)a_{ij}\big) = (ha_{ij} + ka_{ij}) \\ &= (ha_{ij}) + (ka_{ij}) = h\mathbf{A} + k\mathbf{A}\end{aligned}$$

The proofs of the remaining parts are left as exercises. ■

The operation of subtraction, written $\mathbf{A}-\mathbf{B}$, is defined by $\mathbf{A}+(-1)\mathbf{B}$. Thus, $\mathbf{A} - \mathbf{A} = \mathbf{A}+(-1)\mathbf{A} = \mathbf{O}$ by Part (d) of Theorem 0.3.1. Since $\mathbf{A}+(\mathbf{B}-\mathbf{A}) = \mathbf{B}$, it follows that $\mathbf{B} - \mathbf{A}$ is the solution of the matrix equation $\mathbf{A} + \mathbf{X} = \mathbf{B}$. (See also Problem 0.3.9.)

Recall from Section 0.2 that a square matrix $\mathbf{A}$ is symmetric if $\mathbf{A} = \mathbf{A}^{\mathrm{T}}$. If $\mathbf{A}^{\mathrm{T}} = -\mathbf{A}$, then $\mathbf{A}$ is *skew-symmetric*. Skew-symmetric matrices are square for the same reason that symmetric matrices are. The following matrices are skew-symmetric:

$$[0], \qquad \begin{bmatrix} 0 & -1 \\ 1 & 0 \end{bmatrix}, \qquad \begin{bmatrix} 0 & -1 & -2 \\ 1 & 0 & -3 \\ 2 & 3 & 0 \end{bmatrix}$$

The appearance of zeros on the diagonals is not an accident; it is a consequence of the equality $\mathbf{A} = -\mathbf{A}^{\mathrm{T}}$.

Example 0.3.1. Show that every skew-symmetric matrix must have zeros on the diagonal.

Solution. The transpose operation leaves the diagonal entries of $\mathbf{A}$ unaffected. However, $\mathbf{A} = -\mathbf{A}^{\mathrm{T}}$ requires that the diagonal entries be equal to their negatives; that is, $a_{ij} = -a_{ij}$. Hence $a_{ii} = 0$.

Example 0.3.2. Let $\mathbf{A}$ be an arbitrary square matrix. Show that (a) $\mathbf{A}+\mathbf{A}^{\mathrm{T}}$ is symmetric and that (b) $\mathbf{A} - \mathbf{A}^{\mathrm{T}}$ is skew-symmetric.

Solution. (a) Recall that a matrix is symmetric if it is equal to its transpose. So consider $(\mathbf{A} + \mathbf{A}^{\mathrm{T}})$. We have $(\mathbf{A} + \mathbf{A}^{\mathrm{T}})^{\mathrm{T}} = \mathbf{A}^{\mathrm{T}} + (\mathbf{A}^{\mathrm{T}})^{\mathrm{T}}$ by Part (i) of Theorem 0.3.1. Now use $\mathbf{A} = (\mathbf{A}^{\mathrm{T}})^{\mathrm{T}}$ to conclude that $(\mathbf{A}+\mathbf{A}^{\mathrm{T}})^{\mathrm{T}} = \mathbf{A}^{\mathrm{T}}+\mathbf{A}$. Part (b) follows in a similar way.

Example 0.3.3. The definition of scalar multiplication leads to the conclusion that every scalar matrix is a multiple of $\mathbf{I}$, that is,

$$a\mathbf{I} = \begin{bmatrix} a & 0 & & 0 \\ 0 & a & \cdots & 0 \\ \vdots & \vdots & & \vdots \\ 0 & 0 & \cdots & a \end{bmatrix}_{n\times n}$$

Matrices with one entry are identified with their sole entry. That is, we write $[a] = a$ even though this is technically incorrect. This will cause no harm and is very convenient.

PROBLEMS

PART 1

0.3.1. Compute the following combinations for the matrices

$$\mathbf{A} = \begin{bmatrix} 1 & -1 & -2 \\ 2 & 1 & 3 \\ 2 & 3 & 0 \end{bmatrix} \qquad \mathbf{B} = \begin{bmatrix} 0 & 1 & 2 \\ 1 & 0 & -3 \\ 2 & 3 & -1 \end{bmatrix}$$

(*a*) $\mathbf{A} - \mathbf{B}$ (*b*) $5\mathbf{A} + 2\mathbf{B}$ (*c*) $\mathbf{A} + \mathbf{A}^{\mathrm{T}}$
(*d*) $\mathbf{A} - \mathbf{A}^{\mathrm{T}}$ (*e*) $\mathbf{B} - \mathbf{A}$

0.3.2. Describe the matrices that are both symmetric and skew-symmetric.

0.3.3. The square matrix of size $n \times n$ with all entries equal to 1 is denoted by $\mathbf{J}_n$. Find (*a*) $\mathbf{J}_n - \mathbf{I}_n$ and (*b*) $\mathbf{J}_n - (n-1)\mathbf{I}_n$.

0.3.4. Find $\mathbf{A}_{*2} + \mathbf{B}_{*3} + \mathbf{B}_{*1}$ using the matrices **A** and **B** of Problem 0.3.1. (See Section 0.2 for the definition of $\mathbf{A}_{*2}$, $\mathbf{B}_{*3}$ and $\mathbf{B}_{*1}$.)

PART 2

0.3.5. Prove Parts (*a*)–(*j*) of Theorem 0.3.1.

0.3.6. Suppose **A** is an arbitrary square matrix. Define "the symmetric part of **A**" by $\mathbf{A}_s = (\mathbf{A} + \mathbf{A}^{\mathrm{T}})/2$ and the "skew-symmetric part of **A**" by an analogous formula $\mathbf{A}_a = (\mathbf{A} - \mathbf{A}^{\mathrm{T}})/2$ Show that $\mathbf{A}_s$ is symmetric, that $\mathbf{A}_a$ is skew-symmetric, and that $\mathbf{A} = \mathbf{A}_s + \mathbf{A}_a$.

0.3.7. Illustrate the conclusions in Problem 0.3.6 for the matrices in Problem 0.3.1.

0.3.8. Refer to Problem 0.3.6. If **A** is symmetric, what is its skew-symmetric part? If **A** is skew-symmetric, what is its symmetric part?

0.3.9. Show that $\mathbf{A}+\mathbf{X} = \mathbf{B}$ has the *unique* solution $\mathbf{X} = \mathbf{B}-\mathbf{A}$. (*Hint:* Use the definition of $\mathbf{B} - \mathbf{A}$ and substitute this expression for **X**. By using various parts of Theorem 0.3.1, show that $\mathbf{B} - \mathbf{A}$ is a solution. Show that if **Y** is a solution, then **Y** must be $\mathbf{B} - \mathbf{A}$. This last assertion is the meaning of uniqueness in this context.)

0.4 MATRIX MULTIPLICATION: PART 1

The definition of matrix multiplication may seem, at first glance, to be quite artificial. Experience shows that it is functional, and interesting motivations for this definition do exist. (See Section 0.5.)

The process of defining **AB** begins with a special case. Let **A** and **B** be given by

$$\mathbf{A} = [\,a_1 \quad a_2 \quad \ldots \quad a_n\,], \qquad \mathbf{B} = \begin{bmatrix} b_1 \\ b_2 \\ \vdots \\ b_n \end{bmatrix}$$

Then by definition **AB** is the 1×1 matrix, written as scalar

$$\mathbf{AB} = a_1b_1 + a_2b_2 + \cdots + a_nb_n \tag{0.4.1}$$

If $\mathbf{x}$ and $\mathbf{y}$ are column matrices of the same size, Eq. 0.4.1 implies that $\mathbf{x}^T\mathbf{y}$ is the scalar $x_1y_1 + x_2y_2 + \cdots + x_ny_n$, called the *dot product* of $\mathbf{x}$ and $\mathbf{y}$. (In physics $\mathbf{x}^T\mathbf{y}$ is often written $\mathbf{x} \cdot \mathbf{y}$. We use both notations interchangeably.)

Theorem 0.4.1. *For each vector* $\mathbf{x}$, $\mathbf{y}$, *and* $\mathbf{z}$ *and every scalar* k,

$(a)\ \mathbf{x} \cdot \mathbf{y} = \mathbf{y} \cdot \mathbf{x}$ $\qquad (b)\ \mathbf{x} \cdot \mathbf{0} = 0$

$(c)\ \mathbf{x} \cdot (\mathbf{y} + \mathbf{z}) = \mathbf{x} \cdot \mathbf{y} + \mathbf{x} \cdot \mathbf{z}$ $\qquad (d)\ \mathbf{x} \cdot (k\mathbf{y}) = k(\mathbf{x} \cdot \mathbf{y})$

$(e)\ \mathbf{x} \cdot \mathbf{x} = x_1^2 + x_2^2 + \cdots + x_n^2$

Proof. We present one proof and leave the remaining arguments for the exercises. To prove (a), simply write down the definitions

$$\mathbf{x} \cdot \mathbf{y} = x_1y_1 + x_2y_2 + \cdots + x_ny_n, \qquad \mathbf{y} \cdot \mathbf{x} = y_1x_1 + y_2x_2 + \cdots + y_nx_n$$

and note that for numbers, $x_iy_j = y_jx_i$. ■

Now consider the arbitrary matrix

$$\mathbf{A} = \begin{bmatrix} a_{11} & a_{12} & \cdots & a_{1n} \\ a_{21} & a_{22} & \cdots & a_{2n} \\ \vdots & \vdots & & \vdots \\ a_{m1} & a_{m2} & \vdots & a_{mn} \end{bmatrix} = \begin{bmatrix} \mathbf{A}_{1*} \\ \mathbf{A}_{2*} \\ \vdots \\ \mathbf{A}_{m*} \end{bmatrix} \tag{0.4.2}$$

where $\mathbf{A}_{i*}$ denotes the ith row of $\mathbf{A}$ as a row vector. (This notation was introduced in Section 0.2 and, although it violates our notational convention for row vectors, writing the ith row of $\mathbf{A}$ as $\mathbf{A}_{i*}$ is common and convenient.) Then define the product $\mathbf{Ax}$ by

$$\mathbf{Ax} = \begin{bmatrix} \mathbf{A}_{1*}\mathbf{x} \\ \mathbf{A}_{2*}\mathbf{x} \\ \vdots \\ \mathbf{A}_{n*}\mathbf{x} \end{bmatrix} \tag{0.4.3}$$

That is, *the ith entry in the vector* $\mathbf{Ax}$ *is the dot product of the ith row of* $\mathbf{A}$ *with* $\mathbf{x}$. Note the repeated use of Eq. 0.4.1. Since the dot product requires the two vector factors to have the same size, the number of entries in $\mathbf{A}_{i*}$ must be the same as the number of entries of $\mathbf{x}$. But this means that the *number of columns of* $\mathbf{A}$ *is the same as the number of entries of* $\mathbf{x}$. Some examples will help clarify Eq. 0.4.3.

Example 0.4.1. Compute $\mathbf{A1}$ for

$$\mathbf{A} = \begin{bmatrix} 2 & -1 & 1 & -1 \\ 1 & 0 & -1 & 0 \\ 0 & 1 & 1 & 1 \end{bmatrix}, \qquad \mathbf{1} = \begin{bmatrix} 1 \\ 1 \\ 1 \\ 1 \end{bmatrix}$$

Solution. The resulting product is a vector with three entries:

$$\begin{bmatrix} [2 & -1 & 1 & -1]\mathbf{1} \\ [1 & 0 & -1 & 0]\mathbf{1} \\ [0 & 1 & 1 & 1]\mathbf{1} \end{bmatrix} = \begin{bmatrix} 2-1+1-1 \\ 1+0-1+0 \\ 0+1+1+1 \end{bmatrix} = \begin{bmatrix} 1 \\ 0 \\ 3 \end{bmatrix}$$

Example 0.4.2. For each $\mathbf{A}$ and $\mathbf{x}$ find $\mathbf{Ax}$.

(*a*) $\mathbf{A} = \mathbf{O}$ and $\mathbf{x}$ arbitrary (*b*) $\mathbf{A} = \mathbf{J}$ and $\mathbf{x} = \mathbf{1}$.

Solution. Assume that each product is defined; that is, the sizes of $\mathbf{A}$ and $\mathbf{x}$ are such that $\mathbf{Ax}$ is meaningful. The vectors $\mathbf{0}$ and $\mathbf{1}$ are defined in Section 0.2. Recall that $\mathbf{J}_n = [\mathbf{1} \quad \mathbf{1} \quad \dots \quad \mathbf{1}]$ and $\mathbf{O}_n = [\mathbf{0} \quad \mathbf{0} \quad \dots \quad \mathbf{0}]$. Then

$$(a)\ \mathbf{O}_n\mathbf{x} = \begin{bmatrix} \mathbf{0}^T \\ \mathbf{0}^T \\ \vdots \\ \mathbf{0}^T \end{bmatrix} \mathbf{x} = \begin{bmatrix} \mathbf{0}^T\mathbf{x} \\ \mathbf{0}^T\mathbf{x} \\ \vdots \\ \mathbf{0}^T\mathbf{x} \end{bmatrix} = \begin{bmatrix} 0 \\ 0 \\ \vdots \\ 0 \end{bmatrix} = \mathbf{0}, \text{ because } \mathbf{0}^T\mathbf{x} = \mathbf{0}\cdot\mathbf{x} = 0$$

$$(b)\ \mathbf{J}_n\mathbf{1} = \begin{bmatrix} \mathbf{1}^T \\ \mathbf{1}^T \\ \vdots \\ \mathbf{1}^T \end{bmatrix} \mathbf{1} = \begin{bmatrix} \mathbf{1}^T\mathbf{1} \\ \mathbf{1}^T\mathbf{1} \\ \vdots \\ \mathbf{1}^T\mathbf{1} \end{bmatrix} = \begin{bmatrix} n \\ n \\ \vdots \\ n \end{bmatrix} = n\begin{bmatrix} 1 \\ 1 \\ \vdots \\ 1 \end{bmatrix} = n\mathbf{1}, \text{ because } \mathbf{1}\cdot\mathbf{1} = n$$

Example 0.4.3. Show that $\mathbf{Ae}_k$ is the kth column of $\mathbf{A}$. (This is an important example.)

Solution. By definition, $\mathbf{Ae}_k$ is a vector whose ith row is given by $A_{i*}\mathbf{e}_k$. In detail, since $\mathbf{e}_k$ is a vector of zeros except for the single 1 located in its kth row,

$$\mathbf{A}_{i*}\mathbf{e}_k = a_{i1}\cdot 0 + a_{i2}\cdot 0 + \cdots + a_{ik}\cdot 1 + \cdots + a_{in}\cdot 0 = a_{ik}$$

The subscript k in the above equation is arbitrary, and therefore

$$\mathbf{Ae}_k = \begin{bmatrix} \mathbf{A}_{1*}\mathbf{e}_k \\ \mathbf{A}_{2*}\mathbf{e}_k \\ \vdots \\ \mathbf{A}_{m*}\mathbf{e}_k \end{bmatrix} = \begin{bmatrix} a_{1k} \\ a_{2k} \\ \vdots \\ a_{mk} \end{bmatrix} = \mathbf{A}_{*k}$$

The definition of $\mathbf{Ax}$ requires that the number of columns of $\mathbf{A}$ (which is the number of entries in $\mathbf{A}_{j*}$) be the same as the number of entries in $\mathbf{x}$. The resulting product is a vector whose size is $m \times 1$, where m is the number of rows of $\mathbf{A}$. Thus, if $\mathbf{A}$ is $m \times n$ and $\mathbf{x}$ is $n \times 1$, $\mathbf{Ax}$ is defined and is a vector of size $m \times 1$.

Consider the product $\mathbf{x}^T\mathbf{x}$. Here $\mathbf{A} = \mathbf{x}^T$. In terms of Eq. 0.4.3,

$$\mathbf{x}^{\mathrm{T}}\mathbf{x} = [x_1 \quad x_2 \quad \ldots \quad x_n]\begin{bmatrix} x_1 \\ x_2 \\ \vdots \\ x_n \end{bmatrix} = [x_1^2 + x_2^2 + \cdots + x_n^2] = [\mathbf{x} \cdot \mathbf{x}]$$

In terms of Eq. 0.4.1, $\mathbf{x}^{\mathrm{T}}\mathbf{x}$ is the scalar $\mathbf{x} \cdot \mathbf{x}$. As noted at the end of the previous section, we identify the 1×1 matrix with its single entry, and hence the two definitions agree.

The next example shows that the definition of $\mathbf{Ax}$ is useful for representing systems of m equations in n unknowns as a single matrix equation $\mathbf{Ax} = \mathbf{b}$.

Example 0.4.4. Write out the three equations implicit in the equation $\mathbf{Ax} = \mathbf{b}$, where

$$\mathbf{A} = \begin{bmatrix} 2 & -3 & 4 \\ 0 & 2 & 2 \\ 0 & 0 & 1 \end{bmatrix}, \qquad \mathbf{x} = \begin{bmatrix} x \\ y \\ z \end{bmatrix}, \qquad \mathbf{b} = \begin{bmatrix} 7 \\ 0 \\ 1 \end{bmatrix}$$

Solution. The product $\mathbf{Ax}$ is given by

$$\mathbf{Ax} = \begin{bmatrix} 2 & -3 & 4 \\ 0 & 2 & 2 \\ 0 & 0 & 1 \end{bmatrix}\begin{bmatrix} x \\ y \\ z \end{bmatrix} = \begin{bmatrix} 2x - 3y + 4z \\ 2y + 2z \\ z \end{bmatrix} = \begin{bmatrix} 7 \\ 0 \\ 1 \end{bmatrix} \tag{0.4.4}$$

However, two matrices are equal if and only if their corresponding entries are the same. Hence Eq. 0.4.4 implies

$$\begin{aligned} 2x - 3y + 4z &= 7 \\ 2y + 2z &= 0 \\ z &= 1 \end{aligned}$$

Example 0.4.5. Write out the m equations implicit in the equation $\mathbf{Ax} = \mathbf{b}$, where

$$\mathbf{A} = \begin{bmatrix} a_{11} & a_{12} & \cdots & a_{1n} \\ a_{21} & a_{22} & \cdots & a_{2n} \\ \vdots & \vdots & & \vdots \\ a_{m1} & a_{m2} & \cdots & a_{mn} \end{bmatrix}, \qquad \mathbf{x} = \begin{bmatrix} x_1 \\ x_2 \\ \vdots \\ x_n \end{bmatrix}, \qquad \mathbf{b} = \begin{bmatrix} b_1 \\ b_2 \\ \vdots \\ b_m \end{bmatrix}$$

Solution. For $\mathbf{Ax}$ to equal $\mathbf{b}$, it is necessary that each row in the product $\mathbf{Ax}$ equal the corresponding row in $\mathbf{b}$. Since there are m rows in $\mathbf{Ax}$, there are m equations. These equations are

$$\begin{aligned} a_{11}x_1 + a_{12}x_2 + \cdots + a_{1n}x_n &= b_1 \\ a_{21}x_1 + a_{22}x_2 + \cdots + a_{2n}x_n &= b_2 \\ \vdots \qquad \vdots \qquad\quad & \vdots \quad \vdots \\ a_{m1}x_1 + a_{m2}x_2 + \cdots + a_{mn}x_n &= b_m \end{aligned}$$

Theorem 0.4.2. *Let* $\mathbf{A}$ *be* $m \times n$ *and* $\mathbf{x}$ *and* $\mathbf{y}$ *be* $n \times 1$. *Then for each such* $\mathbf{A}$, $\mathbf{x}$, $\mathbf{y}$, *and each scalar* h *and* k,

(a) $\mathbf{A}(k\mathbf{x}) = k\mathbf{Ax}$ $\quad$ (b) $\mathbf{A}(\mathbf{x}+\mathbf{y}) = \mathbf{Ax} + \mathbf{Ay}$

(c) $\mathbf{Ix} = \mathbf{x}$ $\quad$ (d) $\mathbf{A}(h\mathbf{x} + k\mathbf{y}) = h\mathbf{Ax} + k\mathbf{Ay}$

Proof. Refer to the definition (Eq. 0.4.3):

$$(a)\ \mathbf{A}(k\mathbf{x}) = \begin{bmatrix} \mathbf{A}_{1*} \\ \mathbf{A}_{2*} \\ \vdots \\ \mathbf{A}_{n*} \end{bmatrix} \begin{bmatrix} kx_1 \\ kx_2 \\ \vdots \\ kx_n \end{bmatrix} = \begin{bmatrix} \mathbf{A}_{1*}(k\mathbf{x}) \\ \mathbf{A}_{2*}(k\mathbf{x}) \\ \vdots \\ \mathbf{A}_{n*}(k\mathbf{x}) \end{bmatrix} = k \begin{bmatrix} \mathbf{A}_{1*}\mathbf{x} \\ \mathbf{A}_{2*}\mathbf{x} \\ \vdots \\ \mathbf{A}_{n*}\mathbf{x} \end{bmatrix} = k(\mathbf{Ax})$$

$$(b)\ \mathbf{A}(\mathbf{x}+\mathbf{y}) = \begin{bmatrix} \mathbf{A}_{1*} \\ \mathbf{A}_{2*} \\ \vdots \\ \mathbf{A}_{n*} \end{bmatrix} (\mathbf{x}+\mathbf{y}) = \begin{bmatrix} \mathbf{A}_{1*}(\mathbf{x}+\mathbf{y}) \\ \mathbf{A}_{2*}(\mathbf{x}+\mathbf{y}) \\ \vdots \\ \mathbf{A}_{n*}(\mathbf{x}+\mathbf{y}) \end{bmatrix} = \begin{bmatrix} \mathbf{A}_{1*}\mathbf{x} + \mathbf{A}_{1*}\mathbf{y} \\ \mathbf{A}_{2*}\mathbf{x} + \mathbf{A}_{2*}\mathbf{y} \\ \vdots \quad\quad \vdots \\ \mathbf{A}_{n*}\mathbf{x} + \mathbf{A}_{n*}\mathbf{y} \end{bmatrix}$$

$$= \begin{bmatrix} \mathbf{A}_{1*}\mathbf{x} \\ \mathbf{A}_{2*}\mathbf{x} \\ \vdots \\ \mathbf{A}_{n*}\mathbf{x} \end{bmatrix} + \begin{bmatrix} \mathbf{A}_{1*}\mathbf{y} \\ \mathbf{A}_{2*}\mathbf{y} \\ \vdots \\ \mathbf{A}_{n*}\mathbf{y} \end{bmatrix} = \mathbf{Ax} + \mathbf{Ay}$$

$$(c)\ \mathbf{Ix} = \begin{bmatrix} \mathbf{e}_1^{\mathrm{T}} \\ \mathbf{e}_2^{\mathrm{T}} \\ \vdots \\ \mathbf{e}_n^{\mathrm{T}} \end{bmatrix} \mathbf{x} = \begin{bmatrix} \mathbf{e}_1^{\mathrm{T}} \cdot \mathbf{x} \\ \mathbf{e}_2^{\mathrm{T}} \cdot \mathbf{x} \\ \vdots \\ \mathbf{e}_n^{\mathrm{T}} \cdot \mathbf{x} \end{bmatrix} = \begin{bmatrix} x_1 \\ x_2 \\ \vdots \\ x_n \end{bmatrix} = \mathbf{x}$$

(d) $\mathbf{A}(h\mathbf{x} + k\mathbf{y}) = \mathbf{A}(h\mathbf{x}) + \mathbf{A}(k\mathbf{y}) = h\mathbf{Ax} + k\mathbf{Ay}$ follows from Part (b) and Part (a), respectively. ■

PROBLEMS

PART 1

0.4.1. For the matrix

$$\mathbf{A} = \begin{bmatrix} 1 & 0 & -1 \\ 0 & 2 & 2 \\ -1 & 2 & 2 \end{bmatrix}$$

and the vector

$$\mathbf{x} = \begin{bmatrix} x \\ y \\ z \end{bmatrix},$$

(a) Compute the product $\mathbf{w} = \mathbf{Ax}$.
(b) Use the answer in (a) to compute $[x \quad y \quad z]\mathbf{w}$.
(c) Use the answer in (a) to compute $\mathbf{w} \cdot \mathbf{w}$.

0.4.2. Find each of the following vectors:

(*a*) $\begin{bmatrix} 1 & 0 & -1 \\ 0 & 2 & 2 \\ -1 & 2 & 2 \end{bmatrix}\begin{bmatrix} 1 \\ 0 \\ 0 \end{bmatrix}$ (*b*) $\begin{bmatrix} 1 & 0 & -1 \\ 0 & 2 & 2 \\ -1 & 2 & 2 \end{bmatrix}\begin{bmatrix} 0 \\ 1 \\ 0 \end{bmatrix}$ (*c*) $\begin{bmatrix} 1 & 0 & -1 \\ 0 & 2 & 2 \\ -1 & 2 & 2 \end{bmatrix}\begin{bmatrix} 0 \\ 0 \\ 1 \end{bmatrix}$

0.4.3. Given

$$\mathbf{A} = \begin{bmatrix} 0 & -1 & -2 \\ 1 & 0 & -3 \\ 2 & 3 & 0 \end{bmatrix}$$

write $\mathbf{A}_{1*}$, $\mathbf{A}_{2*}$, $\mathbf{A}_{3*}$, $\mathbf{A}_{*1}$, $\mathbf{A}_{*2}$, and $\mathbf{A}_{*3}$.

0.4.4. Which of the following products make sense? If they do not, explain why not. (Assume that $\mathbf{x}$ and $\mathbf{y}$ have the same sizes.)

(*a*) $(\mathbf{x}^T\mathbf{y})(\mathbf{x}^T\mathbf{y})$ (*b*) $(\mathbf{x}\cdot\mathbf{y})(\mathbf{x}\cdot\mathbf{y})$ (*c*) $(\mathbf{x}\cdot\mathbf{y})(\mathbf{x}^T\mathbf{y})$
(*d*) $(\mathbf{x}^T\mathbf{y})\mathbf{x}$ (*e*) $(\mathbf{x}\cdot\mathbf{y})\mathbf{x}$ (*f*) $(\mathbf{x}^T\mathbf{y})\cdot\mathbf{x}$
(*g*) $\mathbf{x}^T\cdot\mathbf{y}$ (*h*) $\mathbf{x}^T\cdot\mathbf{y}^T$

0.4.5. Let $\mathbf{x} = [-1 \quad 1]^T$. Find $\mathbf{y}$ so that $\mathbf{x}\cdot\mathbf{y} = 0$ and $\mathbf{y}\cdot\mathbf{y} = 1$.

PART 2

0.4.6. Suppose $\mathbf{x} \in \mathcal{R}^n$ is real. Show that $\mathbf{x}\cdot\mathbf{x} = 0$ if and only if $\mathbf{x} = \mathbf{0}$.
0.4.7. Find an example in which $\mathbf{x} \in \mathcal{C}^n$ and for which $\mathbf{x}\cdot\mathbf{x} = 0$.
0.4.8. Find $\mathbf{1}\cdot\mathbf{1}$, $\mathbf{1}\cdot\mathbf{e}_1$, $\mathbf{e}_i\cdot\mathbf{e}_i$, and $\mathbf{e}_i\cdot\mathbf{e}_j$ $(i \neq j)$.
0.4.9. Explain why $\mathbf{e}_i^T\mathbf{A} = \mathbf{A}_{i*}$.
0.4.10. Explain why $\mathbf{e}_i\cdot(\mathbf{A}\mathbf{e}_j) = a_{ij}$. What is $\mathbf{e}_i^T\mathbf{A}\mathbf{e}_i$?
0.4.11. If $\mathbf{x} \in \mathcal{R}^n$ show that $\mathbf{x}\cdot\mathbf{x} \geq 0$. Find $\mathbf{x} \in \mathcal{C}^n$ such that $\mathbf{x}\cdot\mathbf{x} < 0$.
0.4.12. Show that $\mathbf{x}\cdot(\mathbf{y}+\mathbf{z}) = \mathbf{x}\cdot\mathbf{y} + \mathbf{x}\cdot\mathbf{z}$.
0.4.13. Show that $\mathbf{x}\cdot(k\mathbf{y}) = k(\mathbf{x}\cdot\mathbf{y})$.
0.4.14. Show that $x \cdot y$

$$\mathbf{x}\cdot(a_1\mathbf{y}_1 + a_2\mathbf{y}_2 + \cdots + a_k\mathbf{y}_k) = a_1\mathbf{x}\cdot\mathbf{y}_1 + a_2\mathbf{x}\cdot\mathbf{y}_2 + \cdots + a_k\mathbf{x}\cdot\mathbf{y}_k$$

0.5 MATRIX MULTIPLICATION: PART 2

Section 0.4 lays the groundwork for the definition of the product of two matrices. This definition is based on the matrix-vector product $\mathbf{Ax}$.

Let $\mathbf{B}_{*1}, \mathbf{B}_{*2}, \ldots, \mathbf{B}_{*n}$ denote the columns of $\mathbf{B}$, so that $\mathbf{B}$ may be written $\mathbf{B} = [\mathbf{B}_{*1} \quad \mathbf{B}_{*2} \quad \ldots \quad \mathbf{B}_{*n}]$. Suppose $\mathbf{A}$ has size such that $\mathbf{AB}_{*j}$ is defined as in Section 0.4. Then we define $\mathbf{AB}$ as follows:

$$\mathbf{AB} = [\mathbf{AB}_{*1} \quad \mathbf{AB}_{*2} \quad \ldots \quad \mathbf{AB}_{*n}] \tag{0.5.1}$$

That is, *the* ith *column of* **AB** *is the product of* **A** *with the* ith *column of* **B**. (This is an example of what has become known as "parallel processing." The computation of the ith column of $\mathbf{AB}$ depends only on a knowledge of $\mathbf{A}$ and of the ith column of $\mathbf{B}$. Thus each product $\mathbf{AB}_{*k}$ can be computed independently and therefore simultaneously on a computer with n arithmetic units.) Because of Eq. 0.5.1, the number of columns of $\mathbf{A}$ must be the same as the number of rows of $\mathbf{B}$. If $\mathbf{A}$ is $m \times n$ and $\mathbf{B}$ is $n \times q$, then $\mathbf{A}$ and $\mathbf{B}$ are *conformable* for the product

AB (in that order). In the product **AB**, **A** is called the *premultiplier* and **B** the *postmultiplier*. It also follows from Eq. 0.5.1 that **AB** has size $m \times q$.

Suppose $\mathbf{C} = \mathbf{AB}$ and c_{ij} is the entry in the (i,j) position of **C**. (c_{ij} is in the ith row, jth column of **AB**.) Let the ith row of **A** be denoted by $\mathbf{A}_{i*}$. Since the jth column of **B** is $\mathbf{B}_{*j}$, the jth column of **C** is $\mathbf{AB}_{*j}$. From Eq. 0.5.1, it follows that

$$c_{ij} = \mathbf{A}_{i*}\mathbf{B}_{*j} \tag{0.5.2}$$

To illustrate Eq. 0.5.2, consider the following product of arbitrary matrices **A** and **B**, in which **A** is conformable with **B**.

$$\mathbf{AB} = \begin{bmatrix} * & * & \cdots & * \\ a_{21} & a_{22} & \cdots & a_{2r} \\ \vdots & \vdots & & \vdots \\ * & * & \cdots & * \end{bmatrix} \begin{bmatrix} b_{11} & * & \cdots & * \\ b_{21} & * & \cdots & * \\ \vdots & \vdots & & \vdots \\ b_{r1} & * & \cdots & * \end{bmatrix} = \begin{bmatrix} * & * & \cdots & * \\ c_{21} & * & \cdots & * \\ \vdots & \vdots & & \vdots \\ * & * & \cdots & * \end{bmatrix}$$

The second row of **A** and first column of **B** are outlined to show how c_{21} is computed. Note that $c_{21} = \mathbf{A}_{2*}\mathbf{B}_{*1} = a_{21}b_{11} + a_{22}b_{21} + \cdots + a_{2r}b_{r1}$.

In general, Eq. 0.5.2 has the expanded form:

$$c_{ij} = a_{i1}b_{1j} + a_{i2}b_{2j} + \cdots + a_{ir}b_{rj} \tag{0.5.3}$$

Three examples follow; they illustrate Eq. 0.5.1 or its equivalent, Eq. 0.5.2, depending on which is more convenient or instructive.

Example 0.5.1. Find **AB** for

$$\mathbf{A} = \begin{bmatrix} 1 & 0 & -1 & 2 \\ 0 & 2 & 1 & 3 \end{bmatrix}, \qquad \mathbf{B} = \begin{bmatrix} 0 & -1 \\ 1 & 1 \\ 2 & 0 \\ 1 & 2 \end{bmatrix}$$

Solution. Since **A** has four columns and **B** has four rows, the product **AB** exists. Moreover, we know that **AB** is 2×2. To find the entries of **AB**, we compute the product of **A** with each of the two columns of **B**:

$$\mathbf{AB}_{*1} = \begin{bmatrix} 1 & 0 & -1 & 2 \\ 0 & 2 & 1 & 3 \end{bmatrix} \begin{bmatrix} 0 \\ 1 \\ 2 \\ 1 \end{bmatrix} = \begin{bmatrix} 0 \\ 7 \end{bmatrix}$$

$$\mathbf{AB}_{*2} = \begin{bmatrix} 1 & 0 & -1 & 2 \\ 0 & 2 & 1 & 3 \end{bmatrix} \begin{bmatrix} -1 \\ 1 \\ 0 \\ 2 \end{bmatrix} = \begin{bmatrix} 3 \\ 8 \end{bmatrix}$$

Hence the product **AB** is given by

$$\mathbf{AB} = [\mathbf{AB}_{*1} \quad \mathbf{AB}_{*2}] = \begin{bmatrix} 0 & 3 \\ 7 & 8 \end{bmatrix}$$

Example 0.5.2. Find **AB** for each of the following matrices.

(a) $\mathbf{A} = \mathbf{B} = \mathbf{J}_n$ (b) $\mathbf{A} = \mathbf{O}_n$, $\mathbf{B}_{n\times q}$ is arbitrary
(c) $\mathbf{A} = \mathbf{I}_n$, $\mathbf{B}_{n\times q}$ is arbitrary (d) $\mathbf{B} = \mathbf{I}_q$, $\mathbf{A}_{n\times q}$ is arbitrary

Solution.

$$(a)\ \mathbf{J}_n\mathbf{J}_n = \mathbf{J}_n[\mathbf{1}\ \ \mathbf{1}\ \ \dots\ \ \mathbf{1}] = [\mathbf{J}_n\mathbf{1}\ \ \mathbf{J}_n\mathbf{1}\ \ \dots\ \ \mathbf{J}_n\mathbf{1}]$$
$$= [n\mathbf{1}\ \ n\mathbf{1}\ \ \dots\ \ n\mathbf{1}] = n[\mathbf{1}\ \ \mathbf{1}\ \ \dots\ \ \mathbf{1}] = n\mathbf{J}_n$$

$$(b)\ \mathbf{OB} = \mathbf{O}[\mathbf{B}_{*1}\ \ \mathbf{B}_{*2}\ \ \dots\ \ \mathbf{B}_{*n}] = [\mathbf{OB}_{*1}\ \ \mathbf{OB}_{*2}\ \ \dots\ \ \mathbf{OB}_{*n}]$$
$$= \mathbf{O}, \text{ because } \mathbf{OB}_{*i} = \mathbf{0}.$$

$$(c)\ \mathbf{IB} = \mathbf{I}[\mathbf{B}_{*1}\ \ \mathbf{B}_{*2}\ \ \dots\ \ \mathbf{B}_{*n}] = [\mathbf{IB}_{*1}\ \ \mathbf{IB}_{*2}\ \ \dots\ \ \mathbf{IB}_{*n}]$$
$$= [\mathbf{B}_{*1}\ \ \mathbf{B}_{*2}\ \ \dots\ \ \mathbf{B}_{*n}] = \mathbf{B}, \text{ since } \mathbf{IB}_{*i} = \mathbf{B}_{*i} \text{ for all } \mathbf{B}_{*i}.$$

$$(d)\ \mathbf{AI} = \mathbf{A}[\mathbf{e}_1\ \ \mathbf{e}_2\ \ \dots\ \ \mathbf{e}_n] = [\mathbf{Ae}_1\ \ \mathbf{Ae}_2\ \ \dots\ \ \mathbf{Ae}_n]$$
$$= [\mathbf{A}_{1*}\ \ \mathbf{A}_{2*}\ \ \dots\ \ \mathbf{A}_{n*}] = \mathbf{A}, \text{ since } \mathbf{Ae}_i = \mathbf{A}_{i*}.$$

Example 0.5.3. Find **AB** for each of the following matrices:

$$(a)\ \mathbf{A} = \begin{bmatrix} 1 & 1 \\ -1 & -1 \end{bmatrix} = \mathbf{B}$$

$$(b)\ \mathbf{A} = \begin{bmatrix} \cos\tau & -\sin\tau \\ \sin\tau & \cos\tau \end{bmatrix},\ \mathbf{B} = \mathbf{A}^{\mathrm{T}}$$

$$(c)\ \mathbf{A} = \mathbf{x},\ \mathbf{B} = \mathbf{x}^{\mathrm{T}}$$

Solution.

(a) $\mathbf{AB} = \mathbf{A}^2 = \mathbf{O}$ by inspection.

$$(b)\ \mathbf{AA}^{\mathrm{T}} = \begin{bmatrix} \cos\tau & -\sin\tau \\ \sin\tau & \cos\tau \end{bmatrix}\begin{bmatrix} \cos\tau & \sin\tau \\ -\sin\tau & \cos\tau \end{bmatrix}$$
$$= \begin{bmatrix} \cos^2\tau + \sin^2\tau & 0 \\ 0 & \sin^2\tau + \cos^2\tau \end{bmatrix} = \begin{bmatrix} 1 & 0 \\ 0 & 1 \end{bmatrix}$$

$$(c)\ \mathbf{xx}^{\mathrm{T}} = \begin{bmatrix} x_1x_1 & x_1x_2 & \cdots & x_1x_n \\ x_2x_1 & x_2x_2 & \cdots & x_2x_n \\ \vdots & \vdots & & \vdots \\ x_nx_1 & x_nx_2 & \cdots & x_nx_n \end{bmatrix}$$

Contrast $\mathbf{xx}^{\mathrm{T}}$ with $\mathbf{x}^{\mathrm{T}}\mathbf{x}$. Both products exist, but the former is an $n \times n$ matrix while the latter is a 1×1 matrix.

The conformability of **A** and **B** does not imply the conformability of **B** and **A**. Indeed, **BA** often fails to exists. For example, if **B** is a vector, then **BA** does not exist unless **A** is a row vector. Thus matrix multiplication is (generally) noncommutative. It is distributive over addition.

Theorem 0.5.1. *Assume that the products* **AB**, **AC**, **DF**, *and* **EF** *exist. Then* (*a*) **A**(**B** + **C**) = **AB** + **AC** *and* (*b*) (**D** + **E**)**F** = **DF** + **EF**.

Proof. Both proofs are simple applications of the definition of matrix multiplication. The details are left to the exercises, Problem 0.5.25. ■

Matrix multiplication is also associative; that is, **A**(**BC**) = (**AB**)**C**. The proof is not difficult, but it is tedious. We state this result as a theorem and leave the proof for the Subsection 0.5.1.

Theorem 0.5.2. *If* **A** *is conformable with* **B** *and* **B** *with* **C**, *then* **A** *is conformable with* **BC**, **AB** *is conformable with* **C**, *and*

$$\mathbf{A}(\mathbf{BC}) = (\mathbf{AB})\mathbf{C} \tag{0.5.4}$$

If **A** is not a square matrix, then the product **AA** does not exist, since **A** is not conformable with itself. On the other hand, **AA** always exists if **A** is a square matrix and, not surprisingly, is written $\mathbf{A}^2$. In this vein, we define $\mathbf{A}^1 = \mathbf{A}$ and by induction, define $\mathbf{A}^{n+1} = \mathbf{A}^n\mathbf{A}$, for each positive integer n. (See Problems 0.5.17 and 0.5.26.)

Transposition and multiplication interact in a simple but by no means obvious way. One might reasonably expect that $(\mathbf{AB})^{\mathrm{T}}$ is related to the product of $\mathbf{A}^{\mathrm{T}}$ and $\mathbf{B}^{\mathrm{T}}$ in some order. In general, if **A** and **B** are conformable, then $\mathbf{B}^{\mathrm{T}}$ and $\mathbf{A}^{\mathrm{T}}$ are always conformable, whereas $\mathbf{A}^{\mathrm{T}}$ and $\mathbf{B}^{\mathrm{T}}$ may not be.

Theorem 0.5.3. *If* **AB** *exists, so does* $\mathbf{B}^{\mathrm{T}}\mathbf{A}^{\mathrm{T}}$, *and*

$$(\mathbf{AB})^{\mathrm{T}} = \mathbf{B}^{\mathrm{T}}\mathbf{A}^{\mathrm{T}} \tag{0.5.5}$$

Proof. The proof consists of comparing the (i,j) entry on both sides of Eq. 0.5.5 and showing that they are identical. Consider, for instance, the (2,1) entry of $\mathbf{B}^{\mathrm{T}}\mathbf{A}^{\mathrm{T}}$. Denote this entry by d_{21}. The following display guides the computation of d_{21}. Here we assume that **A** is $m \times r$ and **B** is $r \times n$:

$$\mathbf{B}^{\mathrm{T}}\mathbf{A}^{\mathrm{T}} = \begin{bmatrix} * & * & \cdots & * \\ b_{12} & b_{22} & \cdots & b_{r2} \\ \vdots & \vdots & & \vdots \\ * & * & \cdots & * \end{bmatrix} \begin{bmatrix} a_{11} & * & \cdots & * \\ a_{12} & * & \cdots & * \\ \vdots & \vdots & & \vdots \\ a_{1r} & * & \cdots & * \end{bmatrix} = \begin{bmatrix} * & * & \cdots & * \\ d_{21} & * & \cdots & * \\ \vdots & \vdots & & \vdots \\ * & * & \cdots & * \end{bmatrix}$$

Thus d_{21} is given by

$$d_{21} = a_{11}b_{12} + a_{12}b_{22} + \cdots + a_{1r}b_{r2} \tag{0.5.6}$$

The (2,1) entry of $(\mathbf{AB})^{\mathrm{T}}$ is the (1,2) entry of **AB**. (Why?) Here is the guide for the computation of the (1,2) entry of **AB**:

$$\mathbf{AB} = \begin{bmatrix} a_{11} & a_{12} & \cdots & a_{1r} \\ * & * & \cdots & * \\ \vdots & \vdots & & \vdots \\ * & * & \cdots & * \end{bmatrix} \begin{bmatrix} * & b_{12} & \cdots & * \\ * & b_{22} & \cdots & * \\ \vdots & \vdots & & \vdots \\ * & b_{r2} & \cdots & * \end{bmatrix} = \begin{bmatrix} * & x & \cdots & * \\ * & * & \cdots & * \\ \vdots & \vdots & & \vdots \\ * & * & \cdots & * \end{bmatrix}$$

Clearly, $x = d_{21}$. The general argument follows this special case with very little alteration. An alternative proof is outlined in Problem 0.5.14. ■

Example 0.5.4. Show that $\mathbf{AA}^{\mathrm{T}}$ and $\mathbf{A}^{\mathrm{T}}\mathbf{A}$ are symmetric.

Solution. First of all, both products always exist regardless of the size of $\mathbf{A}$. If $\mathbf{A}$ is $m \times n$ then $\mathbf{A}^{\mathrm{T}}\mathbf{A}$ is $n \times n$ and $\mathbf{AA}^{\mathrm{T}}$ is $m \times m$. (Why?) The arguments that show the symmetry are easy: $(\mathbf{AA}^{\mathrm{T}})^{\mathrm{T}} = (\mathbf{A}^{\mathrm{T}})^{\mathrm{T}}\mathbf{A}^{\mathrm{T}} = \mathbf{AA}^{\mathrm{T}}$ and, similarly, $(\mathbf{A}^{\mathrm{T}}\mathbf{A})^{\mathrm{T}} = \mathbf{A}^{\mathrm{T}}(\mathbf{A}^{\mathrm{T}})^{\mathrm{T}} = \mathbf{AA}^{\mathrm{T}}$.

0.5.1 The Associativity of Matrix Multiplication

Recall that Theorem 0.5.2 asserts the law of associativity of matrix multiplication, $\mathbf{A}(\mathbf{BC}) = (\mathbf{AB})\mathbf{C}$. We prove this theorem by first proving the special case where $\mathbf{C}$ is a vector.

Lemma 0.1. *Let* $\mathbf{A}$ *be conformable with* $\mathbf{B}$, *and* $\mathbf{c}$ *be a vector conformable with* $\mathbf{AB}$. *Then*

$$\mathbf{A}(\mathbf{Bc}) = (\mathbf{AB})\mathbf{c} \tag{0.5.7}$$

Proof. Let $\mathbf{c}$ have entries $c_1, c_2, \ldots, c_n$. Then it is easy to verify

$$\mathbf{c} = c_1\mathbf{e}_1 + c_2\mathbf{e}_2 + \cdots + c_n\mathbf{e}_n \tag{0.5.8}$$

Hence,

$$(\mathbf{AB})\mathbf{c} = c_1(\mathbf{AB})\mathbf{e}_1 + c_2(\mathbf{AB})\mathbf{e}_2 + \cdots + c_n(\mathbf{AB})\mathbf{e}_n \tag{0.5.9}$$

follows from Eq. 0.5.8 and Theorem 0.4.2(d). The ith column of $\mathbf{AB}$ is given by $(\mathbf{AB})\mathbf{e}_i$ and also by $\mathbf{A}$ times the ith column of $\mathbf{B}$. That is, $(\mathbf{AB})\mathbf{e}_i = \mathbf{AB}_{*i}$, and using this equality in Eq. 0.5.9,

$$\begin{aligned}(\mathbf{AB})\mathbf{c} &= c_1\mathbf{AB}_{*1} + c_2\mathbf{AB}_{*2} + \cdots + c_n\mathbf{AB}_{*n} \\ &= \mathbf{A}(c_1\mathbf{B}_{*1} + c_2\mathbf{B}_{*2} + \cdots + c_n\mathbf{B}_{*n}) \\ &= \mathbf{A}(c_1\mathbf{Be}_1 + c_2\mathbf{Be}_2 + \cdots + c_n\mathbf{Be}_n) \end{aligned} \tag{0.5.10}$$

since $\mathbf{Be}_i = \mathbf{B}_{*1}$. Therefore, from Eq. 0.5.10,

$$\begin{aligned}(\mathbf{AB})\mathbf{c} &= \mathbf{A}(c_1\mathbf{Be}_1 + c_2\mathbf{Be}_2 + \cdots + c_n\mathbf{Be}_n) \\ &= \mathbf{A}(\mathbf{B}(c_1\mathbf{e}_1 + c_2\mathbf{e}_2 + \cdots + c_n\mathbf{e}_n)) = \mathbf{A}(\mathbf{Bc})\end{aligned}$$

by Eq. 0.5.8. ■

Equation 0.5.7 represents a special case of associativity of multiplication in which the right-most matrix is a vector. The general case follows from the special.

Theorem 0.5.4. *If* **A** *is conformable with* **B** *and* **B** *with* **C**, *then* **A** *is conformable with* **BC** *and* **AB** *is conformable with* **C**, *and*

$$\mathbf{A}(\mathbf{BC}) = (\mathbf{AB})\mathbf{C} \tag{0.5.11}$$

Proof. It is easy to check the conformability conditions; the truth of Eq. 0.5.11, however, is less obvious. Note the role of Eq. 0.5.7 in the proof. It is used with $\mathbf{C}_{*j}$ in place of **c**.

$$\begin{aligned}\mathbf{A}(\mathbf{BC}) &= \mathbf{A}(\mathbf{B}[\ldots\mathbf{C}_{*j}\ldots]) = \mathbf{A}[\ldots\mathbf{BC}_{*j}\ldots]\\ &= [\ldots\mathbf{A}(\mathbf{BC}_{*j})\ldots] = [\ldots(\mathbf{AB})\mathbf{C}_{*j}\ldots]\\ &= (\mathbf{AB})[\ldots\mathbf{C}_{*j}\ldots] = (\mathbf{AB})\mathbf{C}\end{aligned}$$

0.5.2 Matrix Multiplication in Graph Theory

Figure 0.6*b* is the digraph representation of the cities connected by Fly-by-Night Airlines. (See Subsection 0.1.3.) The incidence matrix **G** for this graph is given in Fig. 0.6*a*. Consider this question: In how many different ways can a passenger get from P_1 to P_2 with exactly one intermediate stop? The digraph shows that the answer is 2. Now examine the matrix $\mathbf{G}^2$ whose i, j entry is denoted by $g_{ij}^{(2)}$:

$$\mathbf{G}^2 = \begin{bmatrix} 4 & 2 & 1 & 2 & 1\\ 2 & 3 & 1 & 1 & 2\\ 1 & 1 & 2 & 2 & 1\\ 2 & 1 & 2 & 3 & 1\\ 1 & 2 & 1 & 1 & 2 \end{bmatrix} \tag{0.5.12}$$

It is no coincidence that $g_{12}^{(2)}$, the (1,2) entry of $\mathbf{G}^2$, is also 2, for

$$\begin{aligned} g_{12}^{(2)} &= g_{11}g_{12} + g_{12}g_{22} + g_{13}g_{32} + g_{14}g_{42} + g_{15}g_{52}\\ &= g_{13}g_{32} + g_{14}g_{42} + g_{15}g_{52} \end{aligned} \tag{0.5.13}$$

since $g_{11} = g_{22} = 0$. Each of the remaining three terms in Eq. 0.5.13 contributes 1 to the sum $g_{12}^{(2)}$ if and only if both g_{1i} and g_{i2} are 1 for $i = 3, 4, 5$. But this

$$\begin{bmatrix} 0 & 1 & 1 & 1 & 1\\ 1 & 0 & 1 & 1 & 0\\ 1 & 1 & 0 & 0 & 0\\ 1 & 1 & 0 & 0 & 1\\ 1 & 0 & 0 & 1 & 0 \end{bmatrix}$$

(*a*)

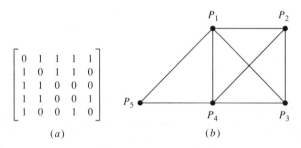

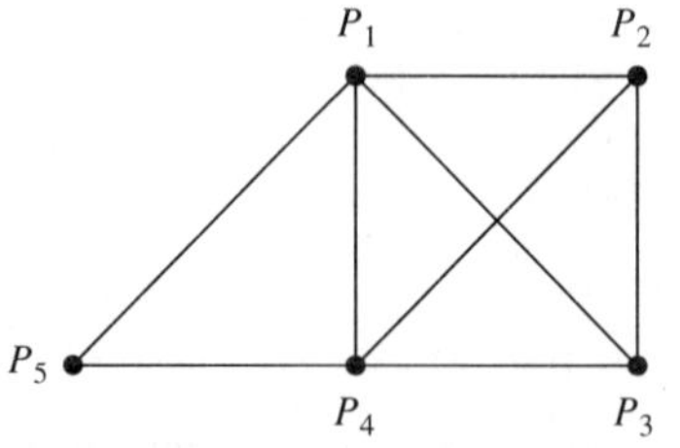

(*b*)

FIGURE 0-6

occurs if and only if one can get from P_1 to P_2 through the stopovers P_3, P_4, or P_5, respectively. It is instructive to interpret each of the entries of $\mathbf{G}^2$ in terms of the routing in Fig. 0.6*b*. (See Problem 0.5.10.)

Example 0.5.5. Consider the problem first raised in Section 0.1.3: Given the incident matrix for the acquaintance network

$$\mathbf{A} = \begin{bmatrix} 0 & 1 & 1 & 0 & 0 \\ 1 & 0 & 1 & 1 & 0 \\ 1 & 1 & 0 & 1 & 0 \\ 0 & 1 & 1 & 0 & 1 \\ 0 & 0 & 0 & 1 & 0 \end{bmatrix} \tag{0.5.14}$$

we find that

$$\mathbf{A}^3 = (a_{ij}^{(3)}) = \begin{bmatrix} 2 & 3 & 4 & 1 & 1 \\ 3 & 2 & 4 & 1 & 1 \\ 4 & 4 & 2 & 4 & 0 \\ 1 & 1 & 4 & 0 & 2 \\ 1 & 1 & 0 & 2 & 0 \end{bmatrix} \tag{0.5.15}$$

To understand why P_4 is not a member of a clique (see Fig. 0.3), note that by definition of matrix multiplication,

$$a_{44}^{(3)} = a_{41}^{(2)} a_{14} + a_{42}^{(2)} a_{24} + a_{43}^{(2)} a_{34} + a_{44}^{(2)} a_{44} + a_{45}^{(2)} a_{54} \tag{0.5.16}$$

where $\mathbf{A}^2 = (a_{ij}^{(2)})$. A typical term in Eq. 0.5.16 is $a_{4i}^{(2)} a_{i4}$, and the value of this product is the number of 3-step connections between P_4 and itself of the form P_4 to P_j to P_i to P_4:

$$\begin{array}{ccc} P_i & & \\ \downarrow & \nwarrow & \\ P_4 & \rightarrow & P_j \end{array} \tag{0.5.17}$$

Now, by definition of incident matrix (Subsection 0.1.3), $a_{i4} = 0$ if there is no edge between P_i and P_4; for example:

$$\begin{array}{ccc} P_i & \leftarrow & P_k \\ & & \uparrow \\ P_4 & \rightarrow & P_j \end{array} \tag{0.5.18}$$

From Eq. 0.5.14 or the digraph, $a_{14} = 0$, $a_{24} = 0$, $a_{34} = 1$, $a_{44} = 0$, $a_{54} = 1$, and hence Eq. 0.5.16 simplifies to

$$a_{44}^{(3)} = a_{43}^{(2)} + a_{45}^{(2)} \tag{0.5.19}$$

As we have seen in the previous example, $a_{4i}^{(2)}$ represents the number of 2-step connections between P_4 and P_i (such as P_4 to P_2 to P_i). However,

$$a_{43}^{(2)} = a_{41}a_{13} + a_{42}a_{23} + a_{43}a_{33} + a_{44}a_{43} + a_{45}a_{53} \tag{0.5.20}$$

and $a_{41} = a_{42} = a_{33} = a_{44} = a_{53} = 0$ shows that $a_{43}^{(2)} = 0$; similarly for $a_{45}^{(2)}$. Hence $a_{44}^{(3)} = 0$. There are no 3-step connections originating and terminating at P_4, so P_4 is not part of a clique.

A more tedious but roughly similar argument can be made for a general incidence matrix for the digraph of an acquaintance network. All of this leads to the general proposition that P_i belongs to a clique if and only if $a_{ii}^{(3)} \neq 0$.

PROBLEMS

PART 1

0.5.1. Compute

$$\begin{bmatrix} -6 & 7 \\ 7 & -8 \end{bmatrix} \begin{bmatrix} 8 & 7 \\ 7 & 6 \end{bmatrix}$$

0.5.2. Compute

$$\begin{bmatrix} 2 & 5 \\ 1 & 3 \end{bmatrix} \begin{bmatrix} 11 & 30 \\ -4 & -11 \end{bmatrix} \begin{bmatrix} 3 & -5 \\ -1 & 2 \end{bmatrix}$$

0.5.3. Verify $\mathbf{A}(\mathbf{B}+\mathbf{C}) = \mathbf{AB} + \mathbf{AC}$, where

$$\mathbf{A} = \begin{bmatrix} 1 & 2 \\ 3 & -1 \end{bmatrix}, \qquad \mathbf{B} = \begin{bmatrix} 0 & 1 \\ 2 & 3 \end{bmatrix}, \qquad \mathbf{C} = \begin{bmatrix} 1 & 1 \\ 0 & 1 \end{bmatrix}$$

0.5.4. Compute the product $\mathbf{AB}$ and explain why $\mathbf{BA}$ does not exist, where

$$\mathbf{A} = \begin{bmatrix} 2 & -1 & 2 \\ 0 & 3 & 0 \\ 2 & 1 & 2 \end{bmatrix}, \qquad \mathbf{B} = \begin{bmatrix} 1 & 0 \\ 2 & 0 \\ 1 & 2 \end{bmatrix}$$

0.5.5. For the matrices of Problem 0.5.4, verify that

$$(a)\ \mathbf{AB} = \begin{bmatrix} \mathbf{A}\begin{bmatrix} 1 \\ 2 \\ 1 \end{bmatrix} & \mathbf{A}\begin{bmatrix} 0 \\ 0 \\ 2 \end{bmatrix} \end{bmatrix} \qquad (b)\ \mathbf{AB} = \begin{bmatrix} [2 & -1 & 2]\mathbf{B} \\ [0 & 3 & 0]\mathbf{B} \\ [2 & 1 & 2]\mathbf{B} \end{bmatrix}$$

0.5.6. Find the following products

$$(a)\ \begin{bmatrix} 2 \\ 3 \\ -1 \end{bmatrix} [1 \ \ 1 \ \ 1] \qquad (b)\ \begin{bmatrix} 1 \\ 1 \\ 1 \end{bmatrix} [2 \ \ 3 \ \ -1] \qquad (c)\ [1 \ \ 1 \ \ 1] \begin{bmatrix} 2 \\ 3 \\ -1 \end{bmatrix}$$

0.5.7. Find

$$[1 \ \ 1 \ \ 1] \begin{bmatrix} 2 \\ 3 \\ -1 \end{bmatrix} [1 \ \ 1 \ \ 1] \begin{bmatrix} 2 \\ 3 \\ -1 \end{bmatrix}$$

0.5.8. Find

$$[x \ \ y \ \ z] \begin{bmatrix} 1 & 0 & -1 \\ 0 & 2 & 2 \\ -1 & 2 & 1 \end{bmatrix} \begin{bmatrix} x \\ y \\ z \end{bmatrix}$$

0.5.9. Verify that

$$(a)\ \mathbf{e}_3^{\mathrm{T}} \begin{bmatrix} 1 & 0 & -1 \\ 0 & 2 & 2 \\ -1 & 2 & 1 \end{bmatrix} = [-1 \ \ 2 \ \ 1] \qquad (b)\ \begin{bmatrix} 1 & 0 & -1 \\ 0 & 2 & 2 \\ -1 & 2 & 1 \end{bmatrix} \mathbf{e}_3 = \begin{bmatrix} -1 \\ 2 \\ 1 \end{bmatrix}$$

0.5.10. Verify Eq. 0.5.12 by computing $\mathbf{G}^2$ for the incidence matrix in Fig. 0.6*a*. Use the digraph to verify that $g_{25}^{(2)} = 2$ is the number of routes between P_2 and P_5 with exactly one stopover. Interpret $g_{11}^{(2)}$.

PART 2

0.5.11. Show that $\mathbf{x}^{\mathrm{T}}(\mathbf{y}\mathbf{x}^{\mathrm{T}})\mathbf{y}$ is a 1×1 matrix whose sole entry is $(\mathbf{x} \cdot \mathbf{y})^2$.

0.5.12. Show that the product of diagonal matrices is a diagonal matrix and find a formula for the diagonal entries of the product.

0.5.13. Let $\mathbf{A}$ be $n \times n$ and $\mathbf{D}_n$ a diagonal matrix. Show that, in general, $\mathbf{A}$ and $\mathbf{D}_n$ do not commute.

0.5.14. Verify Theorem 0.5.3 for the special case in which $\mathbf{B} = \mathbf{e}_i$. Use this result to prove the more general case, in which $\mathbf{B} = \mathbf{b}$. Now use the definition of $\mathbf{AB}$ to prove Theorem 0.5.3.

0.5.15. Under what hypothesis is it true that $(\mathbf{A} + \mathbf{B})^2 = \mathbf{A}^2 + 2\mathbf{AB} + \mathbf{B}^2$?

0.5.16. Show that $(\mathbf{A} + \mathbf{I})^2 = \mathbf{A}^2 + 2\mathbf{A} + \mathbf{I}$ and reconcile your conclusion with the answer to Problem 0.5.15.

0.5.17. By definition $\mathbf{A}^3 = \mathbf{A}^2\mathbf{A}$. Show that $\mathbf{A}^3 = \mathbf{A}\mathbf{A}^2$. What theorem is required to establish this result? Define $\mathbf{A}^4$ and show $\mathbf{A}^4 = \mathbf{A}^2\mathbf{A}^2$.

0.5.18. Recall that $\mathbf{1}^{\mathrm{T}} = [1 \quad 1 \quad \dots \quad 1]$. Describe $\mathbf{1}^{\mathrm{T}}\mathbf{A}$ and $\mathbf{A1}$.

0.5.19. Show that $\mathbf{1}\mathbf{1}^{\mathrm{T}} = \mathbf{J}_n$.

0.5.20. If $\mathbf{AB} = \mathbf{BA}$, show that $(\mathbf{AB})^2 = \mathbf{A}^2\mathbf{B}^2$. Does $\mathbf{AB} = \mathbf{BA}$ imply $(\mathbf{AB})^2 = \mathbf{B}^2\mathbf{A}^2$?

0.5.21. Explain why the product of upper triangular matrices is upper triangular and why the product of lower triangular matrices is lower triangular.

0.5.22. If $\mathbf{A}$ is symmetric, is $\mathbf{A}^2$ symmetric? If $\mathbf{A}$ and $\mathbf{B}$ are symmetric, is $\mathbf{AB}$ symmetric? Suppose $\mathbf{A}$ and $\mathbf{B}$ commute and are symmetric. Is $\mathbf{AB}$ symmetric?

0.5.23. If $\mathbf{A}$ and $\mathbf{B}$ commute, do $\mathbf{A}^{\mathrm{T}}$ and $\mathbf{B}^{\mathrm{T}}$ commute?

0.5.24. Show that $\mathbf{AB}$ can be interpreted: *The* ith *row of* $\mathbf{AB}$ *is the* ith *row of* $\mathbf{A}$ *times* $\mathbf{B}$.

0.5.25. Prove Theorem 0.5.1.

PART 3

0.5.26. For each positive integer n, show that $(\mathbf{A}^{\mathrm{T}})^n = (\mathbf{A}^n)^{\mathrm{T}}$.

0.5.27. Show that $(\mathbf{A} + a\mathbf{I})^2 = \mathbf{A}^2 + 2a\mathbf{A} + a^2\mathbf{I}$ and compare with Problems 0.5.16 and 0.5.17. Use induction on n to prove

$$(\mathbf{A} + a\mathbf{I})^n = \mathbf{A}^n + C\binom{n}{1}a\mathbf{A}^{n-1} + C\binom{n}{2}a^2\mathbf{A}^{n-2} + \cdots + C\binom{n}{n}a^n\mathbf{I}$$

where

$$C\binom{n}{r} = \frac{n!}{r!\,(n-r)!}$$

is the binomial coefficient. ($C\binom{n}{r}$ is the number of ways of choosing r items from a set of n distinguishable items.) The identity

$$C\binom{n}{r} = C\binom{n-1}{r} + C\binom{n-1}{r-1}$$

is needed and may be assumed.

0.6 PECULIARITIES OF MULTIPLICATION

Using the word multiplication to describe **AB** suggests that this complex arithmetical computation is analogous with ordinary scalar multiplication. However, the fact that $\mathbf{AB} \neq \mathbf{BA}$, for most **A** and **B**, shows that we cannot expect too close a resemblance. There are other significant differences between **AB** and ab, a few of which are exhibited in the following examples.

Example 0.6.1. The failure of commutativity is illustrated by the following products:

$$\begin{bmatrix} 1 & 1 \\ -1 & -1 \end{bmatrix}\begin{bmatrix} 1 & -1 \\ -1 & -1 \end{bmatrix} = \begin{bmatrix} 0 & -2 \\ 0 & 2 \end{bmatrix} \neq \begin{bmatrix} 1 & -1 \\ -1 & -1 \end{bmatrix}\begin{bmatrix} 1 & 1 \\ -1 & -1 \end{bmatrix} = \begin{bmatrix} 2 & 2 \\ 0 & 0 \end{bmatrix}$$

Example 0.6.2. It is a fundamental property of numbers that if $ab = 0$, then either a or b is zero. But for matrices, it is possible that $\mathbf{AB} = \mathbf{O}$ when neither **A** nor **B** is zero.

$$\begin{bmatrix} 1 & 1 \\ -1 & -1 \end{bmatrix}\begin{bmatrix} 1 & -1 \\ -1 & -1 \end{bmatrix} = \begin{bmatrix} 0 & 0 \\ 0 & 0 \end{bmatrix}$$

In algebra, the "law of cancellation" asserts that if $a \neq 0$ and $ab = ac$, then $b = c$ (in essence canceling a from both sides of the equation). This is a consequence of the fact that $ab = 0$ implies that either a or b is zero. To see why, suppose $ab = ac$ and $a \neq 0$. Then $ab - ac = a(b - c) = 0$. Since $a \neq 0$, $b - c = 0$; hence $b = c$ as desired. The fact that $\mathbf{AB} = \mathbf{O}$ does not imply that either **A** or **B** is **O** suggests that the law of cancellation may fail for matrices. The next example confirms this.

Example 0.6.3. Let

$$\mathbf{A} = \begin{bmatrix} 1 & 1 \\ 1 & 1 \end{bmatrix}, \qquad \mathbf{B} = \begin{bmatrix} 1 & 1 \\ 0 & 0 \end{bmatrix}$$

Then,

$$\begin{bmatrix} 1 & 1 \\ 1 & 1 \end{bmatrix}\begin{bmatrix} 1 & 1 \\ 0 & 0 \end{bmatrix} = \begin{bmatrix} 1 & 1 \\ 1 & 1 \end{bmatrix} \quad \text{and} \quad \begin{bmatrix} 1 & 1 \\ 1 & 1 \end{bmatrix}\begin{bmatrix} 1 & 0 \\ 0 & 1 \end{bmatrix} = \begin{bmatrix} 1 & 1 \\ 1 & 1 \end{bmatrix}$$

shows that $\mathbf{AB} = \mathbf{J}$ and $\mathbf{AI} = \mathbf{J}$. Hence $\mathbf{AB} = \mathbf{AI}$, but $\mathbf{B} \neq \mathbf{I}$.

If $\mathbf{A}^2 = \mathbf{B}$, then it is not unreasonable to call **A** a *square root* of **B**. But unlike square roots of scalars, some matrices have infinitely many square roots and some have none. Here are some illustrations.

Example 0.6.4. Show that there are no square roots of

$$\mathbf{A} = \begin{bmatrix} 0 & 1 \\ 0 & 0 \end{bmatrix}$$

Solution. Suppose the contrary; that is, assume

$$\begin{bmatrix} a & b \\ c & d \end{bmatrix}^2 = \begin{bmatrix} 0 & 1 \\ 0 & 0 \end{bmatrix}$$

This leads to the following four equations:

(1) $a^2 + bc = 0$ **(2)** $b\,(a + d) = 1$
(3) $c\,(a + d) = 0$ **(4)** $cb + d^2 = 0$

Equations (2) and (3) show that $c = 0$, which, when used in (1) and (4), implies that $a = d = 0$. This contradicts (2).

Example 0.6.5. The following products are easy to verify:

(a) $\begin{bmatrix} 1 & 0 \\ 0 & 1 \end{bmatrix}\begin{bmatrix} 1 & 0 \\ 0 & 1 \end{bmatrix} = \begin{bmatrix} 1 & 0 \\ 0 & 1 \end{bmatrix}$ (b) $\begin{bmatrix} -1 & 0 \\ 0 & -1 \end{bmatrix}\begin{bmatrix} -1 & 0 \\ 0 & -1 \end{bmatrix} = \begin{bmatrix} 1 & 0 \\ 0 & 1 \end{bmatrix}$

(c) $\begin{bmatrix} 0 & 1 \\ 1 & 0 \end{bmatrix}\begin{bmatrix} 0 & 1 \\ 1 & 0 \end{bmatrix} = \begin{bmatrix} 1 & 0 \\ 0 & 1 \end{bmatrix}$ (d) $\begin{bmatrix} -1 & -2 \\ 0 & 1 \end{bmatrix}\begin{bmatrix} -1 & -2 \\ 0 & 1 \end{bmatrix} = \begin{bmatrix} 1 & 0 \\ 0 & 1 \end{bmatrix}$

Since **I** is the matrix analog of 1, Parts (*a*) and (*b*) of Example 0.6.4 can be regarded as the matrix analog of the two square roots of 1. Parts (*c*) and (*d*) hint at a vast array of square roots of **I**. (See Problem 0.6.3.)

PROBLEMS

PART 1

0.6.1. Show that for every α and β

$$\begin{bmatrix} 1 & 1 \\ 1 & 1 \end{bmatrix}\begin{bmatrix} 1+\alpha & -\beta \\ -\alpha & 1+\beta \end{bmatrix} = \begin{bmatrix} 1 & 1 \\ 1 & 1 \end{bmatrix}$$

0.6.2. Show that for every α and β

$$\begin{bmatrix} 1 & 1 \\ 1 & 1 \end{bmatrix}\begin{bmatrix} \alpha & \beta \\ -\alpha & -\beta \end{bmatrix} = \begin{bmatrix} 0 & 0 \\ 0 & 0 \end{bmatrix}$$

0.6.3. Show that for every τ

$$\begin{bmatrix} \cos\tau & \sin\tau \\ \sin\tau & -\cos\tau \end{bmatrix}\begin{bmatrix} \cos\tau & \sin\tau \\ \sin\tau & -\cos\tau \end{bmatrix} = \begin{bmatrix} 1 & 0 \\ 0 & 1 \end{bmatrix}$$

0.6.4. Verify that

$$\mathbf{A}^2 = \begin{bmatrix} -1 & -2 \\ 0 & 1 \end{bmatrix}^2 = \mathbf{I}_2$$

(Note that there is no choice of τ such that **A** can be obtained from

$$\mathbf{T}(\tau) = \begin{bmatrix} \cos\tau & \sin\tau \\ \sin\tau & -\cos\tau \end{bmatrix}$$

This shows that the family $\mathbf{T}(\tau)$ does not contain all the square roots of **I**.)

PART 2

0.6.5. Suppose $\mathbf{AB} = \mathbf{O}$ with $\mathbf{A} \neq \mathbf{O}$ and $\mathbf{B} \neq \mathbf{O}$. For any **C** define **D** by $\mathbf{D} = \mathbf{C} - \mathbf{B}$. Now show that $\mathbf{AC} = \mathbf{AD}$ and $\mathbf{C} \neq \mathbf{D}$. Set $\mathbf{A} = \mathbf{J}_2$ and use the results of this problem and Problem 0.6.2 to obtain the family in Problem 0.6.1.

CHAPTER 1

ELEMENTARY MATRIX THEORY

1.1 INTRODUCTION

This chapter presumes a familiarity with the notational conventions, definitions, and theorems of Chapter 0. A brief summary of these results is provided here for ease of reference and quick review.

1.1.1 Notations and Definitions

The rectangular, $m \times n$ array of numbers defined as having the entry a_{ij} in the ith row, jth column is written $\mathbf{A} = \mathbf{A}_{m \times n} = (a_{ij})$. The *diagonal* of $\mathbf{A}$ is the column vector $\text{diag}(\mathbf{A}) = [a_{11} \quad a_{22} \quad \ldots \quad a_{rr}]^{\mathrm{T}}$, where r is the lesser of m and n. $\mathbf{A}$ is a *square matrix* if $m = n$. $\mathbf{A}$ is *upper trapezoidal* if the entries below the diagonal are zero; it is *upper triangular* if it is square and upper trapezoidal. $\mathbf{A}$ is *lower trapezoidal* if the entries above the diagonal are zero; it is *lower triangular* if it is square and lower trapezoidal. $\mathbf{A}$ is a *diagonal matrix* if it is square and the entries not on the diagonal are zero. A *scalar matrix* is a diagonal matrix all of whose diagonal entries are equal. The *transpose* of $\mathbf{A}$, written $\mathbf{A}^{\mathrm{T}}$, has a_{ji} as the entry in the ith row, jth column. $\mathbf{A}$ is *symmetric* if $\mathbf{A}^{\mathrm{T}} = \mathbf{A}$.

Some special notational conventions follow:

(a) $\mathbf{A}_{*j}$ is the jth column and $\mathbf{A}_{i*}$ the ith row of $\mathbf{A}$

(b) $\mathbf{A}_n = \mathbf{A}_{n \times n}$, ($c$) $\mathbf{O}_n = (0)$, (d) $\mathbf{J}_n = (1)$

(*e*) $\mathbf{I}_n = (\delta_{ij})$, where $\delta_{ij} = \begin{cases} 1 \text{ if } i = j \\ 0 \text{ if } i \neq j \end{cases}$

(*f*) $\mathbf{x} = \begin{bmatrix} x_1 \\ x_2 \\ \vdots \\ x_n \end{bmatrix}$ (*g*) $\mathbf{0} = \begin{bmatrix} 0 \\ 0 \\ \vdots \\ 0 \end{bmatrix}$ (*h*) $\mathbf{1} = \begin{bmatrix} 1 \\ 1 \\ \vdots \\ 1 \end{bmatrix}$

(*i*) $\mathbf{e}_1 = \begin{bmatrix} 1 \\ 0 \\ \vdots \\ 0 \end{bmatrix}$ $\mathbf{e}_2 = \begin{bmatrix} 0 \\ 1 \\ \vdots \\ 0 \end{bmatrix}, \quad \ldots \quad \mathbf{e}_{\mathrm{n}} = \begin{bmatrix} 0 \\ 0 \\ \vdots \\ 1 \end{bmatrix}$

(*j*) $\mathbf{x} \in \mathcal{R}^n$ means that $\mathbf{x}$ is $n \times 1$ and has real entries; $\mathbf{x} \in \mathcal{C}^n$ allows for the possibility of complex entries in $\mathbf{x}$.

1.1.2 Theorems

Matrix algebra requires certain conformability conditions in order that the various arithmetic operations can be defined. All such conditions are implicitly assumed in following theorems. (The complete statements of the theorems are given in Chapter 0.)

(*a*) $\mathbf{A} \pm \mathbf{B} = (a_{ij} \pm b_{ij})$
(*b*) $k\mathbf{A} = (ka_{ij})$
(*c*) $(\mathbf{A} \pm \mathbf{B})^{\mathrm{T}} = \mathbf{A}^{\mathrm{T}} \pm \mathbf{B}^{\mathrm{T}}$
(*d*) $\mathbf{A}_{m\times r}\mathbf{B}_{r\times n} = \mathbf{C}_{m\times n} = (c_{ij} = \sum_{i=1}^{r} a_{ik}b_{kj})$
(*e*) $\mathbf{A(BC)} = \mathbf{(AB)C}$
(*f*) $\mathbf{A(B \pm C)} = \mathbf{AB} \pm \mathbf{AC}$
(*g*) $\mathbf{(B \pm C)\,A} = \mathbf{BA} \pm \mathbf{CA}$
(*h*) $(\mathbf{AB})^{\mathrm{T}} = \mathbf{B}^{\mathrm{T}}\mathbf{A}^{\mathrm{T}}$
(*i*) $\mathbf{AI} = \mathbf{IA}$
(*j*) $\mathbf{OA} = \mathbf{AO} = \mathbf{O}$
(*k*) $\mathbf{AB} \neq \mathbf{BA}$, except in special cases
(*l*) $\mathbf{AB} = \mathbf{AC}$ does not imply $\mathbf{B} = \mathbf{C}$
(*m*) $\mathbf{AB} = \mathbf{O}$ does not imply that either $\mathbf{A} = \mathbf{O}$ or $\mathbf{B} = \mathbf{O}$
(*n*) $\mathbf{Ae}_i = \mathbf{A}_{*i}$, $\quad \mathbf{e}_j^{\mathrm{T}}\mathbf{A} = \mathbf{A}_{j*}$

1.1.3 MATLAB

Like most programming languages, MATLAB utilizes a variety of special notational conventions that vary from standard mathematical usage. This variation is partly due to the peculiarities of entering information into a computer. A guiding principle useful in predicting which notational conventions are likely to be different in MATLAB from those in the text is this: a textbook convention using specialized type faces (such as representing matrices by bold face capitals) or those using subscripts and superscripts, are almost certainly not the conventions used in MATLAB.

Table 1.1 is a shortened version of the more elaborate table, given in Appendix A, of "translations" from text notation to MATLAB. The items selected for this table are those relevant to the material of this chapter and provide a summary of the notation used in Chapter 0.

TABLE 1.1
Translations from text notation to MATLAB

Text	MATLAB	Meaning	Reference
$\mathbf{A}^T$	A.'	Transpose of **A**	Eq. 0.2.10
$\mathbf{A}_{*j}$	A(:, j)	jth column of **A**	pg. 12
$\mathbf{A}_{i*}$	A(i, :)	ith row of **A**	pg. 12
$\mathbf{I}_n$	eye(n)	Identity matrix of size n	Eq. 0.2.9
$\mathbf{O}_n$	zeros(n)	$n \times n$ matrix of zeros	pg. 15
$\mathbf{J}_n$	ones(n)	$n \times n$ matrix of ones	Eq. 0.2.11
$\mathbf{O}_{m\times n}$	zeros(m, n)	$m \times n$ matrix of zeros	pg. 15
$\mathbf{J}_{m\times n}$	ones(m, n)	$m \times n$ matrix of ones	pg. 15
$\mathbf{0}$	zeros(n, 1)	$n \times 1$ vector of zeros	pg. 14
$\mathbf{1}$	ones(n, 1)	$n \times 1$ vector of ones	pg. 14

There are some MATLAB functions that have no notational equivalent in matrix theory. Suppose **A** is $m \times n$ and **x** is $n \times 1$. Then MATLAB returns the ordered pair (m,n) if size(A) is entered after the MATLAB prompt (">>") and returns n if length(x) or length(x') is entered. Entering zeros(A) returns zeros(m,n) (see Table 1.1), ones(A) returns ones(m,n) and eye(A) returns an $m\times n$ matrix with ones on its diagonal. Diag(A) returns a *vector* whose entries are the diagonal entries of **A**, but note that diag(x) returns a *diagonal matrix* whose diagonal is the entries of **x**. Thus, diag(diag(A)) returns a diagonal matrix whose diagonal is the diagonal of **A**. Although these ideas are explored in some detail in the problem set, here is an illustrative example in which only MATLAB notation is used.

Example 1.1.1. Enter the matrix A,

$$\mathbf{A} = \begin{bmatrix} 2 & -1 & 1 & -1 \\ 1 & 0 & -1 & 0 \\ 0 & 1 & 1 & 1 \end{bmatrix}$$

and determine MATLAB's response to the commands:

(*a*) size(A), (*b*) A(:,2), (*c*) A(3,:), (*d*) eye(A), (*e*) diag(A)

Solution. At the MATLAB prompt ("<<") enter

```
A =
    [2  -1   1  -1
     1   0  -1   0
     0   1   1   1]
```

and MATLAB returns

```
A =
     2  -1   1  -1
     1   0  -1   0
     0   1   1   1
```

Now that MATLAB has stored the explicit definition of A, the effects of entering the various functions of A proposed in this example yield:

(*a*) Enter: size(A) Return: ans =

```
3  4
```

(*b*) Enter: A(:,2) Return: ans =

```
-1
 0
 1
```

(*c*) Enter: A(3,:) Return: ans =

```
0  1  1  1
```

(*d*) Enter: eye(A) Return: ans =

```
1  0  0  0
0  1  0  0
0  0  1  0
```

(*e*) Enter: diag:(A) Return: ans =

```
2
0
1
```

The standard mathematical practice of denoting multiplication by writing the factors contiguously, as with $k\mathbf{A}$, is not acceptable in programming languages for essentially the same reason that 2 times 3 cannot be written 23 since 23 is already a defined symbol. Indeed, kA is a legal name for a matrix in MATLAB, but not necessarily the product of k and A. MATLAB follows the common convention of using $*$ as the multiplicative operator so that $k\mathbf{A}$ is written $k *$ A.

Addition and subtraction of matrices poses no problems: A + B and A − B returns the sum and difference of **A** and **B**, respectively. A rather special feature of MATLAB is its treatment of the (technically) meaningless expression A + k. MATLAB interprets A + k as A + $k *$ ones(A). Thus, if we assume $\mathbf{A} = (a_{ij})$,

MATLAB returns the matrix whose entries are $(k + a_{ij})$. For example, zeros(4) + 1 = ones(4).

MATLAB interprets a 1×1 matrix as we do; namely as the scalar which is its own sole entry. For instance, [3] = 3. In particular then, entering $[a] * A$ after the MATLAB prompt returns $a * A$. Indeed, after A and $a = [a]$ are defined, MATLAB returns a ∗ A whether one enters $a * A$ or $[a] * A$. The danger in using $[a] = a$ is that $[a]\mathbf{A}$ is not defined in matrix algebra unless **A** is a row matrix because $[a]$ and **A** are not generally conformable.

The MATLAB notation for **AB** is A ∗ B and for $\mathbf{A}^n$ is A^n. These are the standard programming language notations for multiplication and exponentiation, respectively.

PROBLEMS

PART 1

In Problems 1.1.1–1.1.11,

$$\mathbf{A} = \begin{bmatrix} 5 & -1 & 0 & -3 \\ 1 & 0 & 0 & 2 \\ 2 & 2 & 2 & -2 \\ 0 & -5 & 3 & -3 \end{bmatrix}$$

1.1.1. Extract the first three rows and the last three columns of **A**.

1.1.2. What is the outcome of entering length(diag(A))?

1.1.3. What is the outcome of entering zeros(ones(A)), ones(zeros(A)), eye(ones(A)) and diag(diag(A)? Check your reasoning by entering these matrices after the MATLAB prompt.

1.1.4. What is the result of entering (size(A))', size(A')? Check.

1.1.5. Enter (A')' and compare with A.

1.1.6. What is the MATLAB notation for $\mathbf{I}_4$? $\mathbf{0}_3$? Check by entering your answer after the MATLAB prompt.

1.1.7. Enter diag(A(:,4)). Enter diag(A(4,:)). Explain.

1.1.8. Enter A(:,2:4) and A(:,1:3) and infer from the output the meaning of B(:,*i*:*j*) for arbitrary B, i, and j. What happens if $i > j$?

1.1.9. Repeat Problem 1.1.8 except enter A(2:4,:) and A(1:3,:).

1.1.10. Repeat Problem 1.1.8 except enter A(2:3,1:4).

1.1.11. Repeat Problem 1.1.8 except enter A(:,:) and A(:).

1.1.12. Use proper MATLAB notation to enter the row vector $\mathbf{x}^{\mathrm{T}} = [1 \quad 2 \quad 3 \quad -1]$. Enter eye($x$), diag($x$), ones($x$), zeros($x$).

1.1.13. Enter any $4 * 3$ matrix **B**. Predict the results of entering eye(B), diag(B), diag(B'), (diag(B))', ones(B), diag(ones(B)). Verify your answers.

1.1.14. Use MATLAB to compute the following combinations for the matrices

$$\mathbf{A} = \begin{bmatrix} 1 & -1 & -2 \\ 2 & 1 & 3 \\ 2 & 3 & 0 \end{bmatrix}, \qquad \mathbf{B} = \begin{bmatrix} 0 & 1 & 2 \\ 1 & 0 & -3 \\ 2 & 3 & -1 \end{bmatrix}$$

(*a*) $\mathbf{A} - \mathbf{B}$ (*b*) $5\mathbf{A} + 2\mathbf{B}$ (*c*) $\mathbf{A} + \mathbf{A}^{\mathrm{T}}$ (*d*) $\mathbf{A} - \mathbf{A}^{\mathrm{T}}$ (*e*) $\mathbf{B} - \mathbf{A}$

1.1.15. Use the appropriate notational conventions to enter $\mathbf{J}_4 - \mathbf{I}_4, \mathbf{I}_3 - \mathbf{J}_3$ and zeros(5) + eye(5). What does MATLAB return?

1.1.16. Use MATLAB to find the vectors

$$(a)\begin{bmatrix} 1 & 0 & -1 \\ 0 & 2 & 2 \\ -1 & 2 & 2 \end{bmatrix}\begin{bmatrix} 1 \\ 0 \\ 0 \end{bmatrix} \qquad (b)\begin{bmatrix} 1 & 0 & -1 \\ 0 & 2 & 2 \\ -1 & 2 & 2 \end{bmatrix}\begin{bmatrix} 0 \\ 1 \\ 0 \end{bmatrix} \qquad (c)\begin{bmatrix} 1 & 0 & -1 \\ 0 & 2 & 2 \\ -1 & 2 & 2 \end{bmatrix}\begin{bmatrix} 0 \\ 0 \\ 1 \end{bmatrix}$$

1.1.17. For the matrix

$$\mathbf{A} = \begin{bmatrix} 0 & -1 & -2 \\ 1 & 0 & -3 \\ 2 & 3 & 0 \end{bmatrix}$$

enter the product $\mathbf{e}_2^T\mathbf{A}\mathbf{e}_3$ using MATLAB conventions. Show that MATLAB returns -3.

1.2 PARTITIONED MULTIPLICATION

The definition $\mathbf{AB} = [\mathbf{AB}_{*1} \quad \mathbf{AB}_{*2} \quad \dots \quad \mathbf{AB}_{*n}]$ requires that we interpret $\mathbf{AB}$ as a collections of column matrices. That is, $\mathbf{AB}$ is construed as a row matrix with vector entries! In fact, we go one step further; we permit the entries of $\mathbf{A}$ to be matrices themselves. For example, suppose

$$\mathbf{A} = \begin{bmatrix} 1 & -1 & 0 & 0 & 2 & 3 \\ 0 & 1 & -1 & 0 & 1 & 0 \\ 2 & 2 & 3 & 3 & 0 & 1 \end{bmatrix} \tag{1.2.1}$$

Then $\mathbf{A}$ is *partitioned* by introducing a set of horizontal and vertical lines in the manner shown in Eq. 1.2.2.

$$\mathbf{A} = \left[\begin{array}{cc:cc:cc} 1 & -1 & 0 & 0 & 2 & 3 \\ \hdashline 0 & 1 & -1 & 0 & 1 & 0 \\ 2 & 2 & 3 & 3 & 0 & 1 \end{array}\right] \tag{1.2.2}$$

Then, if we set $\mathbf{A}_{11} = [1 \quad -1], \mathbf{A}_{12} = [0 \quad 0], \mathbf{A}_{13} = [2 \quad 3]$ and

$$A_{21} = \begin{bmatrix} 0 & 1 \\ 2 & 2 \end{bmatrix}, \qquad A_{22} = \begin{bmatrix} -1 & 0 \\ 3 & 3 \end{bmatrix}, \qquad A_{23} = \begin{bmatrix} 1 & 0 \\ 0 & 1 \end{bmatrix}$$

then we may write

$$\mathbf{A} = \begin{bmatrix} \mathbf{A}_{11} & \mathbf{A}_{12} & \mathbf{A}_{13} \\ \mathbf{A}_{21} & \mathbf{A}_{22} & \mathbf{A}_{23} \end{bmatrix}$$

This is a representation of $\mathbf{A}$ as a rectangular array of matrices. Other partitionings of $\mathbf{A}$ are possible; any set of horizontal and vertical lines drawn in $\mathbf{A}$ result in a partitioning of $\mathbf{A}$. For example,

$$\mathbf{A} = \left[\begin{array}{c:cc:ccc} 1 & -1 & 0 & 0 & 2 & 3 \\ 0 & 1 & -1 & 0 & 1 & 0 \\ 2 & 2 & 3 & 3 & 0 & 1 \end{array}\right]$$

$$\mathbf{A} = \left[\begin{array}{cc|cccc} 1 & -1 & 0 & 0 & 2 & 3 \\ 0 & 1 & -1 & 0 & 1 & 0 \\ \hline 2 & 2 & 3 & 3 & 0 & 1 \end{array}\right]$$

All partitionings of **A** have two properties in common: the submatrices in any given "row" have the same number of rows; and the submatrices in a given "column" have the same number of columns. The most commonly used partition is one in which the columns of **A** are viewed as vectors.

The importance of partitioned matrices resides in a remarkable theorem concerning the effect of the partitioning of **A** and **B** on the product **AB**. The statement and proof of the most general theorem of this type is complicated by the complexity of the notation involved. Rather than attempt this, we shall exhibit four examples of the most common applications. The important point to observe is that the *multiplication proceeds as though the entries of the matrices were scalars* rather than matrices. For example,

$$\mathbf{a}^{\mathrm{T}}\mathbf{x} = [a_1 \quad a_2 \quad \ldots \quad a_n]\begin{bmatrix} x_1 \\ x_2 \\ \vdots \\ x_n \end{bmatrix} = a_1x_1 + a_2x_2 + \cdots + a_nx_n \tag{1.2.3}$$

leads to the following analogous formula in which $\mathbf{a}^{\mathrm{T}}$ is replaced by **A** and the entries of $\mathbf{a}^{\mathrm{T}}$ are the columns $\mathbf{A}_{*i}$.

Example 1.2.1. If $\mathbf{A} = [\mathbf{A}_{*1} \quad \mathbf{A}_{*2} \quad \ldots \quad \mathbf{A}_{*n}]$, then

$$\mathbf{Ax} = [\mathbf{A}_{*1} \quad \mathbf{A}_{*2} \quad \ldots \quad \mathbf{A}_{*n}]\begin{bmatrix} x_1 \\ x_2 \\ \vdots \\ x_n \end{bmatrix} = x_1\mathbf{A}_{*1} + x_2\mathbf{A}_{*2} + \cdots + x_n\mathbf{A}_{*n} \tag{1.2.4}$$

Compare Eq. 1.2.4 with Eq. 1.2.3.

Example 1.2.2. Suppose **A**, **B** and **C** are square matrices of (possibly) different sizes. Then

$$\begin{bmatrix} \mathbf{A} & \mathbf{O} & \mathbf{O} \\ \mathbf{O} & \mathbf{B} & \mathbf{O} \\ \mathbf{O} & \mathbf{O} & \mathbf{C} \end{bmatrix}^2 = \begin{bmatrix} \mathbf{A}^2 & \mathbf{O} & \mathbf{O} \\ \mathbf{O} & \mathbf{B}^2 & \mathbf{O} \\ \mathbf{O} & \mathbf{O} & \mathbf{C}^2 \end{bmatrix}$$

Example 1.2.3. Suppose **A** and **C**, and **B** and **D** are conformable matrices. Then

$$[\mathbf{A} \quad \mathbf{B}]\begin{bmatrix} \mathbf{C} \\ \mathbf{D} \end{bmatrix} = [\mathbf{AC} + \mathbf{BD}]$$

Example 1.2.4. Suppose all the products appearing below are defined. It follows that,

$$\begin{bmatrix} \mathbf{A} & \mathbf{B} \\ \mathbf{C} & \mathbf{D} \end{bmatrix} \begin{bmatrix} \mathbf{E} & \mathbf{F} \\ \mathbf{G} & \mathbf{H} \end{bmatrix} = \begin{bmatrix} \mathbf{AE} + \mathbf{BG} & \mathbf{AF} + \mathbf{BH} \\ \mathbf{CE} + \mathbf{DG} & \mathbf{CF} + \mathbf{DH} \end{bmatrix}$$

It is extremely important to note that matrices which are the entries in the left-most factor are premultipliers in the product matrix.

1.2.1 Partitioned Matrices in MATLAB

Entering partitioned matrices in MATLAB is strikingly similar to entering matrices of scalars. For example, enter the matrices **A**, **B**, **C** and **D** by

```
A =           B =            C =          D =
    [0  1         [-1  0         [1  1]       [0  0]
     2  2]          3  3]
```

Assume that these matrices have been entered into MATLAB'S memory. Then MATLAB returns

```
[A  B] =                    [A;B] =
         0  1  -1  0                  0  1
         2  2   3  3                  2  2
                                     -1  0
                                      3  3
```

The next example combines a number of MATLAB functions to generate larger matrices from smaller components.

Example 1.2.5.

(*a*) E = [A zeros(A); zeros(A) eye(A)] returns E =

```
0  1  0  0
2  2  0  0
0  0  1  0
0  0  0  1
```

(*b*) E = [A B] returns E =

```
0  1  -1  0
2  2   3  3
```

(*c*) E = [A zeros(A); zeros(C) C] returns E =

```
0  1  0  0
2  2  0  0
0  0  1  1
```

(*d*) E = [A B; C D] returns E =

```
0  1  -1  0
2  2   3  3
1  1   0  0
```

PROBLEMS

PART 1

In each of the next 4 problems let **A**, **B**, **C** and **D** denote the matrices

$$\mathbf{A} = \begin{bmatrix} 0 & 1 \\ 2 & 2 \end{bmatrix}, \qquad \mathbf{B} = \begin{bmatrix} -1 & 0 \\ 3 & 3 \end{bmatrix}, \qquad \mathbf{C} = [1 \quad 1], \qquad \mathbf{D} = [0 \quad 0]$$

1.2.1. Verify that $\mathbf{C}[\mathbf{A} \quad \mathbf{B}] = [\mathbf{CA} \quad \mathbf{CB}]$.

1.2.2. Verify that

$$\begin{bmatrix} \mathbf{A} & \mathbf{O} \\ \mathbf{O} & \mathbf{B} \end{bmatrix}^2 = \begin{bmatrix} \mathbf{A}^2 & \mathbf{O} \\ \mathbf{O} & \mathbf{B}^2 \end{bmatrix}.$$

1.2.3. Verify that

$$[\mathbf{C} \quad \mathbf{D}]\begin{bmatrix} \mathbf{A} \\ \mathbf{B} \end{bmatrix} = [\mathbf{CA} + \mathbf{DB}].$$

1.2.4. Verify that $\mathbf{A}[\mathbf{A} \quad \mathbf{B}] = [\mathbf{A}^2 \quad \mathbf{AB}]$.

PART 2

1.2.5. Assume that **A** is $n \times n$ and **B** is $m \times m$. Use the definition of matrix multiplication to prove the conclusion of Part 1, Problem 0.2.2.

1.2.6. Assume that **C** is $p \times q$, that **A** is $q \times r$, that **D** is $p \times q$, and **B** $q \times r$. Let

$$\mathbf{E} = [\mathbf{C} \quad \mathbf{D}]\begin{bmatrix} \mathbf{A} \\ \mathbf{B} \end{bmatrix}$$

Show that this product exists and determine the size of **E**. Prove that the conclusion of Problem 1.2.3 is correct.

MATLAB

1.2.7. Use **A**, **B**, **C** and **D** of Part 1 to verify the conclusions of Problems 1.2.1–1.2.4.

1.2.8. Verify the conclusions of Example 1.2.5.

1.3 THE INVERSE MATRIX

In ordinary arithmetic, the purpose of defining division is to express the solution of $ax = b$ as a number, the quotient of b by a. However, we can avoid the division operator entirely by defining the inverse of a, written $a^{-1}(a \neq 0)$, usually called the reciprocal of a, and then expressing the solution of $ax = b$ as $a^{-1}b$. Thus the division operation is replaced by the simpler idea of multiplication by the inverse. It is the purpose of this section to define and understand the notion of inverse in matrix algebra. Our ultimate goal is the determination of solutions to the equation $\mathbf{AX} = \mathbf{B}$, and as we shall see, the inverse is the theoretical tool we need.

For the square matrix **A** we call **X** an *inverse* of **A** if it satisfies the pair of equations:

$$\mathbf{AX} = \mathbf{I}, \qquad \mathbf{XA} = \mathbf{I} \tag{1.3.1}$$

Since $\mathbf{OX} = \mathbf{O}$ for all conformable $\mathbf{X}$, the zero matrix cannot have an inverse. Matrices that have no inverses are called *singular*. Unlike ordinary algebra where only 0 has no inverse, there are many matrices besides $\mathbf{O}$ which are singular. Those matrices with inverses are called *invertible* or *nonsingular*. Since the identity matrix is its own inverse, there is at least one nonsingular matrix. We now prove the important result that there is only one inverse for a nonsingular matrix.

Theorem 1.3.1. *Suppose* $\mathbf{A}$ *is nonsingular. Then* $\mathbf{A}$ *has exactly one inverse.*

Proof. Suppose $\mathbf{B}$ and $\mathbf{C}$ are inverses of $\mathbf{A}$. Then $\mathbf{AC} = \mathbf{I}$ and $\mathbf{BA} = \mathbf{I}$. Now multiply $\mathbf{AC} = \mathbf{I}$ on the left by $\mathbf{B}$ to obtain $\mathbf{B(AC)} = \mathbf{BI} = \mathbf{B}$; so $\mathbf{BAC} = \mathbf{B}$. But $\mathbf{BA} = \mathbf{I}$, so $\mathbf{BAC} = \mathbf{B}$ simplifies to $\mathbf{C} = \mathbf{B}$. (Note the use of associativity.) ■

Since the inverse of $\mathbf{A}$ is unique, we give it a special label. We write $\mathbf{A}^{-1}$ for the inverse of $\mathbf{A}$ by analogy with a^{-1}, the reciprocal (inverse) of a. Equation 1.3.1 shows that if $\mathbf{A}$ is invertible then its inverse is also invertible and its inverse is $\mathbf{A}$; that is, $(\mathbf{A}^{-1})^{-1} = \mathbf{A}$. The existence of $\mathbf{A}^{-1}$ provides the means for the solution of $\mathbf{AX} = \mathbf{B}$.

Theorem 1.3.2. *If* $\mathbf{A}$ *is invertible then the equation* $\mathbf{AX} = \mathbf{B}$ *has the unique solution* $\mathbf{X} = \mathbf{A}^{-1}\mathbf{B}$.

Proof. We show that $\mathbf{A}^{-1}\mathbf{B}$ is a solution by substituting $\mathbf{A}^{-1}\mathbf{B}$ for $\mathbf{X}$ in $\mathbf{AX} = \mathbf{B}$:

$$\mathbf{AX} = \mathbf{A}(\mathbf{A}^{-1}\mathbf{B}) = (\mathbf{AA}^{-1})\mathbf{B} = \mathbf{IB} = \mathbf{B}.$$

Now the proof that the solution is unique. If $\mathbf{C}$ *is any solution, then* $\mathbf{AC} = \mathbf{B}$ *and hence* $\mathbf{A}^{-1}(\mathbf{AC}) = \mathbf{A}^{-1}\mathbf{B}$. *But* $\mathbf{A}^{-1}(\mathbf{AC}) = \mathbf{C}$, *and this combined with* $\mathbf{A}^{-1}(\mathbf{AC}) = \mathbf{A}^{-1}\mathbf{B}$ *shows that* $\mathbf{C} = \mathbf{A}^{-1}\mathbf{B}$. *Note that the proof of existence uses* $\mathbf{AA}^{-1} = \mathbf{I}$, *while uniqueness uses* $\mathbf{A}^{-1}\mathbf{A} = \mathbf{I}$. ■

The relationships among inverses, multiplication, and transposition are given in the next theorem.

Theorem 1.3.3. *If* $\mathbf{A}$ *and* $\mathbf{B}$ *are invertible* $n \times n$ *matrices, then*

(*a*) $(\mathbf{AB})^{-1} = \mathbf{B}^{-1}\mathbf{A}^{-1}$ (*b*) $(\mathbf{A}^{\mathrm{T}})^{-1} = (\mathbf{A}^{-1})^{\mathrm{T}}$ (*c*) $(\mathbf{ABC})^{-1} = \mathbf{C}^{-1}\mathbf{B}^{-1}\mathbf{A}^{-1}$

Proof. The first two assertions are proved by verifying that the conjectured inverses satisfy Eq. 1.3.1.

(*a*) The assertion is that the inverse of $\mathbf{AB}$ is given by $\mathbf{B}^{-1}\mathbf{A}^{-1}$. The following computations show that this is the case:

$$(\mathbf{AB})\mathbf{B}^{-1}\mathbf{A}^{-1} = \mathbf{A}(\mathbf{BB}^{-1})\mathbf{A}^{-1} = \mathbf{AA}^{-1} = \mathbf{I}$$
$$(\mathbf{B}^{-1}\mathbf{A}^{-1})\mathbf{AB} = \mathbf{B}^{-1}(\mathbf{A}^{-1}\mathbf{A})\mathbf{B} = \mathbf{B}^{-1}\mathbf{B} = \mathbf{I}$$

(*b*) Here we assert that the inverse of $\mathbf{A}^T$ is $(\mathbf{A}^{-1})^T$. So we must verify that $\mathbf{A}^T(\mathbf{A}^{-1})^T = \mathbf{I}$ and $(\mathbf{A}^{-1})^T\mathbf{A}^T = \mathbf{I}$. The former follows by transposing the identity $\mathbf{I} = \mathbf{A}^{-1}\mathbf{A}$. For, $\mathbf{I}^T = (\mathbf{A}^{-1}\mathbf{A})^T = \mathbf{A}^T(\mathbf{A}^{-1})^T$. The latter follows similarly by transposing the identity $\mathbf{I} = \mathbf{A}\mathbf{A}^{-1}$. We often write $\mathbf{A}^{-T}$ for $(\mathbf{A}^{-1})^T$.

(*c*) This assertion follows from (*a*). (See Problem 1.3.15.) ■

Neither the definition of inverse nor Theorem 1.3.3 provide a direct means for determining whether a matrix is invertible or singular. In fact, it is often difficult to recognize a singular matrix by inspection. Some useful criteria for singularity are given in the next example.

Example 1.3.1. Show that the following matrices are singular: (*a*) Those with a row or a column of zeros; (*b*) those with two proportional rows or columns.

Solution. (*a*) Consider $\mathbf{AX} = \mathbf{I}$. If $\mathbf{A}$ has a row of zeros, so does the product $\mathbf{AX}$. Thus $\mathbf{AX} = \mathbf{I}$ is impossible and therefore $\mathbf{A}$ must be singular. If $\mathbf{A}$ has a column of zeros, then $\mathbf{A}^T$ has a row of zeros and thus $\mathbf{A}^T$ is singular. But then $\mathbf{A}$ is singular by Theorem 1.3.3(*b*). (*b*) Let $\mathbf{A} = [\mathbf{A}_{*1} \quad \mathbf{A}_{*2} \quad \ldots \quad \mathbf{A}_{*n}]$ and consider $\mathbf{XA} = \mathbf{I}$. Since

$$\mathbf{XA} = \mathbf{X}[\mathbf{A}_{*1} \quad \mathbf{A}_{*2} \quad \ldots \quad \mathbf{A}_{*n}] = [\mathbf{XA}_{*1} \quad \mathbf{XA}_{*2} \quad \ldots \quad \mathbf{XA}_{*n}] = \mathbf{I} \tag{1.3.2}$$

if two columns of $\mathbf{A}$ are proportional, these same columns of $\mathbf{XA} = \mathbf{I}$ are also proportional. But $\mathbf{I}$ has no proportional columns and thus $\mathbf{X}$ cannot exist and satisfy $\mathbf{XA} = \mathbf{I}$. Hence $\mathbf{A}$ is singular. If $\mathbf{A}$ has proportional rows, then $\mathbf{A}^T$ has proportional columns and is therefore singular. By Theorem 1.3.3, it follows that $\mathbf{A}$ is singular.

Example 1.3.2. Explain why the following matrices are singular.

(*a*) $\begin{bmatrix} 1 & 1 & 1 \\ 2 & 2 & 2 \\ 3 & 3 & 3 \end{bmatrix}$ (*b*) $\begin{bmatrix} 1 & 1 & 1 \\ 2 & 2 & 2 \\ 1 & 2 & 3 \end{bmatrix}$ (*c*) $\begin{bmatrix} 0 & 1 & 1 \\ 0 & 2 & 2 \\ 0 & 1 & 0 \end{bmatrix} \mathbf{A}_3$

(*d*) $\mathbf{J}_n$ (*e*) $\mathbf{xx}^T$

Solution. The matrices (*a*), (*b*), (*d*), and (*e*) are singular because, among other things, they have proportional rows (assuming $\mathbf{x}$ has more than one entry); (*c*) is singular for every $\mathbf{A}_3$ because, in the product matrix, the second row is twice the first row. (Why?)

Section 1.4 is devoted to the study of a class of nonsingular matrices called elementary matrices. The inverses of these matrices are easy to obtain by inspection. We illustrate the invertibility of the three types of elementary matrices in the next example.

Example 1.3.3. Find the inverses of

$$(a)\ \mathbf{P} = \begin{bmatrix} 1 & 0 & 0 & 0 \\ 0 & 1 & 0 & 0 \\ 0 & 0 & 0 & 1 \\ 0 & 0 & 1 & 0 \end{bmatrix} \qquad (b)\ \mathbf{M} = \begin{bmatrix} 1 & 0 & 0 & 0 \\ 0 & 1 & 0 & 0 \\ 0 & 0 & a & 0 \\ 0 & 0 & 0 & 1 \end{bmatrix}$$

$$(c)\ \mathbf{E} = \begin{bmatrix} 1 & 0 & 0 & 0 \\ 0 & 1 & 0 & 0 \\ a & 0 & 1 & 0 \\ 0 & 0 & 0 & 1 \end{bmatrix}$$

Solution. The matrix in (a) results from interchanging rows 3 and 4 of $\mathbf{I}_4$. It is easy to see that $\mathbf{PP} = \mathbf{I}$ and, hence, that $\mathbf{P}$ is its own inverse. For (b), consider the following product

$$\begin{bmatrix} 1 & 0 & 0 & 0 \\ 0 & 1 & 0 & 0 \\ 0 & 0 & a & 0 \\ 0 & 0 & 0 & 1 \end{bmatrix}\begin{bmatrix} 1 & 0 & 0 & 0 \\ 0 & 1 & 0 & 0 \\ 0 & 0 & b & 0 \\ 0 & 0 & 0 & 1 \end{bmatrix} = \begin{bmatrix} 1 & 0 & 0 & 0 \\ 0 & 1 & 0 & 0 \\ 0 & 0 & b & 0 \\ 0 & 0 & 0 & 1 \end{bmatrix}\begin{bmatrix} 1 & 0 & 0 & 0 \\ 0 & 1 & 0 & 0 \\ 0 & 0 & a & 0 \\ 0 & 0 & 0 & 1 \end{bmatrix}$$

$$= \begin{bmatrix} 1 & 0 & 0 & 0 \\ 0 & 1 & 0 & 0 \\ 0 & 0 & ab & 0 \\ 0 & 0 & 0 & 1 \end{bmatrix}$$

given any $a \neq 0$, we can choose $b = 1/a$ and thus find the inverse of $\mathbf{M}$. A similar idea holds for the matrices in (c):

$$\begin{bmatrix} 1 & 0 & 0 & 0 \\ 0 & 1 & 0 & 0 \\ a & 0 & 1 & 0 \\ 0 & 0 & 0 & 1 \end{bmatrix}\begin{bmatrix} 1 & 0 & 0 & 0 \\ 0 & 1 & 0 & 0 \\ -a & 0 & 1 & 0 \\ 0 & 0 & 0 & 1 \end{bmatrix} = \begin{bmatrix} 1 & 0 & 0 & 0 \\ 0 & 1 & 0 & 0 \\ -a & 0 & 1 & 0 \\ 0 & 0 & 0 & 1 \end{bmatrix}\begin{bmatrix} 1 & 0 & 0 & 0 \\ 0 & 1 & 0 & 0 \\ a & 0 & 1 & 0 \\ 0 & 0 & 0 & 1 \end{bmatrix}$$

$$= \begin{bmatrix} 1 & 0 & 0 & 0 \\ 0 & 1 & 0 & 0 \\ 0 & 0 & 1 & 0 \\ 0 & 0 & 0 & 1 \end{bmatrix}$$

1.3.1 Inverses in MATLAB

The superscript-free notation for $\mathbf{A}^{-1}$ is inv(A). It is possible to show (as in Problem 1.7.13) that the inverse of a matrix with rational entries is also a matrix with rational entries. However, inv(A) may return a decimal approximation to $\mathbf{A}^{-1}$ even if the entries of $\mathbf{A}$ are integers. For $\mathbf{A}$ with rational entries, use rat(inv(A)) to obtain the entries of $\mathbf{A}^{-1}$ as quotients of integers. However, rat(A) is a symbolic matrix which cannot be an input to further MATLAB operations.

Example 1.3.4. Enter

$$\mathbf{A} = \begin{bmatrix} 1 & 0 & -1 \\ 2 & 2 & 3 \\ 1 & 1 & 0 \end{bmatrix}.$$

Then MATLAB returns

(*a*) inv(A) =

```
 1.0000    0.3333   -0.6667
-1.0000   -0.3333    1.6667
      0    0.3333   -0.6667
```

(*b*) rat(inv(A)) =

```
 1    1/3   -2/3
-1   -1/3    5/3
 0    1/3   -2/3
```

Note that A * rat(inv(A)) yields a meaningless output, as does 3 * rat(inv(A)). However, if B is defined by entering the entries of rat(inv(A)),

B = [1 1/3 − 2/3; − 1 − 1/3 5/3; 0 1/3 − 2/3]

then B * A = A * B = eye(3).

PROBLEMS

PART 1

1.3.1. Apply the definition of inverse to show that if $ad - bc \neq 0$,

$$\begin{bmatrix} a & b \\ c & d \end{bmatrix}^{-1} = (ad - bc)^{-1}\begin{bmatrix} d & -b \\ -c & a \end{bmatrix}$$

Verify this result for the matrix

$$\begin{bmatrix} 1 & 2 \\ -2 & 1 \end{bmatrix}$$

1.3.2. (*a*) Verify that $\mathbf{A}$ and $\mathbf{A}^{-1}$ are indeed inverses:

$$\mathbf{A} = \begin{bmatrix} 1 & 0 & 1 \\ 2 & 1 & 1 \\ 1 & 1 & 2 \end{bmatrix}, \qquad \mathbf{A}^{-1} = \tfrac{1}{2}\begin{bmatrix} 1 & 1 & -1 \\ -3 & 1 & 1 \\ 1 & -1 & 1 \end{bmatrix}$$

(*b*) Suppose $\mathbf{b} = [2 \;\; 0 \;\; 4]^{\mathrm{T}}$. Compute $\mathbf{A}^{-1}\mathbf{b}$ and verify that this vector is a solution of $\mathbf{Ax} = \mathbf{b}$.

1.3.3. Find the inverses of the following matrices by inspection:

$$\mathbf{A} = \begin{bmatrix} a & 0 & 0 & 0 \\ 0 & b & 0 & 0 \\ 0 & 0 & c & 0 \\ 0 & 0 & 0 & d \end{bmatrix}, \qquad \mathbf{B} = \begin{bmatrix} 0 & 0 & 0 & 1 \\ 0 & 0 & 1 & 0 \\ 0 & 1 & 0 & 0 \\ 1 & 0 & 0 & 0 \end{bmatrix}$$

1.3.4. Find the inverse of

$$\mathbf{B} = \begin{bmatrix} 1 & 1 & 1 & 1 \\ 0 & 1 & 1 & 1 \\ 0 & 0 & 1 & 1 \\ 0 & 0 & 0 & 1 \end{bmatrix}$$

PART 2

1.3.5. Apply the definition of inverse to show that $(\mathbf{SAS}^{-1})^{-1} = \mathbf{SA}^{-1}\mathbf{S}^{-1}$.

1.3.6. Apply the definition of inverse to show that $(k\mathbf{A})^{-1} = (1/k)\mathbf{A}^{-1}$.

1.3.7. Consider the matrices, **P**, **M** and **E** of Example 1.3.3. Compute **PM**, **PE**, **ME**, **MP**, **EP**, **EM**. Find the inverses of these six matrices.

1.3.8. Suppose $\mathbf{AB} = \mathbf{C}$ and each matrix is square. Show that **B** is invertible if **A** and **C** are invertible. Show that **A** is invertible if **B** and **C** are invertible.

PART 3

1.3.9. Explain the following product of partitioned matrices:

$$\left[\begin{array}{c|c} \mathbf{A}^{-1} & \mathbf{0} \\ \hline \mathbf{O}^{\mathrm{T}} & 1 \end{array}\right]\left[\begin{array}{c|c} \mathbf{A} & \mathbf{b} \\ \hline \mathbf{c}^{\mathrm{T}} & 1 \end{array}\right] = \left[\begin{array}{c|c} \mathbf{I} & \mathbf{A}^{-1}\mathbf{b} \\ \hline \mathbf{c}^{\mathrm{T}} & 1 \end{array}\right]$$

1.3.10. If **B** is invertible and $\mathbf{B}^2 = \mathbf{B}$, show that $\mathbf{B} = \mathbf{I}$. Exhibit a 2×2 example of a singular $\mathbf{B} \neq \mathbf{O}$ for which $\mathbf{B}^2 = \mathbf{B}$.

1.3.11. If **A** is invertible show that $(\mathbf{A}^n)^{-1} = (\mathbf{A}^{-1})^n$ for each integer $n > 0$. (In view of this result, we write $\mathbf{A}^{-n}$ for either $(\mathbf{A}^n)^{-1}$ or $(\mathbf{A}^{-1})^n$.)

1.3.12. Show that

$$\begin{aligned} &(\mathbf{I} - \mathbf{A})(\mathbf{I} + \mathbf{A} + \mathbf{A}^2 + \cdots + \mathbf{A}^{n-1}) \\ &= (\mathbf{I} + \mathbf{A} + \mathbf{A}^2 + \cdots + \mathbf{A}^{n-1})(\mathbf{I} - \mathbf{A}) = \mathbf{I} - \mathbf{A}^n \end{aligned}$$

1.3.13. Show that $(\mathbf{SAS}^{-1})^n = \mathbf{SA}^n\mathbf{S}^{-1}$, for each integer $n > 0$.

1.3.14. Show that $(\mathbf{SAS}^{-1})^n = \mathbf{SA}^n\mathbf{S}^{-1}$ holds for all integers, provided **A** is invertible. (*Hint:* Define $\mathbf{A}^0 = \mathbf{I}$ and use Problems 1.3.11 and 1.3.13.)

1.3.15. Suppose **A**, **B** and **C** are invertible. Show that $(\mathbf{ABC})^{-1} = \mathbf{C}^{-1}\mathbf{B}^{-1}\mathbf{A}^{-1}$.

MATLAB

1.3.16. Verify the conclusion of Problem 1.3.2.

For each of the following problems enter random matrices **A** and **B** both 5×5.

1.3.17. Verify Theorem 1.3.3.

1.3.18. Verify $(\mathbf{A}^{-1})^{-1} = \mathbf{A}$.

1.4 ELEMENTARY ROW MATRICES

Our next topic is a class of invertible matrices called *elementary matrices*. To motivate our discussion, we need to first study certain operations on the rows of a matrix. The following changes to the rows of **A** are called *elementary row operations*.

Type 1. Interchange two rows of **A**.
Type 2. Multiply a row of **A** by a nonzero scalar.
Type 3. Add a multiple of one row of **A** to another row.

The matrix **A** is *row equivalent* to **B** (or, for short, **A** is equivalent to **B**) if there is a sequence of elementary row operations that transforms **A** into **B**. We portray the equivalence of **A** and **B** with an *arrow diagram:*

$$\mathbf{A} = \mathbf{A}_0 \to \mathbf{A}_1 \to \cdots \mathbf{A}_{k-1} \to \mathbf{A}_k = \mathbf{B} \tag{1.4.1}$$

Each arrow describes the effect of a single elementary row operation and, by definition, $\mathbf{A}_i$ is equivalent to $\mathbf{A}_j$ if $i < j$.

Example 1.4.1. Find the sequence of elementary row operations implicit in the arrow diagram

$$\mathbf{A} = \begin{bmatrix} 1 & 0 & 0 \\ 0 & 0 & 1 \\ 2 & -1 & 0 \end{bmatrix} \to \begin{bmatrix} 1 & 0 & 0 \\ 2 & -1 & 0 \\ 0 & 0 & 1 \end{bmatrix} \to \begin{bmatrix} 1 & 0 & 0 \\ 0 & -1 & 0 \\ 0 & 0 & 1 \end{bmatrix} \to \begin{bmatrix} 1 & 0 & 0 \\ 0 & 1 & 0 \\ 0 & 0 & 1 \end{bmatrix} = \mathbf{I}$$

Solution. Let $\mathbf{A}_1$ and $\mathbf{A}_2$ denote the second and third matrices in the given diagram so $\mathbf{A} \to \mathbf{A}_1 \to \mathbf{A}_2 \to \mathbf{I}$. Then $\mathbf{A} \to \mathbf{A}_1$ is obtained by interchanging rows 2 and 3 of **A**. To obtain $\mathbf{A}_2$ from $\mathbf{A}_1$ add $-2 \times$ row 1 of $\mathbf{A}_1$ to row 2.

The arrow diagram in Eq. 1.4.1 implies a second, "inverse" arrow diagram

$$\mathbf{B} = \mathbf{A}_k \to \cdots \to \mathbf{A}_1 \to \mathbf{A}_0 = \mathbf{A} \tag{1.4.2}$$

To show this, we prove that every step in a diagram is reversible; if $\mathbf{A}_i \to \mathbf{A}_{i+1}$ then $\mathbf{A}_{i+1} \to \mathbf{A}_i$. The proofs for elementary row operations of Types 1 and 2 are straightforward and are left as exercises. (See Problems 1.4.14 and 1.4.15). If $\mathbf{A}_i \to \mathbf{A}_{i+1}$ represents the addition of α times row k to row l, then $\mathbf{A}_{i+1} \to \mathbf{A}_i$ is obtained by adding $-\alpha$ times row k to row l.

Example 1.4.2. Find the elementary row operations that reverse the diagram of Example 1.4.1.

Solution. It is easier to discover the row operations if we first rewrite the diagram of Example 1.4.1 in reverse order. The reversed diagram is given as follows:

$$\mathbf{I} = \begin{bmatrix} 1 & 0 & 0 \\ 0 & 1 & 0 \\ 0 & 0 & 1 \end{bmatrix} \to \begin{bmatrix} 1 & 0 & 0 \\ 0 & -1 & 0 \\ 0 & 0 & 1 \end{bmatrix} \to \begin{bmatrix} 1 & 0 & 0 \\ 2 & -1 & 0 \\ 0 & 0 & 1 \end{bmatrix} \to \begin{bmatrix} 1 & 0 & 0 \\ 0 & 0 & 1 \\ 2 & -1 & 0 \end{bmatrix} = \mathbf{A}$$

The first step is to multiply the second row by -1. The second step is to add 2 times row 1 of **I** to the second row. Finally, to obtain **A**, simply interchange rows 2 and 3 of the matrix to the immediate left of **A** in the diagram. (Compare with the operations used in Example 1.4.1.)

Theorem 1.4.1. *If* **A** *is row equivalent to* **B**, *then* **B** *is row equivalent to* **A**.

Proof. This theorem is simply a formal statement that every arrow diagram is reversible. ■

Recall that in the product **FA**, **F** is called a *premultiplier* of **A**, and **A** is called a *postmultiplier* of **F**. For every elementary row operation on **A**, there is a corresponding premultiplier **F** which has the same effect on **A** as does the elementary row operation. For instance suppose $\mathbf{A} \rightarrow \mathbf{A}_1$. Then there is a nonsingular matrix **F** such that $\mathbf{FA} = \mathbf{A}_1$. These multipliers are called *elementary matrices*. Elementary matrices are easy to construct and they are easily shown to be invertible. For simplicity let us take the special case in which all the matrices are of order 3; the argument for the general case is quite similar. We assert.

1. $\mathbf{P} = \begin{bmatrix} 1 & 0 & 0 \\ 0 & 0 & 1 \\ 0 & 1 & 0 \end{bmatrix}$ interchanges rows 2 and 3 of **A**.

2. $\mathbf{M} = \begin{bmatrix} 1 & 0 & 0 \\ 0 & \alpha & 0 \\ 0 & 0 & 1 \end{bmatrix}$ multiplies row 2 of **A** by α.

3. $\mathbf{E} = \begin{bmatrix} 1 & 0 & 0 \\ \alpha & 1 & 0 \\ 0 & 0 & 1 \end{bmatrix}$ adds α times the first row of **A** to its second row.

These assertions are easily checked by performing the multiplications **PA**, **MA**, and **EA** on the arbitrary matrix **A** of order $3 \times n$. (See Example 1.4.3).

We write **P** for all elementary matrices that interchange rows, **M** for those that multiply a given row by a scalar, and **E** for those that add a multiple of one row to another (distinct) row. We use **F** for any elementary row matrix, regardless of type. By analogy with the classification of elementary row operations, **P** is an elementary matrix of Type 1, **M** is an elementary matrix of Type 2, and **E** is of Type 3.

To understand the technique of constructing elementary row matrices having a specific effect on **A**, suppose it is desired to add -3 times row 2 to row 1. The appropriate elementary row matrix is obtained by applying this elementary row operation to **I**. If **A** is $3 \times n$, then **E** is given by

$$\mathbf{I} \rightarrow \begin{bmatrix} 1 & -3 & 0 \\ 0 & 1 & 0 \\ 0 & 0 & 1 \end{bmatrix} = \mathbf{E}$$

It is easy to ascertain that **EA** is the matrix obtained from **A** by the elementary operation, "add -3 times row 2 to row 1." Consider the next example and compare it with Example 1.4.1.

Example 1.4.3. Find the sequence of elementary matrices representing the elementary operations depicted in the arrow diagram

$$\mathbf{A} = \begin{bmatrix} 1 & 0 & 0 \\ 0 & 0 & 1 \\ 2 & -1 & 0 \end{bmatrix} \to \begin{bmatrix} 1 & 0 & 0 \\ 2 & -1 & 0 \\ 0 & 0 & 1 \end{bmatrix} \to \begin{bmatrix} 1 & 0 & 0 \\ -2 & 1 & 0 \\ 0 & 0 & 1 \end{bmatrix} \to \begin{bmatrix} 1 & 0 & 0 \\ 0 & 1 & 0 \\ 0 & 0 & 1 \end{bmatrix} = \mathbf{I}$$

Solution. The first operation interchanges rows 2 and 3. Hence the first elementary matrix is $\mathbf{P}$ and $\mathbf{PA} = \mathbf{A}_1$.

$$\mathbf{P} = \begin{bmatrix} 1 & 0 & 0 \\ 0 & 0 & 1 \\ 0 & 1 & 0 \end{bmatrix}, \quad \mathbf{PA} = \begin{bmatrix} 1 & 0 & 0 \\ 0 & 0 & 1 \\ 0 & 1 & 0 \end{bmatrix} \begin{bmatrix} 1 & 0 & 0 \\ 0 & 0 & 1 \\ 2 & -1 & 0 \end{bmatrix} = \begin{bmatrix} 1 & 0 & 0 \\ 2 & -1 & 0 \\ 0 & 0 & 1 \end{bmatrix} = \mathbf{A}_1$$

The second elementary matrix multiplies row 2 by -1. Thus the second elementary matrix is $\mathbf{M}$ and $\mathbf{MA}_1 = \mathbf{A}_2$.

$$\mathbf{M} = \begin{bmatrix} 1 & 0 & 0 \\ 0 & -1 & 0 \\ 0 & 0 & 1 \end{bmatrix}, \quad \mathbf{MA}_1 = \begin{bmatrix} 1 & 0 & 0 \\ 0 & -1 & 0 \\ 0 & 0 & 1 \end{bmatrix} \begin{bmatrix} 1 & 0 & 0 \\ 2 & -1 & 0 \\ 0 & 0 & 1 \end{bmatrix} = \begin{bmatrix} 1 & 0 & 0 \\ -2 & 1 & 0 \\ 0 & 0 & 1 \end{bmatrix} = \mathbf{A}_2$$

The last operation adds 2 times row 1 to row 2. So the last elementary matrix is $\mathbf{E}$ and $\mathbf{EA}_2 = \mathbf{I}$.

$$\mathbf{E} = \begin{bmatrix} 1 & 0 & 0 \\ 2 & 1 & 0 \\ 0 & 0 & 1 \end{bmatrix} \quad \mathbf{EA}_2 = \begin{bmatrix} 1 & 0 & 0 \\ 2 & 1 & 0 \\ 0 & 0 & 1 \end{bmatrix} \begin{bmatrix} 1 & 0 & 0 \\ -2 & 1 & 0 \\ 0 & 0 & 1 \end{bmatrix} = \begin{bmatrix} 1 & 0 & 0 \\ 0 & 1 & 0 \\ 0 & 0 & 1 \end{bmatrix} = \mathbf{I}$$

Note that $\mathbf{I} = \mathbf{EA}_2 = \mathbf{EMA}_1 = \mathbf{EMPA}$.

This example can be generalized to show that for every arrow diagram

$$\mathbf{A} = \mathbf{A}_0 \to \cdots \to \mathbf{A}_k = \mathbf{B} \tag{1.4.3}$$

there corresponds an equation of the form

$$\mathbf{F}_k \mathbf{F}_{k-1} \cdots \mathbf{F}_2 \mathbf{F}_1 \mathbf{A} = \mathbf{B} \tag{1.4.4}$$

where $\mathbf{F}_i$ is the elementary matrix such that $\mathbf{F}_i \mathbf{A}_{i-1} = \mathbf{A}_i$.

Theorem 1.4.2. *Every elementary matrix is invertible and its inverse is an elementary matrix of the same type.*

Proof. If $\mathbf{P}$ is of Type 1 then it interchanges two rows and $\mathbf{P}^2 = \mathbf{I}$. If $\mathbf{M}_1$ multiplies row i by $\alpha \neq 0$, define $\mathbf{M}_2$ as the elementary matrix which multiplies row i by $1/\alpha$. Then $\mathbf{M}_1\mathbf{M}_2 = \mathbf{M}_2\mathbf{M}_1 = \mathbf{I}$. Finally, let $\mathbf{E}_1$ add α times row i to row j, and $\mathbf{E}_2$ add $-\alpha$ times row i to row j. Then $\mathbf{E}_1\mathbf{E}_2 = \mathbf{E}_2\mathbf{E}_1 = \mathbf{I}$. ■

Example 1.3.3 illustrates this theorem for representative elementary matrices of size 4×4.

Theorem 1.4.3. *If* **A** *is row equivalent to* **B**, *then there is a nonsingular matrix* **S** *such that* $\mathbf{SA} = \mathbf{B}$.

Proof. By hypothesis there is an arrow diagram from **A** to **B**. By Eq. 1.4.4, $\mathbf{F}_k\mathbf{F}_{k-1}\cdots\mathbf{F}_2\mathbf{F}_1\mathbf{A} = \mathbf{B}$. Set $\mathbf{S} = \mathbf{F}_k\mathbf{F}_{k-1}\cdots\mathbf{F}_2\mathbf{F}_1$. Then $\mathbf{SA} = \mathbf{B}$ and, by Theorem 1.4.2, **S** is the product of nonsingular matrices and is therefore nonsingular by Theorem 1. 3.3(*a*). ■

Corollary 1. *If* **A** *is row equivalent to* **B**, *then either both* **A** *and* **B** *are nonsingular or they both are singular.*

Proof. By the theorem, $\mathbf{SA} = \mathbf{B}$. If **A** is nonsingular, then since **S** is nonsingular, **B** is the product of nonsingular matrices and is therefore nonsingular. Also, $\mathbf{A} = \mathbf{S}^{-1}\mathbf{B}$ shows that **A** is the product of nonsingular matrices if **B** is nonsingular. That is, if either **A** or **B** is nonsingular, then they both are. ■

Corollary 2. *If* **A** *is row equivalent to* **I**, *then* **A** *is nonsingular.*

Proof. This is a special case of Corollary 1, since **I** is nonsingular. ■

Note that Corollary 2 does not assert that every nonsingular matrix is row equivalent to **I**. This statement is the converse of Corollary 2; it is true, important, and interesting. Its proof is in the next section as Theorem 1.5.4. (See also Problem 1.4.20.)

PROBLEMS

PART 1

1.4.1. List all the elementary row matrices of sizes 1×1, 2×2 and 3×3.

1.4.2. Is **I** an elementary matrix? Is $-\mathbf{I}$? Is $\mathbf{F}_1\mathbf{F}_2$?

1.4.3. Construct the elementary matrices of size 4×4 which (*a*) Adds 2 times row 1 to row 3, (*b*) Interchanges rows 4 and 1, (*c*) Multiplies row 1 by -4, (*d*) Adds -2 times row 3 to row 1.

1.4.4. Multiply the matrices in parts (*a*) and (*c*) of Problem 1.4.3.

1.4.5. Find a sequence of elementary matrices so that

$$\begin{bmatrix} 0 & 0 & 0 & a \\ 0 & 0 & b & 0 \\ 0 & c & 0 & 0 \\ d & 0 & 0 & 0 \end{bmatrix} \to \cdots \to \mathbf{I}$$

1.4.6. Compute the product of the elementary matrices found in Problem 1.4.5. Show that this product is the inverse of the matrix given in Problem 1.4.5.

1.4.7. List all the elementary matrices of size 4 that interchange rows. (There are 4 rows taken 2 at a time so there are $4 \times 3/2 = 6$ such matrices.)

1.4.8. Let **A** be the matrix of Example 1.4.3. Find a sequence of elementary matrices that takes **I** to **A**.

PART 2

1.4.9. Is **A** row equivalent to **A**? Explain.

1.4.10. Suppose **A** is row equivalent to **B**. Is $k\mathbf{A}$ row equivalent to $h\mathbf{B}$?

1.4.11. Suppose **A** is row equivalent to **B** and **B** is row equivalent to **C**. Show that **A** is row equivalent to **C** by means of an arrow diagram.

1.4.12. Use Problem 1.4.11 to describe the relationship among the nonsingular matrices which take **A** to **B**, **B** to **C**, and **A** to **C**.

1.4.13. Explain why every pair of matrices in the arrow diagram $\mathbf{A} \to \mathbf{A}_1 \to \cdots \to \mathbf{A}_k \to \mathbf{B}$ is equivalent.

1.4.14. Suppose interchanging rows i and j takes $\mathbf{A}_i$ to $\mathbf{A}_{i+1}$. What elementary row operation takes $\mathbf{A}_{i+1}$ to $\mathbf{A}_i$?

1.4.15. Suppose multiplying row i by α takes $\mathbf{A}_i$ to $\mathbf{A}_{i+1}$. What elementary row operation takes $\mathbf{A}_{i+1}$ to A_i?

1.4.16. Explain why every upper triangular matrix without zeros on the diagonal is row equivalent to **I**. What is the maximum number of elementary operations of each type necessary to convert such an upper triangular matrix to **I**?

1.4.17. Let $\mathbf{R}_n$ be a square matrix whose first row is $\mathbf{r}^{\mathrm{T}}$ and whose last $n-1$ rows are zero. Show that $\mathbf{R}_n$ is row equivalent to $\mathbf{1r}^{\mathrm{T}}$.

1.4.18. Show that **A** and **B** are row equivalent and find a nonsingular **S** such that $\mathbf{SA} = \mathbf{B}$, where

$$\mathbf{A} = \begin{bmatrix} 2 & 2 & 1 \\ 3 & 3 & -2 \\ 1 & 1 & -2 \end{bmatrix}, \qquad \mathbf{B} = \begin{bmatrix} 1 & 1 & 0 \\ 0 & 0 & 1 \\ 0 & 0 & 0 \end{bmatrix}.$$

Explain why **A** is singular.

1.4.19. Use the matrices of Problem 1.4.18 (**A**, **B** and **S**) to find a **T** such that $\mathbf{TB} = \mathbf{A}$. Compute **ST**.

1.4.20. Suppose **A** is row equivalent to **I**. Show that **A** is the product of elementary matrices.

1.5 A TEST FOR INVERTIBILITY

Elementary row operations are powerful tools for the solution of systems of equations. In this section, row operations are used to derive an algorithm which distinguishes singular from invertible matrices and, when the matrix is invertible, determine its inverse.

Theorem 1.5.1. *Each* **A** *is row equivalent to an upper trapezoidal matrix* **U**.

Proof. The idea behind the proof is quite simple; apply elementary row operations to clear the entries below the diagonal starting with column 1 and do the same for each column moving to the right, column by column. Indeed, suppose we have progressed this far:

$$\mathbf{A} \to \mathbf{A}_1 \to \cdots \to \mathbf{A}_k = \begin{bmatrix} * & * & * & * & \cdots & * \\ 0 & * & * & * & \cdots & * \\ 0 & 0 & * & * & \cdots & * \\ 0 & 0 & 0 & a & \cdots & * \\ 0 & 0 & 0 & b & \cdots & * \\ 0 & 0 & 0 & c & \cdots & * \end{bmatrix} \tag{1.5.1}$$

The next step is to clear the entries below the diagonal in the fourth column (a in this case). If $b = c = 0$ there is nothing to do and we move to the fifth column. Otherwise, there are three cases.

Case 1. *Assume $a \neq 0$. Then, using only Type 3 operations,*

$$\begin{bmatrix} * & * & * & * & \cdots & * \\ 0 & * & * & * & \cdots & * \\ 0 & 0 & * & * & \cdots & * \\ 0 & 0 & 0 & a & \cdots & * \\ 0 & 0 & 0 & b & \cdots & * \\ 0 & 0 & 0 & c & \cdots & * \end{bmatrix} \to \begin{bmatrix} * & * & * & * & \cdots & * \\ 0 & * & * & * & \cdots & * \\ 0 & 0 & * & * & \cdots & * \\ 0 & 0 & 0 & a & \cdots & * \\ 0 & 0 & 0 & 0 & \cdots & * \\ 0 & 0 & 0 & c & \cdots & * \end{bmatrix} \to \begin{bmatrix} * & * & * & * & \cdots & * \\ 0 & * & * & * & \cdots & * \\ 0 & 0 & * & * & \cdots & * \\ 0 & 0 & 0 & a & \cdots & * \\ 0 & 0 & 0 & 0 & \cdots & * \\ 0 & 0 & 0 & 0 & \cdots & * \end{bmatrix}$$

Case 2. *Assume $a = 0$, $b \neq 0$. Then, using a Type 1 operation to interchange the fourth and fifth rows, Case 2 reduces to Case 1:*

$$\begin{bmatrix} * & * & * & * & \cdots & * \\ 0 & * & * & * & \cdots & * \\ 0 & 0 & * & * & \cdots & * \\ 0 & 0 & 0 & 0 & \cdots & * \\ 0 & 0 & 0 & b & \cdots & * \\ 0 & 0 & 0 & c & \cdots & * \end{bmatrix} \to \begin{bmatrix} * & * & * & * & \cdots & * \\ 0 & * & * & * & \cdots & * \\ 0 & 0 & * & * & \cdots & * \\ 0 & 0 & 0 & b & \cdots & * \\ 0 & 0 & 0 & 0 & \cdots & * \\ 0 & 0 & 0 & c & \cdots & * \end{bmatrix} \to \begin{bmatrix} * & * & * & * & \cdots & * \\ 0 & * & * & * & \cdots & * \\ 0 & 0 & * & * & \cdots & * \\ 0 & 0 & 0 & b & \cdots & * \\ 0 & 0 & 0 & 0 & \cdots & * \\ 0 & 0 & 0 & 0 & \cdots & * \end{bmatrix}$$

Case 3. *Assume $a = b = 0$ and $c \neq 0$. This case is essentially Case 2 except rows four and six are interchanged:*

$$\begin{bmatrix} * & * & * & * & \cdots & * \\ 0 & * & * & * & \cdots & * \\ 0 & 0 & * & * & \cdots & * \\ 0 & 0 & 0 & 0 & \cdots & * \\ 0 & 0 & 0 & 0 & \cdots & * \\ 0 & 0 & 0 & c & \cdots & * \end{bmatrix} \to \begin{bmatrix} * & * & * & * & \cdots & * \\ 0 & * & * & * & \cdots & * \\ 0 & 0 & * & * & \cdots & * \\ 0 & 0 & 0 & c & \cdots & * \\ 0 & 0 & 0 & 0 & \cdots & * \\ 0 & 0 & 0 & 0 & \cdots & * \end{bmatrix}$$

These cases illustrate how elementary row operations can always be found to clear the entries below the diagonal entry in column i if the entries below the diagonals on all columns to the left of column i are already zero. Note that this technique does not introduce nonzero entries in these "earlier" columns. That is, Eq. 1.5.1 implies

$$\mathbf{A}\to\mathbf{A}_1\to\cdots\to\mathbf{A}_k\to\mathbf{A}_{k+1}=\begin{bmatrix} * & * & * & * & \cdots & * \\ 0 & * & * & * & \cdots & * \\ 0 & 0 & * & * & \cdots & * \\ 0 & 0 & 0 & * & \cdots & * \\ 0 & 0 & 0 & 0 & \cdots & * \\ 0 & 0 & 0 & 0 & \cdots & * \end{bmatrix} \quad \blacksquare$$

Remarks. An alternative way of expressing this theorem is that for each $\mathbf{A}$ there always exists an upper trapezoidal matrix $\mathbf{U}$ such that the diagram $\mathbf{A}\to\mathbf{A}_1\to\cdots\to\mathbf{A}_r\to\mathbf{U}$ is possible. It should be noted that the procedure used in this special case is not restricted by the number of rows and columns of $\mathbf{A}$. A rigorous argument can be based on induction on the number of columns of $\mathbf{A}$. The steps are outlined in Problem 1.5.11.

Theorem 1.5.2. *Suppose* $\mathbf{U}$ *is an upper triangular matrix. Then* $\mathbf{U}$ *is singular if and only if it has a zero diagonal entry.*

Proof. The "if" part is illustrated for the case in which $\mathbf{U}$ is 6×6 and $u_{44}=0$. If the entry $u_{66}=0$ then the last row of $\mathbf{U}$ is a row of zeros, and we are done. If $u_{66}\neq 0$, then multiples of the last row of $\mathbf{U}$ may be used to clear the entries above u_{66} in the last column:

$$\begin{bmatrix} * & * & * & * & * & * \\ 0 & * & * & * & * & * \\ 0 & 0 & * & * & * & * \\ 0 & 0 & 0 & 0 & * & * \\ 0 & 0 & 0 & 0 & * & * \\ 0 & 0 & 0 & 0 & 0 & u_{66} \end{bmatrix} \to\cdots\to \begin{bmatrix} * & * & * & * & * & 0 \\ 0 & * & * & * & * & 0 \\ 0 & 0 & * & * & * & 0 \\ 0 & 0 & 0 & 0 & * & 0 \\ 0 & 0 & 0 & 0 & * & 0 \\ 0 & 0 & 0 & 0 & 0 & u_{66} \end{bmatrix} \tag{1.5.2}$$

Now look at u_{55}. If this entry is zero, then the row 5 is a zero row and $\mathbf{U}$ is equivalent to a singular matrix. By Corollary 1 of Theorem 1.5.3, $\mathbf{U}$ is also singular. Assume instead that this term is not zero. Again, we take suitable multiples of row 5 and add them to the rows above. The next diagram shows why row 4 becomes a row of zeros if $u_{66}\neq 0$ and $u_{55}\neq 0$.

$$\begin{bmatrix} * & * & * & * & * & * \\ 0 & * & * & * & * & * \\ 0 & 0 & * & * & * & * \\ 0 & 0 & 0 & 0 & * & * \\ 0 & 0 & 0 & 0 & u_{55} & * \\ 0 & 0 & 0 & 0 & 0 & * \end{bmatrix} \to\cdots\to \begin{bmatrix} * & * & * & * & 0 & 0 \\ 0 & * & * & * & 0 & 0 \\ 0 & 0 & * & * & 0 & 0 \\ 0 & 0 & 0 & 0 & 0 & 0 \\ 0 & 0 & 0 & 0 & u_{55} & 0 \\ 0 & 0 & 0 & 0 & 0 & * \end{bmatrix} \tag{1.5.3}$$

It is not difficult to see how this argument can be generalized and be made rigorous: Replace u_{66} by u_{nn} and assume $a_{ii}=0$. Using the illustration above, show that $\mathbf{U}$ is equivalent to a matrix whose ith row is a zero row.

Conversely, if no diagonal entry is zero then $\mathbf{U}$ is row equivalent to $\mathbf{I}$ and $\mathbf{U}$ is nonsingular by Corollary 1 of Theorem 1.4.3. $\blacksquare$

Theorems 1.5.1 and 1.5.2 together form the test for singularity mentioned in the introduction to this section. We transform **A** to upper triangular form by repeated elementary row operations. If at any stage we reach a zero entry on the diagonal that cannot be made nonzero by a row interchange with a *later* row, then **A** is singular and we can stop. If, on the other hand, no zero entry appears on the diagonal then **A** is nonsingular.

The next theorem is an extension of the previous two theorems.

Theorem 1.5.3. *The square matrix* **A** *is singular if and only if it is row equivalent to an upper triangular matrix with at least one zero on its diagonal.*

Proof. Theorem 1.5.1 shows that a square matrix **A** is row equivalent to an upper triangular matrix **U**. Hence **A** is singular if and only if **U** is singular by Corollary 1 of Theorem 1.4.3. Theorem 1.5.2 completes the argument. (See Problems 1.4.11 and 1.4.16.) ■

Corollary 1. *The square matrix* **A** *is singular if and only if it is row equivalent to an upper triangular matrix with a row of zeros.*

Proof. This is a consequence of Theorems 1.5.2 and 1.5.3. ■

Example 1.5.1. Use the theorems of this section to establish the singularity of the matrix

$$\mathbf{A} = \begin{bmatrix} 2 & 2 & 1 \\ 3 & 3 & -2 \\ 1 & 1 & -2 \end{bmatrix}$$

Solution. The following diagram,

$$\mathbf{A} = \begin{bmatrix} 2 & 2 & 1 \\ 3 & 3 & -2 \\ 1 & 1 & -2 \end{bmatrix} \rightarrow \begin{bmatrix} 1 & 1 & -2 \\ 3 & 3 & -2 \\ 2 & 2 & 1 \end{bmatrix} \rightarrow \begin{bmatrix} 1 & 1 & -2 \\ 0 & 0 & 4 \\ 2 & 2 & 1 \end{bmatrix} \rightarrow \begin{bmatrix} 1 & 1 & -2 \\ 0 & 0 & 4 \\ 0 & 0 & 5 \end{bmatrix} = \mathbf{U}$$

shows that **A** is row equivalent to **U** and **U** is upper triangular with a zero diagonal entry. Hence, by Theorem 1.5.3, **A** is singular.

The next theorem is not only interesting, it also provides the basis for the computation of $\mathbf{A}^{-1}$.

Theorem 1.5.4. *The matrix* **A** *is nonsingular if and only if it is row equivalent to the identity matrix.*

Proof. We have established that a matrix which is row equivalent to **I** is nonsingular. To prove the converse, first note that **A** is row equivalent to an upper triangular matrix **U** by Theorem 1.5.1. Assume **A** is nonsingular. If **U** were to have a zero on its diagonal, then **U** is singular by Theorem 1.5.2 and then **A** would be singular. Hence **A** is row equivalent to an upper triangular matrix with no zeros on its diagonal. But such a matrix is row equivalent to **I**. Thus $\mathbf{A} \to \cdots \to \mathbf{U} \to \cdots \to \mathbf{I}$, implying that **A** is row equivalent to **I**. ■

Corollary 1, which follows, provides a computationally efficient algorithm that generates the inverse of **A** using elementary row operations.

Corollary 1. *If* **A** *is nonsingular, then the arrow diagram*

$$[\mathbf{A} \quad \mathbf{I}] \to \cdots \to [\mathbf{I} \quad \mathbf{B}] \tag{1.5.4}$$

is possible and, moreover, Eq. 1.5.4 implies $\mathbf{B} = \mathbf{A}^{-1}$.

Proof. Since **A** is nonsingular, $\mathbf{A} \to \cdots \to \mathbf{I}$ follows by Theorem 1.5.4. Application of those row operations that take **A** to **I** to the matrix $[\mathbf{A} \quad \mathbf{I}]$ yields $[\mathbf{A} \quad \mathbf{I}] \to \cdots \to [\mathbf{I} \quad \mathbf{B}]$ for some **B**. So the arrow diagram given by Eq. 1.5.4 is possible. We now show that $\mathbf{B} = \mathbf{A}^{-1}$. By Theorem 1.4.3, there is a nonsingular **S** such that $\mathbf{S}[\mathbf{A} \quad \mathbf{I}] = [\mathbf{I} \quad \mathbf{B}]$. However, since $\mathbf{S}[\mathbf{A} \quad \mathbf{I}] = [\mathbf{SA} \quad \mathbf{S}]$, we have $[\mathbf{SA} \quad \mathbf{S}] = [\mathbf{I} \quad \mathbf{B}]$, and therefore, $\mathbf{SA} = \mathbf{I}$ and $\mathbf{S} = \mathbf{B}$. The latter two equations imply $\mathbf{BA} = \mathbf{I}$. Since **A** is nonsingular and $\mathbf{A}^{-1}$ is unique, $\mathbf{B} = \mathbf{A}^{-1}$.

Example 1.5.2. Use Corollary 1 to find the inverse of

$$\mathbf{A} = \begin{bmatrix} 2 & -1 & 1 \\ 1 & 0 & -1 \\ 0 & 1 & 1 \end{bmatrix}$$

Solution. Form the matrix $[\mathbf{A} \quad \mathbf{I}]$ and compute the arrow diagram $[\mathbf{A} \quad \mathbf{I}] \to \cdots \to [\mathbf{I} \quad \mathbf{B}]$.

$$\left[\begin{array}{ccc|ccc} 2 & -1 & 1 & 1 & 0 & 0 \\ 1 & 0 & -1 & 0 & 1 & 0 \\ 0 & 1 & 1 & 0 & 0 & 1 \end{array}\right] \to \left[\begin{array}{ccc|ccc} 1 & 0 & -1 & 0 & 1 & 0 \\ 2 & -1 & 1 & 1 & 0 & 0 \\ 0 & 1 & 1 & 0 & 0 & 1 \end{array}\right]$$

$$\to \left[\begin{array}{ccc|ccc} 1 & 0 & -1 & 0 & 1 & 0 \\ 0 & -1 & 3 & 1 & -2 & 0 \\ 0 & 1 & 1 & 0 & 0 & 1 \end{array}\right] \to \left[\begin{array}{ccc|ccc} 1 & 0 & -1 & 0 & 1 & 0 \\ 0 & -1 & 3 & 1 & -2 & 0 \\ 0 & 0 & 4 & 1 & -2 & 1 \end{array}\right] \to$$

$$\cdots \to \left[\begin{array}{ccc|ccc} 1 & 0 & -1 & 0 & 1 & 0 \\ 0 & 1 & -3 & -1 & 2 & 0 \\ 0 & 0 & 1 & \tfrac{1}{4} & -\tfrac{1}{2} & \tfrac{1}{4} \end{array}\right] \to$$

$$\cdots \to \left[\begin{array}{ccc|ccc} 1 & 0 & 0 & \tfrac{1}{4} & \tfrac{1}{2} & \tfrac{1}{4} \\ 0 & 1 & 0 & -\tfrac{1}{4} & \tfrac{1}{2} & \tfrac{3}{4} \\ 0 & 0 & 1 & \tfrac{1}{4} & -\tfrac{1}{2} & \tfrac{1}{4} \end{array}\right]$$

Hence,

$$\mathbf{A}^{-1} = \tfrac{1}{4}\begin{bmatrix} 1 & 2 & 1 \\ -1 & 2 & 3 \\ 1 & -2 & 1 \end{bmatrix}$$

Corollary 2. *The matrix* **A** *is nonsingular if and only if it is the product of elementary row matrices.*

Proof. By Theorem 1.5.4, a matrix is nonsingular if it is row equivalent to **I**. Thus, **I** is row equivalent to **A** by Theorem 1.4.1 and there exists an arrow diagram $\mathbf{I} \to \cdots \to \mathbf{A}$. From Eq. 1.4.1, it follows that $\mathbf{F}_k\mathbf{F}_{k-1}\cdots\mathbf{F}_2\mathbf{F}_1\mathbf{I} = \mathbf{A}$. Thus, every nonsingular matrix is the product of elementary matrices. The converse is trivial. ■

The definition of $\mathbf{A}^{-1}$ requires that in order for **A** to be invertible and **X** to be its inverse, both $\mathbf{AX} = \mathbf{I}$ and $\mathbf{XA} = \mathbf{I}$ must hold. However, a much weaker hypothesis suffices.

Corollary 3. *If* **A** *is a square matrix and either* $\mathbf{AB} = \mathbf{I}$ *or* $\mathbf{CA} = \mathbf{I}$, *then* **A** *is invertible.*

Proof. Suppose by way of contradiction that $\mathbf{AB} = \mathbf{I}$ and **A** is singular. Then, by Corollary 1 of Theorem 1.5.3, **A** is row equivalent to **U**, where **U** is an upper triangular matrix with a row of zeros. Hence, by Theorem 1.4.3, there exists a nonsingular **S** such that $\mathbf{SA} = \mathbf{U}$. So $\mathbf{AB} = \mathbf{I}$ implies $\mathbf{SAB} = \mathbf{S}$. Then replacing **SA** by **U** in $\mathbf{SAB} = \mathbf{S}$ leads to $\mathbf{UB} = \mathbf{S}$. However, since **U** has a row of zeros, so does $\mathbf{UB} = \mathbf{S}$, which is impossible since **S** is invertible. Hence, the hypothesis that **A** is singular is contradictory and, therefore, **A** is invertible.

Now assume that $\mathbf{CA} = \mathbf{I}$ and that **C** is singular. Write **B** for **A** and the **A** for **C** in $\mathbf{CA} = \mathbf{I}$. This gives $\mathbf{AB} = \mathbf{I}$ and shows that this second alternative is just the first alternative with a different notation. We conclude that **C** must be invertible. Hence **A** is the inverse of **C** and, thus, **A** is invertible. This shows that **A** must be nonsingular if either there exists a **B** such that $\mathbf{AB} = \mathbf{I}$, or a **C** such that $\mathbf{CA} = \mathbf{I}$. ■

This next corollary deserves a comment. It is easy to show that if either **A** or **B** is nonsingular and the other is singular, then the product must be singular. (See Problem 1.5.9.) It is, surprisingly, a bit harder to establish the fact that if *both* **A** and **B** are singular, then so is **AB** without the use of Theorem 1.5.4. The following Corollary includes both cases.

Corollary 4. *If either* **A** *or* **B** *is singular, so is* $\mathbf{C} = \mathbf{AB}$.

Proof. Suppose, by way of contradiction, that **C** is invertible. Then $\mathbf{C} = \mathbf{AB}$ implies $\mathbf{C}^{-1}\mathbf{AB} = \mathbf{I}$. Set $\mathbf{C}^{-1}\mathbf{A} = \mathbf{Y}$. Hence $\mathbf{YB} = \mathbf{I}$ and, by Corollary 3 of Theorem 1.5.4, **B** is nonsingular, contradicting the hypothesis. ■

PROBLEMS

PART 1

1.5.1. Find the inverse of each of the following elementary matrices:

$$\mathbf{P} = \begin{bmatrix} 0 & 1 & 0 \\ 1 & 0 & 0 \\ 0 & 0 & 1 \end{bmatrix}, \qquad \mathbf{M} = \begin{bmatrix} \alpha & 0 & 0 \\ 0 & 1 & 0 \\ 0 & 0 & 1 \end{bmatrix}, \qquad \mathbf{E} = \begin{bmatrix} 1 & 0 & 0 \\ 0 & 1 & 0 \\ \alpha & 0 & 1 \end{bmatrix}$$

1.5.2. For the matrices in Problem 1.5.1, find $(\mathbf{PEM})^{-1}$ and verify that it is the product of the inverses in the opposite order, $\mathbf{M}^{-1}\mathbf{E}^{-1}\mathbf{P}^{-1}$.

1.5.3. Write each of the following nonsingular matrices as the product of elementary matrices:

$$(a) \begin{bmatrix} 0 & 1 & 0 \\ 1 & 0 & 0 \\ -1 & 0 & 1 \end{bmatrix} \qquad (b) \begin{bmatrix} 0 & 0 & \alpha \\ 0 & \beta & 0 \\ \gamma & 0 & 0 \end{bmatrix} \qquad (c) \begin{bmatrix} 1 & 2 \\ -1 & -3 \end{bmatrix}$$

1.5.4. Consider the 4-step arrow diagram

$$\mathbf{A} = \begin{bmatrix} 1 & -1 & 1 \\ 1 & 0 & 1 \\ 0 & 1 & 1 \end{bmatrix} \rightarrow \begin{bmatrix} 1 & -1 & 1 \\ 0 & 1 & 0 \\ 0 & 1 & 1 \end{bmatrix} \rightarrow \begin{bmatrix} 1 & 0 & 1 \\ 0 & 1 & 0 \\ 0 & 1 & 1 \end{bmatrix} \rightarrow \begin{bmatrix} 1 & 0 & 1 \\ 0 & 1 & 0 \\ 0 & 0 & 1 \end{bmatrix}$$

$$\rightarrow \begin{bmatrix} 1 & 0 & 0 \\ 0 & 1 & 0 \\ 0 & 0 & 1 \end{bmatrix} = \mathbf{I}$$

Find each elementary matrix involved in the transformation of $\mathbf{A}$ to $\mathbf{I}$. Show that the product of these matrices in the appropriate order results in a matrix $\mathbf{S}$ which is the inverse of $\mathbf{A}$.

1.5.5. Use the method of Corollary 1 of Theorem 1.5.4 to find $\mathbf{A}^{-1}$ for the matrix $\mathbf{A}$ of Problem 1.5.4.

PART 2

1.5.6. Use the definition of upper trapezoidal matrix to show that every column matrix is row equivalent to an upper trapezoidal (column) matrix.

1.5.7. Let $\mathbf{C} = \mathbf{AB}$. There are eight ways of assigning the attributes singular and nonsingular to these three matrices. For example, $\mathbf{A}$ and $\mathbf{B}$ nonsingular and $\mathbf{C}$ singular is impossible. Which of these combinations are possible?

1.5.8. Prove that $\mathbf{A}$ and $\mathbf{A}^2$ are either both singular or both nonsingular. Generalize to the pair $\mathbf{A}$ and $\mathbf{A}^k$.

1.5.9. Let $\mathbf{C} = \mathbf{AB}$. If $\mathbf{A}$ is nonsingular and $\mathbf{B}$ is singular, show that $\mathbf{C}$ is singular. (*Hint:* Consider $\mathbf{B} = \mathbf{A}^{-1}\mathbf{C}$ and assume $\mathbf{C}$ is nonsingular.)

1.5.10. If $\mathbf{A}$ and $\mathbf{B}$ are nonsingular $n \times n$ matrices, are they row equivalent? What if $\mathbf{A}$ and $\mathbf{B}$ are singular? Offer examples or proofs.

1.5.11. Prove that a product of any number of matrices is singular if and only if at least one of the factors is singular.

PART 3

1.5.12. Suppose $\mathbf{A}$ is $m \times n$ and that its first $r < n$ columns form an upper trapezoidal matrix. Show that $\mathbf{A}$ is row equivalent to a matrix $\mathbf{B}$ whose first $r + 1$ columns also form an upper trapezoidal matrix. Combine this result with Problem 1.5.6 to provide an inductive proof of Theorem 1.5.1.

1.5.13. Present an argument by induction to show that every upper triangular matrix with a zero on its diagonal is row equivalent to an upper triangular matrix with a row of zeros. Also give an example of a nonsquare matrix for which this assertion is false.

1.5.14. Suppose $\mathbf{A}$ is a square matrix and assume that $[\mathbf{A} \quad \mathbf{B}] \rightarrow \cdots \rightarrow [\mathbf{I} \quad \mathbf{C}]$. Show that $\mathbf{C}$ is the unique solution of $\mathbf{AX} = \mathbf{B}$. (Hint: Model your argument after the proof of Corollary 1 of Theorem 1.5.4.) Hence explain why $\mathbf{C} = \mathbf{A}^{-1}\mathbf{B}$.

1.5.15. If $\mathbf{A}$ is equivalent to $\mathbf{A}_r$ and $\mathbf{B}$ is equivalent to $\mathbf{B}_r$, show that $\mathbf{AB}$ is equivalent to $\mathbf{A}_r\mathbf{B}$. Is $\mathbf{AB}$ equivalent to $\mathbf{AB}_r$? Is $\mathbf{AB}$ equivalent to $\mathbf{A}_r\mathbf{B}_r$?

1.6 DETERMINANTS

Although determinants were invented long before matrices, we view determinants as just one of many possible functions defined on the entries of a square matrix, albeit one of the most important functions. Another interesting function of the entries of the matrix $\mathbf{A}$ is the *trace* of $\mathbf{A}$, written tr($\mathbf{A}$), and defined as the sum of the diagonal entries of $\mathbf{A}$; namely, tr($\mathbf{A}$)= $\sum a_{ii}$. This section discusses a scalar function called *determinant* of $\mathbf{A}$, written det($\mathbf{A}$). (Some authors use the notation $|\mathbf{A}|$.) Under some circumstances,[1] the set of vectors $\{\mathbf{a}_1, \mathbf{a}_2, \ldots, \mathbf{a}_n\}$ defines the edges of an n-dimensional parallelepiped, P, with the origin at one vertex. Then, setting $\mathbf{A} = [\mathbf{a}_1 \quad \mathbf{a}_2 \quad \mathbf{a}_n]$, $|\det(A)|$ is the volume of P. In two and three dimensions, we can establish this result by elementary means. In higher dimensions, we make this our definition.

The definition of det($\mathbf{A}$) is quite intricate. It will be developed in stages.

A *term* of det($\mathbf{A}$) is + or − the product of n entries of $\mathbf{A}$, one from each row and each column. A typical term is, therefore,

$$(\pm)a_{1*}a_{2*}\cdots a_{n*} \tag{1.6.1}$$

The sequence of second subscripts is a permutation of 1,2, . . . ,n. The + sign is chosen if the number of inversions in this sequence is even. The number of inversions is the number of pairs in which a larger number precedes a smaller. There are four inversions in the sequence 1,5,2,4,3: namely, 5,2; 5,4; 5,3; and 4,3. For example, the product $a_{11}a_{22}a_{34}a_{43}$ has one factor from each row and column of $\mathbf{A}_4$. When the correct sign is affixed, this product is a term of det($\mathbf{A}_4$). Since the sequence of second subscripts is 1,2,4,3 and this sequence has one inversion, the term is $-a_{11}a_{22}a_{34}a_{43}$. For any square matrix $\mathbf{A}_n$, the product $a_{11}a_{22}\ldots a_{nn}$ is a term of det($\mathbf{A}_n$), since there are no inversions in the sequence of second (column) subscripts.

There are $n!$ permutations of n integers and hence $n!$ terms in det($\mathbf{A}$). Half of these terms are affixed with a − sign, a result which is by no means obvious although easy to believe on aesthetic grounds. The determinant of $\mathbf{A}_2$ has two terms: $a_{11}a_{22}$ and $-a_{12}a_{21}$. There are three positively signed terms,

[1] The criterion involves an idea presented in Chapter 3.

$a_{11}a_{22}a_{33}$, $a_{12}a_{23}a_{31}$, and $a_{13}a_{21}a_{32}$ in det($\mathbf{A}_3$). The terms with negative signs are $-a_{13}a_{22}a_{31}$, $-a_{12}a_{21}a_{33}$, and $-a_{11}a_{23}a_{32}$. In general, we define det(**A**) as the sum of all $n!$ terms:

$$\det(\mathbf{A}) = \sum(\pm)a_{1*}a_{2*}\cdots a_{n*} \tag{1.6.2}$$

When the definition is applied directly to the arbitrary matrices $\mathbf{A}_2$ and $\mathbf{A}_3$, these familiar formulas are obtained:

$$\det\begin{bmatrix} a_{11} & a_{12} \\ a_{21} & a_{22} \end{bmatrix} = a_{11}a_{22} - a_{12}a_{21} \tag{1.6.3}$$

$$\det\begin{bmatrix} a_{11} & a_{12} & a_{13} \\ a_{21} & a_{22} & a_{23} \\ a_{31} & a_{32} & a_{33} \end{bmatrix} = a_{11}a_{22}a_{33} + a_{12}a_{23}a_{31} + a_{13}a_{21}a_{32} - a_{13}a_{22}a_{31} - a_{11}a_{23}a_{32} - a_{12}a_{21}a_{33}$$

Example 1.6.1. Compute det(**A**) and det(**B**), where

$$\mathbf{A} = \begin{bmatrix} 1 & 1 \\ -1 & -1 \end{bmatrix}, \qquad \mathbf{B} = \begin{bmatrix} \cos\tau & -\sin\tau \\ \sin\tau & \cos\tau \end{bmatrix}$$

Solution. Applying Eq. 1.6.3, we have $\det(\mathbf{A}) = -1 - (-1) = 0$ and $\det(\mathbf{B}) = \cos^2\tau + \sin^2\tau = 1$.

An attempt to evaluate det(**A**) from its definition runs into the staggering prospect of computing $n!$ terms. If n is moderately large, say $n = 100$, then $n!$ is roughly 10^{158} and this number exceeds the (imputed) number of atoms in the universe and the direct computation of det(**A**) is hopeless. Fortunately, the next two theorems provide a computationally feasible method for evaluating determinants.

If $\mathbf{A}_1$ is the result of applying an elementary row operation to **A**, then there is an elementary matrix **F** such that $\mathbf{A}_1 = \mathbf{FA}$. The first theorem, which follows, describes the connection between det($\mathbf{A}_1$) and det(**A**).

Theorem 1.6.1. *Suppose* $\mathbf{A} \to \mathbf{A}_1$. *If*

1. $\mathbf{A}_1$ results from a row interchange in **A**, then $\det(\mathbf{A}) = -\det(\mathbf{A}_1)$.
2. $\mathbf{A}_1$ results from multiplying a row of **A** by $\alpha \neq 0$, then $\alpha\det(\mathbf{A}) = \det(\mathbf{A}_1)$
3. $\mathbf{A}_1$ results from any Type 3 row operation, then $\det(\mathbf{A}) = \det(\mathbf{A}_1)$.

Proof. The proof is not difficult but rather tedious. It is obtained from a careful study of the effect of elementary row operations on the determinant function. We accept this theorem without proof. ■

Corollary 1. *If* **A** *is row equivalent to* **B**, *then there is a nonzero scalar k such that* $\det(\mathbf{A}) = k\det(\mathbf{B})$.

Proof. By hypothesis, $\mathbf{A} \to \cdots \to \mathbf{B}$. The corollary follows from the fact that each elementary row operation introduces a factor that is never zero. Indeed, k is the product of all these factors. ■

Theorem 1.6.2. *The determinant of an upper triangular matrix is the product of its diagonal entries.*

Proof. Let $\mathbf{U}$ be an upper triangular matrix with diagonal $u_{11}, u_{22}, \ldots, u_{nn}$. One of the terms of $\det(\mathbf{U})$ is $u_{11}u_{22}\ldots u_{nn}$. (The term has a positive sign because the column subscripts are in their natural order and hence there are 0 inversions.) All of the other $n! - 1$ terms contain at least one entry of $\mathbf{U}$ below the diagonal. Since these entries are all zero, these terms are zero, and $\det(\mathbf{U}) = u_{11}u_{22}\cdots u_{nn}$. ■

Summarizing. The algorithm to compute $\det(\mathbf{A})$ is essentially the same as the algorithm to convert $\mathbf{A}$ to upper triangular form by elementary row operations. If care is taken so that Type 2 operations are avoided, and $\mathbf{A} \to \cdots \to \mathbf{U}$ then Theorems 1.6.1 and 1.6.2 imply

$$\det \mathbf{A} = (-1)^{\epsilon} u_{11}u_{22}\ldots u_{nn}$$

where the u_{ii} are the diagonal entries of $\mathbf{U}$ and ϵ is the number of row interchanges used in going from $\mathbf{A}$ to $\mathbf{U}$.

An immediate consequence of Theorem 1.6.2 is that the determinant of a diagonal matrix is the product of its diagonal entries. In particular, $\det(\mathbf{I}_n) = \mathbf{1}$ and $\det(k\mathbf{I}_n) = k^n$.

Theorem 1.6.3. $\mathbf{A}$ *is singular if and only if* $\det(\mathbf{A}) = 0$.

Proof. Suppose that $\mathbf{A}$ is nonsingular. Then $\mathbf{A}$ is row equivalent to $\mathbf{I}$ and hence $\det(\mathbf{A}) = k\det(\mathbf{I}) = k$, with $k \neq 0$, by Corollary 1 of Theorem 1.6.1. Now suppose $\mathbf{A}$ is singular. Then $\mathbf{A}$ is row equivalent to an upper triangular matrix $\mathbf{U}$ with a zero diagonal entry. Then $\det(\mathbf{U}) = 0$ by Theorem 1.6.2. So, by Corollary 1, $\det(\mathbf{A}) = k0 = 0$. ■

Example 1.6.2. Find the value of

$$\det\begin{bmatrix} 1 & -1 & 1 \\ 0 & 1 & 1 \\ 2 & 1 & -1 \end{bmatrix}$$

Solution. We have

$$\det\begin{bmatrix} 1 & -1 & 1 \\ 0 & 1 & 1 \\ 2 & 1 & -1 \end{bmatrix} = \det\begin{bmatrix} 1 & -1 & 1 \\ 0 & 1 & 1 \\ 0 & 3 & -3 \end{bmatrix} = \det\begin{bmatrix} 1 & -1 & 1 \\ 0 & 1 & 1 \\ 0 & 0 & -6 \end{bmatrix} = -6$$

Note that each elementary row operation is of Type 3, so no multiplicative factors appear in the sequence of equalities.

Example 1.6.3. Find the value of

$$\det\begin{bmatrix} -1 & 2 & 1 & 1 \\ 0 & 1 & 0 & 0 \\ 0 & 1 & 1 & -1 \\ 2 & 0 & 0 & 3 \end{bmatrix}$$

Solution. We apply elementary row operations of Type 3 as follows:

$$\begin{bmatrix} -1 & 2 & 1 & 1 \\ 0 & 1 & 0 & 0 \\ 0 & 1 & 1 & -1 \\ 2 & 0 & 0 & 3 \end{bmatrix} \to \begin{bmatrix} -1 & 2 & 1 & 1 \\ 0 & 1 & 0 & 0 \\ 0 & 1 & 1 & -1 \\ 0 & 4 & 2 & 5 \end{bmatrix} \to \begin{bmatrix} -1 & 2 & 1 & 1 \\ 0 & 1 & 0 & 0 \\ 0 & 0 & 1 & -1 \\ 0 & 0 & 2 & 5 \end{bmatrix}$$

$$\to \begin{bmatrix} -1 & 2 & 1 & 1 \\ 0 & 1 & 0 & 0 \\ 0 & 0 & 1 & -1 \\ 0 & 0 & 0 & 7 \end{bmatrix}$$

Hence,

$$\det\begin{bmatrix} -1 & 2 & 1 & 1 \\ 0 & 1 & 0 & 0 \\ 0 & 1 & 1 & -1 \\ 2 & 0 & 0 & 3 \end{bmatrix} = \det\begin{bmatrix} -1 & 2 & 1 & 1 \\ 0 & 1 & 0 & 0 \\ 0 & 0 & 1 & -1 \\ 0 & 0 & 0 & 7 \end{bmatrix} = -7$$

Example 1.6.4. Show that $\det(k\mathbf{A}) = (k^n)\det(\mathbf{A})$, where $\mathbf{A}$ is $n \times n$.

Solution. Since $k\mathbf{A}$ has a factor of k in each row of $\mathbf{A}$, we have, by repeated use of Theorem 1.6.1, Part (2), $\det(k\mathbf{A}) = (k^n)\det(\mathbf{A})$.

Example 1.6.5. Suppose $\mathbf{P}$, $\mathbf{M}$, and $\mathbf{E}$ are elementary row matrices of Types 1, 2 and 3, respectively, and that $\mathbf{M}$ multiplies row i of $\mathbf{A}$ by α. Then (*a*) $\det(\mathbf{P}) = -1$, (*b*) $\det(\mathbf{M}) = \alpha$, and (*c*) $\det(\mathbf{E}) = 1$.

Solution. Consider Theorem 1.6.1 with $\mathbf{A} = \mathbf{P}$. Since $\mathbf{P} \to \mathbf{I}$, (*a*) follows by Part (1). If $\mathbf{A} = \mathbf{E}$, we have (*c*) by Part (3). Finally, if $\mathbf{A} = \mathbf{M}$, then $\mathbf{M} \to \mathbf{I}$ and thus $\det(\mathbf{M}) = \alpha\det(\mathbf{I}) = \alpha$ by Part (2) of Theorem 1.6.1.

Example 1.6.6. Show that $\det(\mathbf{FA}) = \det(\mathbf{F})\det(\mathbf{A})$, if $\mathbf{F}$ is any elementary row matrix.

Solution. Set $\mathbf{FA} = \mathbf{A}_1$ and use Theorem 1.6.1 and Example 1.6.5.

Theorem 1.6.4. *For every pair of square matrices* $\mathbf{A}$ *and* $\mathbf{B}$,

$$\det(\mathbf{AB}) = \det(\mathbf{A})\det(\mathbf{B}) \tag{1.6.4}$$

Proof. If $\mathbf{A}$ is singular then so is $\mathbf{AB}$, and Eq. 1.6.4 is the statement $0 = 0$. If $\mathbf{A}$ is nonsingular, it is the product of elementary row matrices by Corollary 2 of Theorem 1.5.4. Suppose for notational convenience that $\mathbf{A} = \mathbf{F}_3\mathbf{F}_2\mathbf{F}_1$. Replace $\mathbf{A}$ in $\mathbf{AB}$ by $\mathbf{F}_3\mathbf{F}_2\mathbf{F}_1$. Then $\det(\mathbf{AB}) = \det(\mathbf{F}_3\mathbf{F}_2\mathbf{F}_1\mathbf{B})$. Now we apply Example 1.6.6 three times and obtain

$$\begin{aligned}\det(\mathbf{AB}) &= \det(\mathbf{F}_3\mathbf{F}_2\mathbf{F}_1\mathbf{B}) = \det(\mathbf{F}_3)\det(\mathbf{F}_2\mathbf{F}_1\mathbf{B}) \\ &= \det(\mathbf{F}_3)\det(\mathbf{F}_2)\det(\mathbf{F}_1\mathbf{B}) \\ &= \det(\mathbf{F}_3)\det(\mathbf{F}_2)\det(\mathbf{F}_1\mathbf{B}) = \det(\mathbf{F}_3)\det(\mathbf{F}_2)\det(\mathbf{F}_1)\det(\mathbf{B})\end{aligned} \tag{1.6.5}$$

By the same token, $\mathbf{A} = \mathbf{F}_3\mathbf{F}_2\mathbf{F}_1$ implies

$$\det(\mathbf{A}) = \det(\mathbf{F}_3)\det(\mathbf{F}_2)\det(\mathbf{F}_1) \tag{1.6.6}$$

We complete the proof by multiplying Eq. 1.6.6 by $\det(\mathbf{B})$ and then comparing this result with Eq. 1.6.5. ■

The factorization of a nonsingular $\mathbf{A}$ into a product of elementary row matrices can also be used to prove that $\det(\mathbf{A}^{\mathrm{T}}) = \det(\mathbf{A})$. We first prove the special case in which $\mathbf{A}$ is an elementary matrix.

Lemma 1. *Let* $\mathbf{F}$ *be an elementary matrix. Then* $\det(\mathbf{F}^{\mathrm{T}}) = \det(\mathbf{F})$.

Proof. Observe that $\mathbf{P}$ and $\mathbf{M}$ are symmetric. So $\mathbf{P} = \mathbf{P}^{\mathrm{T}}$ and $\mathbf{M} = \mathbf{M}^{\mathrm{T}}$ and the assertion of the lemma is trivial. Let $\mathbf{E}$ be the elementary matrix of Type 3 that adds α times row i to row j. Then $\mathbf{E}^{\mathrm{T}}$ adds α times row j to row i and is therefore also Type 3 elementary matrix. But the determinant of an elementary matrix of Type 3 always has value one. Hence $\det(\mathbf{E}^{\mathrm{T}}) = \det(\mathbf{E}) = 1$. ■

Theorem 1.6.5. *For every matrix* $\mathbf{A}$, $\det(\mathbf{A}) = \det(\mathbf{A}^{\mathrm{T}})$.

Proof. If $\mathbf{A}$ is singular so is $\mathbf{A}^{\mathrm{T}}$. The theorem is then trivial, because both determinants are zero. If $\mathbf{A}$ is nonsingular, then $\mathbf{A} = \mathbf{F}_k\mathbf{F}_2\cdots\mathbf{F}_1$ which implies that $\mathbf{A}^{\mathrm{T}} = \mathbf{F}_1^{\mathrm{T}}\mathbf{F}_2^{\mathrm{T}}\cdots\mathbf{F}_k^{\mathrm{T}}$. Thus, $\det(\mathbf{A}) = \det(\mathbf{F}_1)\det(\mathbf{F}_2)\cdots\det(\mathbf{F}_k)$ follows from Theorem 1.6.6. Likewise, $\det(\mathbf{A}^{\mathrm{T}}) = \det(\mathbf{F}_1^{\mathrm{T}})\det(\mathbf{F}_2^{\mathrm{T}})\cdots\det(\mathbf{F}_k^{\mathrm{T}})$. By Lemma 1, $\det(\mathbf{F}_i^{\mathrm{T}}) = \det(\mathbf{F}_i)$ for each i, so $\det(\mathbf{A}) = \det(A^{\mathrm{T}})$. ■

Example 1.6.7. Let $\mathbf{S}_{2n+1}$ be skew-symmetric. Show that $\mathbf{S}_{2n+1}$ is singular.

Solution. By definition, $\mathbf{S}_{2n+1}^{\mathrm{T}} = -\mathbf{S}_{2n+1}$. Hence, by Theorem 1.6.5 and Example 1.6.4,

$$\det(\mathbf{S}_{2n+1}) = \det(-\mathbf{S}_{2n+1}^{\mathrm{T}}) = (-1)^{2n+1}\det(\mathbf{S}_{2n+1}) = -\det\mathbf{S}_{2n+1}$$

Therefore $\det(\mathbf{S}_{2n+1}) = -\det(\mathbf{S}_{2n+1})$ which implies that $\det(\mathbf{S}_{2n+1}) = 0$. Thus $\mathbf{S}_{2n+1}$ is singular by Theorem 1.6.3.

1.6.1 Determinants in MATLAB

The function det(A) invokes the subroutine in MATLAB that calculates det(**A**). If the matrix **A** has integer entries then det(A) returns an integer. MATLAB computes det(A) by first factoring $\mathbf{A} = \mathbf{LU}$ where **U** is upper triangular and **L** is (row-permuted) lower triangular. A fuller discussion of this factorization of **A** is given in Section 2.5.1.

PROBLEMS

PART 1

1.6.1. Find the value of each of the following determinants:

$$(a)\ \det[a] \qquad (b)\ \det\begin{bmatrix} 0 & -1 \\ 1 & 0 \end{bmatrix} \qquad (c)\ \det\begin{bmatrix} 0 & -1 & -2 \\ 1 & 0 & -3 \\ 2 & 3 & 0 \end{bmatrix}$$

$$(d)\ \det\begin{bmatrix} 0 & 0 & 0 & 0 & 1 \\ 0 & 0 & 0 & 1 & 0 \\ 0 & 0 & 1 & 0 & 0 \\ 0 & 1 & 0 & 0 & 0 \\ 1 & 0 & 0 & 0 & 0 \end{bmatrix} \qquad (e)\ \det\begin{bmatrix} 1 & -1 & -2 \\ 2 & 1 & 3 \\ 2 & 3 & 0 \end{bmatrix}$$

$$(f)\ \det\begin{bmatrix} 0 & 1 & -2 \\ 1 & 0 & -3 \\ 2 & 3 & -1 \end{bmatrix}$$

1.6.2. Count the number of inversions in each sequence:

(*a*) 5, 4, 3, 2, 1 (*b*) 1, 5, 3, 4, 2 (*c*) 1, 2, 5, 4, 3.

PART 2

1.6.3. Show that $\det(\mathbf{A}^{-1}) = \det(\mathbf{A})^{-1}$.

1.6.4. Show that $\mathbf{A}^2 = \mathbf{I}$ implies $|\det(\mathbf{A})| = 1$. Find **A** such that $\det(\mathbf{A}) = -1$.

1.6.5. Explain why $\det(\mathbf{S}^{-1}\mathbf{AS}) = \det(\mathbf{A})$.

PART 3

1.6.6. Use the definition of determinant to show that every matrix with a row of zeros has determinant equal to zero.

1.6.7. Show that multiplying a row of **A** by α multiplies every term of det(**A**) by α. Use this fact to prove Theorem 1.6.1, Part (2).

1.6.8. Show that these four steps will interchange rows i and j of **A**: (*a*) Add (-1) times row i to row j. (*b*) Add row j to row i. (*c*). Add (-1) times row i to row j. (*d*) Multiply row j by -1. Hence show that Theorem 1.6.1, Parts (2) and (3) can be used to prove Theorem 1.6.1, Part (1).

1.6.9. Use Theorem 1.6.1 to show that every matrix with two rows proportional has determinant equal to zero.

1.6.10. Use the definition of determinant to show that

$$\det\begin{bmatrix} 0 & 0 & 0 & \cdots & 0 & z \\ 0 & 0 & 0 & \cdots & y & * \\ \vdots & \vdots & \vdots & & \vdots & \vdots \\ 0 & b & * & \cdots & * & * \\ a & * & * & \cdots & * & * \end{bmatrix} = \epsilon ab\cdots yz$$

where ϵ is either 1 or -1.

1.6.11. For the matrix given in Problem 1.6.10, write the elements $a,b,\cdots,z$ with the usual double subscripted notation. Show that the number of inversions of the sequence of second subscripts is $(n-1)+(n-2)+\cdots+1$. Use this fact to prove that the given determinant has value $(-1)^{n(n-1)/2}ab\cdots yz$.

1.6.12. If a term T_i of det(**A**) does not contain the diagonal entry a_{ii}, show that T_i cannot contain all the remaining diagonal entries. That is, T_i is not a product of $n-1$ diagonal entries and one off-diagonal entry.

1.6.13. Show that $\det(\alpha\mathbf{A}) = (\alpha^n)\det(\mathbf{A})$ by using Theorem 1.6.1, Part (2).

1.6.14. Explain why det(**A**) is an integer if **A** has integer entries. If **A** has rational entries, explain why det(**A**) is rational.

MATLAB

1.6.15. Evaluate the determinants in Problem 1.6.1 by use of the "det" function in MATLAB.

1.6.16. For the matrices (*d*)–(*f*) in Part 1.6.1, verify that $\det(\mathbf{A}^{-1}) = (\det(\mathbf{A}))^{-1}$. Recall that $\mathbf{A}^{-1}$ is computed by the function inv(A) in MATLAB.

1.6.17. Repeat Problem 1.6.16 except verify that $\det(\mathbf{A}^2) = (\det(\mathbf{A}))^2$.

1.6.18. Repeat Problem 1.6.16 except verify that $\det(\mathbf{A}^T) = \det(\mathbf{A})$.

1.6.19. Repeat Problem 1.6.16 except verify that $\det(-2\mathbf{A}) = (-2)^n\det(\mathbf{A})$.

1.6.20. Suppose **A** is the matrix given in Problem 1.6.1(*e*), and **B** is the matrix (*f*) in that same problem. Show that $\det(\mathbf{B}^{-1}\mathbf{A}\mathbf{B}) = \det(\mathbf{A})$.

1.6.21. Find an order of magnitude estimate for 100!. Assume that a computer can multiply two numbers in 10^{-7} seconds. How many years will it take to compute det(**A**) from the definition? (Ignore additions and logical operations.)

1.7 COFACTORS, ADJOINTS AND CRAMER'S RULE

This section completes our brief review of the theory of determinants, and may be omitted for most applications.

Suppose **A** has size $n \times n$ and typical entry a_{ij}. We call the matrix obtained from **A** by striking out the row and column containing a_{ij}, the *minor matrix* of a_{ij}. The determinant of this matrix, written M_{ij}, is the *minor* of a_{ij}. The scalar $A_{ij} = (-1)^{i+j}M_{ij}$ is the *cofactor* of a_{ij}, and the matrix whose entries are cofactors will be written cof(**A**). That is,

$$\text{cof}(A) = \begin{bmatrix} A_{11} & A_{12} & \cdots & A_{1n} \\ A_{21} & A_{22} & \cdots & A_{2n} \\ \vdots & \vdots & & \vdots \\ A_{n1} & A_{n2} & \cdots & A_{nn} \end{bmatrix} \tag{1.7.1}$$

Example 1.7.1. Find

$$\operatorname{cof}\begin{bmatrix} 1 & 0 & -1 \\ 0 & 2 & 2 \\ 1 & 1 & 1 \end{bmatrix}$$

Solution. There are 9 terms and hence 9 minors and 9 cofactors. The minors and cofactors for the entries in the first row will be computed and the remaining 6 cofactors left for the exercises.

$$M_{11} - \det\begin{bmatrix} 2 & 2 \\ 1 & 1 \end{bmatrix} = 0, \qquad A_{11} = (-1)^2 M_{11} = 0$$

$$M_{12} = \det\begin{bmatrix} 0 & 2 \\ 1 & 1 \end{bmatrix} = -2, \qquad A_{12} = (-1)^3 M_{12} = 2$$

$$M_{13} = \det\begin{bmatrix} 0 & 2 \\ 1 & 1 \end{bmatrix} = -2, \qquad A_{13} = (-1)^3 M_{13} = -2$$

The remaining 6 entries of cof(**A**) are computed similarly. Using Eq. 1.7.1,

$$\operatorname{cof}\begin{bmatrix} 1 & 0 & -1 \\ 0 & 2 & 2 \\ 1 & 1 & 1 \end{bmatrix} = \begin{bmatrix} 0 & 2 & -2 \\ -1 & 2 & -1 \\ -2 & -2 & 2 \end{bmatrix}$$

The *adjoint* of **A**, written $\mathbf{A}^+$ or adj(**A**), is the transpose of cof(**A**). That is, $\mathbf{A}^+ = (\operatorname{cof}(\mathbf{A}))^{\mathrm{T}} = (A_{ji})$ and

$$\mathbf{A}^+ = \begin{bmatrix} A_{11} & A_{21} & \cdots & A_{n1} \\ A_{12} & A_{22} & \cdots & A_{n2} \\ \vdots & \vdots & & \vdots \\ A_{1n} & A_{2n} & \cdots & A_{nn} \end{bmatrix} = (\operatorname{cof}(\mathbf{A}))^T \tag{1.7.2}$$

The next theorem is implied by the well known "expansion by cofactors" technique for finding det(**A**) as well as the starting point for the proof of "Cramer's Rule." This theorem is offered without proof.

Theorem 1.7.1. *Let* $\mathbf{A}^+$ *be the adjoint of* **A**. *Then*

$$\mathbf{A}\mathbf{A}^+ = \mathbf{A}^+\mathbf{A} = \det(\mathbf{A})\mathbf{I} \tag{1.7.3}$$

Corollary 1. *If* **A** *is nonsingular, then*

$$\mathbf{A}^{-1} = \mathbf{A}^+/\det(\mathbf{A}) \tag{1.7.4}$$

Proof. Equation 1.7.4 follows easily from Eq. 1.7.3, since **A** is nonsingular implies $\det(\mathbf{A}) \neq 0$ by Theorem 1.6.3. ■

If we examine the diagonal entries on the right-hand side of Eq. 1.7.3, we come to the following conclusions which are known collectively as *the expansion of* det(**A**) *by cofactors*. This theorem is also offered without proof.

Theorem 1.7.2. *For each row i of* **A**,

$$\det(\mathbf{A}) = a_{i1}A_{i1} + a_{i2}A_{i2} + a_{in}A_{in} + \cdots a_{nj}A_{nj} \tag{1.7.5}$$

For each column j of **A**,

$$\det(\mathbf{A}) = a_{1j}A_{1j} + \cdots + a_{2j}A_{2j} \tag{1.7.6}$$

There are three major reasons for using expansion by cofactors. First, it is often convenient for computing det(**A**) when the matrix **A** has a highly regular pattern in its entries. Second, it is sometimes used to compute det(**A**) when the entries of **A** are functions of some parameter and the row reduction method becomes excessively cumbersome. And third, this expansion can be used to establish such theoretical results as Cramer's Rule, Theorem 1.7.4, and the Cayley-Hamilton theorem, Section 6.7.

Example 1.7.2. Expand the following determinant using cofactors of the first column:

$$\mathrm{D}_3 = \det\begin{bmatrix} a & a & a \\ b & a & a \\ 0 & b & a \end{bmatrix} \tag{1.7.7}$$

Solution. We can easily verify that the only nonzero terms in the evaluation of D_3 by Eq. 1.7.6 are A_{11} and A_{21}. Hence,

$$A_{11} = \mathrm{M}_{11} = \det\begin{bmatrix} a & a \\ b & a \end{bmatrix} = a^2 - ab;$$

$$A_{21} = -\mathrm{M}_{21} = -\det\begin{bmatrix} a & a \\ b & a \end{bmatrix} = -a^2 + ab$$

yields $\mathrm{D}_3 = a(a^2 - ab) - b(a^2 + ab) = a(a - b)^2$.

The off-diagonal entries in Eq. 1.7.4 lead to the several surprising variations on the expansion by cofactors rule.

Theorem 1.7.3. *For each row i and column j of* **A** *and each* $k \neq i$,

$$0 = a_{i1}A_{k1} + a_{i2}A_{k2} + \cdots + a_{in}A_{kn} \tag{1.7.8}$$

$$0 = a_{1j}A_{1k} + a_{2j}A_{2k} + \cdots + a_{nj}A_{nk} \tag{1.7.9}$$

Proof. Apply the definition of multiplication to the product $\mathbf{AA}^+$. By Eq. 1.7.4 the entry in the ith row, kth column $(i \neq k)$ of $\mathbf{AA}^+$ is an off-diagonal entry of det(**A**)**I**. This entry is zero which implies Eq. 1.7.8. Equation 1.7.9 follows by similar reasoning applied to $\mathbf{A}^+\mathbf{A} = \det(\mathbf{A})\mathbf{I}$. ■

The expression for the inverse of **A** given by Eq. 1.7.5 is not particularly useful for computational purposes since it requires computing n^2+1 determinants. However, it has some theoretical importance. Suppose $\mathbf{Ax} = \mathbf{b}$. Define the n matrices obtained from **A** by replacing, one at a time, each column of **A** by **b**. These matrices are denoted by $\mathbf{A}_j$. For example,

$$\mathbf{A}_2 = \begin{bmatrix} a_{11} & b_1 & \cdots & a_{1n} \\ a_{21} & b_2 & \cdots & a_{2n} \\ \vdots & & & \vdots \\ a_{n1} & b_n & \cdots & a_{nn} \end{bmatrix} \tag{1.7.10}$$

If $\det(\mathbf{A}_j)$ is expanded by cofactors of the entries in the column containing **b**, then for each j,

$$\det(\mathbf{A}_j) = \mathbf{A}_{1j}\mathbf{b}_1 + \mathbf{A}_{2j}\mathbf{b}_2 + \cdots + \mathbf{A}_{nj}\mathbf{b}_n \tag{1.7.11}$$

Theorem 1.7.4. *(Cramer's Rule). Suppose A is invertible. Then the jth component of the solution of* $\mathbf{Ax} = \mathbf{b}$, *namely* x_j, *is given by the quotient*

$$x_j = \det(\mathbf{A}_j)/\det(\mathbf{A}) \tag{1.7.12}$$

Proof. Since **A** is invertible, we have $\mathbf{x} = \mathbf{A}^{-1}\mathbf{b} = (\det(\mathbf{A}))^{-1}\mathbf{A}^{+}\mathbf{b}$, by Eq. 1.7.5. From this formula for **x**, it follows that $\det(\mathbf{A})\mathbf{x} = \mathbf{A}^{+}\mathbf{b}$ and hence

$$\det(\mathbf{A})\mathbf{x} = \mathbf{A}^{+}\mathbf{b} = \begin{bmatrix} A_{11} & A_{21} & \cdots & A_{n1} \\ A_{12} & A_{22} & \cdots & A_{n2} \\ \vdots & \vdots & & \vdots \\ A_{1n} & A_{2n} & \cdots & A_{nn} \end{bmatrix} \begin{bmatrix} b_1 \\ b_2 \\ \vdots \\ b_n \end{bmatrix}$$

$$= \begin{bmatrix} A_{11}b_1 & + & A_{21}b_2 & + & \cdots & + & A_{n1}b_n \\ A_{12}b_1 & + & A_{22}b_2 & + & \cdots & + & A_{n2}b_n \\ \vdots & & \vdots & & & & \vdots \\ A_{1n}b_1 & + & A_{2n}b_2 & + & \cdots & + & A_{nn}b_n \end{bmatrix}$$

From this expression and Eq. 1.7.11 it follows that

$$\det(\mathbf{A})\mathbf{x} = \mathbf{A}^{+}\mathbf{b} = \begin{bmatrix} \det(\mathbf{A}_1) \\ \det(\mathbf{A}_2) \\ \vdots \\ \det(\mathbf{A}_n) \end{bmatrix} \tag{1.7.13}$$

and $\det(\mathbf{A})x_j = \det(\mathbf{A}_j)$ is simply the fact that the jth components in Eq. 1.7.13 are equal. ■

Cramer's Rule, in the familiar form presented here, fails if the number of unknowns is unequal to the number of equations and is inapplicable if **A** is singular. This latter failure is quite significant; Chapters 5 and 6 are concerned primarily with systems having singular coefficient matrices. A more serious difficulty with Cramer's Rule is that its implementation for numerical computations of the solution of $\mathbf{Ax} = \mathbf{b}$ is terribly inefficient. Far better schemes are known and used. See, in particular, Sections 2.4 and 2.5.

PROBLEMS

PART 1

1.7.1. Use Cramer's rule to solve the system $a_1x + a_2y = c_1$, $b_1x + b_2y = c_2$.

1.7.2. Use Cramer's rule to solve the system

$$\begin{aligned} 2x_1 + x_2 - x_3 &= 1 \\ x_1 - x_2 - x_3 &= 0 \\ x_1 + x_2 - x_3 &= 1 \end{aligned}$$

1.7.3. Show

$$\det\begin{bmatrix} x+a & a & a \\ a & x+a & a \\ a & a & x+a \end{bmatrix} = x^2(x+3a)$$

1.7.4. Show

$$\det\begin{bmatrix} x^2 & y^2 & z^2 \\ x & y & z \\ 1 & 1 & 1 \end{bmatrix} = (x-y)(x-z)(y-z)$$

1.7.5. Show

$$\det\begin{bmatrix} 1+a_1 & a_1 & a_1 \\ a_2 & 1+a_2 & a_2 \\ a_3 & a_3 & 1+a_3 \end{bmatrix} = 1 + a_1 + a_2 + a_3$$

1.7.6. Show

$$\det\begin{bmatrix} 0 & a & a \\ a & 0 & a \\ a & a & b \end{bmatrix} = (-a)^2(2a-b)$$

1.7.7. Show that $\mathbf{I}^+ = \mathbf{I}$.

PART 2

1.7.8. Show that $\det(\mathbf{J}_n - n\mathbf{I}_n) = 0$. (*Hint:* Add rows 2 through n to row 1.)

1.7.9. Show that

$$\det\begin{bmatrix} a & a & \cdots & a & a \\ b & a & \cdots & a & a \\ 0 & b & \cdots & a & a \\ \vdots & \vdots & & \vdots & \vdots \\ 0 & 0 & \cdots & b & a \end{bmatrix} = a(a-b)^{n-1}$$

1.7.10. Show that

$$\det\begin{bmatrix} x+a & a & \cdots & a \\ a & x+a & \cdots & a \\ \vdots & \vdots & & \vdots \\ a & a & \cdots & x+a \end{bmatrix} = x^{n-1}(x+na)$$

1.7.11. Show that

$$\det\begin{bmatrix} 0 & a & \cdots & a & a \\ a & 0 & \cdots & a & a \\ \vdots & \vdots & & \vdots & \vdots \\ a & a & \cdots & a & b \end{bmatrix} = (-a)^{n-1}(n(a-b)-a+2b)$$

1.7.12. Show that

$$\det\begin{bmatrix} 1+a_1 & a_1 & \cdots & a_1 \\ a_2 & 1+a_2 & \cdots & a_2 \\ \vdots & \vdots & & \vdots \\ a_n & a_n & \cdots & 1+a_n \end{bmatrix} = 1+a_1+a_2+\cdots+a_n$$

1.7.13. If $\mathbf{A}$ has rational entries, show that $\mathbf{A}^{-1}$ has rational entries. (*Hint:* Explain why $\mathbf{A}^{-1}$ as given by Eq. 1.7.5 is a quotient of rational numbers.)

1.7.14. Derive Eq. 1.7.11 for $j = 1$ by explicitly computing $\det(\mathbf{A}_1)$ by expansion of cofactors of the entries in the first column of $\mathbf{A}_1$.

PART 3

Assume that $\mathbf{A}$ and $\mathbf{B}$ are nonsingular in each of the following problems.

1.7.15. Show that $(\mathbf{AB})^+ = \mathbf{B}^+\mathbf{A}^+$ and hence $(\mathbf{A}^{-1})^+ = (\mathbf{A}^+)^{-1}$.

1.7.16. Show that $(k\mathbf{A})^+ = k^{n-1}\mathbf{A}^+$.

1.7.17. Show that $\det(\mathbf{A}^+) = (\det(\mathbf{A}))^{n-1}$.

1.7.18. Show that $(\mathbf{A}^+)^+ = (\det(\mathbf{A}))^{n-2}\mathbf{A}$.

CHAPTER 2

RANK: THE REDUCED ROW ECHELON FORM AND SYSTEMS OF SIMULTANEOUS EQUATIONS

2.1 INTRODUCTION

This chapter presents four important ideas: (1) the row-reduced echelon form and some of its many implications; (2) rank; (3) the Gaussian elimination process as a means for the solution of $\mathbf{Ax} = \mathbf{b}$; and (4) the notion of linear combinations and linear independence. Each of these themes is presented as a natural consequence of elementary row operations, and in this sense this chapter is a continuation of the ideas put forth in Chapter 1.

2.2 THE REDUCED ROW ECHELON FORM

Elementary row operations are performed on $\mathbf{A}$, usually for the purpose of transforming $\mathbf{A}$ to an equivalent matrix with a simpler or more convenient structure. One such structure, called the *reduced row echelon form,* and written rref for short, is defined by these four criteria:

1. The zero rows, if any, are the last rows of the matrix.
2. The first nonzero entry in a nonzero row is a one. It is called a *leading one*.

3. Each column containing a leading one, called a *leading column,* is a unit vector, $\mathbf{e}_i$, for some i.

4. A leading one in row p is to the left of a leading one in row q whenever $p < q$.

Example 2.2.1. The following matrices are in rref. (The $*$ entries, when they appear, represent arbitrary scalars.)

(*a*) $\mathbf{e}_1$ (*b*) $[1]$ (*c*) $\mathbf{I}$ (*d*) $\mathbf{e}_i^{\mathrm{T}}$ for all i

(*e*) $[\mathbf{I}\ \mathbf{B}]$, for any $\mathbf{B}$ (*f*) $[0\ 0\ 1\ * \cdots *]$

(*g*) $\begin{bmatrix} 1 & 0 \\ 0 & 1 \\ 0 & 0 \\ 0 & 0 \end{bmatrix}$ (*h*) $\begin{bmatrix} 1 & * & 0 & 0 & * \\ 0 & 0 & 1 & 0 & * \\ 0 & 0 & 0 & 1 & * \\ 0 & 0 & 0 & 0 & 0 \end{bmatrix}$ (*i*) $\begin{bmatrix} 1 & * & * & * & * \\ 0 & 0 & 0 & 0 & 0 \\ 0 & 0 & 0 & 0 & 0 \\ 0 & 0 & 0 & 0 & 0 \end{bmatrix}$

(*j*) $\begin{bmatrix} \mathbf{A} & \mathbf{B} \\ \mathbf{O} & \mathbf{O} \end{bmatrix}$ and $\begin{bmatrix} \mathbf{A} & \mathbf{O} \\ \mathbf{O} & \mathbf{I} \end{bmatrix}$ for $\mathbf{A}$ in rref and with no zero rows.

Two comments are in order. First of all, among the vectors $\{\mathbf{e}_i\}$ only $\mathbf{e}_1$ is in rref; and second, the zero matrix is also in rref. Actually, it is unimportant how we fall on the question of whether $\mathbf{O}_{m\times n}$ is in rref, but it is included because it satisfies all four criteria, though it meets conditions (2)–(4) vacuously.

The leading columns of a matrix in rref are unit vectors by definition. Suppose $\mathbf{A}_r$ is in rref with r leading columns; that is, $\mathbf{A}_r$ has exactly r nonzero rows. Then $\mathbf{A}_r$ must contain the unit vectors $\mathbf{e}_1, \mathbf{e}_2, \ldots, \mathbf{e}_r$, because the nonzero rows of $\mathbf{A}_r$ are not separated by zero rows. For instance, compare $\mathbf{A}_r$ with $\mathbf{B}$ and $\mathbf{C}$:

$$\mathbf{A}_r = \begin{bmatrix} 1 & * & 0 & 0 & * \\ 0 & 0 & 1 & 0 & * \\ 0 & 0 & 0 & 1 & * \\ 0 & 0 & 0 & 0 & 0 \end{bmatrix} \qquad \mathbf{B} = \begin{bmatrix} 1 & * & 0 & 0 & * \\ 0 & 0 & 0 & 0 & 0 \\ 0 & 0 & 0 & 1 & * \\ 0 & 0 & 0 & 0 & 0 \end{bmatrix}$$

$$\mathbf{C} = \begin{bmatrix} 1 & * & 0 & 0 & 0 \\ 0 & 0 & 0 & 0 & 1 \\ 0 & 0 & 0 & 1 & 0 \\ 0 & 0 & 0 & 0 & 0 \end{bmatrix}$$

Clearly, $\mathbf{B}$ is not in rref. The presence of the zero row as the second row of $\mathbf{B}$ implies the absence of $\mathbf{e}_2$. On the other hand, even though $\mathbf{C}$ is also not in rref, it contains $\mathbf{e}_1$, $\mathbf{e}_2$, and $\mathbf{e}_3$ since the zero row is at the bottom. Criterion (4) means that if $\mathbf{A}_{*j}$ is a leading column of $\mathbf{A}_r$, say $\mathbf{e}_i$, then $j \geq i$. Each of these remarks should be verified by referring to the matrices given in Example 2.1.1. The next theorem constitutes the fundamental theoretical result on reduced row echelon forms.

Theorem 2.2.1. *Every matrix* $\mathbf{A}$ *is row equivalent to a matrix* $\mathbf{A}_r$ *in reduced row echelon form. Moreover, if* $\mathbf{B}$ *is row equivalent to* $\mathbf{A}$ *and if* $\mathbf{B}$ *is in reduced row echelon form, then* $\mathbf{B} = \mathbf{A}_r$.

Proof. This theorem makes two assertions. The first is that for any $\mathbf{A}$, there is a sequence of elementary row operations such that

$$\mathbf{A} \rightarrow \cdots \rightarrow \mathbf{A}_r \tag{2.2.1}$$

To prove Eq. 2.2.1 modify the inductive argument given in Theorem 1.5.1 (Problems 2.2.10 and 2.2.11 are guides through the crucial steps of the induction.) The second assertion is that $\mathbf{A}_r$ is unique, quite a remarkable result; for although the sequence of row operations that ultimately result in a rref of $\mathbf{A}$ is not unique, the last matrix in the diagram is always $\mathbf{A}_r$. To preserve the flow of this chapter, the proof of this proposition is left for Subsection 2.3.1. However, Examples 2.2.3 and 2.2.4 are pertinent and illuminating. ■

Since the reduced row echelon form is unique, we can identify the columns in $\mathbf{A}$ that will become the leading columns of $\mathbf{A}_r$. We call these columns the *leading columns* of $\mathbf{A}$. The next example illustrates this point.

Example 2.2.2. Find the leading columns of

$$\mathbf{A} = \begin{bmatrix} 0 & 1 & 1 & 1 & 1 \\ 0 & -1 & -1 & 1 & 1 \\ 0 & 1 & 1 & -1 & 2 \end{bmatrix}$$

Solution. We construct the reduced row echelon form of $\mathbf{A}$ to answer the question because it is usually difficult to determine by inspection which are the leading columns of $\mathbf{A}$.

$$\mathbf{A} = \begin{bmatrix} 0 & 1 & 1 & 1 & 1 \\ 0 & -1 & -1 & 1 & 1 \\ 0 & 1 & 1 & -1 & 2 \end{bmatrix} \rightarrow \begin{bmatrix} 0 & 1 & 1 & 1 & 1 \\ 0 & 0 & 0 & 2 & 2 \\ 0 & 0 & 0 & -2 & 1 \end{bmatrix}$$

$$\rightarrow \begin{bmatrix} 0 & 1 & 1 & 1 & 1 \\ 0 & 0 & 0 & 1 & 1 \\ 0 & 0 & 0 & -2 & 1 \end{bmatrix} \rightarrow \begin{bmatrix} 0 & 1 & 1 & 0 & 0 \\ 0 & 0 & 0 & 1 & 1 \\ 0 & 0 & 0 & -2 & 1 \end{bmatrix}$$

$$\rightarrow \begin{bmatrix} 0 & 1 & 1 & 0 & 0 \\ 0 & 0 & 0 & 1 & 1 \\ 0 & 0 & 0 & 0 & 3 \end{bmatrix} \rightarrow \begin{bmatrix} 0 & 1 & 1 & 0 & 0 \\ 0 & 0 & 0 & 1 & 1 \\ 0 & 0 & 0 & 0 & 1 \end{bmatrix}$$

$$\rightarrow \begin{bmatrix} 0 & 1 & 1 & 0 & 0 \\ 0 & 0 & 0 & 1 & 0 \\ 0 & 0 & 0 & 0 & 1 \end{bmatrix} = \mathbf{A}_r$$

The leading columns of $\mathbf{A}$ are its 2nd, 4th and 5th columns,

$$\mathbf{A}_{*2} = \begin{bmatrix} 1 \\ -1 \\ 1 \end{bmatrix}, \quad \mathbf{A}_{*4} = \begin{bmatrix} 1 \\ 1 \\ -1 \end{bmatrix}, \quad \mathbf{A}_{*5} = \begin{bmatrix} 1 \\ 1 \\ 2 \end{bmatrix}$$

because the 2nd, 4th and 5th columns of $\mathbf{A}_r$ are the leading columns of $\mathbf{A}_r$. Similarly, the leading columns of every matrix in the preceding arrow diagram are their 2nd, 4th and 5th columns.

As we shall see in the next section, we can exploit the reduced row echelon form to study the solution set of systems of equations. The actual computation of the solutions, however, uses a somewhat simpler form. (See Section 2.3.) The remainder of this section is devoted to examining the effects of adding and deleting rows and columns of a matrix in rref. Consider a typical matrix in reduced row echelon form:

$$\mathbf{A}_r = \begin{bmatrix} 1 & * & * & 0 & * & 0 & * \\ 0 & 0 & 0 & 1 & * & 0 & * \\ 0 & 0 & 0 & 0 & 0 & 1 & * \\ 0 & 0 & 0 & 0 & 0 & 0 & 0 \end{bmatrix} \tag{2.2.2}$$

Example 2.2.3. If the last column or the last two columns of the matrix $\mathbf{A}_r$ are removed, the resulting matrices are

$$\mathbf{A}_1 = \begin{bmatrix} 1 & * & * & 0 & * & 0 \\ 0 & 0 & 0 & 1 & * & 0 \\ 0 & 0 & 0 & 0 & 0 & 1 \\ 0 & 0 & 0 & 0 & 0 & 0 \end{bmatrix} \quad \mathbf{A}_2 = \begin{bmatrix} 1 & * & * & 0 & * \\ 0 & 0 & 0 & 1 & * \\ 0 & 0 & 0 & 0 & 0 \\ 0 & 0 & 0 & 0 & 0 \end{bmatrix}$$

and these matrices are in reduced row echelon form.

Example 2.2.4. Show that the matrices obtained from $\mathbf{A}_r$, Eq. 2.2.2, by removing either its last row or last two rows are in reduced row echelon form.

Solution. We denote these matrices $\mathbf{A}_3$ and $\mathbf{A}_4$. Then

$$\mathbf{A}_3 = \begin{bmatrix} 1 & * & * & 0 & * & 0 & * \\ 0 & 0 & 0 & 1 & * & 0 & * \\ 0 & 0 & 0 & 0 & 0 & 1 & * \end{bmatrix} \qquad \mathbf{A}_4 = \begin{bmatrix} 1 & * & * & 0 & * & 0 & * \\ 0 & 0 & 0 & 1 & * & 0 & * \end{bmatrix}$$

Here, again, inspection verifies that $\mathbf{A}_3$ and $\mathbf{A}_4$ are in rref.

These last two examples illustrate the point that striking out the last k columns and l rows of a matrix in rref leaves a submatrix which is also in rref. In matrix notation, if $\mathbf{C} = [\mathbf{A}\ \mathbf{B}]$ is in rref, then so is $\mathbf{A}$ (but not necessarily $\mathbf{B}$); and if

$$\mathbf{D} = \begin{bmatrix} \mathbf{E} \\ \mathbf{F} \end{bmatrix}$$

is in rref so is $\mathbf{E}$.

2.2.1 The rref Operator in MATLAB

MATLAB contains the function "rref" and a remarkable function "rrefmovie." Entering rref(A) returns the reduced row echelon form of **A**. Entering rrefmovie(A) returns a sequence of matrices showing, in essence, the steps in the diagram $\mathbf{A} \rightarrow \cdots \rightarrow \mathbf{A}_r$. Beware: MATLAB interchanges rows to reduce round-off errors. Thus, the diagram generated by rrefmovie(A) may not coincide with the diagram one generates by hand computation. (Although the rref of **A** is unique, the diagram that exhibits the steps from **A** to $\mathbf{A}_r$ is by no means unique.)

PROBLEMS

PART 1

2.2.1. Identify the leading columns of each matrix in Example 2.2.1.

2.2.2. Which of the following matrices are in rref? Find the rref of those that are not.

$(a)\ \begin{bmatrix} 1 & 0 & 1 \\ 0 & 0 & 1 \\ 0 & 0 & 0 \end{bmatrix} \quad (b)\ \begin{bmatrix} 0 & 0 \\ 0 & 1 \\ 0 & 0 \end{bmatrix} \quad (c)\ \mathbf{1} \quad (d)\ \mathbf{1}^{\mathrm{T}} \quad (e)\ \mathbf{1}^{\mathrm{T}}\mathbf{1}$

2.2.3. Repeat Problem 2.2.2 for the following matrices:

$(a)\ \mathbf{1}\mathbf{1}^{\mathrm{T}} \quad (b)\ [0] \quad (c)\ [2] \quad (d)\ \begin{bmatrix} 0 & 0 & 1 \\ 0 & 0 & 0 \end{bmatrix} \quad (e)\ \begin{bmatrix} 1 & * & 1 \\ 0 & 0 & 0 \end{bmatrix}$

2.2.4. Repeat Problem 2.2.2 for the following matrices:

$(a)\ \begin{bmatrix} 0 & 1 & 1 \\ 0 & 0 & 0 \end{bmatrix} \quad (b)\ \begin{bmatrix} 1 & * & 1 \\ 0 & 0 & 1 \end{bmatrix} \quad (c)\ \begin{bmatrix} 0 & 0 & 1 & 2 & 3 \\ 0 & 0 & 0 & 0 & 1 \end{bmatrix}$

$(d)\ \begin{bmatrix} 0 & 0 & 1 & 2 & 0 \\ 0 & 0 & 0 & 0 & 1 \end{bmatrix}$

2.2.5. List the leading columns of **A** for each of the matrices in Problems 2.2.2–2.2.4.

2.2.6. Remove the last two columns of the matrices (*h*) and (*i*) of Example 2.2.1 and verify that these matrices are in rref.

2.2.7. Remove the last two columns of each matrix in Problem 2.2.4 and find their rref. For these same matrices, remove the last row and find their rref.

2.2.8. Show by example that **A** in rref does not imply that $\mathbf{A}^{\mathrm{T}}$ is in rref.

2.2.9. Explain why $\mathbf{e}_i$, $i \neq 1$, is never in rref but $\mathbf{e}_i^{\mathrm{T}}$ always is.

PART 2

2.2.10. Show that $\mathbf{A}_r$ has the same zero columns as **A**.

2.2.11. Explain why every column of a nonsingular **A** in rref is a leading column.

2.2.12. Give an example of a 4×4 matrix in rref which has $\mathbf{e}_3$ as a nonleading column. Must this matrix have a leading column which is $\mathbf{e}_1$, $\mathbf{e}_2$, $\mathbf{e}_3$, $\mathbf{e}_4$?

2.2.13. Show that row equivalent matrices have the same reduced row echelon form. What theorem is crucial for the argument?

2.2.14. Show that the number of leading columns of **A** cannot exceed the number of rows of **A**.

2.2.15. Suppose **A** is in rref. Is [**A B**] in rref? Explain. If **A** has no zero rows, does your answer change?

2.2.16. Suppose **A** and **B** are in rref and have the same number of rows. Is [**A B**] in rref? Explain.

2.2.17. What is the rref of $\mathbf{J}_n$?

2.2.18. Suppose $\mathbf{x}^T = [1 \quad x_2 \quad \ldots \quad x_n]$. What is the rref of $\mathbf{x}\mathbf{x}^T$? Of $\mathbf{x}^T\mathbf{x}$?

PART 3

2.2.19. Suppose **A** is in rref. Show that it is always possible to put [**A a**] into reduced row echelon form by at most one elementary operation of Type 1, one operation of Type 2, and $n - 1$ operations of Type 3.

2.2.20. Show that a column matrix can always be transformed into rref form by elementary operations. Use this fact and the conclusion of Problem 2.2.1 to prove by induction the first assertion of Theorem 2.2.1.

2.2.21. Show that if **A** and **B** are row equivalent, then they have precisely the same leading columns and the same number of nonzero rows. What theorems are crucial for this argument?

2.2.22. If **A** is row equivalent to **B**, show that **AT** is row equivalent to **BT**.

MATLAB

2.2.23. Use the MATLAB functions rref(A) and rrefmovie(A) for each of the matrices in Part 1, Problems 2.2.2–2.2.4.

2.2.24. Use the MATLAB function rref(A) to confirm your view of the nature of the rref for the following matrices: (*a*) $\mathbf{e}_3$, (*b*) $\mathbf{O}_{3\times 4}$, (*c*) [3], (*d*) $\mathbf{J}_4$.

2.3 AN APPLICATION OF ROW OPERATIONS TO THE SOLUTION OF Ax = b

As an application of the ideas presented in the previous section, we use the rref of **A** to find the solutions of $\mathbf{Ax} = \mathbf{b}$. This section is not meant to be a complete analysis of this idea; rather it is only a taste of what lies ahead in Sections 2.4 and 2.5.

Cramer's Rule in its familiar form is of limited use in solving $\mathbf{Ax} = \mathbf{b}$ for these reasons: first, it requires that the system have as many equations as unknowns; second, there are $n + 1$ determinants that must be evaluated; and third, the method fails if **A** is singular, even though the singularity of **A** does not preclude the possibility of solving $\mathbf{Ax} = \mathbf{b}$. (Example 2.2.3 is an illustration of this case.) Hence, except for certain theoretical purposes and for matrices of rather small size, the system $\mathbf{Ax} = \mathbf{b}$ is never solved using Cramer's Rule.

Suppose, perhaps after some sequence of elementary row operations are applied to [**A b**], we end up with the system $\mathbf{A}_r\mathbf{x} = \mathbf{c}$, which for the sake of explicitness is given by

$$\begin{bmatrix} 1 & 1 & -1 & 0 \\ 0 & 0 & 0 & 1 \\ 0 & 0 & 0 & 0 \end{bmatrix} \begin{bmatrix} x \\ y \\ z \\ t \end{bmatrix} = \begin{bmatrix} 2 \\ -1 \\ 0 \end{bmatrix} \tag{2.3.1}$$

Interchanging t with y results in the system

$$\begin{bmatrix} 1 & 0 & -1 & 1 \\ 0 & 1 & 0 & 0 \\ 0 & 0 & 0 & 0 \end{bmatrix} \begin{bmatrix} x \\ t \\ z \\ y \end{bmatrix} = \begin{bmatrix} 2 \\ -1 \\ 0 \end{bmatrix} \tag{2.3.2}$$

Both systems, Eq. 2.3.1 and Eq. 2.3.2, represent the same set of equations; only the ordering of the unknowns has been altered. However, in Eq. 2.3.2, the coefficient matrix has its first two columns as its leading columns. In general, if $\mathbf{A}$ has r leading columns, it is always possible to re-order the unknowns in $\mathbf{Ax} = \mathbf{b}$ so that the leading columns of $\mathbf{A}$ are its first r columns. Hence, without loss in generality, we shall assume that the first r columns of $\mathbf{A}_r$ are $\mathbf{e}_1, \mathbf{e}_2, \ldots, \mathbf{e}_r$. (See Subsection 2.3.2)

Theorem 2.3.1. *The systems* $\mathbf{Ax} = \mathbf{b}$ *and* $\mathbf{Bx} = \mathbf{c}$ *have the same solution sets if* $[\mathbf{A}\ \mathbf{b}] \to \cdots \to [\mathbf{B}\ \mathbf{c}]$.

Proof. Consider the system $\mathbf{Ax} = \mathbf{b}$ with the corresponding augmented matrix $[\mathbf{A}\ \mathbf{b}]$. Suppose we apply elementary row operations on this augmented matrix until $[\mathbf{A}\ \mathbf{b}]$ is transformed into $[\mathbf{B}\ \mathbf{c}]$. That is,

$$[\mathbf{A}\ \mathbf{b}] \to \cdots \to [\mathbf{B}\ \mathbf{c}] \tag{2.3.3}$$

Then there exists a nonsingular matrix, $\mathbf{S}$, such that $\mathbf{S}\,[\mathbf{A}\ \mathbf{b}] = [\mathbf{B}\ \mathbf{c}]$. So

$$\mathbf{S}[\mathbf{A}\ \mathbf{b}] = [\mathbf{SA}\ \mathbf{Sb}] = [\mathbf{B}\ \mathbf{c}] \tag{2.3.4}$$

We deduce from the last equality in Eq. 2.3.4 that

$$\mathbf{SA} = \mathbf{B} \qquad \text{and} \qquad \mathbf{Sb} = \mathbf{c} \tag{2.3.5}$$

Now multiply the system $\mathbf{Ax} = \mathbf{b}$ by $\mathbf{S}$ to obtain $\mathbf{SAx} = \mathbf{Sb}$, and then use Eq. 2.3.5 to obtain the equivalent system $\mathbf{Bx} = \mathbf{c}$. Hence, if $\mathbf{x}$ is any solution of $\mathbf{Ax} = \mathbf{b}$, it is also a solution of $\mathbf{Bx} = \mathbf{c}$. Conversely, suppose $\mathbf{x}$ is a solution of $\mathbf{Bx} = \mathbf{c}$. If we multiply $\mathbf{Bx} = \mathbf{c}$ by $\mathbf{S}^{-1}$, we can deduce that $\mathbf{x}$ is also a solution of $\mathbf{Ax} = \mathbf{b}$, because $\mathbf{S}^{-1}\mathbf{B} = \mathbf{A}$ and $\mathbf{S}^{-1}\mathbf{c} = \mathbf{b}$. ■

This theorem is useful when the resulting system $\mathbf{Bx} = \mathbf{c}$ is easier to analyze and solve than the original system $\mathbf{Ax} = \mathbf{b}$. Here are two illustrative examples. In both cases $\mathbf{B} = \mathbf{A}_r$, where $\mathbf{A}_r$ is the rref of $\mathbf{A}$. Systems with one or more solutions are called *consistent,* those with none are *inconsistent*.

Example 2.3.1. Show that the following system is inconsistent.

$$\mathbf{Ax} = \begin{bmatrix} 1 & 1 & 1 & 1 \\ 0 & -1 & -1 & 1 \\ 0 & 1 & 1 & -1 \end{bmatrix} \mathbf{x} = \begin{bmatrix} 1 \\ 1 \\ 2 \end{bmatrix}$$

Solution. Convert the given system to rref:

$$[\mathbf{A}\ \mathbf{b}] \rightarrow \left[\begin{array}{cccc:c} 1 & 0 & 0 & 2 & 2 \\ 0 & 1 & 1 & -1 & -1 \\ 0 & 0 & 0 & 0 & 3 \end{array}\right] \rightarrow \cdots \rightarrow \left[\begin{array}{cccc:c} 1 & 0 & 0 & 2 & 0 \\ 0 & 1 & 1 & -1 & 0 \\ 0 & 0 & 0 & 0 & 1 \end{array}\right] = [\mathbf{A}_r\ \mathbf{c}]$$

The system equivalent to $\mathbf{Ax} = \mathbf{b}$ is

$$\mathbf{A}_r\mathbf{x} = \begin{bmatrix} 1 & 0 & 0 & 2 \\ 0 & 1 & 1 & -1 \\ 0 & 0 & 0 & 0 \end{bmatrix} \mathbf{x} = \mathbf{c} = \begin{bmatrix} 0 \\ 0 \\ 1 \end{bmatrix}$$

This equation is the matrix-vector form of a system with 3 equations in 4 unknowns. The third equation is read from the last row: $0x + 0y + 0z + 0t = 1$. This is a contradiction, so the system $\mathbf{A}_r\mathbf{x} = \mathbf{c}$ has no solutions. Hence, neither does the given system, by Theorem 2.3.1.

It is sometimes thought that systems with fewer equations than unknowns are "under-determined" and therefore must have infinitely many solutions. Example 2.3.1 shows this presumption false. Similarly, systems with more equations than unknowns are often assumed to be inconsistent. The next example shows that this statement cannot be true in general; such systems may be inconsistent or have one solution or even infinitely many solutions.

Example 2.3.2. Show that the following system is consistent.

$$\mathbf{Ax} = \begin{bmatrix} 1 & 1 & 1 & 1 \\ 0 & -1 & -1 & 1 \\ 0 & 1 & 1 & -1 \\ 1 & 0 & 2 & 0 \\ 1 & 2 & 2 & 0 \end{bmatrix} \quad \mathbf{x} = \begin{bmatrix} 1 \\ 1 \\ -1 \\ 2 \\ 0 \end{bmatrix} \tag{2.3.6}$$

Solution. Proceed as in the previous example:

$$[\mathbf{A}\ \mathbf{b}] = \left[\begin{array}{cccc:c} 1 & 1 & 1 & 1 & 1 \\ 0 & -1 & -1 & 1 & 1 \\ 0 & 1 & 1 & -1 & -1 \\ 1 & 0 & 2 & 0 & 2 \\ 1 & 2 & 2 & 0 & 0 \end{array}\right] \rightarrow$$

$$\cdots \rightarrow \left[\begin{array}{cccc:c} 1 & 0 & 0 & 2 & 2 \\ 0 & 1 & 0 & 0 & -1 \\ 0 & 0 & 1 & -1 & 0 \\ 0 & 0 & 0 & 0 & 0 \\ 0 & 0 & 0 & 0 & 0 \end{array}\right] = [\mathbf{A}_r\ \mathbf{c}]$$

But now the equivalent system is

$$\mathbf{A}_r\mathbf{x} = \begin{bmatrix} 1 & 0 & 0 & 2 \\ 0 & 1 & 0 & 0 \\ 0 & 0 & 1 & -1 \\ 0 & 0 & 0 & 0 \\ 0 & 0 & 0 & 0 \end{bmatrix} \mathbf{x} = \begin{bmatrix} 2 \\ -1 \\ 0 \\ 0 \\ 0 \end{bmatrix} \tag{2.3.7}$$

In expanded form, the equations are $x + 2t = 2$, $y = -1$, $z - t = 0$, and two repetitions of the truism $0x + 0y + 0z = 0$. If we set $z = 0$, then $t = 0$, $x = 2$, and $y = -1$, and the vector $\mathbf{x} = [2\ -1\ 0\ 0]^T$ is a solution of Eq. 2.3.7 as well as Eq. 2.3.6. Not only is the system Eq. 2.3.6 consistent, it has infinitely many solutions, one for each choice of z and t.

Example 2.3.3. Show that Cramer's Rule cannot be applied to the following consistent system.

$$\mathbf{A}\mathbf{x} = \begin{bmatrix} 1 & 1 & 1 \\ 0 & -1 & 1 \\ 0 & 1 & -1 \end{bmatrix} \quad \mathbf{x} = \begin{bmatrix} 1 \\ 1 \\ -1 \end{bmatrix} \tag{2.3.8}$$

Solution. Once again compute the rref of the augmented matrix:

$$[\mathbf{A}\mathbf{b}] \to \left[\begin{array}{ccc:c} 1 & 1 & 1 & 1 \\ 0 & -1 & 1 & 1 \\ 0 & 1 & -1 & -1 \end{array}\right] \to \cdots \to \left[\begin{array}{ccc:c} 1 & 0 & 2 & 2 \\ 0 & 1 & -1 & -1 \\ 0 & 0 & 0 & 0 \end{array}\right] = [\mathbf{A}_r\mathbf{c}]$$

The equation represented by the second row is $y - z = -1$. Set $z = 0$. Then $y = -1$. The first row represents the equation $x + 2z = 2$. Hence $x = 2$. Thus there is at least one solution, $\mathbf{x} = [2\quad -1\quad 0]^T$ and the given system is consistent. However, since $\det(\mathbf{A}) = 0$, Cramer's Rule is inapplicable.

2.3.1 The Uniqueness of the Reduced Row Echelon Form[1]

This Subsection is devoted entirely to the proof of Theorem 2.2.1. The proof is constructed by pasting together a collection of intermediate lemmas.

Lemma 2.1. *Suppose* **A** *and* **B** *are in* rref *and are row equivalent. Let* **A**$'$ *and* **B**$'$ *be the result of removing the last k columns of* **A** *and* **B**, *respectively. Then* **A**$'$ *and* **B**$'$ *are in* rref *and are also row equivalent.*

---

[1] This section may be skipped without loss of continuity.

Proof. That $\mathbf{A}'$ and $\mathbf{B}'$ are in reduced row echelon form is easy to see and is illustrated in Example 2.2.3. To prove that $\mathbf{A}'$ and $\mathbf{B}'$ are row equivalent, write $\mathbf{A} = [\mathbf{A}'\ \mathbf{C}]$ and $\mathbf{B} = [\mathbf{B}'\ \mathbf{D}]$. Then there exists a matrix $\mathbf{S}$ such that $\mathbf{SA} = \mathbf{S}[\mathbf{A}'\ \mathbf{C}] = [\mathbf{B}'\ \mathbf{D}]$. Since $\mathbf{S}[\mathbf{A}'\ \mathbf{C}] = [\mathbf{SA}'\ \mathbf{SC}]$, it follows that $\mathbf{SA}' = \mathbf{B}'$. ■

Lemma 2.2. *If* $[\mathbf{A}_r\ \mathbf{c}]$ *is in* rref, *then the system* $\mathbf{A}_r\mathbf{x} = \mathbf{c}$ *is inconsistent if and only if* $\mathbf{c}$ *is a leading column of* $[\mathbf{A}_r\ \mathbf{c}]$.

Proof. Suppose that we have re-labeled the unknowns so that the first r columns of $\mathbf{A}$ are the leading columns. The rref of $[\mathbf{A}\ \mathbf{b}]$ is $[\mathbf{A}_r\ \mathbf{c}]$:

$$\left[\begin{array}{cccc|cccc|c} 1 & 0 & \cdots & 0 & * & * & \cdots & * & c_1 \\ 0 & 1 & \cdots & 0 & * & * & \cdots & * & c_2 \\ \vdots & \vdots & & \vdots & \vdots & \vdots & & \vdots & \vdots \\ 0 & 0 & \cdots & 1 & * & * & \cdots & * & c_r \\ \hline 0 & 0 & \cdots & 0 & 0 & 0 & \cdots & 0 & \beta \\ 0 & 0 & \cdots & 0 & 0 & 0 & \cdots & 0 & 0 \\ \vdots & \vdots & & \vdots & \vdots & \vdots & & \vdots & \vdots \\ 0 & 0 & \cdots & 0 & 0 & 0 & \cdots & 0 & 0 \end{array}\right] \begin{array}{l} \\ \\ \\ \leftarrow r\text{th row} \\ \\ \\ \\ \\ \end{array} \tag{2.3.9}$$

There are two possibilities: If $\beta = 1$ the system is inconsistent because the $(r+1)$st equation is contradictory. In this case $\mathbf{c}$ is a leading column. If $\beta = 0$, then $\mathbf{c}$ is not a leading column and the system has a solution obtained by setting $x_{r+1} = x_{r+2} = \cdots = x_n = 0$ and deducing that $x_i = c_i$, for each i, $i = 1, 2, \ldots, r$. Put in partitioned form, the analysis of the consistent case becomes,

$$\left[\begin{array}{c|c} \mathbf{I}_r & * \\ \hline \mathbf{O} & \mathbf{0} \end{array}\right] \left[\begin{array}{c} \mathbf{x}_r \\ \hline \mathbf{0} \end{array}\right] = \left[\begin{array}{c} \mathbf{I}_r\mathbf{x}_r + * \mathbf{0} \\ \hline \mathbf{O}\mathbf{x}_r + \mathbf{0}\mathbf{0} \end{array}\right] = \left[\begin{array}{c} \mathbf{x}_r \\ \hline \mathbf{0} \end{array}\right] = \left[\begin{array}{c} \mathbf{c} \\ \hline \mathbf{0} \end{array}\right] \tag{2.3.10}$$

which makes evident the nature of the nontrivial solution of $\mathbf{A}_r\mathbf{x} = \mathbf{c}$; namely

$$\mathbf{x}_c = \left[\begin{array}{c} \mathbf{c} \\ \hline \mathbf{0} \end{array}\right] \quad \blacksquare \tag{2.3.11}$$

Lemma 2.3. *If* $[\mathbf{A}_r\ \mathbf{c}]$ *and* $[\mathbf{A}_r\ \mathbf{d}]$ *are in* rref *and are row equivalent, then* $\mathbf{c} = \mathbf{d}$.

Proof. By hypothesis, the systems $\mathbf{A}_r\mathbf{x} = \mathbf{c}$ and $\mathbf{A}_r\mathbf{x} = \mathbf{d}$ are equivalent. Hence, if one is inconsistent so is the other; and then, by Lemma 2.2, $\mathbf{c}$ and $\mathbf{d}$ would be leading columns of $[\mathbf{A}_r\ \mathbf{c}]$ and $[\mathbf{A}_r\ \mathbf{d}]$, respectively. In that case $\mathbf{c} = \mathbf{d}$ and we are done. So we need to consider only the case in which both systems are consistent. There is no loss in generality in assuming that the leading columns of $\mathbf{A}_r$ are its first r columns. (If the leading columns are not the first r columns, they can be made so by re-labeling the unknowns). Then, as shown in Eq. 2.3.10, the system $\mathbf{A}_r\mathbf{x} = \mathbf{c}$ has the solution $\mathbf{x}_c$ so that $\mathbf{A}_r\mathbf{x}_c = \mathbf{c}$. Since the systems $\mathbf{A}_r\mathbf{x} = \mathbf{c}$ and

$\mathbf{A}_r\mathbf{x} = \mathbf{d}$ are equivalent, $\mathbf{x}_c$ must also solve $\mathbf{A}_r\mathbf{x} = \mathbf{d}$. That is, $\mathbf{A}_r\mathbf{x}_c = \mathbf{d}$. Hence, $\mathbf{c} = \mathbf{d}$. ■

Theorem 2.3.2. *(Uniqueness). If* $\mathbf{A}$ *and* $\mathbf{B}$ *are in reduced row echelon form and are row equivalent, then* $\mathbf{A} = \mathbf{B}$.

Proof. The number of rows and columns of $\mathbf{A}$ and $\mathbf{B}$ are the same. If $\mathbf{A}$ is a column matrix, then so is $\mathbf{B}$. The reduced row echelon form for a single column is either $\mathbf{0}$ or $\mathbf{e}_1$. If $\mathbf{A}$ is one and $\mathbf{B}$ the other, then they could not be row equivalent. Hence, if they are column vectors, they must be equal; so we can assume that $\mathbf{A}$ and $\mathbf{B}$ have more than one column.

Suppose $\mathbf{A}$ and $\mathbf{B}$ agree in their first r columns and differ in column $r + 1$. Now remove columns $r + 2, r + 3, \ldots, n$ of both matrices. By Lemma 2.1 the resulting matrices are in rref and are row equivalent. If these truncated matrices are denoted by $[\mathbf{A}_r\ \mathbf{c}]$ and $[\mathbf{A}_r\ \mathbf{d}]$, then they are unequal since $\mathbf{c} \neq \mathbf{d}$ by stipulation. But this contradicts Lemma 2.3. Hence, $\mathbf{A} = \mathbf{B}$. ■

2.3.2 The Leading Columns of A

The system

$$\begin{aligned} x_1 + 2x_2 \qquad &= 1 \\ x_3 &= -1 \end{aligned} \tag{2.3.12}$$

has the augmented matrix

$$\left[\begin{array}{ccc|c} 1 & 2 & 0 & 1 \\ 0 & 0 & 1 & -1 \end{array}\right] \tag{2.3.13}$$

The matrix in Eq. 2.3.13 is in rref and its leading columns are its first and third. The variable x_3 in Eq. 2.3.12 is written after x_2 by convention. It is for this reason that the third rather than the second column in Eq. 2.3.13 is a leading columns. Had x_3 been written before x_2, the system would be

$$\begin{aligned} x_1 + \qquad 2x_2 &= 1 \\ x_3 \qquad &= -1 \end{aligned} \tag{2.3.14}$$

and its augmented matrix is

$$\left[\begin{array}{ccc|c} 1 & 0 & 2 & 1 \\ 0 & 1 & 0 & -1 \end{array}\right] \tag{2.3.15}$$

Now the first two columns of the matrix in Eq. 2.3.15 are leading columns. The augmented matrix Eq. 2.3.15 represents precisely the same system as does Eq. 2.3.13, *provided that column 2 contains the coefficients of* x_3 *and not those of* x_2. This simple re-ordering of the variables permits us to assume that the leading columns of $\mathbf{A}$ are its initial columns, an extremely useful simplification of notation.

In more general terms, suppose that $\mathbf{P}$ is an elementary matrix which interchanges rows i and j of $\mathbf{x}$. Then $\mathbf{y} = \mathbf{Px} = [\cdots x_j \cdots x_i \cdots]^{\mathrm{T}}$.

$$\mathbf{A}' = \mathbf{AP} = \begin{bmatrix} * & \cdots & a_{1j} & \cdots & a_{1i} & \cdots & * \\ * & \cdots & a_{2j} & \cdots & a_{2i} & \cdots & * \\ & & \vdots & & \vdots & & \\ * & \cdots & a_{mj} & \cdots & a_{mi} & \cdots & * \end{bmatrix} \tag{2.3.16}$$

$$\text{ith column} \uparrow \qquad\qquad \uparrow \text{ jth column}$$

Since $\mathbf{P}^2 = \mathbf{I}$, Eq. 2.3.16 implies

$$\mathbf{Ax} = \mathbf{APPx} = \mathbf{A}'\,\mathbf{y} = \mathbf{b} \tag{2.3.17}$$

Only one interchange of the entries of $\mathbf{x}$ is accomplished by Eq. 2.3.17. It should be obvious that a succession of interchanges can be performed on $\mathbf{x}$ so that the result on $\mathbf{A}$, say $\mathbf{A}'$, has its leading columns as its initial columns. In this case, Eq. 2.3.17 takes the form

$$\mathbf{Ax} = \mathbf{AP}_1\mathbf{P}_2\cdots\mathbf{P}_k\mathbf{P}_k\cdots\mathbf{P}_2\mathbf{P}_1\mathbf{x} = \mathbf{A}'\,\mathbf{y} = \mathbf{b} \tag{2.3.18}$$

and $\mathbf{A}'\,\mathbf{y} = \mathbf{b}$ represents exactly the same system as $\mathbf{Ax} = \mathbf{b}$. Moreover, the rref of $\mathbf{A}'$, say $\mathbf{A}'_r$, takes the *canonical form*

$$\mathbf{A}' = \begin{bmatrix} \mathbf{I}_r & * \\ \mathbf{O} & \mathbf{O} \end{bmatrix} \tag{2.3.19}$$

PROBLEMS

PART 1

2.3.1. Find a solution for each system given below:

$$(a)\ \begin{bmatrix} 1 & 2 & 0 & 0 \\ 0 & 0 & 1 & 0 \\ 0 & 0 & 0 & 1 \\ 0 & 0 & 0 & 0 \end{bmatrix}\mathbf{x} = \begin{bmatrix} -1 \\ 2 \\ 1 \\ 0 \end{bmatrix} \qquad (b)\ \begin{bmatrix} 1 & 1 & 1 & 1 \\ 0 & 0 & 0 & 0 \\ 0 & 0 & 0 & 0 \\ 0 & 0 & 0 & 0 \end{bmatrix}\mathbf{x} = \begin{bmatrix} 3 \\ 0 \\ 0 \\ 0 \end{bmatrix}$$

$$(c)\ \begin{bmatrix} 1 & 1 & 1 \\ -1 & 1 & 1 \\ 1 & 1 & -1 \end{bmatrix}\mathbf{x} = \begin{bmatrix} 1 \\ 1 \\ 2 \end{bmatrix} \qquad (d)\ \begin{bmatrix} 1 & 2 & 2 & 0 & 0 & 0 \\ 0 & 0 & 0 & 1 & 1 & 0 \\ 0 & 0 & 0 & 0 & 0 & 1 \end{bmatrix}\mathbf{x} = \begin{bmatrix} -1 \\ 0 \\ 2 \end{bmatrix}$$

2.3.2. If $\mathbf{A}$ is invertible, explain why $\mathbf{A}^{-1}\mathbf{b}$ is always a solution of $\mathbf{Ax} = \mathbf{b}$.

2.3.3. Find all $\mathbf{b}$ so that the following system is inconsistent:

$$\mathbf{Ax} = \begin{bmatrix} 1 & 1 & 1 & 1 \\ 0 & -1 & -1 & 1 \\ 0 & 1 & 1 & -1 \end{bmatrix}\mathbf{x} = \mathbf{b} = \begin{bmatrix} a \\ b \\ c \end{bmatrix}$$

2.3.4. Find all $\mathbf{b}$ so that $\mathbf{J}_n\mathbf{x} = \mathbf{b}$ is consistent.

PART 2

2.3.5. Suppose $\mathbf{x}_h$ is a solution of $\mathbf{Ax} = \mathbf{0}$, and $\mathbf{x}_f$ is a solution of $\mathbf{Ax} = \mathbf{b}$. Show that $k\mathbf{x}_h + \mathbf{x}_f$ is a solution of $\mathbf{Ax} = \mathbf{b}$ for all scalars k.

2.3.6. If $\mathbf{x}_1$ and $\mathbf{x}_2$ are two solutions of $\mathbf{Ax} = \mathbf{b}$, show that $\mathbf{x}_1 - \mathbf{x}_2$ is a solution of $\mathbf{Ax} = \mathbf{0}$.

2.3.7. Prove the following theorem: If $\mathbf{x}_1$ and $\mathbf{x}_2$ are solutions of $\mathbf{Ax} = \mathbf{b} \neq \mathbf{0}$, then $a\mathbf{x}_1 + b\mathbf{x}_2$ is also a solution if and only if $a + b = 1$.

2.3.8. If $\mathbf{b}$ is a column of $\mathbf{A}$, explain why the system $\mathbf{Ax} = \mathbf{b}$ is consistent.

2.3.9. Let $\mathbf{A} = [\mathbf{C}\ \mathbf{D}]$. Suppose that $\mathbf{C}$ is invertible and that the reduced row echelon form of $\mathbf{A}$ has no zero rows. Show that a solution of $[\mathbf{C}\ \mathbf{D}]\mathbf{x} = \mathbf{b}$ is given by $\mathbf{x} = \begin{bmatrix} \mathbf{Cb} \\ \mathbf{O} \end{bmatrix}$. Hence show that $\mathbf{Ax} = \mathbf{b}$ is consistent for all choices of $\mathbf{b}$.

2.4 THE SOLUTION OF Ax = b BY GAUSSIAN ELIMINATION

In this section we suppose that $\mathbf{A}$ is a square, nonsingular matrix, so the system $\mathbf{Ax} = \mathbf{b}$ has as many equations as unknowns. Then, since $\mathbf{A}$ is invertible, it follows that $\mathbf{A}^{-1}\mathbf{b}$ is the unique solution of this system. We could compute $\mathbf{x} = \mathbf{A}^{-1}\mathbf{b}$ by using the ideas presented in Section 1.5; the rref for a nonsingular matrix is $\mathbf{I}$ and hence the diagram,

$$[\mathbf{A}\ \mathbf{b}] \to \cdots \to [\mathbf{I}\ \mathbf{A}^{-1}\mathbf{b}] \tag{2.4.1}$$

is the diagram in Eq. 1.5.4. However, the problem can be solved more efficiently. Consider the diagram

$$[\mathbf{A}\ \mathbf{b}] \to \cdots \to [\mathbf{U}\ \mathbf{c}] \tag{2.4.2}$$

where $\mathbf{U}$ is upper triangular. (This diagram is constructed in the same manner as the diagram in Eq. 2.4.1 except we stop the row reduction process when we reach $\mathbf{U}$ rather than $\mathbf{I}$.) From Theorem 2.3.1, it follows that the systems $\mathbf{Ax} = \mathbf{b}$ and $\mathbf{Ux} = \mathbf{c}$ are equivalent. The process used in constructing the diagram in Eq. 2.4.2 is called *forward elimination* and the diagonal entries of $\mathbf{U}$ are called *pivots*. The system $\mathbf{Ux} = \mathbf{b}$ can be solved by *back substitution,* a process best described by example. Let the augmented matrix of $\mathbf{Ux} = \mathbf{c}$ be given by

$$\left[\begin{array}{ccc|c} 2 & -1 & 1 & 1 \\ 0 & 3 & 1 & 1 \\ 0 & 0 & -1 & 5 \end{array}\right] \tag{2.4.3}$$

The corresponding equations, in the variables x_1, x_2, x_3, are

$$\begin{aligned} 2x_1 - x_2 + x_3 &= 1 \\ 3x_2 + x_3 &= 1 \\ - x_3 &= 5 \end{aligned} \tag{2.2.4}$$

From the third equation $x_3 = -5$. From the second equation and $x_3 = -5$, we obtain $x_2 = 2$. Now substitute $x_2 = 2$ and $x_3 = -5$ into the first equation to obtain $x_1 = 4$. It should be apparent from this example why the process is called back substitution. Indeed, as long as we begin with a nonsingular coefficient matrix **A**, forward elimination can convert **A** into a **U** with no zero diagonal entries. Since **A** is a square matrix, the last equation in the system $\mathbf{Ux} = \mathbf{c}$ determines $\mathbf{x}_n$, the next to the last determines x_{n-1}, and so on. The technique combining forward elimination and back substitution is called *Gaussian elimination*. The pivots are the diagonal entries of **U** and are read from the diagonal of the matrix in Eq. 2.4.3; in this case 2, 3, -1.

Example 2.4.1. Use Gaussian elimination to solve the system

$$\mathbf{Ax} = \begin{bmatrix} 2 & -1 & 1 \\ 2 & 2 & 2 \\ -2 & 4 & -1 \end{bmatrix} \mathbf{x} = \mathbf{b} = \begin{bmatrix} 1 \\ 2 \\ 5 \end{bmatrix}$$

Solution. We begin with forward elimination.

$$[\mathbf{A}\ \mathbf{b}] = \left[\begin{array}{ccc|c} 2 & -1 & 1 & 1 \\ 2 & 2 & 2 & 2 \\ -2 & 4 & -1 & 5 \end{array}\right] \to \cdots \to \left[\begin{array}{ccc|c} 2 & -1 & 1 & 1 \\ 0 & 3 & 1 & 1 \\ 0 & 3 & 0 & 6 \end{array}\right] \to$$

$$\cdots \to \left[\begin{array}{ccc|c} 2 & -1 & 1 & 1 \\ 0 & 3 & 1 & 1 \\ 0 & 0 & -1 & 5 \end{array}\right] = [\mathbf{U}\ \mathbf{c}]$$

Since $[\mathbf{U}\ \mathbf{c}]$ is the system in Eq. 2.4.4, we need not repeat the back substitution. The given system has the unique solution $\mathbf{x} = [4 \quad 2 \quad -5]^{\mathrm{T}}$.

Two difficulties may arise during the forward elimination steps in the Gaussian elimination process. Neither of these difficulties appeared in Example 2.4.1. The first complication appears whenever a diagonal entry is zero. Example 2.4.2 illustrates this case. The second complication is loss of accuracy due to the finite storage capacity of the computer. There is, for example, no way that π can be saved with complete accuracy. Our ability to store only a finite number of the digits of a number may yield large inaccuracies in the computation of the solution of $\mathbf{Ax} = \mathbf{b}$. Example 2.4.3 shows how this can come about.

Example 2.4.2. Use Gaussian elimination to solve the system

$$\mathbf{Ax} = \begin{bmatrix} 0 & -1 & 1 \\ 2 & 2 & 2 \\ 2 & 4 & -1 \end{bmatrix} \mathbf{x} = \begin{bmatrix} 1 \\ 2 \\ 1 \end{bmatrix} = \mathbf{b}$$

Solution. We cannot use the zero entry on the diagonal to clear the entries in the first column. This is due, of course, to the fact that the equations (rows of **A**) are given in such a manner that there is no x_1 variable in the first equation. The solution is obvious. Interchange rows 1 and 2 (or 1 and

3). The following diagram represents the steps in the forward elimination process:

$$\left[\begin{array}{ccc:c} 0 & -1 & 1 & 1 \\ 2 & 2 & 2 & 2 \\ 2 & 4 & -1 & 1 \end{array}\right] \rightarrow \left[\begin{array}{ccc:c} 2 & 2 & 2 & 2 \\ 0 & -1 & 1 & 1 \\ 2 & 4 & -1 & 1 \end{array}\right]$$

$$\rightarrow \left[\begin{array}{ccc:c} 2 & 2 & 2 & 2 \\ 0 & -1 & 1 & 1 \\ 0 & 2 & -3 & -1 \end{array}\right] \rightarrow \left[\begin{array}{ccc:c} 2 & 2 & 2 & 2 \\ 0 & -1 & 1 & 1 \\ 0 & 0 & -1 & 1 \end{array}\right]$$

Back substitution yields $\mathbf{x} = [4\ -2\ -1]^{\mathrm{T}}$. The pivots are $2, -1, -1$.

In order to explain the point of the next example, we must make two assumptions about the way the arithmetical computations are carried out in a computer. We shall assume that only five significant places of accuracy are kept in any computation. Second, a number with more than five significant figures is rounded by "chopping." For example, the number 1.50026 is chopped to 1.5002. With these restrictions in mind, we consider an example which appears in *Computer Methods for Mathematical Computations,* G. E. Forsythe, M. A. Malcolm, C. B. Moler, Prentice-Hall Series in Automatic Computation, Prentice Hall, 1977, Englewood Cliffs, New Jersey.

Example 2.4.3. Use Gaussian elimination to solve the system with augmented matrix

$$\left[\begin{array}{ccc:c} 10 & -7 & 0 & 7 \\ -3 & 2.099 & 6 & 3.901 \\ 5 & -1 & 5 & 6 \end{array}\right]$$

Solution. The first two steps in the forward elimination process are

$$\left[\begin{array}{ccc:c} 10 & -7 & 0 & 7 \\ -3 & 2.099 & 6 & 3.901 \\ 5 & -1 & 5 & 6 \end{array}\right] \rightarrow \cdots \rightarrow \left[\begin{array}{ccc:c} 10 & -7 & 0 & 7 \\ 0 & -0.001 & 6 & 6.001 \\ 0 & 2.5 & 5 & 2.5 \end{array}\right]$$

It is at this point that the limited capacity of the computer plays a role in altering the accuracy of the computations. Multiply the second row by 2500 and add the result to the third row to eliminate 2.5. The product, 2500 $\times 6.001$ is chopped to 15,002. Thus, without row interchanges,

$$\left[\begin{array}{ccc:c} 10 & -7 & 0 & 7 \\ 0 & -0.001 & 6 & 6.001 \\ 0 & 2.5 & 5 & 2.5 \end{array}\right] \rightarrow \left[\begin{array}{ccc:c} 10 & -7 & 0 & 7 \\ 0 & -0.001 & 6 & 6.001 \\ 0 & 0 & 15005 & 15004 \end{array}\right]$$

The third row implies $x_3 = 0.99993$, and if this value is substituted into the second equation, there results: $-0.001\mathrm{x}_2 + 6 \times (0.99993) = 6.001$. Hence $x_2 = -1.5$ and this leads to $x_1 = -0.35$.

However, the coefficient matrix for this system is nonsingular, and it is easy to verify that the unique solution of the given system is $\mathbf{x} = [0 \quad -1 \quad 1]^T$! The discrepancy between the correct answer and the one computed by Gaussian elimination is due to the small value of the second pivot, −0.001. We can illustrate this point quite dramatically. Suppose rows two and three are interchanged just before the last elimination. Then the diagram is

$$\left[\begin{array}{ccc:c} 10 & -7 & 0 & 7 \\ 0 & -0.001 & 6 & 6.001 \\ 0 & 2.5 & 5 & 2.5 \end{array}\right] \to \left[\begin{array}{ccc:c} 10 & -7 & 0 & 7 \\ 0 & 2.5 & 5 & 2.5 \\ 0 & -0.001 & 6 & 6.001 \end{array}\right]$$

$$\to \left[\begin{array}{ccc:c} 10 & -7 & 0 & 7 \\ 0 & 2.5 & 5 & 2.5 \\ 0 & 0 & 6.002 & 6.002 \end{array}\right] \qquad (2.4.5)$$

Clearly $x_3 = 1$, and $2.5x_2 + 5(1) = 2.5$ implies $x_2 = -1$. Finally, $x_1 = 0$.

Example 2.4.3 illustrates an elementary but important principle: Divide each row by the largest entry in the row and then interchange the ith row with the jth row (assuming $i < j$) if this leads to a pivot with a larger numerical value. This explains the interchange of rows 2 and 3 in the diagram in Eq. 2.4.5. The process of using row interchanges with $i < j$ to obtain the largest pivot is called *partial pivoting*. A complete study of these ideas is undertaken in texts on numerical analysis; it suffices for our purposes simply to illustrate the necessity of taking these measures.

In Section 2.5, we explore an implementation of Gaussian elimination known as the **LU** factorization of **A**. It is a first step in the direction of modifying Gaussian elimination so that it can be used in computer programs.

2.4.1 Solving Consistent Systems in MATLAB

MATLAB solves the system $\mathbf{Ax} = \mathbf{b}$ by Gaussian elimination with partial pivoting using a descendant of the LINPACK program. (LINPACK is a modern, highly regarded library of computer programs for solving systems of equations with speed and accuracy. LINPACK was originally written in FORTRAN; the version used by MATLAB is written in C.) Suppose **A** is nonsingular and **b** is some fixed vector of scalars. Then $\mathbf{x} = \mathbf{A}^{-1}\mathbf{b}$, the unique solution of $\mathbf{Ax} = \mathbf{b}$, is computed by the command A\b. The right-hand side need not be a vector; the command A\B returns the matrix inv(A)*B for any matrix **B**, as long as **A** is conformable with **B**. In particular, A\eye(n) returns inv(A). Indeed, inv(A) is actually computed in this manner. (Be careful to distinguish the backward slash "\" from its cousin the forward slash "/". The forward slash is a legal operator in MATLAB used to obtain a least squares solution to inconsistent equations. See Chapter 4, Section 4.10.)

Example 2.4.4. Use \ to find the solution of the system in Example 2.4.2.

Solution. Input **A** and **b**. In response to the command A\b, MATLAB returns

```
A\b =
        4
       -2
       -1
```

Example 2.4.5. For the matrix **A** of Example 2.4.2, find inv(A), rat(inv(A)) and A\I.

Solutions.

```
inv(A) =
         1.6667   -0.5000    0.6667
         0.3333    0         0.3333
        -2.0000    1.0000   -1.0000
```

MATLAB returns the same matrix in response to A\eye(n) as it does in response to inv(A). Finally,

```
rat(inv(A)) =
         5/3   -1/2   2/3
         1/3      0   1/3
         -2       1    -1
```

PROBLEMS

PART 1

2.4.1. Use Gaussian elimination (forward elimination and back substitution) to find the unique solutions of

(*a*) $\begin{bmatrix} 1 & 1 & 1 \\ -1 & -1 & 1 \\ -1 & 1 & -1 \end{bmatrix}\mathbf{x} = \begin{bmatrix} 1 \\ 1 \\ 2 \end{bmatrix}$ (*b*) $\begin{bmatrix} 1 & 1 & 1 \\ -1 & -1 & 1 \\ -1 & 1 & -1 \end{bmatrix}\mathbf{x} = \begin{bmatrix} 1 \\ 1 \\ 1 \end{bmatrix}$

(*c*) $\begin{bmatrix} 1 & 1 & 1 \\ -1 & -1 & 1 \\ -1 & 1 & -1 \end{bmatrix}\mathbf{x} = \begin{bmatrix} 0 \\ 1 \\ 0 \end{bmatrix}$

2.4.2. Repeat Problem 2.4.1 for the systems

(*a*) $\begin{bmatrix} 1 & 0 & 0 & 0 \\ 2 & 0 & 1 & 0 \\ 0 & 1 & -1 & 1 \\ 0 & 0 & 1 & 1 \end{bmatrix}\mathbf{x} = \begin{bmatrix} -1 \\ 2 \\ 1 \\ 0 \end{bmatrix}$ (*b*) $\begin{bmatrix} 1 & 1 & 1 & 1 \\ 1 & 1 & 1 & 0 \\ 1 & 1 & 0 & 0 \\ 1 & 0 & 0 & 0 \end{bmatrix}\mathbf{x} = \begin{bmatrix} 3 \\ 0 \\ 0 \\ 0 \end{bmatrix}$

2.4.3. Find the family of solutions of the following systems by setting $x_3 = t$.

(*a*) $\begin{bmatrix} 1 & 1 & 1 \\ 0 & -1 & 1 \\ 0 & 1 & -1 \end{bmatrix}\mathbf{x} = \begin{bmatrix} 1 \\ 1 \\ -1 \end{bmatrix}$ (*b*) $\begin{bmatrix} 1 & 1 & 1 \\ 0 & -1 & 1 \\ 0 & 1 & -1 \end{bmatrix}\mathbf{x} = \begin{bmatrix} 0 \\ 1 \\ -1 \end{bmatrix}$

2.4.4. Redo Example 2.4.3 in "chopped" arithmetic without partial pivoting but carrying (*a*) 7 decimal places; (*b*) 9 decimal places.

MATLAB

2.4.5. Use \ to find the solutions to the systems in Problem 2.4.1.

2.4.6. Repeat Problem 2.4.5 except use inv(A)*b.

2.4.7. Use \ to find the solutions to the systems in Problem 2.4.2.

2.4.8. Repeat Problem 2.4.7 except use inv(A)*b.

2.4.9. Use \ to find the solution to the systems in Problem 2.4.3. What does MATLAB return after the input inv(A)*b ?

2.4.10. Use \ to compute the solution of the system in Example 2.4.3.

2.5 THE LU FACTORIZATION OF A

In this section it is proved that every nonsingular matrix can be written as the product of a "nearly" lower triangular matrix $\mathbf{L}_p$ and an upper triangular matrix $\mathbf{U}$. This is called the **LU** *factorization* of **A**, the proof of which is given in Theorem 2.5.1. The exact nature of **L** and **U** will be revealed in the course of this proof.

Every nonsingular matrix **A** is row equivalent to an upper triangular matrix **U**. Therefore, there exists a nonsingular matrix $\mathbf{L}_p$ such that $\mathbf{A} = \mathbf{L}_p\mathbf{U}$. It is possible to show (but we do not do so here) that a permutation of the rows of $\mathbf{L}_p$ results in a lower triangular matrix. Matrices which can be made lower triangular by a permutation of their rows are called *permuted lower triangular*. In the example that follows, all the arithmetic is exact and we see why $\mathbf{L}_p$ is often lower triangular in hand computations although it is seldom so in machine computations.

The first step is the careful analysis of the diagram $\mathbf{A} \to \cdots \to \mathbf{U}$. Although the elementary row operations that transform **A** to **U** in this diagram are not unique, they can be restricted to row interchanges and the addition of a multiple of one row to a row below it. To guide us through this analysis, consider the following example in which **A** is given by

$$\mathbf{A} = \begin{bmatrix} 2 & 2 & 1 \\ 2 & 3 & -2 \\ 4 & 1 & -2 \end{bmatrix} \tag{2.5.1}$$

Example 2.5.1. Construct the diagram $\mathbf{A}\to \cdots \to\mathbf{U}$ for the matrix **A** given by Eq. 2.5.1 and find the elementary row matrices corresponding to each row operation. Show that the product of the elementary row matrices is a lower triangular matrix **S** such that $\mathbf{SA} = \mathbf{U}$.

Solution. The steps in the row reduction to upper triangular form are straightforward. We clear each column below the diagonal by elementary row operations of Type 3. (No row interchanges are necessary for this particular matrix.) Each step in the following diagram is labeled to facilitate identifying the corresponding elementary row matrix.

$$\mathbf{A} \underset{1}{\to} \begin{bmatrix} 2 & 2 & 1 \\ 0 & 1 & -3 \\ 4 & 1 & -2 \end{bmatrix} \underset{2}{\to} \begin{bmatrix} 2 & 2 & 1 \\ 0 & 1 & -3 \\ 0 & -3 & -4 \end{bmatrix} \underset{3}{\to} \begin{bmatrix} 2 & 2 & 1 \\ 0 & 1 & -3 \\ 0 & 0 & -13 \end{bmatrix} = \mathbf{U}$$

It is easy to verify that

$$\mathbf{E}_1 = \begin{bmatrix} 1 & 0 & 0 \\ -1 & 1 & 0 \\ 0 & 0 & 1 \end{bmatrix} \qquad \mathbf{E}_2 = \begin{bmatrix} 1 & 0 & 0 \\ 0 & 1 & 0 \\ -2 & 0 & 1 \end{bmatrix} \qquad \mathbf{E}_3 = \begin{bmatrix} 1 & 0 & 0 \\ 0 & 1 & 0 \\ 0 & 3 & 1 \end{bmatrix}$$

$$\mathbf{E}_1\mathbf{A} = \begin{bmatrix} 1 & 0 & 0 \\ -1 & 1 & 0 \\ 0 & 0 & 1 \end{bmatrix} \begin{bmatrix} 2 & 2 & 1 \\ 2 & 3 & -2 \\ 4 & 1 & -2 \end{bmatrix} = \begin{bmatrix} 2 & 2 & 1 \\ 0 & 1 & -3 \\ 4 & 1 & -2 \end{bmatrix}$$

$$\mathbf{E}_2(\mathbf{E}_1\mathbf{A}) = \begin{bmatrix} 1 & 0 & 0 \\ 0 & 1 & 0 \\ -2 & 0 & 1 \end{bmatrix} \begin{bmatrix} 2 & 2 & 1 \\ 0 & 1 & -3 \\ 4 & 1 & -2 \end{bmatrix} = \begin{bmatrix} 2 & 2 & 1 \\ 0 & 1 & -3 \\ 0 & -3 & -4 \end{bmatrix}$$

$$\mathbf{E}_3(\mathbf{E}_2\mathbf{E}_1\mathbf{A}) = \begin{bmatrix} 1 & 0 & 0 \\ 0 & 1 & 0 \\ 0 & 3 & 1 \end{bmatrix} \begin{bmatrix} 2 & 2 & 1 \\ 0 & 1 & -3 \\ 0 & -3 & -4 \end{bmatrix} = \begin{bmatrix} 2 & 2 & 1 \\ 0 & 1 & -3 \\ 0 & 0 & -13 \end{bmatrix} = \mathbf{U}$$

It should be clear why each elementary matrix in the example is a lower triangular matrix. Since the product of lower triangular matrices is lower triangular, $\mathbf{S} = \mathbf{E}_3\mathbf{E}_2\mathbf{E}_1$ is lower triangular. Indeed,

$$\mathbf{S} = \mathbf{E}_3\mathbf{E}_2\mathbf{E}_1 = \begin{bmatrix} 1 & 0 & 0 \\ -1 & 1 & 0 \\ -5 & 3 & 1 \end{bmatrix}$$

$$\mathbf{SA} = \begin{bmatrix} 1 & 0 & 0 \\ -1 & 1 & 0 \\ -5 & 3 & 1 \end{bmatrix} \begin{bmatrix} 2 & 2 & 1 \\ 2 & 3 & -2 \\ 4 & 1 & -2 \end{bmatrix} = \begin{bmatrix} 2 & 2 & 1 \\ 0 & 1 & -3 \\ 0 & 0 & -13 \end{bmatrix} = \mathbf{U}$$

The inverse of a lower triangular matrix is also lower triangular. So set $\mathbf{L} = \mathbf{S}^{-1}$, and from $\mathbf{SA} = \mathbf{U}$ it follows that $\mathbf{S} = \mathbf{LU}$. For the matrix $\mathbf{A}$ of the previous example,

$$\mathbf{S}^{-1} = \mathbf{L} = \begin{bmatrix} 1 & 0 & 0 \\ 1 & 1 & 0 \\ 2 & -3 & 1 \end{bmatrix} \qquad \mathbf{LU} = \begin{bmatrix} 1 & 0 & 0 \\ 1 & 1 & 0 \\ 2 & -3 & 1 \end{bmatrix} \begin{bmatrix} 2 & 2 & 1 \\ 0 & 1 & -3 \\ 0 & 0 & -13 \end{bmatrix}$$

$$= \mathbf{A} = \begin{bmatrix} 2 & 2 & 1 \\ 2 & 3 & -2 \\ 4 & 1 & -2 \end{bmatrix}$$

as expected. Except for the need to interchange rows to preserve accuracy or to exchange a zero diagonal entry with a nonzero entry, Example 2.5.1 and the observations that follow it, illustrate the general argument.

If some row interchanges are used in the diagram $\mathbf{A} \to \cdots \to \mathbf{U}$, then $\mathbf{L}$ will not be lower triangular. As previously remarked, it is possible to show that $\mathbf{L}$ can be made lower triangular by a sequence of row interchanges. The next theorem is the formal statement of the "**LU** factorization theorem."

Theorem 2.5.1. *For every matrix* **A** *there is an upper triangular matrix* **U** *and a permuted lower triangular matrix* $\mathbf{L}_p$ *such that*

$$\mathbf{A} = \mathbf{L}_p\mathbf{U} \tag{2.5.2}$$

In general, $\mathbf{L}_p$ is a matrix which can be made lower triangular by row interchanges. That is, there exists a sequence of elementary matrices of Type 1, $\mathbf{P}_1$, $\mathbf{P}_2, \ldots, \mathbf{P}_k$, such that $\mathbf{P}_k\mathbf{P}_{k-1}\ldots\mathbf{P}_1\mathbf{L}_p = \mathbf{L}$, where **L** is a lower triangular matrix. Using this relationship between $\mathbf{L}_p$ and **L** leads to the following alternative form of Theorem 2.5.1.

Corollary 1. *For every matrix* **A**, *there is a permutation of the rows of* **A** *leading to* $\mathbf{A}'$, *an upper triangular matrix* **U**, *and a lower triangular matrix* **L** *such that*

$$\mathbf{A}' = \mathbf{LU} \tag{2.5.3}$$

Proof. Suppose $\mathbf{P}_k\mathbf{P}_{k-1}\ldots\mathbf{P}_1\mathbf{L}_p = \mathbf{L}$. Then set $\mathbf{A}' = \mathbf{P}_k\mathbf{P}_{k-1}\ldots\mathbf{P}_1\mathbf{A}$ and multiply Eq. 2.5.2 by $\mathbf{P}_k\mathbf{P}_{k-1}\ldots\mathbf{P}_1$ to obtain

$$\mathbf{A}' = \mathbf{P}_k\mathbf{P}_{k-1}\ldots\mathbf{P}_1\mathbf{A} = \mathbf{P}_k\mathbf{P}_{k-1}\ldots\mathbf{P}_1\mathbf{L}_p\mathbf{U} = \mathbf{LU}. \blacksquare \tag{2.5.4}$$

The rationale for finding the **LU** factorization of **A** lies in its use in solving the system $\mathbf{Ax} = \mathbf{b}$. Once **L** and **U** are found, the solution of the triangular systems $\mathbf{Ly} = \mathbf{b}$ for **y**, and then $\mathbf{Ux} = \mathbf{y}$ for **x**, offers a solution of $\mathbf{Ax} = \mathbf{b}$. This can easily be seen because $\mathbf{Ax} = (\mathbf{LU})\mathbf{x} = \mathbf{L}(\mathbf{Ux}) = \mathbf{Ly} = \mathbf{b}$. This method of solving $\mathbf{Ax} = \mathbf{b}$ has been extensively investigated and is the method of choice for all but special circumstances. A full discussion of the advantages and limitations of the **LU** factorization technique belongs to the field of numerical analysis.

2.5.1 LU Factorization in MATLAB

MATLAB used the **LU** factorization to compute $\mathbf{A}^{-1}$ and det(**A**) by means of the formulas

$$\mathbf{A}^{-1} = \mathbf{U}^{-1}\mathbf{L}^{-1} \qquad \det(\mathbf{A}) = \det(\mathbf{L})\det(\mathbf{U})$$

To obtain the matrices **L** and **U** from **A**, invoke the "double assignment" notation [L U] = lu(A). Then MATLAB returns L and U. Since the computation of **L** and **U** is done so as to preserve accuracy, **L** is seldom returned as a lower triangular matrix. (See Theorem 2.5.1 and Example 2.5.2.). The file mplu.m given in Appendix B returns the lower triangular matrix **L**, the upper triangular matrix **U**, and a permutation matrix **P** such that $\mathbf{LU} = \mathbf{A}'$ and $\mathbf{PA}' = \mathbf{A}$. (See Eqs. 2.5.3 and 2.3.4 and Problems 2.5.13 and 2.5.14.

Example 2.5.2. Use the matrix of Example 2.5.1 and the assignment [LU] = lu(A) to find the **LU** factorization of **A**.

Solution. At the MATLAB prompt define

```
A =
        [2  2   1
         2  3  -2
         4  1  -2]
```

Then [L U] = lu(A) returns

```
L =                      U =
     0.5  0.6  1.0            4.0  1.0  -2.0
     0.5  1.0  0              0    2.5  -1.0
     1.0  0    0              0    0     2.6
```

Note that **L** is a row permuted lower triangular matrix and that **LU** = **A**. In the notation of this section, **L** is written $\mathbf{L}_p$.

PROBLEMS

PART 1

2.5.1. Find the **LU** factorization of

$$(a)\ \mathbf{A} = \begin{bmatrix} 1 & a \\ 1 & b \end{bmatrix} \qquad (b)\ \mathbf{A} = \begin{bmatrix} 1 & a \\ c & b \end{bmatrix}$$

2.5.2. Find the **LU** factorizations of

$$(a) \begin{bmatrix} 1 & 1 & 1 \\ -1 & 1 & 1 \\ 0 & 0 & -1 \end{bmatrix} \quad (b) \begin{bmatrix} 1 & 1 & 1 \\ 0 & 1 & 1 \\ 0 & 1 & -1 \end{bmatrix} \quad (c) \begin{bmatrix} 1 & 1 & 1 \\ -1 & 1 & 1 \\ 0 & 1 & -1 \end{bmatrix}$$

$$(d) \begin{bmatrix} 1 & 1 & 1 \\ -1 & 1 & 1 \\ 1 & 1 & -1 \end{bmatrix}$$

2.5.3. Show that det(**A**) = det(**L**) det(**U**) for the matrix in Problem 2.5.2 (*d*).

2.5.4. Compute $\mathbf{L}_p\mathbf{U}$ and verify that $\mathbf{A} = \mathbf{L}_p\mathbf{U}$, where

$$\mathbf{A} = \begin{bmatrix} 2 & 2 & 1 \\ 2 & 3 & -2 \\ 4 & 1 & -2 \end{bmatrix} \qquad \mathbf{L}_p = \begin{bmatrix} 0.5 & 0.6 & 1.0 \\ 0.5 & 1.0 & 0 \\ 1.0 & 0 & 0 \end{bmatrix} \qquad \mathbf{U} = \begin{bmatrix} 4.0 & 1.0 & -2.0 \\ 0 & 2.5 & -1.0 \\ 0 & 0 & 2.6 \end{bmatrix}$$

2.5.5. For the matrices **A**, **U** and $\mathbf{L}_p$ in Problem 2.5.4, find $\mathbf{P}_1, \mathbf{P}_2, \ldots, \mathbf{P}_k$ so that $\mathbf{L} = \mathbf{P}_k\mathbf{P}_{k-1}\ldots\mathbf{P}_1\mathbf{L}_p$ is lower triangular. Define $\mathbf{A}' = \mathbf{P}_k\mathbf{P}_{k-1}\ldots\mathbf{P}_1\mathbf{A}$ and find the **LU** factorization of $\mathbf{A}'$.

2.5.6. Use the notation in Problem 2.5.5 to solve $\mathbf{A}'\,\mathbf{x} = \mathbf{b}$ by solving $\mathbf{Ly} = \mathbf{b}$ and $\mathbf{Ux} = \mathbf{y}$ for these **b**:

$$(a) \begin{bmatrix} 1 \\ -1 \\ 0 \end{bmatrix} \quad (b) \begin{bmatrix} 1 \\ 1 \\ 1 \end{bmatrix} \quad (c) \begin{bmatrix} 1 \\ 1 \\ -1 \end{bmatrix} \quad (d) \begin{bmatrix} 1 \\ -1 \\ 1 \end{bmatrix}$$

PART 2

2.5.7. Verify the following factorization of **A**:

$$\mathbf{A} = \begin{bmatrix} 2 & 2 & 1 \\ 2 & 3 & -2 \\ 4 & 1 & -2 \end{bmatrix} = \begin{bmatrix} 1 & 0 & 0 \\ 1 & 1 & 0 \\ 2 & -3 & 1 \end{bmatrix} \begin{bmatrix} 2 & 2 & 1 \\ 0 & 1 & -3 \\ 0 & 0 & -13 \end{bmatrix}$$

$$= \begin{bmatrix} 1 & 0 & 0 \\ 1 & 1 & 0 \\ 2 & -3 & 1 \end{bmatrix} \begin{bmatrix} 2 & 0 & 0 \\ 0 & 1 & 0 \\ 0 & 0 & -13 \end{bmatrix} \begin{bmatrix} 1 & 1 & 0.5 \\ 0 & 1 & -3 \\ 0 & 0 & 1 \end{bmatrix}$$

2.5.8. Use the **LU** factorization theorem to show that the nonsingular matrix **A** can be factored $\mathbf{A} = \mathbf{LDU}$, where **L** and **U** are lower and upper triangular matrices respectively, and **L** and **U** have 1's on their diagonals.

2.5.9. If no partial pivoting is used in the diagram $\mathbf{A} \to \cdots \to \mathbf{U}$, explain why the diagonal of the matrix **L** in the **LU** factorization of **A** is $\{1, 1, \ldots, 1\}$. Moreover, if **A** is symmetric show that $\mathbf{A} = \mathbf{LDL}^{\mathrm{T}}$.

PART 3

2.5.10. Refer to Problem 2.5.9 for hypotheses and notation. Show that the factorization $\mathbf{A} = \mathbf{LDU}$ is unique. (*Hint:* Assume that $\mathbf{A} = \mathbf{L}_1\mathbf{D}_1\mathbf{U}_1$. Then $\mathbf{LDU} = \mathbf{L}_1\mathbf{D}_1\mathbf{U}_1$ implies $\mathbf{L}_1^{-1}\mathbf{LD} = \mathbf{D}_1\mathbf{U}_1\mathbf{U}^{-1}$. But the left-hand side is lower triangular and the right-hand side is upper triangular. Hence both sides are diagonal matrices.) The representation $\mathbf{A} = \mathbf{LDU}$ is called the **LDU** *factorization theorem*.

MATLAB

2.5.11. Use the assignment [L U] = lu(A) to find the **LU** factorization of the matrices in Problem 2.5.2.

2.5.12. Use the assignment [L U] = lu(A) to find the **LU** factorization of the matrix $\mathbf{A}'$ in Problem 2.5.5.

Use [P,L,U,p] = mplu(A) in place of [L U] = lu(A) in the next two problems. (See Appendix B.)

2.5.13. The matrix in Example 2.5.2. Verify that $\mathbf{LU} = \mathbf{PA} = \mathbf{A}'$.

2.5.14. The matrices in Problems 2.5.2 and 2.5.5.

2.6 SPANS, LINEAR INDEPENDENCE AND RANK

2.6.1 Spans and Linear Combinations

Suppose that $\mathbf{u}_1, \mathbf{u}_2, \ldots, \mathbf{u}_k$ belong to $\mathcal{R}^n$. Sums of the form

$$\alpha_1\mathbf{u}_1 + \alpha_2\mathbf{u}_2 + \cdots + \alpha_k\mathbf{u}_k \tag{2.6.1}$$

play a central role in linear algebra. Such sums are called *linear combinations* of $\{\mathbf{u}_1, \mathbf{u}_2, \ldots, \mathbf{u}_k\}$ and the real scalars $\alpha_1, \alpha_2, \ldots, \alpha_k$, are called *weights*. We shall assume without any further remarks that $k \geq 1$. The set of all linear combinations of $\{\mathbf{u}_1, \mathbf{u}_2, \ldots, \mathbf{u}_k\}$, is called the *span* of $\{\mathbf{u}_1, \mathbf{u}_2, \ldots, \mathbf{u}_k\}$. This set is written $span\{\mathbf{u}_1, \mathbf{u}_2, \ldots, \mathbf{u}_k\}$.

Example 2.6.1. The span of

$$\left\{\begin{bmatrix}1\\0\\1\end{bmatrix}, \begin{bmatrix}-1\\2\\1\end{bmatrix}\right\}$$

is the set of linear combinations,

$$\alpha\begin{bmatrix}1\\0\\1\end{bmatrix} + \beta\begin{bmatrix}-1\\2\\1\end{bmatrix} = \begin{bmatrix}\alpha-\beta\\2\beta\\\alpha+\beta\end{bmatrix}$$

There are no restrictions on the weights, so choosing all weights zero is possible. Thus $\mathbf{0} \in \mathcal{R}^n$ belongs to every span of n-tuples. For a given $\mathbf{b}$ and the fixed set of vectors $\{\mathbf{u}_1,\mathbf{u}_2,\ldots,\mathbf{u}_k\}$, we ask whether there exist weights $\alpha_1,\alpha_2,\ldots,\alpha_k$, such that

$$\mathbf{b} = \alpha_1\mathbf{u}_1 + \alpha_2\mathbf{u}_2 + \cdots + \alpha_k\mathbf{u}_k \tag{2.6.2}$$

If such a set of weights exists, then $\mathbf{b} \in span\{\mathbf{u}_1,\mathbf{u}_2,\ldots,\mathbf{u}_k\}$.

Example 2.6.2. Interpret the vector $\mathbf{x} = [x\ y]^{\mathrm{T}}$ as the point P with coordinates (x,y). Show that the span of $\mathbf{x}_0 = [1\ 1]^{\mathrm{T}}$ is the line $x = y$.

Solution. $Span\{\mathbf{x}_0\}$ is the set of all vectors of the form $\alpha\mathbf{x}_0 = [\alpha\ \alpha]^{\mathrm{T}}$. So $x = \alpha = y$. (See Fig. 2.1.)

Example 2.6.3. Show that the span of $\{\mathbf{x}_1,\mathbf{x}_2\}$ is the plane, $x + y - z = 0$, where

$$\mathbf{x}_1 = \begin{bmatrix}1\\0\\1\end{bmatrix} \qquad \mathbf{x}_2 = \begin{bmatrix}-1\\2\\1\end{bmatrix}.$$

Solution. The span of these vectors is given by

$$\alpha\mathbf{x}_1 + \beta\mathbf{x}_2 = \begin{bmatrix}\alpha-\beta\\2\beta\\\alpha+\beta\end{bmatrix}$$

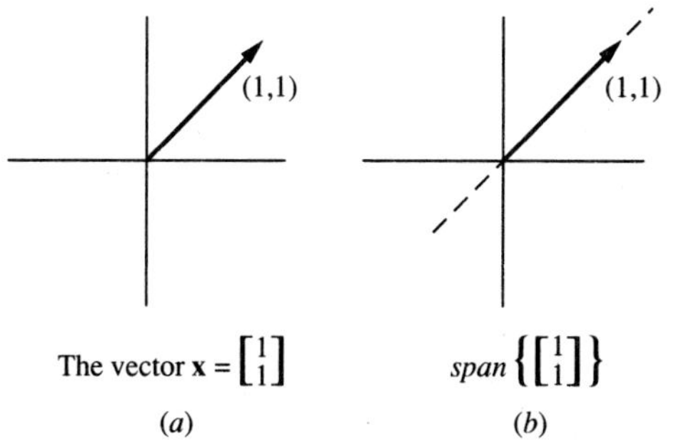

FIGURE 2-1
Illustration of Example 2.6.2.

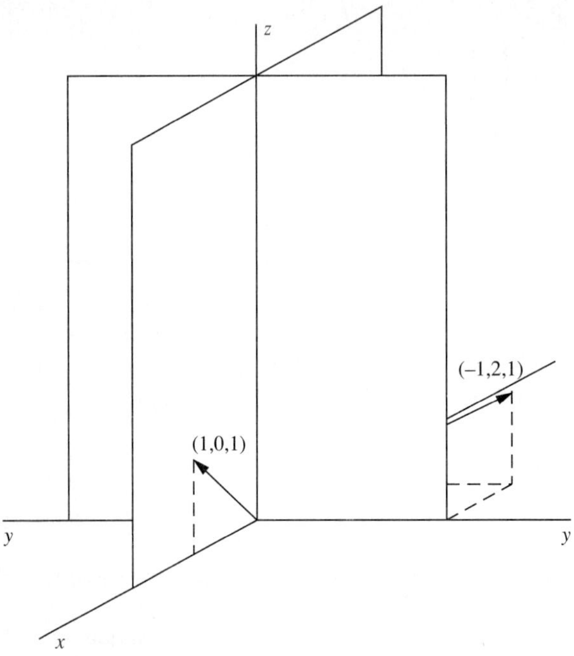

(a)

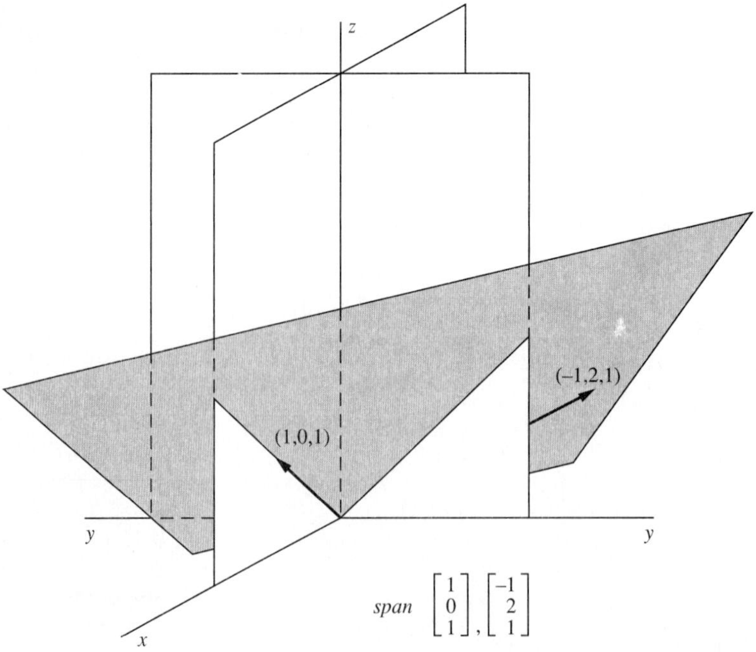

(b)

FIGURE 2-2
(a) Vectors in 3-space; (b) a span in 3-space.

(See Example 2.6.1.) Thus $x = \alpha - \beta, y = 2\beta$, and $z = \alpha + \beta$. Eliminating α and β from these equations yields the equation $x+y-z = 0$. The plane defined by this equation is sketched in Fig. 2.2.

Example 2.6.4. The only vector in $span\{\mathbf{0}\}$ is $\mathbf{0}$ and every n-tuple is in $span\{\mathbf{e}_1, \mathbf{e}_2, \ldots, \mathbf{e}_n\}$.

2.6.2 Linear Independence and Dependence

The special case in which $\mathbf{b} = \mathbf{0}$ in Eq. 2.6.2 is of particular importance. Clearly, $\mathbf{0}$ is always in the span of any set of vectors; when all the weights are zero, so is the sum. It is useful to avoid this triviality by requiring that at least one of the weights be nonzero; then, if $\mathbf{0}$ is a nontrivial combination of the set $\{\mathbf{u}_1, \mathbf{u}_2, \ldots, \mathbf{u}_k\}$, we say that $\{\mathbf{u}_1, \mathbf{u}_2, \ldots, \mathbf{u}_k\}$ is *linearly dependent*. The specific equation

$$\mathbf{0} = \alpha_1\mathbf{u}_1 + \alpha_2\mathbf{u}_2 + \cdots + \alpha_k\mathbf{u}_k \tag{2.6.3}$$

exhibiting $\mathbf{0}$ as a nontrivial combination of $\mathbf{u}_1, \mathbf{u}_2, \ldots, \mathbf{u}_k$ is called a *dependency relationship,* provided at least one of the weights in Eq. 2.6.3 is nonzero. If there is no set of weights for which Eq. 2.6.3 holds, other than the trivial case, $\alpha_1 = \alpha_2 = \cdots = \alpha_k = 0$, then $\{\mathbf{u}_1, \mathbf{u}_2, \ldots, \mathbf{u}_k\}$ is said to be *linearly independent*. Thus every set $\{\mathbf{u}_1, \mathbf{u}_2, \ldots, \mathbf{u}_k\}$ is either linearly independent or dependent. The next theorem is an alternative and somewhat more intuitively appealing way of expressing linear dependence.

Theorem 2.6.1. *The set $\mathcal{S} = \{\mathbf{u}_1, \mathbf{u}_2, \ldots, \mathbf{u}_k\}$ is linearly dependent if and only if some vector in $\mathcal{S}$ is a linear combination of the other vectors in $\mathcal{S}$.*

Proof. If $\mathcal{S}$ is linearly dependent then the dependency relationship in Eq. 2.6.3 holds for some set of weights not all zero. Suppose, to be specific, that $\alpha_1 \neq 0$. Then Eq. 2.6.3 implies

$$\mathbf{u}_1 = (-\alpha_2/\alpha_1)\mathbf{u}_2 + (-\alpha_k/\alpha_1)\mathbf{u}_2 + \cdots + (-\alpha_k/\alpha_1)\mathbf{u}_k \tag{2.6.4}$$

Thus $\mathbf{u}_1 \in span\{\mathbf{u}_2, \mathbf{u}_3, \ldots, \mathbf{u}_k\}$. For the converse see Problem 2.6.13. ■

Here are three examples to clarify these definitions. The first shows that a set containing the zero vector is dependent; the second shows that sets in which one vector is a multiple of another are also dependent.

Example 2.6.5. The set $\{\mathbf{u}_1 = \mathbf{0}, \mathbf{u}_2, \ldots, \mathbf{u}_k\}$ is linearly dependent.

Solution. The given set is linearly dependent because there exists a nontrivial dependency relationship: $\mathbf{0} = 1\mathbf{u}_1 + 0\mathbf{u}_2 + \cdots + 0\mathbf{u}_k$.

Example 2.6.6. Show that the set $\{\mathbf{u}_1, \mathbf{u}_2 = a\mathbf{u}_1, \ldots, \mathbf{u}_k\}$ is linearly dependent by finding a dependency relationship.

Solution. The dependency relationship: $\mathbf{0} = a\mathbf{u}_1 - \mathbf{u}_2$. That is, the weights are $a_1 = a$, $a_2 = -1$, $a_3 = \cdots = a_k = 0$.

Example 2.6.7. Show that the set $\mathcal{S} = \{\mathbf{e}_1, \mathbf{e}_2, \ldots, \mathbf{e}_k\}$ is linearly independent.

Solution. It should be obvious that none of the vectors in $\mathcal{S}$ is a linear combination of the other vectors in $\mathcal{S}$.

Suppose $\mathbf{U} = [\mathbf{u}_1 \quad \mathbf{u}_2 \quad \mathbf{u}_k]$ and $\mathbf{a} = [\alpha_1 \quad \alpha_2 \quad \alpha_k]^{\mathrm{T}}$. Then

$$\mathbf{Ua} = \alpha_1\mathbf{u}_1 + \alpha_2\mathbf{u}_2 + \cdots + \alpha_k\mathbf{u}_k = \mathbf{b} \tag{2.6.5}$$

Thus $\mathbf{b} \in span\{\mathbf{u}_1, \mathbf{u}_2, \ldots, \mathbf{u}_k\}$ if and only if there is a vector of weights, $\mathbf{a}$, such that $\mathbf{Ua} = \mathbf{b}$. If $\mathbf{b} = \mathbf{0}$, Eq. 2.6.5 implies that $\mathbf{Ua} = \mathbf{0}$ has a nontrivial solution if and only if there exist weights, not all zero, for which

$$\alpha_1\mathbf{u}_1 + \alpha_2\mathbf{u}_2 + \cdots + \alpha_k\mathbf{u}_k = \mathbf{0} \tag{2.6.6}$$

For example, if the vectors $\mathbf{e}_1$, $\mathbf{e}_2$, and $\mathbf{e}_3$ are 4-tuples then, as a special case of Eq. 2.6.6, $\{\mathbf{e}_1, \mathbf{e}_1 + \mathbf{e}_2, \mathbf{e}_1 + \mathbf{e}_2 + \mathbf{e}_3\}$ is linearly independent since

$$\mathbf{Ua} = \begin{bmatrix} 1 & 1 & 1 \\ 0 & 1 & 1 \\ 0 & 0 & 1 \\ 0 & 0 & 0 \end{bmatrix} \mathbf{a} = \mathbf{0}$$

has $\mathbf{a} = \mathbf{0}$ as the only solution of this system. The solution to the problem posed in Example 2.6.7 can be handled similarly. These remarks can be put in the form of a theorem.

Theorem 2.6.2. *The columns of* $\mathbf{A}$ *are linearly independent if and only if the homogeneous system* $\mathbf{Ax} = \mathbf{0}$ *has only the trivial solution.*

Example 2.6.8. Use Theorem 2.6.2 to determine whether the following sets of vectors are linearly dependent. If linearly dependent, find the weights in the dependency relationship:

(*a*) $\left\{ \begin{bmatrix} 1 \\ 0 \\ -1 \end{bmatrix}, \begin{bmatrix} 1 \\ 1 \\ -1 \end{bmatrix} \right\}$ (*b*) $\left\{ \begin{bmatrix} 1 \\ 0 \\ -1 \end{bmatrix}, \begin{bmatrix} 1 \\ 1 \\ -1 \end{bmatrix}, \begin{bmatrix} 0 \\ -1 \\ 0 \end{bmatrix} \right\}$

Solution. (*a*) The relevant systems are

$$\begin{bmatrix} 1 & 1 \\ 0 & 1 \\ -1 & -1 \end{bmatrix} \mathbf{x} = \mathbf{0} \quad \text{and its row equivalent form} \begin{bmatrix} 1 & 0 \\ 0 & 1 \\ 0 & 0 \end{bmatrix} \mathbf{x} = \mathbf{0}$$

Since the latter system, evidently, has only the trivial solution, the vectors in Part (*a*) are linearly independent. For Part (*b*), bypass the step of writing the system down and proceed directly with the conversion of the coefficient matrix to reduced row echelon form.

$$\mathbf{A} = \begin{bmatrix} 1 & 1 & 0 \\ 0 & 1 & -1 \\ -1 & -1 & 0 \end{bmatrix} \rightarrow \begin{bmatrix} 1 & 1 & 0 \\ 0 & 1 & -1 \\ 0 & 0 & 0 \end{bmatrix} \rightarrow \begin{bmatrix} 1 & 0 & 1 \\ 0 & 1 & -1 \\ 0 & 0 & 0 \end{bmatrix} = \mathbf{A}_r$$

A solution of the system $\mathbf{A}_r\mathbf{x} = \mathbf{0}$ can be found by inspection. Specifically, $x_1 = 1$, $x_2 = -1$, $x_3 = -1$ and a dependency relationship is

$$\begin{bmatrix} 1 \\ 0 \\ -1 \end{bmatrix} + (-1)\begin{bmatrix} 1 \\ 1 \\ -1 \end{bmatrix} + (-1)\begin{bmatrix} 0 \\ -1 \\ 0 \end{bmatrix} = 0$$

2.6.3 Rank

In view of the need to solve homogeneous systems to determine whether a set of vectors is linearly dependent, the system $\mathbf{Ax} = \mathbf{0}$ will be analyzed more deeply. (The complete theory is presented in Section 3.5.) To do this conveniently, we need the concept of rank. The *rank* of $\mathbf{A}$, written rank($\mathbf{A}$), is the number of nonzero rows in the row echelon form of $\mathbf{A}$. Since the reduced row echelon form is unique, the rank is well defined. Note that only the zero matrix has rank zero. Every other matrix has rank at least 1 and no more than the number of its rows. Since each nonzero row in rref($\mathbf{A}$) defines a leading one and therefore a leading column, the rank is also no greater than the number of columns of $\mathbf{A}$.

Theorem 2.6.3. *The homogeneous system* $\mathbf{Ax} = \mathbf{0}$ *has nontrivial solutions if and only if the rank of* $\mathbf{A}$ *is less than the number of columns of* $\mathbf{A}$.

Proof. Suppose $\mathbf{A}$ is $m \times n$ and rank($\mathbf{A}$) $= r < n$. The proof is most easily visualized by assuming that $\mathbf{A}_r$, the rref of $\mathbf{A}$, has the representation

$$\mathbf{A}_r = \left[\begin{array}{cccc|ccc} 1 & 0 & \cdots & 0 & 0 & * & \cdots & * \\ 0 & 1 & \cdots & 0 & 0 & * & \cdots & * \\ \vdots & \vdots & & \vdots & \vdots & \vdots & & \vdots \\ 0 & 0 & \cdots & 0 & 1 & * & \cdots & * \\ \hline 0 & 0 & \cdots & 0 & 0 & 0 & \cdots & 0 \\ \vdots & \vdots & & \vdots & \vdots & \vdots & & \vdots \\ 0 & 0 & \cdots & 0 & 0 & 0 & \cdots & 0 \end{array}\right] = \left[\begin{array}{c|c} \mathbf{I}_r & \mathbf{C} \\ \hline \mathbf{O} & \mathbf{O} \end{array}\right]$$

This is no loss in generality; see Subsection 2.3.2. Note that rank($\mathbf{A}$) is r and there are at least $r + 1$ columns. Hence $\mathbf{C}$ has at least one column and

$$\mathbf{A}_r\mathbf{x} = \left[\begin{array}{c|c} \mathbf{I}_r & \mathbf{C} \\ \hline \mathbf{O} & \mathbf{O} \end{array}\right]\left[\begin{array}{c} \mathbf{z} \\ \hline \mathbf{y} \end{array}\right] = 0$$

has a nontrivial solution

$$\mathbf{x} = \left[\begin{array}{c} -\mathbf{Cy} \\ \hline \mathbf{y} \end{array}\right] \tag{2.6.7}$$

for every choice of $\mathbf{y} \neq 0$. (See Problem 2.6.16.)

On the other hand, if $r = \text{rank}(\mathbf{A}) = n$, then $\mathbf{A}_r\mathbf{x} = \mathbf{0}$ takes the simpler partitioned form,

$$\mathbf{A}_r\mathbf{x} = \begin{bmatrix} \mathbf{I}_r \\ \text{---} \\ \mathbf{O} \end{bmatrix} \mathbf{x} = \mathbf{0}$$

Clearly, only $\mathbf{x} = \mathbf{0}$ can solve the system $\mathbf{A}_r\mathbf{x} = \mathbf{0}$. ■

Theorem 2.6.3 can be translated into a theorem on linear independence as illustrated by the following corollaries.

Corollary 1. *The set* $\{\mathbf{a}_1, \mathbf{a}_2, \ldots, \mathbf{a}_k\}$ *is linearly dependent if and only if the rank of* $\mathbf{A} = [\mathbf{a}_1 \quad \mathbf{a}_2 \quad \mathbf{a}_k]$ *is less than* k.

Proof. By Theorem 2.6.2, the given set is linearly dependent if $\mathbf{Ax} = \mathbf{0}$ has nontrivial solutions. By Theorem 2.6.3, this is the case if and only if rank($\mathbf{A}$) is less than the number of columns of $\mathbf{A}$. ■

Corollary 2. *The matrix* $\mathbf{A}$ *is singular if and only if its set of columns (or rows) is a linearly dependent set.*

Proof. A singular matrix has at least one zero row in its reduced row echelon form. Hence the rank of a singular matrix is less than the number of its columns. By Corollary 1, the columns form a linearly dependent set. Since $\mathbf{A}^{\mathrm{T}}$ is also singular, the same conclusion holds for the rows of $\mathbf{A}$.

Conversely, if either the rows or columns of $\mathbf{A}$ are linearly dependent sets then Corollary 1 implies that $\mathbf{A}$ is singular. ■

Corollary 3. *Suppose* $\mathcal{S} = \{\mathbf{a}_1, \mathbf{a}_2, \ldots, \mathbf{a}_k\}$ *is a set of* k m*-tuples. Then* $\mathcal{S}$ *is linearly dependent if* $k > m$.

Proof. Since the rank of a matrix cannot exceed the number of its rows, the hypothesis of this corollary guarantees that $\mathbf{A} = [\mathbf{a}_1 \quad \mathbf{a}_2 \quad \mathbf{a}_k]$ has rank less than k. Hence, by Corollary 1, $\mathcal{S}$ is linearly dependent. ■

We remark in passing that some authors use the term *row rank* for what we have called rank.

PROBLEMS

PART 1

2.6.1. Which of the following sets are linearly independent? For those that are linearly dependent, determine a dependency relationship.

(*a*) $\left\{\begin{bmatrix}1\\0\\1\end{bmatrix}, \begin{bmatrix}1\\1\\-1\end{bmatrix}, \begin{bmatrix}-1\\1\\-3\end{bmatrix}\right\}$ (*b*) $\left\{\begin{bmatrix}1\\0\\0\end{bmatrix}, \begin{bmatrix}1\\1\\0\end{bmatrix}, \begin{bmatrix}1\\1\\1\end{bmatrix}\right\}$ (*c*) $\left\{\begin{bmatrix}1\\0\\1\end{bmatrix}, \begin{bmatrix}1\\1\\-1\end{bmatrix}, \begin{bmatrix}1\\1\\3\end{bmatrix}\right\}$

2.6.2. Repeat Problem 2.6.1 for the sets:

$$(a)\ \left\{\begin{bmatrix}2\\0\\1\end{bmatrix},\begin{bmatrix}4\\-2\\3\end{bmatrix},\begin{bmatrix}1\\-1\\1\end{bmatrix}\right\}\quad (b)\ \left\{\begin{bmatrix}2\\0\\1\end{bmatrix},\begin{bmatrix}1\\1\\0\end{bmatrix},\begin{bmatrix}0\\0\\1\end{bmatrix},\begin{bmatrix}1\\-1\\1\end{bmatrix}\right\}\quad (c)\ \left\{\begin{bmatrix}1\\1\\3\end{bmatrix},\begin{bmatrix}-1\\0\\-2\end{bmatrix},\begin{bmatrix}1\\2\\4\end{bmatrix}\right\}$$

2.6.3. Repeat Problem 2.6.1 for the sets:

$$(a)\ \left\{\begin{bmatrix}1\\1\\0\\1\end{bmatrix},\begin{bmatrix}-1\\2\\0\\0\end{bmatrix},\begin{bmatrix}0\\0\\1\\0\end{bmatrix},\begin{bmatrix}1\\-1\\-1\\1\end{bmatrix}\right\}\quad (b)\ \left\{\begin{bmatrix}-1\\0\\0\\1\end{bmatrix},\begin{bmatrix}2\\-1\\1\\1\end{bmatrix},\begin{bmatrix}0\\-1\\1\\3\end{bmatrix}\right\}$$

$$(c)\ \left\{\begin{bmatrix}1\\0\\1\\1\end{bmatrix},\begin{bmatrix}0\\2\\1\\0\end{bmatrix},\begin{bmatrix}5\\2\\0\\-3\end{bmatrix},\begin{bmatrix}1\\-1\\1\\0\end{bmatrix}\right\}$$

2.6.4. Find an integer k so that the following set is linearly dependent:

$$\left\{\begin{bmatrix}k\\-1\\1\end{bmatrix},\begin{bmatrix}1\\k\\-1\end{bmatrix},\begin{bmatrix}-1\\1\\k\end{bmatrix}\right\}$$

2.6.5. Find a dependency relationship among the columns of **A**:

$$\mathbf{A}=\begin{bmatrix}1&1&-1&1\\1&0&1&2\\2&1&0&3\\-1&1&0&0\end{bmatrix}$$

2.6.6. Find a dependency relationship among the rows of the matrices of Problem 2.6.5.

2.6.7. Find a dependency relationship among the columns of

$$\mathbf{B}=\begin{bmatrix}1&1&1&-1\\2&1&0&1\\3&2&1&0\\0&-1&1&0\end{bmatrix}$$

(*Note:* The columns of **B** are obtained from the columns of **A** in Problem 2.6.5 by a permutation.)

2.6.8. Which of the following sets are linearly independent?

$$(a)\ \left\{\begin{bmatrix}1\\0\\*\\*\\0\\*\end{bmatrix},\begin{bmatrix}0\\1\\*\\*\\0\\*\end{bmatrix},\begin{bmatrix}0\\0\\*\\*\\1\\*\end{bmatrix}\right\}\quad (b)\ \left\{\begin{bmatrix}1\\0\\0\\0\\*\\*\end{bmatrix},\begin{bmatrix}0\\1\\0\\0\\*\\*\end{bmatrix},\begin{bmatrix}1\\2\\1\\0\\*\\*\end{bmatrix},\begin{bmatrix}1\\2\\1\\1\\*\\*\end{bmatrix}\right\}\quad (c)\ \left\{\begin{bmatrix}*\\0\\0\\1\\*\\0\end{bmatrix},\begin{bmatrix}*\\1\\0\\0\\*\\0\end{bmatrix},\begin{bmatrix}*\\2\\1\\0\\*\\2\end{bmatrix},\begin{bmatrix}*\\1\\1\\0\\*\\0\end{bmatrix}\right\}$$

$$(d)\ \left\{\begin{bmatrix}1\\0\\0\end{bmatrix},\begin{bmatrix}*\\1\\0\end{bmatrix},\begin{bmatrix}*\\*\\1\end{bmatrix}\right\}\quad (e)\ \left\{\begin{bmatrix}0\\1\\1\end{bmatrix},\begin{bmatrix}1\\1\\0\end{bmatrix},\begin{bmatrix}1\\0\\1\end{bmatrix}\right\}$$

PART 2

2.6.9. If $\{\mathbf{x}_1, \mathbf{x}_2, \mathbf{x}_3, \mathbf{x}_4\}$ is linearly independent, so is $\{\mathbf{x}_1, \mathbf{x}_2, \mathbf{x}_3\}$. Why? Generalize to sets with k vectors.

2.6.10. If $\{\mathbf{x}_1, \mathbf{x}_2, \mathbf{x}_3\}$ is linearly dependent, so is $\{\mathbf{x}_1, \mathbf{x}_2, \mathbf{x}_3, \mathbf{x}_4\}$ for any $\mathbf{x}_4$. Why? Generalize to sets with k vectors.

2.6.11. Prove that $\{\mathbf{x}_1\}$ is linearly independent if and only if $\mathbf{x}_1 \neq \mathbf{0}$.

2.6.12. If $\{\mathbf{x}_1, \mathbf{x}_2, \ldots, \mathbf{x}_k\}$ is linearly independent and $k > 1$, show that none of the vectors in this set is a linear combination of the others.

2.6.13. If $\mathbf{x}_0$ is a linear combination of $\{\mathbf{x}_1, \mathbf{x}_2, \ldots, \mathbf{x}_k\}$, show that the set $\{\mathbf{x}_0, \mathbf{x}_1, \mathbf{x}_2, \ldots, \mathbf{x}_k\}$ is linearly dependent.

2.6.14. Given the linearly dependent set $\{\mathbf{x}_1, \mathbf{x}_2, \ldots, \mathbf{x}_k\}$ in which no vector is $\mathbf{0}$ and $k > 1$. Suppose the dependency relationship is

$$\mathbf{0} = a_1\mathbf{x}_1 + a_2\mathbf{x}_2 + \cdots + a_k\mathbf{x}_k.$$

Show that at least two weights are nonzero.

2.6.15. If $\{\mathbf{x}_1, \mathbf{x}_2, \mathbf{x}_3, \mathbf{x}_4\}$ is linearly independent and $\mathbf{S}$ is nonsingular, prove that $\{\mathbf{S}\mathbf{x}_1, \mathbf{S}\mathbf{x}_2, \mathbf{S}\mathbf{x}_3, \mathbf{S}\mathbf{x}_4\}$ is linearly independent. Explain the necessity of the hypothesis that $\mathbf{S}$ is nonsingular.

2.6.16. Show that

$$\mathbf{x} = \begin{bmatrix} -\mathbf{C}\mathbf{y} \\ \hline \mathbf{y} \end{bmatrix} \quad \text{is a nontrivial solution of} \quad \left[\begin{array}{c|c} \mathbf{I}_r & \mathbf{C} \\ \hline \mathbf{O} & \mathbf{O} \end{array}\right] \mathbf{x} = \mathbf{0}$$

for every choice of $\mathbf{y} \neq \mathbf{0}$.

2.6.17. If $\{\mathbf{x}_1, \mathbf{x}_2\}$ is linearly dependent, show that either $\mathbf{x}_1 = \alpha\mathbf{x}_2$ or $\mathbf{x}_2 = \alpha\mathbf{x}_1$ for some scalar α.

PART 3

2.6.18. Suppose $\{\mathbf{x}_1, \mathbf{x}_2, \ldots, \mathbf{x}_n\}$ is an arbitrary set of n-tuples. Let $\mathbf{S}$ be singular. Show that $\{\mathbf{S}\mathbf{x}_1, \mathbf{S}\mathbf{x}_2, \ldots, \mathbf{S}\mathbf{x}_n\}$ is linearly dependent.

2.6.19. Suppose $\{\mathbf{x}_1, \mathbf{x}_2, \ldots, \mathbf{x}_k\}$ is an arbitrary set of n-tuples. Let $\mathbf{S}$ be a square matrix of size n and rank $r < n$. Show that $\{\mathbf{S}\mathbf{x}_1, \mathbf{S}\mathbf{x}_2, \ldots, \mathbf{S}\mathbf{x}_k\}$ is linearly dependent if $k > r$.

2.7 RANK: A SECOND LOOK

As we have seen in Section 2.6, the number of nonzero rows in the reduced row echelon form is a well-defined parameter of a matrix $\mathbf{A}$, called its rank. It is important to recall that if $\mathbf{A}$ and $\mathbf{B}$ are row equivalent, then they have the same rank because they have the same reduced row echelon forms.

Example 2.7.1. Justify the following assertions:

(*a*) If $\mathbf{A}_n$ nonsingular, then $\text{rank}(\mathbf{A}) = n$.
(*b*) $\text{rank}(\mathbf{J}_n) = 1$.
(*c*) If $\mathbf{b} \neq \mathbf{0}$ then $\text{rank}(\mathbf{b}) = 1$.
(*d*) If $\mathbf{A}_{m\times n}$ has at least $m - r$ zero rows, then $\text{rank}(\mathbf{A}) \leq r$.

Solution. (*a*) If $\mathbf{A}$ is nonsingular its reduced row echelon form is the identity and hence $\text{rank}(\mathbf{A}_n) = n$. (*b*) The matrix $\mathbf{J}_n$ is a square matrix of size n each of whose entries is 1. Hence the row echelon form of $\mathbf{J}_n$ has first row $\mathbf{1}^{\mathrm{T}}$, and all other rows $\mathbf{0}^{\mathrm{T}}$. Thus $\text{rank}(\mathbf{J}_n) = 1$. (*c*) If $\mathbf{b} \neq \mathbf{0}$, then $\mathbf{b}_r = \mathbf{e}_1$ and $\text{rank}(\mathbf{b}) = 1$. (Why?) If $\mathbf{b} = \mathbf{0}$, $\text{rank}(\mathbf{b}) = 0$. (*d*) The rref of $\mathbf{A}$ must also have at least $m - r$ rows of zeros and therefore at most r nonzero rows. Hence $\text{rank}(\mathbf{A}) \leq r$.

Theorem 2.7.1. *If* $\mathbf{A}$ *has size* $m \times n$*, then* $\text{rank}(\mathbf{A}) \leq m$ *and* $\text{rank}(\mathbf{A}) \leq n$.

Proof. See Section 2.6. ■

Theorem 2.7.2. *For every pair of conformable matrices* $\mathbf{A}$ *and* $\mathbf{B}$,

$$\text{rank}(\mathbf{AB}) \leq \text{rank}(\mathbf{A}) \tag{2.7.1}$$

Proof. Suppose $\mathbf{A}$ is $m \times n$ with rank r. Let $\mathbf{A}_r$ be the rref of $\mathbf{A}$. Since $\mathbf{A}$ is row equivalent to $\mathbf{A}_r$, there exists a nonsingular $\mathbf{S}$ such that $\mathbf{SA} = \mathbf{A}_r$. Hence $\mathbf{SAB} = \mathbf{A}_r\mathbf{B}$ and therefore $\mathbf{AB}$ is row equivalent to $\mathbf{A}_r\mathbf{B}$. Thus $\text{rank}(\mathbf{AB}) = \text{rank}(\mathbf{A}_r\mathbf{B})$, so it suffices to determine $\text{rank}(\mathbf{A}_r\mathbf{B})$. If the ith row of $\mathbf{A}_r$ is a zero row, then so is the ith row of $\mathbf{A}_r\mathbf{B}$. Since $\text{rank}(\mathbf{A}) = r$ and $\mathbf{A}$ is $m \times n$, $\mathbf{A}_r$ has exactly $m - r$ zero rows. Thus $\mathbf{A}_r\mathbf{B}$ has at least $m - r$ zero rows and therefore its rank is at most r. Hence from this and from Example 2.7.1(*d*), it follows that $\text{rank}(\mathbf{AB}) = \text{rank}(\mathbf{A}_r\mathbf{B}) \leq r = \text{rank}(\mathbf{A})$. ■

Theorem 2.7.3. *If* $\mathbf{B}$ *is nonsingular, then*

$$\text{rank}(\mathbf{BA}) = \text{rank}(\mathbf{A}) \quad \text{and} \quad \text{rank}(\mathbf{AB}) = \text{rank}(\mathbf{A}) \tag{2.7.2}$$

Proof. Since $\mathbf{B}$ is nonsingular $\mathbf{BA}$ is row equivalent to $\mathbf{A}$, and row equivalent matrices have the same rank. Hence the first equality in Eq. 2.7.2 holds. However, the second equality cannot be proved so easily because $\mathbf{AB}$ and $\mathbf{A}$ are not necessarily row equivalent. For example, $\mathbf{A}$ and $\mathbf{AB}$ are not row equivalent when $\mathbf{A}$ and $\mathbf{B}$ are given as follows:

$$\mathbf{A} = \begin{bmatrix} 1 & 0 \\ 0 & 0 \end{bmatrix} \qquad \mathbf{B} = \begin{bmatrix} 0 & 1 \\ 1 & 0 \end{bmatrix} \qquad \mathbf{AB} = \begin{bmatrix} 1 & 0 \\ 0 & 0 \end{bmatrix}\begin{bmatrix} 0 & 1 \\ 1 & 0 \end{bmatrix} = \begin{bmatrix} 0 & 1 \\ 0 & 0 \end{bmatrix}$$

To complete the proof of Theorem 2.7.3, we resort to a clever trick. We know $\text{rank}(\mathbf{ABB}^{-1}) = \text{rank}(\mathbf{A})$. However, Theorem 2.7.2 implies the inequalities, $\text{rank}(\mathbf{ABB}^{-1}) \leq \text{rank}(\mathbf{AB}) \leq \text{rank}(\mathbf{A})$. Thus

$$\text{rank}(\mathbf{A}) = \text{rank}(\mathbf{ABB}^{-1}) \leq \text{rank}(\mathbf{AB}) \leq \text{rank}(\mathbf{A}),$$

so the inequalities are equalities, and therefore $\text{rank}(\mathbf{AB}) = \text{rank}(\mathbf{A})$. ■

Theorem 2.7.3 shows that $\text{rank}(\mathbf{AB}) < \text{rank}(\mathbf{A})$ implies $\mathbf{B}$ is singular. However, the converse is false; that is, $\text{rank}(\mathbf{AB}) = \text{rank}(\mathbf{A})$ can occur even though $\mathbf{B}$ is singular. The most that can be said is that for arbitrary $\mathbf{A}$ and $\mathbf{B}$, $\text{rank}(\mathbf{AB}) \leq \text{rank}(\mathbf{A})$. Here are two illustrations.

Example 2.7.2. Determine the ranks of $\mathbf{A}$ and $\mathbf{A}^2$ for

$$\mathbf{A} = \begin{bmatrix} 1 & 0 \\ 0 & 0 \end{bmatrix}$$

Solution. Clearly rank($\mathbf{A}$) = 1. Since $\mathbf{A}^2 = \mathbf{A}$ and rank($\mathbf{A}^2$) = 1, we find rank($\mathbf{AA}$) = rank($\mathbf{A}$) = 1 in spite of the fact that $\mathbf{A}$ is singular.

Example 2.7.3. Compute the ranks of $\mathbf{A}$, $\mathbf{A}^2$, $\mathbf{A}^3$ and $\mathbf{A}^4$, where

$$\mathbf{A} = \begin{bmatrix} 0 & 1 & 0 & 0 \\ 0 & 0 & 1 & 0 \\ 0 & 0 & 0 & 1 \\ 0 & 0 & 0 & 0 \end{bmatrix}$$

Solution. Here are the powers of $\mathbf{A}$:

$$\mathbf{A} = \begin{bmatrix} 0 & 1 & 0 & 0 \\ 0 & 0 & 1 & 0 \\ 0 & 0 & 0 & 1 \\ 0 & 0 & 0 & 0 \end{bmatrix} \qquad \mathbf{A}^2 = \begin{bmatrix} 0 & 0 & 1 & 0 \\ 0 & 0 & 0 & 1 \\ 0 & 0 & 0 & 0 \\ 0 & 0 & 0 & 0 \end{bmatrix}$$

$$\mathbf{A}^3 = \begin{bmatrix} 0 & 0 & 0 & 1 \\ 0 & 0 & 0 & 0 \\ 0 & 0 & 0 & 0 \\ 0 & 0 & 0 & 0 \end{bmatrix} \qquad \mathbf{A}^4 = \begin{bmatrix} 0 & 0 & 0 & 0 \\ 0 & 0 & 0 & 0 \\ 0 & 0 & 0 & 0 \\ 0 & 0 & 0 & 0 \end{bmatrix}$$

Since each of the powers of $\mathbf{A}$ are in reduced row echelon form, we can read the ranks directly from the matrices; rank($\mathbf{A}$) = 3, rank($\mathbf{A}^2$) = 2, rank($\mathbf{A}^3$) = 1, and rank($\mathbf{A}^4$) = 0.

It is not obvious that there is a relationship between the ranks of $\mathbf{A}$ and $\mathbf{A}^{\mathrm{T}}$ unless $\mathbf{A}$ is nonsingular, in which case rank($\mathbf{A}$) = rank($\mathbf{A}^{\mathrm{T}}$) = n, because nonsingular matrices have rank equal to their size. However, if $\mathbf{A}$ is in rref, the rank of its transpose is obvious. For example,

$$\operatorname{rank}\begin{bmatrix} 1 & -1 & 0 & 3 & 0 & 2 \\ 0 & 0 & 1 & 2 & 0 & 0 \\ 0 & 0 & 0 & 0 & 1 & -5 \\ 0 & 0 & 0 & 0 & 0 & 0 \end{bmatrix}^{\mathrm{T}} = 3 = \operatorname{rank}\begin{bmatrix} 1 & 0 & 0 & 0 \\ -1 & 0 & 0 & 0 \\ 0 & 1 & 0 & 0 \\ 3 & 2 & 0 & 0 \\ 0 & 0 & 1 & 0 \\ 2 & 0 & -5 & 0 \end{bmatrix}$$

This is true in general.

$$\operatorname{rank}(\mathbf{A}_r) = \operatorname{rank}(\mathbf{A}_r)^{\mathrm{T}} \tag{2.7.3}$$

The proof of Eq. 2.7.3 is left for Problem 2.7.17. In fact a more general theorem is true.

Theorem 2.7.4. rank($\mathbf{A}$) = rank($\mathbf{A}^{\mathrm{T}}$)

Proof. The proof consists of establishing the chain of equalities

$$\text{rank}(\mathbf{A}) = \text{rank}(\mathbf{A}_r) = \text{rank}\left(\mathbf{A}_r\right)^{\mathrm{T}} = \text{rank}(\mathbf{A}^{\mathrm{T}}) \qquad (2.7.4)$$

The first equality is simply the statement that two row equivalent matrices have the same rank. The second equality is Eq. 2.7.3. To prove the third equality consider $\mathbf{SA} = \mathbf{A}_r$ Then $\mathbf{A}^{\mathrm{T}}\mathbf{S}^{\mathrm{T}} = (\mathbf{A}_r)^{\mathrm{T}}$ and hence $\mathbf{A}^{\mathrm{T}} = (\mathbf{A}_r)^{\mathrm{T}}\mathbf{S}^{-\mathrm{T}}$. Thus

$$\text{rank}(\mathbf{A}^{\mathrm{T}}) = \text{rank}\left((\mathbf{A}_r)^{\mathrm{T}}\mathbf{S}^{-\mathrm{T}}\right) = \text{rank}(\mathbf{A}_r)^{\mathrm{T}}$$

by Theorem 2.7.3. ■

Many writers define the number of nonzero rows in the rref of **A** as the row rank of **A**. Then the column rank of **A** is defined (essentially) as the row rank of $\mathbf{A}^{\mathrm{T}}$. However, because of Theorem 2.7.4, it is unnecessary to distinguish between row and column rank, and this is the position taken in this text.

Theorem 2.7.5. *For every* **A** *and* **B** *that are conformable, we have*

$$\text{rank}(\mathbf{AB}) \le \text{rank}(\mathbf{B})$$

Proof. First note that $\text{rank}(\mathbf{AB}) = \text{rank}\left((\mathbf{AB})\right)^{\mathrm{T}}$ by Theorem 2.7.4. But

$$\text{rank}\left((\mathbf{AB})^{\mathrm{T}}\right) = \text{rank}(\mathbf{B}^{\mathrm{T}}\mathbf{A}^{\mathrm{T}}) \le \text{rank}(\mathbf{B}^{\mathrm{T}}) = \text{rank}(\mathbf{B})$$

using Theorem 2.7.2 and Theorem 2.7.4. Combining these two observations completes the proof. ■

One useful application of the notion of rank is as a test for the existence of solutions to $\mathbf{Ax} = \mathbf{b}$. Recall that a system with at least one solution is consistent; a system with no solutions is inconsistent.

Theorem 2.7.6. *The system* $\mathbf{Ax} = \mathbf{b}$ *is consistent if and only if* $\text{rank}(\mathbf{A}) = \text{rank}\left([\mathbf{A}\ \mathbf{b}]\right)$.

Proof. Suppose the rank of **A** is r and the rref of **A** is $\mathbf{A}_r$. Then for some **c**, the rref of $[\mathbf{A}\ \mathbf{b}]$ is $[\mathbf{A}_r\ \mathbf{c}]$. Clearly $\text{rank}\left([\mathbf{A}_r\ \mathbf{c}]\right) = \text{rank}\left([\mathbf{A}\ \mathbf{b}]\right)$ is either r or $r+1$. Assume that the unknowns in the system $\mathbf{Ax} = \mathbf{b}$ have been ordered (Section 2.3) so that $[\mathbf{A}_r\ \mathbf{c}]$ is given by

$$\left[\begin{array}{cccc|cccc|c}
1 & 0 & \cdots & 0 & * & * & \cdots & * & c_1 \\
0 & 1 & \cdots & 0 & * & * & \cdots & * & c_2 \\
\vdots & \vdots & & \vdots & \vdots & \vdots & & \vdots & \vdots \\
0 & 0 & \cdots & 1 & * & * & \cdots & * & c_r \\
\hline
0 & 0 & \cdots & 0 & 0 & 0 & \cdots & 0 & \beta \\
0 & 0 & \cdots & 0 & 0 & 0 & \cdots & 0 & 0 \\
\vdots & \vdots & & \vdots & \vdots & \vdots & & \vdots & \vdots \\
0 & 0 & \cdots & 0 & 0 & 0 & \cdots & 0 & 0
\end{array}\right]$$

Then $\mathbf{Ax} = \mathbf{b}$ is inconsistent if and only if $\beta \neq 0$. But $\beta \neq 0$ if and only if $1 + \text{rank}(\mathbf{A}) = \text{rank}([\mathbf{A}\ \mathbf{b}])$, in which case $\mathbf{c} = \mathbf{e}_{r+1}$ since $[\mathbf{A}_r\ \mathbf{c}]$ is in rref. ■

We say that $\mathbf{A}_{m \times n}$ has *full column rank* if $\text{rank}(\mathbf{A}) = n$ and *full row rank* if $\text{rank}(\mathbf{A}) = m$. For example,

$$\begin{bmatrix} 2 & * & * \\ 0 & 1 & * \\ 0 & 0 & -1 \\ 0 & 0 & 0 \end{bmatrix} \quad \begin{bmatrix} 1 & * \\ 0 & 3 \\ 0 & 0 \\ 0 & 0 \end{bmatrix} \quad \begin{bmatrix} 4 \\ 0 \\ 0 \\ 0 \end{bmatrix} \quad \begin{bmatrix} 1 & * & * & * \\ 0 & 1 & * & * \\ 0 & 0 & -1 & * \\ 0 & 0 & 0 & 2 \end{bmatrix}$$

are matrices with full column rank and

$$\begin{bmatrix} 2 & * & * \\ 0 & 1 & * \\ 0 & 0 & -1 \end{bmatrix} \quad \begin{bmatrix} 3 & * & * \\ 0 & 0 & -1 \end{bmatrix} \quad \begin{bmatrix} 4 & 1 & * \end{bmatrix}$$

are matrices with full row rank. Note that nonsingular matrices have full row and column rank, and that a matrix with full row rank has no zero rows in its reduced row echelon form. Clearly, if $\mathbf{A}_{m \times n}$ has full column rank then $\text{rank}(\mathbf{A}) = n \leq m$, since the rank of $\mathbf{A}$ cannot exceed the number of its rows. Likewise, if $\mathbf{A}_{m \times n}$ has full row rank, $m \leq n$ by Theorem 2.7.1. The notion of full row rank is used to formulate the following corollary to Theorem 2.7.6:

Corollary 1. *The system* $\mathbf{Ax} = \mathbf{b}$ *is consistent for every* $\mathbf{b}$ *if and only if* $\mathbf{A}$ *has full row rank.*

Proof. If $\mathbf{A}$ is $m \times n$ then $\mathbf{A}$ has full row rank means $\text{rank}(\mathbf{A}) = m$. Since $[\mathbf{A}\ \mathbf{b}]$ has m rows, its rank is m, independent of $\mathbf{b}$. By Theorem 2.7.6, $\mathbf{Ax} = \mathbf{b}$ is consistent. ■

The homogeneous system $\mathbf{Ax} = \mathbf{0}$ is always consistent, since the ranks of $\mathbf{A}$ and $[\mathbf{A}\ \mathbf{0}]$ are clearly equal. (Of course, no elaborate argument is needed to establish the consistency of $\mathbf{Ax} = \mathbf{0}$; $\mathbf{x} = \mathbf{0}$ is always a solution.) For homogeneous systems, the question is not one of consistency but of uniqueness of solutions. If $\mathbf{A}$ is nonsingular, then the answer is easy; $\mathbf{0}$ is the only solution of $\mathbf{Ax} = \mathbf{0}$. If the system's matrix is singular or not square, the issue is more complicated. The notion of rank is particularly well suited to these cases.

Theorem 2.7.7. *The homogeneous system* $\mathbf{Ax} = \mathbf{0}$ *has the unique solution* $\mathbf{x} = \mathbf{0}$ *if and only if* $\mathbf{A}$ *has full column rank.*

Proof. This is a re-phrasing of Theorem 2.6.3. Suppose $\mathbf{A}$ has k columns. Then, if $\mathbf{A}$ has full column rank, $\text{rank}(\mathbf{A}) = k$, and by Theorem 2.6.3, $\mathbf{x} = \mathbf{0}$ is the only solution of $\mathbf{Ax} = \mathbf{0}$. On the other hand, if $\mathbf{Ax} = \mathbf{0}$ has only the trivial solution, then $\text{rank}(\mathbf{A}) = k$, also by Theorem 2.6.3. Thus $\mathbf{A}$ has full column rank. ■

Corollary 1. *If the inhomogeneous system* $\mathbf{Ax} = \mathbf{b}$ *is consistent, then it has a unique solution if and only if* $\mathbf{A}$ *has full column rank.*

Proof. Suppose $\mathbf{A}$ has full column rank and $\mathbf{x}_1$ and $\mathbf{x}_2$ are two solutions of $\mathbf{Ax} = \mathbf{b}$. Then $\mathbf{A}(\mathbf{x}_1 - \mathbf{x}_2) = \mathbf{Ax}_1 - \mathbf{Ax}_2 = \mathbf{b} - \mathbf{b} = \mathbf{0}$ shows that the homogeneous system $\mathbf{Ax} = \mathbf{0}$ has the solution $\mathbf{x}_1 - \mathbf{x}_2$. However, by Theorem 2.7.7, $\mathbf{x}_1 - \mathbf{x}_2 = \mathbf{0}$ and therefore $\mathbf{x}_1 = \mathbf{x}_2$. Conversely, suppose $\mathbf{A}$ does not have full column rank. Then, there is a nontrivial solution of $\mathbf{Ax} = \mathbf{0}$. Suppose this solution is $\mathbf{y} \neq \mathbf{0}$. Then $\mathbf{A}(\mathbf{y} + \mathbf{x}_1) = \mathbf{Ay} + \mathbf{Ax}_1 = \mathbf{0} + \mathbf{b} = \mathbf{b}$. Hence $\mathbf{x}_1$ and $\mathbf{y} + \mathbf{x}_1$ are distinct solutions of $\mathbf{Ax} = \mathbf{b}$. ■

PROBLEMS

PART 1

2.7.1. Find the rank of each matrix in Problem 2.2.1.

2.7.2. Find the rank of each matrix in Problem 2.2.2.

2.7.3. Find the rank of each matrix in Problem 2.2.3.

2.7.4. Exhibit two 2×2 matrices which are row equivalent but whose transposes are not.

2.7.5. Find the ranks of

$$(a)\ \begin{bmatrix} 3 & 1 & 1 & 1 \\ 1 & 3 & 1 & 1 \\ 1 & 1 & 3 & 1 \\ 1 & 1 & 1 & 3 \end{bmatrix} \qquad (b)\ \begin{bmatrix} -3 & 1 & 1 & 1 \\ 1 & -3 & 1 & 1 \\ 1 & 1 & -3 & 1 \\ 1 & 1 & 1 & -3 \end{bmatrix}$$

$$(c)\ \begin{bmatrix} 2 & 1 & 1 \\ 1 & 2 & 1 \\ 1 & 1 & 2 \end{bmatrix} \qquad (d)\ \begin{bmatrix} -2 & 1 & 1 \\ 1 & -2 & 1 \\ 1 & 1 & -2 \end{bmatrix}$$

2.7.6. Construct a matrix in reduced row echelon form in which $\mathbf{e}_1$ is a column, but not a leading column.

2.7.7. Explain why either $\text{rank}(\mathbf{A}) = \text{rank}([\mathbf{A}\ \mathbf{b}])$ or $1 + \text{rank}(\mathbf{A}) = \text{rank}([\mathbf{A}\ \mathbf{b}])$.

PART 2

2.7.8. Explain why $\text{rank}(\mathbf{A}) \leq \text{rank}([\mathbf{A}\ \mathbf{B}])$. Find a condition on $\mathbf{A}$ that ensures equality.

2.7.9. Extend Theorem 2.7.6 to the system $\mathbf{Ax} = \mathbf{b}$, where $\mathbf{A}$ is $m \times n$ and $\mathbf{X}$ is $n \times p$.

2.7.10. Show that

$$\text{rank}\left(\begin{bmatrix} \mathbf{A} & \mathbf{O} \\ \mathbf{O} & \mathbf{B} \end{bmatrix}\right) = \text{rank}(\mathbf{A}) + \text{rank}(\mathbf{B})$$

2.7.11. If $\mathbf{A}$ is row equivalent to $\mathbf{B}$, show that $\text{rank}(\mathbf{A}^{\mathrm{T}}) = \text{rank}(\mathbf{B}^{\mathrm{T}})$.

2.7.12. Suppose $\mathbf{A}$ is $m \times k$ and $\mathbf{B}$ is $k \times m$ and $k \neq m$. Show that $\mathbf{AB}$ and $\mathbf{BA}$ exist but both cannot be nonsingular. Hence, prove that either $\mathbf{AA}^{\mathrm{T}}$ or $\mathbf{A}^{\mathrm{T}}\mathbf{A}$ is singular.

2.7.13. Find the ranks of the following $n \times n$ matrices,

$$(a)\ \begin{bmatrix} n-1 & 1 & \cdots & 1 \\ 1 & n-1 & \cdots & 1 \\ \vdots & \vdots & & \vdots \\ 1 & 1 & \cdots & n-1 \end{bmatrix} \qquad (b)\ \begin{bmatrix} 1-n & 1 & \cdots & 1 \\ 1 & 1-n & \cdots & 1 \\ \vdots & \vdots & & \vdots \\ 1 & 1 & \cdots & 1-n \end{bmatrix}$$

2.7.14. Explain why rank(**A**) = 0 implies **A** = **0**.

2.7.15. By selecting the appropriate values of $*$ in the matrices

$$(a)\begin{bmatrix} * & * & * \\ 0 & 0 & 0 \\ 0 & 0 & 0 \end{bmatrix} \qquad (b)\begin{bmatrix} * & * & * \\ * & * & * \\ 0 & 0 & 0 \end{bmatrix} \qquad (c)\begin{bmatrix} 0 & 0 & 0 \\ 0 & 0 & 0 \\ * & * & * \end{bmatrix}$$

construct examples showing that each of the following can occur:

(*a*) rank(**A** + **B**) = rank(**A**) + rank(**B**).
(*b*) rank(**A** − **B**) = rank(**A**) − rank(**B**).
(*c*) rank(**AB**) = rank(**A**), but rank(**AB**) < rank(**B**).
(*d*) rank(**AB**) < rank(**A**) and rank(**AB**) < rank(**B**).
(*e*) rank(**AB**) = rank(**A**) = rank(**B**).
(*f*) rank(**AB**) = rank(**B**), but rank(**AB**) < rank(**A**).

2.7.16. Suppose **A** has full row and column rank. Show that **A** must be square and invertible. (*Hint:* Use Theorem 2.7.1 to show that **A** is square, and Corollary 1 of Theorem 2.7.6 to show that **AX** = **I** has a solution.)

2.7.17. Prove Eq. 2.7.3

CHAPTER 3

LINEAR ALGEBRA IN N DIMENSIONS

3.1 INTRODUCTION

Analytic geometry, a remarkably fruitful invention of René Descartes, combines geometric visualization with algebraic formalism. While it is most often used to bring geometric intuition to bear on the study of algebraic questions, geometry is benefited by the merger as well. Since our geometric intuition is limited to three dimensional space, it might be thought that an "analytic geometry" in more than three dimensions is not only hopeless but, even if possible, not worth the effort. But it is one of the main goals of this chapter to show that such a generalization is possible, intuitively plausible, and very useful.

The challenge in doing so is twofold: first to discern which parts of analytic geometry are fundamental and generalize to arbitrary dimensions; and, second, to invent a notation that not only captures geometric content, but is natural and easy to use. While our notational demands are resolved by describing points in n dimensional space by vectors of n-tuples, the theory of vector spaces provides a satisfactory answer to the first challenge.

Our theory is suggestive and natural, especially for linear equations, because we can often "see" what is happening in n dimensions through sketches that are two and three dimensional. It is productive because it lends insight into the solution of old problems as well as solves new problems. The theory of the simplex method is an example of the latter, (Sections 9.6–9.10) and the geometric interpretation of the solution of systems of linear equations demonstrates the former. Indeed, the major application in this chapter is the theory of systems of linear equations.

3.2 VECTOR SPACES OF *n*-TUPLES

Sets are a crucial ingredient of all mathematical theories, and matrix theory is no exception. We have many occasions to consider sets of matrices and vectors: the set of all matrices row equivalent to **A**; the set of all nonsingular matrices; the span of a set of vectors; and so on. Among all conceivable sets of vectors, there are some that are singled out for special attention because of their extraordinary usefulness. In this section, we study the most important of these sets, the so-called (real) vector spaces of n-tuples. To do so, it is necessary to establish certain notational and conceptual conventions.

We shall assume that all sets of vectors are sets of real n-tuples (for some n), are always nonempty, and are denoted by capital letters of the form illustrated by $\mathcal{C}, \mathcal{R}, \mathcal{V}, \mathcal{S}, \mathcal{W}$. By $\mathcal{W} \subseteq \mathcal{V}$ we mean that $\mathcal{W}$ is a subset of $\mathcal{V}$; that is, each member of $\mathcal{W}$ is a member of $\mathcal{V}$. This notation includes the possibility that $\mathcal{V} = \mathcal{W}$. With these conditions understood, it follows that linear combinations of vectors from any fixed set are defined.

Definition 3.2.1. *A (nonempty) set of vectors $\mathcal{V} \subseteq \mathcal{R}^n$ is a vector space of n-tuples if the following condition is met: If $\mathbf{x} \in \mathcal{V}$ and $\mathbf{y} \in \mathcal{V}$, then $\alpha\mathbf{x} + \beta\mathbf{y} \in \mathcal{V}$ for each scalar α and β.*

Example 3.2.1. Interpret the vector $\mathbf{x} = [x \quad y]^T$ as the point with coordinates (x,y). Show that the set of all vectors lying on the line $y = mx$ is a vector space.

Solution. The vectors

$$\mathbf{x}_1 = \begin{bmatrix} x_1 \\ y_1 \end{bmatrix}, \qquad \mathbf{x}_2 = \begin{bmatrix} x_2 \\ y_2 \end{bmatrix}$$

lie on the line $y = mx$, if and only if $y_1 = mx_1$ and $y_2 = mx_2$. Hence

$$\alpha\mathbf{x}_1 + \beta\mathbf{x}_2 = \alpha\begin{bmatrix} x_1 \\ mx_1 \end{bmatrix} + \beta\begin{bmatrix} x_2 \\ mx_2 \end{bmatrix} = \begin{bmatrix} \alpha x_1 + \beta x_2 \\ \alpha m x_1 + \beta m x_2 \end{bmatrix}$$

$$= \begin{bmatrix} \alpha x_1 + \beta x_2 \\ m(\alpha x_1 + \beta x_2) \end{bmatrix}$$

shows that $\alpha\mathbf{x}_1 + \beta\mathbf{x}_2$ also lies on the line $y = mx$ for each α and β. Thus by definition the given set of vectors is a vector space.

An immediate conclusion following from the definition of vector space is that every vector space contains the zero vector, since we may always set $\alpha = \beta = 0$. Here is an example of a set of vectors which fails this test and, therefore, is not a vector space.

Example 3.2.2. The set of all vectors of the form $[1 \quad c_1 \quad c_2 \quad 0]^{\mathrm{T}}$ is not a vector space because $[1 \quad c_1 \quad c_2 \quad 0]^{\mathrm{T}} = \mathbf{0}^{\mathrm{T}}$ cannot be satisfied for any choice of c_1 and c_2. (This set is not without interest; such sets are studied in Section 3.7.)

A second conclusion following from the definition of vector space is that the span (the set of all linear combinations) of every finite set of vectors belonging to the vector space $\mathcal{V}$ must be a subset of $\mathcal{V}$. More interesting, every span is itself a vector space. The proof of this theorem is very instructive.

Theorem 3.2.1. *The set* $\mathcal{S} = span\{\mathbf{x}_1,\mathbf{x}_2,\ldots,\mathbf{x}_k\}$ *is a vector space.*

Proof. Suppose $\mathbf{y}$ and $\mathbf{z}$ belong to $\mathcal{S}$. We need to show that $\alpha\mathbf{y} + \beta\mathbf{z}$ also belongs to $\mathcal{S}$ for all scalars α and β. By definition, there are weights $a_1,a_2,\ldots,a_k$ and $b_1,b_2,\ldots,b_k$ such that

$$\mathbf{y} = a_1\mathbf{x}_1 + a_2\mathbf{x}_2 + \cdots + a_k\mathbf{x}_k \text{ and } \mathbf{z} = b_1\mathbf{x}_1 + b_2\mathbf{x}_2 + \cdots + b_k\mathbf{x}_k$$

By a little algebra, we obtain

$$\alpha\mathbf{y} + \beta\mathbf{z} = (\alpha a_1 + \beta b_1)\mathbf{x}_1 + (\alpha a_2 + \beta b_2)\mathbf{x}_2 + \cdots + (\alpha a_k + \beta b_k)\mathbf{x}_k$$

which shows that for every α and β, $\alpha\mathbf{y} + \beta\mathbf{z}$ is a linear combination of the vectors $\{\mathbf{x}_1,\mathbf{x}_2,\ldots,\mathbf{x}_k\}$ and therefore is a vector in $\mathcal{S}$. ■

Example 3.2.3. Show that the set of all vectors of the form $[0 \quad c \quad d \quad 0]^{\mathrm{T}}$ is a vector space.

Solution. The argument given here is typical of the methods used to show that a given set is a vector space. We show that all vectors in the set lie in the span of some fixed, finite set of vectors in the set. In this case it is easy:

$$\begin{bmatrix} 0 \\ c \\ d \\ 0 \end{bmatrix} = c\begin{bmatrix} 0 \\ 1 \\ 0 \\ 0 \end{bmatrix} + d\begin{bmatrix} 0 \\ 0 \\ 1 \\ 0 \end{bmatrix}$$

So every vector of the form $[0 \quad c \quad d \quad 0]^{\mathrm{T}}$ is a linear combination of the vectors $[0 \quad 1 \quad 0 \quad 0]^{\mathrm{T}}$ and $[0 \quad 0 \quad 1 \quad 0]^{\mathrm{T}}$. Alternatively, let

$$\mathbf{c}_1 = \begin{bmatrix} 0 \\ c \\ d \\ 0 \end{bmatrix} \qquad \mathbf{c}_2 = \begin{bmatrix} 0 \\ e \\ f \\ 0 \end{bmatrix}$$

be typical vectors in the given set. Then

$$\alpha\mathbf{c}_1 + \beta\mathbf{c}_2 = \alpha\begin{bmatrix} 0 \\ c \\ d \\ 0 \end{bmatrix} + \beta\begin{bmatrix} 0 \\ e \\ f \\ 0 \end{bmatrix} = \begin{bmatrix} 0 \\ \alpha c \\ \alpha d \\ 0 \end{bmatrix} + \begin{bmatrix} 0 \\ \beta e \\ \beta f \\ 0 \end{bmatrix} = \begin{bmatrix} 0 \\ \alpha c + \beta e \\ \alpha d + \beta f \\ 0 \end{bmatrix}$$

shows that for all scalars α and β, $\alpha\mathbf{c}_1+\beta\mathbf{c}_2$ is of the form $[0 \quad c \quad d \quad 0]^{\mathrm{T}}$. Hence the given set is a vector space by definition.

Example 3.2.4. Show that the set of all solutions of $\mathbf{Ax} = \mathbf{0}$ is a vector space.

Solution. Suppose the set of all solutions is denoted by $\mathcal{N}$. Let $\mathbf{y}$ and $\mathbf{z}$ be any vectors in $\mathcal{N}$. Then $\mathbf{Ay} = \mathbf{0}$ and $\mathbf{Az} = \mathbf{0}$. But, for any α and β, $\mathbf{A}(\alpha\mathbf{y} + \beta\mathbf{z}) = \alpha\mathbf{Ay} + \beta\mathbf{Az} = \alpha\mathbf{0} + \beta\mathbf{0} = \mathbf{0}$ shows that $\alpha\mathbf{y} + \beta\mathbf{z} \in \mathcal{N}$.

Example 3.2.4 provides one of the prime motivations for the study of vector spaces. Call the set of all solutions of the homogeneous system $\mathbf{Ax} = \mathbf{0}$, the *null space* or the *solution space* of $\mathbf{A}$. This is one of the three vector spaces associated with $\mathbf{A}$ which is studied in this chapter. A second space associated with $\mathbf{A}$ is its *column space* defined as the span of the columns of $\mathbf{A}$; and the third is the span of the rows of $\mathbf{A}$, called the *row space* of $\mathbf{A}$. All but the most passing reference to these spaces is deferred to Sections 3.4 and 3.5.

Example 3.2.5. Show that the set of all vectors with n components is a vector space.

Solution. It should be obvious that this set satisfies the definition of vector space. It is interesting to observe that this set is at once the span of $\{\mathbf{e}_1, \mathbf{e}_2, \ldots, \mathbf{e}_n\}$ and the column space of $\mathbf{I}_n$.

$\mathcal{R}^n$ is itself a vector space, the span of $\{\mathbf{e}_1, \mathbf{e}_2, \ldots, \mathbf{e}_n\}$. Another set whose span is $\mathcal{R}^n$ is given in the next example. Sets whose span is $\mathcal{V}$ are called *spanning sets* of $\mathcal{V}$. Such sets are said to span $\mathcal{V}$. It is important to bear in mind that spanning sets of $\mathcal{V}$ are finite sets of vectors in $\mathcal{V}$. Thus

$$\left\{ \begin{bmatrix} 1 \\ 0 \\ 0 \\ 0 \end{bmatrix}, \begin{bmatrix} 0 \\ 1 \\ 0 \\ 0 \end{bmatrix}, \begin{bmatrix} 0 \\ 0 \\ 1 \\ 0 \end{bmatrix}, \begin{bmatrix} 0 \\ 0 \\ 0 \\ 1 \end{bmatrix} \right\}$$

is NOT a spanning set for the vector space $\mathcal{V}$ of Example 3.2.3, even though

$$\begin{bmatrix} 0 \\ c \\ d \\ 0 \end{bmatrix} = 0 \begin{bmatrix} 1 \\ 0 \\ 0 \\ 0 \end{bmatrix} + c \begin{bmatrix} 0 \\ 1 \\ 0 \\ 0 \end{bmatrix} + d \begin{bmatrix} 0 \\ 0 \\ 1 \\ 0 \end{bmatrix} + 0 \begin{bmatrix} 0 \\ 0 \\ 0 \\ 1 \end{bmatrix}$$

The reason is that $\mathbf{e}_1$ and $\mathbf{e}_4$ do not belong to $\mathcal{V}$ and the definition of spanning set for $\mathcal{V}$ requires that they do. *Span*$\{\mathbf{e}_1, \mathbf{e}_2, \mathbf{e}_3, \mathbf{e}_4\} = \mathcal{R}^4 \neq \mathcal{V}$.

Example 3.2.6. Show that $\{\mathbf{u}_1, \mathbf{u}_2, \ldots, \mathbf{u}_n\}$ is another spanning set of $\mathcal{R}^n$, where

$$\mathbf{u}_1 = \mathbf{e}_1, \mathbf{u}_2 = \mathbf{e}_1 + \mathbf{e}_2, \ldots, \mathbf{u}_n = \mathbf{e}_1 + \mathbf{e}_2 + \cdots + \mathbf{e}_n$$

Solution. In expanded form, the given set is

$$\mathbf{u}_1 = \begin{bmatrix} 1 \\ 0 \\ 0 \\ \vdots \\ 0 \\ 0 \end{bmatrix} \quad \mathbf{u}_2 = \begin{bmatrix} 1 \\ 1 \\ 0 \\ \vdots \\ 0 \\ 0 \end{bmatrix} \quad \cdots \quad \mathbf{u}_{n-1} = \begin{bmatrix} 1 \\ 1 \\ 1 \\ \vdots \\ 1 \\ 0 \end{bmatrix} \quad \mathbf{u}_n = \begin{bmatrix} 1 \\ 1 \\ 1 \\ \vdots \\ 1 \\ 1 \end{bmatrix}$$

To show that these vectors span $\mathcal{R}^n$ it is necessary to show that for every vector $\mathbf{b} \in \mathcal{R}^n$ there is a set of weights $\{w_1, w_2, \ldots, w_n\}$ such that

$$\mathbf{b} = w_1\mathbf{u}_1 + w_2\mathbf{u}_2 + \cdots + w_n\mathbf{u}_n \tag{3.2.1}$$

Denote by $\mathbf{A}$ the matrix whose columns are the given vectors; that is, $\mathbf{A} = [\mathbf{u}_1 \ \ \mathbf{u}_2 \ \ \ldots \ \ \mathbf{u}_n]$. Let $\mathbf{w}$ be the vector of weights. Then $\{\mathbf{u}_1, \mathbf{u}_2, \ldots, \mathbf{u}_n\}$ spans $\mathcal{R}^n$ if and only if we can solve $\mathbf{Aw} = \mathbf{b}$ for every choice of $\mathbf{b}$ because Eq. 3.2.1 may be written

$$\mathbf{Aw} = \mathbf{b} = w_1\mathbf{u}_1 + w_2\mathbf{u}_2 + \cdots + w_n\mathbf{u}_n \tag{3.2.2}$$

Since $\mathbf{A}$ is invertible (why?), this is possible, and indeed, $\mathbf{w} = \mathbf{A}^{-1}\mathbf{b}$. For instance,

$$w_1\begin{bmatrix} 1 \\ 0 \\ 0 \end{bmatrix} + w_2\begin{bmatrix} 1 \\ 1 \\ 0 \end{bmatrix} + w_3\begin{bmatrix} 1 \\ 1 \\ 1 \end{bmatrix} = \mathbf{b} = \begin{bmatrix} a \\ b \\ c \end{bmatrix}$$

may be written in matrix form as

$$\mathbf{Aw} = \begin{bmatrix} 1 & 1 & 1 \\ 0 & 1 & 1 \\ 0 & 0 & 1 \end{bmatrix} \mathbf{w} = \begin{bmatrix} a \\ b \\ c \end{bmatrix}$$

But since

$$\mathbf{A}^{-1} = \begin{bmatrix} 1 & -1 & 0 \\ 0 & 1 & -1 \\ 0 & 0 & 1 \end{bmatrix}$$

$\mathbf{A}^{-1}\mathbf{b} = \mathbf{w} = [a - b \quad b - c \quad c]^{\mathrm{T}}$ and hence

$$\begin{bmatrix} a \\ b \\ c \end{bmatrix} = (a - b)\begin{bmatrix} 1 \\ 0 \\ 0 \end{bmatrix} + (b - c)\begin{bmatrix} 1 \\ 1 \\ 0 \end{bmatrix} + c\begin{bmatrix} 1 \\ 1 \\ 1 \end{bmatrix}$$

The next example illustrates an important point: the span of a set of vectors is unaltered if the vectors are multiplied by nonzero scalars or if a multiple of one vector is added to another vector.

Example 3.2.7. Let $\mathcal{S} = span\{\mathbf{x}_1, \mathbf{x}_2, \mathbf{x}_3\}$. Show that the sets $\{\mathbf{x}_2, \mathbf{x}_3, \mathbf{x}_1\}$, $\{\mathbf{x}_1, \alpha\mathbf{x}_2, \mathbf{x}_3\}$ and $\{\mathbf{x}_1, \alpha\mathbf{x}_1 + \mathbf{x}_2, \mathbf{x}_3\}$ also span $\mathcal{S}$, if $\alpha \neq 0$.

Solution. Let $\mathbf{z}$ be any vector in $\mathcal{S}$. By hypothesis,

$$\mathbf{z} = a_1\mathbf{x}_1 + a_2\mathbf{x}_2 + a_3\mathbf{x}_3$$

Clearly $\mathbf{z}$ is a linear combination of the vectors $\{\mathbf{x}_2, \mathbf{x}_3, \mathbf{x}_1\}$. It is also a linear combination of $\{\mathbf{x}_1, \alpha\mathbf{x}_2, \mathbf{x}_3\}$, since

$$\mathbf{z} = a_1\mathbf{x}_1 + (a_2/\alpha)\alpha\mathbf{x}_2 + a_3\mathbf{x}_3$$

And $\mathbf{z}$ is a linear combination of the vectors in $\{\mathbf{x}_1, \alpha\mathbf{x}_1 + \mathbf{x}_2, \mathbf{x}_3\}$, since

$$\mathbf{z} = (a_1 - \alpha a_2)\mathbf{x}_1 + a_2(\alpha\mathbf{x}_1 + \mathbf{x}_2) + a_3\mathbf{x}_3$$

Our last objective is to show that every vector space $\mathcal{V}$ is the span of some set of vectors lying in $\mathcal{V}$. This is an important result because it enables us to represent every vector space as a set of linear combinations of a fixed, finite set of vectors, each of which belongs to the vector space.

Theorem 3.2.2. *If $\mathcal{V}$ is a vector space of n-tuples containing at least one nonzero vector, then it is always possible to find a finite set of linearly independent vectors in $\mathcal{V}$ whose span is $\mathcal{V}$.*

Proof. Assume that $\mathbf{x}_1 \in \mathcal{V}, \mathbf{x}_1 \neq 0$. If $span\{\mathbf{x}_1\} = \mathcal{V}$, we are done. If not, there exists $\mathbf{x}_2 \in \mathcal{V}$ not in the span of $\{\mathbf{x}_1\}$. The set $\{\mathbf{x}_1, \mathbf{x}_2\}$ is linearly independent by Theorem 2.6.1. Consider $span\{\mathbf{x}_1, \mathbf{x}_2\}$. If it is $\mathcal{V}$, we are done. If not, there exists $\mathbf{x}_3 \in \mathcal{V}$ not in $span\{\mathbf{x}_1, \mathbf{x}_2\}$ and thus $\{\mathbf{x}_1, \mathbf{x}_2, \mathbf{x}_3\}$ is a linearly independent set, again by Theorem 2.6.1. This process can be continued until either we have spanned $\mathcal{V}$ or $\{\mathbf{x}_1,\mathbf{x}_2,\ldots,\mathbf{x}_n, \mathbf{x}_{n+1}\}$ is linearly independent. However, by Corollary 3 of Theorem 2.6.3, there cannot be a set of $n+1$ n-tuples that are linearly independent. Hence for some $1 \leq k \leq n$, $span\{\mathbf{x}_1,\ldots,\mathbf{x}_k\} = \mathcal{V}$.

Theorems 3.2.1 and 3.2.2 assert that every span is a vector space containing the vectors in the spanning set, and every vector space is a span of some finite set of vectors in the space. A slight variation of this idea is shown in the next example. ■

Example 3.2.8. Find a linearly independent spanning set for $\mathcal{R}^4$ containing the vectors $\mathbf{x}_1 = [1 \;\; 1 \;\; 0 \;\; -1]^{\mathrm{T}}$ and $\mathbf{x}_2 = [0 \;\; 0 \;\; 1 \;\; 1]^{\mathrm{T}}$.

Solution. Look for vectors not in the span of $\{\mathbf{x}_1, \mathbf{x}_2\}$. Since the fourth entries in $\mathbf{x}_1$ and $\mathbf{x}_2$ are nonzero, any nonzero vector in $\mathcal{R}^4$ with a zero in its fourth entry will not be in the span of $\{\mathbf{x}_1, \mathbf{x}_2\}$. It suffices to choose $\mathbf{x}_3 = [1\ 0\ 0\ 0]^{\mathrm{T}}$. A more instructive method is used to select the fourth vector. Let $\mathbf{x}_4 = [a \;\; b \;\; c \;\; d]^{\mathrm{T}}$. Then, by Corollary 1 of Theorem 2.6.2, the columns of $\mathbf{S} = [\mathbf{x}_1 \; \mathbf{x}_2 \; \mathbf{x}_3 \; \mathbf{x}_4]$ are linearly independent if and only if the rank of $\mathbf{S}$ is 4. (Why?) The rank of $\mathbf{S}$ is found from its rref:

$$\mathbf{S} = [\mathbf{x}_1\ \mathbf{x}_2\ \mathbf{x}_3\ \mathbf{x}_4] = \begin{bmatrix} 1 & 0 & 1 & a \\ 1 & 0 & 0 & b \\ 0 & 1 & 0 & c \\ -1 & 1 & 0 & d \end{bmatrix} \to \cdots \to \begin{bmatrix} 1 & 0 & 0 & b \\ 0 & 1 & 0 & c \\ 0 & 0 & 1 & a-b \\ 0 & 0 & 0 & d-c+b \end{bmatrix}$$

Hence rank($\mathbf{S}$) = 4, provided $d - c + b \neq 0$. One solution is $a = b = c = 0$ and $d = 1$. Then $\mathbf{S} = [\mathbf{x}_1 \quad \mathbf{x}_2 \quad \mathbf{e}_1 \quad \mathbf{e}_4]$ and hence $span\{\mathbf{x}_1, \mathbf{x}_2, \mathbf{e}_1, \mathbf{e}_4\} = \mathcal{R}^n$.

3.2.1 Subspaces

Suppose $\mathcal{W}$ and $\mathcal{V}$ are two sets of vectors such that every vector in $\mathcal{W}$ belongs to $\mathcal{V}$; that is, $\mathcal{W} \subseteq \mathcal{V}$. Subsets of $\mathcal{V}$ are called proper subsets if they are neither empty nor all of $\mathcal{V}$. If $\mathcal{W}$ and $\mathcal{V}$ are vector spaces and $\mathcal{W} \subseteq \mathcal{V}$ then $\mathcal{W}$ is a *subspace* of $\mathcal{V}$.

Sets that span $\mathcal{V}$ will not be spanning sets of $\mathcal{W}$ if $\mathcal{W}$ is a proper subset of $\mathcal{V}$. (Why?) It follows from the definition of subspace that every vector space of n-tuples is a subspace of $\mathcal{R}^n$, and the "trivial" space $\{\mathbf{0}_n\}$ is a subspace of every vector space of n-tuples. The subspaces of $\mathcal{R}^2$ (other than $\{\mathbf{0}_2\}$ and $\mathcal{R}^2$ itself) are lines through the origin. (See Example 2.6.2.) In $\mathcal{R}^3$, the proper subspaces are lines and planes through the origin. Lines and planes in $\mathcal{R}^3$ which do not pass through the origin cannot correspond to subspaces of $\mathcal{R}^3$, because $\mathbf{0}_3$ is not in these sets, and every vector space of 3-tuples must contain $\mathbf{0}_3$.

PROBLEMS

PART 1

3.2.1. Show that no nonempty subset of the solutions of $\mathbf{Ax} = \mathbf{b}$, $\mathbf{b} \neq \mathbf{0}$, can be a vector space.

3.2.2. Show that the set of all vectors of the following forms are vector spaces, by finding spanning sets.

(*a*) $\begin{bmatrix} \alpha \\ \beta \\ \gamma \\ \delta \end{bmatrix}$ (*b*) $\begin{bmatrix} \alpha \\ \beta \\ \gamma \\ \delta \end{bmatrix}, \begin{matrix} \alpha + \beta = 0 \\ \gamma + \delta = 0 \end{matrix}$ (*c*) $\begin{bmatrix} \alpha \\ \beta \\ \gamma \\ \delta \end{bmatrix}, \alpha + \beta = 0$

(*d*) $\begin{bmatrix} \alpha \\ \beta \\ \gamma \\ \delta \end{bmatrix}, \alpha + \beta + \gamma = 0$

3.2.3. Repeat Problem 3.2.2 for the sets

(*a*) $\begin{bmatrix} \alpha \\ 2\alpha \\ -\alpha \\ 0 \end{bmatrix}$ (*b*) $\begin{bmatrix} \alpha \\ -\alpha \\ 0 \\ 0 \end{bmatrix}$

3.2.4. Find a vector not in the span of

$$\left\{\begin{bmatrix}1\\2\\2\end{bmatrix}, \begin{bmatrix}1\\1\\1\end{bmatrix}, \begin{bmatrix}-1\\0\\0\end{bmatrix}\right\}$$

3.2.5. Is the set of all vectors of the form $[\alpha\ \beta\ \gamma]^{\mathrm{T}}$, with $\alpha\beta = 0$ and γ arbitrary, a vector space? If not, what property is violated? If so, find a spanning set.

3.2.6. Is $\mathcal{R}^3$ a subspace of $\mathcal{R}^4$? Is

$$span\left\{\begin{bmatrix}1\\0\\0\\0\end{bmatrix}, \begin{bmatrix}0\\1\\0\\0\end{bmatrix}, \begin{bmatrix}0\\0\\1\\0\end{bmatrix}\right\}$$

a subspace of $\mathcal{R}^4$?

PART 2

3.2.7. Consider the set $\{\mathbf{x}_1, \mathbf{x}_2, \mathbf{x}_3\}$ and the set of all vectors of the form $\mathbf{x}_1 + a_2\mathbf{x}_2 + a_3\mathbf{x}_3$. Is this latter set ever a vector space?

3.2.8. Explain why $\{\mathbf{e}_1, \mathbf{e}_2, \mathbf{e}_3, \mathbf{e}_4\}$ spans the vector space given in Problem 3.2.2(*a*), but does not span the other vector spaces in that problem.

3.2.9. Consider the set of all n-tuples with nonnegative entries. Is this set a vector space? Explain.

3.2.10. Let $\mathbf{x} = [x_1\ \ x_2\ \ \ldots\ \ x_n]^{\mathrm{T}}$ and suppose $x_1 + x_2 + \cdots + x_n = 0$. Consider the set of all such n-tuples. Is this set a vector space? Explain.

3.2.11. Let $\mathcal{V}$ and $\mathcal{W}$ be vector spaces of n-tuples. Let $\mathcal{V} \cap \mathcal{W}$ be the set of all vectors in both $\mathcal{V}$ and $\mathcal{W}$. Show that this "intersection" is nonempty and is also a vector space.

3.2.12. Let $\mathcal{V}$ and $\mathcal{U}$ be vector spaces of n-tuples. Let $\mathcal{V} \cup \mathcal{U}$ be the set of all vectors which are in either $\mathcal{V}$ or $\mathcal{U}$. Are there circumstances in which $\mathcal{V} \cup \mathcal{U}$ is a vector space? Explain.

3.2.13. Let $\mathcal{V}$ and $\mathcal{U}$ be vector spaces of n-tuples, and define $\mathcal{T} = \mathcal{V} \oplus \mathcal{U}$ as the set of vectors $\{\mathbf{v} + \mathbf{u} : \mathbf{v} \text{ in } \mathcal{V} \text{ and } \mathbf{u} \text{ in } \mathcal{U}\}$. Show that $\mathcal{T}$ is a vector space. ($\mathcal{T}$ is called the *direct sum* of $\mathcal{U}$ and $\mathcal{V}$.)

3.2.14. Prove the following theorem: If $\{\mathbf{u}_1, \mathbf{u}_2, \ldots, \mathbf{u}_r\}$ and $\{\mathbf{v}_1, \mathbf{v}_2, \ldots, \mathbf{v}_s\}$ are linearly independent sets of vectors in $\mathcal{R}^n$ and $r + s > n$, then there exists $\mathbf{y} \neq \mathbf{0}$ which is in $span\{\mathbf{u}_1, \mathbf{u}_2, \ldots, \mathbf{u}_r\}$ and $span\{\mathbf{v}_1, v_2, \ldots, \mathbf{v}_s\}$. That is $span\{\mathbf{u}_1, \mathbf{u}_2, \ldots, \mathbf{u}_r\}$ and $span\{\mathbf{v}_1, \mathbf{v}_2, \ldots, \mathbf{v}_s\}$ have at least one nonzero vector in common.

3.3 BASES AND DIMENSION

Every vector space, other than the the trivial spaces $\{\mathbf{0}_n\}$, has many spanning sets. Among all these spanning sets we are interested in those that are linearly independent. Theorem 3.2.2 guarantees the existence of a linearly independent spanning set for every nontrivial vector space. Such sets are important enough to warrant a labelled definition.

Definition 3.3.1. *A linearly independent spanning set for the nontrivial vector space $\mathcal{V}$ is called a basis for $\mathcal{V}$.*

Theorem 3.3.1. *If $\{\mathbf{x}_1,\mathbf{x}_2,\ldots,\mathbf{x}_n\}$ and $\{\mathbf{y}_1,\mathbf{y}_2,\ldots,\mathbf{y}_m\}$ are each bases for the vector space $\mathcal{V}$, then $n = m$.*

Proof. Suppose $\{\mathbf{x}_1,\mathbf{x}_2,\ldots,\mathbf{x}_n\}$ and $\{\mathbf{y}_1,\mathbf{y}_2,\ldots,\mathbf{y}_m\}$ are each bases for the vector space $\mathcal{V}$. Let $\mathbf{X} = [\mathbf{x}_1 \quad \mathbf{x}_2 \quad \ldots \quad \mathbf{x}_n]$ and $\mathbf{Y} = [\mathbf{y}_1 \quad \mathbf{y}_2 \quad \ldots \quad \mathbf{y}_m]$. Since $\{\mathbf{x}_1,\mathbf{x}_2,\ldots,\mathbf{x}_n\}$ and $\{\mathbf{y}_1,\mathbf{y}_2,\ldots,\mathbf{y}_m\}$ are bases for $\mathcal{V}$, they are linearly independent sets. By Corollary 1 of Theorem 2.6.3,

$$\text{rank}(\mathbf{X}) = n, \ \text{rank}(\mathbf{Y}) = m \tag{3.3.1}$$

Suppose $m \neq n$; say $m < n$. Then since $\{\mathbf{y}_1,\mathbf{y}_2,\ldots,\mathbf{y}_m\}$ spans $\mathcal{V}$, every vector in $\mathcal{V}$ is some linear combination of these vectors. That is $\mathbf{Ya}_i = \mathbf{x}_i$ for each $i = 1,2,\ldots,n$. Thus, setting $\mathbf{A} = [\mathbf{a}_1 \quad \mathbf{a}_2 \quad \ldots \quad \mathbf{a}_n]$,

$$\mathbf{YA} = \mathbf{Y}[\mathbf{a}_1 \quad \mathbf{a}_2 \quad \ldots \quad \mathbf{a}_n] = [\mathbf{Ya}_1 \quad \mathbf{Ya}_2 \quad \ldots \quad \mathbf{Ya}_n] = \mathbf{X}$$

Hence, rank($\mathbf{YA}$) = rank($\mathbf{X}$). But by Theorem 2.7.2, rank($\mathbf{YA}$) $\leq$ rank($\mathbf{Y}$). Thus, using Eq. 3.3.1, n = rank($\mathbf{X}$) = rank($\mathbf{YA}$) $\leq$ rank($\mathbf{Y}$) $= m$, contradicting $m < n$. Hence $m \geq n$. Since $m > n$ is also seen to lead to a contradiction by the same argument with the roles of $\{\mathbf{y}_1,\mathbf{y}_2,\ldots,\mathbf{y}_m\}$ and $\{\mathbf{x}_1,\mathbf{x}_2,\ldots,\mathbf{x}_n\}$ reversed, it follows that $m = n$. ■

Definition 3.3.2. *The dimension of $\mathcal{V}$ (written* dim($\mathcal{V}$)*) is the number of vectors in any basis of $\mathcal{V}$. The dimension of $\{\mathbf{0}_n\}$ is zero.*

Example 3.3.1. Find the dimension of the vector space spanned by

$$\left\{\mathbf{x}_1 = \begin{bmatrix} 1 \\ 0 \\ -1 \end{bmatrix}, \mathbf{x}_2 = \begin{bmatrix} 1 \\ 1 \\ -1 \end{bmatrix}, \mathbf{x}_3 = \begin{bmatrix} 0 \\ -1 \\ 0 \end{bmatrix}\right\}$$

Solution. The given set is linearly dependent with a dependency relationship deduced in Example 2.6.8(*b*):

$$\begin{bmatrix} 1 \\ 0 \\ -1 \end{bmatrix} - \begin{bmatrix} 1 \\ 1 \\ -1 \end{bmatrix} - \begin{bmatrix} 0 \\ -1 \\ 0 \end{bmatrix} = \begin{bmatrix} 0 \\ 0 \\ 0 \end{bmatrix} \tag{3.3.2}$$

Moreover, $\{\mathbf{x}_1, \mathbf{x}_2\}$ is linearly independent. From Eq. 3.3.2 it follows that $\mathbf{x}_1 - \mathbf{x}_2 = \mathbf{x}_3$ and therefore $span\{\mathbf{x}_1, \mathbf{x}_2\} = span\{\mathbf{x}_1, \mathbf{x}_2, \mathbf{x}_3\}$. Thus, $\{\mathbf{x}_1, \mathbf{x}_2\}$ is a basis for $span\{\mathbf{x}_1, \mathbf{x}_2, \mathbf{x}_3\}$ and $\dim(span\{\mathbf{x}_1, \mathbf{x}_2, \mathbf{x}_3\}) = 2$.

The definition of dimension presented above corresponds to our intuitive understanding of the term. For instance, the vector space $\mathcal{R}^2 = span\{\mathbf{e}_1, \mathbf{e}_2\}$. That is, $\mathcal{R}^2$ is the set of all vectors with 2 components. When a vector's components are identified with the coordinates of a point, it is clear that $\mathcal{R}^2$ corresponds to all points in the plane. The same is true for the correspondence between the vectors in $\mathcal{R}^3$ and the points in the three dimensional space of solid analytic geometry. These ideas are explored in greater detail in Sections 3.7.

Theorem 3.3.2. *Suppose* $\mathcal{W}$ *is a subspace of* $\mathcal{V}$. *Then* $\dim(\mathcal{W}) < \dim(\mathcal{V})$ *if and only if* $\mathcal{W} \neq \mathcal{V}$.

Proof. Suppose $\mathcal{W} \neq \mathcal{V}$. Choose a basis for $\mathcal{W}$, say $\{\mathbf{w}_1, \mathbf{w}_2, \ldots, \mathbf{w}_s\}$. Then each vector $\mathbf{w}_i$ is in $\mathcal{W}$ and, therefore, in $\mathcal{V}$. Since $\{\mathbf{w}_1, \mathbf{w}_2, \ldots, \mathbf{w}_s\}$ is linearly independent and $\mathcal{W} \neq \mathcal{V}$, it follows that $\mathcal{W}$ is a proper subset of $\mathcal{V}$, and hence that $\{\mathbf{w}_1, \mathbf{w}_2, \ldots, \mathbf{w}_s\}$ cannot span $\mathcal{V}$. Thus there is a vector $\mathbf{v} \in \mathcal{V}$ such that $\{\mathbf{w}_1, \mathbf{w}_2, \ldots, \mathbf{w}_s, \mathbf{v}\}$ is a linearly independent set of vectors belonging to $\mathcal{V}$. It follows that the dimension of $\mathcal{V}$ must be at least $s + 1$. The converse is trivial. ■

PROBLEMS

PART 1

3.3.1. Find bases and the dimensions of the space spanned by the vectors:

$$(a)\ \left\{\begin{bmatrix}1\\0\\1\\0\end{bmatrix}, \begin{bmatrix}1\\0\\1\\1\end{bmatrix}\right\} \qquad (b)\ \left\{\begin{bmatrix}0\\1\\1\\1\end{bmatrix}, \begin{bmatrix}1\\1\\1\\0\end{bmatrix}, \begin{bmatrix}1\\1\\0\\1\end{bmatrix}\right\} \qquad (c)\ \left\{\begin{bmatrix}0\\1\\0\\1\end{bmatrix}, \begin{bmatrix}1\\0\\1\\0\end{bmatrix}, \begin{bmatrix}0\\0\\1\\1\end{bmatrix}\right\}$$

3.3.2. Find a basis and the dimension of each of the following spans:

$$(a)\ \begin{bmatrix}\alpha\\\beta\\\gamma\\\delta\end{bmatrix} \qquad (b)\ \begin{bmatrix}\alpha\\\beta\\\gamma\\\delta\end{bmatrix}, \begin{matrix}\alpha + \beta = 0\\ \gamma + \delta = 0\end{matrix} \qquad (c)\ \begin{bmatrix}\alpha\\\beta\\\gamma\\\delta\end{bmatrix}, \alpha + \beta = 0$$

$$(d)\ \begin{bmatrix}\alpha\\\beta\\\gamma\\\delta\end{bmatrix}, \alpha + \beta + \gamma = 0$$

3.3.3. Find the bases and the dimensions of the spaces spanned by:

$$(a)\ \begin{bmatrix}\alpha\\2\alpha\\-\alpha\\0\end{bmatrix} \qquad (b)\ \begin{bmatrix}\alpha\\-\alpha\\0\\0\end{bmatrix} \qquad (c)\ \left\{\begin{bmatrix}1\\2\\2\end{bmatrix}, \begin{bmatrix}1\\1\\1\end{bmatrix}, \begin{bmatrix}-1\\0\\0\end{bmatrix}\right\}$$

3.3.4. Give a plausible reason for defining the dimension of $\{\mathbf{0}_n\}$ as 0.

PART 2

3.3.5. What are the possible dimensions of $span\{\mathbf{x}_1, \mathbf{x}_2\}$?

3.3.6. Give an example of two vector spaces $\mathcal{V}$ and $\mathcal{W}$, each belonging to $\mathcal{R}^2$, which shows that $\dim(\mathcal{V}) = \dim(\mathcal{W})$ does not imply that $\mathcal{V} = \mathcal{W}$.

3.3.7. If $\mathcal{S}$ is a vector space of 2-tuples and $\dim(\mathcal{S}) = 2$, show that $\mathcal{S} = \mathcal{R}^2$. Contrast this with the result in Problem 3.3.6.

PART 3

3.3.8. Suppose $\{\mathbf{x}_1, \mathbf{x}_2, \ldots, \mathbf{x}_n\}$ is a basis for $\mathcal{R}^n$ and $\mathbf{S}$ is nonsingular. Show that $\{\mathbf{S}\mathbf{x}_1, \mathbf{S}\mathbf{x}_2, \ldots, \mathbf{S}\mathbf{x}_n\}$ is another basis for $\mathcal{R}^n$. (Hint: Consider the product $\mathbf{SX}$, where $\mathbf{X} = [\mathbf{x}_1 \quad \mathbf{x}_2 \quad \ldots \quad \mathbf{x}_n]$.)

3.3.9. Let $\mathcal{V}$ and $\mathcal{W}$ be vector spaces of n-tuples, and define $\mathcal{S} = \mathcal{V} \cap \mathcal{W}$ as the set of vectors in both $\mathcal{V}$ and $\mathcal{W}$. Show that $\mathcal{S}$ is a vector space and prove that $\dim(\mathcal{S}) \leq \dim(\mathcal{V})$ and $\dim(\mathcal{S}) \leq \dim(\mathcal{W})$. (See Problem 3.2.11.)

3.3.10. Define $\mathcal{T} = \mathcal{W} \oplus \mathcal{V}$ (See Problem 3.2.13). Prove that $\dim(\mathcal{T}) \geq \dim(\mathcal{V})$ and $\dim(\mathcal{T}) \geq \dim(\mathcal{W})$.

3.3.11. If $\mathcal{V}$ is a vector space of n-tuples and $\dim(\mathcal{V}) = n$, show that $\mathcal{V} = \mathcal{R}^n$.

3.3.12. Suppose $\{\mathbf{x}_1, \mathbf{x}_2, \ldots, \mathbf{x}_k\}$ is linearly independent and $\mathbf{x}_i \in \mathcal{V}$ for $i = 1, 2, \ldots, k$. Explain why $\dim(\mathcal{V}) \geq k$.

3.3.13. Suppose $\{\mathbf{x}_1, \mathbf{x}_2, \ldots, \mathbf{x}_k\}$ is a spanning set of $\mathcal{V}$, $\mathbf{x}_1 \in \mathcal{V}$ for $i = 1, 2, \ldots, k$. Explain why $\dim(\mathcal{V}) \leq k$.

3.3.14. Use the answers to Problems 3.3.12 and 3.3.13 to interpret the statement: A basis is a minimal spanning set and a maximal independent set.

3.4 THE ROW AND COLUMN SPACES OF A

The *row space* of **A** is the span of the rows (considered as vectors) of **A**. We denote this space by $row(\mathbf{A})$. The *column space* is the span of the columns of **A**, and is denoted by $col(\mathbf{A})$. The column space of **A** is the row space of $\mathbf{A}^T$. That is, $row(\mathbf{A}^T) = col(\mathbf{A})$. Our goal is to find a basis and the dimension of each of these vector spaces. Although these vector spaces can differ vastly (for one thing, if **A** is $m \times n$ $row(\mathbf{A}) \subseteq \mathcal{R}^n$ and $col(\mathbf{A}) \subseteq \mathcal{R}^m$), they do have one thing in common—they have the same dimension, namely $rank(\mathbf{A})$. This is Corollary 2 of Theorem 3.4.1.

Theorem 3.4.1. *If* **A** *is row equivalent to* **B** *then* $row(\mathbf{A}) = row(\mathbf{B})$.

Proof. If we can prove that $\mathbf{A} \rightarrow \mathbf{A}_1$ implies $row(\mathbf{A}) = row(\mathbf{A}_1)$, where $\mathbf{A}_1$ is the result of applying one row operation to **A**, the proof of the theorem then follows by repeating the argument for each step in the diagram $\mathbf{A} \rightarrow \cdots \rightarrow \mathbf{B}$. The details are generalizations of the arguments presented in the solution of Example 3.3.2. (See Problem 3.4.11.) ■

Corollary 1. *The set of nonzero rows in the rref of* **A** *is a basis for* $row(\mathbf{A})$, *and, therefore, the dimension of the row space is the rank of* **A**.

Proof. It should be obvious that the nonzero rows of $\mathbf{A}_r$ are linearly independent and span $row(\mathbf{A}_r)$. By Theorem 3.4.1, $row(\mathbf{A}) = row(\mathbf{A}_r)$ and hence these rows span **A**. Thus $\dim(row(\mathbf{A})) = rank(\mathbf{A})$. (See Problem 3.4.14.) ■

Corollary 2. *For each* $\mathbf{A}$, $rank(\mathbf{A}) = \dim(col(\mathbf{A})) = \dim(row(\mathbf{A}))$

Proof. Corollary 1 asserts that for each $\mathbf{A}$, $\dim(row(\mathbf{A})) = \text{rank}(\mathbf{A})$. Hence $\dim(row(\mathbf{A}^T)) = \dim(col(\mathbf{A})) = \text{rank}(\mathbf{A}^T)$. By Theorem 2.7.4, $\text{rank}(\mathbf{A}^T) = \text{rank}(\mathbf{A})$. ■

Theorem 3.4.1 asserts that $row(\mathbf{A})$ is unaltered by row operations. The same cannot be said for $col(\mathbf{A})$. For instance, the column space of $\mathbf{J}_3$ is $span\{\mathbf{1}_3\}$, while the column space of the rref of $\mathbf{J}_3$ is $span\{\mathbf{e}_1\}$. These one dimensional spaces are not the same; they represent different lines in $\mathcal{R}^3$. Although the row equivalence of $\mathbf{A}$ and $\mathbf{B}$ does not imply $col(\mathbf{A}) = col(\mathbf{B})$, it is true that $\dim(col(\mathbf{A})) = \dim(col(\mathbf{B}))$.

Corollary 3. *If* $\mathbf{A}$ *and* $\mathbf{B}$ *are row equivalent then* $\dim(col(\mathbf{A})) = \dim(col(\mathbf{B}))$.

Proof. Since $\mathbf{A}$ is row equivalent to $\mathbf{B}$, $\text{rank}(\mathbf{A}) = \text{rank}(\mathbf{B})$. By Corollary 2 of Theorem 3.4.1, $col(\mathbf{A})$ and $col(\mathbf{B})$, have same dimension, $\text{rank}(\mathbf{A})$. ■

Since the rref of $\mathbf{A}$ is unique, the nonzero rows of $\mathbf{A}_r$ are also uniquely defined. These rows form a special basis for $row(\mathbf{A})$, called the *canonical basis* of $row(\mathbf{A})$. We can exploit the uniqueness of the canonical basis to test whether the spans of two sets are the same vector spaces. This is done by first constructing matrices *whose row spaces are the vector spaces in question*. Then the canonical basis of each matrix is compared. If they are identical, except for zero rows, then the two vector spaces are the same; otherwise, the given vectors spaces are distinct.

Example 3.4.1. Show that these vector spaces are the same: The set consisting of all vectors of the form $[\alpha \quad \beta \quad \gamma \quad \delta]^T$, $\alpha + \beta + \gamma = \delta$, and the span of

$$\left\{ \mathbf{a}_1 = \begin{bmatrix} -1 \\ 1 \\ 1 \\ 1 \end{bmatrix}, \mathbf{a}_2 = \begin{bmatrix} 1 \\ -1 \\ 1 \\ 1 \end{bmatrix}, \mathbf{a}_3 = \begin{bmatrix} 1 \\ 1 \\ -1 \\ 1 \end{bmatrix} \right\}$$

Solution. The idea is to compare the canonical bases for each of the given vector spaces. Begin by constructing the matrix $\mathbf{A}$ whose rows are the vectors $\mathbf{a}_1$, $\mathbf{a}_2$ and $\mathbf{a}_3$ and then finding the rref of $\mathbf{A}$.

$$\mathbf{A} = \begin{bmatrix} -1 & 1 & 1 & 1 \\ 1 & -1 & 1 & 1 \\ 1 & 1 & -1 & 1 \end{bmatrix} \to \begin{bmatrix} -1 & 1 & 1 & 1 \\ 0 & 0 & 2 & 2 \\ 0 & 2 & 0 & 2 \end{bmatrix} \to \begin{bmatrix} -1 & 1 & 1 & 1 \\ 0 & 1 & 0 & 1 \\ 0 & 0 & 1 & 1 \end{bmatrix}$$

$$\to \begin{bmatrix} 1 & 0 & 0 & 1 \\ 0 & 1 & 0 & 1 \\ 0 & 0 & 1 & 1 \end{bmatrix}$$

Hence the canonical basis for $span\{\mathbf{a}_1,\mathbf{a}_2,\mathbf{a}_3\}$ is

$$\left\{\begin{bmatrix}1\\0\\0\\1\end{bmatrix},\begin{bmatrix}0\\1\\0\\1\end{bmatrix},\begin{bmatrix}0\\0\\1\\1\end{bmatrix}\right\}$$

On the other hand, given that $\delta = \alpha + \beta + \gamma$, it follows that

$$\begin{bmatrix}\alpha\\\beta\\\gamma\\\delta\end{bmatrix} = \begin{bmatrix}\alpha\\\beta\\\gamma\\\alpha+\beta+\gamma\end{bmatrix} = \alpha\begin{bmatrix}1\\0\\0\\1\end{bmatrix} + \beta\begin{bmatrix}0\\1\\0\\1\end{bmatrix} + \gamma\begin{bmatrix}0\\0\\1\\1\end{bmatrix}$$

Since both vector spaces are spanned by the same basis, the spaces are identical.

Theorem 3.4.2. *The set of leading columns of* $\mathbf{A}$ *is a basis for* $col(\mathbf{A})$.

Proof. Suppose $\mathbf{A}_r$ is the rref of $\mathbf{A}$ and rank($\mathbf{A}$) $= r$. Then $\mathbf{A}$ is row equivalent to $\mathbf{A}_r$ and hence there exists a nonsingular matrix $\mathbf{S}$ such that $\mathbf{A} = \mathbf{S}\mathbf{A}_r$. The set of leading columns of $\mathbf{A}_r$ is the set $\{\mathbf{e}_1,\mathbf{e}_2,\ldots,\mathbf{e}_r\}$ and by definition $\{\mathbf{S}\mathbf{e}_1,\mathbf{S}\mathbf{e}_2,\ldots,\mathbf{S}\mathbf{e}_r\}$ is the set of leading columns of $\mathbf{A}$. But this set is linearly independent (since it is a subset of the set of columns of the nonsingular matrix $\mathbf{S}$); each vector is a column of $\mathbf{A}$ (indeed, a leading column of $\mathbf{A}$); and there are r = rank($\mathbf{A}$) = dim($col(\mathbf{A})$) of them. ■

An example will be useful to clarify this result and illustrate its applications. The basic tool is an "auxiliary" matrix $\mathbf{A}$ whose columns are the vectors under study.

Example 3.4.2. Let

$$\mathcal{S} = \left\{\begin{bmatrix}-1\\1\\1\end{bmatrix},\begin{bmatrix}1\\-1\\1\end{bmatrix},\begin{bmatrix}1\\1\\-1\end{bmatrix},\begin{bmatrix}1\\1\\1\end{bmatrix}\right\}$$

Find a basis for $span(\mathcal{S})$ from among the vectors in $\mathcal{S}$. Find dim($span$ ($\mathcal{S}$)).

Solution. Identifying the vectors in $\mathcal{S}$ with the rows of a matrix $\mathbf{R}$ and finding the canonical basis for $row(\mathbf{R})$ can be used to determine dim($span(\mathcal{S})$) but will fail to provide a basis for $span(\mathcal{S})$ from among the vectors in $\mathcal{S}$. To see this consider the following:

$$\mathbf{R} = \begin{bmatrix}-1 & 1 & 1\\1 & -1 & 1\\1 & 1 & -1\\1 & 1 & 1\end{bmatrix} \to \cdots \to \begin{bmatrix}1 & 0 & 0\\0 & 1 & 0\\0 & 0 & 1\\0 & 0 & 0\end{bmatrix}$$

and hence rank(**R**) = 3 and

$$\left\{\begin{bmatrix}1\\0\\0\end{bmatrix},\begin{bmatrix}0\\1\\0\end{bmatrix},\begin{bmatrix}0\\0\\1\end{bmatrix}\right\}$$

is the canonical basis for $row(\mathbf{R}) = span(\mathcal{S})$. Note that not a single one of these vectors is in $\mathcal{S}$! On the other hand, if we construct the auxiliary matrix **A** so that $col(\mathbf{A})$ is the span of the given vectors, then we can identify the leading columns of **A** by finding the leading columns of $\mathbf{A}_r$.

$$\mathbf{A} = \begin{bmatrix}-1 & 1 & 1 & 1\\ 1 & -1 & 1 & 1\\ 1 & 1 & -1 & 1\end{bmatrix} \rightarrow \cdots \rightarrow \begin{bmatrix}1 & 0 & 0 & 1\\ 0 & 1 & 0 & 1\\ 0 & 0 & 1 & 1\end{bmatrix}$$

Hence the first three columns of **A** are its leading columns. Thus, the set of vectors

$$\left\{\begin{bmatrix}-1\\1\\1\end{bmatrix},\begin{bmatrix}1\\-1\\1\end{bmatrix},\begin{bmatrix}1\\1\\-1\end{bmatrix}\right\}$$

form a basis for $span(\mathcal{S})$ from the given four vectors of $\mathcal{S}$, and this span has dimension 3.

PROBLEMS

PART 1

3.4.1. Find bases and the dimensions of the the row and column spaces of the following matrices:

$(a)\begin{bmatrix}1 & 1 & -1\\ 0 & 1 & 1\\ 1 & -1 & -3\end{bmatrix}$ $(b)\begin{bmatrix}1 & 1 & 1\\ 0 & 1 & 1\\ 0 & 0 & 1\end{bmatrix}$ $(c)\begin{bmatrix}1 & 1 & 1\\ 0 & 1 & 1\\ 1 & -1 & 3\end{bmatrix}$

3.4.2. Repeat Problem 3.4.1 for the matrices:

$(a)\begin{bmatrix}2 & 4 & 1\\ 0 & -2 & -1\\ 1 & 3 & 1\end{bmatrix}$ $(b)\begin{bmatrix}2 & 1 & 0 & 1\\ 0 & 0 & 0 & -1\\ 1 & 0 & 1 & 1\end{bmatrix}$ $(c)\begin{bmatrix}1 & -1 & 1 & 0 & 0\\ 1 & 0 & 2 & 0 & 0\\ 3 & -2 & 4 & 1 & 1\end{bmatrix}$

3.4.3. Repeat Problem 3.4.1 for the matrices:

$(a)\begin{bmatrix}1 & -1 & 0 & 1\\ 1 & 2 & 0 & -1\\ 0 & 0 & 1 & -1\\ 1 & 0 & 0 & 1\end{bmatrix}$ $(b)\begin{bmatrix}1 & 2 & 0\\ 0 & -1 & -1\\ 0 & 1 & 1\\ 1 & 1 & 3\end{bmatrix}$ $(c)\begin{bmatrix}1 & 0 & 5 & 1 & 1\\ 0 & 2 & 2 & -1 & 0\\ 1 & 1 & 0 & 1 & 1\\ 1 & 0 & -3 & 0 & 1\end{bmatrix}$

$(d)\begin{bmatrix}1 & 1 & -1 & 1\\ 1 & 0 & 1 & 2\\ 2 & 1 & 0 & 3\\ -1 & 1 & 0 & 0\end{bmatrix}$

3.4.4. Repeat Problem 3.4.1 for the matrices:
(*a*) $[1 \quad \mathbf{c}_m^{\mathrm{T}}]$ (*b*) $[\mathbf{0}_n^{\mathrm{T}} \quad 1 \quad \mathbf{c}_m^{\mathrm{T}}]$ (*c*) $\mathbf{O}_{m\times n}$ (*d*) $\mathbf{J}_n$.

3.4.5. What are the row and column spaces of nonsingular matrices?

PART 2

3.4.6. Find $\mathbf{A}$ and $\mathbf{B}$ such that $\mathbf{A}$ is row equivalent to $\mathbf{B}$ but $col(\mathbf{A}) \neq col(\mathbf{B})$.

3.4.7. If $\mathbf{A}$ has full row rank, show that $col([\mathbf{A} \quad \mathbf{B}]) = col(\mathbf{A})$.

3.4.8. If $\mathbf{A}_{m\times n}$ has full column rank, show that $row(\mathbf{A}) = \mathcal{R}^n$.

3.4.9. Find a basis for the column space of $\mathbf{J}_n - n\mathbf{I}_n$.

3.4.10. Find a vector $\mathbf{v}_0$ in $\mathcal{R}^4$ so that $span\{\mathbf{v}_1, \mathbf{v}_2, \mathbf{v}_3, \mathbf{v}_0\} = \mathcal{R}^4$, given

$$\mathbf{v}_1 = \begin{bmatrix} 1 \\ 0 \\ -1 \\ 0 \end{bmatrix} \qquad \mathbf{v}_2 = \begin{bmatrix} 1 \\ 1 \\ -1 \\ 1 \end{bmatrix} \qquad \mathbf{v}_3 = \begin{bmatrix} 0 \\ 0 \\ -2 \\ 1 \end{bmatrix}$$

PART 3

3.4.11. Let $\mathbf{F}$ be an elementary row matrix. Show that $row(\mathbf{FA}) = row(\mathbf{A})$.

3.4.12. Show that $\dim(row(\mathbf{AB})) \le \dim(row(\mathbf{A}))$ and $\dim(row(\mathbf{AB})) \le \dim(row(\mathbf{B}))$.

3.4.13. Show that $\dim(col(\mathbf{AB})) \le \dim(col(\mathbf{A}))$ and $\dim(col(\mathbf{AB})) \le \dim(col(\mathbf{B}))$.

3.4.14. Show that the nonzero rows of $\mathbf{A}_r$ must be linearly independent by completing the following argument. Suppose the contrary, that $\mathbf{A}_r$ is in rref and the nonzero rows form a linearly dependent set. Show that there exists a nonsingular matrix $\mathbf{S}$ such that $\mathbf{SA}_r$ has rank less than $\mathbf{A}_r$. This is a contradiction.

3.4.15. Prove: If $\mathbf{A}$ is row equivalent to $\mathbf{B}$ and some subset of the columns of $\mathbf{A}$ are linearly dependent, then the same subset of the columns of $\mathbf{B}$ is linearly dependent. Moreover, the weights in the dependency relationship for the columns of $\mathbf{A}$ can be used as the weights in the dependency relationship for the columns of $\mathbf{B}$.

3.4.16. Show that $col(\mathbf{A}+\mathbf{B}) \subseteq col([\mathbf{A}\ \mathbf{B}])$ and that $\dim(col([\mathbf{A}\ \mathbf{B}])) \le \dim(col(\mathbf{A})) + \dim(col(\mathbf{B}))$. Thus deduce, $\text{rank}(\mathbf{A}+\mathbf{B}) \le \text{rank}(\mathbf{A}) + \text{rank}(\mathbf{B})$.

3.4.17. Use Problem 3.4.16 to establish $|\text{rank}(\mathbf{A}) - \text{rank}(\mathbf{B})| \le \text{rank}(\mathbf{A}+\mathbf{B})$. Hint: $\text{rank}(\mathbf{A}) = \text{rank}(\mathbf{A}+\mathbf{B}-\mathbf{B}) \le \text{rank}(\mathbf{A}+\mathbf{B}) + \text{rank}(-\mathbf{B}) = \text{rank}(\mathbf{A}+\mathbf{B}) + \text{rank}(\mathbf{B})$.

3.5 THE NULL SPACE OF A

The primary goal of this section is to determine the set of solutions of $\mathbf{Ax} = \mathbf{0}$, where $\mathbf{A}$ is $m \times n$ and $\text{rank}(\mathbf{A}) = r$. This important vector space is called the null space of $\mathbf{A}$ and is written $null(\mathbf{A})$. One of the highlights of this section is the theorem that relates the parameters, n, $\text{rank}(\mathbf{A})$, and $\dim(null(\mathbf{A}))$ by the simple formula

$$\dim(null(\mathbf{A})) = n - r \tag{3.5.1}$$

The quantity $\dim(null(\mathbf{A}))$ is called the *nullity of* $\mathbf{A}$ and we reserve the symbol η for this parameter. Thus Eq. 3.5.1 may be written $\eta + r = n$. (See Theorem 3.5.3.) We begin the study of $null(\mathbf{A})$ by presenting an algorithm which supplies a basis for this space. This algorithm is similar to the one used to compute $\mathbf{A}^{-1}$.

Suppose $\mathbf{R}$ is the rref of $\mathbf{A}^{\mathrm{T}}$. Then there exists an arrow diagram

$$[\mathbf{A}^{\mathrm{T}} \quad \mathbf{I}] \to \cdots \to [\mathbf{R} \quad \mathbf{N}] = \begin{bmatrix} \mathbf{R}_1 & \mathbf{N}_1 \\ \mathbf{O} & \mathbf{N}_2 \end{bmatrix} \tag{3.5.2}$$

where $\mathbf{R}_1$ has no zero rows and is the rref of $\mathbf{A}^{\mathrm{T}}$ and

$$\mathbf{R} = \begin{bmatrix} \mathbf{R}_1 \\ \mathbf{O} \end{bmatrix}, \quad \mathbf{N} = \begin{bmatrix} \mathbf{N}_1 \\ \mathbf{N}_2 \end{bmatrix} \tag{3.5.3}$$

The algorithm is the arrow diagram in Eq. 3.5.2.

In Section 3.5.1 we shall show the set of columns of $\mathbf{N}_2^{\mathrm{T}}$ is a basis for $null(\mathbf{A})$. (Hence, among other things, $\mathbf{A}\mathbf{N}_2^{\mathrm{T}} = \mathbf{O}$.) A few illustrations will explain the use of Eq. 3.5.2. One final note: the algorithm in Eq. 3.5.2 does not require that $[\mathbf{R}\ \mathbf{N}]$ be in rref; it is sufficient that $\mathbf{R}$ is the rref of $\mathbf{A}^{\mathrm{T}}$. If, however, $[\mathbf{R}\ \mathbf{N}]$ is in rref, then the set of columns of $\mathbf{N}_2^{\mathrm{T}}$ is the canonical basis for $null(\mathbf{A})$. In either case, the set of columns of $\mathbf{R}_1^{\mathrm{T}}$ is the canonical basis for $row(\mathbf{A}^{\mathrm{T}}) = col(\mathbf{A})$.

Example 3.5.1. Find the null and column spaces of the matrix

$$\mathbf{A} = \begin{bmatrix} 1 & 2 & 0 & -1 & -2 \\ 1 & 2 & 1 & 0 & -1 \\ 0 & 0 & 1 & 1 & 1 \\ 1 & 2 & 2 & 1 & 0 \end{bmatrix}$$

Solution. We find the rref of $[\mathbf{A}^{\mathrm{T}} \quad \mathbf{I}]$.

$$[\mathbf{A}^{\mathrm{T}} \quad \mathbf{I}] = \left[\begin{array}{cccc|ccccc} 1 & 1 & 0 & 1 & 1 & 0 & 0 & 0 & 0 \\ 2 & 2 & 0 & 2 & 0 & 1 & 0 & 0 & 0 \\ 0 & 1 & 1 & 2 & 0 & 0 & 1 & 0 & 0 \\ -1 & 0 & 1 & 1 & 0 & 0 & 0 & 1 & 0 \\ -2 & -1 & 1 & 0 & 0 & 0 & 0 & 0 & 1 \end{array}\right] \to$$

$$\cdots \to \left[\begin{array}{cccc|ccccc} 1 & 0 & -1 & -1 & 0 & 0 & 0 & -1 & 0 \\ 0 & 1 & 1 & 2 & 0 & 0 & 0 & 2 & -1 \\ \hline 0 & 0 & 0 & 0 & 1 & 0 & 0 & -1 & 1 \\ 0 & 0 & 0 & 0 & 0 & 1 & 0 & -2 & 2 \\ 0 & 0 & 0 & 0 & 0 & 0 & 1 & -2 & 1 \end{array}\right]$$

Thus,

$$col(\mathbf{A}) = span\left\{\begin{bmatrix} 1 \\ 0 \\ -1 \\ -1 \end{bmatrix}, \begin{bmatrix} 0 \\ 1 \\ 1 \\ 2 \end{bmatrix}\right\} \quad \text{and}$$

$$null(\mathbf{A}) = span\left\{\begin{bmatrix} 1 \\ 0 \\ 0 \\ -1 \\ 1 \end{bmatrix}, \begin{bmatrix} 0 \\ 1 \\ 0 \\ -2 \\ 2 \end{bmatrix}, \begin{bmatrix} 0 \\ 0 \\ 1 \\ -2 \\ 1 \end{bmatrix}\right\}$$

Example 3.5.2. Find a basis and the dimension of the null space of $\mathbf{J}_4$.

Solution. Since the rank of $\mathbf{J}_4$ is 1, $\eta = 3$ is an implication of Eq. 3.5.1. We confirm this result and find the canonical basis of $null(\mathbf{J}_4)$ by use of the algorithm in Eq. 3.5.2.

$$\left[\begin{array}{cccc|cccc} 1 & 1 & 1 & 1 & 1 & 0 & 0 & 0 \\ 1 & 1 & 1 & 1 & 0 & 1 & 0 & 0 \\ 1 & 1 & 1 & 1 & 0 & 0 & 1 & 0 \\ 1 & 1 & 1 & 1 & 0 & 0 & 0 & 1 \end{array}\right] \rightarrow$$

$$\cdots \rightarrow \left[\begin{array}{cccc|cccc} 1 & 1 & 1 & 1 & 1 & 0 & 0 & 0 \\ \hline 0 & 0 & 0 & 0 & -1 & 1 & 0 & 0 \\ 0 & 0 & 0 & 0 & -1 & 0 & 1 & 0 \\ 0 & 0 & 0 & 0 & -1 & 0 & 0 & 1 \end{array}\right] = [\mathbf{NJ}_4 \quad \mathbf{N}]$$

Although $\mathbf{NJ}_4$ is in rref, $[\mathbf{NJ}_4\ \mathbf{N}]$ is not. Nonetheless, the last three rows of $\mathbf{N}$ form a basis for $null(\mathbf{J}_4)$, but not the canonical basis.

$$null(\mathbf{J}_4) = span\left\{\begin{bmatrix} -1 \\ 1 \\ 0 \\ 0 \end{bmatrix}, \begin{bmatrix} -1 \\ 0 \\ 1 \\ 0 \end{bmatrix}, \begin{bmatrix} -1 \\ 0 \\ 0 \\ 1 \end{bmatrix}\right\}$$

confirming that the nullity of $\mathbf{J}_4$ is 3.

Example 3.5.3. Find the bases for the null, column and row spaces of

$$\mathbf{A} = \begin{bmatrix} 1 & 0 & 0 \\ 1 & -1 & 1 \\ 1 & -1 & 1 \\ 1 & 1 & -1 \end{bmatrix}$$

and verify Eq. 3.5.1.

Solution. Compute the rref of $[\mathbf{A}^{\mathrm{T}} \quad \mathbf{I}]$.

$$\left[\begin{array}{cccc|ccc} 1 & 1 & 1 & 1 & 1 & 0 & 0 \\ 0 & -1 & -1 & 1 & 0 & 1 & 0 \\ 0 & 1 & 1 & -1 & 0 & 0 & 1 \end{array}\right] \rightarrow \cdots \rightarrow \left[\begin{array}{cccc|ccc} 1 & 0 & 0 & 2 & 1 & 1 & 0 \\ 0 & 1 & 1 & -1 & 0 & -1 & 0 \\ \hline 0 & 0 & 0 & 0 & 0 & 1 & 1 \end{array}\right]$$

Thus,

$$null(\mathbf{A}) = span\left\{\begin{bmatrix} 0 \\ 1 \\ 1 \end{bmatrix}\right\} \quad \text{and} \quad col(\mathbf{A}) = span\left\{\begin{bmatrix} 1 \\ 0 \\ 0 \\ 2 \end{bmatrix}, \begin{bmatrix} 0 \\ 1 \\ 1 \\ -1 \end{bmatrix}\right\}$$

and these are canonical bases for their respective spaces. Columns 1 and 2 are leading columns of $\mathbf{A}^{\mathrm{T}}$, hence rows 1 and 2 of $\mathbf{A}$ is a basis for $row(\mathbf{A})$. Finally, $r = 2$, $\eta = 1$, and $n = 3$.

Example 3.5.4. Find bases for the row space, column space and null space of **A**, and verify Eq. 3.5.1 where **A** is given as follows:

$$\mathbf{A} = \begin{bmatrix} 1 & 1 & 0 & 1 \\ 2 & 2 & 0 & 2 \\ 0 & 1 & 1 & 2 \\ -1 & 0 & 1 & 1 \\ -2 & -1 & 1 & 0 \end{bmatrix}$$

Solution. Once again we reduce $[\mathbf{A}^T \;\; \mathbf{I}]$ to $[\mathbf{R} \;\; \mathbf{N}]$:

$$\left[\begin{array}{ccccc|cccc} 1 & 2 & 0 & -1 & -2 & 1 & 0 & 0 & 0 \\ 1 & 2 & 1 & 0 & -1 & 0 & 1 & 0 & 0 \\ 0 & 0 & 1 & 1 & 1 & 0 & 0 & 1 & 0 \\ 1 & 2 & 2 & 1 & 0 & 0 & 0 & 0 & 1 \end{array}\right] \rightarrow$$

$$\cdots \rightarrow \left[\begin{array}{ccccc|cccc} 1 & 2 & 0 & -1 & -2 & 1 & 0 & 0 & 0 \\ 0 & 0 & 1 & 1 & 1 & -1 & 1 & 0 & 0 \\ \hline 0 & 0 & 0 & 0 & 0 & 1 & 0 & 2 & -1 \\ 0 & 0 & 0 & 0 & 0 & 0 & 1 & 1 & -1 \end{array}\right]$$

Hence,

$$null(\mathbf{A}) = span\left\{\begin{bmatrix} 1 \\ 0 \\ 2 \\ -1 \end{bmatrix}, \begin{bmatrix} 0 \\ 1 \\ 1 \\ -1 \end{bmatrix}\right\} \qquad col(\mathbf{A}) = span\left\{\begin{bmatrix} 1 \\ 2 \\ 0 \\ -1 \\ -2 \end{bmatrix}, \begin{bmatrix} 0 \\ 0 \\ 1 \\ 1 \\ 1 \end{bmatrix}\right\}$$

$$row(\mathbf{A}) = span\left\{\begin{bmatrix} 1 \\ 1 \\ 0 \\ 1 \end{bmatrix}, \begin{bmatrix} 0 \\ 1 \\ 1 \\ 2 \end{bmatrix}\right\}$$

Clearly $\eta = 2$, and $n - r = 2$.

Example 3.5.5. Find a matrix **B** whose null space is spanned by

$$\mathbf{c}_1 = \begin{bmatrix} 1 \\ 0 \\ 0 \\ -1 \end{bmatrix} \qquad \mathbf{c}_2 = \begin{bmatrix} 1 \\ 1 \\ 1 \\ 0 \end{bmatrix}$$

Solution. Define $\mathbf{C} = [\mathbf{c}_1 \;\; \mathbf{c}_2]$. If $\mathbf{c}_1$ and $\mathbf{c}_2$ are to belong to $null(\mathbf{B})$, then $\mathbf{BC} = \mathbf{O}$. In terms of the algorithm in Eq. 3.5.2, $\mathbf{C}^T\mathbf{B}^T = \mathbf{O}^T$ so that we set $\mathbf{C} = \mathrm{A}^T$ and the algorithm begins with $[\mathbf{C} \;\; \mathbf{I}]$ and returns $\mathbf{B} = \mathbf{N}_2$:

$$[\mathbf{C} \;\; \mathbf{I}] = \left[\begin{array}{cc|cccc} 1 & 1 & 1 & 0 & 0 & 0 \\ 0 & 1 & 0 & 1 & 0 & 0 \\ 0 & 1 & 0 & 0 & 1 & 0 \\ -1 & 0 & 0 & 0 & 0 & 1 \end{array}\right] \rightarrow \cdots \rightarrow \left[\begin{array}{cc|cccc} 1 & 1 & 1 & 0 & 0 & 0 \\ 0 & 1 & 0 & 1 & 0 & 0 \\ \hline 0 & 0 & 0 & -1 & 1 & 0 \\ 0 & 0 & 1 & -1 & 0 & 1 \end{array}\right]$$

Hence

$$\mathbf{B} = \mathbf{N}_2 = \begin{bmatrix} 0 & -1 & 1 & 0 \\ 1 & -1 & 0 & 1 \end{bmatrix}$$

Example 3.5.6. Find a matrix **A** whose null space is spanned by

$$\mathbf{c}_1 = \begin{bmatrix} 1 \\ 0 \\ 0 \\ -1 \end{bmatrix} \qquad \mathbf{c}_2 = \begin{bmatrix} 1 \\ 1 \\ 1 \\ 0 \end{bmatrix} \qquad \mathbf{c}_3 = \begin{bmatrix} 0 \\ 1 \\ 1 \\ 0 \end{bmatrix}$$

Solution. The relevant matrix is $[\mathbf{C} \quad \mathbf{I}] = [\mathbf{c}_1 \quad \mathbf{c}_2 \quad \mathbf{c}_3 \quad \mathbf{I}]$. Then

$$[\mathbf{C} \quad \mathbf{I}] = \left[\begin{array}{ccc|cccc} 1 & 1 & 0 & 1 & 0 & 0 & 0 \\ 0 & 1 & 1 & 0 & 1 & 0 & 0 \\ 0 & 1 & 1 & 0 & 0 & 0 & 0 \\ -1 & 0 & 0 & 0 & 0 & 0 & 1 \end{array}\right] \rightarrow \cdots \rightarrow \left[\begin{array}{ccc|cccc} 1 & 1 & 0 & 1 & 0 & 0 & 0 \\ 0 & 1 & 1 & 0 & 1 & 1 & 1 \\ \hline 0 & 0 & 0 & 0 & -1 & 1 & 0 \\ 0 & 0 & 0 & 1 & -1 & 0 & 1 \end{array}\right]$$

which yields the same null space as in Example 3.5.5.

The reason that the same matrix solves both Example 3.5.5 and 3.5.6 is the fact that $\mathbf{c}_3$ is in the span of $\{\mathbf{c}_1, \mathbf{c}_2\}$ and hence $null(\mathbf{A}) = span\{\mathbf{c}_1, \mathbf{c}_2\} = span\{\mathbf{c}_1, \mathbf{c}_2, \mathbf{c}_3\}$. Contrast this with the next example.

Example 3.5.7. Find a matrix **A** whose null space is spanned by

$$\mathbf{c}_1 = \begin{bmatrix} 1 \\ 0 \\ 0 \\ -1 \end{bmatrix} \qquad \mathbf{c}_2 = \begin{bmatrix} 1 \\ 1 \\ 1 \\ 0 \end{bmatrix} \qquad \mathbf{c}_3 = \begin{bmatrix} 1 \\ 0 \\ 0 \\ 0 \end{bmatrix}$$

Solution. The computation is now

$$[\mathbf{C} \quad \mathbf{I}] = \left[\begin{array}{ccc|cccc} 1 & 1 & 1 & 1 & 0 & 0 & 0 \\ 0 & 1 & 0 & 0 & 1 & 0 & 0 \\ 0 & 1 & 0 & 0 & 0 & 1 & 0 \\ -1 & 0 & 0 & 0 & 0 & 0 & 1 \end{array}\right] \rightarrow \cdots \rightarrow \left[\begin{array}{ccc|cccc} 1 & 1 & 0 & 1 & 0 & 0 & 0 \\ 0 & 1 & 0 & 0 & 1 & 0 & 0 \\ 0 & 0 & 1 & 0 & -1 & 0 & 0 \\ \hline 0 & 0 & 0 & 0 & -1 & 1 & 0 \end{array}\right]$$

Hence $\mathbf{A} = [0 \quad -1 \quad 1 \quad 0]$. Since rank(**A**) $= 1$, $\eta = 3$, the given vectors are a basis for the null space of **A**.

If **A** has full column rank so that **R** contains no zero rows, then the null space of **A** contains only **0**, because $\mathbf{Ax} = \mathbf{0}$ has the unique solution $\mathbf{x} = \mathbf{0}$. In this case Eq. 3.5.2 becomes

$$\mathbf{N}[\mathbf{A}^T \quad \mathbf{I}] = [\mathbf{R} \quad \mathbf{N}] = [\mathbf{R}_1 \quad \mathbf{N}_1]$$

and $\mathbf{N}_2$ does not appear.

3.5.1. The Proof of the Algorithm

The algorithm in Eq. 3.5.2 purports to provide a basis for $null(\mathbf{A})$. The proof is accomplished by showing that the columns of $\mathbf{N}_2^{\mathrm{T}}$ are $n-r$ linearly independent vectors in the null space of $\mathbf{A}$. This is Theorem 3.5.1. Theorem 3.5.2 asserts that $\dim(null(\mathbf{A})) = n-r$. Together, these theorems establish that the set of columns of $\mathbf{N}_2^{\mathrm{T}}$ is a basis for $null(\mathbf{A})$.

Before we present the details of the proof, it is instructive to re-do Example 3.5.3, with the notational addendum that each row is now labeled.

$$\left[\begin{array}{cccc:ccc:c} 1 & 1 & 1 & 1 & 1 & 0 & 0 & \mathbf{r}_1 \\ 0 & -1 & -1 & 1 & 0 & 1 & 0 & \mathbf{r}_2 \\ 0 & 1 & 1 & -1 & 0 & 0 & 1 & \mathbf{r}_3 \end{array}\right]$$

$$\rightarrow \left[\begin{array}{cccc:ccc:c} 1 & 1 & 1 & 1 & 1 & 0 & 0 & \mathbf{r}_1 \\ 0 & -1 & -1 & 1 & 0 & 1 & 0 & \mathbf{r}_2 \\ 0 & 0 & 0 & 0 & 0 & 1 & 1 & \mathbf{r}_3+\mathbf{r}_2 \end{array}\right]$$

Thus $\mathbf{r}_3+\mathbf{r}_2 = \mathbf{0}^{\mathrm{T}}$. In terms of $\mathbf{A}$, this means that its second and third columns sum to zero, because $\mathbf{r}_i^{\mathrm{T}}$ is the ith column of $\mathbf{A}$. That is,

$$\begin{bmatrix} 1 & 0 & 0 \\ 1 & -1 & 1 \\ 1 & -1 & 1 \\ 1 & 1 & -1 \end{bmatrix}\begin{bmatrix} 0 \\ 1 \\ 1 \end{bmatrix} = \mathbf{0}$$

Hence $[0 \quad 1 \quad 1]^{\mathrm{T}}$ is a vector in the null space of $\mathbf{A}$. The proof that the algorithm provides a basis for $null(\mathbf{A})$ is simply an abstracted elaboration of this idea.

Throughout this section, we assume that $\mathbf{A}$ is $m \times n$, $\mathrm{rank}(\mathbf{A}) = r$, and $\mathbf{R}$ is the rref of $\mathbf{A}^{\mathrm{T}}$.

Theorem 3.5.1. *Using the notation of Eq. 3.5.2 and Eq. 3.5.3, the columns of* $\mathbf{N}_2^{\mathrm{T}}$ *are* $n-r$ *linearly independent solutions of* $\mathbf{Ax} = \mathbf{0}$.

Proof. It follows from the arrow diagram in Eq. 3.5.2 that there exists a nonsingular matrix $\mathbf{S}$ such that $\mathbf{S}[\mathbf{A}^{\mathrm{T}} \quad \mathbf{I}] = [\mathbf{R} \quad \mathbf{N}]$. Thus $\mathbf{SA}^{\mathrm{T}} = \mathbf{R}$ and $\mathbf{S} = \mathbf{N}$. Hence $\mathbf{NA}^{\mathrm{T}} = \mathbf{R}$. Since $\mathbf{N}$ is nonsingular,

$$\mathrm{rank}(\mathbf{R}) = \mathrm{rank}(\mathbf{NA}^{\mathrm{T}}) = \mathrm{rank}(\mathbf{A}^{\mathrm{T}}) = r$$

This implies that $\mathbf{R}$ has $n-r$ rows of zeros. Suppose $\mathbf{R}$ and $\mathbf{N}$ are partitioned,

$$\mathbf{R} = \begin{bmatrix} \mathbf{R}_r \\ \mathbf{O} \end{bmatrix} \qquad \mathbf{N} = \begin{bmatrix} \mathbf{N}_1 \\ \mathbf{N}_2 \end{bmatrix} \tag{3.5.4}$$

In this partitioning $\mathbf{R}_r$ is $r \times m$ with all nonzero rows, $\mathbf{O}$ is $(n-r) \times m$, $\mathbf{N}_1$ is $r \times n$, and $\mathbf{N}_2$ is $(n-r) \times n$. (Note: $\mathbf{N}$ is $n \times n$.) Hence $\mathbf{N}[\mathbf{A}^{\mathrm{T}} \quad \mathbf{I}] = [\mathbf{R} \quad \mathbf{N}]$ may be written

$$\mathbf{N}[\mathbf{A}^{\mathrm{T}}\ \mathbf{I}] = [\mathbf{NA}^{\mathrm{T}}\ \mathbf{N}] = \begin{bmatrix} \mathbf{R}_1 & \mathbf{N}_1 \\ \mathbf{O} & \mathbf{N}_2 \end{bmatrix} \tag{3.5.5}$$

Also,

$$\mathbf{R} = \mathbf{NA}^{\mathrm{T}} = \begin{bmatrix} \mathbf{N}_1 \\ \mathbf{N}_2 \end{bmatrix} \mathbf{A}^{\mathrm{T}} = \begin{bmatrix} \mathbf{N}_1\mathbf{A}^{\mathrm{T}} \\ \mathbf{N}_2\mathbf{A}^{\mathrm{T}} \end{bmatrix} \tag{3.5.6}$$

Now substitute Eq. 3.5.6 into Eq. 3.5.5 to obtain

$$\begin{bmatrix} \mathbf{N}_1\mathbf{A}^{\mathrm{T}} & \mathbf{N}_1 \\ \mathbf{N}_2\mathbf{A}^{\mathrm{T}} & \mathbf{N}_2 \end{bmatrix} = \begin{bmatrix} \mathbf{R}_1 & \mathbf{N}_1 \\ \mathbf{O} & \mathbf{N}_2 \end{bmatrix} \tag{3.5.7}$$

from which it follows that $\mathbf{N}_2\mathbf{A}^{\mathrm{T}} = \mathbf{O}$; and by taking transposes $\mathbf{AN}_2^{\mathrm{T}} = \mathbf{O}$. Since $\mathbf{N}$ is nonsingular, every subset of its rows is linearly independent. Hence the columns of $\mathbf{N}_2^{\mathrm{T}}$ are linearly independent. Since $\mathbf{R}_1$ has r rows, so does $\mathbf{N}_1$ and, hence, there are $n - r$ columns in $\mathbf{N}_2^{\mathrm{T}}$. ■

Theorem 3.5.2. *Let* $\eta = \dim(null(\mathbf{A}))$. *Then*

$$\eta = n - r \tag{3.5.8}$$

Proof. Suppose $\{\mathbf{x}_1,\mathbf{x}_2,\ldots,\mathbf{x}_\eta\}$ is a basis for $null(\mathbf{A})$. Define a $n \times n$ nonsingular matrix $\mathbf{N}$ whose last η columns are $\mathbf{x}_1,\mathbf{x}_2,\ldots,\mathbf{x}_\eta$. Write $\mathbf{N}$ in the expanded form as follows:

$$\mathbf{N} = [\mathbf{N}_1 \quad \mathbf{X}] = [\mathbf{n}_1 \quad \mathbf{n}_2 \quad \ldots \quad \mathbf{n}_{n-\eta} \quad \mathbf{x}_1 \quad \mathbf{x}_2 \quad \ldots \quad \mathbf{x}_\eta]$$

Hence

$$\begin{aligned} \mathbf{AN} &= [\mathbf{AN}_1 \quad \mathbf{AX}] = [\mathbf{AN}_1 \quad \mathbf{Ax}_1 \quad \mathbf{Ax}_2 \quad \ldots \quad \mathbf{Ax}_\eta] \\ &= [\mathbf{AN}_1 \quad \mathbf{0} \quad \mathbf{0} \quad \ldots \quad \mathbf{0}] = [\mathbf{AN}_1 \quad \mathbf{O}] \end{aligned} \tag{3.5.9}$$

By Eq. 3.5.9 and the fact that $\mathbf{N}$ is nonsingular, it follows that

$$\mathrm{rank}[\mathbf{AN}_1 \quad \mathbf{O}] = \mathrm{rank}(\mathbf{AN}) = \mathrm{rank}(\mathbf{A}) = r.$$

Hence, among the n columns of $[\mathbf{AN}_1 \quad \mathbf{O}]$ there are at least r nonzero columns. But $\mathbf{O}$ has η zero columns, so that η cannot exceed $n - r$. Hence

$$\eta \leq n - r \tag{3.5.10}$$

By Theorem 3.5.1, we know that there are at least $n - r$ linearly independent vectors in $null(\mathbf{A})$. This and Eq. 3.5.10 proves Eq. 3.5.8. ■

Corollary 1. *The set of columns of* $\mathbf{N}_2^{\mathrm{T}}$ *is a basis of* $null(\mathbf{A})$.

Proof. From Theorem 3.5.1, the columns of $\mathbf{N}_2^{\mathrm{T}}$ are $n - r$ linearly independent vectors in $null(\mathbf{A})$. By Theorem 3.5.2 these vectors must comprise a basis, because if $col(\mathbf{N}_2^{\mathrm{T}}) \neq null(\mathbf{A})$, then $\dim(null(\mathbf{A})$ would exceed $n - r$. ■

3.5.2 MATLAB

To implement the algorithm in Eq. 3.5.2 in MATLAB, we simply invoke the function rref[A′, eye(n)] and read off the rows of $\mathbf{N}_2$.

Example 3.5.8. Use MATLAB to find the null space and column space of A given in Example 3.5.1:

$$\mathbf{A} = \begin{bmatrix} 1 & 2 & 0 & -1 & -2 \\ 1 & 2 & 1 & 0 & -1 \\ 0 & 0 & 1 & 1 & 1 \\ 1 & 2 & 2 & 1 & 0 \end{bmatrix}.$$

Solution. Input the entries of **A** and invoke rref[A′, eye(5)]:

rref[A′, eye(5)] =

$$\begin{matrix} 1 & 0 & -1 & -1 & 0 & 0 & 0 & -1 & 0 \\ 0 & 1 & 1 & 2 & 0 & 0 & 0 & 2 & -1 \\ 0 & 0 & 0 & 0 & 1 & 0 & 0 & -1 & 1 \\ 0 & 0 & 0 & 0 & 0 & 1 & 0 & -2 & 2 \\ 0 & 0 & 0 & 0 & 0 & 0 & 1 & -2 & 1 \end{matrix}$$

which is exactly the conclusion reached in Example 3.5.1.

MATLAB has the command null(A), which provides a matrix **N** whose columns form a basis for the null space of **A**. The basis found by MATLAB contains vectors which are normalized to have certain properties; namely, they form an "orthonormal set." The definition and usefulness of this type of basis are presented in Chapter 4. Also see Appendix B, m null(A).

Example 3.5.9. Use null(A) to find the null space of A of Example 3.5.4.

Solution. After entering A,

```
N = null(A)
    -0.5774    0.0000
     0.5774   -0.5774
    -0.5774   -0.5774
     0.0000    0.5774
```

This basis for *null*(A) can be compared with the basis given in Example 3.5.4 by finding the rref of N′.

```
rref(N')
ans =
    1.0000         0    2.0000   -1.0000
         0    1.0000    1.0000   -1.0000
```

PROBLEMS

PART 1

3.5.1. Find a basis for the null space of the coefficient matrices of the following systems and verify that $\eta + \text{rank}(\mathbf{A}) = n$.

$$\begin{aligned}(a)\ x_1 + x_2 - x_3 + x_4 &= 0\\ (b)\ x_1 - x_2 + x_3 + x_4 &= 0\\ x_4 &= 0\\ (c)\ x_1 + x_2 - x_3 + x_4 &= 0\\ x_3 - 2x_4 &= 0\end{aligned}$$

3.5.2. Repeat Problem 3.5.1 for the systems:

$$\begin{aligned}(a)\ x_1 - x_2 + x_3 + x_4 &= 0\\ x_2 + x_3 + x_4 &= 0\\ (b)\qquad x_1 + x_2 - x_3 &= 0\\ x_1 - 2x_2 - x_3 &= 0\\ (c)\qquad x_1 + x_2 - x_3 &= 0\\ 3x_1 + 4x_2 - x_3 &= 0\\ x_1 + 2x_2 + x_3 &= 0\end{aligned}$$

3.5.3. Repeat Problem 3.5.1 for the systems:
(*a*) $\mathbf{J}_n\mathbf{x} = \mathbf{0}$. (*b*) $\mathbf{u}\mathbf{u}^{\mathrm{T}}\mathbf{x} = \mathbf{0}$, $\mathbf{u} = [1 \quad u_2 \quad \ldots \quad u_n]^{\mathrm{T}}$.

3.5.4. Find the null space for each of the following matrices:

$$(a)\begin{bmatrix} 2 & 4 & 1\\ 0 & -2 & -1\\ 1 & 3 & 1\end{bmatrix} \qquad (b)\begin{bmatrix} 2 & 1 & 0 & 1\\ 0 & 0 & 0 & -1\\ 1 & 0 & 1 & 1\end{bmatrix} \qquad (c)\begin{bmatrix} 1 & -1 & 1 & 0 & 0\\ 1 & 0 & 2 & 0 & 0\\ 3 & -2 & 4 & 1 & 1\end{bmatrix}$$

3.5.5. Repeat Problem 3.5.4 for the matrices
(*a*) $\mathbf{J}_4$ (*b*) $\mathbf{u}\mathbf{u}^{\mathrm{T}}$, $\mathbf{u} = [1 \quad 0 \quad 1]^{\mathrm{T}}$ (*c*) $\mathbf{A} = [1 \quad a \quad b]^{\mathrm{T}}, ab \neq 0$.
(*d*) The transpose of each matrix in Problem 3.5.4.

3.5.6. Repeat Problem 3.5.4 for the matrices:

$$(a)\begin{bmatrix} 1 & -1 & 0 & 1\\ 1 & 2 & 0 & -1\\ 0 & 0 & 1 & -1\\ 1 & 0 & 0 & 1\end{bmatrix} \qquad (b)\begin{bmatrix} -1 & 2 & 0\\ 0 & -1 & -1\\ 0 & 1 & 1\\ 1 & 1 & 3\end{bmatrix}$$

$$(c)\begin{bmatrix} 1 & 0 & 5 & 1\\ 0 & 2 & 2 & -1\\ 1 & 1 & 0 & 1\\ 1 & 0 & -3 & 0\end{bmatrix} \qquad (d)\begin{bmatrix} -1 & 1\\ 1 & 2\\ 0 & 3\\ 0 & 0\end{bmatrix} \qquad (e)\begin{bmatrix} 1 & 1 & 1\\ 0 & 1 & 1\\ 1 & -1 & 3\end{bmatrix}$$

$$(f)\begin{bmatrix} 1 & 1 & 1\\ 0 & 1 & 1\\ 1 & -1 & -3\end{bmatrix} \qquad (g)\begin{bmatrix} 1 & 1 & 1\\ 0 & 1 & 1\\ 1 & 0 & 0\end{bmatrix} \qquad (h)\begin{bmatrix} 1 & 1 & 1\\ 0 & 1 & 1\\ 0 & 0 & 1\end{bmatrix}$$

3.5.7. Find matrices whose null space is spanned by

$$(a)\left\{\begin{bmatrix}1\\0\\1\\0\end{bmatrix}\right\} \qquad (b)\left\{\begin{bmatrix}1\\0\\1\\0\end{bmatrix},\begin{bmatrix}0\\1\\0\\1\end{bmatrix}\right\} \qquad (c)\left\{\begin{bmatrix}1\\0\\1\\0\end{bmatrix},\begin{bmatrix}0\\1\\0\\1\end{bmatrix},\begin{bmatrix}1\\1\\1\\1\end{bmatrix}\right\} \qquad (d)\left\{\begin{bmatrix}1\\0\\1\\0\end{bmatrix},\begin{bmatrix}0\\1\\0\\1\end{bmatrix},\begin{bmatrix}1\\1\\0\\0\end{bmatrix}\right\}$$

3.5.8. Repeat Problem 7 for the matrices spanned by

$$(a)\ \left\{\begin{bmatrix}1\\0\\1\\0\end{bmatrix},\begin{bmatrix}0\\1\\0\\1\end{bmatrix},\begin{bmatrix}1\\1\\0\\0\end{bmatrix},\begin{bmatrix}1\\1\\1\\1\end{bmatrix}\right\}\qquad (b)\ \left\{\begin{bmatrix}1\\0\\1\\0\end{bmatrix},\begin{bmatrix}0\\1\\0\\1\end{bmatrix},\begin{bmatrix}1\\1\\0\\0\end{bmatrix},\begin{bmatrix}0\\0\\0\\1\end{bmatrix}\right\}\qquad (c)\ \left\{\begin{bmatrix}1\\0\\-1\\1\\2\end{bmatrix},\begin{bmatrix}0\\1\\0\\-1\\0\end{bmatrix},\begin{bmatrix}1\\1\\1\\0\\1\end{bmatrix}\right\}$$

PART 2

3.5.9. Show that $null(\mathbf{A})$ is $\{\mathbf{0}\}$ if and only if $\mathbf{A}$ has full column rank.

3.5.10. Is $null(\mathbf{A}) = null(\mathbf{A}^T)$? Suppose $\mathbf{A}$ is square ?

3.5.11. Show that if $\mathbf{A}$ is row equivalent to $\mathbf{B}$ then $null(\mathbf{A}) = null(\mathbf{B})$.

PART 3

3.5.12. Suppose $\mathbf{A}$ is $m \times n$ and rank($\mathbf{A}$) $= r$. What is the dimension of $null(\mathbf{A}^T)$?

3.5.13. Suppose the columns of $\mathbf{U}_{n\times k}$ are linearly independent and form a basis for the null space of $\mathbf{A}$. Show that rank($\mathbf{A}$) $= n - k$.

3.5.14. Suppose $\mathbf{A}$ and $\mathbf{B}$ have the same number of columns. Explain why

$$null\begin{bmatrix}\mathbf{A}\\ \text{---}\\ \mathbf{B}\end{bmatrix} = null(\mathbf{A}) \cap null(\mathbf{B})$$

3.5.15. Show that $\dim(null(\mathbf{AB})) \geq \dim(null(\mathbf{B}))$ and find examples for which $\dim(null(\mathbf{AB})) < \dim(null(\mathbf{A}))$.

MATLAB

Use rref[A′, eye(n)] and null(A) commands in MATLAB to solve the following seven problems.

3.5.16. Problem 3.5.1

3.5.17. Problem 3.5.2.

3.5.18. Problem 3.5.4.

3.5.19. Problem 3.5.5 (a) and (b)

3.5.20. Problem 3.5.6.

3.5.21. Problem 3.5.7.

3.5.22. Problem 3.5.8.

3.5.23. Use null(A) to verify the answers given in Examples 3.5.1–3.5.3.

3.5.24. Use null(A) to verify the answers given in Examples 3.5.5–3.5.6.

3.5.25. Redo Problems 3.5.16–3.5.24 using mnull.m. (See Appendix B.)

3.6 THE GENERAL SOLUTION OF Ax = b

We are now in a position to answer three important questions concerning $\mathbf{Ax} = \mathbf{b}$, for $\mathbf{b} \neq \mathbf{0}$. First, is the system consistent? Second, if the system is consistent, does it have exactly one solution? And lastly, if it has more than one solution, how can we characterize the set of solutions? The answer to all three questions follows from knowledge of the rref of $[\mathbf{A}\ \ \mathbf{b}]$ (which we shall denote by $[\mathbf{A}_r\ \ \mathbf{c}]$) and the null space of $\mathbf{A}$. The issue of consistency is settled by Theorem 2.7.6:

The system $\mathbf{Ax} = \mathbf{b}$ *is consistent if and only if rank*($\mathbf{A}$) $=$ *rank*$[\mathbf{A}\ \ \mathbf{b}]$.

Here is another theorem on the consistency of the system, $\mathbf{Ax} = \mathbf{b}$.

Theorem 3.6.1. *The system* $\mathbf{Ax} = \mathbf{b}$ *is consistent if and only if* $\mathbf{b} \in col(\mathbf{A})$.

Proof. The proof simply consists of recalling the definition of $col(\mathbf{A})$ and noting that $\mathbf{Ax}$ is a linear combination of the columns of $\mathbf{A}$. Thus, if $\mathbf{x}$ is a solution of $\mathbf{Ax} = \mathbf{b}$, $\mathbf{b}$ is a linear combination of the columns with weights given by the entries of $\mathbf{x}$. ■

It is somewhat surprising that the existence of a multiplicity of solutions to $\mathbf{Ax} = \mathbf{b}$ does not depend on the choice of $\mathbf{b}$, but rather on the nature of the solutions of the corresponding homogeneous system $\mathbf{Ax} = \mathbf{0}$.

Theorem 3.6.2. *Suppose that the system* $\mathbf{Ax} = \mathbf{b}$ *is consistent. Then* $\mathbf{Ax} = \mathbf{b}$ *has a unique solution if and only if the corresponding homogeneous system,* $\mathbf{Ax} = \mathbf{0}$, *has only the trivial solution.*

Proof. Suppose that $\mathbf{Ax} = \mathbf{0}$ has only the trivial solution $\mathbf{x} = \mathbf{0}$. If $\mathbf{Ax} = \mathbf{b}$ has solutions $\mathbf{x}_1$ and $\mathbf{x}_2$, then $\mathbf{A}(\mathbf{x}_1 - \mathbf{x}_2) = \mathbf{Ax}_1 - \mathbf{Ax}_2 = \mathbf{b} - \mathbf{b} = \mathbf{0}$. But then $\mathbf{x}_1 - \mathbf{x}_2 = \mathbf{0}$ and hence $\mathbf{x}_1 = \mathbf{x}_2$. This proves that $\mathbf{Ax} = \mathbf{b}$ cannot have two solutions if $\mathbf{Ax} = \mathbf{0}$ has only the trivial solution. So, now assume that $\mathbf{Ax} = \mathbf{0}$ has a nontrivial solution $\mathbf{z}$. (That is, $\mathbf{Az} = \mathbf{0}$ and $\mathbf{z} \neq \mathbf{0}$.) Suppose that $\mathbf{x}_p$ is a solution of $\mathbf{Ax} = \mathbf{b}$. (There must be at least one solution because we are assuming that $\mathbf{Ax} = \mathbf{b}$ is consistent.) Then

$$\mathbf{A}(\mathbf{x}_p + a\mathbf{z}) = \mathbf{Ax}_p + a\mathbf{Az} = \mathbf{b} + \mathbf{0} = \mathbf{b}$$

for every scalar a. Hence, if $\mathbf{Ax} = \mathbf{0}$ has a nontrivial solution then $\mathbf{Ax} = \mathbf{b}$ has infinitely many solutions. ■

There are a variety of ways to express the fact that a homogeneous system has only the trivial solution, one of which is Theorem 2.7.7:

The system $\mathbf{Ax} = \mathbf{0}$ *has a unique solution if and only if* $\mathbf{A}$ *has full column rank.*

We now turn to the last question posed in the introduction: How can we describe the totality of solutions of $\mathbf{Ax} = \mathbf{b}$ when this system has more than one solution? The answer turns on our ability to describe the totality of the solutions to the corresponding homogeneous system $\mathbf{Ax} = \mathbf{0}$.

Let $\{\mathbf{n}_1, \mathbf{n}_2, \ldots, \mathbf{n}_\eta\}$ be a basis for $null(\mathbf{A})$ and $\mathbf{N} = [\mathbf{n}_1 \quad \mathbf{n}_2 \quad \ldots \quad n_\eta]$. Then for every choice of weights, the combination

$$\mathbf{x}_h = a_1\mathbf{n}_1 + a_2\mathbf{n}_2 + \cdots + a_\eta\mathbf{n}_\eta = \mathbf{Na} \qquad (3.6.1)$$

is a solution of $\mathbf{Ax} = \mathbf{0}$. The solution $\mathbf{x}_h$ depends upon the choice of basis for $null(\mathbf{A})$ and the choice of weights $\mathbf{a}$. However, regardless of the choice of basis, the set of all linear combinations of the basis vectors is the set of all solutions of $\mathbf{Ax} = \mathbf{0}$. For this reason Eq. 3.6.1 is often called a *general solution* of $\mathbf{Ax} = \mathbf{0}$.

Theorem 3.6.3. *If* $\mathbf{x}_g$ *and* $\mathbf{x}_p$ *are solutions of* $\mathbf{Ax} = \mathbf{b}$ *and* $\{\mathbf{n}_1,\mathbf{n}_2,\ldots,\mathbf{n}_\eta\}$ *is a basis for* $null(\mathbf{A})$, *then there exists a vector of weights* $\mathbf{a}$ *such that*

$$\mathbf{x}_g = \mathbf{x}_p + \mathbf{x}_h = \mathbf{x}_p + a_1\mathbf{x}_1 + a_2\mathbf{x}_2 + \cdots + a_s\mathbf{x}_s = \mathbf{Na} + \mathbf{x}_p \tag{3.6.2}$$

Proof. Since $\mathbf{A}(\mathbf{x}_g - \mathbf{x}_p) = \mathbf{b} - \mathbf{b} = \mathbf{0}$, $\mathbf{x}_g - \mathbf{x}_p$ is in the span of $\{\mathbf{x}_1,\mathbf{x}_2,\ldots,\mathbf{x}_\eta\}$. Thus there exists $\mathbf{a}$ such that $\mathbf{Na} = \mathbf{x}_q - \mathbf{x}_p$. ■

The family of solutions $\mathbf{x}_p + \mathbf{Na}$ is called a *general solution* of $\mathbf{Ax} = \mathbf{b}$. It is important to realize that every solution of $\mathbf{Ax} = \mathbf{b}$ can be obtained by selecting the weights in Eq. 3.6.2 appropriately—which is the motivation for the terminology "general solution." However, the general solution is by no means unique. There are infinitely many choices of basis for $null(\mathbf{A})$, and even for a given basis, there are usually infinitely many choices for $\mathbf{x}_p$. By contrast, the general solution of $\mathbf{Ax} = \mathbf{b}$ reduces to the "singleton" $\mathbf{A}^{-1}\mathbf{b}$ if $\mathbf{A}$ is invertible. This is consistent with Theorem 3.6.3, because the corresponding homogeneous system, $\mathbf{Ax} = \mathbf{0}$, has only $\mathbf{x} = \mathbf{0}$ as a solution, and thus Eq. 3.6.2 reduces to $\mathbf{x}_g = \mathbf{x}_p = \mathbf{A}^{-1}\mathbf{b}$.

The formula $\mathbf{Na} + \mathbf{x}_p$ for a general solution is also a prescription for determining the general solution. The system $\mathbf{Ax} = \mathbf{b}$ is first solved for any solution $\mathbf{x}_p$ and then a basis for the null space of $\mathbf{A}$ is found. (See Sections 2.3, 3.6.1, and 3.6.2, and Problem 3.6.17.)

3.6.1 An Algorithm for the General Solution of $\mathbf{Ax} = \mathbf{b}$

The technique used to obtain the basis for the null space of $\mathbf{A}$ can be modified to provide the general solution of $\mathbf{Ax} = \mathbf{b}$. Consider the following arrow diagram in which some combination of the rows of $\mathbf{A}^{\mathrm{T}}$ are used to clear the entries below $\mathbf{A}^{\mathrm{T}}$:

$$\left[\begin{array}{c|c} \mathbf{A}^{\mathrm{T}} & \mathbf{I} \\ \hline -\mathbf{b}^{\mathrm{T}} & \mathbf{0}^{\mathrm{T}} \end{array}\right] \rightarrow \cdots \rightarrow \left[\begin{array}{c|c} \mathbf{A}^{\mathrm{T}} & \mathbf{I} \\ \hline \mathbf{0}^{\mathrm{T}} & \mathbf{c}^{\mathrm{T}} \end{array}\right] \tag{3.6.4}$$

This is possible if and only if $\mathbf{b}^{\mathrm{T}}$ is in the span of the rows of $\mathbf{A}^{\mathrm{T}}$ which is to say, if and only if $\mathbf{b}$ is in the column space of $\mathbf{A}$. But $\mathbf{b}$ is in the column space of $\mathbf{A}$ if and only if $\mathbf{Ax} = \mathbf{b}$ is consistent. Our claim is that $\mathbf{c}$ in Eq. 3.6.4 is a solution of $\mathbf{Ax} = \mathbf{b}$. Note that the last row in Eq. 3.6.4 is not interchanged with any other row nor do we multiply this row by any constant. See also Eq. 3.6.7 to follow.

Theorem 3.6.4. *Suppose* $\mathbf{Ax} = \mathbf{b}$ *consistent. Then the arrow diagram Eq. 3.6.4 provides a solution* $\mathbf{c}$ *of* $\mathbf{Ax} = \mathbf{b}$.

Proof. The arrow diagram in Eq. 3.6.4 is equivalent to the following partitioned multiplication:

$$\left[\begin{array}{c|c} \mathbf{I} & \mathbf{0} \\ \hline \mathbf{s}^{\mathrm{T}} & 1 \end{array}\right]\left[\begin{array}{c|c} \mathbf{A}^{\mathrm{T}} & \mathbf{I} \\ \hline -\mathbf{b}^{\mathrm{T}} & \mathbf{0}^{\mathrm{T}} \end{array}\right] = \left[\begin{array}{c|c} \mathbf{IA}^{\mathrm{T}} - \mathbf{0b}^{\mathrm{T}} & \mathbf{II} + \mathbf{00}^{\mathrm{T}} \\ \hline \mathbf{s}^{\mathrm{T}}\mathbf{A}^{\mathrm{T}} - \mathbf{b}^{\mathrm{T}} & \mathbf{s}^{\mathrm{T}}\mathbf{I} + \mathbf{0}^{\mathrm{T}} \end{array}\right]$$

$$= \left[\begin{array}{c|c} \mathbf{A}^{\mathrm{T}} & \mathbf{I} \\ \hline \mathbf{s}^{\mathrm{T}}\mathbf{A}^{\mathrm{T}} - \mathbf{b}^{\mathrm{T}} & \mathbf{s}^{\mathrm{T}} \end{array}\right] = \left[\begin{array}{c|c} \mathbf{A}^{\mathrm{T}} & \mathbf{I} \\ \hline \mathbf{0}^{\mathrm{T}} & \mathbf{c}^{\mathrm{T}} \end{array}\right] \tag{3.6.5}$$

Hence $\mathbf{s}^{\mathrm{T}}\mathbf{A}^{\mathrm{T}} - \mathbf{b}^{\mathrm{T}} = \mathbf{0}^{\mathrm{T}}$ and $\mathbf{s}^{\mathrm{T}} = \mathbf{c}^{\mathrm{T}}$. Therefore, $\mathbf{Ac} = \mathbf{b}$. ∎

The last matrix in Eq. 3.6.5 is the starting point for the determination of a span for $null(\mathbf{A})$. Indeed, both steps can be combined in the same sequence of elementary row operations.

$$\left[\begin{array}{c|c} \mathbf{A}^{\mathrm{T}} & \mathbf{I} \\ \hline -\mathbf{b}^{\mathrm{T}} & \mathbf{0}^{\mathrm{T}} \end{array}\right] \to \cdots \to \left[\begin{array}{c|c} \mathbf{A}^{\mathrm{T}} & \mathbf{I} \\ \hline \mathbf{0}^{\mathrm{T}} & \mathbf{c}^{\mathrm{T}} \end{array}\right] \to \cdots \to \left[\begin{array}{c|c} \mathbf{R} & \mathbf{N} \\ \hline \mathbf{0}^{\mathrm{T}} & \mathbf{c}^{\mathrm{T}} \end{array}\right] \tag{3.6.6}$$

In order that $\mathbf{c}^{\mathrm{T}}$ (a solution of $\mathbf{x}^{\mathrm{T}}\mathbf{A}^{\mathrm{T}} = \mathbf{b}^{\mathrm{T}}$) not be confused with the rows of $\mathbf{N}_2$ (solutions of $\mathbf{x}^{\mathrm{T}}\mathbf{A}^{\mathrm{T}} = \mathbf{0}^{\mathrm{T}}$), it is best not to use a row interchange involving the last row of

$$\left[\begin{array}{c|c} \mathbf{A}^{\mathrm{T}} & \mathbf{I} \\ \hline -\mathbf{b}^{\mathrm{T}} & \mathbf{0}^{\mathrm{T}} \end{array}\right]$$

in the row reduction of Eq. 3.6.6. If Eq. 3.6.6 is implemented by some computer program such as MATLAB, it may not be easy to locate $\mathbf{c}^{\mathrm{T}}$ because the row containing $-\mathbf{b}^{\mathrm{T}}$ might well be interchanged with some higher row. One variation on Eq. 3.6.6 that avoids this difficulty is to divide the algorithm into two stages: first, find the canonical basis for $\mathbf{A}^{\mathrm{T}}$ and a basis for $null(\mathbf{A})$ by using $[\mathbf{A}^{\mathrm{T}} \quad \mathbf{I}] \to \cdots \to [\mathbf{R} \quad \mathbf{N}]$ as in Eq. 3.5.2. Then, as a separate computation use Eq. 3.6.6 in the special form

$$\left[\begin{array}{c|c|c} \mathbf{R}_1 & \mathbf{O} & \mathbf{I} \\ \hline -\mathbf{b}^{\mathrm{T}} & \mathbf{I} & \mathbf{0}^{\mathrm{T}} \end{array}\right] \to \cdots \to \left[\begin{array}{c|c|c} \mathbf{R}_1 & \mathbf{O} & \mathbf{I} \\ \hline \mathbf{0}^{\mathrm{T}} & \mathbf{I} & \mathbf{c}^{\mathrm{T}} \end{array}\right] \tag{3.6.7}$$

The submatrix

$$\left[\begin{array}{c} \mathbf{O} \\ \hline \mathbf{I} \end{array}\right]$$

in the middle of the matrices in Eq. 3.6.7 prohibits interchanging the last row with an earlier row and prohibits the multiplication of the last row by any scalar. (Why?)

Example 3.6.1. Find a general solution of

$$\begin{bmatrix} 1 & 2 & 0 & -1 & -2 \\ 1 & 2 & 1 & 0 & -1 \\ 0 & 0 & 1 & 1 & 1 \\ 1 & 2 & 2 & 1 & 0 \end{bmatrix} \mathbf{x} = \begin{bmatrix} -1 \\ 0 \\ 1 \\ 1 \end{bmatrix}$$

Solution. The computation is based on the arrow diagram Eq. 3.6.6:

$$\left[\begin{array}{cccc|ccccc} 1 & 1 & 0 & 1 & 1 & 0 & 0 & 0 & 0 \\ 2 & 2 & 0 & 2 & 0 & 1 & 0 & 0 & 0 \\ 0 & 1 & 1 & 2 & 0 & 0 & 1 & 0 & 0 \\ -1 & 0 & 1 & 1 & 0 & 0 & 0 & 1 & 0 \\ -2 & -1 & 1 & 0 & 0 & 0 & 0 & 0 & 0 \\ \hline 1 & 0 & -1 & -1 & 0 & 0 & 0 & 0 & 0 \end{array}\right] \rightarrow$$

$$\cdots \rightarrow \left[\begin{array}{cccc|ccccc} 1 & 0 & -1 & -1 & 1 & 0 & -1 & 0 & 0 \\ 0 & 1 & 1 & 2 & 0 & 0 & 1 & 0 & 0 \\ \hline 0 & 0 & 0 & 0 & -2 & 1 & 0 & 0 & 0 \\ 0 & 0 & 0 & 0 & 1 & 0 & -1 & 1 & 0 \\ 0 & 0 & 0 & 0 & 2 & 0 & -1 & 0 & 1 \\ \hline 0 & 0 & 0 & 0 & -1 & 0 & 1 & 0 & 0 \end{array}\right]$$

The vectors that comprise a basis for $null(\mathbf{A})$ and a solution of $\mathbf{Ax} = \mathbf{b}$ are given in the previous diagram. The last row in the matrix on the right defines $\mathbf{c}^{\mathrm{T}}$ and the three rows above it define $\mathbf{x}_1^{\mathrm{T}}$, $\mathbf{x}_2^{\mathrm{T}}$, and $\mathbf{x}_3^{\mathrm{T}}$:

$$\mathbf{c} = \begin{bmatrix} -1 \\ 0 \\ 1 \\ 0 \\ 0 \end{bmatrix} \qquad \mathbf{x}_1 = \begin{bmatrix} -2 \\ 1 \\ 0 \\ 0 \\ 0 \end{bmatrix} \qquad \mathbf{x}_2 = \begin{bmatrix} 1 \\ 0 \\ -1 \\ 1 \\ 0 \end{bmatrix} \qquad \mathbf{x}_3 = \begin{bmatrix} 2 \\ 0 \\ -1 \\ 0 \\ 1 \end{bmatrix}$$

Hence, a general solution is

$$\mathbf{x}_g = \begin{bmatrix} -1 \\ 0 \\ 1 \\ 0 \\ 0 \end{bmatrix} + a_1 \begin{bmatrix} -2 \\ 1 \\ 0 \\ 0 \\ 0 \end{bmatrix} + a_2 \begin{bmatrix} 1 \\ 0 \\ -1 \\ 1 \\ 0 \end{bmatrix} + a_3 \begin{bmatrix} 2 \\ 0 \\ -1 \\ 0 \\ 1 \end{bmatrix}.$$

Example 3.6.2. Use the algorithm in Eq. 3.6.6 to show that the following system is inconsistent:

$$\begin{bmatrix} 1 & 2 & 0 & -1 & -2 \\ 1 & 2 & 1 & 0 & -1 \\ 0 & 0 & 1 & 1 & 1 \\ 1 & 2 & 2 & 1 & 0 \end{bmatrix} \mathbf{x} = \begin{bmatrix} 1 \\ 0 \\ 0 \\ 0 \end{bmatrix}$$

Solution. The computation is essentially a repetition of that performed in the previous example. The last row shows that $-\mathbf{b}^{\mathrm{T}}$ is not a linear combination of the rows of $\mathbf{A}^{\mathrm{T}}$.

$$
\left[\begin{array}{rrrr|rrrrr}
1 & 1 & 0 & 1 & 1 & 0 & 0 & 0 & 0 \\
2 & 2 & 0 & 2 & 0 & 1 & 0 & 0 & 0 \\
0 & 1 & 1 & 2 & 0 & 0 & 1 & 0 & 0 \\
-1 & 0 & 1 & 1 & 0 & 0 & 0 & 1 & 0 \\
-2 & -1 & 1 & 0 & 0 & 0 & 0 & 0 & 0 \\
\hline
-1 & 0 & 0 & 0 & 0 & 0 & 0 & 0 & 0
\end{array}\right] \rightarrow
$$

$$
\cdots \rightarrow \left[\begin{array}{rrrr|rrrrr}
1 & 0 & -1 & -1 & 1 & 0 & -1 & 0 & 0 \\
0 & 1 & 1 & 2 & 0 & 0 & 1 & 0 & 0 \\
\hline
0 & 0 & 0 & 0 & -2 & 1 & 0 & 0 & 0 \\
0 & 0 & 0 & 0 & 1 & 0 & -1 & 1 & 0 \\
0 & 0 & 0 & 0 & 2 & 0 & -1 & 0 & 1 \\
\hline
0 & 0 & 1 & 1 & 1 & 0 & -1 & 0 & 0
\end{array}\right]
$$

Example 3.6.3. Find those vectors **b** for which the following system is consistent, and express the general solution in terms of the entries of **b**:

$$
\mathbf{Ax} = \begin{bmatrix} 1 & 1 & 1 & 1 \\ 1 & -1 & -1 & 1 \\ 2 & 0 & 0 & 2 \end{bmatrix} \mathbf{x} = \mathbf{b} = \begin{bmatrix} \alpha \\ \beta \\ \gamma \end{bmatrix}
$$

Solution. In this example, there is a row with arbitrary parameters.

$$
\left[\begin{array}{rrr|rrrr}
1 & 1 & 2 & 1 & 0 & 0 & 0 \\
1 & -1 & 0 & 0 & 1 & 0 & 0 \\
1 & -1 & 0 & 0 & 0 & 1 & 0 \\
1 & 1 & 2 & 0 & 0 & 0 & 1 \\
\hline
-\alpha & -\beta & -\gamma & 0 & 0 & 0 & 0
\end{array}\right] \rightarrow
$$

$$
\cdots \rightarrow \left[\begin{array}{ccc|cccc}
1 & 1 & 2 & 1 & 0 & 0 & 0 \\
0 & 1 & 1 & .5 & -.5 & 0 & 0 \\
\hline
0 & 0 & 0 & 0 & -1 & 1 & 0 \\
0 & 0 & 0 & -1 & 0 & 0 & 1 \\
\hline
0 & 0 & \gamma + \alpha + \beta & .5(\alpha + \beta) & .5(\alpha - \beta) & 0 & 0
\end{array}\right]
$$

In order for the given system to be consistent, it is necessary and sufficient that $\gamma = \alpha + \beta$. Assuming this, a general solution is

$$
\mathbf{x} = a_1 \begin{bmatrix} -1 \\ 0 \\ 0 \\ 1 \end{bmatrix} + a_2 \begin{bmatrix} 0 \\ -1 \\ 1 \\ 0 \end{bmatrix} + \begin{bmatrix} (\alpha + \beta)/2 \\ (\alpha - \beta)/2 \\ 0 \\ 0 \end{bmatrix}, \gamma = \alpha + \beta
$$

Note that the system given in Example 3.6.5 is either inconsistent, if $\gamma \neq \alpha + \beta$, or has infinitely many solutions. It is not possible to find a **b** such that there is only one solution. This is due to the existence of infinitely many solutions of the associated homogeneous system $\mathbf{Ax} = \mathbf{0}$.

3.6.2 Superposition Principles

A typical theme in modeling linear phenomena is that the output of a sum of inputs is the sum of the individual outputs. For example, in a passive electrical network containing resistors, capacitors, and inductors, the voltage drop between two points in the network due to an impressed voltage $\sin\omega t + \sin 2\omega t$ is the sum of the voltage drops due to $\sin\omega t$ and $\sin 2\omega t$ individually. Engineers call this phenomena "superposition." There are a variety of superposition principles. For the case of linear, inhomogeneous, algebraic systems $\mathbf{Ax} = \mathbf{b}$, a fundamental superposition theorem is

Theorem 3.6.5. *If* $\mathbf{x}_1$ *is a solution of* $\mathbf{Ax} = \mathbf{b}_1$ *and* $\mathbf{x}_2$ *is a solution of* $\mathbf{Ax} = \mathbf{b}_2$, *then* $a\mathbf{x}_1 + b\mathbf{x}_2$ *is a solution of* $\mathbf{Ax} = a\mathbf{b}_1 + b\mathbf{b}_2$.

Proof. The proof is an easy consequence of the elementary properties of matrix multiplication and addition:

$$\mathbf{A}(a\mathbf{x}_1 + b\mathbf{x}_2) = \mathbf{A}(a\mathbf{x}_1) + \mathbf{A}(b\mathbf{x}_2) = a\mathbf{Ax}_1 + b\mathbf{Ax}_2 = a\mathbf{b}_1 + b\mathbf{b}_2$$

Suppose that $\mathbf{y}$ and $\mathbf{z}$ both solve $\mathbf{Ax} = \mathbf{b}$. What can be said about $a\mathbf{y} + b\mathbf{z}$? If $\mathbf{b} = \mathbf{0}$, then $a\mathbf{y} + b\mathbf{z}$ is a solution of $\mathbf{Ax} = \mathbf{0}$. It is not, in general, a solution of $\mathbf{Ax} = \mathbf{b} \neq \mathbf{0}$. Contrast this with Theorem 3.6.4.

There is an important special case that arises in the theory of linear inequalities. If $a + b = 1$ then

$$\mathbf{A}(a\mathbf{y} + b\mathbf{z}) = \mathbf{A}(a\mathbf{y}) + \mathbf{A}(b\mathbf{z}) = a\mathbf{Ay} + b\mathbf{Az} = (a + b)\mathbf{b} = \mathbf{b}$$

shows that $a\mathbf{y} + b\mathbf{z}$ is a solution. (See Chapter 9.) ■

3.6.3 The General Solution in MATLAB

Null(A) returns **N** and A\b returns a particular solution of A ∗ x = b. These two commands are sufficient to express the general solution; N * a + A\b. One note of caution, however. MATLAB returns A\b even if the system is inconsistent! (MATLAB computes the "least squares solution" of A ∗ x = b if this system is inconsistent; see Sections 4.9 and 4.10.) See also msoln(A,b) in Appendix B.

Example 3.6.4. Solve the system in Example 3.6.1 by means of A\b. Assuming A and b has been entered,

```
A\b
ans =
         0
    -.5000
   -1.0000
         0
         0
```

Example 3.6.5. Solve the system in Example 3.6.2 by means of A\b. Assuming A and b has been entered,

```
A\b
ans =
        0
   -.3333
    .3333
        0
        0
```

Of course, this is not a solution of A * x = b.

In these two problems we have omitted the step null(A) since this part has been covered in the previous section.

PROBLEMS

PART 1

3.6.1. Find the general solution of the following systems:

$(a)\ x_1 + x_2 - x_3 + x_4 = 1 \qquad (b)\ \begin{aligned} x_1 - x_2 + x_3 + x_4 &= 0 \\ x_4 &= 1 \end{aligned}$

3.6.2. Repeat Problem 3.6.1 for the systems:

$(a)\ \begin{aligned} x_1 + x_2 - x_3 + x_4 &= 1 \\ x_3 - 2x_4 &= 0 \end{aligned} \qquad (b)\ \begin{aligned} x_1 - x_2 + x_3 + x_4 &= 1 \\ x_2 + x_3 + x_4 &= 1 \end{aligned}$

3.6.3. Repeat Problem 3.6.1 for the systems:

$(a)\ \begin{aligned} x_1 + x_2 - x_3 &= 2 \\ x_1 - 2x_2 - x_3 &= -1 \end{aligned} \qquad (b)\ \begin{aligned} x_1 + x_2 - x_3 &= 1 \\ 3x_1 + 4x_2 - x_3 &= 1 \\ x_1 + 2x_2 + x_3 &= -1 \end{aligned}$

3.6.4. Assume that $\mathbf{a} = [1 \quad a_2 \quad \dots \quad a_n]^{\mathrm{T}}$. Find the general solution of the following systems: $(a)\ \mathbf{J}_n\mathbf{x} = \mathbf{1} \qquad (b)\ \mathbf{a}^{\mathrm{T}}\mathbf{x} = 1$

3.6.5. Which of the systems in Problems 3.6.1–3.6.3 have full row rank? Full column rank?

3.6.6. Let $\mathbf{b} = [1 \quad -1 \quad 0 \quad 1]^{\mathrm{T}}$. Find the general solution of the system $\mathbf{Ax} = \mathbf{b}$ for each $\mathbf{A}$ given below:

$$(a)\begin{bmatrix} 1 & -1 & 0 & 1 \\ 1 & 2 & 0 & -1 \\ 0 & 0 & 1 & -1 \\ 1 & 0 & 0 & 1 \end{bmatrix} \qquad (b)\begin{bmatrix} 1 & 2 & 1 \\ 0 & -1 & -1 \\ 0 & 1 & -1 \\ 1 & 1 & 3 \end{bmatrix} \qquad (c)\begin{bmatrix} 1 & 0 & 5 & 1 & 1 \\ 1 & 2 & 2 & -1 & 0 \\ 0 & 1 & 0 & 1 & 1 \\ 1 & 0 & -3 & 0 & 1 \end{bmatrix}$$

3.6.7. Let $\mathbf{b} = \mathbf{e}_1$. Find the general solution of the system $\mathbf{Ax} = \mathbf{b}$ for each of the given matrices:

$$(a)\begin{bmatrix} 2 & 4 & 2 \\ 0 & -2 & -1 \\ 1 & 3 & 1 \end{bmatrix} \qquad (b)\begin{bmatrix} 2 & 1 & 0 & 1 \\ 0 & 0 & 0 & -1 \\ 1 & 0 & 1 & 1 \end{bmatrix} \qquad (c)\begin{bmatrix} 1 & -1 & 1 & 0 & 0 \\ 1 & 0 & 2 & 0 & 0 \\ 3 & -2 & 4 & 1 & 1 \end{bmatrix}$$

3.6.8. Find the general solution of the systems $\mathbf{Ax} = \mathbf{b}$ for the given matrices $\mathbf{A}$ and vectors $\mathbf{b}$:

$$(a)\ \mathbf{A} = \begin{bmatrix} 1 & 1 & 1 \\ 0 & 1 & 1 \\ 1 & -3 & 3 \end{bmatrix}, \quad \mathbf{b} = \begin{bmatrix} 2 \\ 1 \\ 0 \end{bmatrix} \qquad (b)\ \mathbf{A} = \begin{bmatrix} 1 & 1 & 1 \\ 0 & 1 & 1 \\ 1 & -1 & 3 \end{bmatrix}, \quad \mathbf{b} = \begin{bmatrix} 2 \\ 2 \\ 2 \end{bmatrix}$$

3.6.9. Find the general solution of the systems $\mathbf{Ax} = \mathbf{b}$ for the given matrices $\mathbf{A}$ and vectors $\mathbf{b}$:

$$(a)\ \mathbf{A} = \begin{bmatrix} 1 & 1 & 1 \\ 0 & 1 & 1 \\ 0 & 0 & 1 \end{bmatrix}, \quad \mathbf{b} = \begin{bmatrix} 2 \\ 1 \\ 0 \end{bmatrix} \qquad (b)\ \mathbf{A} = \begin{bmatrix} 1 & 1 & 1 \\ 0 & 1 & 1 \\ 1 & -1 & 3 \end{bmatrix}, \quad \mathbf{b} = \begin{bmatrix} 2 \\ 2 \\ -2 \end{bmatrix}$$

PART 2

3.6.10. Prove that if $\mathbf{A}$ has full row rank, then $\mathbf{Ax} = \mathbf{b}$ is consistent. Select $\mathbf{A}$ in row echelon normal form and provide examples for Problems 3.6.2–3.6.5. Assume $\mathbf{A}$ is $m \times n$ and $\text{rank}(\mathbf{A}) = \text{r}$.

3.6.11. Suppose $m = r < n$. Show that $\mathbf{Ax} = \mathbf{b}$ has infinitely many solutions regardless of the choice of $\mathbf{b}$.

3.6.12. Suppose $m = r = n$. Show that $\mathbf{Ax} = \mathbf{b}$ has a unique solution regardless of the choice of $\mathbf{b}$.

3.6.13. Suppose $n = r < m$. Show that $\mathbf{Ax} = \mathbf{b}$ is inconsistent or has a unique solution depending on the choice of $\mathbf{b}$.

3.6.14. Suppose $r < m$ and $r < n$. Show that $\mathbf{Ax} = \mathbf{b}$ is inconsistent or has infinitely many solutions depending on the choice of $\mathbf{b}$.

3.6.15. Suppose that $\mathbf{x}_1$ and $\mathbf{x}_2$ are solutions of $\mathbf{Ax} = \mathbf{b}, \mathbf{b} \neq \mathbf{0}$. Show that $\alpha\mathbf{x}_1 + \beta\mathbf{x}_2$ is also a solution of $\mathbf{Ax} = \mathbf{b}$ if and only if $\alpha + \beta = 1$.

3.6.16. Suppose $\mathbf{Ax} = \mathbf{b}, \mathbf{b} \neq \mathbf{0}$ has a general solution

$$\mathbf{x}_g = \mathbf{x}_p + a_1\mathbf{x}_1 + a_2\mathbf{x}_2 + \cdots + a_s\mathbf{x}_s$$

Show that the set $\{\mathbf{x}_p, \mathbf{x}_1, \mathbf{x}_2, \ldots, \mathbf{x}_s\}$ is linearly independent. (Hint: Show that $\mathbf{x}_p = a_1\mathbf{x}_1 + a_2\mathbf{x}_2 + \cdots + a_s\mathbf{x}_s$ is impossible.)

3.6.17. Formulate a procedure for obtaining a particular solution of $\mathbf{Ax} = \mathbf{b}$ which relies on the diagram $[\mathbf{A} \quad \mathbf{b}] \to \cdots \to [\mathbf{R} \quad \mathbf{c}]$ where $\mathbf{R}$ is the rref of $\mathbf{A}$.

MATLAB

Use A\b and null(A) to write the general solution of the following eight problems.

3.6.18. Problem 3.6.1.

3.6.19. Problem 3.6.2.

3.6.20. Problem 3.6.3.

3.6.21. Problem 3.6.6.

3.6.22. Problem 3.6.7.

3.6.23. Problem 3.6.8.

3.6.24. Problem 3.6.9.

3.6.25. Verify the general solution given for Example 3.6.1.

3.6.26. Use msoln(A,b) to solve Problems 3.6.1–3.6.3. (See Appendix B.)

3.6.27. Use msoln(A,b) to solve Problems 3.6.5–3.6.9. (See Appendix B.)

3.7 LINES AND PLANES IN n DIMENSIONS

Vector spaces of n-tuples correspond to rather special geometric objects in n-dimensional space, of which lines and planes are the easiest to visualize. Indeed, lines through the origin are the geometric representations of one-dimensional vector spaces, and planes through the origin are the geometric representation of two-dimensional vector spaces. To represent lines and planes that do not pass through the origin, we need to study "translates" of vector spaces. The set of all expressions of the form

$$\mathbf{y}_0 + a_1\mathbf{y}_1 + a_2\mathbf{y}_2 + \cdots + a_k\mathbf{y}_k \tag{3.7.1}$$

is the *translate* of the span of $\{\mathbf{y}_1, \mathbf{y}_2, \ldots, \mathbf{y}_k\}$ by the vector $\mathbf{y}_0$. By definition, a line in n-dimensional space (n-space for short), is the linear function of α given by

$$\mathbf{x}(\alpha) = \mathbf{x}_0 + \alpha\mathbf{x}_1 \tag{3.7.2}$$

where $\mathbf{x}_0$ and $\mathbf{x}_1 \neq \mathbf{0}$ are vectors in $\mathcal{R}^n$ and $-\infty < \alpha < \infty$. Thus, a line is the translate of $span\{\mathbf{x}_1\}$ by $\mathbf{x}_0$. Equation 3.7.2 is known as a *parametric representation* of a line. The next two examples illustrate Eq. 3.7.2 and show that in $\mathcal{R}^2$ and $\mathcal{R}^3$, the parametric representations of a line can be used to find the more familiar Cartesian equations.

Example 3.7.1. Find the Cartesian equation of the line passing through (1,1) with slope ½.

Solution. A line through the origin with slope ½ passes through the point (2,1); hence, each point on this line is a multiple of $\mathbf{x}_1 = [2 \quad 1]^T$. The set of all multiples of $\mathbf{x}_1$ is $span\{\mathbf{x}_1\}$. The line passing through (1,1) parallel to $span\{\mathbf{x}_1\}$ is the translate of $span\{\mathbf{x}_1\}$ by $\mathbf{x}_0 = [1 \quad 1]^T$. So, from Eq. 3.7.2, the parametric equation for the line is given by

$$\begin{bmatrix} x \\ y \end{bmatrix} = \begin{bmatrix} 1 \\ 1 \end{bmatrix} + \alpha \begin{bmatrix} 2 \\ 1 \end{bmatrix}$$

Therefore, $x = 1 + 2\alpha$ and $y = 1 + \alpha$, which yields the equation $x = 2y - 1$. This line has slope ½ and passes through (1,1). (See Fig. 3.1*a*.)

Example 3.7.2. Find the Cartesian equation for the line through the origin and the point with coordinates (1, 2, −1).

Solution. The vector $\mathbf{x}_1 = [1 \quad 2 \quad -1]^T$ corresponds to the point with coordinates (1,2,−1). Each vector in $span\{\mathbf{x}_1\}$ corresponds to a point on the given line. In this example $\mathbf{x}_0 = \mathbf{0}$, since we want the line to pass through the origin. Let (x,y,z) be the coordinates of a point on the line in question. Equation 3.7.1 yields the expression

$$\begin{bmatrix} x \\ y \\ z \end{bmatrix} = \alpha \begin{bmatrix} 1 \\ 2 \\ -1 \end{bmatrix} = \begin{bmatrix} \alpha \\ 2\alpha \\ -\alpha \end{bmatrix}$$

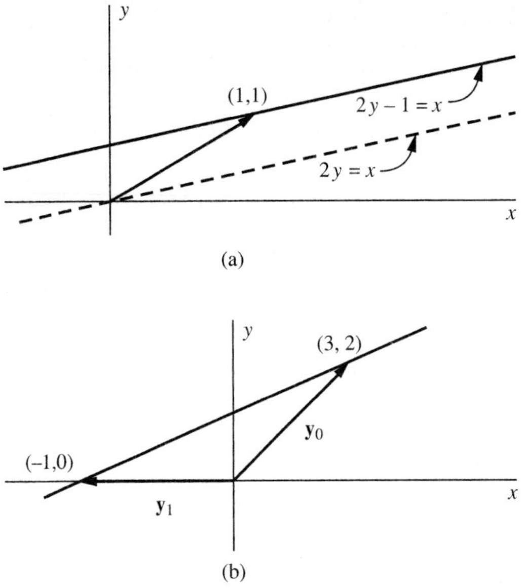

FIGURE 3-1
(*a*) The line passing through (1,1) with slope ½; (*b*) the line passing through (−1,0) and (3,2).

Hence, $x = \alpha$, $y = 2\alpha$, $z = -\alpha$ is the parametric form of the equation of the line. Eliminating α leads to the Cartesian equations $x = y/2 = -z$.

To determine the equation of the line passing through two fixed points, it is convenient to rewrite Eq 3.7.1 in another form. Set $\mathbf{y}_0 = \mathbf{x}_0$ and $\mathbf{y}_1 = \mathbf{x}_1 + \mathbf{x}_0$. Then,

$$\mathbf{x}(\alpha) = \mathbf{x}_0 + \alpha\Big((\mathbf{x}_1 + \mathbf{x}_0) - \mathbf{x}_0\Big) = (1-\alpha)\mathbf{y}_0 + \alpha\mathbf{y}_1 \tag{3.7.3}$$

In this form, $\mathbf{x}(0) = \mathbf{y}_0$ and $\mathbf{x}(1) = \mathbf{y}_1$, and the line passes through the points $\mathbf{y}_1$ and $\mathbf{y}_0$.

Example 3.7.3. Find the equation of the line passing through the points (3,2) and (−1,0).

Solution. Define $\mathbf{y}_0 = [3 \quad 2]^T$ and $\mathbf{y}_1 = [-1 \quad 0]^T$. Then the parametric equation of the line is given by Eq. 3.7.3:

$$\mathbf{x} = \begin{bmatrix} x \\ y \end{bmatrix} = (1-\alpha)\begin{bmatrix} 3 \\ 2 \end{bmatrix} + \alpha\begin{bmatrix} -1 \\ 0 \end{bmatrix}$$

So, $x = 3 - 4\alpha$, and $y = 2 - 2\alpha$. Eliminating the parameter α yields the Cartesian equation $2y - 1 = x$. (See Example 3.7.1 and Figure 3.1*b*.)

A plane in n-space is the linear function of two parameters:

$$\mathbf{x}(\alpha_1, \alpha_2) = \mathbf{x}_0 + \alpha_1\mathbf{x}_1 + \alpha_2\mathbf{x}_2 \tag{3.7.4}$$

where $\{\mathbf{x}_1, \mathbf{x}_2\}$ is linearly independent and $-\infty < \alpha_1, \alpha_2 < \infty$. Thus a plane is the translate of the span of the linearly independent set $\{\mathbf{x}_1, \mathbf{x}_2\}$ by $\mathbf{x}_0$. Now set $\mathbf{y}_0 = \mathbf{x}_0$, $\mathbf{y}_1 = \mathbf{x}_1 + \mathbf{x}_0$, and $\mathbf{y}_2 = \mathbf{x}_2 + \mathbf{x}_0$ in Eq. 3.7.4 to obtain

$$\begin{aligned}\mathbf{x}(\alpha_1, \alpha_2) &= \mathbf{x}_0 + \alpha_1\big((\mathbf{x}_1 + \mathbf{x}_0) - \mathbf{x}_0\big) + \alpha_2\big((\mathbf{x}_2 + \mathbf{x}_0) - \mathbf{x}_0\big) \\ &= (1 - \alpha_1 - \alpha_2)\mathbf{y}_0 + \alpha_1\mathbf{y}_1 + \alpha_2\mathbf{y}_2 \end{aligned} \tag{3.7.5}$$

Clearly, $\mathbf{x}(0,0) = \mathbf{y}_0$, $\mathbf{x}(1,0) = \mathbf{y}_1$ and $\mathbf{x}(0,1) = \mathbf{y}_2$, so the plane given by Eq. 3.7.5 contains the three points $\mathbf{y}_0$, $\mathbf{y}_1$ and $\mathbf{y}_2$. Equations 3.7.4 and 3.7.5 are called the *parametric equations* of the plane. The following examples illustrate the solutions of various problems that can arise in the study of planes in $\mathcal{R}^n$.

Example 3.7.4. Find the Cartesian equation for the plane passing through the points (1,1,1), (1,0,2) and (0,2,2).

Solution. The plane containing these points is obtained by representing these points by vectors,

$$\mathbf{y}_0 = \begin{bmatrix}1\\1\\1\end{bmatrix} \qquad \mathbf{y}_1 = \begin{bmatrix}1\\0\\2\end{bmatrix} \qquad \mathbf{y}_2 = \begin{bmatrix}0\\2\\2\end{bmatrix}$$

and substituting into Eq. 3.7.5. Set $\beta_1 = 1 - \alpha_1 - \alpha_2$, $\beta_2 = \alpha_1$, and $\beta_3 = \alpha_2$. Then the equation of the plane is

$$\mathbf{x} = \begin{bmatrix}x\\y\\z\end{bmatrix} = \beta_1\begin{bmatrix}1\\1\\1\end{bmatrix} + \beta_2\begin{bmatrix}1\\0\\2\end{bmatrix} + \beta_3\begin{bmatrix}0\\2\\2\end{bmatrix} \qquad \beta_1 + \beta_2 + \beta_3 = 1 \tag{3.7.6}$$

Equation 3.7.6 is the parametric equation of the plane. To find the Cartesian equation, eliminate the parameters β_1, β_2, and β_3 in Eq. 3.7.6. To do so, first note that Eq. 3.7.6 can be written

$$\begin{bmatrix}1 & 1 & 0\\1 & 0 & 2\\1 & 2 & 2\\\hline 1 & 1 & 1\end{bmatrix}\begin{bmatrix}\beta_1\\\beta_2\\\beta_3\end{bmatrix} = \begin{bmatrix}x\\y\\z\\\hline 1\end{bmatrix}$$

where the last row is the equation, $\beta_1 + \beta_2 + \beta_3 = 1$. We apply row operations to the augmented matrix of this system to obtain

$$\left[\begin{array}{ccc|c}1 & 1 & 0 & x\\1 & 0 & 2 & y\\1 & 2 & 2 & z\\\hline 1 & 1 & 1 & 1\end{array}\right] \rightarrow \cdots \rightarrow \left[\begin{array}{ccc|c}1 & 1 & 0 & x\\0 & -1 & 2 & y-x\\0 & 1 & 2 & z-x\\\hline 0 & 0 & 1 & 1-x\end{array}\right] \rightarrow \left[\begin{array}{ccc|c}1 & 1 & 0 & x\\0 & -1 & 2 & y-xy\\0 & 0 & 4 & z-2x+y\\\hline 0 & 0 & 1 & 1-x\end{array}\right]$$

$$\rightarrow \left[\begin{array}{ccc|c}1 & 1 & 0 & x\\0 & -1 & 2 & y-xy\\0 & 0 & 4 & z-2x+y\\\hline 0 & 0 & 4 & 4-4x\end{array}\right] \rightarrow \left[\begin{array}{ccc|c}1 & 1 & 0 & x\\0 & -1 & 2 & y-xy\\0 & 0 & 4 & z-2x+y\\\hline 0 & 0 & 0 & 4-2x-z-y\end{array}\right]$$

The last row shows that $4 - 2x - y - z = 0$. It is easy to verify that the points in question do lie on this plane.

Example 3.7.5. Show that the following planes in $\mathcal{R}^4$ are the same:

$$\mathbf{x}(\alpha,\beta) = \begin{bmatrix} 1 \\ -1 \\ 0 \\ 1 \end{bmatrix} + \alpha \begin{bmatrix} 0 \\ 1 \\ 0 \\ -1 \end{bmatrix} + \beta \begin{bmatrix} 2 \\ -1 \\ 1 \\ 2 \end{bmatrix}, \quad \mathbf{y}(\gamma,\delta) = \begin{bmatrix} -1 \\ 1 \\ -1 \\ -2 \end{bmatrix} + \gamma \begin{bmatrix} 2 \\ -2 \\ 1 \\ 3 \end{bmatrix} + \delta \begin{bmatrix} 4 \\ -3 \\ 2 \\ 5 \end{bmatrix}$$

Solution. In both cases, the planes are represented as translates of vector spaces, and the first task is to show that these vector spaces are the same. This is done by finding canonical bases for each of these spaces and showing that these bases are identical. Canonical bases are found by constructing matrices whose row spaces are the vector spaces at hand:

$$\begin{bmatrix} 0 & 1 & 0 & -1 \\ 2 & -1 & 1 & 2 \end{bmatrix} \to \cdots \to \begin{bmatrix} 1 & 0 & .5 & .5 \\ 0 & 1 & 0 & -1 \end{bmatrix}$$

$$\begin{bmatrix} 2 & -2 & 1 & 3 \\ 4 & -3 & 2 & 5 \end{bmatrix} \to \cdots \to \begin{bmatrix} 1 & 0 & .5 & .5 \\ 0 & 1 & 0 & -1 \end{bmatrix}$$

Hence, the two planes are translates of the same vector space. The next and last step is to show that these planes contain at least one common point; for then they are identical. (Why? See Problem 3.7.15.) To do this, choose a convenient set of values for α and β, say $\alpha = \beta = 0$, and show that $\mathbf{x}(0,0) = \mathbf{y}(\gamma,\delta)$ has the solution $\gamma = 1$, $\delta = 0$; that is, $\mathbf{x}(0,0) = \mathbf{y}(1,0)$.

The intersection of two planes is either empty, or it is a line or, if the planes are identical, a plane. (This latter case occurred in Example 3.7.5.) If the equations are given in Cartesian form, say,

$$a_{11}x_1 + a_{12}y_2 + a_{13}z_3 = b_1$$
$$a_{21}x_1 + a_{22}y_2 + a_{23}z_3 = b_2$$

then the intersection is found by solving this system. The problem is somewhat less transparent if the planes are given parametrically.

Example 3.7.6. Find the intersection of the planes

$$\mathbf{x}(\alpha,\beta) = \begin{bmatrix} 1 \\ -1 \\ 0 \\ 1 \end{bmatrix} + \alpha \begin{bmatrix} 0 \\ 1 \\ 0 \\ -1 \end{bmatrix} + \beta \begin{bmatrix} 2 \\ -1 \\ 1 \\ 2 \end{bmatrix}, \quad \mathbf{y}(\gamma,\delta) = \begin{bmatrix} -1 \\ 1 \\ -1 \\ -2 \end{bmatrix} + \gamma \begin{bmatrix} 2 \\ -2 \\ 1 \\ 3 \end{bmatrix} + \delta \begin{bmatrix} 1 \\ -1 \\ 0 \\ 0 \end{bmatrix}$$

Solution. Set $\mathbf{x}(\alpha,\beta) = \mathbf{y}(\gamma,\delta)$ to determine α, β, γ, and δ. This leads to the equations

$$\begin{bmatrix} 1 \\ -1 \\ 0 \\ 1 \end{bmatrix} + \alpha \begin{bmatrix} 0 \\ 1 \\ 0 \\ -1 \end{bmatrix} + \beta \begin{bmatrix} 2 \\ -1 \\ 1 \\ 2 \end{bmatrix} = \begin{bmatrix} -1 \\ 1 \\ -1 \\ -2 \end{bmatrix} + \gamma \begin{bmatrix} 2 \\ -2 \\ 1 \\ 3 \end{bmatrix} + \delta \begin{bmatrix} 1 \\ -1 \\ 0 \\ 0 \end{bmatrix}$$

Or, by combining terms,

$$\alpha\begin{bmatrix}0\\1\\0\\-1\end{bmatrix}+\beta\begin{bmatrix}2\\-1\\1\\2\end{bmatrix}-\gamma\begin{bmatrix}2\\-2\\1\\3\end{bmatrix}-\delta\begin{bmatrix}1\\-1\\0\\0\end{bmatrix}=\begin{bmatrix}0&2&-2&-1\\1&-1&2&1\\0&1&-1&0\\-1&2&-3&0\end{bmatrix}\begin{bmatrix}\alpha\\\beta\\\gamma\\\delta\end{bmatrix}=\begin{bmatrix}-2\\2\\-1\\-3\end{bmatrix}$$

We solve this inhomogeneous system by means of the algorithm in Eq. 3.6.6.

$$\left[\begin{array}{cccc|cccc}0&1&0&-1&1&0&0&0\\2&-1&1&2&0&1&0&0\\-2&2&-1&-3&0&0&1&0\\-1&1&0&0&0&0&0&1\\\hline 2&-2&1&3&0&0&0&0\end{array}\right]\rightarrow$$

$$\cdots\rightarrow\left[\begin{array}{cccc|cccc}1&0&0&-1&0&1&1&-1\\0&1&0&-1&0&1&1&0\\0&0&1&3&0&0&-1&2\\\hline 0&0&0&0&1&-1&-1&0\\\hline 0&0&0&0&0&0&1&0\end{array}\right]$$

The general solution can now be expressed in parametric form as

$$\begin{bmatrix}\alpha\\\beta\\\gamma\\\delta\end{bmatrix}=\begin{bmatrix}0\\0\\1\\0\end{bmatrix}+t\begin{bmatrix}1\\-1\\-1\\0\end{bmatrix}\tag{3.7.8}$$

Hence $\alpha = t$, $\beta = -t$, $\gamma = 1 - t$, and $\delta = 0$. Then

$$\mathbf{x}(t,-t)=\begin{bmatrix}1\\-1\\0\\1\end{bmatrix}+t\begin{bmatrix}0\\1\\0\\-1\end{bmatrix}-t\begin{bmatrix}2\\-1\\1\\2\end{bmatrix}=\begin{bmatrix}1\\-1\\0\\1\end{bmatrix}+t\begin{bmatrix}-2\\2\\-1\\-3\end{bmatrix}\qquad 3.7.9$$

$$-\ \mathbf{y}(1-t,0)$$

3.7.1 Affine Spaces

Lines and planes are two examples of translates of vector spaces. We call any translate of a vector space an *affine space*. Let $\{\mathbf{y}_1,\mathbf{y}_2,\ldots,\mathbf{y}_k\}$ be a basis for the vector space $\mathcal{V}$. Then the set of all combinations of the form

$$\mathbf{y}_0 + a_1\mathbf{y}_1 + \cdots + a_k\mathbf{y}_k \tag{3.7.10}$$

is a translate of $\mathcal{V}$ and is therefore an affine space. The vector $\mathbf{y}_0$ need not be in $\mathcal{V}$, but if it is, then the affine space is $\mathcal{V}$ itself. (See Problem 3.7.26.) The following example illuminates this observation.

Example 3.7.7. Show that the affine space $\mathcal{A}$ is a vector space if and only if $\mathbf{0} \in \mathcal{A}$.

Solution. Suppose $\mathcal{A}$ is the translate of the vector space $\mathcal{V}$ by $\mathbf{y}_0$ and that $\{\mathbf{y}_1,\mathbf{y}_2,\ldots,\mathbf{y}_k\}$ is a basis for $\mathcal{V}$. If $\mathbf{0} \in \mathcal{A}$, then

$$\mathbf{0} = \mathbf{y}_0 + b_1\mathbf{y}_1 + b_2\mathbf{y}_2 + \cdots + b_k\mathbf{y}_k$$

for some set of weights $\{b_1,b_2,\ldots,b_k\}$ and this implies that $\mathbf{y}_0 \in \mathcal{V}$. Hence all vectors in $\mathcal{A}$ lie in the span of $\{\mathbf{y}_1,\mathbf{y}_2,\ldots,\mathbf{y}_k\}$ and, therefore, $\mathcal{A}$ is a vector space. Of course, if $\mathbf{0} \notin \mathcal{A}$, then $\mathcal{A}$ cannot be a vector space.

Example 3.7.8. The set of all solutions of $\mathbf{Ax} = \mathbf{b}$ is the affine space, the translate of *null*(**A**) by a particular solution of $\mathbf{Ax} = \mathbf{b}$. This is true since if $\mathbf{Ay}_0 = \mathbf{b}$ and $\{\mathbf{y}_1,\mathbf{y}_2,\ldots,\mathbf{y}_k\}$ is a basis for *null*(**A**), then a general solution of $\mathbf{Ax} = \mathbf{b}$ is given by $\mathbf{y}_0 + a_1\mathbf{y}_1 + \cdots + a_k\mathbf{y}_k$. (See Section 3.6, Theorem 3.6.3.)

Theorem 3.7.1. *The set of all linear combinations*

$$a_0\mathbf{y}_0 + a_1\mathbf{y}_1 + a_2\mathbf{y}_2 + \cdots + a_k\mathbf{y}_k \tag{3.7.11}$$

subject to the restriction that

$$a_0 + a_1 + \cdots + a_k = 1 \tag{3.7.12}$$

is an affine space, specifically, the translate of $\{\mathbf{y}_1 - \mathbf{y}_0, \mathbf{y}_2 - \mathbf{y}_0,\ldots,\mathbf{y}_n - \mathbf{y}_0\}$ *by* $\mathbf{y}_0$.

Proof. Since $a_0 + a_1 + \cdots + a_k = 1$, it follows that

$$\begin{aligned} &a_0 y_0 + a_1\mathbf{y}_1 + \cdots + a_k\mathbf{y}_k \\ &= (1 - a_1 - a_2 \ldots - a_k)\mathbf{y}_0 + a_1\mathbf{y}_1 + \cdots + a_k\mathbf{y}_k \\ &= y_0 + a_1(\mathbf{y}_1 - \mathbf{y}_0) + \cdots + a_k(\mathbf{y}_k - \mathbf{x}_0) \ \blacksquare \end{aligned}$$

The linear combination given in Eq. 3.7.11 subject to the constraint Eq 3.7.12 is called *an affine combination of* $\{\mathbf{y}_0,\mathbf{y}_1,\ldots,\mathbf{y}_k\}$. Theorem 3.7.1 asserts that the set of all affine combinations of $\{\mathbf{y}_0,\mathbf{y}_1,\ldots,\mathbf{y}_k\}$. is an affine space. This result is analogous to the theorem that the set of all linear combinations of $\{y_0, y_1, \ldots, y_k\}$ is a vector space.

Theorem 3.7.1 is sometimes used as an alternative definition of affine space, in which case the definition given in the text is stated as a theorem. As a special case of the affine space of all solutions of $\mathbf{Ax} = \mathbf{b}$, let $\mathbf{A}$ be the row vector $\mathbf{a}^T$. The set of all solutions of $\mathbf{a}^T\mathbf{x} = \mathbf{b}$, $\mathbf{a} \neq \mathbf{0}$, is called a *hyperplane*. If $\mathbf{a} \neq 0 \in \mathcal{R}^n$, then rank(**A**) = 1 and, hence, the dimension of $null(\mathbf{A}) = n - 1$. Hence, a hyperplane is a translate of a vector space of $n - 1$ dimensions. In particular, a line in two-space (say, $2x - y = -2$) and a plane in three-space (say, $3x + 2y + z = 4$) are hyperplanes. (But a plane in four-space is not because a plane is two-dimensional, and a hyperplane in $\mathcal{R}^4$ must be three-dimensional by definition.) Now we tackle the problem of determining the Cartesian equation of a hyperplane that contains n given points. (See Examples 3.7.4 and 3.7.8.)

Example 3.7.9. Show that the Cartesian equation of the hyperplane containing the points represented by the vectors $\mathbf{y}_1, \mathbf{y}_2, \ldots, \mathbf{y}_n$, $\mathbf{y}_i \in \mathcal{R}^n$, where $\{\mathbf{y}_1, \mathbf{y}_2, \ldots, \mathbf{y}_n\}$ is linearly independent, is given by

$$(\mathbf{1}^{\mathrm{T}}\mathbf{Y}^{-1})\mathbf{x} = 1 \tag{3.7.13}$$

Solution. (Here $\mathbf{a}^{\mathrm{T}} = \mathbf{1}^{\mathrm{T}}\mathbf{Y}^{-1}$.) Let $\mathbf{x}$ represent the point with coordinates $(x_1, x_2, \ldots, x_n)$ lying in the affine space in Eq. 3.7.11, $k = n - 1$. Then

$$\mathbf{x} = a_0\mathbf{y}_0 + a_1\mathbf{y}_1 + a_2\mathbf{y}_2 + \cdots + a_{n-1}\mathbf{y}_{n-1} \tag{3.7.14}$$

$$a_0 + a_1 + a_2 + \cdots + a_k = 1 \tag{3.7.15}$$

Since $\{\mathbf{y}_1\mathbf{y}_2, \ldots, \mathbf{y}_n\}$ is linearly independent and $\mathbf{y}_i \in \mathcal{R}^n$, the matrix $\mathbf{Y} = [\mathbf{y}_1 \ \ \mathbf{y}_2 \ \ \ldots \ \ \mathbf{y}_n]$ is nonsingular. Set $\mathbf{a} = [a_1 \ \ a_2 \ \ \ldots \ \ \mathbf{a}_n]^{\mathrm{T}}$. Then Eq. 3.7.14 and Eq. 3.7.15 may be written

$$\mathbf{Ya} = \mathbf{x} \tag{3.7.16}$$

$$\mathbf{1}^{\mathrm{T}}\mathbf{a} = 1 \tag{3.7.17}$$

From Eq. 3.7.16 it follows that $\mathbf{a} = \mathbf{Y}^{-1}\mathbf{x}$. Equation 3.7.13 follows by substituting this expression into Eq. 3.7.17.

Example 3.7.10. Use Eq. 3.7.17 to find the Cartesian equation of the hyperplane

$$\mathbf{x} = \begin{bmatrix} x \\ y \\ z \\ t \end{bmatrix} = b_1\begin{bmatrix} 1 \\ -1 \\ 0 \\ 0 \end{bmatrix} + b_2\begin{bmatrix} 1 \\ 0 \\ -1 \\ 0 \end{bmatrix} + b_3\begin{bmatrix} 1 \\ 0 \\ 0 \\ -1 \end{bmatrix} + b_4\begin{bmatrix} 1 \\ 1 \\ 1 \\ 1 \end{bmatrix},$$

$$b_1 + b_2 + b_3 + b_4 = 1$$

Solution. Compute $\mathbf{Y}^{-1}$ in the standard manner and obtain

$$\mathbf{Y}^{-1} = 1/4\begin{bmatrix} 1 & -3 & 1 & 1 \\ 1 & 1 & -3 & 1 \\ 1 & 1 & 1 & -3 \\ 1 & 1 & 1 & 1 \end{bmatrix}$$

Then $\mathbf{1}^{\mathrm{T}}\mathbf{Y}^{-1} = [1 \ \ 0 \ \ 0 \ \ 0]$ and hence,

$$\mathbf{1}^{\mathrm{T}}\mathbf{Y}^{-1}\mathbf{x} = [1 \ \ 0 \ \ 0 \ \ 0]\mathbf{x} = x = 1.$$

The Cartesian equation of this hyperplane is $x = 1$, y, z and t arbitrary.

Example 3.7.11. Find the Cartesian equation of the hyperplane containing $\mathbf{e}_1, \mathbf{e}_2, \ldots, \mathbf{e}_n$.

Solution. In this example $\mathbf{Y} = \mathbf{I}_n$ and hence $\mathbf{1}^T\mathbf{I}\mathbf{x} = \mathbf{1}^T\mathbf{x} = 1$. Thus, $\mathbf{a}^T = \mathbf{1}^T$ and the given hyperplane has the equation $x_1 + x_2 + \cdots + x_n = 1$.

Example 3.7.12. Find the Cartesian equation for the plane passing through the points (1,1,1), (1,0,2) and (0,2,2).

Solution. (This is a repeat of Example 3.7.4. Note that a plane in three-space is an affine space.) The plane containing these points is obtained by representing these points as vectors and then proceeding as in Example 3.7.9

$$\mathbf{y}_0 = \begin{bmatrix} 1 \\ 1 \\ 1 \end{bmatrix}, \quad \mathbf{y}_1 = \begin{bmatrix} 1 \\ 0 \\ 2 \end{bmatrix}, \quad \mathbf{y}_2 = \begin{bmatrix} 0 \\ 2 \\ 2 \end{bmatrix}, \quad \mathbf{Y} = \begin{bmatrix} 1 & 1 & 0 \\ 1 & 0 & 2 \\ 1 & 2 & 2 \end{bmatrix}$$

$$\mathbf{Y}^{-1} = 1/4 \begin{bmatrix} 4 & 2 & -2 \\ 0 & -2 & 2 \\ -2 & 1 & 1 \end{bmatrix}$$

Hence, $\mathbf{1}^T\mathbf{Y}^{-1} = [1/2 \quad 1/4 \quad 1/4]$ and therefore

$$\mathbf{1}^T\mathbf{Y}^{-1}\mathbf{x} = [1/2 \quad 1/4 \quad 1/4] \begin{bmatrix} x \\ y \\ z \end{bmatrix} = \tfrac{1}{2}x + \tfrac{1}{4}y + \tfrac{1}{4}z = 1$$

(Compare with the answer to Example 3.7.4.)

PROBLEMS

PART 1

3.7.1. Find the parametric and Cartesian equations of the lines passing through the points,
(*a*) (1,0) and (0,1) (*b*) (−1,1,1) and (0,1,−1)
(*c*) (1,2) and (−1,2) (*d*) (1,1,1,1) and (2,1,0,2)

3.7.2. Find the parametric and Cartesian equations of the line passing through (1,1,−1), parallel to the line through the origin and the point (1,1,1).

3.7.3. Find the parametric and Cartesian equations of the line of intersection of the planes $x + y - z = 1$ and $x - 2y + 2z = 2$.

3.7.4. Find the parametric and Cartesian equations of the line of intersection of the hyperplanes $x - y + z - t = 0$, $x + y + z + t = 1$ and $y - z - t = 2$.

3.7.5. Find the parametric and Cartesian equations of the plane passing through the points:
(*a*) (1,0,0), (0,1,0) and (0,0,1) (*b*) (1,0,0,0), (0,1,0,0) and (0,0,1,0)
(*c*) (1,0,0,1), (0,1,0,1) and (0,0,1,1)

3.7.6. Find the Cartesian equation of the line given parametrically by Eq. 3.7.9.

3.7.7. Find the Cartesian equation of the planes of Example 3.7.6:

$$(a)\ \mathbf{x}(\alpha,\beta) = \begin{bmatrix} 1 \\ -1 \\ 0 \\ 1 \end{bmatrix} + \alpha \begin{bmatrix} 0 \\ 1 \\ 0 \\ -1 \end{bmatrix} + \beta \begin{bmatrix} 2 \\ -1 \\ 1 \\ 2 \end{bmatrix}$$

$$(b)\ \mathbf{y}(\gamma,\delta) = \begin{bmatrix} -1 \\ 1 \\ -1 \\ -2 \end{bmatrix} + \gamma \begin{bmatrix} 2 \\ -2 \\ 1 \\ 3 \end{bmatrix} + \delta \begin{bmatrix} 1 \\ -1 \\ 0 \\ 0 \end{bmatrix}$$

3.7.8. Use the Cartesian equations of the planes obtained as answers to Problems 3.7.6(*a*) and 3.7.6(*b*) to find the equation of the line common to both planes, and compare with the answer to Problem 3.7.5.

3.7.9. Find the Cartesian equation of the plane given by

$$\mathbf{x}(\alpha, \beta) = \begin{bmatrix} 1 \\ 1 \\ 1 \\ 1 \end{bmatrix} + \alpha \begin{bmatrix} 0 \\ 1 \\ 0 \\ -1 \end{bmatrix} + \beta \begin{bmatrix} 0 \\ -1 \\ 1 \\ 0 \end{bmatrix}$$

3.7.10. Find the Cartesian equation of the line given by

$$\mathbf{x}(\alpha) = \begin{bmatrix} 1 \\ 1 \\ 1 \\ 1 \end{bmatrix} + \alpha \begin{bmatrix} 0 \\ 1 \\ 0 \\ -1 \end{bmatrix}$$

3.7.11. Write the plane $3x - 2y - z = 2$ as a translate of a vector space.

3.7.12. Write the line $x - 1 = y$ as the translate of a vector space.

3.7.13. Write the hyperplane $x + 2y + 3z + 4t = 4$ as the translate of a vector space.

3.7.14. Repeat Problem 3.7.11 for the line $x - 1 = y = 2z + 1$.

3.7.15. Explain why two planes (or two lines) are identical if they are translates of the same vector space and have a point in common.

3.7.16. Represent the set of all solutions of $2x - y + 2z - t = 2$ as an affine space.

3.7.17. Represent the set of all solutions of $2x - y + 2z - t = 2,\ y + z = 1$ as an affine space.

3.7.18. Represent the set of all solutions of $2x - y + 2z - t = 2,\ y + z = 1,\ z + t = 0$ as an affine space.

3.7.19. Find the hyperplane in $\mathcal{R}^2$ containing the vectors $\mathbf{e}_1,\ \mathbf{e}_1 + \mathbf{e}_2$.

3.7.20. Find the hyperplane in $\mathcal{R}^3$ containing $\mathbf{e}_1,\ \mathbf{e}_1 + \mathbf{e}_2,\ \mathbf{e}_1 + \mathbf{e}_2 + \mathbf{e}_3$.

3.7.21. Find and sketch an affine space containing (1,−1) and (2,1).

PART 2

3.7.22. Explain why the following parametric equation is a line rather than a plane:

$$\mathbf{x}(\alpha,\beta) = \begin{bmatrix} 1 \\ 1 \\ 1 \\ 1 \end{bmatrix} + \alpha \begin{bmatrix} 0 \\ 1 \\ 0 \\ -1 \end{bmatrix} + \beta \begin{bmatrix} 0 \\ -1 \\ 0 \\ 1 \end{bmatrix}$$

3.7.23. Solve the problem stated as Example 3.7.5 by using the technique used in Example 3.7.6.

3.7.24. Show that the following planes are parallel:

$$\mathbf{x}(\alpha,\beta) = \begin{bmatrix} 1 \\ -1 \\ 0 \\ 0 \end{bmatrix} + \alpha \begin{bmatrix} 0 \\ 1 \\ 0 \\ -1 \end{bmatrix} + \beta \begin{bmatrix} 2 \\ -1 \\ 1 \\ 2 \end{bmatrix} \qquad \mathbf{y}(\gamma,\delta) = \begin{bmatrix} -2 \\ 0 \\ -2 \\ -2 \end{bmatrix} + \gamma \begin{bmatrix} 2 \\ 0 \\ 1 \\ 1 \end{bmatrix} + \delta \begin{bmatrix} 2 \\ -2 \\ 1 \\ 3 \end{bmatrix}$$

3.7.25. Show that the following sets are all affine spaces:

$$(a) \begin{bmatrix} 1 \\ -1 \\ \alpha \\ 1+\alpha \end{bmatrix} \qquad (b) \begin{bmatrix} 1 \\ -1 \\ \alpha \\ \beta \end{bmatrix} \qquad (c) \begin{bmatrix} 1 \\ \alpha \\ \beta \\ \gamma \end{bmatrix}$$

3.7.26. Show that the affine space defined by Eq. 3.7.10 is a vector space if and only if $\mathbf{y}_0 \in \mathcal{V}$.

PART 3

3.7.27. Explain why the solution of $\mathbf{Ax} = \mathbf{b}$ represents a line if $\mathbf{A}$ is $m \times n$, rank($\mathbf{A}$) = $n - 1$, and the system is consistent.

3.7.28. Reword Problem 3.7.27 so that the solution represents a plane.

3.7.29. Suppose $\mathcal{A}$ is an affine space and $\mathbf{x}_1, \mathbf{x}_2, \ldots, \mathbf{x}_k$ belong to $\mathcal{A}$. Show that every affine combination of these vectors belongs to $\mathcal{A}$.

3.7.30. Suppose $\mathbf{x} = \mathbf{x}_0 + \alpha\mathbf{x}_1 + \beta\mathbf{x}_2$ and $y = \mathbf{y}_0 + \gamma\mathbf{y}_1 + \delta\mathbf{y}_2$ are planes. Devise a criterion based on the rank of the matrix, $[\mathbf{x}_1 \quad \mathbf{x}_2 \quad -\mathbf{y}_1 \quad -\mathbf{y}_2 \quad \mathbf{x}_0 - \mathbf{y}_0]$, which shows that these planes are (*a*) Coincident; (*b*) Parallel; (*c*) Neither.

3.7.31. Find a basis for $\mathcal{R}^n$ that contains $n-1$ vectors in the hyperplane $\mathbf{a}^{\mathrm{T}}\mathbf{x} = 1$, where $\mathbf{a} = [1 \quad a_2 \quad \ldots \quad a_n]^{\mathrm{T}}$.

3.7.32. Formulate a definition of the dimension of an affine space.

3.7.33. Suppose $\mathcal{U}$ is the intersection of affine spaces. Show that $\mathcal{U}$ is either empty or is an affine space.

3.8 COORDINATE SYSTEMS AND BASES

Suppose $\mathcal{V} \neq \{\mathbf{0}\}$ is a k-dimensional subspace of $\mathcal{R}^n$ and $\mathcal{B}_V = \{\mathbf{v}_1, \mathbf{v}_2, \ldots, \mathbf{v}_k\}$ is a basis for $\mathcal{V}$. As usual, set $\mathbf{V} = [\mathbf{v}_1 \quad \mathbf{v}_2 \quad \ldots \quad \mathbf{v}_k]$ so that $\mathcal{V} = col(\mathbf{V})$. Suppose $\mathbf{x} \in \mathcal{V}$. Then there is a set of weights $\{x_1, x_2, \ldots, x_k\}$ such that

$$\mathbf{x} = x_1\mathbf{v}_1 + x_2\mathbf{v}_2 + \cdots + x_k\mathbf{v}_k \tag{3.8.1}$$

or equivalently

$$\mathbf{x} = \mathbf{V}\mathbf{x}_v, \qquad \mathbf{x}_v = \begin{bmatrix} x_1 \\ x_2 \\ \vdots \\ x_k \end{bmatrix} \tag{3.8.2}$$

We call the ordered set $(x_1,x_2,\ldots,x_k)$ the *coordinates of* $\mathbf{x}$ *relative to the basis* $\mathcal{B}_V$ *and* $\mathbf{x}_v$ the *coordinate vector of* $\mathbf{x}$ *relative to* $\mathcal{B}_V$. For example,

$$\mathcal{V} = span\left\{\mathbf{v}_1 = \begin{bmatrix} -1 \\ 0 \\ 1 \\ 0 \end{bmatrix}, \mathbf{v}_2 = \begin{bmatrix} 0 \\ 1 \\ 2 \\ 1 \end{bmatrix}\right\}$$

is a two-dimensional subspace of $\mathcal{R}^4$. Then

$$\mathbf{1} = \begin{bmatrix} 1 \\ 1 \\ 1 \\ 1 \end{bmatrix} = (-1)\begin{bmatrix} -1 \\ 0 \\ 1 \\ 0 \end{bmatrix} + (1)\begin{bmatrix} 0 \\ 1 \\ 2 \\ 1 \end{bmatrix} = (-1)\mathbf{v}_1 + (1)\mathbf{v}_2$$

shows that the coordinates of $\mathbf{1}$ relative to $\{\mathbf{v}_1,\mathbf{v}_2\}$ are $(-1,1)$.

Theorem 3.8.1. *For fixed* $\mathbf{x} \in \mathcal{V}$ *and* $\mathcal{B}_V$, *a fixed basis for* $\mathcal{V}$, *the set of coordinates and the coordinate vector relative to* $\mathcal{B}_V$ *are unique.*

Proof. Suppose $\mathbf{b}$ and $\mathbf{c}$ are two coordinate vectors of $\mathbf{x}$ relative to $\mathcal{B}_V$. Then $\mathbf{x} = \mathbf{Vc} = \mathbf{Vb}$, and these relationships imply $\mathbf{V}(\mathbf{c} - \mathbf{b}) = \mathbf{0}$. However, since the columns of $\mathbf{V}$ are linearly independent, $\mathbf{c} - \mathbf{b} = \mathbf{0}$ by Theorem 2.7.7. ■

The definition of coordinate vector can be applied to $\mathcal{V} = \mathcal{R}^n$ where the basis for $\mathcal{V}$ is chosen as the *standard basis* $\mathcal{E} = \{\mathbf{e}_1,\mathbf{e}_2,\ldots,\mathbf{e}_n\}$. Then

$$\mathbf{x} = \begin{bmatrix} x_1 \\ x_2 \\ \vdots \\ x_k \end{bmatrix} = x_1\mathbf{e}_1 + x_2\mathbf{e}_2 + \cdots + x_n\mathbf{e}_n = \mathbf{I}\mathbf{x}_e$$

and $\mathbf{x} = \mathbf{x}_e$ is its own coordinate vector relative to the standard basis. For this reason, vectors given without explicit reference to a basis may be taken as the coordinate vector relative to $\mathcal{E}$.

Example 3.8.1. Find the coordinates for each vector in the plane

$$\mathbf{x} = s\mathbf{v}_1 + t\mathbf{v}_2 = s\begin{bmatrix} -1 \\ 0 \\ 1 \\ 0 \end{bmatrix} + t\begin{bmatrix} 0 \\ 1 \\ 2 \\ 1 \end{bmatrix}$$

Solution. Clearly, $\mathbf{x}$ is in the plane implies that its coordinates are (s,t) relative to the basis $\{\mathbf{v}_1,\mathbf{v}_2\}$. The set of all coordinate vectors relative to this basis is $\mathcal{R}^2$.

Theorem 3.8.2. *The set of all coordinate vectors relative to the k-dimensional vector space* $\mathcal{V} \neq \{\mathbf{0}\} \in \mathcal{R}^n$ *is the vector space* $\mathcal{R}^k$.

Proof. Equation 3.8.1 and the uniqueness theorem shows that we may establish a one to one correspondence[1] between the set of all coordinate vectors relative to $\mathcal{V}$ and all vectors in $\mathcal{R}^k$. ■

Since there are infinitely many bases for a given, nontrivial vector space, there are infinitely many coordinate vectors for each fixed vector in the vector space. What is the connection between these coordinate vectors? To answer this important question let us introduce a second basis for $\mathcal{V}$; namely, $\mathcal{B}_W = \{\mathbf{w}_1, \mathbf{w}_2, \ldots, \mathbf{w}_k\}$ and set $\mathbf{W} = [\mathbf{w}_1 \quad \mathbf{w}_2 \quad \ldots \quad \mathbf{w}_k]$. First, we prove the following useful lemma:

Lemma 3.1. *Suppose* $\mathbf{s}_i$ *is the coordinate vector of* $\mathbf{w}_i$ *relative to the basis* $\mathcal{B}_V$ *and define* $\mathbf{S} = [\mathbf{s}_1 \quad \mathbf{s}_2 \quad \ldots \quad \mathbf{s}_k]$. *Then* $\mathbf{S}$ *is* $k \times k$ *and is invertible and*

$$\mathbf{W} = \mathbf{VS} \tag{3.8.3}$$

Proof. By definition of coordinate vector relative to a basis,

$$\mathbf{w}_i = \mathbf{V}\mathbf{s}_i$$

Hence,

$$\mathbf{VS} = \mathbf{V}[\mathbf{s}_1 \quad \mathbf{s}_2 \quad \ldots \quad \mathbf{s}_k] = [\mathbf{V}\mathbf{s}_1 \quad \mathbf{V}\mathbf{s}_2 \quad \ldots \quad \mathbf{V}\mathbf{s}_k] = \mathbf{W}$$

To show that $\mathbf{S}$ is invertible we show that its columns are linearly independent. We do this by considering $\mathbf{Sx} = \mathbf{0}$. Then from Eq. 3.8.3

$$\mathbf{VSx} = \mathbf{Wx} = \mathbf{0}$$

But the columns of $\mathbf{W}$ are linearly independent so $\mathbf{Wx} = \mathbf{0}$ implies that $\mathbf{x} = \mathbf{0}$ and, as a result, $\mathbf{Sx} = \mathbf{0}$ has only the trivial solution. ■

Let $\mathbf{x}_v$ and $\mathbf{x}_w$ be the coordinate vectors of $\mathbf{x}$ relative to $\mathcal{B}_V$ and $\mathcal{B}_W$, respectively. Then, by Eq. 3.8.2

$$\mathbf{x} = \mathbf{V}\mathbf{x}_v \qquad \text{and} \qquad \mathbf{x} = \mathbf{W}\mathbf{x}_w \tag{3.8.4}$$

From Lemma 3.1, $\mathbf{W} = \mathbf{VS}$ and, by substitution into $\mathbf{x} = \mathbf{W}\mathbf{x}_W$,

$$\mathbf{x} = \mathbf{V}(\mathbf{S}\mathbf{x}_w)$$

Thus $\mathbf{S}\mathbf{x}_w$ and $\mathbf{x}_v$ are both coordinates of $\mathbf{x}$ relative to the basis $\mathcal{B}_V$ and, since the coordinate vector is unique for a specific basis, $\mathbf{S}\mathbf{x}_w = \mathbf{x}_v$. (Note that $\mathbf{V}$ and $\mathbf{W}$ are $n \times k$ but $\mathbf{S}$ is $k \times k$.) This proves

Theorem 3.8.3. *Suppose* $\mathcal{B}_V$ *and* $\mathcal{B}_W$ *are two bases for the k-dimensional sub-*

[1] The definitions and theorems presented here are valid for a wider class of vector spaces than spaces of n-tuples. In that larger context, this theorem gains far greater significance.

space $\mathcal{V} \neq \{\mathbf{0}\}$ *of* $\mathcal{R}^n$ *and that* $\mathbf{x} \in \mathcal{V}$. *Then, if* $\mathbf{x}_v$ *and* $\mathbf{x}_w$ *are coordinate vectors of* $\mathbf{x}$ *relative to* $\mathcal{B}_v$ *and* $\mathcal{B}_w$, *respectively, and* $\mathbf{S}$ *is defined as in Lemma 3.1,*

$$\mathbf{x}_w = \mathbf{S}^{-1}\mathbf{x}_v \tag{3.8.5}$$

Corollary 1. *If* $\mathcal{V} = \mathcal{R}^n$ *and* $\mathcal{B}_v = \mathcal{E}$ *is the standard basis for* $\mathcal{R}^n$, *then*

$$\mathbf{x}_w = \mathbf{W}^{-1}\mathbf{x}. \tag{3.8.6}$$

Proof. Relative to the standard basis, $\mathbf{x}$ is its own coordinate vector and $\mathbf{V} = \mathbf{I}$ and, therefore, $\mathbf{W} = \mathbf{S}$. Thus Eq. 3.8.6 follows from Eq. 3.8.5. In fact, $\mathbf{x}_w$ can be computed by row reductions as follows:

$$[\mathbf{W} \quad \mathbf{x}] \to \cdots \to [\mathbf{I} \quad \mathbf{x}_w] \; \blacksquare \tag{3.8.7}$$

Example 3.8.2. Find the coordinate vector of $\mathbf{x} = [1 \quad -1 \quad 1]^T$ relative to the basis

$$\mathcal{B}_W = \left\{ \mathbf{w}_1 = \begin{bmatrix} 1 \\ 0 \\ 0 \end{bmatrix}, \quad \mathbf{w}_2 = \begin{bmatrix} 1 \\ 1 \\ 0 \end{bmatrix}, \quad \mathbf{w}_3 = \begin{bmatrix} 1 \\ 1 \\ 1 \end{bmatrix} \right\}$$

Solution.

$$\left[\begin{array}{ccc:c} 1 & 1 & 1 & 1 \\ 0 & 1 & 1 & -1 \\ 0 & 0 & 1 & 1 \end{array}\right] \to \cdots \to \left[\begin{array}{ccc:c} 1 & 0 & 0 & 2 \\ 0 & 1 & 0 & -2 \\ 0 & 0 & 1 & 1 \end{array}\right]$$

and hence $\mathbf{x}_w = \mathbf{W}^{-1}\mathbf{x} = \begin{bmatrix} 2 \\ -2 \\ 1 \end{bmatrix}$. As a check,

$$\begin{bmatrix} 1 \\ -1 \\ 1 \end{bmatrix} = (2)\begin{bmatrix} 1 \\ 0 \\ 0 \end{bmatrix} + (-2)\begin{bmatrix} 1 \\ 1 \\ 0 \end{bmatrix} + (1)\begin{bmatrix} 1 \\ 1 \\ 1 \end{bmatrix}$$

Example 3.8.3. Consider the two bases for $\mathcal{V}$,

$$\mathcal{B}_V = \left\{ \mathbf{v}_1 = \begin{bmatrix} 1 \\ -1 \\ 1 \end{bmatrix}, \quad \mathbf{v}_2 = \begin{bmatrix} 0 \\ 1 \\ 1 \end{bmatrix} \right\}, \; \mathcal{B}_W = \left\{ \mathbf{w}_1 = \begin{bmatrix} 1 \\ 0 \\ 2 \end{bmatrix}, \quad \mathbf{w}_2 = \begin{bmatrix} 1 \\ -2 \\ 0 \end{bmatrix} \right\}$$

Find the coordinates for the vectors $\mathbf{w}_1$ and $\mathbf{w}_2$ relative to $\mathcal{B}_V$.

Solution. Define

$$\mathbf{V} = \begin{bmatrix} 1 & 0 \\ -1 & 1 \\ 1 & 1 \end{bmatrix} \qquad \mathbf{W} = \begin{bmatrix} 1 & 1 \\ 0 & -2 \\ 2 & 0 \end{bmatrix}$$

By Eq. 3.8.5, $\mathbf{VS} = \mathbf{W}$ and the columns of $\mathbf{S}$ are the required coordinate vectors. Since $\mathbf{V}$ is not square, we cannot invert $\mathbf{V}$ in $\mathbf{VS} = \mathbf{W}$ to find S. Instead, we use the more general technique given by algorithm Eq. 3.6.4 of Section 3.6:

$$\begin{bmatrix} \mathbf{V}^T & \mathbf{I} \\ -\mathbf{W}^T & \mathbf{O} \end{bmatrix} = \left[\begin{array}{ccc|cc} 1 & -1 & 1 & 1 & 0 \\ 0 & 1 & 1 & 0 & 1 \\ \hline -1 & 0 & -2 & 0 & 0 \\ -1 & 2 & 0 & 0 & 0 \end{array}\right] \rightarrow$$

$$\cdots \rightarrow \left[\begin{array}{ccc|cc} 1 & -1 & 1 & 1 & 0 \\ 0 & 1 & 1 & 0 & 1 \\ \hline 0 & 0 & 0 & 1 & 1 \\ 0 & 0 & 0 & 1 & -1 \end{array}\right] = \begin{bmatrix} \mathbf{V}^T & \mathbf{I} \\ -\mathbf{O} & \mathbf{S}^T \end{bmatrix}$$

Hence

$$\mathbf{S} = [\mathbf{s}_1 \quad \mathbf{s}_2] = \begin{bmatrix} 1 & 1 \\ 1 & -1 \end{bmatrix}$$

and, therefore, $\mathbf{s}_1 = [1 \quad 1]^T$ and $\mathbf{s}_2 = [1 \quad -1]^T$ are the coordinate vectors of $\mathbf{w}_1$ and $\mathbf{w}_2$ relative to $\mathcal{B}_V$, respectively.

Example 3.8.4. Let

$$\mathcal{B}_W = \left\{ \begin{bmatrix} \cos\theta \\ \sin\theta \end{bmatrix}, \begin{bmatrix} -\sin\theta \\ \cos\theta \end{bmatrix} \right\} \quad \text{and } \mathbf{x} = \begin{bmatrix} x \\ y \end{bmatrix}.$$

Then

$$\mathbf{W} = \begin{bmatrix} \cos\theta & -\sin\theta \\ \sin\theta & \cos\theta \end{bmatrix} \quad \text{and} \quad \mathbf{W}^{-1} = \begin{bmatrix} \cos\theta & \sin\theta \\ -\sin\theta & \cos\theta \end{bmatrix}$$

So, from Corollary 1 of Theorem 3.8.3,

$$\mathbf{x}_W = \mathbf{W}^{-1}\mathbf{x} = \begin{bmatrix} \cos\theta & \sin\theta \\ -\sin\theta & \cos\theta \end{bmatrix} \mathbf{x} = \begin{bmatrix} x\cos\theta + y\sin\theta \\ -x\sin\theta + y\cos\theta \end{bmatrix} \tag{3.8.8}$$

If we let $\mathbf{x}_W = \begin{bmatrix} X \\ Y \end{bmatrix}$, then Eq. 3.8.8 implies

$$\begin{aligned} X &= x\cos\theta + y\sin\theta \\ Y &= -x\sin\theta + y\cos\theta \end{aligned} \tag{3.8.9}$$

Equations 3.8.9 relate the coordinates (x,y) of the point P to the coordinates of the same point relative to a frame rotated by an angle θ. For example, if the coordinates of the point P are (1,1) in the x,y frame, then they are $(\sqrt{2},0)$ in the X, Y frame if the x,y frame is rotated $\pi/4$ radians. This follows from Eq. 3.8.9 because $\sin\pi/4 = \cos\pi/4 = \sqrt{2}/2$. See Fig. 3.2.

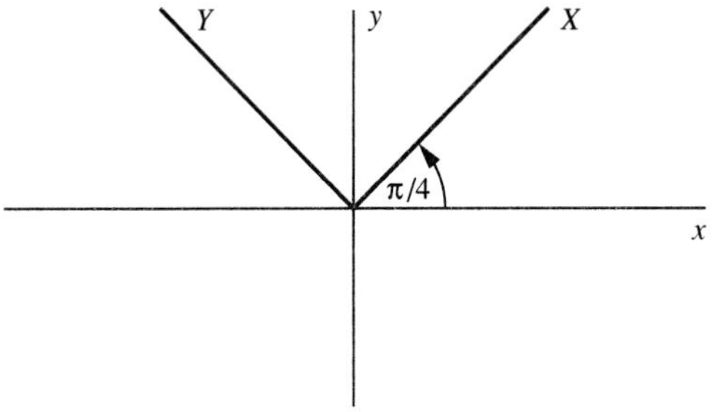

FIGURE 3-2
Depiction of the X,Y frame if the x,y frame is rotated $\pi/4$ radians.

Suppose $\mathbf{x}_v$ and $\mathbf{y}_v$ are the coordinate vectors of $\boldsymbol{x}$ and $\boldsymbol{y}$ relative to the basis $\mathcal{B}_v$ of $\mathcal{R}^n$. Suppose also that $\mathbf{x}_v$ and $\mathbf{y}_v$ are related by

$$\mathbf{y}_v = \mathbf{A}\mathbf{x}_v \tag{3.8.10}$$

for some $n \times n$ matrix $\mathbf{A}$. Now, suppose that $\mathbf{x}_w$ and $\mathbf{y}_w$ are the coordinate vectors of $\mathbf{x}$ and $\mathbf{y}$ relative to a second basis $\diamond$ of $\mathcal{R}^n$. How are $\mathbf{x}_w$ and $\mathbf{y}_w$ related? Theorem 3.8.3 provides the answer. In the notation of that theorem

$$\mathbf{S}^{-1}\mathbf{x}_v = \mathbf{x}_w \quad \text{and} \quad \mathbf{S}^{-1}\mathbf{y}_v = \mathbf{y}_w \tag{3.8.11}$$

If Eq. 3.8.10 is premultiplied by $\mathbf{S}^{-1}$ we obtain $\mathbf{S}^{-1}\mathbf{y}_v = \mathbf{S}^{-1}\mathbf{A}\mathbf{x}_v$. Now using Eq. 3.8.11 we find

$$\mathbf{y}_w = \mathbf{S}^{-1}\mathbf{y}_v = \mathbf{S}^{-1}\mathbf{A}\mathbf{x}_v = \mathbf{S}^{-1}\mathbf{A}\mathbf{S}\mathbf{x}_w \tag{3.8.12}$$

The transformation of $\mathbf{A}$ to $\mathbf{S}\mathbf{A}\mathbf{S}^{-1}$ is one of the prime motivations for the entire theory developed in Chapter 5.

PROBLEMS

PART 1

In each of the following three problems two bases for $\mathcal{V}$ are given by

$$\mathcal{B}_V = \left\{ \mathbf{v}_1 = \begin{bmatrix} 1 \\ -1 \\ 0 \\ 1 \end{bmatrix}, \quad \mathbf{v}_2 = \begin{bmatrix} 0 \\ 1 \\ 1 \\ 0 \end{bmatrix}, \quad \mathbf{v}_3 = \begin{bmatrix} 0 \\ 0 \\ -1 \\ 1 \end{bmatrix} \right\}$$

$$\mathcal{B}_W = \left\{ \mathbf{w}_1 = \begin{bmatrix} 1 \\ 0 \\ 0 \\ 2 \end{bmatrix}, \quad \mathbf{w}_2 = \begin{bmatrix} 0 \\ 1 \\ 0 \\ 1 \end{bmatrix}, \quad \mathbf{w}_3 = \begin{bmatrix} 0 \\ 0 \\ 1 \\ -1 \end{bmatrix} \right\}$$

3.8.1. Find the coordinate vectors of $\mathbf{w}_1$,$\mathbf{w}_2$ and $\mathbf{w}_3$ relative to $\mathcal{B}_V$ and the matrix $\mathbf{S}$ relating $\mathbf{W} = [\mathbf{w}_1 \quad \mathbf{w}_2 \quad \mathbf{w}_3]$ to $\mathbf{V} = [\mathbf{v}_1 \quad \mathbf{v}_2 \quad \mathbf{v}_3]$.

3.8.2. Find the coordinate vectors of $\mathbf{v}_1$, $\mathbf{v}_2$ and $\mathbf{v}_3$ relative to $\mathcal{B}_W$ and the matrix $\mathbf{S}$ relating $\mathbf{V} = [\mathbf{v}_1 \quad \mathbf{v}_2 \quad \mathbf{v}_3]$ to $\mathbf{W} = [\mathbf{w}_1 \quad \mathbf{w}_2 \quad \mathbf{w}_3]$. What is the relationship between the matrices $\mathbf{S}$ of this problem and of Problem 3.8.1?

3.8.3. Suppose $\mathbf{x}$, $\mathbf{y}$, $\mathbf{z}$ are given relative to the standard basis. Find their coordinate vectors relative to $\mathcal{B}_V$.

$$\mathbf{x} = \begin{bmatrix} 1 \\ -1 \\ 0 \\ 1 \end{bmatrix} \qquad \mathbf{y} = \begin{bmatrix} 1 \\ 0 \\ 1 \\ 1 \end{bmatrix} \qquad \mathbf{z} = \begin{bmatrix} 1 \\ -2 \\ 0 \\ 0 \end{bmatrix}$$

3.8.4. Repeat Problem 3.8.3 by using $\mathcal{B}_W$ instead of $\mathcal{B}_V$. Here are two bases for $\mathcal{R}^4$:

$$\mathcal{B}_V = \left\{ \mathbf{v}_1 = \begin{bmatrix} 1 \\ -1 \\ 0 \\ 1 \end{bmatrix}, \quad \mathbf{v}_2 = \begin{bmatrix} 0 \\ 1 \\ 1 \\ 0 \end{bmatrix}, \quad \mathbf{v}_3 = \begin{bmatrix} 0 \\ 0 \\ -1 \\ 1 \end{bmatrix}, \quad \mathbf{v}_4 = \begin{bmatrix} 0 \\ 0 \\ 0 \\ 1 \end{bmatrix} \right\}$$

$$\mathcal{B}_W = \left\{ \mathbf{w}_1 = \begin{bmatrix} 1 \\ 0 \\ 0 \\ 2 \end{bmatrix}, \quad \mathbf{w}_2 = \begin{bmatrix} 0 \\ 1 \\ 0 \\ 1 \end{bmatrix}, \quad \mathbf{w}_3 = \begin{bmatrix} 0 \\ 0 \\ 1 \\ 1 \end{bmatrix}, \quad \mathbf{w}_4 = \begin{bmatrix} 0 \\ 0 \\ 0 \\ 1 \end{bmatrix} \right\}$$

3.8.5. Use the bases $\mathcal{B}_V$ and $\mathcal{B}_W$ of Problem 3.8.4. Set

$$\mathbf{A} = \begin{bmatrix} 1 & 1 & 1 & 1 \\ -1 & 0 & 1 & -1 \\ 0 & 1 & 2 & 0 \\ 2 & 1 & 0 & 2 \end{bmatrix}, \qquad \mathbf{x} = \begin{bmatrix} 1 \\ 1 \\ 0 \\ 0 \end{bmatrix}, \qquad \mathbf{y} = \begin{bmatrix} 2 \\ -1 \\ 1 \\ 3 \end{bmatrix}.$$

Then $\mathbf{Ax} = \mathbf{y}$.

(*a*) Assume that $\mathbf{x} = \mathbf{x}_e$ and $\mathbf{y} = \mathbf{y}_e$ are given relative to the standard basis $\mathcal{E}$. Let $\mathbf{x}_v$ be the coordinate vector of $\mathbf{x}$ relative to $\mathcal{B}_V$. Find $\mathbf{y}_v$ and verify Eq. 3.8.11 by finding $\mathbf{B} = \mathbf{S}^{-1}\mathbf{AS}$. (Note that $\mathcal{E}$ plays the role of $\mathcal{B}_V$ and $\mathcal{B}_W$ is now $\mathcal{B}_V$.)

(*b*) Let $\mathbf{x}_w$ be the coordinate vector of $\mathbf{x}$ relative to $\mathcal{B}_W$. Find $\mathbf{y}_w$ and verify Eq. 3.8.11 by finding $\mathbf{C} = \mathbf{S}^{-1}\mathbf{AS}$. (Note that $\mathcal{E}$ plays the role of $\mathcal{B}_V$.)

(*c*) Referring to parts (*a*) and (*b*), discover a relationship between $\mathcal{B}$ and $\mathbf{C}$.

PART 2

3.8.6. Suppose $\mathcal{V} \neq \{\mathbf{0}\}$ is a k-dimensional subspace of $\mathcal{R}^n$ and $\mathcal{B}_V = \{\mathbf{v}_1, \mathbf{v}_2, \ldots, \mathbf{v}_k\}$ is a basis for $\mathcal{V}$. What are the coordinate vectors of $\mathbf{v}_i$ relative to $\mathcal{B}_V$?

3.8.7. Suppose $\mathbf{x}_v$ is the coordinate vector of $\mathbf{x}$ relative to a basis $\mathcal{B}_V$ of $\mathcal{R}^n$. Find an expression for $\mathbf{x}$ relative to $\mathcal{E}$ in terms of $\mathbf{x}_V$ and $\mathbf{V}$.

3.8.8 Suppose $\mathbf{A}_{m \times n}$ has full column rank (i.e., the columns of $\mathbf{A}$ are linearly independent so that rank$(\mathbf{A}) = n$). Suppose $\mathbf{b} = \mathbf{Ax}$. What is the coordinate vector of $\mathbf{b}$ relative to the columns of $\mathbf{A}$ considered as a basis of *col*$(\mathbf{A})$?

CHAPTER 4

ORTHOGONALITY AND ITS CONSEQUENCES

4.1 INTRODUCTION

All bases share the property of being spanning sets for the vector spaces in which they reside. Thus if $\mathbf{b} \in \mathcal{V}$ and $\mathcal{B}_V = \{\mathbf{v}_1, \mathbf{v}_2, \ldots, \mathbf{v}_k\}$ is any basis for $\mathcal{V}$, then there are scalars $\{a_1, a_2, \ldots, a_k\}$, dependent on $\mathbf{b}$ and $\mathcal{B}_V$ such that,

$$\sum_{i=1}^{k} a_i \mathbf{v}_i = \mathbf{b} \tag{4.1.1}$$

The determination of the weights a_i in Eq. 4.1.1 amounts to finding the solution of the inhomogeneous system $\mathbf{Va} = \mathbf{b}$, where, as usual, $\mathbf{V}$ has as its columns the vectors $\mathbf{v}_1, \mathbf{v}_2, \ldots, \mathbf{v}_k$, and $\mathbf{a} = [a_1 \quad a_2 \quad \ldots \quad a_k]^{\mathrm{T}}$.

Experience with coordinate systems in physics and geometry suggests that bases whose vectors are mutually perpendicular are convenient frames of reference for the solution of Eq. 4.1.1. See, for instance, Example 4.3.3. The standard basis for $\mathcal{R}^3$, $\mathcal{E} = \{\mathbf{i} = \mathbf{e}_1, \mathbf{j} = \mathbf{e}_2, \mathbf{k} = \mathbf{e}_3\}$ is the most familiar example. One reason for its prominence, besides its simplicity, is that the distance between the points (x_1, y_1, z_1) and (x_2, y_2, z_2) is given by the Pythagorean theorem,

$$\sqrt{(x_1 - x_2)^2 + (y_1 - y_2)^2 + (z_1 - z_2)^2}$$

a statement which is false for oblique frames.

It is our intention to define and study bases which share the simplicity and convenience of $\{\mathbf{i}, \mathbf{j}, \mathbf{k}\}$. To do so requires an analysis of the notion of orthogonality in vector (sub)spaces of $\mathcal{R}^n$.

The theory of orthogonality presented here is an introduction to an extensive and important body of literature, among which the theory of Fourier series can be counted as one of the most prominent. Sections 4.9 and 4.10 discuss the theory of least squares, a subject with many applications in the physical and social sciences.

4.2 INNER PRODUCTS AND NORMS

In the previous chapters we ignored questions which dealt with the notion of distance. However, if the correspondence between n-dimensional geometry and vector spaces of n-tuples is to be complete, we must introduce metric concepts, which in this case are inner product, norm, and distance.

For the n-tuples $\mathbf{x} \in \mathcal{R}^n$ and $\mathbf{y} \in \mathcal{R}^n$,

$$\mathbf{x} = \begin{bmatrix} x_1 \\ x_2 \\ \vdots \\ x_n \end{bmatrix}, \qquad \mathbf{y} = \begin{bmatrix} y_1 \\ y_2 \\ \vdots \\ y_n \end{bmatrix}$$

the scalar denoted by $< \mathbf{x}, \mathbf{y} >$ and defined by

$$< \mathbf{x}, \mathbf{y} >= x_1y_1 + x_2y_2 + \cdots + x_ny_n \tag{4.2.1}$$

is called the *inner product* of $\mathbf{x}$ and $\mathbf{y}$. Note that the inner product is also the dot product $\mathbf{x} \cdot \mathbf{y}$, and the matrix product $\mathbf{x}^{\mathrm{T}}\mathbf{y}$ (with the usual convention that 1×1 matrices are identified with their sole scalar entry).

Theorem 4.2.1. *For each* $\mathbf{A}_{m\times n}$, $\mathbf{x} \in \mathcal{R}^n$ *and* $\mathbf{y} \in \mathcal{R}^m$,

$$< \mathbf{Ax}, \mathbf{y} > \;=\; < \mathbf{x}, \mathbf{A}^{\mathrm{T}}\mathbf{y} >$$

Proof. Write $< \mathbf{Ax}, \mathbf{y} > = (\mathbf{Ax})^{\mathrm{T}}\mathbf{y}$. Then $(\mathbf{Ax})^{\mathrm{T}}\mathbf{y} = \mathbf{x}^{\mathrm{T}}\mathbf{A}^{\mathrm{T}}\mathbf{y} = \mathbf{x}^{\mathrm{T}}(\mathbf{A}^{\mathrm{T}}\mathbf{y})$. But $\mathbf{x}^{\mathrm{T}}(\mathbf{A}^{\mathrm{T}}\mathbf{y}) = < \mathbf{x}, \mathbf{A}^{\mathrm{T}}\mathbf{y} >$. ■

For ease of reference, here is a list of the familiar properties of the dot product cast in inner product notation:

$$\left.\begin{aligned}
&(a)\ < \mathbf{x}, \mathbf{y} > \;=\; < \mathbf{y}, \mathbf{x} > \\
&(b)\ < \mathbf{x}, \mathbf{x} > \geq 0 \\
&(c)\ < k\mathbf{x}, \mathbf{y} > \;=\; < \mathbf{x}, k\mathbf{y} > \;=\; k < \mathbf{x}, \mathbf{y} > \\
&(d)\ < \mathbf{x}, \mathbf{x} > \;=\; 0 \text{ if and only if } \mathbf{x} = \mathbf{0} \\
&(e)\ < \mathbf{x} + \mathbf{y}, \mathbf{z} > \;=\; < \mathbf{x}, \mathbf{z} > + < \mathbf{y}, \mathbf{z} > \\
&(f)\ < a_1\mathbf{x}_1 + a_2\mathbf{x}_2 + \cdots + a_k\mathbf{x}_k, \mathbf{z} > \\
&\qquad = a_1 < \mathbf{x}_1, \mathbf{z} > + a_2 < \mathbf{x}_2, \mathbf{z} > + \cdots + a_k < \mathbf{x}_k, \mathbf{z} >
\end{aligned}\right\} \tag{4.2.2}$$

The *norm* of $\mathbf{x}$, written $\|\mathbf{x}\|$, is defined by

$$\|\mathbf{x}\| = \sqrt{<\mathbf{x},\mathbf{x}>} \tag{4.2.3}$$

and is used to define the length of the vector $\mathbf{x}$. In $\mathcal{R}^2$, $\|\mathbf{x}\| = \sqrt{x^2+y^2}$, and so the norm of $\mathbf{x}$ is the length of the line segment from the origin to the point with coordinates (x, y). Similarly, the norm in $\mathcal{R}^3$ corresponds to the length of the vector from (0,0,0) terminating at the point (x, y, z). For this reason the norm as defined by Eq. 4.2.3 is called the *euclidean norm*. Other norms are possible and, in certain circumstances, quite convenient. For example, in the theory of stochastic processes $\|\mathbf{x}\| = \max\{|x_1|, |x_2|, \ldots, |x_n|\}$ is a norm which is more convenient than the euclidean norm.

The definition of euclidean norm requires that $\mathbf{x}$ be real, otherwise it would be possible to have vectors with negative length. (The norm of $[2i \quad 1]^{\mathrm{T}}$ is -3.) As we will see in Chapter 6, restricting vectors to $\mathcal{R}^n$ is too limiting. A generalization of the euclidean norm suitable for studying the "length" of vectors with complex entries is presented in Subsection 4.2.1 to follow. We use the euclidean inner product and norm throughout this chapter unless explicitly stated to the contrary.

Example 4.2.1. Establish the following results for $\mathbf{x}$ and $\mathbf{y} \in \mathcal{R}^n$

(a) $\|\mathbf{x}\| \geq 0$ with equality if and only if $\mathbf{x} = \mathbf{0}$.
(b) $\|a\mathbf{x}\| = |a|\|\mathbf{x}\|$, for each scalar a and each vector $\mathbf{x}$.
(c) $\|\mathbf{x}+\lambda\mathbf{y}\|^2 = \|\mathbf{x}\|^2 + 2\lambda <\mathbf{x},\mathbf{y}> +\lambda^2\|\mathbf{y}\|^2$, for each λ and all $\mathbf{x}$ and $\mathbf{y}$.

Solution. Parts (a) and (b) are set as Problem 4.2.6. The proof of (c) is a consequence of the definition of norm and Theorem 4.2.1:

$$\begin{aligned}\|\mathbf{x}+\lambda\mathbf{y}\|^2 &= <\mathbf{x}+\lambda\mathbf{y}, \mathbf{x}+\lambda\mathbf{y}> \\ &= <\mathbf{x},\mathbf{x}> + <\mathbf{x},\lambda\mathbf{y}> + <\lambda\mathbf{y},\mathbf{x}> + <\lambda\mathbf{y},\lambda\mathbf{y}>\end{aligned}$$

Use

$$\|\mathbf{x}\|^2 = <\mathbf{x},\mathbf{x}>, \qquad <\lambda\mathbf{x},\mathbf{y}> = <\lambda\mathbf{y},\mathbf{x}> = \lambda <\mathbf{x},\mathbf{y}>$$

and

$$<\lambda\mathbf{y},\lambda\mathbf{y}> = \lambda^2\|\mathbf{y}\|^2$$

in the above equation to obtain

$$\|\mathbf{x}+\lambda\mathbf{y}\|^2 = \|\mathbf{x}\|^2 + 2\lambda <\mathbf{x},\mathbf{y}> + \lambda^2\|\mathbf{y}\|^2$$

A vector $\mathbf{q}$ is a *unit* vector if its norm is one; that is if $\|\mathbf{q}\| = 1$. It is always possible to rescale a nonzero vector so that its norm is one. To see this, suppose $\|\mathbf{x}\| = L \neq 0$ and set $\mathbf{q} = \mathbf{x}/L$. By Example 4.2.1$(b)$, $\|\mathbf{q}\| = \|\mathbf{x}/L\| = \|\mathbf{x}\|/L = 1$.

Theorem 4.2.2. *(The Schwarz Inequality). For each* $\mathbf{x}$ *and* $\mathbf{y}$,

$$|<\mathbf{x},\ \mathbf{y}>| \leq \|\mathbf{x}\|\,\|\mathbf{y}\| \tag{4.2.4}$$

Proof. Assume that $\{\mathbf{x}, \mathbf{y}\}$ is linearly independent so that $\mathbf{x} + \lambda\mathbf{y} \neq \mathbf{0}$ for every choice of the scalar λ. By Part (c) of Example 4.2.1,

$$0 < \|\mathbf{x} + \lambda\mathbf{y}\|^2 = \|\mathbf{x}\|^2 + 2\lambda < \mathbf{x}, \mathbf{y} > + \lambda^2\|\mathbf{y}\|^2 \tag{4.2.5}$$

Let $a = \|\mathbf{y}\|^2$, $b = < \mathbf{x}, \mathbf{y} >$ and $c = \|\mathbf{x}\|^2$. Then Inequality 4.2.5 becomes

$$a\lambda^2 + 2b\lambda + c > 0. \tag{4.2.6}$$

However, since $a > 0$, Inequality 4.2.6 is possible if and only if $a^2\lambda + 2b\lambda + c$ has no real roots, and this occurs if and only if the discriminant, $b^2 - ac$, is negative. That is,

$$b^2 - ac = < \mathbf{x}, \mathbf{y} >^2 - \|\mathbf{x}\|^2\|\mathbf{y}\|^2 < 0$$

from which Inequality 4.2.5 follows. Finally, if $\{\mathbf{x}, \mathbf{y}\}$ is linearly dependent, then $| < \mathbf{x}, \mathbf{y} > | = \|\mathbf{x}\|\,\|\mathbf{y}\|$. (See Problem 4.2.15.) ■

Corollary 1. $\|\mathbf{x} + \mathbf{y}\| \leq \|\mathbf{x}\| + \|\mathbf{y}\|$ (4.2.7)

Proof. Choose $\lambda = 1$ in Inequality 4.2.5 and use $| < \mathbf{x}, \mathbf{y} > | \leq \|\mathbf{x}\|\,\|\mathbf{y}\|$ to obtain

$$\|\mathbf{x} + \mathbf{y}\|^2 = \|\mathbf{x}\|^2 + 2 < \mathbf{x}, \mathbf{y} > + \|\mathbf{y}\|^2 \leq \|\mathbf{x}\|^2 + 2\|\mathbf{x}\|\,\|\mathbf{y}\| + \|\mathbf{y}\|^2 = (\|\mathbf{x}\| + \|\mathbf{y}\|)^2$$ ■

It is natural to define the distance between points as the length of the vector between them. Since the norm measures length, the distance between $\mathbf{x}$ and $\mathbf{y}$, written $\mathrm{d}(\mathbf{x}, \mathbf{y})$, is defined as the length of $\mathbf{x} - \mathbf{y}$:

$$\mathrm{d}(\mathbf{x}, \mathbf{y}) = \|\mathbf{x} - \mathbf{y}\| \tag{4.2.8}$$

For vectors in $\mathcal{R}^2$, Eq. 4.2.8 reduces to the familiar

$$\|\mathbf{x} - \mathbf{y}\| = \sqrt{(x_1 - y_1)^2 + (x_2 - y_2)^2} \tag{4.2.9}$$

The distance function, Eq. 4.2.8, has certain properties that one expects of distance: the distance between $\mathbf{x}$ and $\mathbf{y}$ is equal to the distance between $\mathbf{y}$ and $\mathbf{x}$, and is always positive unless $\mathbf{x} = \mathbf{y}$, in which case it is zero.

Example 4.2.2. Show: (a) $\mathrm{d}(\mathbf{x}, \mathbf{y}) = \mathrm{d}(\mathbf{y}, \mathbf{x})$. (b) $\mathrm{d}(\mathbf{x}, \mathbf{y}) > 0$ if $\mathbf{x} \neq \mathbf{y}$. (c) $\mathrm{d}(\mathbf{x}, \mathbf{y}) = 0$ if and only if $\mathbf{x} = \mathbf{y}$.

Solution. (a) $\mathrm{d}(\mathbf{x}, \mathbf{y}) = \|\mathbf{x} - \mathbf{y}\| = \|-(\mathbf{y} - \mathbf{x})\| = \|(\mathbf{y} - \mathbf{x})\| = \mathrm{d}(\mathbf{y}, \mathbf{x})$. Parts (b) and (c) depend on Parts (b) and (d) of Eq. 4.2.2.

A less obvious consequence of the definition of a distance function is the so-called *triangle inequality:*

$$\mathrm{d}(\mathbf{x}, \mathbf{y}) \leq \mathrm{d}(\mathbf{x}, \mathbf{z}) + \mathrm{d}(\mathbf{z}, \mathbf{y}) \tag{4.2.10}$$

valid for every set of vectors $\mathbf{x}$, $\mathbf{y}$ and $\mathbf{z}$. (See Fig. 4.1.) The proof is a simple consequence of Corollary 1. Set $\mathbf{s} = \mathbf{x} - \mathbf{z}$ and $\mathbf{t} = \mathbf{z} - \mathbf{y}$. Then $\mathbf{s} + \mathbf{t} = \mathbf{x} - \mathbf{y}$. Equation 4.2.7 implies

$$\|\mathbf{s} + \mathbf{t}\| = \|\mathbf{x} - \mathbf{y}\| \leq \|\mathbf{s}\| + \|\mathbf{t}\| = \|\mathbf{x} - \mathbf{z}\| + \|\mathbf{z} - \mathbf{y}\|.$$

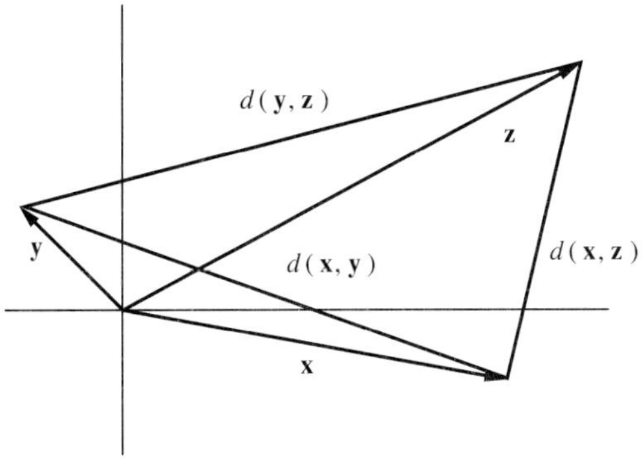

FIGURE 4-1
The triangle inequality.

Just as the norm provides a measure of length for vectors in n-space, the inner product is used to define the notion of direction. The cosine of the angle between $\mathbf{x}$ and $\mathbf{y}$ is defined by the expression

$$<\mathbf{x}, \mathbf{y}> = \|\mathbf{x}\|\,\|\mathbf{y}\| \cos\vartheta, \qquad 0 \le \vartheta \le \pi \tag{4.2.11}$$

Two remarks are in order. First, Eq. 4.2.11 defines a cosine because the ratio $<\mathbf{x}, \mathbf{y}> \|\mathbf{x}\|^{-1}\|\mathbf{y}\|^{-1}$ is between -1 and 1 by the Schwarz Inequality. Second, Eq. 4.2.11 reduces to the law of cosines in two and three dimensions. (See Problem 4.2.20.) By far, the most important application of Eq. 4.2.11 occurs when $\cos\vartheta = 0$ so that $\vartheta = \pi/2$. In this case, $\mathbf{x}$ and $\mathbf{y}$ are perpendicular. If $<\mathbf{x}, \mathbf{y}> = 0$ then $\mathbf{x}$ is said to be *orthogonal* to $\mathbf{y}$, written $\mathbf{x}\perp\mathbf{y}$.

If $\mathbf{y} = \mathbf{0}$, then $\mathbf{x}\perp\mathbf{y}$ for all $\mathbf{x}$. And, as a matter of fact, $\mathbf{0}$ is the only such vector. (To see this, note that if there is a $\mathbf{y}$ such that $\mathbf{x}\perp\mathbf{y}$ for every $\mathbf{x}$, then select $\mathbf{x} = \mathbf{y}$ and since $\mathbf{y}\perp\mathbf{y}$, $<\mathbf{y}, \mathbf{y}> = \|\mathbf{y}\|^2 = 0$. But only the zero vector has zero norm. See also Problem 4.2.12.)

The definitions of orthogonality and the product $\mathbf{Ax}$ lead to the observation that *every vector in the row space of* $\mathbf{A}$ *is orthogonal to every vector in the null space of* $\mathbf{A}$. More will be said about this in Section 4.7.

Given the vectors $\mathbf{x}$ and $\mathbf{y}$, $\mathbf{x} - \mathbf{y}$ may be interpreted as the third side in a triangle whose other sides are $\mathbf{x}$ and $\mathbf{y}$. By definition, this triangle is a right triangle if $\mathbf{x}\perp\mathbf{y}$. The *Pythagorean theorem* in two- or three-space asserts that $\mathbf{x}\perp\mathbf{y}$ implies

$$\|\mathbf{x} - \mathbf{y}\|^2 = \|\mathbf{x}\|^2 + \|\mathbf{y}\|^2 \tag{4.2.12}$$

In fact an n-dimensional version of Eq. 4.2.12 can be proved.

Example 4.2.3. Prove $\|\mathbf{x} - \mathbf{y}\|^2 = \|\mathbf{x}\|^2 + \|\mathbf{y}\|^2$ if and only if $\mathbf{x}\perp\mathbf{y}$.

Solution. Since $\|\mathbf{x} - \mathbf{y}\|^2 = \|\mathbf{x}\|^2 - 2 <\mathbf{x}, \mathbf{y}> + \|\mathbf{y}\|^2$, the result follows if and only if $<\mathbf{x}, \mathbf{y}> = 0$.

Example 4.2.4. Verify $\mathbf{x}\perp\mathbf{y}$ and Eq. 4.2.12 for $\mathbf{x}$ and $\mathbf{y}$ given by,

$$\mathbf{x} = \begin{bmatrix} 1 \\ -1 \\ 1 \\ 2 \end{bmatrix} \qquad \mathbf{y} = \begin{bmatrix} -1 \\ 0 \\ 3 \\ -1 \end{bmatrix}$$

Solution. The arithmetic is simple: $\|\mathbf{x}\|^2 = 1+1+1+4 = 7$; $\|\mathbf{y}\|^2 = 1+0+9+1 = 11$, $\|\mathbf{x}-\mathbf{y}\|^2 = 4+1+4+9 = 18$. Thus, $\|\mathbf{x}-\mathbf{y}\|^2 = \|\mathbf{x}\|^2 + \|\mathbf{y}\|^2$ and $<\mathbf{x},\mathbf{y}> = -1+0+3-2 = 0$.

4.2.1 Alternative Norms[1]

The euclidean norm and the hermitian norm (to follow) arise from setting $\mathbf{x} = \mathbf{y}$ in an inner product. Alternatively, we can begin by defining the norm of $\|\mathbf{x}\|$ as a function which satisfies these conditions:

1. $\|\mathbf{x}\| \geq 0$ for all $\mathbf{x}$.
2. $\|\mathbf{x}\| = 0$ if and only if $\mathbf{x} = \mathbf{0}$.
3. $\|k\mathbf{x}\| = |k|\,\|\mathbf{x}\|$ for all $\mathbf{x}$ and k.

Example 4.2.1 shows that the euclidean norm is a norm according to this abstract definition. Two other norms (besides the hermitian norm) appear quite frequently.

$$\begin{aligned} \|\mathbf{x}\|_1 &= |x_1| + |x_2| + \cdots + |x_n| \\ \|\mathbf{x}\|_\infty &= \max\{|x_1|, |x_2|, \ldots, |x_n|\} \end{aligned} \tag{4.2.13}$$

Indeed, $\|\mathbf{x}\|_\infty$ is a convenient norm in the study of Markov processes.

Although less interesting from our point of view, the function

$$\|\mathbf{x}\|_p = (|x_1|^p + |x_2|^p + \cdots + |x_n|^p)^{1/p}$$

is a norm for each positive integer p. Note that $p = 2$ leads to the euclidean norm and $p = 1$ leads to $\|\mathbf{x}\|_1$. The proof that the functions given in Eq. 4.2.13 are norms is left for the Problem 4.2.24.

MATLAB returns these norms as a result of entering norm(x,1) and norm(x,inf) respectively.

4.2.2 Hermitian Inner Products and Norms[2]

One way to avoid the unsatisfactory situation that vectors with complex entries[3] may have negative lengths is to generalize the definition of inner product. The following definition turns out to be eminently satisfactory:

$$<\mathbf{x},\mathbf{y}> = \overline{x}_1 y_1 + \overline{x}_2 y_2 + \cdots + \overline{x}_n y_n = (\overline{\mathbf{x}})^{\mathrm{T}}\mathbf{y} \tag{4.2.14}$$

---

[1]This subsection may be skipped on first reading.

[2]This chapter does not depend on a reading of this subsection.

[3]A review of complex numbers appears in Section 5.2.

Note that $\|\mathbf{x}\| \geq 0$ for $\mathbf{x} \in \mathscr{C}^n$ and for real vectors, Eq. 4.2.14 becomes Eq. 4.2.1. Equation 4.2.14 defines the *hermitian inner product*. With a few minor exceptions (see Example 4.2.5), all the theorems of this section remain true when the euclidean inner products and norms are replaced by the hermitian inner products and norms. Here are the three exceptions:

Example 4.2.5. Show that

$(a) <\mathbf{x}, \mathbf{y}> = <\overline{\mathbf{y}, \mathbf{x}}> \qquad (b) <a\mathbf{x}, \mathbf{y}> = \overline{a}<\mathbf{x}, \mathbf{y}>$
$(c) <\mathbf{A}\mathbf{x}, \mathbf{y}> = <\mathbf{x}, (\overline{\mathbf{A}})^{\mathrm{T}}\mathbf{y}>$

Solution.
(*a*) From Eq. 4.2.14,

$$<\overline{\mathbf{y}, \mathbf{x}}> = \overline{\overline{y}_1 x_1 + \overline{y}_2 x_2 + \cdots + \overline{y}_n x_n} = \overline{\overline{y}_1 x_1} + \overline{\overline{y}_2 x_2} + \cdots + \overline{\overline{y}_n x_n}$$
$$= \overline{\overline{y}}_1 \overline{x}_1 + \overline{\overline{y}}_2 \overline{x}_2 + \cdots + \overline{\overline{y}}_n \overline{x}_n = y_1 \overline{x}_1 + y_2 \overline{x}_2 + \cdots + y_n \overline{x}_n = <\mathbf{x}, \mathbf{y}>$$
$$(b) < a\mathbf{x}, \mathbf{y}> = \overline{a\,x_1}y_1 + \overline{a\,x_2}y_2 + \cdots + \overline{a\,x_n}y_n$$
$$= \overline{a}\,\overline{x}_1 y_1 + \overline{a}\,\overline{x}_2 y_2 + \cdots + \overline{a}\,\overline{x}_n y_n = \overline{a} <\mathbf{x}, \mathbf{y}>$$
$$(c) <\mathbf{A}\mathbf{x}, \mathbf{y}> = (\overline{\mathbf{A}\mathbf{x}})^{\mathrm{T}}\mathbf{y} = (\overline{\mathbf{x}})^{\mathrm{T}}\left((\overline{\mathbf{A}})^{\mathrm{T}}\mathbf{y}\right) = <\mathbf{x}, (\overline{\mathbf{A}})^{\mathrm{T}}\mathbf{y}>$$

Although the Schwarz Inequality holds for the hermitian inner product and norm, the proof is not a simple generalization of the proof given above. The details of this argument and a more elaborate treatment of hermitian inner products is given in Section 6.1.

PROBLEMS

PART 1

4.2.1. Find the norms of the following vectors:

$(a)\ \mathbf{e}_k \qquad (b)\ \mathbf{1} \qquad (c)\ [a] \qquad (d)\ \mathbf{1}^{\mathrm{T}}\mathbf{x} \qquad (e) \begin{bmatrix} 1 \\ -1 \\ 1 \end{bmatrix} \qquad (f) \begin{bmatrix} \sin\tau \\ \cos\tau \end{bmatrix}$

4.2.2. Find the inner products:

$(a) <\mathbf{e}_i, \mathbf{e}_j>,\ i \neq j. \qquad (b) <\mathbf{e}_i, \mathbf{e}_i>. \qquad (c) <\mathbf{1}, \mathbf{x}>.$
$(d) <\mathbf{0}, \mathbf{x}>. \qquad (e) <\mathbf{e}_i, \mathbf{x}>.$

$(f) < \begin{bmatrix} a \\ -b \end{bmatrix}, \begin{bmatrix} b \\ a \end{bmatrix} >.$

4.2.3. Find the inner products:

$(a) < \begin{bmatrix} 1 \\ -2 \\ 0 \\ 1 \end{bmatrix}, \begin{bmatrix} 2 \\ -1 \\ 3 \\ -4 \end{bmatrix} > \qquad (b) < \begin{bmatrix} \sqrt{x} \\ \sqrt{y} \end{bmatrix}, \begin{bmatrix} \sqrt{x} \\ \sqrt{y} \end{bmatrix} > \qquad (c) < \begin{bmatrix} \sin\tau \\ \cos\tau \end{bmatrix}, \begin{bmatrix} \sin\tau \\ \cos\tau \end{bmatrix} >$

4.2.4. Find a nonzero vector with complex entries whose norm, as defined by Eq. 4.2.3, is zero.

PART 2

4.2.5. Prove Parts (*a*) through (*d*) and (*f*) of Eq. 4.2.2.

4.2.6. Prove Parts (*a*) and (*b*) of Example 4.2.1 for **x** and **y** in $\mathcal{R}^n$ and in $\mathcal{C}^n$.

4.2.7. Show that the angle between $[1 \quad 1]^T$ and $[1 \quad 0]^T$ is $\pi/4$ (measured counterclockwise). Verify this by using Eq. 4.2.11.

4.2.8. If $\mathbf{x} \perp \mathbf{y}$ and $\mathbf{y} \perp \mathbf{z}$ does it follow that $\mathbf{x} \perp \mathbf{z}$? Explain.

4.2.9. If $\mathbf{x} \perp \mathbf{y}$ and $\mathbf{x} \perp \mathbf{z}$ does it follow that $\mathbf{x} \perp (\mathbf{y} + \mathbf{z})$? Explain.

4.2.10. Find α so that $(\mathbf{b} - \alpha\mathbf{u}) \perp \mathbf{u}$, given that $\|\mathbf{u}\| = 1$.

4.2.11. Given $\|\mathbf{u}\| = 1$, show that $(\mathbf{u}\mathbf{u}^T)^2 = \mathbf{u}\mathbf{u}^T$.

4.2.12. Suppose $\mathcal{V}$ is a vector space with basis $\mathcal{B}_V = \{\mathbf{v}_1, \mathbf{v}_2, \ldots, \mathbf{v}_k\}$. If $\mathbf{y} \in \mathcal{V}$ and is orthogonal to each vector $\mathbf{v}_i \in \mathcal{B}_V$, show that $\mathbf{y} = \mathbf{0}$.

4.2.13. Show that $(\mathbf{u}\mathbf{u}^T)^2 = \|\mathbf{u}\|^2(\mathbf{u}\mathbf{u}^T)$.

PART 3

4.2.14. At what point in the proof of the Schwarz Inequality, Theorem 4.2.3, is the hypothesis used that $\{\mathbf{x}, \mathbf{y}\}$ is linearly independent?

4.2.15. Show that equality holds Theorem 4.2.3 if and only if $\{\mathbf{x}, \mathbf{y}\}$ is linearly dependent.

4.2.16. Suppose $\mathbf{x}_0$ is a solution of $\mathbf{A}\mathbf{x} = \mathbf{b}$ and $\mathbf{y}_0^T$ is a solution of $\mathbf{y}^T\mathbf{A} = \mathbf{0}^T$. Prove that $\mathbf{b} \perp \mathbf{y}_0$.

4.2.17. Show that $\|\mathbf{x} + \mathbf{y}\|^2 + \|\mathbf{x} - \mathbf{y}\|^2 = 2(\|\mathbf{x}\|^2 + \|\mathbf{y}\|^2)$. Find a geometric interpretation for this theorem in $\mathcal{R}^2$.

4.2.18. Suppose **y** is orthogonal to $\mathbf{x}_1, \mathbf{x}_2, \ldots, \mathbf{x}_k$. Show that **y** is orthogonal to every vector in $span\{\mathbf{x}_1, \mathbf{x}_2, \ldots, \mathbf{x}_k\}$.

4.2.19. Show that the ith column of **A** is orthogonal to the transpose of the jth row of $\mathbf{A}^{-1}$, provided $i \neq j$.

4.2.20. Suppose **x** and **y** are two-tuples. Let ϑ be the angle between them. Use the law of cosines to show that $\|\mathbf{x} - \mathbf{y}\|^2 = \|\mathbf{x}\|^2 + \|\mathbf{y}\|^2 - 2\|\mathbf{x}\|\,\|\mathbf{y}\|\cos\vartheta$. (See Fig. 4.2.) Use (*c*) of Example 4.2.1 with $\lambda = -1$ and the result just established to prove Eq. 4.2.11.

4.2.21. Show that every vector in *null*(**A**) is orthogonal to every vector in *row*(**A**).

4.2.22. Show that $\|\mathbf{x}+\mathbf{y}\|^2 - \|\mathbf{x}-\mathbf{y}\|^2 = 4 < \mathbf{x}, \mathbf{y} >$ and provide a geometric interpretation in $\mathcal{R}^2$.

4.2.23. Prove the Schwarz Inequality for vectors in $\mathcal{R}^2$ by writing out the expressions for $< \mathbf{x}, \mathbf{y} >$, $\|\mathbf{x}\|$ and $\|\mathbf{y}\|$.

4.2.24. Show that $\|\mathbf{x}\|_1$ and $\|\mathbf{x}\|_\infty$ satisfy conditions (1)–(3) in Section 4.2.1.

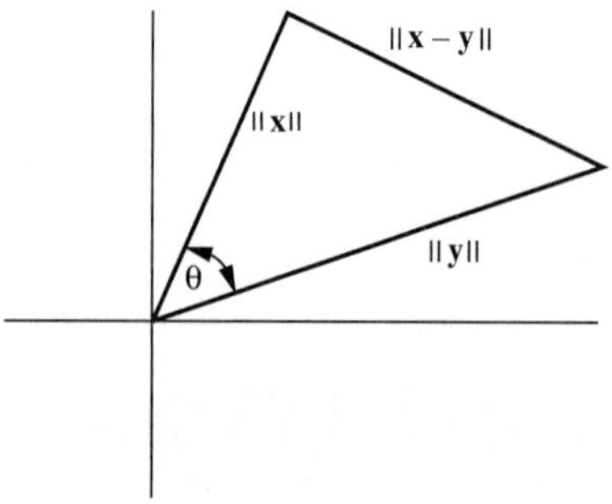

FIGURE 4-2
The law of cosines whose sides have length $\|\mathbf{x}\|$, $\|\mathbf{y}\|$ and $\|\mathbf{x} - \mathbf{y}\|$.

MATLAB

Use the commands norm(x,1), norm(x,2), and norm(x,inf) to compute the norms of the following vectors:

4.2.25. (*a*) $\mathbf{e}_4 \in \mathfrak{R}^6$ (*b*) $\mathbf{1}_5$ (*c*) $[-3]$ (*d*) $\begin{bmatrix} 1 \\ -1 \\ 1 \end{bmatrix}$

4.2.26. (*a*) $i\mathbf{e}_4$ (*b*) $[2-7i]$ (*c*) $\begin{bmatrix} 1 & + & i \\ -1 & - & i \\ & i & \end{bmatrix}$

4.2.27. Find $|2-3i|$ by using norm(x,1), norm(x,2), and norm(x,inf). Explain.

4.2.28. Deduce the definition of norm(x,inf) by experimenting with various vectors, x.

4.2.29. Experiment with sufficiently many x to conjecture a relationship between the magnitudes of norm(x,1), norm(x,2), and norm(x,inf).

4.3 ORTHONORMAL BASES

Recall that vectors $\mathbf{x} \in \mathfrak{R}^n$ and $\mathbf{y} \in \mathfrak{R}^n$ are called *orthogonal* (written $\mathbf{x}\perp\mathbf{y}$) if $<\mathbf{x},\mathbf{y}>=0$. In view of the definition of $<\mathbf{x},\mathbf{y}>$, the zero vector is orthogonal to all vectors. The set of vectors $\{\mathbf{x}_1,\mathbf{x}_2,\ldots,\mathbf{x}_k\}$ is an *orthogonal* set if $<\mathbf{x}_i,\mathbf{x}_j>=0$ for each i and j, $i \neq j$. It is called an *orthonormal* set if it is orthogonal *and* $<\mathbf{x}_i,\mathbf{x}_i>=1$. In brief, $\{\mathbf{x}_1,\mathbf{x}_2,\ldots,\mathbf{x}_k\}$ is orthonormal if $<\mathbf{x}_i,\mathbf{x}_j>=\delta_{ij}$. (Recall that $\delta_{ij}=0$ if $i \neq j$ and $\delta_{ii}=1$. The symbol δ_{ij} is called the *Kroneker delta* and is read "delta ij".) The set of unit vectors $\{\mathbf{e}_1,\mathbf{e}_2,\ldots,\mathbf{e}_k\}$, $\mathbf{e}_i \in \mathfrak{R}^n$, $n \geq k$ is a simple example of an orthonormal set.

Example 4.3.1. Show that the following set of vectors form an orthogonal set of vectors for any choice of x:

$$\left\{\mathbf{v}_1 = \begin{bmatrix} 1 \\ 0 \\ 1 \end{bmatrix}, \mathbf{v}_2 = \begin{bmatrix} -1 \\ 0 \\ 1 \end{bmatrix}, \mathbf{v}_3 = \begin{bmatrix} 0 \\ x \\ 0 \end{bmatrix}\right\}$$

Solution. It is clear from the placement of the zero entries that $\mathbf{v}_3$ is orthogonal to $\mathbf{v}_1$ and $\mathbf{v}_2$. Also, $<\mathbf{v}_1,\mathbf{v}_2>=(1)(-1)+0+1=0$.

Theorem 4.3.1. *If* $\{\mathbf{x}_1,\mathbf{x}_2,\ldots,\mathbf{x}_k\}$ *is an orthonormal set, then it is linearly independent.*

Proof. To show that a set of vectors is linearly independent it is necessary to show that only the trivial combination yields the zero vector. Consider, then, the linear combination,

$$a_1\mathbf{x}_1 + a_2\mathbf{x}_2 + \cdots + a_k\mathbf{x}_k = \mathbf{0} \tag{4.3.1}$$

For each i, the inner product of both sides of Eq. 4.3.1 with $\mathbf{x}_i$ leads to

$$a_1 <\mathbf{x}_1,\mathbf{x}_i> + a_2 <\mathbf{x}_2,\mathbf{x}_i> + \cdots + a_k <\mathbf{x}_k,\mathbf{x}_i> = <\mathbf{0},\mathbf{x}_i> = 0 \tag{4.3.2}$$

But, for each j, $< \mathbf{x}_j, \mathbf{x}_i > = \delta_{ij}$ so that Eq. 4.3.2 becomes $a_i < \mathbf{x}_i, \mathbf{x}_i > = 0$. Since $\mathbf{x}_i \neq \mathbf{0}$, $\|\mathbf{x}_i\|^2 = < \mathbf{x}_i, \mathbf{x}_i > 0$ and, therefore, $a_i = 0$. But i is arbitrary. Thus all the weights are zero. ■

Example 4.3.2. Suppose $\{\mathbf{x}_1, \mathbf{x}_2, \ldots, \mathbf{x}_k\}$, $\mathbf{x}_i \neq \mathbf{0}$, $i = 1, 2, \ldots, k$, is an orthogonal set. Show that $\{\mathbf{q}_1, \mathbf{q}_2, \ldots, \mathbf{q}_k\}$ is orthonormal if $\mathbf{q}_i = \mathbf{x}_i \|\mathbf{x}_i\|^{-1}$.

Solution. The vector $\mathbf{q}_i$ is simply a re-scaling of $\mathbf{x}_i$, and we have already shown in the paragraph following Example 4.2.1 that $\|\mathbf{q}_i\| = 1$. Here is a repeat of that argument in slightly altered notation and generality:

$$< \mathbf{q}_i, \mathbf{q}_j > = < \frac{\mathbf{x}_i}{\|\mathbf{x}_i\|}, \frac{\mathbf{x}_j}{\|\mathbf{x}_j\|} > = \|\mathbf{x}_j\|^{-1}\|\mathbf{x}_i\|^{-1} < \mathbf{x}_i, \mathbf{x}_j > = 0 \qquad \text{if } i \neq j$$

$$< \mathbf{q}_i, \mathbf{q}_i > = < \frac{\mathbf{x}_i}{\|\mathbf{x}_i\|}, \frac{\mathbf{x}_i}{\|\mathbf{x}_i\|} > = \|\mathbf{x}_i\|^{-2} < \mathbf{x}_i, \mathbf{x}_i > = \|\mathbf{x}_i\|^{-2}\|\mathbf{x}\|^2 = 1$$

As an example illustrating the convenience of working with orthonormal sets, consider the problem of determining the weights in the linear combination

$$a_1\mathbf{q}_1 + a_2\mathbf{q}_2 + \cdots + a_k\mathbf{q}_k = \mathbf{b} \tag{4.3.3}$$

where $\mathcal{Q} = \{\mathbf{q}_1, \mathbf{q}_2, \ldots, \mathbf{q}_k\}$ is assumed orthonormal and $\mathbf{b} \in \mathcal{G}$. To find a_i, multiply both sides of Eq. 4.3.3 by $\mathbf{q}_i^{\mathrm{T}}$ and exploit the orthogonality relationships, $\mathbf{q}_i^{\mathrm{T}}\mathbf{q}_j = \delta_{ij}$. Thus,

$$a_1\mathbf{q}_i^{\mathrm{T}}\mathbf{q}_1 + a_2\mathbf{q}_i^{\mathrm{T}}\mathbf{q}_2 + \cdots + a_k\mathbf{q}_i^{\mathrm{T}}\mathbf{q}_k = \mathbf{q}_i^{\mathrm{T}}\mathbf{b}$$

and hence $\mathbf{a}_i = \mathbf{q}_i^{\mathrm{T}}\mathbf{b}$. By using these values for a_i, Eq. 4.3.3 can be written

$$< \mathbf{b}, \mathbf{q}_1 > \mathbf{q}_1 + < \mathbf{b}, \mathbf{q}_2 > \mathbf{q}_2 + \cdots + < \mathbf{b}, \mathbf{q}_k > \mathbf{q}_k = \mathbf{b} \tag{4.3.4}$$

Define the *component of* $\mathbf{b}$ *in the direction* $\mathbf{q}_i$ as the scalar $< \mathbf{b}, \mathbf{q}_i >$. Thus, the weights in Eq. 4.3.4 are the components of $\mathbf{b}$ in the directions $\mathbf{q}_i$.

Example 4.3.3. Find the weights in $\mathbf{b} = a_1\mathbf{q}_1 + a_2\mathbf{q}_2 + a_3\mathbf{q}_3$, where

$$\mathbf{b} = \begin{bmatrix} 2 \\ 0 \\ 1 \\ 1 \end{bmatrix} \qquad \mathbf{q}_1 = 1/2\begin{bmatrix} 1 \\ 1 \\ 1 \\ 1 \end{bmatrix} \qquad \mathbf{q}_2 = 1/2\begin{bmatrix} 1 \\ -1 \\ -1 \\ 1 \end{bmatrix} \qquad \mathbf{q}_3 = 1/2\begin{bmatrix} -1 \\ 1 \\ -1 \\ 1 \end{bmatrix}$$

Solution. It is a simple matter of verifying definitions to show that the set $\{\mathbf{q}_1, \mathbf{q}_2, \mathbf{q}_3\}$ is orthonormal and that the three inner products are $< \mathbf{q}_1, \mathbf{b} > = 2$, $< \mathbf{q}_2, \mathbf{b} > = 1$, and $< \mathbf{q}_3, \mathbf{b} > = -1$. These are the components of $\mathbf{b}$ in the mutual orthogonal directions, $\mathbf{q}_1$, $\mathbf{q}_2$, and $\mathbf{q}_3$. Hence, the weights are $a_1 = 2$, $a_2 = 1$, and $a_3 = -1$. Finally, write $\mathbf{b}$ as the following linear combination of the vectors $\mathbf{q}_1$, $\mathbf{q}_2$, and $\mathbf{q}_3$:

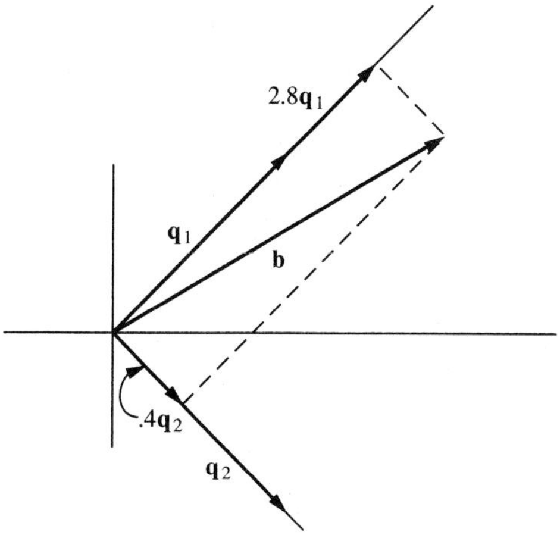

FIGURE 4-3
The components of **b** in the direction $\mathbf{q}_1$, and $\mathbf{q}_2$.

$$\mathbf{b} = \begin{bmatrix} 2 \\ 0 \\ 1 \\ 1 \end{bmatrix} = 2\begin{bmatrix} 1/2 \\ 1/2 \\ 1/2 \\ 1/2 \end{bmatrix} + \begin{bmatrix} 1/2 \\ -1/2 \\ -1/2 \\ 1/2 \end{bmatrix} - \begin{bmatrix} -1/2 \\ 1/2 \\ -1/2 \\ 1/2 \end{bmatrix}$$

Example 4.3.4. Find the components of $\mathbf{b} = [2\ 2]^T$ in the directions $\mathbf{q}_1 = [.6\ \ .8]^T$ and $\mathbf{q}_2 = [.8\ \ -.6]^T$.

Solution. The components are $< \mathbf{q}_1, \mathbf{b} > = 2.8$ and $< \mathbf{q}_2, \mathbf{b} > = .4$. Hence,

$$\mathbf{b} = (2.8)\begin{bmatrix} .6 \\ .8 \end{bmatrix} + (.4)\begin{bmatrix} .8 \\ -.6 \end{bmatrix} = \begin{bmatrix} 2 \\ 2 \end{bmatrix}$$

Figure 4.3 shows the relationships between **b**, $2.8\mathbf{q}_1$, and $.4\mathbf{q}_2$. Note that $2.8\mathbf{q}_1$ and $.4\mathbf{q}_2$ form the two sides of a right triangle whose hypotenuse is the vector **b**.

4.3.1 The Projection of b into $\mathcal{V}$

Suppose $\mathbf{b} \in \mathcal{R}^n$ and $\mathcal{V}$ is a subspace of $\mathcal{R}^n$. Define a *projection of* **b** *into* $\mathcal{V}$ as a vector $\mathbf{b}_\perp \in \mathcal{V}$ with the property that $\mathbf{b} - \mathbf{b}_\perp$ is orthogonal to every vector in $\mathcal{V}$. It is not difficult to find a projection of **b** into $\mathcal{V}$ if there is an orthonormal set which is a basis for $\mathcal{V}$. (Such a basis is called an *orthonormal* basis for $\mathcal{V}$. In Section 4.4, we will show how to construct an orthonormal basis for any subspace of $\mathcal{R}^n$.)

Theorem 4.3.2. *(Uniqueness). Let* $\mathbf{b} \in \mathcal{R}^n$ *and* $\mathbf{b}_\perp$ *and* $\mathbf{c}_\perp$ *be two projections of* **b** *into* $\mathcal{V}$. *Then* $\mathbf{b}_\perp = \mathbf{c}_\perp$.

Proof. By definition $\mathbf{b}-\mathbf{b}_\perp$ and $\mathbf{b}-\mathbf{c}_\perp$ are orthogonal to all vectors in $\mathcal{V}$. Hence $(\mathbf{b}-\mathbf{c}_\perp)-(\mathbf{b}-\mathbf{b}_\perp) = \mathbf{b}_\perp - \mathbf{c}_\perp$ is also orthogonal to all vectors in $\mathcal{V}$. Since $\mathcal{V}$ is a vector space, $\mathbf{b}_\perp - \mathbf{c}_\perp \in \mathcal{V}$, and hence $\mathbf{b}_\perp - \mathbf{c}_\perp = \mathbf{0}$. (See Section 4.2, Problem 4.2.18.) ■

Theorem 4.3.2 tells us that the projection of $\mathbf{b}$ into $\mathcal{V}$ is unique, if it exists. We show that the projection exists by finding its representation as a linear combination of an orthonormal basis for $\mathcal{V}$. Again, suppose that $\{\mathbf{q}_1,\mathbf{q}_2,\ldots,\mathbf{q}_k\}$ is an orthonormal basis for $\mathcal{V}$ and, for convenience, set $\mathbf{Q} = [\mathbf{q}_1 \quad \mathbf{q}_2 \quad \ldots \quad \mathbf{q}_k]$. Define $\mathbf{b}_q$ by

$$\begin{aligned}\mathbf{b}_q &= <\mathbf{b},\mathbf{q}_1>\mathbf{q}_1 + <\mathbf{b},\mathbf{q}_2>\mathbf{q}_2 + \cdots + <\mathbf{b},\mathbf{q}_k>\mathbf{q}_k \\ &= \mathbf{Q}\mathbf{Q}^{\mathrm{T}}\mathbf{b} \qquad (4.3.5)\end{aligned}$$

Theorem 4.3.3. *(Existence). The vector* $\mathbf{b}_q$ *is the projection of* $\mathbf{b}$ *into* $\mathcal{V} = span\{\mathbf{q}_1,\mathbf{q}_2,\ldots,\mathbf{q}_k\}$.

Proof. Since $\mathbf{b}_q \in \mathcal{V}$,

$$\mathbf{b}_q = <\mathbf{b}_q,\mathbf{q}_1>\mathbf{q}_1 + <\mathbf{b}_q,\mathbf{q}_2>\mathbf{q}_2 + \cdots + <\mathbf{b}_q,\mathbf{q}_k>\mathbf{q}_k \qquad (4.3.6)$$

follows from Eq. 4.3.4. Subtracting Eq. 4.3.6 from Eq. 4.3.5 yields

$$\mathbf{0} = <\mathbf{b}-\mathbf{b}_q,\mathbf{q}_1>\mathbf{q}_1 + <\mathbf{b}-\mathbf{b}_q,\mathbf{q}_2>\mathbf{q}_2 + \cdots + <\mathbf{b}-\mathbf{b}_q,\mathbf{q}_k>\mathbf{q}_k$$

from which it follows that $<\mathbf{b}-\mathbf{b}_q,\mathbf{q}_i> = 0$. Hence $\mathbf{b}-\mathbf{b}_q$ is orthogonal to each of the basis vectors and therefore to all vectors in $\mathcal{V}$. Therefore, by definition and the uniqueness theorem, $\mathbf{b}_q = \mathbf{b}_\perp$. ■

One of the most persuasive reasons for studying projections is that the projection of $\mathbf{b}$ into $\mathcal{V}$ is the vector in $\mathcal{V}$ "nearest" $\mathbf{b}$. The following theorem is fundamental to the theory of least squares, Section 4.10.

Theorem 4.3.4. *Suppose* $\mathbf{v} \in \mathcal{V}$ *and* $\mathbf{b}_\perp$ *is the projection of* $\mathbf{b}$ *into* $\mathcal{V}$. *Then*

$$\|\mathbf{b}-\mathbf{b}_\perp\| \le \|\mathbf{b}-\mathbf{v}\| \qquad (4.3.7)$$

Proof. The vectors $(\mathbf{b}-\mathbf{b}_\perp)$ and $(\mathbf{b}_\perp-\mathbf{v})$ are orthogonal because $(\mathbf{b}_\perp-\mathbf{v}) \in \mathcal{V}$ and $(\mathbf{b}-\mathbf{b}_\perp)$ is orthogonal to all vectors in $\mathcal{V}$. By the Pythagorean Theorem, Example 4.2.3,

$$\|\mathbf{b}-\mathbf{v}\|^2 = \|(\mathbf{b}-\mathbf{b}_\perp)-(\mathbf{v}-\mathbf{b}_\perp)\|^2 = \|\mathbf{b}-\mathbf{b}_\perp\|^2 + \|\mathbf{v}-\mathbf{b}_\perp\|^2$$

which implies Eq. 4.3.7 since $\|\mathbf{b}_\perp-\mathbf{v}\|^2 \ge 0$. ■

For $\mathcal{V} = span\{\mathbf{q}_1\}$, $\mathbf{b}_\perp = <\mathbf{b},\mathbf{q}_1>\mathbf{q}_1$. Equation 4.3.5 shows, therefore, that the projection of $\mathbf{b}$ into $span\{\mathbf{q}_1,\mathbf{q}_2,\ldots,\mathbf{q}_k\}$ is the sum of the projections of $\mathbf{b}$ into each $span\{\mathbf{q}_i\}$, $i = 1,2,\ldots,k$. The special case in which $\mathbf{q}_i = \mathbf{e}_i$ results in the common definition of the "component of $\mathbf{b}$ in the direction $\mathbf{e}_i$" as the ith

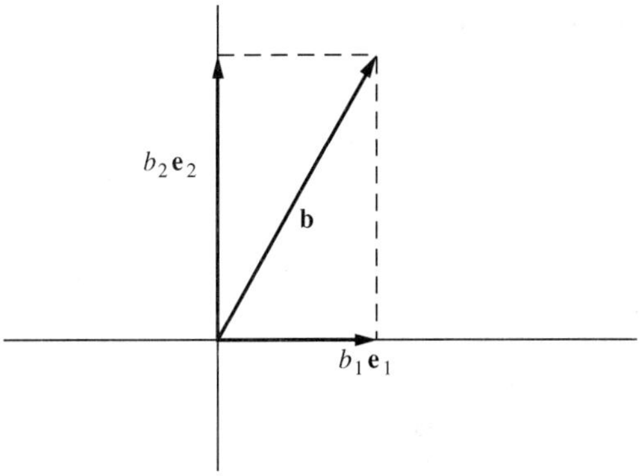

FIGURE 4-4
The components of **b** in the directions $\mathbf{e}_1$ and $\mathbf{e}_2$.

entry of **b**. That is, the projection of **b** into the span of $\{\mathbf{e}_1, \mathbf{e}_2, \ldots, \mathbf{e}_k\}$ is given by

$$\mathbf{b}_\perp = b_1\mathbf{e}_1 + b_2\mathbf{e}_2 + \cdots + b_k\mathbf{e}_k$$

An example in two-space is given in Fig. 4.4.

Example 4.3.5. For the vectors **b**, $\mathbf{q}_1$, and $\mathbf{q}_2$ to follow, construct $\mathbf{b}_\perp$ and show that $\mathbf{b} - \mathbf{b}_\perp$ is orthogonal to $\mathbf{q}_1$ and $\mathbf{q}_2$.

$$\mathbf{b} = \begin{bmatrix} 1 \\ 1 \\ 1 \end{bmatrix} \qquad \mathbf{q}_1 = \frac{1}{\sqrt{2}}\begin{bmatrix} 1 \\ 1 \\ 0 \end{bmatrix} \qquad \mathbf{q}_2 = \frac{1}{\sqrt{3}}\begin{bmatrix} 1 \\ -1 \\ 1 \end{bmatrix}$$

Solution. First compute the components of **b** in the directions of $\mathbf{q}_1$ and $\mathbf{q}_2$. These are $<\mathbf{b}, \mathbf{q}_1>= \sqrt{2}$ and $<\mathbf{b}, \mathbf{q}_2>= 1/\sqrt{3}$. Then, by definition,

$$\mathbf{b} - \mathbf{b}_\perp = \begin{bmatrix} 1 \\ 1 \\ 1 \end{bmatrix} - \sqrt{2}\mathbf{q}_1 - \frac{1}{\sqrt{3}}\mathbf{q}_2 = \begin{bmatrix} 1 \\ 1 \\ 1 \end{bmatrix} - \begin{bmatrix} 1 \\ 1 \\ 0 \end{bmatrix} - 1/3\begin{bmatrix} 1 \\ -1 \\ 1 \end{bmatrix} = 1/3\begin{bmatrix} -1 \\ 1 \\ 2 \end{bmatrix}$$

And $\mathbf{b} - \mathbf{b}_\perp$ is orthogonal to $\mathbf{q}_1$ and $\mathbf{q}_2$.

Example 4.3.6. Find the projection of $\mathbf{b} = [0\ 0\ 0\ 1]^T$ into the span of the orthonormal basis given in Example 4.3.3.

Solution. Since $<\mathbf{b}, \mathbf{q}_i>= 1/2$ for $i = 1, 2, 3$, the projection is

$$\mathbf{b}_\perp = 1/2\begin{bmatrix} \tfrac{1}{2} \\ \tfrac{1}{2} \\ \tfrac{1}{2} \\ \tfrac{1}{2} \end{bmatrix} + 1/2\begin{bmatrix} \tfrac{1}{2} \\ -\tfrac{1}{2} \\ -\tfrac{1}{2} \\ \tfrac{1}{2} \end{bmatrix} + 1/2\begin{bmatrix} -\tfrac{1}{2} \\ \tfrac{1}{2} \\ -\tfrac{1}{2} \\ \tfrac{1}{2} \end{bmatrix} = 1/4\begin{bmatrix} 1 \\ 1 \\ -1 \\ 3 \end{bmatrix} \neq \mathbf{b}$$

We can use the fact that $\mathbf{b} - \mathbf{b}_\perp$ is orthogonal to all vectors in the span of $\{\mathbf{q}_1, \mathbf{q}_2, \ldots, \mathbf{q}_k\}$ to resolve the following problem: Given the orthonormal set

$\{\mathbf{q}_1, \mathbf{q}_2, \ldots, \mathbf{q}_{n-1}\}$, $\mathbf{q}_i \in \mathcal{R}^n$, find $\mathbf{q}_n$ so that $\{\mathbf{q}_1, \mathbf{q}_2, \ldots, \mathbf{q}_{n-1}, \mathbf{q}_n\}$ is an orthonormal basis for $\mathcal{R}^n$. The following example illustrates the method.

Example 4.3.7. Find an orthogonal basis for $\mathcal{R}^4$ which contains the vectors $\mathbf{q}_1$, $\mathbf{q}_2$, $\mathbf{q}_3$ of Example 4.3.3.

Solution. Choose a vector $\mathbf{b}$ not in the span of $\mathbf{q}_1, \mathbf{q}_2, \mathbf{q}_3$. Since $n - 1$ vectors cannot span an n-dimensional space, such a vector always exists. In this specific example, $\mathbf{b} = [0\ 0\ 0\ 1]^{\mathrm{T}} \notin span\{\mathbf{q}_1, \mathbf{q}_2, \mathbf{q}_3\}$ is obtained by inspection. From the work in Example 4.3.6,

$$\mathbf{b}_\perp = 1/4\begin{bmatrix} 1 \\ 1 \\ -1 \\ 3 \end{bmatrix}, \qquad \mathbf{b} - \mathbf{b}_\perp = 1/4\begin{bmatrix} -1 \\ -1 \\ 1 \\ 1 \end{bmatrix}.$$

We verify that $\mathbf{b} - \mathbf{b}_\perp$ is orthogonal to $\mathbf{q}_1$, $\mathbf{q}_2$, and $\mathbf{q}_3$. Thus $\mathbf{q}_4 = 2(\mathbf{b} - \mathbf{b}_\perp)$ and the orthonormal basis is $\{\mathbf{q}_1, \mathbf{q}_2, \mathbf{q}_3, \mathbf{q}_4\}$. In general, the required basis is $\{\mathbf{q}_1, \mathbf{q}_2, \ldots, \mathbf{q}_{n-1}, \mathbf{q}_n\}$, where $\mathbf{q}_n = (\mathbf{b} - \mathbf{b}_\perp)\|\mathbf{b} - \mathbf{b}_\perp\|^{-1}$.

The vector $\mathbf{b}$ can also be obtained in specific cases by exploiting the fact that the (transposes) of the rows of $\mathbf{A}$ are orthogonal to the solutions of $\mathbf{Ax} = \mathbf{0}$. (Why?) So define $\mathbf{Q} = [\mathbf{q}_1\ \ \mathbf{q}_2\ \ \cdots\ \ \mathbf{q}_{n-1}]$. Since rank($\mathbf{Q}$) is $n - 1$, the null space of $\mathbf{Q}^{\mathrm{T}}$ is one-dimensional. That is, there is one independent solution of $\mathbf{Q}^{\mathrm{T}}\mathbf{x} = \mathbf{0}$ and this solution, suitably normalized, is $\mathbf{q}_n$. The algorithm in Eq. 3.5.2 requires the reduction $\mathbf{A}^{\mathrm{T}}$ to rref to find *null*($\mathbf{A}$). In this example, $\mathbf{A}^{\mathrm{T}} = (\mathbf{Q}^{\mathrm{T}})^{\mathrm{T}} = \mathbf{Q}$. Since $null(\mathbf{Q}) = null(2\mathbf{Q})$ and the arthmetic is simpler with $2\mathbf{Q}$ than $\mathbf{Q}$, we work with $2\mathbf{Q}$.

$$[2\mathbf{Q}\ \mathbf{I}] = \left[\begin{array}{ccc|cccc} 1 & 1 & -1 & 1 & 0 & 0 & 0 \\ 1 & -1 & 1 & 0 & 1 & 0 & 0 \\ 1 & -1 & -1 & 0 & 0 & 1 & 0 \\ 1 & 1 & 1 & 0 & 0 & 0 & 1 \end{array}\right] \to$$

$$\cdots \to \left[\begin{array}{ccc|cccc} 1 & 1 & -1 & 1 & 0 & 0 & 0 \\ 0 & 2 & -2 & 1 & -1 & 0 & 0 \\ 0 & 0 & -2 & 0 & -1 & 1 & 0 \\ \hline 0 & 0 & 0 & -1 & -1 & 1 & 1 \end{array}\right]$$

Hence, it follows that

$$null(\mathbf{Q}^{\mathrm{T}}) = span\left\{\begin{bmatrix} -1 \\ -1 \\ 1 \\ 1 \end{bmatrix}\right\}$$

which, after normalization, is $\mathbf{b} - \mathbf{b}_\perp$.

Equation 4.3.5,

$$\mathbf{b}_q = <\mathbf{b}, \mathbf{q}_1> \mathbf{q}_1 + <\mathbf{b}, \mathbf{q}_2> \mathbf{q}_2 + \cdots + <\mathbf{b}, \mathbf{q}_k> \mathbf{q}_k = \mathbf{QQ}^{\mathrm{T}}\mathbf{b}$$

represents $\mathbf{b}_\perp$ as a linear combination of the vectors which span $\mathcal{V}$. In the terminology of Section 3.8, the vector

$$\mathbf{Q}^T\mathbf{b} = \begin{bmatrix} <\mathbf{b}, \mathbf{q}_1> \\ <\mathbf{b}, \mathbf{q}_2> \\ \vdots \\ <\mathbf{b}, \mathbf{q}_k> \end{bmatrix}$$

is the coordinate vector of $\mathbf{b}_\perp$ relative to the basis $\{\mathbf{q}_1, \mathbf{q}_2, \ldots, \mathbf{q}_k\}$ of $\mathcal{V}$ because $\mathbf{Q}\mathbf{Q}^T\mathbf{b} = \mathbf{b}_\perp$. The coordinate vector of $\mathbf{b}_\perp$ relative to other bases for $\mathcal{V}$ is discussed in Section 4.9.

PROBLEMS

PART 1

4.3.1. Verify that the following set forms an orthonormal basis for $\mathcal{R}^4$.

$$\left\{ \mathbf{q}_1 = 1/2\begin{bmatrix} 1 \\ 1 \\ 1 \\ 1 \end{bmatrix}, \mathbf{q}_2 = 1/2\begin{bmatrix} 1 \\ -1 \\ -1 \\ 1 \end{bmatrix}, \mathbf{q}_3 = 1/2\begin{bmatrix} -1 \\ 1 \\ -1 \\ 1 \end{bmatrix}, \mathbf{q}_4 = 1/2\begin{bmatrix} 1 \\ 1 \\ -1 \\ -1 \end{bmatrix} \right\}$$

4.3.2. Find the projections of the vectors $\mathbf{b}$, given below, into $span\{\mathbf{q}_1, \mathbf{q}_2, \mathbf{q}_3\}$, where $\mathbf{q}_1$, $\mathbf{q}_2$, and $\mathbf{q}_3$ are given in Problem 4.3.1:

$$(a)\begin{bmatrix} 1 \\ 0 \\ 1 \\ 1 \end{bmatrix} \quad (b)\begin{bmatrix} 0 \\ 0 \\ 1 \\ 0 \end{bmatrix} \quad (c)\begin{bmatrix} 0 \\ 0 \\ 0 \\ 1 \end{bmatrix} \quad (d)\begin{bmatrix} -1 \\ 1 \\ 1 \\ 1 \end{bmatrix}$$

4.3.3. Show that the following set is an orthogonal basis for $\mathcal{R}^3$:

$$\left\{ \begin{bmatrix} 1 \\ 1 \\ 1 \end{bmatrix}, \begin{bmatrix} 1 \\ 0 \\ -1 \end{bmatrix}, \begin{bmatrix} 1 \\ -2 \\ 1 \end{bmatrix} \right\}$$

4.3.4. Find all vectors $\mathbf{x} = [x\ y\ z]^T$ so that $\left\{ \begin{bmatrix} 1 \\ 1 \\ 1 \end{bmatrix}, \begin{bmatrix} 1 \\ 0 \\ -1 \end{bmatrix}, \begin{bmatrix} x \\ y \\ z \end{bmatrix} \right\}$ is an orthogonal basis for $\mathcal{R}^3$.

4.3.5. Convert the basis in Problem 4.3.3 into an orthonormal basis.

4.3.6. Find the components of $\mathbf{b}$ in the direction of each of the vectors

$$\mathbf{q}_1 = \frac{1}{\sqrt{3}}\begin{bmatrix} 1 \\ 1 \\ 1 \end{bmatrix} \qquad \mathbf{q}_2 = \frac{1}{\sqrt{6}}\begin{bmatrix} 1 \\ -2 \\ 1 \end{bmatrix}$$

for the $\mathbf{b}$ given below:

$$(a)\ \mathbf{b} = \begin{bmatrix} 1 \\ 0 \\ 1 \end{bmatrix} \quad (b)\ \mathbf{b} = \begin{bmatrix} 0 \\ 0 \\ 1 \end{bmatrix} \quad (c)\ \mathbf{b} = \begin{bmatrix} 1 \\ 0 \\ 0 \end{bmatrix} \quad (d)\ \mathbf{b} = \begin{bmatrix} -1 \\ 0 \\ 1 \end{bmatrix}$$

4.3.7. Compare the sum of the answers to (b) and (c) of Problem 4.3.6 with the answer to (a) of the same Problem.

4.3.8. For each $\mathbf{b}$ in Problem 4.3.6 compute $\mathbf{b} - \mathbf{b}_\perp$ and verify $\mathbf{b} - \mathbf{b}_\perp$ is orthogonal to every vector in $\mathcal{R}^3$.

4.3.9. Find $\mathbf{b}_\perp$ for the basis given in Example 4.3.3 for

(a) $\mathbf{b} = \mathbf{0}$ (b) $\mathbf{b} = \mathbf{q}_1$ (c) $\mathbf{b} = \mathbf{e}_1$ (d) $\mathbf{b} = \mathbf{e}_2$ (e) $\mathbf{b} = \mathbf{e}_3$.

4.3.10. Given $\mathbf{b} = [1 \quad 0 \quad 0 \quad 0]^{\mathrm{T}}$ and the orthonormal basis of Example 4.3.3, find $\mathbf{b}_\perp$ and $\mathbf{b} - \mathbf{b}_\perp$.

PART 2

4.3.11. Suppose $\{\mathbf{q}_1, \mathbf{q}_2, \mathbf{q}_3\}$ and $\{\mathbf{p}_1, \mathbf{p}_2, \mathbf{p}_3\}$ are orthonormal sets. Show that the following is an orthogonal set and find the norms of each vector:

$$\left\{\begin{bmatrix} \mathbf{q}_1 \\ \hline \mathbf{p}_1 \end{bmatrix}, \begin{bmatrix} \mathbf{q}_2 \\ \hline \mathbf{p}_2 \end{bmatrix}, \begin{bmatrix} \mathbf{q}_3 \\ \hline \mathbf{p}_3 \end{bmatrix}\right\}$$

4.3.12. Suppose $\{\mathbf{q}_1,\mathbf{q}_2,\ldots,\mathbf{q}_{n-1}\}$ is a set of orthonormal vectors. Show that $null(\mathbf{Q}^{\mathrm{T}})$ is one-dimensional. Suppose $\mathbf{x}_0 \neq \mathbf{0}$ solves $\mathbf{Q}^{\mathrm{T}}\mathbf{x} = \mathbf{0}$. Show that $\mathbf{x}_0 \perp \mathbf{q}_i$ for all i, $i = 1, 2, \ldots, n-1$.

4.3.13. Show that $\|\mathbf{q}_1 - \mathbf{q}_2\| = \sqrt{2}$ for orthonormal vectors, $\mathbf{q}_1$ and $\mathbf{q}_2$, each in $\mathcal{R}^n$.

4.3.14. Show that the following set is orthonormal for each choice of ϕ and ϑ:

$$\left\{\begin{bmatrix} \sin\varphi \ \cos\vartheta \\ \sin\varphi \ \sin\vartheta \\ \cos\varphi \end{bmatrix}, \begin{bmatrix} -\sin\vartheta \\ \cos\vartheta \\ 0 \end{bmatrix}, \begin{bmatrix} \cos\varphi \ \cos\vartheta \\ \cos\varphi \ \sin\vartheta \\ -\sin\varphi \end{bmatrix}\right\}$$

4.3.15. Prove:

(a) $\mathbf{u} \perp \mathbf{v}$ if and only if $\|\mathbf{u} + \mathbf{v}\| = \|\mathbf{u} - \mathbf{v}\|$

(b) $(\mathbf{u} - \mathbf{v}) \perp (\mathbf{u} + \mathbf{v})$ if and only if $\|\mathbf{u}\| = \|\mathbf{v}\|$.

4.3.16. Suppose $\mathbf{x} \in \mathcal{R}^n$, $\mathbf{y} \in \mathcal{R}^m$ and $\mathbf{A}$ is $m \times n$.

(a) Show that $< \mathbf{Ax}, \mathbf{y} >= 0$ for all $\mathbf{x}$ and $\mathbf{y}$, implies that $\mathbf{A} = \mathbf{O}$.

(b) By using (a), show that $< \mathbf{Ax}, \mathbf{y} >=< \mathbf{Bx}, y >$ for all $\mathbf{x}$ and $\mathbf{y}$, implies $\mathbf{A} = \mathbf{B}$.

4.3.17. Define $\mathbf{Q} = [\mathbf{q}_1 \quad \mathbf{q}_2 \quad \cdots \quad \mathbf{q}_k]$ where $\{\mathbf{q}_1,\mathbf{q}_2,\ldots,\mathbf{q}_k\}$ is an orthonormal basis for $\mathcal{V}$. Show that $\mathbf{QQ}^{\mathrm{T}}\mathbf{b} = \mathbf{b}_\perp$.

MATLAB

Use the expression $\mathbf{b}_\perp = \mathbf{QQ}^{\mathrm{T}}\mathbf{b}$ to solve the following problems.

4.3.18. Problems 4.3.6 and 4.3.8.

4.3.19. Problem 4.3.9.

4.3.20. Problem 4.3.10.

4.3.21. Verify the conclusion in Example 4.3.5 and compute $\|\mathbf{b} - \mathbf{b}_\perp\|$.

4.3.22. Verify the conclusion in Example 4.3.6 and compute $\|\mathbf{b} - \mathbf{b}_\perp\|$.

4.3.23. Verify the conclusion in Example 4.3.7 and compute $\|\mathbf{b} - \mathbf{b}_\perp\|$.

4.4 ORTHOGONAL MATRICES

Given an orthonormal basis $\{\mathbf{q}_1,\mathbf{q}_2,\ldots,\mathbf{q}_k\}$ for the vector space $\mathcal{V} \subseteq \mathcal{R}^n$, it is often convenient to interpret $\mathcal{V}$ as the column space of $\mathbf{Q}$, where $\mathbf{Q} = [\mathbf{q}_1 \quad \mathbf{q}_2 \quad \cdots \quad \mathbf{q}_k]$.

We call such $\mathbf{Q}$ *orthonormal*.[4] If $\mathbf{Q}_{m \times n}$ is orthonormal then $m \geq n$ because the columns of $\mathbf{Q}$ are linearly independent. Also,

$$\mathbf{Q}^{\mathrm{T}}\mathbf{Q} = \mathbf{I}_n \tag{4.4.1}$$

since $\mathbf{Q}^{\mathrm{T}}\mathbf{Q} = (\mathbf{q}_i^{\mathrm{T}}\mathbf{q}_j) = (\delta_{ij})$. In fact, if Eq. 4.4.1 holds for the matrix $\mathbf{Q}$, then the columns of $\mathbf{Q}$ form an orthonormal basis for $col(\mathbf{Q})$. Note that $\mathbf{Q}\mathbf{Q}^{\mathrm{T}} \neq \mathbf{I}_m$ if $m \neq n$. For example, let $\mathbf{Q} = \mathbf{1}_2/\sqrt{2}$. Then

$$\mathbf{Q}^{\mathrm{T}}\mathbf{Q} = \mathbf{1}_1 = [1] \qquad \mathbf{Q}\mathbf{Q}^{\mathrm{T}} = 1/2\begin{bmatrix} 1 & 1 \\ 1 & 1 \end{bmatrix}$$

If $m = n$, then we call the square matrix $\mathbf{Q}$ orthogonal.

Note that orthogonal matrices are simply square orthonormal matrices. Equation 4.4.1 leads to the following remarkable theorem.

Theorem 4.4.1. *The matrix* $\mathbf{Q}$ *is orthogonal if and only if* $\mathbf{Q}^{\mathrm{T}} = \mathbf{Q}^{-1}$.

Proof. For square matrices, Eq. 4.4.1 implies $\mathbf{Q}\mathbf{Q}^{\mathrm{T}} = \mathbf{I}$ and, hence, $\mathbf{Q}^{\mathrm{T}}$ is the inverse of $\mathbf{Q}$. If, conversely, $\mathbf{Q}^{\mathrm{T}}$ is the inverse of $\mathbf{Q}$, then $\mathbf{Q}$ is square and Eq. 4.4.1 holds and hence the columns of $\mathbf{Q}$ are orthonormal. ■

Example 4.4.1. Show that for all φ, $\begin{bmatrix} \cos\varphi & -\sin\varphi \\ \sin\varphi & \cos\varphi \end{bmatrix}$ is orthogonal.

Solution. A matter of computation using $\cos^2\varphi + \sin^2\varphi = 1$.

Example 4.4.2. Show that $\det(\mathbf{Q}) = \pm 1$ if $\mathbf{Q}$ is orthogonal.

Solution. From $\mathbf{I} = \mathbf{Q}^{\mathrm{T}}\mathbf{Q}$ it follows that

$$\det(\mathbf{I}) = 1 = \det(\mathbf{Q}^{\mathrm{T}}\mathbf{Q}) = \det(\mathbf{Q}^{\mathrm{T}})\det(\mathbf{Q}) = \det^2(\mathbf{Q})$$

since $\det(\mathbf{Q}^{\mathrm{T}}) = \det(\mathbf{Q})$.

Without any conditions on $\mathbf{A}$, little can be said about the relationships between $\mathbf{x}$ and $\mathbf{Ax}$. For instance, if $\mathbf{x} \perp \mathbf{y}$, it surely cannot be concluded that $\mathbf{Ax} \perp \mathbf{Ay}$. If $\mathbf{A}$ is an orthogonal matrix, the situation is strikingly different. The next theorem and its corollary illustrate this point. The theorem and its corollary assert that orthonormal matrices preserve inner products and norms.

Theorem 4.4.2. *If* $\mathbf{Q}$ *is orthonormal, then* $< \mathbf{Qx}, \mathbf{Qy} > = < \mathbf{x}, \mathbf{y} >$.

---

[4]This terminology is not conventional. We adopt it because matrices with orthonormal columns appear with great regularity and no specific name for them has been generally accepted. This would ordinarily cause no confusion except that square matrices with orthonormal columns are commonly known as orthogonal matrices. In this text, then, orthogonal matrices form a subset of the class of orthonormal matrices.

Proof. The conclusion follows from $< \mathbf{Qx}, \mathbf{Qy} > = (\mathbf{Qx})^{\mathrm{T}}(\mathbf{Qy}) = \mathbf{x}^{\mathrm{T}}\mathbf{Q}^{\mathrm{T}}\mathbf{Qy} = \mathbf{x}^{\mathrm{T}}\mathbf{Iy} = \mathbf{x}^{\mathrm{T}}\mathbf{y} = < \mathbf{x}, \mathbf{y} >$. ■

Corollary 1. *If* $\mathbf{Q}$ *is orthonormal, then* $\|\mathbf{Qx}\| = \|\mathbf{x}\|$.

Proof. Set $\mathbf{y} = \mathbf{x}$ in Theorem 4.4.2. Then, the conclusion of Theorem 4.4.2 becomes $\|\mathbf{Qx}\|^2 = < \mathbf{Qx}, \mathbf{Qx} > = < \mathbf{x}, \mathbf{x} > = \|\mathbf{x}\|^2$. And, since the norm is nonnegative, $\|\mathbf{Qx}\| = \|\mathbf{x}\|$. ■

Example 4.4.3. Show that $\mathbf{Q}_1$ and $\mathbf{Q}_2$ are orthonormal implies that $\mathbf{Q}_1\mathbf{Q}_2$ is orthonormal.

Solution. The proof amounts to verifying $(\mathbf{Q}_1\mathbf{Q}_2)^{\mathrm{T}}(\mathbf{Q}_1\mathbf{Q}_2) = \mathbf{I}$.

Recall from the previous section that the projection of $\mathbf{b}$ into the span of the orthonormal set $\{\mathbf{q}_1, \mathbf{q}_2, \ldots, \mathbf{q}_k\}$ is denoted by $\mathbf{b}_\perp$ and given by

$$\mathbf{b}_\perp = < \mathbf{b}, \mathbf{q}_1 > \mathbf{q}_1 + < \mathbf{b}, \mathbf{q}_2 > \mathbf{q}_2 + \cdots + < \mathbf{b}, \mathbf{q}_k > \mathbf{q}_k \qquad (4.4.2)$$

If $\mathbf{Q} = [\mathbf{q}_1 \quad \mathbf{q}_2 \quad \ldots \quad \mathbf{q}_k]$, then $\mathbf{b}_\perp$ is in the column space of $\mathbf{Q}$. One can infer by direct computation that

$$\mathbf{Q}(\mathbf{Q}^{\mathrm{T}}\mathbf{b}) = \mathbf{b}_\perp \qquad (4.4.3)$$

Now $\mathbf{Q}(\mathbf{Q}^{\mathrm{T}}\mathbf{b})$ is a linear combination of the columns of $\mathbf{Q}$ with weights given by the entries in $\mathbf{Q}^{\mathrm{T}}\mathbf{b}$. Equations 4.4.2 and 4.4.3 show that these weights are $\mathbf{q}_i^{\mathrm{T}}\mathbf{b} = < \mathbf{b}, \mathbf{q}_i >$. Finally, if $\mathbf{Q} = \mathbf{q}$, then it follows from Eq. 4.4.3 that the projection of $\mathbf{b}$ into the column space of $\mathbf{Q}$ is given by $\mathbf{qq}^{\mathrm{T}}\mathbf{b} = < \mathbf{b}, \mathbf{q} > \mathbf{q}$. Hence, the projection of $\mathbf{b}$ into $span\{\mathbf{q}_1, \mathbf{q}_2, \ldots, \mathbf{q}_k\}$ is the sum of the projections of $\mathbf{b}$ into $span\{\mathbf{q}_i\}$, $i = 1, 2, \ldots, k$.

Example 4.4.4. If $\mathbf{Q}_{m\times n}$ is orthonormal, show that $\mathbf{U} = \mathbf{I} - 2\mathbf{QQ}^{\mathrm{T}}$ is a symmetric, orthogonal matrix; that is, $\mathbf{U}^2 = \mathbf{I}$.

Solution. The matrix $\mathbf{U} = \mathbf{I} - 2\mathbf{QQ}^{\mathrm{T}}$ is $m \times m$ and since

$$\mathbf{U}^{\mathrm{T}} = (\mathbf{I} - 2\mathbf{QQ}^{\mathrm{T}})^{\mathrm{T}} = \mathbf{I}^{\mathrm{T}} - 2(\mathbf{QQ}^{\mathrm{T}})^{\mathrm{T}} = \mathbf{I} - 2\mathbf{QQ}^{\mathrm{T}} = \mathbf{U}$$

it follows that $\mathbf{U}$ is symmetric. Finally, $\mathbf{U}^{\mathrm{T}}\mathbf{U} = \mathbf{I} - 4\mathbf{QQ}^{\mathrm{T}} + 4\mathbf{QQ}^{\mathrm{T}} = \mathbf{I}$.

There is a special case of Example 4.4.4 that has some independent interest in numerical matrix theory. Let $\mathbf{Q} = \mathbf{u}$, where $\mathbf{u}$ is a unit vector. So, (trivially) $\mathbf{Q}$ has orthonormal columns. Let $\mathbf{U} = \mathbf{I} - 2\mathbf{uu}^{\mathrm{T}}$. Then $\mathbf{U}$ is an orthogonal matrix called a *Householder matrix*. (See Subsection 4.8.1.) For example, let $\mathbf{u}^{\mathrm{T}} = \sqrt{2}/2\ [1\ 1\ 0]$. Then, it follows that

$$\mathbf{U} = \mathbf{I} - 2\mathbf{uu}^{\mathrm{T}} = \mathbf{I} - \begin{bmatrix} 1 \\ 1 \\ 0 \end{bmatrix} [1\ 1\ 0] = \begin{bmatrix} 0 & -1 & 0 \\ -1 & 0 & 0 \\ 0 & 0 & 1 \end{bmatrix}$$

PROBLEMS

PART 1

4.4.1. Find a matrix $\mathbf{Q}$ which is orthogonal and whose first two columns are

$$\mathbf{q}_1 = 1/3\begin{bmatrix} -2 \\ 1 \\ 2 \end{bmatrix}, \qquad \mathbf{q}_2 = 1/3\begin{bmatrix} 1 \\ -2 \\ 2 \end{bmatrix}.$$

4.4.2. Verify that $< \mathbf{Qx}, \mathbf{Qy} > = < \mathbf{x}, \mathbf{y} >$ and $\|\mathbf{Qx}\|^2 = \|\mathbf{x}\|^2$ for $\mathbf{Q}$, $\mathbf{x}$, $\mathbf{y}$ given by

$$\mathbf{Q} = 1/2\begin{bmatrix} 1 & 1 & -1 & 1 \\ 1 & -1 & 1 & 1 \\ 1 & -1 & -1 & -1 \\ 1 & 1 & 1 & -1 \end{bmatrix},$$

(*a*) $\mathbf{x} = \begin{bmatrix} 1 \\ 1 \\ 0 \\ 0 \end{bmatrix}, \quad \mathbf{y} = \begin{bmatrix} 1 \\ 1 \\ 1 \\ 1 \end{bmatrix}$

(*b*) $\mathbf{x} = \mathbf{e}_1, \quad \mathbf{y} = \begin{bmatrix} -1 \\ 2 \\ -1 \\ 2 \end{bmatrix}$ (*c*) $\mathbf{x} = \mathbf{e}_2, \quad \mathbf{y} = \begin{bmatrix} a \\ b \\ c \\ d \end{bmatrix}$

(*d*) $\mathbf{x} = \mathbf{e}_1, \quad \mathbf{y} = \mathbf{e}_2$

4.4.3. Show that $\mathbf{I} - \mathbf{J}_4/2$ is an orthogonal matrix. (Recall $\mathbf{J}_n = (1)_n$.)

4.4.4. Verify that $\mathbf{Q}(\varphi) = \begin{matrix} \cos\varphi & -\sin\varphi \\ \sin\varphi & \cos\varphi \end{matrix}$ is an orthogonal matrix for all φ. Explain why $\begin{bmatrix} 0 & 1 \\ 1 & 0 \end{bmatrix}$ is an orthogonal matrix which is distinct from $\mathbf{Q}(\varphi)$.

4.4.5. Compute the orthogonal matrix $\mathbf{I} - 2\mathbf{Q}\mathbf{Q}^{\mathrm{T}}$ for these matrices $\mathbf{Q}$:

(*a*) $1/2\begin{bmatrix} 1 & -1 \\ -1 & 1 \\ -1 & -1 \\ 1 & 1 \end{bmatrix}$ (*b*) $1/2\begin{bmatrix} 1 & -1 & 1 \\ -1 & 1 & 1 \\ -1 & -1 & 1 \\ 1 & 1 & 1 \end{bmatrix}$ (*c*) $1/2\begin{bmatrix} 1 & -1 & 1 & 1 \\ -1 & 1 & 1 & 1 \\ -1 & -1 & 1 & -1 \\ 1 & 1 & 1 & -1 \end{bmatrix}$

(*d*) $\mathbf{e}_1$ (*e*) $[1\ 1\ 1\ 1]/2$ (*f*) $[1\ -1]\sqrt{2}/2$

4.4.6. Let

$$\mathbf{Q} = 1/2\begin{bmatrix} 1 & 1 \\ 1 & -1 \\ 1 & -1 \\ 1 & 1 \end{bmatrix} \text{ and } \mathbf{P} = 1/2\begin{bmatrix} -1 & 1 \\ 1 & 1 \\ -1 & -1 \\ 1 & -1 \end{bmatrix}.$$

Find $\mathbf{S}$ such that $\mathbf{QS} = \mathbf{P}$ and verify that $\mathbf{S}$ is orthogonal.

PART 2

4.4.7. Show: If $\mathbf{u} \in \mathcal{R}^2$ with $\|\mathbf{u}\| = 1$, then there exists φ such that

$$\mathbf{u} = \begin{bmatrix} a \\ b \end{bmatrix} = \begin{bmatrix} \cos\varphi \\ \sin\varphi \end{bmatrix}$$

4.4.8. Show that $\mathbf{Q}_1(\varphi)$ and $\mathbf{Q}_2(\vartheta)$ are orthogonal matrices for all φ and ϑ but that there is no φ and ϑ for which $\mathbf{Q}_1(\varphi) = \mathbf{Q}_2(\vartheta)$, where

$$\mathbf{Q}_1(\varphi) = \begin{bmatrix} \cos\varphi & \sin\varphi \\ -\sin\varphi & \cos\varphi \end{bmatrix} \qquad \mathbf{Q}_2(\varphi) = \begin{bmatrix} \cos\vartheta & \sin\vartheta \\ \sin\vartheta & -\cos\vartheta \end{bmatrix}$$

4.4.9. Let $\mathbf{x} = [1\ \ 1]^{\mathrm{T}}$. Plot $\mathbf{Q}_1(\pi/4)\mathbf{x}$, $\mathbf{Q}_2(\pi/4)\mathbf{x}$, $\mathbf{Q}_1(\pi/4)\mathbf{Q}_2(\pi/4)\mathbf{x}$, and $\mathbf{Q}_2(\pi/4)$ $\mathbf{Q}_1(\pi/4)\mathbf{x}$ where the orthogonal matrices are those given in Problem 4.4.8

4.4.10. Suppose $\mathbf{Q}_1$ and $\mathbf{Q}_2$ are orthogonal matrices. Show that

$$\left[\begin{array}{c|c} \mathbf{Q}_1 & \mathbf{O} \\ \hline \mathbf{O} & \mathbf{Q}_2 \end{array}\right]$$

is also orthogonal.

4.4.11. Show that the following matrix is orthogonal for all ϑ and all φ:

$$\begin{bmatrix} \sin\varphi\cos\vartheta & -\sin\vartheta & \cos\varphi\cos\vartheta \\ \sin\varphi\sin\vartheta & \cos\vartheta & \cos\varphi\sin\vartheta \\ \cos\varphi & 0 & -\sin\varphi \end{bmatrix}$$

4.4.12. Use $< \mathbf{Ax}, \mathbf{y} > = < \mathbf{x}, \mathbf{A}^{\mathrm{T}}\mathbf{y} >$ (Theorem 4.2.1) to construct an alternative proof of Theorem 4.4.2.

4.4.13. For every square $\mathbf{A}$, orthogonal $\mathbf{Q}$, and positive integer k show that $(\mathbf{Q}^{\mathrm{T}}\mathbf{AQ})^k = \mathbf{Q}^{\mathrm{T}}\mathbf{A}^k\mathbf{Q}$. If $\mathbf{A}$ is invertible, show that this result is true for every integer k. (Define $\mathbf{A}^0 = \mathbf{I}$.)

4.4.14. Construct an orthogonal, symmetric matrix which is not $\mathbf{I}$. Show that there are only two orthogonal, skew-symmetric matrices which are 2×2; namely,

$$\begin{bmatrix} 0 & \mp 1 \\ \pm 1 & 0 \end{bmatrix}$$

PART 3

4.4.15. Suppose $\mathbf{A}$ is a square matrix and $< \mathbf{Ax}, \mathbf{Ay} > = < \mathbf{x}, \mathbf{y} >$ for all $\mathbf{x}$ and for all $\mathbf{y}$. Prove that $\mathbf{A}$ must be orthogonal. (Assume that $\mathbf{x}$ and $\mathbf{y}$ belong to $\mathcal{R}^n$ and note that this is the converse of Theorem 4.4.2.)

4.4.16. Suppose $\mathbf{A}$ is a square matrix and $\|\mathbf{Ax}\| = \|\mathbf{x}\|$ for all $\mathbf{x}$. Show that $\mathbf{A}$ is orthogonal. Hint: Set $\mathbf{x} = \mathbf{y} - \mathbf{z}$ and expand $\|\mathbf{A}(\mathbf{y}-\mathbf{z})\|^2$. Now use the result proved in Problem 4.4.15. (Note that this is the converse of the theorem implicit in Corollary 1 of Theorem 4.4.2.)

4.4.17. Show that a symmetric matrix $\mathbf{Q}$ is orthogonal if and only if it satisfies $\mathbf{Q}^2 = \mathbf{I}$. Show that a skew-symmetric matrix $\mathbf{Q}$ is orthogonal if and only if it satisfies $\mathbf{Q}^2 = -\mathbf{I}$.

4.4.18. Let $S = a^2 + b^2 + c^2 + d^2$, $S \neq 0$, and set

$$\mathbf{Q}(a, b, c, d) = 1/S \begin{bmatrix} a^2 + b^2 - c^2 - d^2 & 2(bc - ad) & 2(bd + ac) \\ 2(ad + bc) & a^2 - b^2 + c^2 - d^2 & 2(cd - ab) \\ 2(bd - ac) & 2(ab + cd) & a^2 - b^2 - c^2 + d^2 \end{bmatrix}$$

Show that $\mathbf{Q}^{-1} = \mathbf{Q}^{\mathrm{T}} = \mathbf{Q}[a, -b, -c, -d]$ and $\det(\mathbf{Q}) = 1$. Hence, $\mathbf{Q}$ is orthogonal. (If a, b, c, d are integers, $\mathbf{Q}$ is a family of real orthogonal matrices with rational entries. Moreover, all such orthogonal matrices are of this type. This remarkable result appears in a letter to the editor, *The American Mathematical Monthly,* vol. 94, no. 8, pp. 757, 758, by J. Cremona.)

4.5 THE GRAM–SCHMIDT METHOD

Every orthonormal set of vectors is linearly independent. The converse is false, of course. Indeed, a "random" basis for a vector space is unlikely to have any mutually orthogonal vectors. However, it is possible to replace the given basis by another basis for the same vector space, the latter basis being orthonormal. One means for doing so is known as the *Gram–Schmidt method,* an iterative technique which exploits the fact that the difference between $\mathbf{b}$ and its projection into $\mathcal{V}$ is orthogonal to $\mathcal{V}$. (See Section 4.3.1.)

We begin by assuming that the nonempty set $\{\mathbf{u}_1, \mathbf{u}_2, \dots, \mathbf{u}_m\}$ contains no zero vectors. Define $span\{\mathbf{u}_1, \mathbf{u}_2, \dots, \mathbf{u}_m\} = \mathcal{V}$ and, since we do not assume that $\{\mathbf{u}_1, \mathbf{u}_2, \dots, \mathbf{u}_m\}$ is linearly independent, $\dim(\mathcal{V}) = k \le m$. The idea is to construct the projection of $\mathbf{u}_i$ into the subspace of $\mathcal{V}$, $span\{\mathbf{u}_1, \mathbf{u}_2, \dots, \mathbf{u}_{i-1}\}$, $i \le k$. If $\mathbf{u}_i$ belongs to $span\{\mathbf{u}_1, \mathbf{u}_2, \dots, \mathbf{u}_{i-1}\}$ then the projection is $\mathbf{u}_i$ itself and, as we shall see, this messes up the algorithm. For this reason, if $\mathbf{u}_i$ belongs to $span\{\mathbf{u}_1, \mathbf{u}_2, \dots, \mathbf{u}_{i-1}\}$, we ignore $\mathbf{u}_i$ and use $\mathbf{u}_{i+1}$ in its place and check to see whether $\mathbf{u}_{i+1}$ belongs to $span\{\mathbf{u}_1, \mathbf{u}_2, \dots, \mathbf{u}_{i-1}\}$. If it does, then we use $\mathbf{u}_{i+2}$ and so on until either we find $\mathbf{u}_j \notin span\{\mathbf{u}_1, \mathbf{u}_2, \dots, \mathbf{u}_{i-1}\}$ and we use $\mathbf{u}_j$ in place of $\mathbf{u}_i$, or we run out of vectors in $span\{\mathbf{u}_1, \mathbf{u}_2, \dots, \mathbf{u}_m\}$ and the algorithm terminates. We simplify the presentation of the algorithm by assuming that at each stage $\mathbf{u}_i \notin span\{\mathbf{u}_1, \mathbf{u}_2, \dots, \mathbf{u}_{i-1}\}$. (The MATLAB implementation of the algorithm permits $\{\mathbf{u}_1, \mathbf{u}_2, \dots, \mathbf{u}_m\}$ to be linearly dependent. See Section 4.5.1.)

STEP 1. (This is the initializing step.) Define $\mathbf{v}_1 = \mathbf{u}_1$ and $r_1 = \|\mathbf{v}_1\|$. Then $\mathbf{q}_1 = \mathbf{v}_1/r_1$ is a unit vector. Note that $\mathbf{q}_1$ is defined because $r_1 \neq 0$.

STEP 2. Define $\mathbf{v}_2 = \mathbf{u}_2 - (\mathbf{u}_2)_\perp$, where $(\mathbf{u}_2)_\perp$ is the projection of $\mathbf{u}_2$ into $span\{\mathbf{q}_1\}$. That is,

$$\mathbf{v}_2 = \mathbf{u}_2 - \langle \mathbf{q}_1, \mathbf{u}_2 \rangle \mathbf{q}_1, \qquad r_2 = \|\mathbf{v}_2\| \tag{4.5.1}$$

By construction, $\mathbf{v}_2$ is orthogonal to $\mathbf{q}_1$. If $\mathbf{v}_2 = \mathbf{0}$, then by Eq. 4.5.1, $\mathbf{u}_2 \in span\{\mathbf{q}_1\} = span\{\mathbf{u}_i\}$. This contradicts the assumption that $\{\mathbf{u}_1, \mathbf{u}_2, \dots, \mathbf{u}_m\}$ is linearly independent. Hence $\mathbf{v}_2 \neq \mathbf{0}$ and we can define the unit vector $\mathbf{q}_2 = \mathbf{v}_2/r_2$. Note that $span\{\mathbf{q}_1, \mathbf{q}_2\} = span\{\mathbf{u}_1, \mathbf{u}_2\}$.

STEP 3. Define $\mathbf{v}_3 = \mathbf{u}_3 - (\mathbf{u}_3)_\perp$, where $(\mathbf{u}_3)_\perp$ is the projection of $\mathbf{u}_3$ into $span\{\mathbf{q}_1, \mathbf{q}_2\}$. That is,

$$\mathbf{v}_3 = \mathbf{u}_3 - \langle \mathbf{q}_1, \mathbf{u}_3 \rangle \mathbf{q}_1 - \langle \mathbf{q}_2, \mathbf{u}_3 \rangle \mathbf{q}_2, \qquad r_3 = \|\mathbf{v}_3\|$$

Again, $\mathbf{v}_3 \neq \mathbf{0}$ since we are assuming that $\{\mathbf{q}_1, \mathbf{q}_2\}$ is linearly independent. Then $r_3 \neq 0$ and we are able to define the unit vector $\mathbf{q}_3 = \mathbf{v}_3/r_3$, which by construction is orthogonal to $\mathbf{q}_1$ and $\mathbf{q}_2$.

It is important to write down the explicit formula that generates $\mathbf{v}_j$ and thus $\mathbf{q}_i$ from $\{\mathbf{q}_1, \mathbf{q}_2, \ldots, \mathbf{q}_{j-1}\}$:

STEP *j*. Define $\mathbf{v}_j = \mathbf{u}_j - (\mathbf{u}_j)_\perp$, where $(\mathbf{u}_j)_\perp$ is the projection of $\mathbf{u}_j$ into $span\{\mathbf{q}_1, \mathbf{q}_2, \ldots, \mathbf{q}_{j-1}\}$. That is,[5]

$$\mathbf{v}_j = \mathbf{u}_j - \sum_{i=1}^{j-1} < \mathbf{u}_j, \mathbf{q}_i > \mathbf{q}_i, \quad j = 1, 2, \ldots, k \tag{4.5.2}$$

$$r_j = \|\mathbf{v}_j\| \qquad \mathbf{q}_j = \mathbf{v}_j / r_j, \quad j = 1, 2, \ldots, k \tag{4.5.3}$$

Since we assume the set $\{\mathbf{u}_1, \mathbf{u}_2, \ldots, \mathbf{u}_k\}$ is linearly independent, it then follows that $r_j \neq 0$ and $\mathbf{q}_j = \mathbf{v}_j / r_j$ is a unit vector orthogonal to $\mathbf{q}_i$ for all $i < j$. The same holds for $\mathbf{q}_j$ since $\mathbf{q}_j = r_j \mathbf{v}_j$.

The pair of Eq. 4.5.2 and Eq. 4.5.3 define the Gram–Schmidt method for $1 < j \leq k$. It is an iteration scheme that replaces each $\mathbf{u}_j$ with $\mathbf{q}_j$ such that $span\{\mathbf{u}_1, \mathbf{u}_2, \ldots, \mathbf{u}_j\} = span\{\mathbf{q}_1, \mathbf{q}_2, \ldots, \mathbf{q}_j\}$. Some examples will help explain the use of this technique.

Example 4.5.1. Use the Gram–Schmidt method to find an orthonormal basis for the space spanned by the vectors,

$$\{\mathbf{u}_1, \mathbf{u}_2, \mathbf{u}_3\} = \left\{ \begin{bmatrix} 1 \\ 1 \\ 0 \end{bmatrix}, \begin{bmatrix} 1 \\ 0 \\ 0 \end{bmatrix}, \begin{bmatrix} 1 \\ 1 \\ 1 \end{bmatrix} \right\}$$

Solution. If we were just interested in finding an orthonormal basis for the space spanned by $\{\mathbf{u}_1, \mathbf{u}_2, \mathbf{u}_3\}$, we would have nothing to do. For $\{\mathbf{u}_1, \mathbf{u}_2, \mathbf{u}_3\}$ spans $\mathcal{R}^3$ and so does the set of unit vectors $\{\mathbf{e}_1, \mathbf{e}_2, \mathbf{e}_3\}$. The Gram–Schmidt method provides us with something more: $\mathbf{q}_1 \in span\{\mathbf{u}_1\}$; $\mathbf{q}_1$ and $\mathbf{q}_2 \in span\{\mathbf{u}_1, \mathbf{u}_2\}$; and, finally, $\mathbf{q}_1$, $\mathbf{q}_2$, and $\mathbf{q}_3 \in span\{\mathbf{u}_1, \mathbf{u}_2, \mathbf{u}_3\}$. So, following the steps outlined above:

$$\mathbf{v}_1 = \mathbf{u}_1 = \begin{bmatrix} 1 \\ 1 \\ 0 \end{bmatrix}, \quad r_1 = \|\mathbf{v}_1\| = \sqrt{2}, \quad \mathbf{q}_1 = \mathbf{v}_1/\sqrt{2}$$

$$\mathbf{v}_2 = \begin{bmatrix} 1 \\ 0 \\ 0 \end{bmatrix} - < \begin{bmatrix} 1 \\ 0 \\ 0 \end{bmatrix}, \mathbf{q}_1 > \mathbf{q}_1 = \begin{bmatrix} 1 \\ 0 \\ 0 \end{bmatrix} - 1/2 \begin{bmatrix} 1 \\ 1 \\ 0 \end{bmatrix} = 1/2 \begin{bmatrix} 1 \\ -1 \\ 0 \end{bmatrix}$$

---

[5]The empty sum $\sum_1^0$ is defined as 0.

$$r_2 = \|\mathbf{v}_2\| = \frac{1}{\sqrt{2}}, \quad \mathbf{q}_2 = \frac{\mathbf{v}_2}{\sqrt{2}}$$

$$\mathbf{v}_3 = \begin{bmatrix} 1 \\ 1 \\ 1 \end{bmatrix} - < \begin{bmatrix} 1 \\ 1 \\ 0 \end{bmatrix}, \mathbf{q}_1 > \mathbf{q}_1 - < \begin{bmatrix} 1 \\ 1 \\ 1 \end{bmatrix}, \mathbf{q}_2 > \mathbf{q}_2$$

$$= \begin{bmatrix} 1 \\ 1 \\ 1 \end{bmatrix} - \frac{1}{2}(2)\begin{bmatrix} 1 \\ 1 \\ 0 \end{bmatrix} - \frac{1}{2}(0)\begin{bmatrix} 1 \\ -1 \\ 1 \end{bmatrix} = \begin{bmatrix} 0 \\ 0 \\ 1 \end{bmatrix} \qquad \mathbf{r}_3 = \|\mathbf{v}_3\| = 1, \; \mathbf{q}_3 = \mathbf{v}_3$$

Therefore, the orthonormal basis is

$$\left\{ \frac{1}{\sqrt{2}}\begin{bmatrix} 1 \\ 1 \\ 0 \end{bmatrix}, \frac{1}{\sqrt{2}}\begin{bmatrix} 1 \\ -1 \\ 0 \end{bmatrix}, \begin{bmatrix} 0 \\ 0 \\ 1 \end{bmatrix} \right\}$$

Example 4.5.2. Use the Gram–Schmidt method to find an orthonormal basis for the span of the vectors

$$\mathbf{u}_1 = \begin{bmatrix} 1 \\ 1 \\ 1 \\ 1 \end{bmatrix}, \qquad \mathbf{u}_2 = \begin{bmatrix} 1 \\ 0 \\ 0 \\ 1 \end{bmatrix}, \qquad \mathbf{u}_3 = \begin{bmatrix} -1 \\ 0 \\ -2 \\ 1 \end{bmatrix}$$

Solution. Following the steps in the algorithm,

$$\mathbf{v}_1 = \mathbf{u}_1 = \begin{bmatrix} 1 \\ 1 \\ 1 \\ 1 \end{bmatrix}, r_1 = 2, \mathbf{q}_1 = \frac{\mathbf{v}_1}{2}$$

$$\mathbf{v}_2 = \begin{bmatrix} 1 \\ 0 \\ 0 \\ 1 \end{bmatrix} - 1/4 < \begin{bmatrix} 1 \\ 0 \\ 0 \\ 1 \end{bmatrix}, \begin{bmatrix} 1 \\ 1 \\ 1 \\ 1 \end{bmatrix} > \begin{bmatrix} 1 \\ 1 \\ 1 \\ 1 \end{bmatrix} = 1/2\begin{bmatrix} 1 \\ -1 \\ 1 \\ 1 \end{bmatrix}, r_2 = \|\mathbf{v}_2\| = 1, \mathbf{q}_2 = \mathbf{v}_2$$

$$\mathbf{v}_3 = \begin{bmatrix} -1 \\ 0 \\ -2 \\ 1 \end{bmatrix} - 1/4 < \begin{bmatrix} -1 \\ 0 \\ -2 \\ 1 \end{bmatrix}, \begin{bmatrix} 1 \\ 1 \\ 1 \\ 1 \end{bmatrix} > \begin{bmatrix} 1 \\ 1 \\ 1 \\ 1 \end{bmatrix} - 1/4 < \begin{bmatrix} -1 \\ 0 \\ -2 \\ 1 \end{bmatrix}, \begin{bmatrix} 1 \\ -1 \\ -1 \\ 1 \end{bmatrix} > \begin{bmatrix} 1 \\ -1 \\ -1 \\ 1 \end{bmatrix}$$

$$= \begin{bmatrix} -1 \\ 0 \\ -2 \\ 1 \end{bmatrix} + 1/2\begin{bmatrix} 1 \\ 1 \\ 1 \\ 1 \end{bmatrix} - 1/2\begin{bmatrix} 1 \\ -1 \\ -1 \\ 1 \end{bmatrix} = \begin{bmatrix} -1 \\ 1 \\ -1 \\ 1 \end{bmatrix}, \mathbf{r}_3 = \|\mathbf{v}_3\| = 2, \mathbf{q}_3 = \frac{\mathbf{v}_3}{2}$$

The orthonormal basis spanning the same space spanned by $\{\mathbf{u}_1, \mathbf{u}_2, \mathbf{u}_3\}$ is given by

$$\left\{ 1/2\begin{bmatrix} 1 \\ 1 \\ 1 \\ 1 \end{bmatrix}, 1/2\begin{bmatrix} 1 \\ -1 \\ -1 \\ 1 \end{bmatrix}, 1/2\begin{bmatrix} -1 \\ 1 \\ -1 \\ 1 \end{bmatrix} \right\}$$

4.5.1 Orthonormal Bases in MATLAB

The command Q = orth(A) returns a matrix $\mathbf{Q}$ whose orthonormal columns span the column space of $\mathbf{A}$. That is, $col(\mathbf{A}) = col(\mathbf{Q})$. Since a set of orthonormal vectors must be linearly independent, $col(\mathbf{A}) = col(\mathbf{Q})$ implies that the number of columns of $\mathbf{Q}$ is rank($\mathbf{A}$), the dimension of $col(\mathbf{A})$. One implication of this fact is that $\mathbf{Q}$ is orthonormal but not necessarily orthogonal. Moreover, MATLAB uses a variation of the Gram–Schmidt method that is superior in numerical accuracy to the one described above. This results in an orthonormal basis that may differ from the one given by the iteration, Eq. 4.5.2. The following example illustrates some of the features of orth(A).

Example 4.5.3. Let $\mathbf{A}$, $\mathbf{B}$ and $\mathbf{C}$ be given by

$$\mathbf{A} = \begin{bmatrix} 1 & 1 & 1 \\ 1 & 0 & 1 \\ 0 & 0 & 1 \end{bmatrix} \qquad \mathbf{B} = \begin{bmatrix} 1 & 1 & 1 \\ 1 & 1 & 0 \\ 1 & 0 & 0 \end{bmatrix} \qquad \mathbf{C} = \begin{bmatrix} 2 & 1 & 1 \\ -1 & 0 & -1 \\ 1 & 1 & 0 \end{bmatrix}$$

Orthogonal bases for the column spaces of these matrices are obtained by orth(X). MATLAB returns the following

```
orth(A) =

     0.5774    0.4082   -0.7071
     0.5774    0.4082    0.7071
     0.5774   -0.4082    0.0000

orth(B) =

     0.5774    0.4082   -0.7071
     0.5774    0.4082    0.7071
     0.5774   -0.4082    0.0000

orth(C) =

     0.8165         0
    -0.4082   -0.7071
     0.4082   -0.7071
```

It is easy to verify that $col(\mathbf{A}) = col(\text{orth}(\mathbf{A})) = col(\text{orth}(\mathbf{B}))$. Note also that the columns of orth($\mathbf{C}$) span the two dimensional space $col(\mathbf{C})$.

The projection of **b** into $\mathcal{V}$ was computed in Section 4.3 by assuming that an orthonormal basis for $\mathcal{V}$ is known. For $\mathcal{V} = col(\mathbf{A})$, we can use orth(A) to find $\mathbf{b}_\perp$. Assume **A** and **b** have been entered and define Q = orth(A). Then the command Q * Q' * b returns the projection of **b** into $\mathcal{V}$.

Example 4.5.4. Suppose $\mathbf{b} = [1 \quad -1 \quad 1]^T$ and C is given as in Example 4.5.3. Then orth(C)*orth(C)'*b returns the projection of **b** into the column space of **C**:

```
orth(C)*orth(C)'*b
ans =
        1.3333
       -0.6667
        0.6667
```

Example 4.5.5. Repeat Example 4.5.4 using **B** of Example 4.5.3 in place of **C**.

Solution. Since the columns of **B** span R^3, we expect the projection of **b** to be itself. This is readily verified:

```
orth(C)*orth(C)'*b
ans =
        1.0000
       -1.0000
        1.0000
```

PROBLEMS

PART 1

Use the Gram–Schmidt method to find an orthonormal basis for the space spanned by the following sets of vectors in Problems 4.5.1–4.5.5.

4.5.1. $\left\{\begin{bmatrix}1\\1\\1\end{bmatrix}, \begin{bmatrix}1\\1\\0\end{bmatrix}, \begin{bmatrix}1\\0\\0\end{bmatrix}\right\}$

4.5.2. $\left\{\begin{bmatrix}1\\1\\1\end{bmatrix}, \begin{bmatrix}1\\0\\0\end{bmatrix}, \begin{bmatrix}1\\1\\0\end{bmatrix}\right\}$

4.5.3. $\left\{\begin{bmatrix}1\\1\\0\end{bmatrix}, \begin{bmatrix}1\\1\\1\end{bmatrix}, \begin{bmatrix}1\\0\\0\end{bmatrix}\right\}$

4.5.4. $\left\{\begin{bmatrix}1\\0\\0\end{bmatrix}, \begin{bmatrix}1\\1\\1\end{bmatrix}, \begin{bmatrix}1\\1\\0\end{bmatrix}\right\}$

4.5.5. $\left\{\begin{bmatrix}1\\0\\0\end{bmatrix}, \begin{bmatrix}1\\1\\0\end{bmatrix}, \begin{bmatrix}1\\1\\1\end{bmatrix}\right\}$

4.5.6. Use the Gram–Schmidt method on the linearly dependent set

$$\left\{\begin{bmatrix}1\\0\\1\end{bmatrix}, \begin{bmatrix}2\\-1\\1\end{bmatrix}, \begin{bmatrix}1\\-1\\0\end{bmatrix}\right\}$$

4.5.7. Let $\mathbf{q}_1$ and $\mathbf{q}_2$ denote the first two vectors in the orthonormal bases generated in Problems 4.5.1–4.5.4. Let $\mathbf{b} = [1 \quad -2 \quad 1]^T$. Find $\mathbf{b}_\perp$ for each set $\{\mathbf{q}_1, \mathbf{q}_2\}$ and verify that $\mathbf{b} - \mathbf{b}_\perp$ is orthogonal to every vector in $span\{\mathbf{q}_1, \mathbf{q}_2\}$.

4.5.8. Find an orthonormal basis for the vector space spanned by

$$\left\{\begin{bmatrix}1\\0\\0\\1\end{bmatrix}, \begin{bmatrix}-1\\0\\-2\\1\end{bmatrix}, \begin{bmatrix}1\\1\\1\\1\end{bmatrix}\right\}$$

and compare with the basis found in Example 4.5.2.

PART 2

4.5.9. Suppose $abc \neq 0$. Explain why the Gram–Schmidt method leads to the same orthonormal basis for $span\{\mathbf{u}_1, \mathbf{u}_2, \mathbf{u}_3\}$ and $span\{a\mathbf{u}_1, b\mathbf{u}_2, c\mathbf{u}_3\}$.

4.5.10. If $a_1b_2c_3 \neq 0$, explain why the Gram–Schmidt method leads to the same orthonormal basis for $span\{\mathbf{u}_1, \mathbf{u}_2, \mathbf{u}_3\}$ and $span\{a_1\mathbf{u}_1, b_1\mathbf{u}_1 + b_2\mathbf{u}_2, c_1\mathbf{u}_1 + c_2\mathbf{u}_2 + c_3\mathbf{u}_3\}$.

4.5.11. Explain why the Gram–Schmidt method leads to different orthonormal bases for $span\{\mathbf{u}_1, \mathbf{u}_2, \mathbf{u}_3\}$ and $span\{\mathbf{u}_1, \mathbf{u}_2+\mathbf{u}_3, \mathbf{u}_3\}$. Contrast this conclusion with the result in Problem 4.5.10 above.

PART 3

4.5.12. Formulate and prove a generalization of the result stated in Problem 4.5.10, applied to $span\{\mathbf{u}_1,\mathbf{u}_2,\ldots,\mathbf{u}_k\}$.

4.5.13. Use Eq. 4.5.1 to show that $r_i = 0$ implies that $\{\mathbf{u}_1,\mathbf{u}_2,\ldots,\mathbf{u}_i\}$ must be linearly dependent.

MATLAB

4.5.14. Use orth(X) to find orthonormal bases for the matrices in Problems 4.5.1–4.5.5.

4.5.15. Repeat Problem 4.5.15 for the matrix in Problem 4.5.6.

4.5.16. Verify the results given in Example 4.5.3.

4.5.17. Use the set of vectors given in Problem 4.5.8 to find an orthonormal basis for their span.

4.6 THE QR FACTORIZATION

The Gram–Schmidt process can be applied to the columns of $\mathbf{A}$ (viewing the columns of $\mathbf{A}$ as a spanning set of $col(\mathbf{A})$) and this leads to the factorization of

A into an orthogonal matrix **Q** whose columns span *col*(**A**) and an upper triangular matrix **R**. Indeed, this factorization (or decomposition, as it is sometimes called) is nothing more than a matrix formulation of the equations defining the Gram–Schmidt process, Eq. 4.5.2:

$$\mathbf{v}_j = \mathbf{u}_j - \sum_{i=1}^{j-1} < \mathbf{u}_j, \mathbf{q}_i > \mathbf{q}_i, \; r_j = \|\mathbf{v}_j\| \tag{4.6.1}$$

$$\mathbf{q}_j = \mathbf{v}_j / r_j, \; j = 1, 2, \ldots, k \tag{4.6.2}$$

To see how this comes about, first rewrite Eq. 4.6.2 as $\mathbf{v}_j = r_j \mathbf{q}_j$ and define $r_{ij} =< \mathbf{u}_j, \mathbf{q}_i >=< \mathbf{q}_i, \mathbf{u}_j >, \; i < j$. Next solve for $\mathbf{u}_j$ in Eq. 4.6.1.

$$\mathbf{u}_j = r_j \mathbf{q}_j + \sum_{i=1}^{j-1} r_{ij} \mathbf{q}_i, \; j = 1, 2, \ldots, k \tag{4.6.3}$$

Now set $\mathbf{A} = [\mathbf{u}_1 \;\; \mathbf{u}_2 \;\; \ldots \;\; \mathbf{u}_k]$ and $\mathbf{Q} = [\mathbf{q}_1 \;\; \mathbf{q}_2 \;\; \ldots \;\; \mathbf{q}_k]$. Finally, define **R** by

$$\mathbf{R} = [\mathbf{r}_1 \;\; \mathbf{r}_2 \;\; \ldots \;\; \mathbf{r}_k] = \begin{bmatrix} r_1 & r_{12} & \cdots & r_{1k} \\ 0 & r_2 & \cdots & r_{2k} \\ \vdots & \vdots & & \vdots \\ 0 & 0 & \cdots & r_k \end{bmatrix} \tag{4.6.4}$$

Then, with a little effort, it follows that Eq. 4.6.3 has the matrix formulation, $\mathbf{A} = \mathbf{QR}$ called the **QR** *factorization* or *decomposition* of **A**. Note that

$$\mathbf{u}_j = \mathbf{Q}\mathbf{r}_j, \; j = 1, 2, \ldots, k \tag{4.6.5}$$

Theorem 4.6.1. *Assume that* $\mathbf{A}_{m \times n}$ *has full column rank. Then there exists an orthonormal matrix* $\mathbf{Q}_{m \times n}$ *and a nonsingular, upper triangular matrix* **R** *such that* $\mathbf{A} = \mathbf{QR}$.

Proof. The assumption that **A** has full column rank implies that the columns of **A** form a linearly independent set. Hence, the Gram–Schmidt method generates **Q** as above. Since the diagonal entries of **R** are nonzero, **R** is nonsingular. ■

Example 4.6.1. Construct the **QR** factorization of the matrix

$$\mathbf{A} = \begin{bmatrix} 1 & 1 & 1 \\ 1 & 0 & 1 \\ 0 & 0 & 1 \end{bmatrix}$$

Solution. The columns of **A** are the vectors, $\mathbf{u}_1$, $\mathbf{u}_2$, and $\mathbf{u}_3$ given in Example 4.5.1. In that example, the vectors $\mathbf{q}_1$, $\mathbf{q}_2$, and $\mathbf{q}_3$ and $r_1 = \sqrt{2}$, $r_2 = 1/\sqrt{2}$, $r_3 = 1$ were computed. There remains the computation of r_{12}, r_{13}, and r_{23}. By definition, these scalars are the inner products,

$$r_{12} = < \mathbf{u}_2, \mathbf{q}_1 > = < \begin{bmatrix} 1 \\ 0 \\ 0 \end{bmatrix}, \frac{1}{\sqrt{2}} \begin{bmatrix} 1 \\ 1 \\ 0 \end{bmatrix} > = \frac{\sqrt{2}}{2},$$

$$r_{13} = < \mathbf{u}_3, \mathbf{q}_1 > = < \begin{bmatrix} 1 \\ 1 \\ 1 \end{bmatrix}, \frac{1}{\sqrt{2}} \begin{bmatrix} 1 \\ 1 \\ 0 \end{bmatrix} > = \sqrt{2}$$

$$r_{23} = < \mathbf{u}_3, \mathbf{q}_2 > = < \begin{bmatrix} 1 \\ 1 \\ 1 \end{bmatrix}, \frac{1}{\sqrt{2}} \begin{bmatrix} 1 \\ -1 \\ 0 \end{bmatrix} > = 0$$

All this leads to

$$\mathbf{A} = \begin{bmatrix} 1 & 1 & 1 \\ 1 & 0 & 1 \\ 0 & 0 & 1 \end{bmatrix} = \mathbf{QR} = \frac{1}{\sqrt{2}} \begin{bmatrix} 1 & 1 & 0 \\ 1 & -1 & 0 \\ 0 & 0 & \sqrt{2} \end{bmatrix} \frac{\sqrt{2}}{2} \begin{bmatrix} 2 & 1 & 2 \\ 0 & 1 & 0 \\ 0 & 0 & \sqrt{2} \end{bmatrix}$$

Example 4.6.2. Find the **QR** factorization of the matrix

$$\mathbf{A} = \begin{bmatrix} 1 & 1 & -1 \\ 1 & 0 & 0 \\ 1 & 0 & -2 \\ 1 & 1 & 1 \end{bmatrix}$$

Solution. The columns of **A** are the vectors of Example 4.5.2. From the work done in that example,

$$\mathbf{Q} = 1/2 \begin{bmatrix} 1 & 1 & -1 \\ 1 & -1 & 1 \\ 1 & -1 & -1 \\ 1 & 1 & 1 \end{bmatrix}$$

Next, compute

$$r_{12} = < \begin{bmatrix} 1 \\ 0 \\ 0 \\ 1 \end{bmatrix}, 1/2 \begin{bmatrix} 1 \\ 1 \\ 1 \\ 1 \end{bmatrix} > = 1, \qquad r_{13} = < \begin{bmatrix} -1 \\ 0 \\ -2 \\ 1 \end{bmatrix}, 1/2 \begin{bmatrix} 1 \\ 1 \\ 1 \\ 1 \end{bmatrix} > = -1,$$

$$r_{23} = < \begin{bmatrix} -1 \\ 0 \\ -2 \\ 1 \end{bmatrix}, 1/2 \begin{bmatrix} 1 \\ -1 \\ -1 \\ 1 \end{bmatrix} > = 1$$

Since $r_1 = 2$, $r_2 = 1$, and $r_3 = 2$, **R** is determined. The factorization of **A** is then given by

$$\mathbf{A} = \begin{bmatrix} 1 & 1 & -1 \\ 1 & 0 & 0 \\ 1 & 0 & -2 \\ 1 & 1 & 1 \end{bmatrix} = \mathbf{QR} = 1/2 \begin{bmatrix} 1 & 1 & -1 \\ 1 & -1 & 1 \\ 1 & -1 & -1 \\ 1 & 1 & 1 \end{bmatrix} \begin{bmatrix} 2 & 1 & -1 \\ 0 & 1 & 1 \\ 0 & 0 & 2 \end{bmatrix}$$

The **QR** factorization of $\mathbf{A}_{m \times n}$ provides some interesting and important insights into the system $\mathbf{Ax} = \mathbf{b}$. When the **QR** factorization of **A** is known, the solution of the system $\mathbf{Ax} = \mathbf{b}$ is particularly simple. The reason for this simplicity is easy to see. $\mathbf{QRx} = \mathbf{b}$ implies $\mathbf{Rx} = \mathbf{Q}^T\mathbf{b}$ because $\mathbf{Q}^T\mathbf{Q} = \mathbf{I}$. (Note that $\mathbf{Q}$ need not be square in order that $\mathbf{Q}^T\mathbf{Q} = \mathbf{I}$; all that is required is that $\mathbf{Q}$ be orthonormal.) Since $\mathbf{R}$ is upper triangular, the system $\mathbf{Rx} = \mathbf{Q}^T\mathbf{b}$ can be solved by back substitution. There is a further observation relative to the systems $\mathbf{Ax} = \mathbf{b}$ and $\mathbf{Rx} = \mathbf{Q}^T\mathbf{b}$. The system $\mathbf{Ax} = \mathbf{b}$ may not be consistent because, for one thing, $m > n$ is not excluded. Indeed, this is exactly the situation that arises in the fitting of data by a line of best fit. However, $\mathbf{Rx} = \mathbf{Q}^T\mathbf{b}$ is always consistent since $\mathbf{R}$ is nonsingular. The solution of $\mathbf{Rx} = \mathbf{Q}^T\mathbf{b}$ provides the "best fit" of the data given in $\mathbf{Ax} = \mathbf{b}$. (See Section 4.10.)

Example 4.6.3. Use the **QR** factorization of **A** to solve

$$\mathbf{Ax} = \begin{bmatrix} 1 & 1 & -1 \\ 1 & 0 & 0 \\ 1 & 0 & -2 \\ 1 & 1 & 1 \end{bmatrix} \mathbf{x} = \begin{bmatrix} 0 \\ 1 \\ 3 \\ -2 \end{bmatrix}$$

Solution. From Example 4.6.2, this system can be written

$$\mathbf{QRx} = 1/2 \begin{bmatrix} 1 & 1 & -1 \\ 1 & -1 & 1 \\ 1 & -1 & -1 \\ 1 & 1 & 1 \end{bmatrix} \begin{bmatrix} 2 & 1 & -1 \\ 0 & 1 & 1 \\ 0 & 0 & 2 \end{bmatrix} \mathbf{x} = \begin{bmatrix} 0 \\ 1 \\ 3 \\ -2 \end{bmatrix}$$

Multiply this system by $\mathbf{Q}^T$ to obtain

$$\mathbf{Q}^T\mathbf{QRx} = \mathbf{Rx} = \begin{bmatrix} 2 & 1 & -1 \\ 0 & 1 & 1 \\ 0 & 0 & 2 \end{bmatrix} \mathbf{x} = 1/2 \begin{bmatrix} 1 & 1 & 1 & 1 \\ 1 & -1 & -1 & 1 \\ -1 & 1 & -1 & 1 \end{bmatrix} \begin{bmatrix} 0 \\ 1 \\ 3 \\ -2 \end{bmatrix} = \begin{bmatrix} 1 \\ -3 \\ -2 \end{bmatrix}$$

The last row shows that $2z = -2$ and hence $z = -1$. The second row leads to $y + z = -3$ from which we get $y = -2$. Finally, the first row asserts that $2x + y - z = 1$. Thus, $x = 1$ and hence $\mathbf{x} = [1\ -2\ -1]^T$.

Let $\mathcal{V} = span\{\mathbf{u}_1, \mathbf{u}_2, \ldots, \mathbf{u}_k\}$. Then $\mathcal{V}$ is also $span\{\mathbf{q}_1, \mathbf{q}_2, \ldots, \mathbf{q}_k\}$. Now Eq. 4.6.5 and Eq. 3.8.2 show that $\mathbf{r}_i$ is the coordinate vector of $\mathbf{u}_i$ relative to the basis $\{\mathbf{q}_1, \mathbf{q}_2, \ldots, \mathbf{q}_k\}$. (See Section 3.8 for the relevant definitions and theorems.) Thus the **QR** factorization theorem is the "change of basis" formula of Lemma 3.1, Section 3.8. In the terminology of Section 3.8, $\mathbf{R} = \mathbf{S}$. We shall have more to say about this interpretation and its consequences in Section 4.8.

One last remark: the Gram–Schmidt process described in Sections 4.5 and 4.6 is flawed by difficulties due to numerical considerations. Without special care, the resulting matrices **Q** and **R** are often unacceptably inaccurate. Because of this difficulty, other more elaborate schemes have been developed that are modifications of the Gram–Schmidt method as derived here. The interested reader is encouraged to seek out texts on numerical methods in linear algebra for a discussion of this important topic.

4.6.1 The QR Factorization in MATLAB

For any $\mathbf{A}_{m\times n}$ the MATLAB command [Q,R] = qr(A) produces an orthogonal matrix $\mathbf{Q}_m$ whose columns span $\mathcal{R}^m$ (which may not be $col(\mathbf{A})$) and an upper trapezoidal matrix $\mathbf{R}_{m\times n}$ such that rank(**A**) = rank(**R**). If rank(**A**) = r, then **R** has its last $n-r$ zero rows and these rows are the last rows of **R**. A variety of examples will clarify this MATLAB command.

Note that MATLAB provides a **QR** decomposition which differs from the one given in the text in that if **A** is $m \times n$ then **Q** is always $m \times m$ and **R** is $m \times n$. In the text, **Q** is $m \times n$ and **R** is $n \times n$.

Example 4.6.4. Use the command [Q,R] = qr(A) to find the **QR** factorization of the following matrices:

$$(a)\ \mathbf{A} = \begin{bmatrix} 1 \\ 1 \\ 1 \\ 1 \end{bmatrix} \qquad (b)\ \mathbf{A} = \begin{bmatrix} 1 & 1 \\ 1 & 0 \\ 1 & 0 \\ 1 & 1 \end{bmatrix} \qquad (c)\ \mathbf{A} = \begin{bmatrix} 1 & 1 & 2 \\ 1 & 0 & 1 \\ 1 & 0 & 1 \\ 1 & 1 & 2 \end{bmatrix}$$

Solution. In response to [Q,R] = qr(A), MATLAB returns

(*a*) Q =

```
   -0.5000   -0.5000   -0.5000   -0.5000
   -0.5000    0.8333   -0.1667   -0.1667
   -0.5000   -0.1667    0.8333   -0.1667
   -0.5000   -0.1667   -0.1667    0.8333
```

R =

```
   -2
    0
    0
    0
```

(*b*) Q =

```
   -0.5000    0.5000   -0.1000   -0.7000
   -0.5000    0.5000   -0.7000    0.1000
   -0.5000   -0.5000    0.7000   -0.1000
   -0.5000    0.5000    0.1000    0.7000
```

R =

```
   -2   -1.0000
    0    1.0000
    0         0
    0         0
```

(*c*) Q =

```
   -0.5000    0.5000   -0.5000   -0.5000
   -0.5000   -0.5000    0.5000   -0.5000
   -0.5000   -0.5000   -0.5000    0.5000
   -0.5000    0.5000    0.5000    0.5000
```

R =

```
   -2   -1.0000   1.0000
    0    1.0000   1.0000
    0         0   2.0000
    0         0        0
```

Example 4.6.5. Use the command [Q,R] = qr(A) to find the **QR** factorization of the following matrices:

$$(a)\ \mathbf{A} = [1 \quad 1 \quad -1] \qquad (b)\ \mathbf{A} = \begin{bmatrix} 1 & 1 & -1 \\ 1 & 0 & 0 \end{bmatrix}$$

Solution. In response to [Q,R] = qr(A), MATLAB returns

(*a*) Q =

1

R =

1 1 −1

(*b*) Q =

−0.7071 −0.7071
−0.7071 0.7071

R =

−1.4142 −0.7071 0.7071
0 −0.7071 0.7071

PROBLEMS

PART 1

4.6.1. Find the **QR** factorization of these matrices:

$$(a)\begin{bmatrix} 1 & 0 \\ -1 & 1 \end{bmatrix} \quad (b)\begin{bmatrix} 0 & 1 \\ 1 & -1 \end{bmatrix} \quad (c)\begin{bmatrix} 1 & 1 \\ 1 & 2 \end{bmatrix}$$

4.6.2. Find the **QR** factorization of $\mathbf{A}_1$ where

$$\mathbf{A}_1 = \begin{bmatrix} 1 & 1 & -1 \\ 1 & 0 & -1 \\ 0 & 0 & -1 \end{bmatrix} = \mathbf{A}\begin{bmatrix} 1 & 0 & 0 \\ 0 & 1 & 0 \\ 0 & 0 & -1 \end{bmatrix}$$

and **A** is given in Example 4.6.1. Compare with the factorization of **A** given in that example.

4.6.3. Repeat Problem 4.6.2 with $\mathbf{A}_2$ in place of $\mathbf{A}_1$,

$$\mathbf{A}_2 = \begin{bmatrix} 1 & -1 & 1 \\ 1 & 0 & 1 \\ 0 & 0 & 1 \end{bmatrix} = \mathbf{A}\begin{bmatrix} 1 & 0 & 0 \\ 0 & -1 & 0 \\ 0 & 0 & 1 \end{bmatrix}$$

4.6.4. Repeat Problem 4.6.2 with $\mathbf{A}_3$ in place of $\mathbf{A}_1$,

$$\mathbf{A}_3 = \begin{bmatrix} -1 & 2 & 0 \\ -1 & 1 & 0 \\ 0 & 0 & 1 \end{bmatrix} = \mathbf{A}\begin{bmatrix} -1 & 0 & -1 \\ 0 & 1 & 0 \\ 0 & 0 & 1 \end{bmatrix}$$

PART 2

4.6.5. If **A** has the **QR** factorization $\mathbf{A} = \mathbf{QR}$, show that $\mathbf{A}^T\mathbf{A} = \mathbf{R}^T\mathbf{R}$.

4.6.6. Find the **QR** factorization of **U** where

$$\mathbf{U} = \begin{bmatrix} 1 & 1 & \cdots & 1 \\ 0 & 1 & \cdots & 1 \\ \vdots & \vdots & & \vdots \\ 0 & 0 & \cdots & 1 \end{bmatrix}$$

4.6.7. What is the **QR** factorization of an orthogonal matrix?

4.6.8. If **R** is a diagonal matrix, show that $\mathbf{A} = \mathbf{QR}$ has orthogonal columns.

4.6.9. If **A** is a diagonal matrix, what is its **QR** factorization?

MATLAB

4.6.10. Verify the result given in Example 4.6.4.
4.6.11. Verify the result given in Example 4.6.5.
4.6.12. Use [Q,R] = qr(A) to find the **QR** factorization of each matrix in Problem 4.5.1.
4.6.13. Repeat Problem 4.6.12 for the matrix $\mathbf{A}_1$ in Problem 4.6.2.
4.6.14. Repeat Problem 4.6.12 for the matrix $\mathbf{A}_2$ in Problem 4.6.3.
4.6.15. Repeat Problem 4.6.12 for the matrix $\mathbf{A}_3$ in Problem 4.6.4.
4.6.16. Repeat Problem 4.6.12 for the matrix **U** in Problem 4.6.6, where **U** is 4×4.
4.6.17. Verify the factorization for the matrix **A** in Example 4.6.1.
4.6.18. Verify the factorization for the matrix **A** in Example 4.6.2.
4.6.19. Verify the factorization for the matrix **A** in Example 4.6.3.

4.7 COMPLEMENTARY ORTHOGONAL VECTOR SPACES

One of the most remarkable examples of orthogonality is implicit in the definition of matrix multiplication and the assertion that $\mathbf{x}_0$ is a solution of $\mathbf{Ax} = \mathbf{0}$. For, if $\mathbf{Ax}_0 = \mathbf{0}$, then $\mathbf{x}_0$ is orthogonal to each of the rows of **A**, assuming **A** and $\mathbf{x}_0$ are real. From this, it follows that $\mathbf{x}_0$ is orthogonal to every vector in the row space of **A**. In fact, every vector in $null(\mathbf{A})$ is orthogonal to every vector in $col(\mathbf{A}^{\mathrm{T}}) = row(\mathbf{A})$. Vector spaces which are mutually orthogonal in this sense are of sufficient importance to warrant a brief discussion.

Let $\mathcal{V}$ and $\mathcal{W}$ be two nonempty subspaces of $\mathcal{R}^n$. Suppose every vector in $\mathcal{W}$ is orthogonal to every vector in $\mathcal{V}$. Then every vector in $\mathcal{V}$ is orthogonal to every vector in $\mathcal{W}$ (why?) and we call $\mathcal{V}$ and $\mathcal{W}$ *mutually orthogonal* vector spaces. If $\mathcal{V}$ and $\mathcal{W}$ are mutually orthogonal vector spaces and $\dim(\mathcal{V})+\dim(\mathcal{W}) = n$, then $\mathcal{W}$ is written $\mathcal{V}^{\perp}$, or equivalently $\mathcal{V} = \mathcal{W}^{\perp}$, and the two subspaces are called *orthogonal complements*. For example, if

$$\mathbf{v}_1 = \begin{bmatrix} 1 \\ 0 \\ -2 \\ 0 \end{bmatrix}, \qquad \mathbf{v}_2 = \begin{bmatrix} 0 \\ 1 \\ 0 \\ -4 \end{bmatrix}$$

then $span\{\mathbf{v}_1\}$ and $span\{\mathbf{v}_2\}$ are mutually orthogonal, one-dimensional subspaces of $\mathcal{R}^4$. They are not orthogonal complements because the sum of their dimensions is only two. On the other hand, let $\mathbf{v}_3 = [1 \quad 1]^{\mathrm{T}}$ and $\mathbf{v}_4 = [-1 \quad 1]^{\mathrm{T}}$. Then $span\{\mathbf{v}_3\}$ and $span\{\mathbf{v}_4\}$ are orthogonal complements because these spans are mutually orthogonal vector spaces and the sum of their dimensions is two.

There is a paradoxical aspect to the definition of mutually orthogonal vector spaces. Two planes in $\mathcal{R}^3$ which pass through the origin are representations of vector spaces. Suppose the planes are perpendicular, say the y,z-plane and the x,y-plane. These planes are not mutually orthogonal subspaces of $\mathcal{R}^3$, for example, the vector from (0,0,0) to (0,1,1) is in the y,z-plane but is not orthogonal to any vector in the x,y-plane. (See Fig. 4.5.) The paradox is resolved

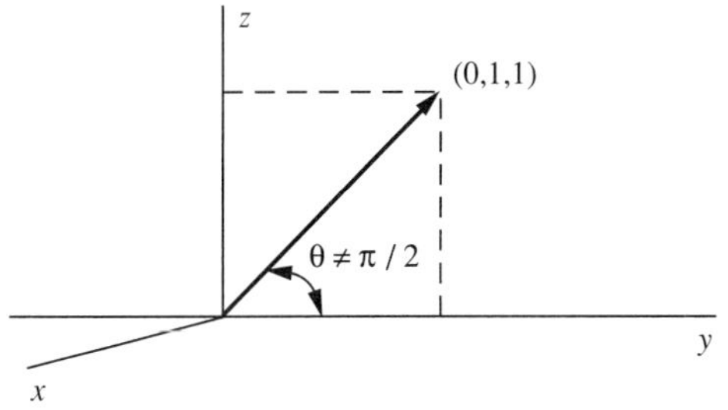

FIGURE 4-5
Perpendicular planes in $\mathcal{R}^3$ are not mutually orthogonal.

when it is realized that the conditions necessary for a pair of vector spaces to be mutually orthogonal are more stringent than the conditions used to define the perpendicularity of planes in $\mathcal{R}^3$. It is possible for two planes to represent mutually orthogonal vector subspaces of $\mathcal{R}^n$, $n \geq 4$, but it is not possible in $\mathcal{R}^3$ because planes are two-dimensional and hence $\dim(\mathcal{V}) + \dim(\mathcal{W}) = 4$. One last point: given $\mathcal{V}$, there remains to prove that there always exists $\mathcal{V}^{\perp}$. This is Corollary 1 of Theorem 4.7.1.

Example 4.7.1. Show that

$$\mathcal{V} = span\left\{\begin{bmatrix}1\\1\\0\\0\end{bmatrix}, \begin{bmatrix}-1\\1\\0\\0\end{bmatrix}\right\}, \qquad \mathcal{W} = span\left\{\begin{bmatrix}0\\0\\1\\0\end{bmatrix}, \begin{bmatrix}0\\0\\0\\1\end{bmatrix}\right\}$$

are orthogonal complements.

Solution. Because of the positioning of the zero entries, it is obvious that every vector in $\mathcal{W}$ is orthogonal to every vector in $\mathcal{V}$. Hence $\mathcal{W}$ and $\mathcal{V}$ are mutually orthogonal. Since $\dim(\mathcal{V}) = \dim(\mathcal{W}) = 2$, it follows by definition, that $\mathcal{W} = \mathcal{V}^{\perp}$. Note that $\mathcal{V}$ and $\mathcal{V}^{\perp}$ are planes in $\mathcal{R}^4$.

Theorem 4.7.1. $null(\mathbf{A})^{\perp} = row(\mathbf{A})$ (4.7.1)

Proof. Suppose that $\mathbf{A}$ is $m \times n$ and $\text{rank}(\mathbf{A}) = r$. We have already seen that every solution of $\mathbf{Ax} = \mathbf{0}$ is orthogonal to every vector in $row(\mathbf{A})$; that is, these subspaces of $\mathbf{A}$ are mutually orthogonal. To show that they are orthogonal complements we need to prove that $\dim(row(\mathbf{A})) + \dim(null(\mathbf{A})) = n$, since $row(\mathbf{A})$ and $null(\mathbf{A})$ are subspaces of $\mathcal{R}^n$. But $\dim(row\mathbf{A}) = r$ and $\dim(null\mathbf{A}) = n - r$ follows from Eq. 3.5.1. ■

If $\mathcal{V}$ is a vector space of n-tuples, the set of all vectors not in $\mathcal{V}$ is not a vector space even when the zero vector is adjoined to this set (with some trivial exceptions). However, the set of all vectors *orthogonal* to every vector in $\mathcal{V}$ is a vector space; indeed, it is $\mathcal{V}^{\perp}$.

Corollary 1. *Let* $\mathcal{V} \subseteq \mathcal{R}^n$. *Then there exists* $\mathcal{W} \subseteq \mathcal{R}^n$ *such that* $\mathcal{W} = \mathcal{V}^{\perp}$.

Proof. Construct $\mathbf{V}$ so that $row(\mathbf{V}) = \mathcal{V}$. Then $\mathcal{W} = null(\mathbf{V})$. See also Problem 4.7.16. ■

Example 4.7.2. Find a basis for the orthogonal complement of

$$\mathcal{V} = span\left\{\begin{bmatrix}1\\1\\1\\0\end{bmatrix}, \begin{bmatrix}-1\\1\\3\\-2\end{bmatrix}\right\}$$

Solution. This problem could be done by inspection. The point in offering the following analysis is to illustrate the use of Theorem 4.7.1. Construct $\mathbf{V}$ whose rows are the given vectors and determine a basis for its null space in the standard manner. (See Section 3.5.)

$$\left[\begin{array}{ccc:cccc}1 & -1 & 1 & 0 & 0 & 0\\1 & 1 & 0 & 1 & 0 & 0\\1 & 3 & 0 & 0 & 1 & 0\\0 & -2 & 0 & 0 & 0 & 1\end{array}\right] \rightarrow \cdots \rightarrow \left[\begin{array}{ccc:ccc}1 & -1 & 1 & 0 & 0 & 0\\0 & 2 & -1 & 1 & 0 & 0\\0 & 0 & 1 & -2 & 1 & 0\\0 & 0 & -1 & 1 & 0 & 1\end{array}\right]$$

From the last two rows we obtain

$$\mathbf{x}_1 = \begin{bmatrix}1\\-2\\1\\0\end{bmatrix}, \qquad \mathbf{x}_2 = \begin{bmatrix}-1\\1\\0\\1\end{bmatrix}$$

Thus $\{\mathbf{x}_1, \mathbf{x}_2\}$ is a basis for $null(\mathbf{V})$ and hence for $\mathcal{V}^{\perp}$.

Example 4.7.3. Show that

$(a)\ (\mathcal{V}^{\perp})^{\perp} = \mathcal{V}$ $\qquad (b)\ (null(\mathbf{A}^{\mathrm{T}}))^{\perp} = col(\mathbf{A})$
$(c)\ (row(\mathbf{A}))^{\perp} = null(\mathbf{A})$ $\qquad (d)\ (col(\mathbf{A})^{\perp} = null(\mathbf{A}^{\mathrm{T}})$

Solution. (a) is a consequence of the definition of orthogonal complements. (b) is Theorem 4.7.1 with $\mathbf{A}^{\mathrm{T}}$ replacing $\mathbf{A}$ and $row(\mathbf{A}^{\mathrm{T}}) = col(\mathbf{A})$. (c) follows from (a) and Theorem 4.7.1. (d) follows from (c) with $\mathbf{A}^{\mathrm{T}}$ replacing $\mathbf{A}$.

Example 4.7.4. It is always possible to find $\mathbf{B}$ such that $null(\mathbf{B}) = col(\mathbf{A})$ by exploiting Theorem 4.7.1 and the algorithm described in Section 3.5. (In particular, see Example 3.5.5.) For the matrix

$$\mathbf{A} = \begin{bmatrix}1 & 0\\-1 & 1\\1 & 1\\0 & 1\end{bmatrix}$$

consider the following arrow diagram:

$$[\mathbf{A} \quad \mathbf{I}] = \left[\begin{array}{rr|rrrr} 1 & 0 & 1 & 0 & 0 & 0 \\ -1 & 1 & 0 & 1 & 0 & 0 \\ 1 & 1 & 0 & 0 & 1 & 0 \\ 0 & 1 & 0 & 0 & 0 & 1 \end{array}\right] \rightarrow \left[\begin{array}{rr|rrrr} 1 & 0 & 1 & 0 & 0 & 0 \\ 0 & 1 & 1 & 1 & 0 & 0 \\ \hline 0 & 0 & -2 & -1 & 1 & 0 \\ 0 & 0 & -1 & -1 & 0 & 1 \end{array}\right]$$

The matrix **B** is the 2×4 submatrix in the bottom two rows, last four columns of the rightmost matrix. The connection between this example and Theorem 4.7.1 is developed further in Problem 4.7.15.

In view of the restriction $\dim(\mathcal{V}) + \dim(\mathcal{V}^{\perp}) = n$, three-dimensional space has only two varieties of orthogonal complements. The first is a plane through the origin and its orthogonal complement, the line through the origin perpendicular to the plane. The second is $\mathcal{R}^3$ and its complement $\{\mathbf{0}_3\}$. The fact that planes and the lines perpendicular to them can be interpreted as pairs of orthogonal complementary sets can be used to justify and generalize a familiar result in analytic geometry:

The plane passing through (x_1, y_1, z_1) and perpendicular to the line from the origin to (a, b, c) is

$$a(x - x_1) + b(y - y_1) + c(z - z_1) = 0 \tag{4.7.2}$$

Moreover, by setting $\mathbf{a} = [a_1 \quad a_2 \quad a_3]^{\mathrm{T}}$, $\mathbf{x} = [x \quad y \quad z]^{\mathrm{T}}$, and $\mathbf{x}_1 = [x_1 \quad y_1 \quad z_1]^{\mathrm{T}}$, Eq. 4.7.2 may be written in the equivalent forms,

$$\mathbf{a}^{\mathrm{T}}(\mathbf{x} - \mathbf{x}_1) = 0 \tag{4.7.3}$$
$$\mathbf{a}^{\mathrm{T}}\mathbf{x} = \mathbf{a}^{\mathrm{T}}\mathbf{x}_1$$

If $\mathbf{a}$, $\mathbf{x}$ and $\mathbf{x}_1$ all belong to $\mathcal{R}^n$ then the set of all $\mathbf{x}$ satisfying $\mathbf{a}^{\mathrm{T}}\mathbf{x} = b$, for fixed $\mathbf{a}$ and b, is a *hyperplane* in $\mathcal{R}^n$. (See Section 3.2.) The next example illustrates the "complementary orthogonal" subspace method of obtaining the equations of planes.

Example 4.7.5. Find a plane passing through the point $(-1,1,1)$ and perpendicular to the line,

$$\mathcal{V} = span\left\{\begin{bmatrix} 1 \\ 1 \\ 1 \end{bmatrix}\right\}$$

Solution. By elementary analytic geometry and Eq. 4.7.3, the equation is given by $(x + 1) + (y - 1) + (z - 1) = 0$, or alternatively $x + y + z = 1$. Of course, this is the method of choice. What follows is significantly more complicated. It has the virtue, however, of clarifying the notions and techniques of this section.

The null space of the matrix $\mathbf{V} = [1 \ 1 \ 1]$ is the set of all vectors orthogonal to $\mathcal{V}$. It is easy to see that *null*($\mathbf{V}$) is spanned by the basic vectors

$$\mathbf{x}_1 = \begin{bmatrix} -1 \\ 1 \\ 0 \end{bmatrix}, \qquad \mathbf{x}_2 = \begin{bmatrix} -1 \\ 0 \\ 1 \end{bmatrix}$$

Hence, the desired plane is the translate of *null*(**V**) by $[-1\ 1\ 1]^{\mathrm{T}}$. (See Section 3.7.) Specifically,

$$\mathbf{x} = \begin{bmatrix} -1 \\ 1 \\ 1 \end{bmatrix} + \alpha\mathbf{x}_1 + \beta\mathbf{x}_2 = \begin{bmatrix} -1 \\ 1 \\ 1 \end{bmatrix} + \alpha\begin{bmatrix} -1 \\ 1 \\ 0 \end{bmatrix} + \beta\begin{bmatrix} -1 \\ 0 \\ 1 \end{bmatrix}$$

Thus $x = -1 - \alpha - \beta$, $y = 1 + \alpha$, $z = 1 + \beta$. If the parameters α and β are eliminated from these equations, the Cartesian equation of the plane is found to be $x + y + z = 1$.

The notion of orthogonal subspaces provides yet another criterion for the consistency of $\mathbf{Ax} = \mathbf{b}$, often called the *Fredholm Alternative*.

Theorem 4.7.2. *The system* $\mathbf{Ax} = \mathbf{b}$ *is consistent if and only if* $\mathbf{b}$ *is orthogonal to all solutions of* $\mathbf{A}^{\mathrm{T}}\mathbf{y} = \mathbf{0}$.

Proof. The assertion "$\mathbf{Ax} = \mathbf{b}$ is consistent" implies "$\mathbf{b} \in col(\mathbf{A})$." The assertion "$\mathbf{b}$ is orthogonal to all solutions of $\mathbf{A}^{\mathrm{T}}\mathbf{y} = \mathbf{0}$" is equivalent to "$\mathbf{b} \perp \mathbf{y}$ for all $\mathbf{y} \in null(\mathbf{A}^{\mathrm{T}})$." Thus the theorem may be rephrased:

The vector $\mathbf{b} \in col(\mathbf{A})$ *if and only if* $\mathbf{b} \in null(\mathbf{A}^{\mathrm{T}})$.

But this is precisely the result listed as (*c*) in Example 4.7.4. ■

PROBLEMS

PART 1

4.7.1. Find the orthogonal complements of these vector spaces:

$$(a)\ span\left\{\begin{bmatrix} 1 \\ 1 \\ 0 \\ -1 \end{bmatrix}\right\} \quad (b)\ span\left\{\begin{bmatrix} 1 \\ 1 \\ 0 \\ -1 \end{bmatrix}, \begin{bmatrix} 0 \\ 1 \\ 1 \\ 1 \end{bmatrix}\right\} \quad (c)\ span\left\{\begin{bmatrix} 1 \\ 1 \\ 0 \\ -1 \end{bmatrix}, \begin{bmatrix} 0 \\ 1 \\ 1 \\ 1 \end{bmatrix}, \begin{bmatrix} -1 \\ 0 \\ 1 \\ 0 \end{bmatrix}\right\}$$

4.7.2. Find orthogonal bases for each of the orthogonal complements of the spans given in Problem 4.7.1.

4.7.3. Find a basis for the orthogonal complement of

$$col\begin{bmatrix} 1 & 1 \\ 0 & 0 \\ -1 & 0 \\ 0 & 1 \end{bmatrix}$$

4.7.4. Find a basis for the orthogonal complement of

$$null\begin{bmatrix} -1 & 0 \\ 1 & 1 \\ 1 & 0 \\ 1 & 1 \end{bmatrix}$$

4.7.5. Find a plane perpendicular to the line $span\{[0 \quad 1 \quad 1]^T\}$ and passing through the point $(-1,1,0)$ by finding a basis for the orthogonal complement of $span\{[0 \quad 1 \quad 1]^T\}$.

PART 2

4.7.6. Formulate a definition that captures the idea of perpendicular planes. Contrast your definition with the definition of mutually orthogonal vector spaces in $\mathcal{R}^3$.

4.7.7. Suppose $\mathbf{V}^T\mathbf{U} = \mathbf{O}$. Show that $col(\mathbf{V})$ and $col(\mathbf{U})$ are mutually orthogonal vector spaces.

4.7.8. Show that $(\mathcal{V}^{\perp})^{\perp} = \mathcal{V}$.

4.7.9. Suppose $\mathcal{V} \subseteq \mathcal{R}^n$ is a vector space. Let $\mathcal{S}$ contain $\mathbf{0}$ and all vectors not in $\mathcal{V}$. Show that $\mathcal{S}$ is not generally a vector space. Under what circumstances is $\mathcal{S}$ a vector space?

4.7.10. (*a*) What is the orthogonal complement of a line through the origin in $\mathcal{R}^2$? In $\mathcal{R}^3$? In $\mathcal{R}^n$?
(*b*) What is the orthogonal complement of $\mathcal{R}^n$? Of $\{\mathbf{0}\}$?
(*c*) What is the orthogonal complement of a plane in $\mathcal{R}^4$?
(*d*) What is the orthogonal complement of a plane in $\mathcal{R}^2$?

PART 3

4.7.11. Suppose $\mathbf{a}$ and $\mathbf{x}_1$ are given. What is a basis and the dimension of the orthogonal complement of the hyperplane, $\mathbf{a}^T(\mathbf{x} - \mathbf{x}_1) = 0$?

4.7.12. Suppose $\{\mathbf{v}_1,\mathbf{v}_2,\ldots,\mathbf{v}_k\}$ and $\{\mathbf{u}_1,\mathbf{u}_2,\ldots,\mathbf{u}_j\}$ are bases for $\mathcal{V}$ and $\mathcal{V}^{\perp}$, respectively. Prove that $\{\mathbf{v}_1,\mathbf{v},\ldots,\mathbf{v}_k,\mathbf{u}_1,\mathbf{u}_2,\ldots,\mathbf{u}_j\}$ is a basis for $\mathcal{R}^n$. Is $\mathbf{A} = [\mathbf{v}_1 \quad \mathbf{v}_2 \quad \ldots \quad \mathbf{v}_k \quad \mathbf{u}_1 \quad \mathbf{u}_2 \quad \ldots \quad \mathbf{u}_j]$ an orthogonal matrix?

4.7.13. Suppose $\mathcal{V}$ and $\mathcal{V}^{\perp}$ are orthogonal complements in $\mathcal{R}^n$ and $\mathbf{x} \in \mathcal{R}^n$. Show that there exists $\mathbf{v} \in \mathcal{V}$ and $\mathbf{u} \in \mathcal{V}^{\perp}$ such that $\mathbf{x} = \mathbf{u} + \mathbf{v}$. Show that $\mathbf{x} = \mathbf{v}_1 + \mathbf{u}_1$ implies $\mathbf{v}_1 = \mathbf{v}$ and $\mathbf{u}_1 = \mathbf{u}$.

4.7.14. Suppose $\mathbf{A}$ is symmetric. Prove: $(null(\mathbf{A}))^{\perp} = col(\mathbf{A})$ and $(col(\mathbf{A}))^{\perp} = \text{null}(\mathbf{A})$.

4.7.15. Show that the rows of the matrix $\mathbf{B}$ of Example 4.7.4 are solutions of $\mathbf{A}^T\mathbf{y} = \mathbf{0}$. From this fact, explain why the technique illustrated in this example yields $\mathbf{B}$ such that $null(\mathbf{B}) = col(\mathbf{A})$.

4.7.16. Let $\mathcal{V} \subseteq \mathcal{R}^n$ be a vector space and $\mathcal{S}$ the set of all vectors orthogonal to every vector in $\mathcal{V}$. Show, without reference to Theorem 4.7.1 or its corollary, that $\mathcal{S} = \mathcal{V}^{\perp}$.

4.8 ORTHOGONAL PROJECTIONS

The words "projection" and "projector" have well established meanings in ordinary speech. The fact that these terms are adopted for technical purposes suggests that we wish to incorporate some of this meaning into the definition. The projection of a vector into the x,y-plane is shown as the shadow cast by light rays perpendicular or oblique to the screen (the x,y-plane). Figure 4.6 displays a perpendicular projection. The perpendicular projection exhibits two properties which are the ones we wish to exploit: first, the projection of a vector lying in the plane is the vector itself—and this is true for oblique as well as perpendicular projections; and second, the difference between the object (the vector) and its image (the projection) is a vector perpendicular to the screen (the plane). Our understanding

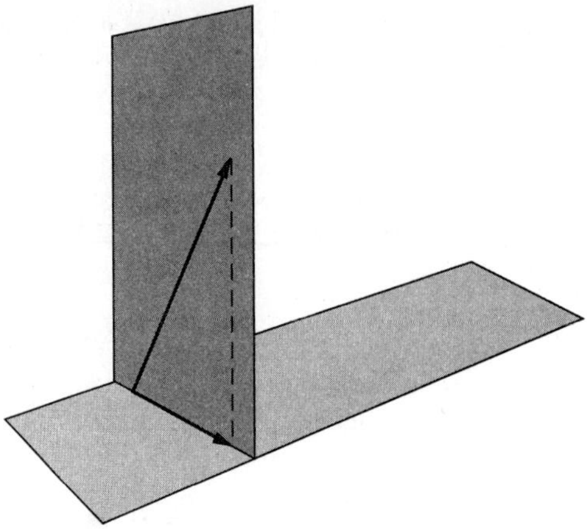

FIGURE 4-6
A perpendicular projection.

of projections suggests that the projection described in Fig. 4.6 is a single point if the vector is perpendicular to the x, y-plane. In the context of vector space theory, the projector is a matrix and the screen is its column space.

In Section 4.3 we defined the projection of **b** into a vector space $\mathcal{V}$ with emphasis on the projected vector. In this section our interest is centered on the operation that does the projection.

Definition 4.8.1. *A matrix* **P** *is a projector if for each* **b** *and* **z**

$$(a)\ \mathbf{P}(\mathbf{Pb}) = \mathbf{Pb} \qquad (4.8.1)$$
$$(b)\ (\mathbf{b} - \mathbf{Pb}) \perp \mathbf{Pz}$$

Property (a) is meant to capture the idea that the projection of a vector already on the screen is the vector itself, that is, **P** projects **Pb** into **Pb**. Property (b) is the orthogonality requirement; $\mathbf{b} - \mathbf{Pb}$ issorthogonal to all vectors in the column space of **P**. Thus, if **P** is a projector, $\mathbf{Pb} = \mathbf{b}_{\perp}$ is the projection of **b** into $col(\mathbf{P})$. (See Section 4.3.) The next theorem and its converse completely characterize projectors in terms of two algebraic properties: **P** must be symmetric and idempotent. (Some authors call **P** an orthogonal projector. Since we shall have no occasion to treat any other variety of projector, we can safely use the simpler appellation.)

Theorem 4.8.1. **P** *is a projector if and only if it has these properties:*

$$(a)\ \mathbf{P}^{\mathrm{T}} = \mathbf{P} \qquad (4.8.2)$$
$$(b)\ \mathbf{P}^2 = \mathbf{P}$$

Proof. Let **b** be an arbitrary vector and **P** a projector. By definition, $\mathbf{P}^2\mathbf{b} = \mathbf{Pb}$, and since this must hold for all **b**, it holds for $\mathbf{b} = \mathbf{e}_i$. But $\mathbf{P}^2\mathbf{e}_i = \mathbf{P}e_i$ shows that the ith columns of $\mathbf{P}^2$ and $\mathbf{P}$ are identical for each i. That is, $\mathbf{P}^2 = \mathbf{P}$. We now show that $\mathbf{P}$ is symmetric. A vector in the column space of $\mathbf{P}$ is given by $\mathbf{Pz}$ for some $\mathbf{z}$. By definition, $\mathbf{Pz} \perp (\mathbf{b} - \mathbf{Pb})$ for all $\mathbf{z}$ and all $\mathbf{b}$. So,

$$0 = (\mathbf{Pz})^{\mathrm{T}}(\mathbf{b} - \mathbf{Pb}) = \mathbf{z}^{\mathrm{T}}(\mathbf{P}^{\mathrm{T}} - \mathbf{P}^{\mathrm{T}}\mathbf{P})\mathbf{b}$$

By choosing $\mathbf{z} = \mathbf{e}_i$ and $\mathbf{b} = \mathbf{e}_j$, it follows that the (i, j) entry of $\mathbf{P}^{\mathrm{T}} - \mathbf{P}^{\mathrm{T}}\mathbf{P}$ is zero and, hence, $\mathbf{P}^{\mathrm{T}} - \mathbf{P}^{\mathrm{T}}\mathbf{P} = \mathbf{O}$. Therefore, $\mathbf{P}^{\mathrm{T}} = \mathbf{P}^{\mathrm{T}}\mathbf{P}$. Since $\mathbf{P}^{\mathrm{T}}\mathbf{P}$ is symmetric, so is $\mathbf{P}^{\mathrm{T}}$ and so is $\mathbf{P}$.

Now the converse. Assume that $\mathbf{P}$ satisfies Eq. 4.8.2. Two facts must be shown: first, $\mathbf{P}(\mathbf{Pb}) = \mathbf{Pb}$ for each $\mathbf{b}$, and, second, that $< \mathbf{Pz}, \mathbf{b} - \mathbf{Pb} >= 0$ for all $\mathbf{z}$ and all $\mathbf{b}$. The former is an immediate consequence of Eq. 4.8.2(b). The latter follows because $\mathbf{P}^2 = \mathbf{P}$ and $\mathbf{P}^{\mathrm{T}} = \mathbf{P}$ imply

$$< \mathbf{Pz}, \mathbf{b} - \mathbf{Pb} > = (\mathbf{Pz})^{\mathrm{T}}(\mathbf{b} - \mathbf{Pb}) = \mathbf{z}^{\mathrm{T}}(\mathbf{Pb} - \mathbf{P}^2\mathbf{b}) = \mathbf{z}^{\mathrm{T}}\mathbf{0} = 0. \blacksquare$$

If $\mathbf{P}$ is nonsingular, $\mathbf{P}^2 = \mathbf{P}$ implies that $\mathbf{P} = \mathbf{I}$ since we can multiply both sides by $\mathbf{P}^{-1}$. So the only interesting projectors are those that are singular and not $\mathbf{O}$. ($\mathbf{O}$ is the trivial projector.)

Example 4.8.1. Show that these matrices are projectors: (a) $\mathbf{QQ}^{\mathrm{T}}$, where $\mathbf{Q}$ an orthonormal matrix. (b) $\mathbf{I} - \mathbf{P}$, where $\mathbf{P}$ is a projector. (c) $\mathbf{J}_n/n$.

Solution. (a) The matrix $\mathbf{QQ}^{\mathrm{T}}$ is symmetric and $(\mathbf{QQ}^{\mathrm{T}})^{\mathrm{T}}(\mathbf{QQ}^{\mathrm{T}}) = \mathbf{QIQ}^{\mathrm{T}} = \mathbf{QQ}^{\mathrm{T}}$. By Theorem 4.8.1, $\mathbf{QQ}^{\mathrm{T}}$ is a projector. (b) $\mathbf{I} - \mathbf{P}$ is symmetric and $\mathbf{P}^2 = \mathbf{P}$ imply

$$(\mathbf{I} - \mathbf{P})(\mathbf{I} - \mathbf{P}) = \mathbf{I} - 2\mathbf{P} + \mathbf{P}^2 = \mathbf{I} - \mathbf{P}$$

Finally, to prove (c) note that $\mathbf{J}_n$ is symmetric and $\mathbf{J}_n^2 = n\mathbf{J}_n$ so that $(\mathbf{J}_n/n)^2 = \mathbf{J}_n/n$.

Example 4.8.2. The projector

$$\mathbf{P} = 1/9\begin{bmatrix} 5 & -4 & 2 \\ -4 & 5 & 2 \\ 2 & 2 & 8 \end{bmatrix}$$

projects the vector $\mathbf{b} = [\alpha \quad \beta \quad \gamma]^{\mathrm{T}}$ into the plane $z = 2x + 2y$. To see why note that

$$\mathbf{Pb} = 1/9\begin{bmatrix} 5 & -4 & 2 \\ -4 & 5 & 2 \\ 2 & 2 & 8 \end{bmatrix}\begin{bmatrix} \alpha \\ \beta \\ \gamma \end{bmatrix} = 1/9\begin{bmatrix} 5\alpha & - & 4\beta & + & 2\gamma \\ -4\alpha & + & 5\beta & + & 2\gamma \\ 2\alpha & + & 2\beta & + & 8\gamma \end{bmatrix} = \begin{bmatrix} x \\ y \\ z \end{bmatrix}$$

Now, verify

$$\begin{aligned} 2x + 2y &= \tfrac{2}{9}(5\alpha - 4\beta + 2\gamma) + \tfrac{2}{9}(-4\alpha + 5\beta + 2\gamma) \\ &= \tfrac{2}{9}(\alpha + \beta + 4\gamma) = z \end{aligned}$$

The vectors $\mathbf{b} = \beta[2 \quad 2 \quad -1]^{\mathrm{T}}$ lie along a line perpendicular to $z = 2x + 2y$ and this is confirmed by the computation $\mathbf{Pb} = \mathbf{0}$. The projector $\mathbf{I} - \mathbf{P}$ projects into the line spanned by $[2 \quad 2 \quad -1]^{\mathrm{T}}$.

Example 4.8.3. The orthonormal vectors

$$\mathbf{q}_1 = \frac{\sqrt{5}}{15}\begin{bmatrix} 5 \\ -4 \\ 2 \end{bmatrix}, \qquad \mathbf{q}_2 = \frac{\sqrt{5}}{5}\begin{bmatrix} 0 \\ 1 \\ 2 \end{bmatrix} \tag{4.8.3}$$

span the column space of the projector $\mathbf{P}$ of Example 4.8.2. (See Problem 4.8.10.) The projection of $\mathbf{b} = [1 \quad 1 \quad 1]^{\mathrm{T}}$ into this column space of $\mathbf{P}$ is given in Eq. 4.8.2, $\mathbf{Pb} = [1\ 1\ 4]^{\mathrm{T}}/3$. On the other hand, from Theorem 4.3.2, the projection of $\mathbf{b}$ onto a vector space spanned by an orthonormal basis is given by $\mathbf{b}_{\perp} = <\mathbf{b}, \mathbf{q}_1> \mathbf{q}_1 + <\mathbf{b}, \mathbf{q}_2> \mathbf{q}_2$; that is,

$$\mathbf{b}_{\perp} = <\begin{bmatrix} 1 \\ 1 \\ 1 \end{bmatrix}, \frac{\sqrt{5}}{15}\begin{bmatrix} 5 \\ -4 \\ 2 \end{bmatrix}> \left(\frac{\sqrt{5}}{15}\begin{bmatrix} 5 \\ -4 \\ 2 \end{bmatrix}\right) + <\begin{bmatrix} 1 \\ 1 \\ 1 \end{bmatrix}, \frac{\sqrt{5}}{5}\begin{bmatrix} 0 \\ 1 \\ 2 \end{bmatrix}> \left(\frac{\sqrt{5}}{5}\begin{bmatrix} 0 \\ 1 \\ 2 \end{bmatrix}\right)$$

$$= 1/15\begin{bmatrix} 5 \\ -4 \\ 2 \end{bmatrix} + 3/5\begin{bmatrix} 0 \\ 1 \\ 2 \end{bmatrix} = 1/3\begin{bmatrix} 1 \\ 1 \\ 4 \end{bmatrix} = \mathbf{Pb}$$

$\mathbf{QQ}^{\mathrm{T}}$ is a projector because it is a symmetric, idempotent matrix, and $\mathbf{QQ}^{\mathrm{T}}\mathbf{b}$ lies in $col(\mathbf{Q})$ since $\mathbf{Q}(\mathbf{Q}^{\mathrm{T}}\mathbf{b})) = \mathbf{QQ}^{\mathrm{T}}\mathbf{b}$. Finally, $\mathbf{QQ}^{\mathrm{T}}\mathbf{b} = \mathbf{b}_{\perp}$. (Equation 4.3.4 of Section 4.3.) On the other hand, the general projector $\mathbf{P}$ is not usually orthogonal. If $\mathbf{P}$ is a projector and an orthogonal matrix, then $\mathbf{P}$ is nonsingular, and, therefore, $\mathbf{P} = \mathbf{I}$. This case is uninteresting.

Deeper insight is gained into the nature of projectors by the fact that the column spaces of $\mathbf{P}$ and $\mathbf{I} - \mathbf{P}$ are complementary orthogonal subspaces. Example 4.8.2 shows this in a simple case. The result is true in general.

Theorem 4.8.2. *For every projector* $\mathbf{P}$, $(col(\mathbf{P}))^{\perp} = col(\mathbf{I} - \mathbf{P})$.

Proof. Since $\mathbf{P}$ is symmetric, its row space and column space are identical. So, by Theorem 4.7.1, $(col(\mathbf{P}))^{\perp} = (row(\mathbf{P}))^{\perp} = null(\mathbf{P})$. Thus, all that is needed is to show that $null(\mathbf{P}) = col(\mathbf{I} - \mathbf{P})$. To do this, assume that $\mathbf{p} \in col(\mathbf{I} - \mathbf{P})$. Then, there exists a vector $\mathbf{z}$ such that $(\mathbf{I} - \mathbf{P})\mathbf{z} = \mathbf{p}$. Multiplying this equation by $\mathbf{P}$ yields $\mathbf{P}(\mathbf{I} - \mathbf{P})\mathbf{z} = \mathbf{Pp}$. However,

$$\mathbf{P}(\mathbf{I} - \mathbf{P})\mathbf{z} = (\mathbf{P} - \mathbf{P}^2)\mathbf{z} = \mathbf{0}$$

Thus, $\mathbf{Pp} = \mathbf{0}$ so $\mathbf{p} \in null(\mathbf{P})$. That is, $col(\mathbf{I} - \mathbf{P}) \subseteq null(\mathbf{P})$. Next, suppose $\mathbf{p}$ is in the null space of $\mathbf{P}$. Then $\mathbf{Pp} = \mathbf{0}$ and, therefore, $(\mathbf{I} - \mathbf{P})\mathbf{p} = \mathbf{p} - \mathbf{Pp} = \mathbf{p}$. This shows that $\mathbf{p} \in col(\mathbf{I} - \mathbf{P})$. Hence, $null(\mathbf{P}) \subseteq col(\mathbf{I} - \mathbf{P})$. Therefore, $null(\mathbf{P}) = col(\mathbf{I} - \mathbf{P})$. ■

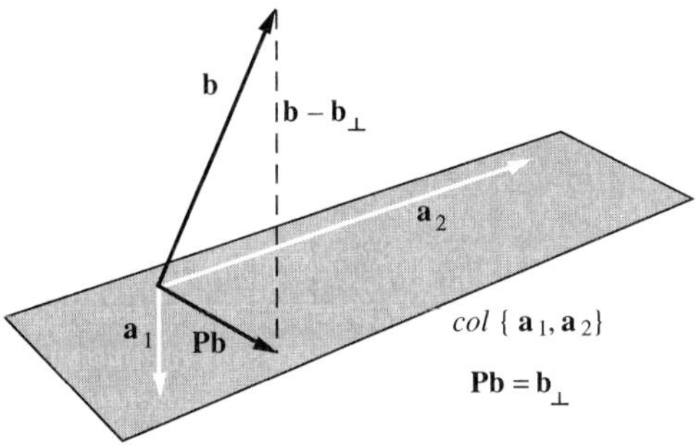

FIGURE 4-7
The projection of **b** into *col*(**A**).

Perhaps the most important reason for studying projections is that the projection provides a solution to the problem of finding the best approximation to **b** from vectors in *col*(**P**). See Fig. 4.7. The plane in this figure is meant to suggest the column space of **P**. It is geometrically obvious that the length of $\mathbf{b} - \mathbf{Pb}$ is less than or equal to the length of $\mathbf{b} - \mathbf{u}$ for any **u** in the plane. We can make all of this quite precise.

Theorem 4.8.3. *Let* **P** *be a projector and* **b** *an arbitrary vector. Then for each* $\mathbf{u} \in col(\mathbf{P})$,

$$\|\mathbf{b} - \mathbf{Pb}\| \leq \|\mathbf{b} - \mathbf{u}\| \tag{4.8.4}$$

Proof. Since **Pb** is a projection into *col*(**P**), this is Theorem 4.3.4 with a different notation. ■

The inequality in Eq. 4.8.4 can be interpreted as the solution to the following optimization problem: Find $\mathbf{u}_m \in \mathcal{V}$ such that $\|\mathbf{b} - \mathbf{u}\|$ is minimized for all $\mathbf{u} \in \mathcal{V}$. The solution is provided by Theorem 4.8.3. Choose $\mathbf{u}_m$ as the projection of **b** into $\mathcal{V}$, that is, $\mathbf{u}_m = \mathbf{Pb}$. To effect this solution numerically, find an orthonormal basis for $\mathcal{V}$, and let **Q** have this basis as its columns. Then $\mathbf{u} = \mathbf{QQ}^{\mathrm{T}}\mathbf{b}$, because $\mathbf{QQ}^{\mathrm{T}}$ projects **b** into $col(\mathbf{Q}) = \mathcal{V}$, and $\mathbf{u}_m = \mathbf{Pb} = \mathbf{QQ}^{\mathrm{T}}\mathbf{b}$ follows from Theorem 4.8.3. Note that $\mathbf{u}_m = \mathbf{b}$ if $\mathbf{b} \in \mathcal{V}$, by setting $\mathbf{u} = \mathbf{b}$ in Eq. 4.8.4.

Example 4.8.4. Find **u** in $span\{\mathbf{q}_1, \mathbf{q}_2, \mathbf{q}_3\}$ such that $\|\mathbf{b} - \mathbf{u}\|^2$ is minimal, where $\mathbf{b}$, $\mathbf{q}_1$, $\mathbf{q}_2$, and $\mathbf{q}_3$ are:

$$\mathbf{b} = \begin{bmatrix} 1 \\ 0 \\ 0 \\ 0 \end{bmatrix}, \qquad \mathbf{q}_1 = 1/2\begin{bmatrix} 1 \\ 1 \\ 1 \\ 1 \end{bmatrix}, \qquad \mathbf{q}_2 = 1/2\begin{bmatrix} 1 \\ -1 \\ -1 \\ 1 \end{bmatrix}, \qquad \mathbf{q}_3 = 1/2\begin{bmatrix} -1 \\ 1 \\ -1 \\ 1 \end{bmatrix}$$

Solution. Write

$$\mathbf{Q} = 1/2\begin{bmatrix} 1 & 1 & -1 \\ 1 & -1 & 1 \\ 1 & -1 & -1 \\ 1 & 1 & 1 \end{bmatrix}$$

and compute

$$\mathbf{u} = \mathbf{Q}\mathbf{Q}^{\mathrm{T}}\mathbf{b} = 1/2\begin{bmatrix} 1 & 1 & -1 \\ 1 & -1 & 1 \\ 1 & -1 & -1 \\ 1 & 1 & 1 \end{bmatrix} 1/2\begin{bmatrix} 1 & 1 & 1 & 1 \\ 1 & -1 & -1 & 1 \\ -1 & 1 & -1 & 1 \end{bmatrix}\begin{bmatrix} 1 \\ 0 \\ 0 \\ 0 \end{bmatrix}$$

$$= 1/4\begin{bmatrix} 1 & 1 & -1 \\ 1 & -1 & 1 \\ 1 & -1 & -1 \\ 1 & 1 & 1 \end{bmatrix}\begin{bmatrix} 1 \\ 1 \\ -1 \end{bmatrix} = 1/4\begin{bmatrix} 3 \\ -1 \\ 1 \\ 1 \end{bmatrix}$$

4.8.1 Reflectors

By analogy with "projector" and "projection" we wish to construct a matrix **R** which reflects **b** in $\mathcal{V}$. Figure 4.8 provides a geometric motivation for the definition of the reflection of **b** with respect to $\mathcal{V} = col(\mathbf{P})$.

$$(\mathbf{b} - \mathbf{Rb}) = 2(\mathbf{b} - \mathbf{Pb})$$

Indeed, we make this our definition: if **P** is a projector, call **R** a *reflector relative to col*(**P**) if $(\mathbf{I} - \mathbf{R}) = 2(\mathbf{I} - \mathbf{P})$, or equivalently, if

$$\mathbf{R} = 2\mathbf{P} - \mathbf{I} \tag{4.8.5}$$

We call $\mathbf{b}_R = \mathbf{Rb}$ the *reflection of* **b** *in col*(**P**).

Theorem 4.8.4. *Reflectors are symmetric, orthogonal matrices.*

Proof. It is obvious from the definition that **R** is symmetric. That **R** is orthogonal follows from

$$\mathbf{R}^{\mathrm{T}}\mathbf{R} = \mathbf{R}^2 = (2\mathbf{P} - \mathbf{I})^2 = \mathbf{I} - 4\mathbf{P} + 4\mathbf{P}^2 = \mathbf{I} \ \blacksquare$$

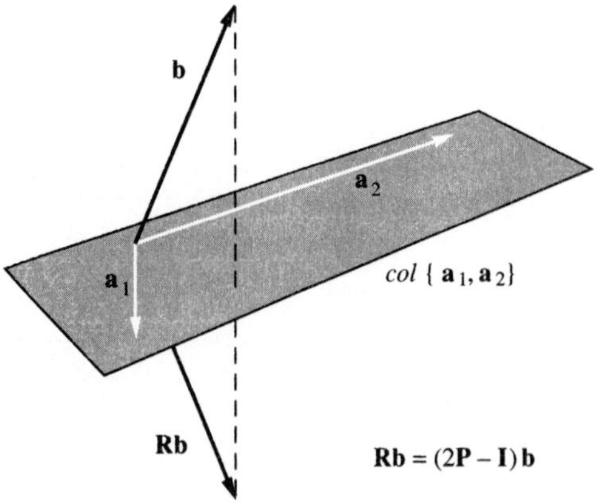

FIGURE 4-8
Reflection of **b** relative to $\mathcal{V} = col(\mathbf{P})$.

Our intuition suggests that the reflection of $\mathbf{b}_R$ should be $\mathbf{b}$ and the reflection of a vector in $col(\mathbf{P})$ is itself. Both conjectures are true.

Example 4.8.5. Show that

(*a*) $\mathbf{Rb}_R = \mathbf{b}$
(*b*) $\mathbf{b} \in col(\mathbf{P})$ implies $\mathbf{b}_R = \mathbf{b}$

Solution. (*a*) $\mathbf{Rb}_R = \mathbf{R}^2\mathbf{b} = \mathbf{Ib} = \mathbf{b}$. (*b*) If $\mathbf{b} \in col(\mathbf{P})$, then $\mathbf{Pb} = \mathbf{b}$ and, from Eq. 4.8.5, it follows that

$$\mathbf{b}_R = (2\mathbf{P} - \mathbf{I})\mathbf{b} = (2\mathbf{Pb} - \mathbf{b}) = 2\mathbf{b} - \mathbf{b} = \mathbf{b}$$

Remarks. (1) Part (*a*) of Example 4.8.5 shows that the reflection of a reflection is itself, and Part (*b*) shows that the reflection of an object in the "mirror" is also itself. Both results confirm our usage of reflector to describe the effects of $\mathbf{R}$. (2) We have defined reflectors relative to $\mathcal{V}$ if $\mathcal{V}$ is the column space of some projector. For an arbitrary vector space $\mathcal{V} \neq \{\mathbf{0}\} \subseteq \mathcal{R}^n$, the projector relative to $\mathcal{V}$ can be found by first constructing an orthonormal basis for $\mathcal{V}$, say $\{\mathbf{q}_1, \mathbf{q}_2, \ldots, \mathbf{q}_k\}$ and setting $\mathbf{Q} = [\mathbf{q}_1 \quad \mathbf{q}_2 \quad \ldots \quad \mathbf{q}_k]$. Then $\mathcal{V} = col(\mathbf{Q})$ and $\mathbf{P} = \mathbf{QQ}^\mathrm{T}$ is a projector into $\mathcal{V}$. Now set $\mathbf{R} = 2\mathbf{QQ}^\mathrm{T} - \mathbf{I}$. Then $\mathbf{R}$ is a reflector relative to $\mathcal{V}$.

Example 4.8.6. Suppose $\mathbf{R}$ is a projector relative to $col(\mathbf{P})$, show that $-\mathbf{R}$ is a reflector relative to $col(\mathbf{I} - \mathbf{P})$.

Solution. Consider the reflector $\mathbf{R}' = 2(\mathbf{I} - \mathbf{P}) - \mathbf{I}$ relative to the column space of $\mathbf{I} - \mathbf{P}$. Then $\mathbf{R}' = \mathbf{I} - 2\mathbf{P} = -\mathbf{R}$.

One of the more useful reflectors is the Householder matrix $\mathbf{R} = \mathbf{I} - 2\mathbf{uu}^\mathrm{T} = -(2\mathbf{uu}^\mathrm{T} - \mathbf{I})$, where $\|\mathbf{u}\| = 1$ so that $\mathbf{uu}^\mathrm{T}$ is a projector. Hence, by Example 4.8.6, $\mathbf{I} - 2\mathbf{uu}^\mathrm{T}$ is a reflector relative to $\mathbf{I} - \mathbf{uu}^\mathrm{T}$. (Note that if $\mathbf{P} = \mathbf{uu}^\mathrm{T}$, then $\mathbf{I} - \mathbf{P} = \mathbf{I} - \mathbf{uu}^\mathrm{T}$.) Theorem 4.9.3 provides a reflector relative to $col(\mathbf{A})$.

PROBLEMS

PART 1

In the next four Problems, let $\mathbf{b}$, $\mathbf{q}_1$, $\mathbf{q}_2$, and $\mathbf{q}_3$ be defined as in Example 4.8.4.

4.8.1. Find $\mathbf{u}_m$ in $span\{\mathbf{q}_1, \mathbf{q}_2\}$. ($\mathbf{u}_m$ minimizes $\|\mathbf{b} - \mathbf{u}\|$ for $\mathbf{u} \in span\{\mathbf{q}_1, \mathbf{q}_2\}$.) Compare $\|\mathbf{u}_m\|$ with the answer obtained in Example 4.8.4.

4.8.2. Repeat Problem 4.8.1 except use $span\{\mathbf{q}_1, \mathbf{q}_3\}$.

4.8.3. Repeat Problem 4.8.1 except use $span\{\mathbf{q}_2, \mathbf{q}_3\}$.

4.8.4. Let $\mathbf{Q} = [\mathbf{q}_1 \quad \mathbf{q}_2]$. Compute $\mathbf{P} = \mathbf{QQ}^\mathrm{T}$ and $\mathbf{I} - \mathbf{P}$.

4.8.5. List all the projectors, $\mathbf{P}_{2\times 2}$.

4.8.6. Show directly that $\mathbf{J}_2/2$ and $\mathbf{J}_3/3$ are projectors. Find the orthogonal complements of $col(\mathbf{J}_2)$ and $col(\mathbf{J}_3)$.

4.8.7. Construct a matrix which projects $\mathbf{b} \in \mathcal{R}^3$ into the x,z-plane.

4.8.8. Construct a matrix which projects $\mathbf{b} \in \mathcal{R}^3$ into the y-axis. Compare the matrix in this problem with the answer to Problem 4.8.7.

4.8.9. Construct a matrix which projects $\mathbf{b} \in \mathcal{R}^3$ into the line passing through the origin and the point (1,1,1).

4.8.10. For $\mathbf{q}_1$, $\mathbf{q}_2$, and $\mathbf{P}$ of Example 4.8.3, show that $span\{\mathbf{q}_1, \mathbf{q}_2\}$ is the column space of $\mathbf{P}$ by showing that these column spaces are the plane $z = 2x + 2y$.

PART 2

4.8.11. Suppose $\mathbf{P}_1$ and $\mathbf{P}_2$ are projectors. Is $\mathbf{P}_1\mathbf{P}_2$ a projector? What happens if we add the hypothesis, $\mathbf{P}_1\mathbf{P}_2 = \mathbf{P}_2\mathbf{P}_1$? Explain.

4.8.12. Suppose $\mathbf{P}_1$ and $\mathbf{P}_2$ are projectors and $\mathbf{P}_1\mathbf{P}_2 = -\mathbf{P}_2\mathbf{P}_1$, then $\mathbf{P}_1+\mathbf{P}_2$ is a projector. Prove this assertion.

4.8.13. If $\mathbf{P}$ is a projector, show that $2\mathbf{P} - \mathbf{I}$ is an orthogonal matrix.

4.8.14. Show that $\mathbf{u}\mathbf{u}^{\mathrm{T}}$ is a projector if and only if $\|\mathbf{u}\| = 1$.

4.8.15. Show that an orthogonal matrix which is also a projector must be $\mathbf{I}$.

4.8.16. Show that $\mathbf{U}\mathbf{U}^{\mathrm{T}}$ is a projector if and only if $\mathbf{U}^{\mathrm{T}}\mathbf{U}$ is a projector. Here is an example:

$$\mathbf{U}^{\mathrm{T}} = 1/3\begin{bmatrix} 1 & -2 & 2 \\ -2 & 1 & 2 \end{bmatrix}$$

4.8.17. If $\mathbf{P}$ is a projector, show that $(null(\mathbf{P}))^{\perp} = null(\mathbf{I} - \mathbf{P})$.

4.8.18. Find the projector which projects $\mathbf{b} \in \mathcal{R}^3$ into the plane given by $x + y + z = 0$.

4.8.19. Let $\mathbf{P}$ be the projector given in Example 4.8.2. Find $2\mathbf{P} - \mathbf{I}$ and sketch $\mathbf{b}$ and $(2\mathbf{P} - \mathbf{I})\mathbf{b}$, where $\mathbf{b} = [1\ 0\ 1]^{\mathrm{T}}$.

4.8.20. Let $\mathbf{R}$ be a reflector. Show that $(\mathbf{I} \pm \mathbf{R})/2$ are projectors.

4.9 THE NORMAL EQUATIONS AND PROJECTIONS INTO COL(A)

Suppose the system $\mathbf{Ax} = \mathbf{b}$ is inconsistent so that $\mathbf{b} \notin col(\mathbf{A})$ and for each $\mathbf{x}$, $\|\mathbf{b} - \mathbf{Ax}\| > 0$. Define $\mathbf{r} = \mathbf{b} - \mathbf{Ax}$ and call this the *residual vector* and its norm, $r = \|\mathbf{r}\|$, the *residual*. The residual is a measure of the "closeness" of a given $\mathbf{x}$ to a solution; it is a nonnegative function of $\mathbf{x}$ and is always positive for inconsistent systems. We show here that there is a unique $\mathbf{x} \in \mathcal{R}^n$, written $\mathbf{x}_m$, which minimizes the residual. In fact, $\mathbf{x}_m$ is the solution of $\mathbf{Ax} = \mathbf{b}_\perp$, where $\mathbf{b}_\perp$ is the projection of $\mathbf{b}$ into $col(\mathbf{A})$ and the minimum residual, r_m, is given by $r_m = \|\mathbf{b} - \mathbf{Ax}_m\|$. In the previous section, $\mathbf{b}_\perp$ was found by constructing an orthonormal basis for $col(\mathbf{A})$. In this section, we find this projection without computing an orthonormal basis.

Assume that $\mathbf{Ax} = \mathbf{b}$ is inconsistent and that $\mathbf{A}$ has full column rank. This guarantees that $\mathbf{A}$ has at least as many rows as columns. The system,

$$\mathbf{A}^{\mathrm{T}}\mathbf{Ax} = \mathbf{A}^{\mathrm{T}}\mathbf{b} \tag{4.9.1}$$

is called the *normal equations corresponding* to $\mathbf{Ax} = \mathbf{b}$. As we shall prove, the solution to the normal equations is unique and more importantly, it minimizes the residual.

Theorem 4.9.1. *If* $\mathbf{A}$ *has full column rank, then the normal equations have a unique solution* $\mathbf{x}_m$ *and* $\mathbf{Ax}_m$ *is the projection of* $\mathbf{b}$ *into* $col(\mathbf{A})$. *Moreover, for all* $\mathbf{x}$,

$$r_m = \|\mathbf{b} - \mathbf{Ax}_m\| \leq \|\mathbf{b} - \mathbf{Ax}\| \tag{4.9.2}$$

Proof. By the QR factorization theorem, $\mathbf{A} = \mathbf{QR}$, $\mathbf{R}$ is nonsingular and $col(\mathbf{A}) = col(\mathbf{Q})$. Also, $\mathbf{Q} = \mathbf{AR}^{-1}$ and $\mathbf{A}^{\mathrm{T}}\mathbf{A} = \mathbf{R}^{\mathrm{T}}\mathbf{Q}^{\mathrm{T}}\mathbf{QR} = \mathbf{R}^{\mathrm{T}}\mathbf{R}$. Given $\mathbf{b}$, it follows from Eq. 4.3.5 that

$$\mathbf{b}_{\perp} = \mathbf{QQ}^{\mathrm{T}}\mathbf{b} = \mathbf{AR}^{-1}\mathbf{R}^{-\mathrm{T}}\mathbf{A}^{\mathrm{T}}\mathbf{b} = \mathbf{A}(\mathbf{R}^{\mathrm{T}}\mathbf{R})^{-1}\mathbf{A}^{\mathrm{T}}\mathbf{b} = \mathbf{A}(\mathbf{A}^{\mathrm{T}}\mathbf{A})^{-1}\mathbf{A}^{\mathrm{T}}\mathbf{b} \tag{4.9.3}$$

On the other hand, Eq. 4.9.1 has the unique solution $\mathbf{x}_m = (\mathbf{A}^{\mathrm{T}}\mathbf{A})^{-1}\mathbf{A}^{\mathrm{T}}\mathbf{b}$. (This solution exists and is unique because $(\mathbf{A}^{\mathrm{T}}\mathbf{A})^{-1}$ exists. Note that $\mathbf{A}$ need not be square so that neither $\mathbf{A}$ nor $\mathbf{A}^{\mathrm{T}}$ have inverses.) Substituting $\mathbf{x}_m$ into Eq. 4.9.3 leads to $\mathbf{b}_{\perp} = \mathbf{Ax}_m$. For each $\mathbf{x}$, $\mathbf{Ax}$ is in $col(\mathbf{A})$ and, therefore, Eq. 4.9.2 follows from Theorem 4.8.3. ■

Corollary 1. $r_m = 0$ *if and only if* $\mathbf{b}_{\perp} = \mathbf{b}$.

Proof. If $\mathbf{b}_{\perp} = \mathbf{b}$ then $\mathbf{x}_m = \mathbf{b}$ and $r_m = 0$ from Eq. 4.9.2. Conversely, if $r_m = \|\mathbf{b} - \mathbf{Ax}_m\| = 0$, $\mathbf{b} - \mathbf{Ax}_m = \mathbf{0}$ and, therefore, $\mathbf{b} = \mathbf{Ax}_m = \mathbf{b}_{\perp}$. ■

Corollary 2. $r_m^2 = \min\|\mathbf{b} - \mathbf{Ax}\|^2 = \|\mathbf{b}\|^2 - \|\mathbf{Ax}_m\|^2$ (4.9.4)

Proof. Consider the identity $\|\mathbf{b}\|^2 = \|(\mathbf{b}-\mathbf{b}_{\perp})+\mathbf{b}_{\perp}\|^2$. By definition of projection, $(\mathbf{b}-\mathbf{b}_{\perp})$ is orthogonal to $\mathbf{b}_{\perp}$ since $(\mathbf{b}-\mathbf{b}_{\perp})$ is orthogonal to all vectors in $col(\mathbf{A})$ and $\mathbf{b}_{\perp} \in col(\mathbf{A})$. Hence, by the Pythagorean theorem,

$$\|\mathbf{b}\|^2 = \|(\mathbf{b} - \mathbf{b}_{\perp}) + \mathbf{b}_{\perp}\|^2 = \|(\mathbf{b} - \mathbf{b}_{\perp})\|^2 + \|\mathbf{b}_{\perp}\|^2 \tag{4.9.5}$$

By Theorem 4.9.1, $r_m = \|(\mathbf{b} - \mathbf{b}_{\perp}\|^2 = \min\|(\mathbf{b} - \mathbf{Ax}\|^2$ and $\mathbf{Ax}_m = \mathbf{b}_{\perp}$. Using these facts, Eq. 4.9.5 is Eq. 4.9.4. ■

The proof of Theorem 4.9.1 does more than simply show that there is a solution to the normal equations, it provides an answer to the question of finding the projection of $\mathbf{b}$ onto $col(\mathbf{A})$ when $\mathbf{A}$ is not orthogonal.

Theorem 4.9.2. *Let* $\mathcal{V} \subseteq \mathcal{R}^n$ *be a vector space and* $\{\mathbf{a}_1,\mathbf{a}_2,\ldots,\mathbf{a}_k\}$ *be a basis for* $\mathcal{V}$. *Define* $\mathbf{A} = [\mathbf{a}_1 \ \ \mathbf{a}_2 \ \ \ldots \ \ \mathbf{a}_k]$. *Then the projection of* $\mathbf{b}$ *into* $\mathcal{V}$ *is the vector in* $\mathcal{V}$ *given by*

$$\mathbf{b}_{\perp} = \mathbf{A}(\mathbf{A}^{\mathrm{T}}\mathbf{A})^{-1}\mathbf{A}^{\mathrm{T}}\mathbf{b} \tag{4.9.6}$$

Proof. The conclusion has already been established. ■

An alternative argument consists of showing that $\mathbf{A}(\mathbf{A}^{\mathrm{T}}\mathbf{A})^{-1}\mathbf{A}^{\mathrm{T}}$ is a projection matrix and that it projects $\mathbf{b}$ into $col(\mathbf{A})$.

Theorem 4.9.3. *If* $\mathbf{A}$ *has full column rank, then*

(*a*) $\mathbf{P} = \mathbf{A}(\mathbf{A}^{\mathrm{T}}\mathbf{A})^{-1}\mathbf{A}^{\mathrm{T}}$ is a projector into $col(\mathbf{A})$ and
(*b*) $\mathbf{R} = 2\mathbf{A}(\mathbf{A}^{\mathrm{T}}\mathbf{A})^{-1}\mathbf{A}^{\mathrm{T}} - \mathbf{I}$ is a reflector relative to $col(\mathbf{A})$

Proof. The details of showing that $\mathbf{P}$ is symmetric and $\mathbf{P}^2 = \mathbf{P}$ is left for Problem 4.9.15. Since $\mathbf{Pb} = \mathbf{A}\left((\mathbf{A}^T\mathbf{A})^{-1}\mathbf{A}^T\mathbf{b}\right)$, $\mathbf{Pb} \in col(\mathbf{A})$ and this proves that $\mathbf{P}$ projects into $col(\mathbf{A})$. Part (*b*) follows from the definition of reflector, Eq. 4.8.5, and because $\mathbf{R} = 2\mathbf{P} - \mathbf{I}$. ■

In the terminology of Section 3.8, $\mathbf{b}_\perp = \mathbf{A}\mathbf{x}_m$ shows that $\mathbf{x}_m$ is the coordinate vector of $\mathbf{b}_\perp$ relative to the basis $\{\mathbf{a}_1, \mathbf{a}_2, \ldots, \mathbf{a}_k\}$ of $col(\mathbf{A})$. Indeed, the derivation of $\mathbf{b}_\perp = \mathbf{A}\mathbf{x}_m$ from the $\mathbf{QR}$ factorization theorem is precisely the computation that relates the coordinate vector $\mathbf{Q}^T\mathbf{b}$ of $\mathbf{b}_\perp$ relative to columns of $\mathbf{Q}$ to the coordinate vector $\mathbf{A}\mathbf{x}_m$ of $\mathbf{b}_\perp$ relative to the columns of $\mathbf{A}$. In this interpretation, $\mathbf{A} = \mathbf{QR}$ is the formula $\mathbf{W} = \mathbf{VS}$ of Section 3.8. (See Lemma 3.1 and Theorem 3.8.3.)

Example 4.9.1. Find the projection of $\mathbf{b}$ into $span\{\mathbf{a}_1, \mathbf{a}_2\}$, where

$$\mathbf{b} = \begin{bmatrix} 0 \\ 4 \\ 2 \\ 4 \end{bmatrix}, \qquad \mathbf{a}_1 = \begin{bmatrix} 1 \\ 1 \\ 1 \\ 1 \end{bmatrix}, \qquad \mathbf{a}_2 = \begin{bmatrix} -1 \\ 0 \\ 1 \\ 2 \end{bmatrix}$$

Solution. Construct $\mathbf{b}_\perp$ from Eq. 4.9.6 as follows:

$$\mathbf{A} = \begin{bmatrix} 1 & -1 \\ 1 & 0 \\ 1 & 1 \\ 1 & 2 \end{bmatrix} \qquad \mathbf{A}^T\mathbf{A} = \begin{bmatrix} 1 & 1 & 1 & 1 \\ -1 & 0 & 1 & 2 \end{bmatrix} \begin{bmatrix} 1 & -1 \\ 1 & 0 \\ 1 & 1 \\ 1 & 2 \end{bmatrix} = \begin{bmatrix} 4 & 2 \\ 2 & 6 \end{bmatrix}$$

$$\mathbf{A}^T\mathbf{b} = \begin{bmatrix} 1 & 1 & 1 & 1 \\ -1 & 0 & 1 & 2 \end{bmatrix} \begin{bmatrix} 0 \\ 4 \\ 2 \\ 4 \end{bmatrix} = \begin{bmatrix} 1 & 0 \\ 1 & 0 \end{bmatrix}$$

Therefore,

$$\mathbf{b}_\perp = \mathbf{A}(\mathbf{A}^T\mathbf{A})^{-1}\mathbf{A}^T\mathbf{b} = \begin{bmatrix} 1 & -1 \\ 1 & 0 \\ 1 & 1 \\ 1 & 2 \end{bmatrix} \begin{bmatrix} 4 & 2 \\ 2 & 6 \end{bmatrix}^{-1} \begin{bmatrix} 1 & 0 \\ 1 & 0 \end{bmatrix} = \begin{bmatrix} 1 & -1 \\ 1 & 0 \\ 1 & 1 \\ 1 & 2 \end{bmatrix} \begin{bmatrix} 2 \\ 1 \end{bmatrix} = \begin{bmatrix} 1 \\ 2 \\ 3 \\ 4 \end{bmatrix}$$

Note that $\mathbf{x}_m = (\mathbf{A}^T\mathbf{A})^{-1}\mathbf{A}^T\mathbf{b} = [2\ 1]^T$.

In Problem 4.9.2, the task is set to find an orthonormal basis for $span\{\mathbf{a}_1, \mathbf{a}_2\}$ and use Corollary 2 of Theorem 4.9.2 in place of Eq. 4.9.8 to compute $\mathbf{b}_\perp$.

Example 4.9.2. Find a projector $\mathbf{P}$ which projects $\mathbf{x} \in \mathfrak{R}^3$ into the plane $x + y + z = 0$.

Solution. Construct $\mathbf{A}$ so that $col(\mathbf{A})$ is the set of vectors lying in the given plane. To do this, first find a basis for the vectors whose entries satisfy $z = -x - y$. Since

$$\begin{bmatrix} x \\ y \\ z \end{bmatrix} = \begin{bmatrix} x \\ y \\ -x-y \end{bmatrix} = \begin{bmatrix} x \\ 0 \\ -x \end{bmatrix} = \begin{bmatrix} 0 \\ y \\ -y \end{bmatrix} = x\begin{bmatrix} 1 \\ 0 \\ -1 \end{bmatrix} + y\begin{bmatrix} 0 \\ 1 \\ -1 \end{bmatrix}$$

The vectors $\mathbf{x}_1 = [1 \quad 0 \quad -1]^{\mathrm{T}}$ and $\mathbf{x}_2 = [0 \quad 1 \quad -1]^{\mathrm{T}}$ form a basis for all vectors of the form $[x \quad y \quad -x \quad -y]^{\mathrm{T}}$. Hence

$$\mathbf{A} = \begin{bmatrix} 1 & 0 \\ 0 & 1 \\ -1 & -1 \end{bmatrix}$$

defines a matrix whose column space is the set of vectors lying in the given plane. Thus, from Theorem 4.9.3, $\mathbf{P} = \mathbf{A}(\mathbf{A}^{\mathrm{T}}\mathbf{A})^{-1}\mathbf{A}^{\mathrm{T}}$ is the required projector. After some elementary but tedious computation,

$$\mathbf{P} = 1/3\begin{bmatrix} 2 & -1 & -1 \\ -1 & 2 & -1 \\ -1 & -1 & 2 \end{bmatrix}$$

It is easy to verify that $\mathbf{P}$ is idempotent; it is clearly symmetric. The vector $\mathbf{y} = [2 \quad 3 \quad -5]^{\mathrm{T}}$ is in the given plane and $\mathbf{Py} = \mathbf{y}$ supports the contention that $\mathbf{P}$ projects into the plane $x + y + z = 0$. The vector $\mathbf{z} = [1\ 1\ 1]^{\mathrm{T}}$ is normal to this plane and $\mathbf{Pz} = \mathbf{0}$ as expected from a projector. Problems 4.9.5 and 4.9.6 investigate the related projector $\mathbf{I} - \mathbf{P}$.

4.9.1 MATLAB

We can use MATLAB to compute the projection of $\mathbf{b}$ into $col(\mathbf{A})$ by finding an orthonormal $\mathbf{Q}$ such that $col(\mathbf{A}) = col(\mathbf{Q})$. The command orth(A) accomplishes this end as we have seen in Section 4.5.1.

PROBLEMS

PART 1

4.9.1. (*a*) Consider the system

$$\begin{bmatrix} 1 & 1 \\ 1 & -1 \\ 2 & 0 \end{bmatrix}\begin{bmatrix} x \\ y \end{bmatrix} = \begin{bmatrix} 0 \\ 0 \\ 1 \end{bmatrix}$$

Show that $\|\mathbf{r}\|^2 = 6x^2 + 2y^2 - 4x + 1$ and hence deduce that $r_m^2 = 1/3$. Show that this minimum is obtained for $x = 1/3$, $y = 0$.

(*b*) Compute the solution of the normal equations corresponding to the system in Part(*a*).

(*c*) Verify that $r_m^2 = \|\mathbf{b}\|^2 - \|\mathbf{Ax}_m\|^2$.

4.9.2. Repeat Problem 4.9.1, except use $\mathbf{b} = [1 \quad 1 \quad 1]^{\mathrm{T}}$.

4.9.3. Repeat Problem 4.9.1, except use $\mathbf{b} = [1 \quad 0 \quad 1]^{\mathrm{T}}$. Show that $r_m = 0$ and explain why this implies that $\mathbf{b} \in col(\mathbf{A})$.

4.9.4. Find the projection of $\mathbf{b} = [1 \;\; -1 \;\; 1]^{\mathrm{T}}$ into the column space of

$$\mathbf{A} = \begin{bmatrix} 1 & 1 \\ 1 & -1 \\ 2 & 0 \end{bmatrix}$$

by computing the related projector, $\mathbf{P} = \mathbf{A}(\mathbf{A}^{\mathrm{T}}\mathbf{A})^{-1}\mathbf{A}^{\mathrm{T}}$.

4.9.5. Verify the computation of $\mathbf{P}$ of Example 4.9.2. Describe the vector space into which $\mathbf{I} - \mathbf{P}$ projects $\mathbf{x} \in \mathcal{R}^3$.

4.9.6. Find the projection of $\mathbf{x} = [1 \;\; -1 \;\; 0]^{\mathrm{T}}$ into the plane of $x + y + z = 0$. What does your answer say about $\mathbf{x}$ and its relation to the given plane?

4.9.7. Find the distance between the point (1,1,1) and the plane $x + y + z = 0$ by using the results of Example 4.9.2 and the fact that the distance from a point to a plane is the length of the perpendicular from the point to the plane.

4.9.8. Find an orthonormal basis for the vectors in the plane, $x + y + z = 0$. Let $\mathbf{Q}$ be the matrix whose columns are the orthonormal vectors comprising the basis. Compute $\mathbf{Q}\mathbf{Q}^{\mathrm{T}}$, verify that it is a projector and compare with $\mathbf{P}$ given in Example 4.9.2.

4.9.9. Find an orthonormal basis for $col(\mathbf{A})$, where $\mathbf{A}$ is the matrix of Example 4.9.1. Now use Eq. 4.3.5 to find $\mathbf{b}_{\perp}$ and compare with the answer given in Example 4.9.1.

4.9.10. Find a projector $\mathbf{P}$ which projects $\mathbf{x} \in \mathcal{R}^2$ into the line $y = x$. Onto what line does $\mathbf{I} - \mathbf{P}$ project? Find the projections of $\mathbf{e}_1$ and $\mathbf{e}_2$ by $\mathbf{P}$. On the same graph, sketch the vectors $\mathbf{e}_1$, $\mathbf{e}_2$, the line $y = x$, and their projections by $\mathbf{P}$. Do the same for the projector $\mathbf{I} - \mathbf{P}$.

4.9.11. Find a projector $\mathbf{P}$ which projects $\mathbf{x} \in \mathcal{R}^3$ into the line, $y = x = z$. Show that $\mathbf{I} - \mathbf{P}$ projects $\mathbf{x}$ into a plane. Find the Cartesian equations of this plane and a line normal to it passing through the origin.

PART 2

4.9.12. What are the normal equations corresponding to the invertible matrix $\mathbf{A}$? Find $\mathbf{x}_m$ and r_m.

4.9.13. Suppose $\mathbf{e}_i \in \mathcal{R}^n$. Find the normal equations corresponding to the system $[\mathbf{e}_1 \;\; \mathbf{e}_2 \;\; \ldots \;\; \mathbf{e}_k]\mathbf{x} = \mathbf{b}$ where $k < n$; also, determine $\mathbf{x}_m$ and r_m.

4.9.14. (*a*) If $\mathbf{A}_{m\times n}$ and $m \neq n$ has full column rank, show that $\mathbf{A}\mathbf{A}^{\mathrm{T}}$ is singular.
(*b*) If $\mathbf{A}$ has full column rank and is square, show that $\mathbf{A}\mathbf{A}^{\mathrm{T}}$ is invertible.

4.9.15. Show that $\mathbf{A}(\mathbf{A}^{\mathrm{T}}\mathbf{A})^{-1}\mathbf{A}^{\mathrm{T}}$ is a projector.

PART 3

4.9.16. Let $\mathbf{1} \in \mathcal{R}^n$, $\mathbf{a} \neq \mathbf{0} \in \mathcal{R}^n$, $\mathbf{T} = [\mathbf{1} \;\; \mathbf{a}]$, $\Sigma a_i = 0$ and $S = \Sigma a_i^2 \neq 0$. Find the normal equations corresponding to the system $\mathbf{T}\mathbf{x} = \mathbf{e}_i$. Find $\mathbf{x}_m$ and r_m.

4.9.17. Repeat Problem 4.9.15 except that $\mathbf{T} = [\mathbf{1} \;\; \mathbf{a} \;\; \mathbf{c}]$, $\Sigma c_i = 0$ and $\mathbf{a}^{\mathrm{T}}\mathbf{c} = 0$. What are the normal equations if $\mathbf{a}^{\mathrm{T}}\mathbf{c} = 1$?

4.9.18. (*a*) Show that $<\mathbf{c} - \mathbf{d}, \mathbf{c} - \mathbf{d}> = (\|\mathbf{c}\| - \|\mathbf{d}\|)^2 + 2(\|\mathbf{c}\|\,\|\mathbf{d}\| - <\mathbf{c}, \mathbf{d}>)$.
(*b*) What theorem asserts that $\|\mathbf{c}\|\,\|\mathbf{d}\| - <\mathbf{c}, \mathbf{d}>$ is always nonnegative?
(*c*) Now set $\mathbf{c} = \mathbf{b}$, $\mathbf{d} = \mathbf{A}\mathbf{x}_m$. Show that $\|\mathbf{c}\|\,\|\mathbf{d}\| - <\mathbf{c}, \mathbf{d}> = 0$ and thereby offer an alternative proof for Corollary 2 of Theorem 4.9.1.

4.9.19. Let **A** be $m \times n$, $m \geq n$ and suppose **A** has full column rank. Define $r^2(\mathbf{x}) = \|\mathbf{b} - \mathbf{A}\mathbf{x}\|^2$.

(*a*) Show that $r^2 = \sum_{i=1}^{m} \left(b_i - \sum_{j=1}^{n} a_{ij} x_j\right)^2$.

(*b*) Find $\partial r / \partial x_j$ for $j = 1, 2, \ldots, n$.

(*c*) Show that $\partial r / \partial x_j = 0$ for all j leads to the normal equations corresponding to $\mathbf{A}\mathbf{x} = \mathbf{b}$.

(*d*) Use (*c*) to show that $t = < \mathbf{a}, \mathbf{b} > \|\mathbf{a}\|^{-2}$ minimizes $\|\mathbf{b} - t\mathbf{a}\|^2$ and that $\mathbf{b}_\perp = t\mathbf{a}$.

MATLAB

4.9.20. Verify $r_m^2 = 1/3$ in Problem 4.9.1 for A = [1 1; 1 −1; 2 0] and b = [1/3 0]' by computing norm(b − orth(A)*orth(A)'*b,2).

4.9.21. Repeat Problem 4.9.4 using the command orth(A) appropriately.

4.10 LEAST SQUARES FIT OF DATA

This section is a brief introduction to the theory of least squares, a subject of enormous importance and distinguished history dating back at least to Gauss. It is an application of the ideas developed in Sections 4.2 through 4.9. None of the work that follows this section depends on the material developed here and, hence, this section may be omitted without loss of continuity.

The problem we wish to study arises in the attempt to fit experimental data by a smooth curve that in some sense represents a "best fit." There are statistical reasons for defining best fit in the manner we do, but such justification is best left to texts on statistics. We study those examples of curve fitting usually classified under the rubrics of "linear regression," "multiple regression," and "least squares estimation."

Suppose an experiment is run in which Y_i is the measured output from an input X_i. For instance, Y_i might be voltage across a resistor through which passes a current of X_i ohms. Assume on theoretical grounds that X_i and Y_i are linearly related. If these data are plotted for five values, then the plot illustrated in Fig. 4.8 is obtained. The line drawn in Fig. 4.9 represents an attempt to predict

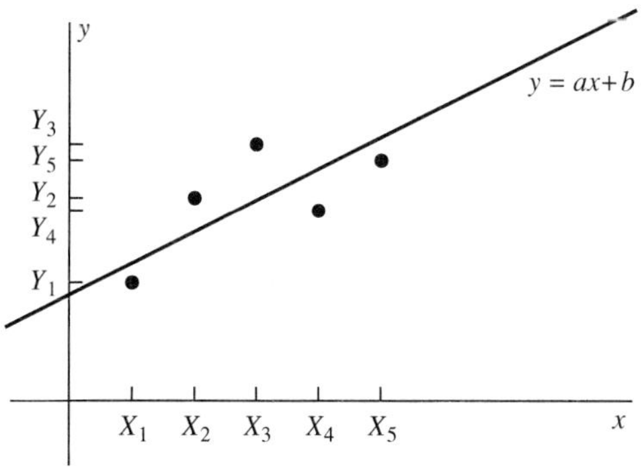

FIGURE 4-9
A candidate for the best fit of linear data.

Y_i given X_i. In general, the results of n data points, (X_i, Y_i), $i = 1, 2, \ldots, n$, can be presented in tabular form as in Table 4.1. The presumed equation relating x to y is $y = a + bx$ and hence the predicted value for $x = X_i$ is given by $y_i = a + bX_i$. The unknowns, a and b, are thus vastly overdetermined by these n equations. The differences $Y_i - y_i = Y_i - (a + bX_i)$ measure how far the predicted values differ from the experimental values. The object is to choose a and b so that

$$\sum_{i=1}^{n} [Y_i - (a + bX_i)]^2 \tag{4.10.1}$$

is minimized. For such a and b, the line $y = a + bx$ is called the *linear regression equation* or the *line of regression of y on x* and since the requirement for determining a and b is the minimization of a sum of squares, the method is known as the *least squares fit of data*.

We now face the task of finding a and b. Refer to Table 4.1. The expression

$$\mathbf{r} = \begin{bmatrix} Y_1 - y_1 \\ Y_2 - y_2 \\ \vdots \\ Y_n - y_n \end{bmatrix} = \begin{bmatrix} Y_1 \\ Y_2 \\ \vdots \\ Y_n \end{bmatrix} - \begin{bmatrix} 1 & X_1 \\ 1 & X_2 \\ \vdots & \vdots \\ 1 & X_n \end{bmatrix} \begin{bmatrix} a \\ b \end{bmatrix} \tag{4.10.2}$$

represents the vector of differences between the predicted and the measured y values. Thus finding a and b that minimizes the sum of squares in Eq. 4.10.2 is equivalent to minimizing $\|\mathbf{r}\| = \|\mathbf{b} - \mathbf{Ax}\|$ for

$$\mathbf{b} = \begin{bmatrix} Y_1 \\ Y_2 \\ \vdots \\ Y_n \end{bmatrix} \qquad \mathbf{A} = \begin{bmatrix} 1 & X_1 \\ 1 & X_2 \\ \vdots & \vdots \\ 1 & X_n \end{bmatrix} \qquad \mathbf{x} = \begin{bmatrix} a \\ b \end{bmatrix} \tag{4.10.3}$$

The solution of this problem has been obtained in Theorem 4.9.1. That is, $\mathbf{x} = \mathbf{x}_m$, where $\mathbf{x}_m$ is the solution of the normal equations associated with $\mathbf{Ax} = \mathbf{b}$. In the case of the linear regression equations, the normal equations are obtained from the (typically inconsistent) system

TABLE 4.1
Results of n data points

Input	Experiment	Predicted
X_1	Y_1	$y_1 = a + bX_1$
X_2	Y_2	$y_2 = a + bX_2$
$\vdots$	$\vdots$	$\vdots$
X_n	Y_n	$y_n = a + bX_n$

$$\mathbf{Ax} = \begin{bmatrix} 1 & X_1 \\ 1 & X_2 \\ \vdots & \vdots \\ 1 & X_n \end{bmatrix} \begin{bmatrix} a \\ b \end{bmatrix} = \mathbf{b} = \begin{bmatrix} Y_1 \\ Y_2 \\ \vdots \\ Y_n \end{bmatrix} \tag{4.10.4}$$

The normal equations are $\mathbf{A}^{\mathrm{T}}\mathbf{Ax} = \mathbf{A}^{\mathrm{T}}\mathbf{b}$; hence Eq. 4.10.4 leads to

$$\begin{bmatrix} n & \sum X_i \\ \sum X_i & \sum X_i^2 \end{bmatrix} \begin{bmatrix} a \\ b \end{bmatrix} = \begin{bmatrix} \sum Y_i \\ \sum X_i Y_i \end{bmatrix} \tag{4.10.5}$$

Suppose $\overline{X}$ and $\hat{s}_x^2$ be the *mean* and *standard deviation* of $X_1, X_2, \ldots, X_n$. Likewise, suppose $\overline{Y}$ and $\hat{s}_y^2$ are the mean and standard deviation of $Y_1, Y_2, \ldots, Y_n$ and $\hat{s}_{xy}$ is the *covariance,* that is,

$$\overline{X} = \sum X_i/n \qquad \overline{Y} = \sum Y_i/n \qquad \hat{s}_x^2 = \sum X_i^2/n - (\overline{X})^2 \tag{4.10.6}$$

$$\hat{s}_y^2 = \sum Y_i^2/n - (\overline{Y})^2 \qquad \hat{s}_{xy} = \sum X_i Y_i/n - (\overline{XY}) \tag{4.10.7}$$

Applying elementary row operations to the augmented matrix of the normal Eqs. 4.10.5, 4.10.6 and 4.10.7 yields

$$\left[\begin{array}{cc|c} n & \sum X_i & \sum Y_i \\ \sum X_1 & \sum X_i^2 & \sum X_i Y_i \end{array}\right] \to \left[\begin{array}{cc|c} 1 & \overline{X} & \overline{Y} \\ \overline{X} & \sum X_i^2/n & \sum X_i Y_i/n \end{array}\right]$$

$$\to \left[\begin{array}{cc|c} 1 & \overline{X} & \overline{Y} \\ 0 & \hat{s}_x^2 & \hat{s}_{xy} \end{array}\right] \to \left[\begin{array}{cc|c} 1 & 0 & Y - \overline{X}\hat{s}_{xy}\hat{s}_x^{-2} \\ 0 & 1 & \hat{s}_{xy}\hat{s}_x^{-2} \end{array}\right]$$

from which we deduce the values of a and b. First b, then a:

$$b = \frac{\hat{s}_{xy}}{\hat{s}_x^2} = \frac{(\sum X_i Y_i/n) - \overline{XY}}{(\sum X_i^2/n) - X^{-2}} \qquad a = \overline{Y} - b\overline{X} \tag{4.10.8}$$

Example 4.10.1. Blood is drawn from volunteers to determine the effects of a new experimental drug designed to lower cholesterol levels. The following data shows the results of varying the dosage from 0 units to 1 unit in steps of 0.2 of a unit. The data are presented in Table 4.2 and graphed in Figure 0.4. The units for the cholesterol level are milligrams per unit volume of blood.

TABLE 4.2
Drug dosages and cholesterol levels

Drug Dosage: D	0.0	0.2	0.4	0.6	0.8	1.0
Cholesterol: C	289	273	254	226	213	189

The data looks as though C and D are linearly related. If we assume that this is so, what line best fits the data? Or put equivalently, given $C = a + bD$, what choices should be made for the constants a and b to achieve a least squares fit?

Solution. Begin by computing $\overline{D}$, $\overline{C}$, $\hat{s}_D^2$ and $\hat{s}_{DC}$. (The computation of a and b by this method is extremely sensitive to errors of truncation in the intermediate steps. We have kept four decimal places and then rounded to two places for a and b.) These values are $\overline{D} = 0.5$, $\overline{C} = 240.67$, $\hat{s}_D^2 = .11667$, and $\hat{s}_{DC} = -11.80$. Then, by Eq. 4.46, $b = -101.14$, and $a = 291.24$. Hence, $C = (291.24) - (101.14)D$ is the best linear fit of the data. We predict, for instance, that $C = 215$ if $D = .75$. (See Figure 0.4.)

The next example illustrates how a change of variable can cast a problem of exponential curve fitting into one in which the linear regression model is appropriate.

Example 4.10.2. Suppose there are theoretical reasons for assuming that the data in Table 4.3 should lie on a decreasing exponential of the form $y = Me^{-kx}$.

TABLE 4.3
Data on a decreasing exponential

x	1.0	1.5	2.0	2.5	3.0	3.5
y	3.00	2.34	1.82	1.42	1.10	0.86

By taking the logarithm of the equation $y = Me^{-kx}$, it follows that the equation $z = \ln y = \ln M - kx$ is linear in x. A tabulation of the same data with ln y used in place of y leads to Table 4.4.

TABLE 4.4
Data from Table 4.3

x	1.0	1.5	2.0	2.5	3.0	3.5
$z = \ln y$	1.0986	0.8502	0.5988	0.3507	0.0953	−0.1508

The line of regression of $\ln y$ on x is computed by finding to four significant places the means, $\overline{X} = 2.2500$ and $\overline{Z} = 0.4738$, and the standard deviations $\hat{s}_x^2 = .7292$ and $\hat{s}_{xz} = -.3650$. Use Eq. 4.46 to compute $b = -k = -0.5005$ and $a = \ln M = 1.5999$. Hence, $y = 4.95 \times e^{-0.50x}$.

The previous example illustrates how an exponential fit may be interpreted as a linear fit in $\ln y$.

A problem in which an attempt is made to fit data to a power curve $y = Mx^{-k}$, is linear in ln y as a function of ln x.

Example 4.10.3. Fit $y = Mx^{-k}$ to the data in Example 4.10.2, by finding the line of regression of $z = \ln y$ on $t = \ln x$. Here z and t are related by $z = \ln M - k \ln x = \ln M - kt$, resulting from $\ln y = \ln(Mx^{-k})$.

Solution. The data are given in Table 4.5:

TABLE 4.5
Data from Example 4.10.2

$t = \ln x$	0.0000	0.4055	0.6931	0.9163	1.986	1.2528
$z = \ln y$	1.0986	0.8502	0.5988	0.3507	0.0953	−0.1508

Compute $\overline{T} = .7277, \overline{Z} = .4738, \hat{s}_{TZ} = -.2286$, and $\hat{s}_T^2 = .1806$. Hence, $b = -k = -1.2685$, $a = \ln \quad M = 1.3949$, and $y = 4.03x^{-1.27}$.

If the mean of $X_1, X_2, \ldots, X_n$ is zero (a case that will occur if the X values are equally spaced and symmetric about 0), then the normal equations become

$$\begin{bmatrix} n & 0 \\ 0 & \sum X_i^2 \end{bmatrix} \begin{bmatrix} a \\ b \end{bmatrix} = \begin{bmatrix} \sum Y_i \\ \sum X_i Y_i \end{bmatrix}$$

and hence $a = \overline{Y}$, $b = \mathbf{x}^{\mathrm{T}}\mathbf{y}\|\mathbf{x}\|^{-2}$, where the vector notation seems particularly appropriate in these circumstances.

The theory of multiple regression is a generalization to m variables of the ideas we have used above for curve fitting in one variable. Unfortunately, the notation used in statistics is not the preferred notation in matrix analysis. The following compromise is adopted here. Let w be a function of the m variables $x, y, \ldots, z$. Determine weights $a, b, \ldots, d$ so that

$$w = a + bx + cy + \cdots + dz \tag{4.10.9}$$

best fits the data

$$\left.\begin{array}{l} (x_1, y_1, \ldots, z_1, w_1) \\ (x_2, y_2, \ldots, z_2, w_2) \\ (x_n, y_n, \ldots, z_n, w_n) \end{array}\right\} \tag{4.10.10}$$

When these values are substituted into Eq. 4.10.9 there follows the (typically inconsistent) system

$$\begin{aligned} w_1 &= a + bx_1 + cy_1 + \cdots + dz_1 \\ w_2 &= a + bx_2 + cy_2 + \cdots + dz_2 \\ &\vdots \qquad\qquad\qquad\quad \vdots \\ w_n &= a + bx_n + cy_n + \cdots + dz_n \end{aligned} \tag{4.10.11}$$

In matrix form these equations lead to

$$\begin{bmatrix} 1 & x_1 & y_1 & \cdots & z_1 \\ 1 & x_2 & y_2 & \cdots & z_2 \\ \vdots & & & & \vdots \\ 1 & x_n & y_n & \cdots & z_n \end{bmatrix} \begin{bmatrix} a \\ b \\ \vdots \\ d \end{bmatrix} = \begin{bmatrix} w_1 \\ w_2 \\ \vdots \\ w_n \end{bmatrix} \tag{4.10.12}$$

The normal equations are obtained by multiplying both sides of Eq. 4.10.12 by $\mathbf{A}^{\mathrm{T}}$ obtaining

$$\begin{bmatrix} n & \sum x_i & \sum y_i & \cdots & \sum z_i \\ \sum x_i & \sum x_i^2 & \sum x_i y_i & \cdots & \sum x_i z_i \\ \vdots & & & & \vdots \\ \sum z_i & \sum z_i x_i & \sum z_i y_i & \cdots & \sum z_i^2 \end{bmatrix} \begin{bmatrix} a \\ b \\ \vdots \\ d \end{bmatrix} = \begin{bmatrix} \sum w_i \\ \sum x_i w_i \\ \vdots \\ \sum z_i w_i \end{bmatrix} \tag{4.10.14}$$

The system Eq. 4.10.14 defines the normal equations for the solution of the multiple regression problem and is an m-variable generalization of the one dimensional linear regression equations Eq. 4.10.5. One special case deserves at least passing reference: If $y = x^2, \ldots, z = x^m$ then Eq. 4.10.9 becomes $w = a + bx + cx^2 + \cdots + dx^m$ and the process of fitting data is known as *polynomial regression*. The normal equations Eq. 4.10.14 then take the form

$$\begin{bmatrix} n & \sum x_i & \sum x_i^2 & \cdots & \sum x_i^n \\ \sum x_i & \sum x_i^2 & \sum x_i^3 & \cdots & \sum x_i^{m+1} \\ \vdots & & & & \vdots \\ \sum x_i^m & \sum x_i^{m+1} & \sum x_i^{m+1} & \cdots & \sum x_i^{2m} \end{bmatrix} \begin{bmatrix} a \\ b \\ \vdots \\ d \end{bmatrix} = \begin{bmatrix} \sum w_i \\ \sum w_i x_i \\ \vdots \\ \sum w_i x_i^m \end{bmatrix} \tag{4.10.15}$$

4.10.1 Least Square Solutions in MATLAB

The symbol \ is used to command MATLAB to solve the system $\mathbf{Ax} = \mathbf{b}$. If $\mathbf{A}$ is invertible then A\b returns the vector $\mathbf{A}^{-1}\mathbf{b}$. If $\mathbf{A}$ has full column rank but $m > n$ then A/b returns the least squares solution.

Example 4.10.4. Solve the problem given as Example 4.10.1.

Solution. We use (4.10.4). Enter D = [0.0; 0.2; 0.4; 0.6; 0.8; 1.0], C = [289; 273; 254; 226; 213; 189] and A = [ones(D) D]. In response to A\C MATLAB returns

```
ans =
        291.2381
      - 101.1429
```

Example 4.10.5. Solve the problem given as Example 4.10.2.

Solution. Again use (4.10.4) as follows. First enter x = [1; 1.5; 2; 2.5; 3; 3.5], y = [3; 2.34; 1.82; 1.42; 1.10; .86] and A = [ones(x) x]. MATLAB interprets log(y) as a vector whose entries are the natural logarithms of the entries of y. Thus in response to A\log(y), MATLAB returns

```
ans =
        1.6001
      - 0.5006
```

Example 4.10.6. Solve the problem given as Example 4.10.3.

Solution. In this instance define A = [ones(x) log(x)] and enter A\log(y).

PROBLEMS

PART 1

4.10.1. Compute $\overline{C}$, $\overline{D}$,$\sum C_i^2$, $\sum D_i^2$, and $\sum C_i D_i$ for the data in Table 4.2 and verify the regression equation derived in Example 4.10.1. Keep at least four decimal places of accuracy at each step. Repeat the calculations using only two places of accuracy and compare the regression equations.

4.10.2. Compute X, Z, $\sum X_i^2$, $\sum Y_i^2$, and $\sum X_i Y_i$ for the data in Table 4.4 and verify the conclusions given in Example 4.10.2.

4.10.3. Use the data in Table 4.5 of Example 4.10.3 to answer Problem 4.10.2.

4.10.4. The release of radioactive fallout from the Chernobyl accident has been tabulated in units of millions of curies (MCi) as a function of time in days. These data[6] were obtained:

time, t (days)	0	1	2	3	4	5	6	7	8	9
fallout, R (MCi)	12.8	4	3.4	2.6	2	2	4	5	7	8

Sketch the data and find the best quadratic fit.

4.10.5. Over the course of this century the number of years of life left to a 65 year old woman on the average has increased from 12.2 years in 1900 to 18.6 years in 1985. Find the regression of future lifetime on t (years) given these data:

t (date)	1900	1930	1959	1970	1985
L (yrs)	12.2	12.8	14.6	15.8	18.6

4.10.6. The serum concentrations of penicillin in units/ml diminishes as a function of time (hours) as tabulated below:

t (hrs)	0.5	1.0	1.5	2.0	2.5	3.0	3.5	4.0
P (u/ml)	7.80	4.00	2.50	1.75	1.48	1.25	1.20	1.15

Sketch the data and find the best exponential fit.

[6]John F. Ahearne, "Nuclear Power after Chernobyl," *Science,* 8 May 1987.

PART 2

4.10.7. Let $\mathbf{1} \in \mathcal{R}^n$. Use the notations $\mathbf{1}^{\mathrm{T}}\mathbf{x}$, $\|\mathbf{x}\|$, $\mathbf{x}^{\mathrm{T}}\mathbf{y}$, and rewrite the following expressions:
(*a*) The system Eq. 4.10.5.
(*b*) Equations 4.10.6 and 4.10.7.

4.10.8. Derive Eq. 4.10.5 from Eq. 4.10.4.

4.10.9. Simplify Eq. 4.10.14 in the event that $\overline{X} = \overline{Y} = \cdots = \overline{Z} = 0$. What is the value of a in this case?

4.10.10. The system $\mathbf{Ax} = \mathbf{b}$ of Eq. 4.10.4 is generally inconsistent. Show that this is not the case if the data lie on a line. What solution can you anticipate from the corresponding normal equations? Is your expectation fulfilled?

4.10.11. Prove the following alternative expressions for $\hat{s}_x^2$ and $\hat{s}_{xy}$:
(*a*) $\hat{s}_x^2 = \sum(X_i - \overline{X})^2/n$
(*b*) $\hat{s}_{xy} = \sum(X_i - \overline{X})(Y_i - \overline{Y})/n$

4.10.12. Solve the normal equations 4.10.14 for the regression plane that best fits the n points (X_i, Y_i, W_i).

4.10.13. Use the results proved in Problem 4.10.5 to derive the following alternative expressions for b, given by Eq. 4.10.6:

$$b = \frac{\hat{s}_{xy}}{\hat{s}_x^2} = \frac{\sum(X_i - \overline{X})(Y_i - \overline{Y})}{\sum(X_i - \overline{X})^2}$$

PART 3

4.10.14. Find the equation of the line of regression of x on y by reconstructing the theory with Y_i replacing X_i. Explain why this line is different, in general, from the regression of y on x. Illustrate by reversing the roles of C and D in Example 4.10.1.

4.10.15. Let $\mathrm{f}(a, b)$ be defined by

$$\mathrm{f}(a, b) = \sum_{i=1}^{n} [Y_i - (a + bX_i)]^2$$

Find the minimum of $\mathrm{f}(a, b)$ by setting $\partial\mathrm{f}/\partial a = \partial\mathrm{f}/\partial b = 0$. Show that these equations lead to the normal equations.

4.10.16. Suppose m measurements are made at one value of x; say, (X_0, Y_i), for $i = 1, 2, \ldots, m$. Suppose we wish the line $y = a$ that best fits this data in a least squares sense. Find a by constructing a function $\mathrm{f}(a)$ analogous to $\mathrm{f}(a, b)$ and setting $d\mathrm{f}/da = 0$. Can this work be placed in the context of the theory of the normal equations?

CHAPTER 5

THE EIGENVALUE-EIGENVECTOR PROBLEM

PART 1 THEORY

5.1 INTRODUCTION

Three broad classes of problems arise from various interpretations of the transformation $\mathbf{y} = \mathbf{A}\mathbf{x}$, in which $\mathbf{A}$ is assumed square, and $\mathbf{x}$ and $\mathbf{y}$ are given by

$$\mathbf{x} = \begin{bmatrix} x_1 \\ x_2 \\ \vdots \\ x_n \end{bmatrix} \qquad \mathbf{y} = \begin{bmatrix} y_1 \\ y_2 \\ \vdots \\ y_n \end{bmatrix}$$

First, if $\mathbf{y}$ is given, say $\mathbf{y} = \mathbf{b}$, then $\mathbf{y} = \mathbf{A}\mathbf{x}$ is simply the familiar problem of solving a system of algebraic, linear equations, $\mathbf{A}\mathbf{x} = \mathbf{b}$. Second, if $\mathbf{y} = \mathbf{x}_{k+1}$ and $\mathbf{x}$ is rewritten $\mathbf{x} = \mathbf{x}_k$, then $\mathbf{y} = \mathbf{A}\mathbf{x}$ becomes $\mathbf{x}_{k+1} = \mathbf{A}\mathbf{x}_k$. In this form $\mathbf{y} = \mathbf{A}\mathbf{x}$ represents a system of linear difference equations with constant coefficients. (An application appears in Section 5.10. See also Section 0.1.6.) Third, interpret $\mathbf{x}$ and $\mathbf{y}$ as a function of t, $\mathbf{x} = \mathbf{x}(t)$ and $\mathbf{y} = \mathbf{x}'(t)$, the derivative of $\mathbf{x}(t)$ with respect to t. Then $\mathbf{y} = \mathbf{A}\mathbf{x}$ becomes $\mathbf{x}'(t) = \mathbf{A}\mathbf{x}(t)$, and this is a system of linear differential equations of first order with constant coefficients. (See Sections 5.9 and 5.11.)

For any problem that has the form $\mathbf{y} = \mathbf{Ax}$ (the illustrations mentioned above being three such cases), the entries in $\mathbf{y}$ are linear combinations of the entries in $\mathbf{x}$. The system $\mathbf{y} = \mathbf{Ax}$ is significantly easier to handle if each entry in $\mathbf{y}$, y_i, depended on only a few of the entries in $\mathbf{x}$. Indeed, this is one of the main motivations for the reduction of $\mathbf{A}$ to upper triangular form in the solution of $\mathbf{Ax} = \mathbf{b}$ by Gaussian elimination. The most favorable circumstance occurs if $\mathbf{A}$ is diagonal, in which case each y_i is proportional to its corresponding x_i. This raises the question of whether $\mathbf{y} = \mathbf{Ax}$ can be replaced by an "equivalent" system in which the matrix operator is diagonal. The answer is often yes, and here are two explanations of how this could happen.

Let us view $\mathbf{Ax} = \mathbf{y}$ as a transformation of $\mathbf{x}$ to $\mathbf{y}$ where $\mathbf{x}$ and $\mathbf{y}$ are coordinate vectors relative to the standard basis $\mathscr{E} = \{\mathbf{e}_1, \mathbf{e}_2, \ldots, \mathbf{e}_n\}$ for $\mathscr{R}^n$. In this context our question may be phrased, is there a basis $\mathscr{B}_v$ for $\mathscr{R}^n$ in which the coordinate vectors for $\mathbf{x}$ and $\mathbf{y}$ are related by a diagonal matrix? (See Section 3.8.) Let $\mathbf{x}_v$ and $\mathbf{y}_v$ be the coordinate vectors of $\mathbf{x}$ and $\mathbf{y}$ relative to $\mathscr{B}_v$. Then $\mathbf{y}_v = \mathbf{S}^{-1}\mathbf{ASx}_v$, where the columns of $\mathbf{S}$ are the vectors comprising the basis $\mathscr{B}_v$. We search for $\mathscr{B}_v$, and by implication $\mathbf{S}$, such that $\mathbf{S}^{-1}\mathbf{AS}$ is a diagonal matrix.

Alternately, we may view $\mathbf{S}^{-1}\mathbf{x}_v = \mathbf{x}$ as a change of variables from $\mathbf{x}_v$ to $\mathbf{x}$. Now set $\mathbf{S}^{-1}\mathbf{y} = \mathbf{y}_v$. Then, if $\mathbf{y} = \mathbf{Ax}$ is multiplied by $\mathbf{S}^{-1}$, we obtain $\mathbf{S}^{-1}\mathbf{y} = \mathbf{S}^{-1}\mathbf{Ax}$ into which we substitute the expressions for $\mathbf{x}_v$ and $\mathbf{y}_v$

$$\mathbf{S}^{-1}\mathbf{y} = \mathbf{y}_v = \mathbf{S}^{-1}\mathbf{Ax} = \mathbf{S}^{-1}\mathbf{ASx}_v$$

That is, $\mathbf{y}_v = \mathbf{S}^{-1}\mathbf{ASx}_v$, and both interpretations lead to the same problem: find an invertible matrix $\mathbf{S}$ such that $\mathbf{S}^{-1}\mathbf{AS}$ is diagonal. This is the central issue addressed in this chapter.

The solution to this problem requires the determination of the roots of an nth-degree polynomial. For this reason, it is desirable to review the elementary theory of polynomial equations. This review is presented in Section 5.2 in which appear two broad themes: first, a review of the algebra of complex numbers; and then, the relationship between the roots of the polynomial and its factors. Sections 5.3 through 5.7 resolve the issue of when $\mathbf{S}^{-1}\mathbf{AS}$ is diagonal and how $\mathbf{S}$ may be found. These sections comprise Part 1 of this chapter. Part 2, Sections 5.8 through 5.11, presents various extensions and applications.

5.2 COMPLEX NUMBERS AND THE ROOTS OF POLYNOMIAL EQUATIONS

Until this chapter it was convenient to restrict the set of scalars to real numbers and unnecessary to do otherwise. However, as will become evident, even for real $\mathbf{A}$, complex scalars may be an important factor in the full analysis of $\mathbf{A}$. This section is designed to pave the way for this transition by providing a review of some of the basic ideas in complex arithmetic and the solution of polynomial equations.

A number c is complex if it is of the form $a + ib$, where a and b are real and $i^2 = -1$. The real numbers are a subset of the complex numbers obtained by selecting $b = 0$. The real numbers a and b are called the *real* and *imaginary parts of* c and are written $\text{Re}(c) = a$ and $\text{Im}(c) = b$. Thus, c may be written $c = \text{Re}(c) + i\text{Im}(c)$. If $c = a + ib$, then $\bar{c} = a - ib$ is called the *complex conjugate of* c. In terms of c and $\bar{c}$, $\text{Re}(c) = (c + \bar{c})/2$ and $\text{Im}(c) = (c - \bar{c})/2$. A number of elementary arithmetic results connected with complex numbers are listed below; more are reserved for the problems.

Theorem 5.2.1. *For complex numbers c and d*

(*a*) $c = 0$ *if and only if* $a = 0$ *and* $b = 0$
(*b*) $\overline{(c + d)} = \bar{c} + \bar{d}$ *and* $\overline{cd} = \overline{c}\overline{d}$
(*c*) $c\bar{c} = |c|^2 = \text{Re}^2(c) + \text{Im}^2(c) > 0$
(*d*) $\text{Re}(c + d) = \text{Re}(c) + \text{Re}(d)$ and $\text{Im}(c + d) = \text{Im}(c) + \text{Im}(d)$
(*e*) *For each real* k, $\text{Re}(kc) = k\text{Re}(c)$ *and* $\text{Im}(kc) = k\text{Im}(c)$
(*f*) $|c| \geq |\text{Re}(c)|, \quad |c| \geq |\text{Im}(c)|$

Proof. The proofs for parts (*c*) and (*f*) follow; the remaining arguments are presented as exercises.

Suppose $c = a + ib$. Then, by definition of $\bar{c}$,

$$c\bar{c} = (a + ib)(a - ib) = a^2 + iab - iab + b^2 = a^2 + b^2$$

and $a^2 + b^2 \geq 0$ because a and b are real. Part (*f*) follows from (*c*) by elementary considerations of inequality relationships: since $\text{Re}(c)$ and $\text{Im}(c)$ are real, $|c|^2 = \text{Re}^2(c) + \text{Im}^2(c) \geq \text{Re}^2(c)$ and, similarly, $|c|^2 \geq \text{Im}^2(c)$. ■

Example 5.2.1. Use the results in Theorem 5.2.1 to prove that $1/c = \bar{c}/|c|^2$ and find $\text{Re}(1/c)$ and $\text{Im}(1/c)$.

Solution. Let $c = a + ib$ so that $\bar{c} = a - ib$. Then,

$$\frac{1}{c} = \frac{\bar{c}}{c\bar{c}} = \frac{\bar{c}}{|c|^2} = \frac{a - ib}{a^2 + b^2}$$

from Part (*c*) of Theorem 5.2.1. Next,

$$\frac{a - ib}{a^2 + b^2} = \frac{a}{a^2 + b^2} - \frac{ib}{a^2 + b^2}$$

Therefore,

$$\text{Re}\left[\frac{1}{c}\right] = \frac{a}{a^2 + b^2}, \qquad \text{Im}\left[\frac{1}{c}\right] = -\frac{b}{a^2 + b^2}$$

Denote by p (and if necessary q) any polynomial of degree n of the form

$$p(\lambda) = (-\lambda)^n + c_{n-1}(-\lambda)^{(n-1)} + \cdots + c_0 \tag{5.2.1}$$

The coefficients may not be real, although commonly they are. In any case, the fundamental theorem of algebra states that the equation $p(\lambda) = 0$ has a root among the complex numbers. The next theorem contains this result and a related factorization.

Theorem 5.2.2. *For every polynomial*

$$p(\lambda) = (-\lambda)^n + c_{n-1}(-\lambda)^{n-1} + \cdots + c_0$$

there exist n complex numbers $\lambda_1, \lambda_2, \ldots, \lambda_n$, *not necessarily distinct, such that*

$$p(\lambda_k) = 0 \qquad \text{for each } k = 1, 2, \ldots, n \tag{5.2.2}$$

$$p(\lambda) = (\lambda_1 - \lambda)(\lambda_2 - \lambda)\cdots(\lambda_n - \lambda) \tag{5.2.3}$$

$$p(\lambda) = (-\lambda)^n + (\lambda_1 + \lambda_2 + \cdots + \lambda_n)(-\lambda)^{n-1} + \cdots + (\lambda_1\lambda_2\cdots\lambda_n) \tag{5.2.4}$$

Moreover, if $p(r) = 0$, *then* $r = \lambda_k$ *for some k.*

Proof. The first two equalities are corollaries of the fundamental theorem of algebra. Equation 5.2.2 asserts that a polynomial of degree n has n roots; the second equation asserts that for each root λ_k, $p(\lambda)$ has a factor $(\lambda_k - \lambda)$. The third equation is implied by the second. ■

The expression for $p(\lambda)$ given in Eq. 5.2.4 yields these connections between the roots of $p(\lambda)$ and its coefficients: The *sum* of the roots is c_{n-1}; the *product* of the roots is c_0.

In the event that all the coefficients c_i in Eq. 5.2.1 are real and r is a root of $p(\lambda)$, then so is $\bar{r}$. To see why this must be so, we note

$$0 = \bar{0} = \overline{p(r)} = \overline{(-r)^n + c_{n-1}(-r)^{n-1} + \cdots + c_0} \tag{5.2.5}$$

Since c_k is real by assumption, $\bar{c}_k = c_k$. This result and Theorem 5.2.1 imply that Eq. 5.2.5 can be simplified as follows

$$0 = \overline{p(r)} = \overline{(-r)^n} + c_{n-1}\overline{(-r)^{n-1}} + \cdots + c_0$$

However, $\overline{(-r)^k} = (-\bar{r})^k$, and this implies

$$0 = \overline{p(r)} = (-\bar{r})^n + c_{n-1}(-\bar{r})^{n-1} + \cdots + c_0 = p(\bar{r})$$

Thus $\bar{r}$ is a root, as asserted.

Example 5.2.2. Find a polynomial of degree 3 whose roots are 0, -1, and 1.

Solution. By Eq. 5.2.3, $p(x) = -x(-1 - x)(1 - x)$. Hence, if these three factors are multipled, $p(x) = -x^3 + x$ results. Now confirm that $c_2 = \lambda_1 + \lambda_2 + \lambda_3 = 0$ and $c_0 = \lambda_1\lambda_2\lambda_3 = 0$.

5.2.1 The Roots of Unity

The equation $x^n - 1 = 0$ plays an important role in many diverse areas of mathematics. The roots of this equation are called the nth *roots of unity,* because each root satisfies $x^n = 1$.

It is common to define ω by

$$\omega = \cos(2\pi/\text{n}) + i \sin(2\pi/\text{n}) = e^{2\pi i/n} \tag{5.2.6}$$

(The second equality in Eq. 5.2.6 is the Euler formula, familiar to students of elementary differential equations.) Then the solutions of $x^n - 1 = 0$ are given by the n powers of ω. For each integer k, $k = 1, 2, \ldots, n$,

$$\omega^k = (e^{2\pi i/n})^k = e^{2\pi ik/n} = \cos(2k\pi/n) + i \sin(2\pi k/n) \tag{5.2.7}$$

In particular, for $k = n$,

$$\omega^n = \cos(2n\pi/n) + i \sin(2\pi n/n) = \cos(2\pi) + i \sin(2\pi) = 1$$

Note that if k and m are integers satisfying $0 < k < m < n$, then $\omega^k \neq \omega^m$. Finally, $(\omega^k)^n = (\omega^n)^k = 1$, and hence, $1, \omega, \omega^2, \ldots, \omega^{n-1}$ are n distinct nth roots of $x^n - 1$.

Example 5.2.3. Find the roots for each of the following polynomials:

$(a)\ x^3 - 1 \qquad (b)\ x^4 - 1 \qquad (c)\ x^8 - 1$

Solution. (a) To find the three cube roots of unity, use the following trigonometric facts

$$\cos(2\pi/3) = -1/2 \qquad \cos(4\pi/3) = -1/2$$
$$\sin(2\pi/3) = \sqrt{3}/2 \qquad \sin(4\pi/3) = -\sqrt{3}/2$$

Then, from Eq. 5.2.7 with $n = 3$,

$$\begin{aligned} x_1 &= \omega = \cos(2\pi/3) + i \sin(2\pi/3) = -1/2 + i\sqrt{3}/2 \\ x_2 &= \omega^2 = \cos(4\pi/3) + i \sin(4\pi/3) = -1/2 - i\sqrt{3}/2 \\ x_3 &= \omega^3 = \cos(6\pi/3) + i \sin(6\pi/3) = 1 \end{aligned}$$

(b) Two roots are found by inspection; they are 1 and -1. In the present notation, these roots arise from $x_4 = 1$ and

$$\omega^2 = x_2 = \cos(4\pi/4) + i \sin(4\pi/4) = -1$$

The remaining roots are

$$\begin{aligned} x_1 &= \omega = \cos(2\pi/4) + i \sin(2\pi/4) = i \\ x_3 &= \omega^3 = \cos(6\pi/4) + i \sin(6\pi/4) = -i. \end{aligned}$$

(c) From Eq. 5.2.7,

$$x_1 = \omega = \cos(2\pi/8) + i \sin(2\pi/8) = (1 + i)\sqrt{2}/2$$

It is a good exercise in complex arithmetic to verify that $x_2 = \omega^2 = i$.

$$x_4 = \omega^4 = -1$$
$$x_6 = \omega^6 = -i.$$

Of course,

$$x_8 = \omega^8 = 1$$

Finally,

$$x_3 = \omega^3 = (-1 + i)\sqrt{2}/2, \qquad x_5 = \omega^5 = (-1 - i)\sqrt{2}/2$$

5.2.2 Vector Spaces of Complex *n*-tuples

The vector space $\mathcal{R}^n$ is the set of all real n-tuples. In the succeeding sections we will have occasion to study vectors and matrices whose entries are complex numbers. The set of all n-tuples (vectors) with complex entries is denoted by $\mathcal{C}^n$. Note that $span\{\mathbf{e}_1, \mathbf{e}_2, \ldots, \mathbf{e}_n\} = \mathcal{R}^n$ if the weights are assumed real but is $\mathcal{C}^n$ if the weights are allowed to range over the complex numbers. Thus, $\mathcal{V} = span\{\mathbf{x}_1, \mathbf{x}_2, \ldots, \mathbf{x}_k\}$ is ambiguous; its meaning depends on the allowable set of weights. We resolve this ambiguity by convention: if no comments are made to the contrary, we assume that the weights are real, that $\{\mathbf{x}_1, \mathbf{x}_2, \ldots, \mathbf{x}_k\}$ is a set of real vectors, and, therefore, $\mathcal{V} \subseteq \mathcal{R}^n$. If any of the vectors in $\{\mathbf{x}_1, \mathbf{x}_2, \ldots, \mathbf{x}_k\}$ contains complex entries, then $\mathcal{V} \subseteq \mathcal{C}^n$; that is, the weights in $span\{\mathbf{x}_1, \mathbf{x}_2, \ldots, \mathbf{x}_k\}$ range over the complex numbers.

5.2.3 Polynomials and Roots in MATLAB

Polynomials are represented in MATLAB as the entries in a row vector. The first entry is the coefficient of the highest power and the succeeding entries are the coefficients of the corresponding powers in descending order. Thus, p = [1 0 −1] is the MATLAB notation for the polynomial $x^2 - 1$.

There are five MATLAB commands related directly to polynomials, of which the following three are relevant here: (1) roots(p), (2) poly(r), and (3) polyval(x,y). We illustrate these commands in order.

The command r = roots(p) returns a column vector whose entries are the roots of $p(x) = 0$.

Example 5.2.4. Use MATLAB to compute the 5th roots of unity.

Solution. The five 5th roots of unity are the solutions of $x^5 - 1 = 0$. So define $p = [1 \quad 0 \quad 0 \quad 0 \quad 0 \quad -1]$. Then r = roots(p) returns

```
r =
   - 0.8080 + 0.5878i
   - 0.8080 - 0.5878i
     0.3090 + 0.9511i
     0.3090 - 0.9511i
     1.0000
```

If the entries of the column vector **r** are the roots of the polynomial $p(x) = 0$, the command poly(r) returns the coefficients of the polynomial $Kp(x)$ as a row vector, where K is a scaling factor, so that $Kp(x)$ is monic (the coefficient of the highest power of x is 1). The coefficients of p(x) are given in descending order, and except for round-off errors and scaling, r = roots(p) and p = poly(r) are inverses. That is, r = roots(poly(r)) and p = poly(roots(r)). (Poly accepts row or column vectors as arguments.)

Example 5.2.5. Verify r = roots(poly(r)) and p = poly(roots(r)) for the polynomial $p(x) = (3-x)(1-x)^2(1+x^2) = -x^5 + 5x^4 - 8x^3 + 8x^2 - 7x + 3$.

Solution. The roots of $p(x)$ are $r_1 = 3, r_2 = r_3 = 1, r_4 = i, r_5 = -i$. Hence,

$$r = [3 \quad 1 \quad 1 \quad \text{sqrt}(-1), \quad -\text{sqrt}(-1)]$$

and after r is entered,

```
p = poly(r)
    1   - 5  8   - 8  7   - 3
```

which are the coefficients of $-p(x)$. Next

```
s = roots(p)
    3
  - 0.0000 + 1.0000i
  - 0.0000 - 1.0000i
    1.0000
    1.0000
```

The appearance of the zeros after the decimal point is a sign that the displayed quantities are truncated from numbers stored by MATLAB, and that at least one of these numbers is not an integer. Since the correct answers are integers, the process of computing the roots accumulated some error. Indeed, the "format long" command shows the two unit roots are stored as .99999997198611 and 1.00000002801390. This explains the next computation.

```
q = poly(s)
    1.0000       -5.0000      8.0000      -8.0000 - 0.0000i
    7.0000 - 0.0000i       - 3.0000 - 0.0000i
```

Example 5.2.6. Suppose $p(x)$ is a polynomial entered into MATLAB as the row vector p of its coefficients. Suppose that **x** is a vector. The vector of values $p(\mathbf{x})$ is obtained by the command polyval(p,x). Polyval accepts row or column vectors for x and returns a vector of the same size. Enter p and r from Example 5.2.5. Then, (*a*) polyval(p, [1 3 2])

ans =

0 0 −5

(*b*) polyval(p,r)

ans =

0 0 0 0

(*c*) polyval(p, r′)

ans =

0
0
0
0
0

(*d*) polyval(p, [1; 2; sqrt(−1)])

ans =

0
−5
0

PROBLEMS

PART 1

5.2.1. Let $c = 3 - 2i$ and $d = 1 + i$. Find
(*a*) $\mathrm{Re}(cd)$ (*b*) $\mathrm{Im}(c\bar{d})$ (*c*) $\mathrm{Re}(c+\bar{d})$ (*d*) $\mathrm{Im}(c+\bar{d})$ (*e*) $\mathrm{Im}(i\bar{c})$
(*f*) $\mathrm{Re}(id)$ (*g*) c^2 (*h*) $(1+i)^2/4$ (*i*) $\mathrm{Re}(c/d)$ (*j*) $\mathrm{Re}(c/\bar{d})$

5.2.2. Use the result in Example 5.2.1 to show that $d/c = \bar{c}d/|c|^2$.

5.2.3. Show that $1/c = \bar{c}$ if $a^2 + b^2 = 1$.

5.2.4. Verify Eq. 5.2.4 for the polynomials
(*a*) $p_2(\lambda) = (1 - \lambda)(-1 - \lambda)$ (*b*) $p_3(\lambda) = (1 - \lambda)(2 - \lambda)(3 - \lambda)$
(*c*) $p_2(\lambda) = (r_1 - \lambda)(\bar{r}_1 - \lambda)$

5.2.5. Given that $r_1 = 1 - i\sqrt{2}$, $r_2 = 1 + i\sqrt{2}$, and $r_3 = 1$ are the roots of the polynomial $p_3(\lambda) = (-\lambda)^3 + c_2(-\lambda)^2 + c_1(-\lambda) + c_0$, find the scalars c_0, c_1, and c_2 and verify Eq. 5.2.4.

5.2.6. Verify the arithmetic in the solution of Example 5.2.3(*c*).

5.2.7. Let $\omega = \cos(2\pi/3) + i\sin(2\pi/3)$. Show that $1 + \omega + \omega^2 = 0$ and $1 + \omega^2 + \omega^4 = 0$.

PART 2

5.2.8. Prove Theorem 5.2.1 by resorting directly to the definitions.

5.2.9. Suppose $p(\lambda) = \lambda^3 - \lambda^2 + 2\lambda - 3$. Show that $\lambda^3 p(1/\lambda) = -3\lambda^3 + 2\lambda^2 - \lambda + 1$. Without computing the roots of $p(\lambda)$, express the roots of $\lambda^3 p(1/\lambda)$ in terms of the roots of $p(\lambda)$.

5.2.10. Show:
(*a*) $\omega^{-k} = \omega^{n-k}$ (*b*) $\omega^{n+k} = \omega^k$

PART 3

5.2.11. Suppose $a = |a|e^{i\alpha}$. Show that the roots of $x^n - a = 0$ are $\omega^k |a|^{1/n} e^{i\alpha/k}$, $k = 1, 2, \ldots, n$.

5.2.12. Show that $1 + \omega + \omega^2 + \cdots + \omega^{n-1} = 0$ by considering $(1 - \omega)(1 + \omega + \omega^2 + \cdots + \omega^{n-1})$.

MATLAB

5.2.13. Find the roots of $p(\lambda) = \lambda^3 - \lambda^2 + 2\lambda - 3$ and $\lambda^3 p(1/\lambda) = -3\lambda^3 + 2\lambda^2 - \lambda + 1$.

5.2.14. Find the roots of $x^8 - 1 = 0$ and compare with the answer in Example 5.2.3(*c*).

5.2.15. Define $w = \cos(2\pi/7) + i\sin(2\pi/7)$, and $p(x) = 1 + x + x^2 + \cdots + x^6$. Use polyval to evaluate $p(w^k)$ for $k = 1, 2, 3, \ldots, 8$.

5.3 THE CHARACTERISTIC EQUATION

The solution of the algebraic *eigenvector-eigenvalue* problem for the square matrix $\mathbf{A}$ is a nonzero vector $\mathbf{x}$ and a scalar λ such that

$$\mathbf{Ax} = \lambda\mathbf{x}, \qquad \mathbf{x} \neq \mathbf{0} \tag{5.3.1}$$

The scalar λ is an *eigenvalue* of $\mathbf{A}$ and the vector $\mathbf{x} \neq \mathbf{0}$ is an *eigenvector* corresponding to λ. The scalar λ and the vector $\mathbf{x}$ related by Eq. 5.3.1 is called an *eigenpair*. In general, the vectors $\mathbf{Ay}$ and $\mathbf{y}$ are unrelated geometrically. For eigenvectors, however, Eq. 5.3.1 asserts that $\mathbf{Ax}$ and $\mathbf{x}$ are proportional. Thus, the points represented by the eigenvector $\mathbf{x}$ and the vector $\mathbf{Ax}$ lie on the same line through the origin.

Clearly, $\mathbf{Ax} = \lambda\mathbf{x}$ is equivalent to $\mathbf{Ax} - \lambda\mathbf{x} = \mathbf{0}$, so by writing $\lambda\mathbf{x} = \lambda\mathbf{Ix}$, Eq. 5.3.1 becomes

$$(\mathbf{A} - \lambda\mathbf{I})\mathbf{x} = \mathbf{0}, \qquad \mathbf{x} \neq \mathbf{0} \tag{5.3.2}$$

If $\mathbf{A} - \lambda\mathbf{I}$ is nonsingular, Eq. 5.3.2 has only the trivial solution $\mathbf{x} = \mathbf{0}$ (which is not an eigenvector by definition). Thus, to find the eigenvectors of $\mathbf{A}$, first find those λ for which $\mathbf{A} - \lambda\mathbf{I}$ is singular, and then solve the homogeneous system in Eq. 5.3.2. This leads to the crucial observation that eigenvalues are specifically those scalars for which $\mathbf{A} - \lambda\mathbf{I}$ is singular; that is, those λ for which

$$\det(\mathbf{A} - \lambda\mathbf{I}) = 0 \tag{5.3.3}$$

since a matrix is singular if and only if its determinant is 0. (See Theorem 1.6.3.) Set $c_{\mathbf{A}}(\lambda) = \det(\mathbf{A} - \lambda\mathbf{I})$. (If no confusion can arise as to which matrix is meant, then $c(\lambda)$ is written instead of the more cumbersome $c_{\mathbf{A}}(\lambda)$.) The *characteristic equation of* $\mathbf{A}$ is $c(\lambda) = 0$. The eigenvalues are the zeros of the characteristic equation.

Example 5.3.1. Find the eigenvalues of each of the following matrices

$$(a)\begin{bmatrix} 1 & 1 \\ 4 & 1 \end{bmatrix} \qquad (b)\begin{bmatrix} a & * \\ 0 & b \end{bmatrix} \qquad (c)\ [a] \qquad (d)\begin{bmatrix} 0 & -1 \\ 1 & 0 \end{bmatrix}$$

Solution. For (a) the characteristic equation is given by

$$\det\left\{\begin{bmatrix} 1 & 1 \\ 4 & 1 \end{bmatrix} - \lambda\mathbf{I}\right\} = \det\left\{\begin{bmatrix} 1-\lambda & 1 \\ 4 & 1-\lambda \end{bmatrix}\right\} = (1-\lambda)^2 - 4 = 0$$

The eigenvalues are the roots of $(1-\lambda)^2 - 4 = 0$; namely, $\lambda_1 = -1$ and $\lambda_2 = 3$. For (b), the characteristic equation is once again a quadratic,

$$\det\left\{\begin{bmatrix} a & * \\ 0 & b \end{bmatrix} - \lambda\mathbf{I}\right\} = \det\left\{\begin{bmatrix} a-\lambda & * \\ 0 & b-\lambda \end{bmatrix}\right\} = (a-\lambda)(b-\lambda) = 0$$

Thus, the eigenvalues of this matrix are its two diagonal entries, $\lambda_1 = a$ and $\lambda_2 = b$, and are independent of the (1,2) entry. The 1×1 matrix $[a]$ has the single eigenvalue $\lambda_1 = a$. Finally, for the matrix in (*d*), we have

$$\det\left\{\begin{bmatrix} 0 & -1 \\ 1 & 0 \end{bmatrix} - \lambda\mathbf{I}\right\} = \det\left\{\begin{bmatrix} -\lambda & -1 \\ 1 & -\lambda \end{bmatrix}\right\} = \lambda^2 + 1 = 0$$

The eigenvalues are imaginary: $\lambda_1 = -i$ and $\lambda_2 = i$.

In general,

$$c(\lambda) = \det(\mathbf{A} - \lambda\mathbf{I}) = \det\begin{bmatrix} a_{11} - \lambda & a_{12} & \dots & a_{n1} \\ a_{21} & a_{22} - \lambda & \dots & a_{n2} \\ \vdots & \vdots & & \vdots \\ a_{n1} & a_{n2} & \dots & a_{nn} - \lambda \end{bmatrix} \tag{5.3.4}$$

Example 5.3.2. Show that the eigenvalues of an upper triangular matrix are its diagonal entries.

Solution. From Eq. 5.3.4 it follows that $\mathbf{A} - \lambda\mathbf{I}$ is upper triangular if $\mathbf{A}$ is. Since the determinant of an upper triangular matrices is the product of its diagonal entries, $c(\lambda) = (a_{11} - \lambda)(a_{22} - \lambda)\cdots(a_{nn} - \lambda)$. Clearly, the characteristic polynomial of $\mathbf{A}$ does not determine the entries of $\mathbf{A}$.

The determinant of $\mathbf{A}$ is a sum of $n!$ terms, where the set of second subscripts of each term is a permutation of $\{1, 2, \dots, n\}$. (See Section 1.6.) Thus, $c(\lambda) = \det(\mathbf{A} - \lambda\mathbf{I})$ is a polynomial (in λ) of degree n, called the *characteristic polynomial* of $\mathbf{A}$. One can learn more about this polynomial by a careful study of the terms of $\det(\mathbf{A} - \lambda\mathbf{I})$. Suppose the term T of $\det(\mathbf{A})$ has the factor a_{ij}, $i \neq j$; that is,

$$T = (\pm)a_{1*}a_{2*}\cdots a_{ij}\cdots a_{n*}$$

Then T cannot contain the factors a_{ii} or a_{jj}, or it would have two factors from the same row or column. Therefore, except for the "diagonal" term $a_{11}a_{22}\cdots a_{nn}$, every term in $\det(\mathbf{A})$ has $n - 2$ or fewer diagonal entries as factors. In the expansion of $\det(\mathbf{A} - \lambda\mathbf{I})$, this last observation translates into the statement that every term contains $n - 2$ or fewer factors with λ, except for the diagonal term, which contains exactly n factors with λ. Hence,

$$c(\lambda) = \underbrace{(a_{11} - \lambda)(a_{22} - \lambda)\cdots(a_{nn} - \lambda)}_{\text{diagonal terms}} + \underbrace{p_{n-2}(\lambda)}_{\text{remaining terms}} \tag{5.3.5}$$

where $p_{n-2}(\lambda)$ is a polynomial of degree $n - 2$ or less in λ. This shows that $c(\lambda)$ is a polynomial of degree n. The nth and $(n - 1)$th degree terms are obtained by multiplying out the first product on the right-hand side of Eq. 5.3.5, since the highest power of λ that can occur in the remaining terms is $n - 2$. If we set $\text{tr}(\mathbf{A}) = a_{11} + a_{22} + \cdots + a_{nn}$ (read "trace of $\mathbf{A}$"), then Eq. 5.3.5 implies the representation

$$\det(\mathbf{A} - \lambda\mathbf{I}) = c(\lambda) = (-\lambda)^n + \text{tr}(\mathbf{A})(-\lambda)^{n-1} + \cdots + c_0 \tag{5.3.6}$$

Equation 5.3.6 is an identity in λ. Since Eq. 5.3.6 is true for all λ, it is true for $\lambda = 0$. Thus $\det(\mathbf{A}) = c(0) = c_0$. This proves the following theorem.

Theorem 5.3.1. *The characteristic polynomial of* **A** *is given by*

$$c(\lambda) = (-\lambda)^n + \operatorname{tr}(\mathbf{A})(-\lambda)^{n-1} + \cdots + \det(\mathbf{A}) \tag{5.3.7}$$

Now suppose that the n roots of $c(\lambda)$ (the eigenvalues of **A**) are denoted by $\lambda_1, \lambda_2, \ldots, \lambda_n$. Then $c(\lambda) = (\lambda_1 - \lambda)(\lambda_2 - \lambda)\ldots(\lambda_n - \lambda)$ and, therefore,

$$c(\lambda) = (-\lambda)^n + (\lambda_1 + \lambda_2 + \cdots + \lambda_n)(-\lambda)^{n-1} + \cdots + (\lambda_1\lambda_2\cdots\lambda_n)$$

(See Theorem 5.2.2.) By comparing this representation with that in Eq. 5.3.7, we deduce the elementary but remarkable connection between the eigenvalues of **A** and its trace and determinant.

Theorem 5.3.2. *For each square matrix* **A**,

$$(a)\ \det(\mathbf{A}) = \lambda_1\lambda_2\cdots\lambda_n \tag{5.3.8}$$

$$(b)\ \operatorname{tr}(\mathbf{A}) = \lambda_1 + \lambda_2 + \cdots + \lambda_n \tag{5.3.9}$$

Corollary 1. *The matrix* **A** *is singular if and only if* $\lambda = 0$ *is an eigenvalue of* **A**.

Proof. The proof is an immediate consequence of Eq. 5.3.3 or Eq. 5.3.8, since **A** is singular if and only if $\det(\mathbf{A}) = 0$. ■

Example 5.3.3. Verify Theorem 5.3.2 for the matrix

$$\mathbf{A} = \begin{bmatrix} 1 & 2 & 4 \\ 0 & 2 & 0 \\ 0 & 2 & 1 \end{bmatrix}$$

Solution. Compute

$$c(\lambda) = \det(\mathbf{A} - \lambda\mathbf{I}) - \det\begin{bmatrix} 1-\lambda & 2 & 4 \\ 0 & 2-\lambda & 0 \\ 0 & 2 & 1-\lambda \end{bmatrix}$$

$$= (1-\lambda)\det\begin{bmatrix} 2-\lambda & 0 \\ 2 & 1-\lambda \end{bmatrix} = (1-\lambda)^2(2-\lambda)$$

As expected, $c(\lambda)$ is a cubic. Its three roots are $\lambda_1 = \lambda_2 = 1$ and $\lambda_3 = 2$. Theorem 5.3.2 is verified by the computations $\operatorname{tr}(\mathbf{A}) = 4$ and $\det(\mathbf{A}) = 2$.

Example 5.3.4. Verify Theorem 5.3.2 for the matrix

$$\mathbf{A} = \begin{bmatrix} -1 & 3 & 0 \\ 3 & 7 & 0 \\ 0 & 0 & 6 \end{bmatrix}$$

Solution. Compute

$$c(\lambda) = \det(\mathbf{A} - \lambda\mathbf{I}) = \det\begin{bmatrix} -1-\lambda & 3 & 0 \\ 3 & 7-\lambda & 0 \\ 0 & 0 & 6-\lambda \end{bmatrix}$$

$$= (6-\lambda)\det\begin{bmatrix} -1-\lambda & 3 \\ 3 & 7-\lambda \end{bmatrix} = (6-\lambda)(\lambda+2)(\lambda-8)$$

Hence, $\lambda_1 = 6, \lambda_2 = -2, \lambda_3 = 8$. We have $\text{tr}(\mathbf{A}) = 12$ and $\det(\mathbf{A}) = -96$, which is in agreement with $\lambda_1 + \lambda_2 + \lambda_3 = 12$ and $\lambda_1\lambda_2\lambda_3 = -96$.

The set of all eigenvalues of **A** is known as the *spectrum* of **A**. The *spectral radius* of **A**, written $\rho(\mathbf{A})$, is the maximum of the absolute values of the eigenvalues of **A**. That is,

$$\rho(\mathbf{A}) = \max\{|\lambda_1|, |\lambda_2|, \ldots, |\lambda_n|\} \tag{5.3.10}$$

Thus, for instance, $\rho(\mathbf{A}) = 8$ for the matrix of Example 5.3.4.

5.3.1 The Characteristic Equation and the Eigenvalues in MATLAB

The command eig(A) returns the eigenvalues of **A** as the entries in a column vector.

Example 5.3.5. Suppose

```
A =
    [1  2  4
     0  2  0
     0  2  1]
```

then eig(A) returns

```
ans =
     1
     1
     2
```

Poly(A) returns the coefficients of $\det(\lambda\mathbf{I} - \mathbf{A}) = (-1)^n c_{\mathbf{A}}(\lambda)$ as a row vector. The coefficients are presented in decreasing order. For the matrix in Example 5.3.5, $c_A(\Lambda) = -\lambda^3 + 4\lambda^2 - 5\lambda + 2$, so that

```
poly(A) =
          1    - 4    5    - 2
```

Roots(poly(A)) provides an alternative method for finding eigenvalues of **A**.

Example 5.3.6. For the matrix **A** in Example 5.3.3, roots(poly(A)) returns

$$\begin{aligned}\text{ans} =&\\ &2.0000\\ &1.0000 + 0.0000i\\ &1.0000 - 0.0000i\end{aligned}$$

PROBLEMS

PART 1

Find the characteristic equation, the eigenvalues, and the spectral radius of each of the matrices in Part 1. (Recall that $|a + ib|^2 = a^2 + b^2$.)

5.3.1. (*a*) $\begin{bmatrix} 1 & 1 \\ -1 & -1 \end{bmatrix}$ (*b*) $\begin{bmatrix} \cos\tau & -\sin\tau \\ \sin\tau & \cos\tau \end{bmatrix}$ (*c*) $\begin{bmatrix} 0 & a \\ a & 0 \end{bmatrix}$

(*d*) $\begin{bmatrix} 0 & -a \\ a & 0 \end{bmatrix}$

5.3.2. (*a*) $\begin{bmatrix} 2 & -1 & -1 \\ 1 & 1 & 0 \\ 0 & 1 & 1 \end{bmatrix}$ (*b*) $\begin{bmatrix} -1 & 1 & -1 \\ 0 & -1 & 0 \\ 1 & 1 & 1 \end{bmatrix}$ (*c*) $\begin{bmatrix} 2 & 1 & -1 \\ 1 & 0 & 0 \\ 0 & 1 & 1 \end{bmatrix}$

5.3.3. (*a*) $\begin{bmatrix} 1 & 1 & 0 \\ 0 & 1 & 1 \\ 0 & 0 & 1 \end{bmatrix}$ (*b*) $\begin{bmatrix} 1 & 1 & 0 \\ 0 & 1 & 0 \\ 0 & 0 & 1 \end{bmatrix}$ (*c*) $\begin{bmatrix} 1 & 0 & 0 \\ 0 & 1 & 0 \\ 0 & 0 & 1 \end{bmatrix}$

5.3.4. (*a*) $\begin{bmatrix} 0 & 0 & 1 \\ 1 & 0 & 0 \\ 0 & 1 & 0 \end{bmatrix}$ (*b*) $\begin{bmatrix} -1 & 2 & 3 \\ 0 & 0 & 0 \\ 1 & 1 & 1 \end{bmatrix}$ (*c*) $\begin{bmatrix} 0 & 1 & 0 \\ 0 & 0 & 1 \\ 5 & 6 & 0 \end{bmatrix}$

(*d*) $\begin{bmatrix} 1 & 1 & 1 \\ 1 & 1 & 1 \\ a & b & (a+b)/2 \end{bmatrix}$ (*e*) $\begin{bmatrix} 1 & -2 & 1 \\ 1 & 1 & -2 \\ -2 & 1 & 1 \end{bmatrix}$

5.3.5. (*a*) $\begin{bmatrix} 1 & i \\ -i & -1 \end{bmatrix}$ (*b*) $\begin{bmatrix} 1 & i \\ i & -1 \end{bmatrix}$ (*c*) $\begin{bmatrix} 0 & ia \\ ia & 0 \end{bmatrix}$ (*d*) $\begin{bmatrix} 0 & -ia \\ ia & 0 \end{bmatrix}$

5.3.6. (*a*) $\begin{bmatrix} 1 & 0 \\ 2 & 3 \end{bmatrix}$ (*b*) $\begin{bmatrix} 2 & 2 \\ 0 & 1 \end{bmatrix}$ (*c*) $\begin{bmatrix} 0 & 0 & 0 \\ 2 & 1 & 0 \\ 0 & 4 & 1 \end{bmatrix}$ (*d*) $\begin{bmatrix} -1 & 2 & 0 \\ 0 & 2 & 6 \\ 0 & 4 & 5 \end{bmatrix}$

(*e*) $[0]$ (*f*) $\begin{bmatrix} 0 & -1 \\ 1 & 0 \end{bmatrix}$ (*g*) $\begin{bmatrix} 0 & -1 & -2 \\ 1 & 0 & -3 \\ 2 & 3 & 0 \end{bmatrix}$ (*h*) $\begin{bmatrix} 1 & -1 & -2 \\ 2 & 1 & 3 \\ 2 & 3 & 0 \end{bmatrix}$

5.3.7. $\begin{bmatrix} 2 & 0 & 3 & 0 \\ 0 & 2 & 0 & 3 \\ 3 & 0 & 2 & 0 \\ 0 & 3 & 0 & 2 \end{bmatrix}$

5.3.8. (*a*) $\begin{bmatrix} 1 & 1 & 1 \\ 0 & 2 & 1 \\ 2 & 1 & 0 \end{bmatrix}$ (*b*) $\begin{bmatrix} -1 & 1 & 1 \\ -3 & 3 & 1 \\ -1 & 1 & 1 \end{bmatrix}$ (*c*) $\begin{bmatrix} 2 & -1 & 1 \\ 3 & -2 & 1 \\ 1 & -1 & 2 \end{bmatrix}$

(*d*) $\begin{bmatrix} -2 & 1 & 2 \\ -5 & 4 & -2 \\ 1 & 1 & -1 \end{bmatrix}$

5.3.9. (*a*) $\begin{bmatrix} 2 & 2 & -1 \\ -1 & -1 & 1 \\ 2 & 4 & -1 \end{bmatrix}$ (*b*) $\begin{bmatrix} 0 & -1 & 1 \\ 2 & -3 & 2 \\ -2 & 2 & -3 \end{bmatrix}$ (*c*) $\begin{bmatrix} -1 & 1 & 1 \\ 2 & 0 & 2 \\ 3 & 3 & 1 \end{bmatrix}$

(*d*) $\begin{bmatrix} 2 & 1 & 1 \\ -1 & 0 & 1 \\ 2 & 2 & 3 \end{bmatrix}$ (*e*) $\begin{bmatrix} 0 & -2 & 1 \\ -2 & 3 & -2 \\ 1 & -2 & 0 \end{bmatrix}$ (*f*) $\begin{bmatrix} 2 & -2 & -1 \\ 1 & -1 & -1 \\ -2 & 4 & 3 \end{bmatrix}$

(*g*) $\begin{bmatrix} 0 & 1 & 2 \\ 1 & 0 & -3 \\ 2 & 3 & 0 \end{bmatrix}$

5.3.10. (*a*) $\begin{bmatrix} 2 & 0 & 1 \\ 1 & 3 & 1 \\ 1 & 0 & 2 \end{bmatrix}$ (*b*) $\begin{bmatrix} -1 & 0 & 2 \\ 1 & 1 & 1 \\ 2 & 0 & -1 \end{bmatrix}$ (*c*) $\begin{bmatrix} 2 & 0 & 1 \\ 1 & 1 & 1 \\ 1 & 0 & 2 \end{bmatrix}$

(*d*) $\begin{bmatrix} 3 & 0 & 2 \\ 1 & 1 & -1 \\ -2 & 0 & 1 \end{bmatrix}$ (*e*) $\begin{bmatrix} 3 & 0 & 2 \\ 1 & 1 & 1 \\ -2 & 0 & -1 \end{bmatrix}$ (*f*) $\begin{bmatrix} 1 & 1 & -5/4 \\ 1 & 1 & 1 \\ 1 & 1 & 1 \end{bmatrix}$

(*g*) $\begin{bmatrix} 0 & 1 & 0 \\ 0 & 0 & 1 \\ 1 & -3 & 3 \end{bmatrix}$

5.3.11. (*a*) $\begin{bmatrix} 0 & 1 & 0 \\ 1 & 0 & 0 \\ 0 & 0 & 1 \end{bmatrix}$ (*b*) $\begin{bmatrix} 0 & 0 & 1 \\ 1 & 0 & 0 \\ 0 & 1 & 0 \end{bmatrix}$ (*c*) $\begin{bmatrix} 1 & 1 & -1 \\ 1 & 1 & 1 \\ 1 & 1 & 1 \end{bmatrix}$

PART 2

5.3.12. Show that the characteristic equations of $\mathbf{A}^T$ and $\mathbf{A}$ are identical by proving $\det(\mathbf{A}^T - \lambda\mathbf{I}) = \det\left((\mathbf{A} - \lambda\mathbf{I})^T\right)$.

5.3.13. How are the eigenvalues of **A** and **B** related to those of

$$\begin{bmatrix} \mathbf{A} & \mathbf{O} \\ \mathbf{O} & \mathbf{B} \end{bmatrix}$$

5.3.14. Find the characteristic equation and show that $a + b + c, r$, and s are the eigenvalues of

$$\mathbf{A} = \begin{bmatrix} a & b & c \\ a - r & b + r & c \\ a - s & b & c + s \end{bmatrix}$$

5.3.15. Find the characteristic equation and show that $d, a+b$, and $a-d$ are the eigenvalues of

$$\mathbf{A} = \begin{bmatrix} a & 0 & b \\ c & d & c \\ b & 0 & a \end{bmatrix}$$

5.3.16. Find the characteristic equation of the matrices

$$(a)\ \begin{bmatrix} 0 & 1 & 0 \\ 0 & 0 & 1 \\ r^3 & -3r^2 & 3r \end{bmatrix} \quad (b)\ \begin{bmatrix} 0 & 1 & 0 \\ 0 & 0 & 1 \\ -r & 1 & r \end{bmatrix} \quad (c)\ \begin{bmatrix} 2-s & s & s \\ 1 & 0 & -1 \\ 0 & 1 & 2 \end{bmatrix}$$

5.3.17. Expand the determinants:

$$\det\begin{bmatrix} a_{11}-\lambda & a_{12} \\ a_{21} & a_{22}-\lambda \end{bmatrix} \qquad \det\begin{bmatrix} a_{11}-\lambda & a_{12} & a_{31} \\ a_{21} & a_{22}-\lambda & a_{23} \\ a_{31} & a_{32} & a_{33}-\lambda \end{bmatrix}$$

and verify the fact that every term except the one consisting of the product of the diagonal entries is of degree $n-2$ or less in λ.

5.3.18. Suppose λ is an eigenvalue of **A**, so that there exists a nonzero vector **x** such that $\mathbf{Ax} = \lambda\mathbf{x}$. Use this formulation of the eigenvalue-eigenvector problem to derive the following:
(*a*) $k+\lambda$ is an eigenvalue of $\mathbf{A} + k\mathbf{I}$.
(*b*) $k\lambda$ is an eigenvalue of $k\mathbf{A}$.
(*c*) If **A** is invertible, $1/\lambda$ is an eigenvalue of $\mathbf{A}^{-1}$.

5.3.19. Explain why each of the following statements is true: The scalar λ is an eigenvalue λ of **A** if
(*a*) $\mathbf{A} - \lambda\mathbf{I}$ is singular.
(*b*) $\det(\mathbf{A} - \lambda\mathbf{I}) = 0$.
(*c*) there is an $\mathbf{x} \neq \mathbf{0}$ such that $\mathbf{Ax} = \lambda\mathbf{x}$.
(*d*) $c(\lambda) = 0$.

PART 3

5.3.20. Let $c_{\mathbf{B}}(\lambda)$ be the characteristic polynomial of $\mathbf{B} = k\mathbf{A}$. Show that

$$c_{\mathbf{B}}(\lambda) = (k\lambda_1 - \lambda)(k\lambda_2 - \lambda)\cdots(k\lambda_n - \lambda)$$

where $\lambda_1, \lambda_2, \ldots, \lambda_n$ are the eigenvalues of **A**. How are the eigenvalues of **A** related to those of **B**? Compare with Problem 5.3.18.

5.3.21. Let $c_{\mathbf{B}}(\lambda)$ be the characteristic polynomial of $\mathbf{B} = \mathbf{A} + k\mathbf{I}$. Show that

$$c_{\mathbf{B}}(\lambda) = (k + \lambda_1 - \lambda)(k + \lambda_2 - \lambda)\cdots(k + \lambda_n - \lambda)$$

where $\lambda_1, \lambda_2, \ldots, \lambda_n$ are the eigenvalues of **A**. How are the eigenvalues of **A** related to those of **B**? Compare with Problem 5.3.18.

5.3.22. Let $c(\lambda)$ be the characteristic polynomial of **A** and $c_{\mathbf{B}}(\lambda)$ be the characteristic polynomial of $\mathbf{B} = \mathbf{A}^{-1}$.
(*a*) Show that

$$\begin{aligned} c_{\mathbf{B}}(\lambda) &= (-\lambda)^n \det(\mathbf{B})(\lambda_1 - 1/\lambda)(\lambda_2 - 1/\lambda)\cdots(\lambda_n - 1/\lambda) \\ &= (\lambda_1^{-1} - \lambda)(\lambda_2^{-1} - \lambda)\cdots(\lambda_n^{-1} - \lambda) \end{aligned}$$

where $\lambda_1, \lambda_2, \ldots, \lambda_n$ are the eigenvalues of $\mathbf{A}$. How are the eigenvalues of $\mathbf{A}$ related to those of $\mathbf{A}^{-1}$?

(*b*) Show that $\mathbf{c_B}(\lambda) = \det(\mathbf{A}^{-1})(-\lambda)^n c(1/\lambda)$. By studying the coefficients of the polynomial $\mathbf{c_B}(\lambda)$ and $(-\lambda)^n c(1/\lambda)$, prove that the coefficient of λ in the characteristic equation of $\mathbf{A}$ is $c_1 = \det(\mathbf{A})\operatorname{tr}(\mathbf{A}^{-1})$.

5.3.23. Show by example that there is no connection between the characteristic equations of $\mathbf{A}$ and $\mathbf{B}$ if $\mathbf{A}$ and $\mathbf{B}$ are row-equivalent but otherwise unrelated. ($\mathbf{A}$ is row-equivalent to $\mathbf{B}$ if there exists a nonsingular $\mathbf{S}$ such that $\mathbf{SA} = \mathbf{B}$. In other words, there is a sequence of elementary row operations that take $\mathbf{A}$ into $\mathbf{B}$.)

5.3.24. Let $\prod_{i=2}^{n-1} x_i = x_2 x_3 \cdots x_{n-1}$ and suppose

$$\mathbf{A} = \begin{bmatrix} a_{11} & 0 & \ldots & 0 & a_{1n} \\ a_{21} & a_{22} & \ldots & 0 & a_{2n} \\ \vdots & & & & \\ a_{n1} & 0 & \ldots & 0 & a_{nn} \end{bmatrix}$$

Show that $c_{\mathbf{A}}(\lambda) = [\lambda^2 - (a_{11} + a_{nn})\lambda + a_{11}a_{nn} - a_{1n}a_{n1}] \prod_{i=2}^{n-1}(a_{ii} - \lambda)$ is the characteristic equation of $\mathbf{A}$.

MATLAB

Use the MATLAB command roots(poly(A)) or eig(A) to find the eigenvalues of the following matrices.

5.3.26. Problem 5.3.1(*a*).

5.3.27. Problem 5.3.2(*a*)–(*c*).

5.3.28. Problem 5.3.3(*a*)–(*c*).

5.3.29. Problem 5.3.4(*a*)–(*c*).

5.3.30. Problem 5.3.5(*a*), (*b*).

5.3.31. Problem 5.3.6.

5.3.32. Problem 5.3.7.

5.3.33. Problem 5.3.8.

5.3.34. Problem 5.3.9.

5.3.35. Problem 5.3.10

5.3.36. Use the MATLAB command magic(n) to find the magic square of size $n \times n$ for $n = 3, 4, 5$. Find the eigenvalues of each of these magic squares. (See Section 0.1.1.)

5.3.37. Find the eigenvalues of the matrix $\mathbf{P}$ of Section 5.1.

5.3.38. Enter

$$\mathbf{A} = \begin{bmatrix} 1 & 1 & 1 \\ 0 & 2 & 1 \\ 2 & 1 & 0 \end{bmatrix}$$

and compare the eigenvalues of $\mathbf{A}$ with those of $\mathbf{A}^2$, and $\mathbf{A}^2 + 2\mathbf{A} + \mathbf{I}$.

5.3.39. What does MATLAB return in response to poly(eig(A))? Explain.

5.4 THE EIGENVECTORS OF A

For each eigenvalue λ of $\mathbf{A}$, there exist nonzero vectors $\mathbf{x}$ such that $\mathbf{Ax} = \lambda\mathbf{x}$. Each such vector is an eigenvector corresponding to λ. The set consisting of the eigenvectors corresponding to λ and the zero vector is a vector space known as the *eigenspace* of λ, written $\mathscr{E}(\lambda)$. However, even for real **A**, the eigenvalues may not be real, and hence the entries of the corresponding eigenvector need not be real. We write $\mathbf{x} \in \mathscr{C}^n$ instead of $\mathbf{x} \in \mathscr{R}^n$ to denote that **x** is an n-tuple with (possibly) complex entries. Thus, for example, $\mathscr{E}(\lambda) \subseteq \mathscr{C}^n$.

Theorem 5.4.1. *If λ is an eigenvalue of* **A** *then the set of all vectors satisfying* $\mathbf{Ax} = \lambda\mathbf{x}$ *is the vector space* $\mathscr{E}(\lambda) = null(\mathbf{A} - \lambda\mathbf{I})$, *called the eigenspace of* λ. *Moreover, dim* $(\mathscr{E}(\lambda)) = n - \text{rank}(\mathbf{A} - \lambda\mathbf{I})$.

Proof. The set of vectors satisfying $\mathbf{Ax} = \lambda\mathbf{x}$ are precisely those that satisfy $(\mathbf{A} - \lambda\mathbf{I})\mathbf{x} = \mathbf{0}$. Hence, $\mathscr{E}(\lambda) = null(\mathbf{A} - \lambda\mathbf{I})$. By Theorem 3.5.2, dim $(\mathscr{E}(\lambda)) = n - \text{rank}(\mathbf{A} - \lambda\mathbf{I})$. ■

Example 5.4.1. Find all the eigenspaces of

$$\mathbf{A} = \begin{bmatrix} 1 & 1 \\ 4 & 1 \end{bmatrix}$$

Solution. In Example 5.3.1(a), the eigenvalues of **A** were found to be $\lambda_1 = -1$ and $\lambda_2 = 3$. There are two eigenspaces, one for each eigenvalue. We find the eigenspace associated with $\lambda_1 = -1$ by solving the system

$$(\mathbf{A} + \mathbf{I})\mathbf{x} = \begin{bmatrix} 2 & 1 \\ 4 & 2 \end{bmatrix}\mathbf{x} = \mathbf{0}$$

The singular coefficient matrix confirms that $\lambda = -1$ is an eigenvalue. A set of linearly independent solutions of this system is obtained by elementary row operations on the augmented system $[(\mathbf{A} + \mathbf{I})^T \quad \mathbf{I}]$:

$$[(\mathbf{A} + \mathbf{I})^T \quad \mathbf{I}] = \begin{bmatrix} 2 & 4 & 1 & 0 \\ 1 & 2 & 0 & 1 \end{bmatrix} \rightarrow \cdots \rightarrow \begin{bmatrix} 1 & 2 & ½ & 0 \\ 0 & 0 & -½ & 1 \end{bmatrix}$$

Hence, the vector $\mathbf{x}_1 = [-½ \quad 1]^T$ is a basis for the null space of $\mathbf{A} + \lambda\mathbf{I}$ and, therefore, the eigenspace is one-dimensional. That is, $\mathscr{E}(-1) = span\{\mathbf{x}_1\}$. It is easily verified that $\mathbf{Ax}_1 = (-1)\mathbf{x}_1$.

The second eigenspace is obtained in the same manner using $\lambda = 3$. The diagram

$$\begin{bmatrix} -2 & 4 & 1 & 0 \\ 1 & -2 & 0 & 1 \end{bmatrix} \rightarrow \cdots \rightarrow \begin{bmatrix} -1 & ½ & ½ & 0 \\ 0 & 0 & ½ & 1 \end{bmatrix}$$

leads to the conclusion that $\mathscr{E}(3) = span\{[½ \quad 1]^T\}$ and, therefore, that this eigenspace is also one-dimensional.

Example 5.4.2. Find the eigenspaces of

$$\mathbf{A} = \begin{bmatrix} 1 & 1 & 2 \\ 0 & 1 & 0 \\ 0 & 0 & 1 \end{bmatrix}$$

Solution. The characteristic equation is $c(\lambda) = (1-\lambda)^3$. Hence, all three eigenvalues are identical. Therefore, there is only one eigenspace. Its dimension depends on rank($\mathbf{A} - \lambda\mathbf{I}$). In this case, we have rank($\mathbf{A} - \mathbf{I}$) = 1 and hence $\dim\left(\mathscr{E}(1)\right) = 3 - 1 = 2$. The eigenspace is found from

$$(\mathbf{A} - \mathbf{I})\mathbf{x} = \begin{bmatrix} 0 & 1 & 2 \\ 0 & 0 & 0 \\ 0 & 0 & 0 \end{bmatrix} \mathbf{x} = 0$$

This leads to the linearly independent eigenvectors $\mathbf{x}_1 = [1 \quad 0 \quad 0]^T$ and $\mathbf{x}_2 = [0 \quad -2 \quad 1]^T$. Thus,

$$\mathscr{E}(1) = span\left\{\begin{bmatrix} 1 \\ 0 \\ 0 \end{bmatrix}, \begin{bmatrix} 0 \\ -2 \\ 1 \end{bmatrix}\right\}$$

Example 5.4.3. Find the eigenspaces of

$$\mathbf{A} = \begin{bmatrix} 1 & 1 & 2 \\ 0 & 1 & 1 \\ 0 & 0 & 1 \end{bmatrix}$$

Solution. Again the characteristic equation is $c(\lambda) = (1-\lambda)^3$, and all three eigenvalues are identical. The sole eigenspace has dimension 1 since the rank of $\mathbf{A} - \mathbf{I}$ is 2. In contrast to the previous example, we find the set of solutions of the homogeneous system

$$(\mathbf{A} - \mathbf{I})\mathbf{x} = \begin{bmatrix} 0 & 1 & 2 \\ 0 & 0 & 1 \\ 0 & 0 & 0 \end{bmatrix} \mathbf{x} = 0$$

is one-dimensional, as expected. Explicitly, $\mathscr{E}(1) = span\{[1 \quad 0 \quad 0]^T\}$.

In some instances it is possible to bypass the definitions and find the eigenvalues and eigenvectors by exploiting the various theorems proved in this section and Section 5.3.

Example 5.4.4. Find the eigenspaces of the matrix $\mathbf{J}_n = [1 \quad 1 \quad \ldots \quad 1]$

Solution. By definition

$$\mathbf{J}_n = \begin{bmatrix} 1 & 1 & \ldots & 1 \\ 1 & 1 & \ldots & 1 \\ \vdots & \vdots & & \vdots \\ 1 & 1 & \ldots & 1 \end{bmatrix}$$

Clearly, $\mathbf{J}_n$ is singular and, hence, $\lambda = 0$ is an eigenvalue. Because rank($\mathbf{J}_n - 0\mathbf{I}$) = rank($\mathbf{J}_n$) = 1, the eigenspace associated with $\lambda = 0$ is $(n-1)$-dimensional. A basis for this eigenspace is the set

$$\left\{ \mathbf{x}_1 = \begin{bmatrix} -1 \\ 1 \\ 0 \\ \vdots \\ 0 \end{bmatrix}, \quad \mathbf{x}_2 = \begin{bmatrix} -1 \\ 0 \\ 1 \\ \vdots \\ 0 \end{bmatrix}, \ldots, \mathbf{x}_{n-1} = \begin{bmatrix} -1 \\ 0 \\ 0 \\ \vdots \\ 1 \end{bmatrix} \right\}$$

It will be shown in the next section that the dimension of the eigenspace is a lower bound for the number of times a given eigenvalue can be repeated as a root of $c(\lambda)$. Applied to this example, it follows that $\lambda = 0$ must be repeated at least $n - 1$ times. Therefore $c(\lambda) = (0 - \lambda)^{n-1}(\lambda_n - \lambda) = 0$ is the characteristic equation. Since $\mathrm{tr}(\mathbf{J}_n) = n = 0 + 0 + \cdots + 0 + \lambda_n$ (by Theorem 5.3.2), it follows that $\lambda_n = n$. The eigenspace associated with this eigenvalue is obtained by inspection: $\mathcal{E}(n) = span\{\mathbf{1}\}$.

5.4.1 Eigenvectors in MATLAB

Eig(A) is the MATLAB command that returns a column vector whose entries are the eigenvalues of **A**. The eigenvectors are obtained by [X,D] = eig(A), where **D** is a diagonal matrix whose diagonal entries are the eigenvalues of **A**, and **X** is a matrix whose columns are the eigenvectors of **A**. The *i*th column of **X** and the (*i*, *i*) entry of **D** is an eigenpair. Moreover, MATLAB returns an orthonormal basis of eigenvectors for each eigenspace. In particular, if $\dim\left(\mathcal{E}(\lambda)\right) = 1$ and $\mathbf{x} \in \mathcal{E}(\lambda)$, then MATLAB returns $\mathbf{x}/\|\mathbf{x}\|$.

Example 5.4.5. Use the command [X,D] = eig(A) to find the eigenvalues and eigenvectors of $\mathbf{J}_4$.

Solution. First set J = ones(4). Then [X,D] = eig(J) returns the pair of matrices X and D:

```
X =
   -0.3829    0.5660    0.5320    0.5000
    0.8511    0.1579   -0.0254    0.5000
   -0.3325    0.0812   -0.7955    0.5000
   -0.1357   -0.8051    0.2889    0.5000

D =
   -0.0000    0          0         0
    0        -0.0000     0         0
    0         0          0.0000    0
    0         0          0         4.0000
```

The first three columns of X are three orthonormal eigenvectors of $\mathbf{J}_4$ corresponding to the eigenvalue 0. The last column of X is the eigenvector of $\mathbf{J}_4$ of norm 1, corresponding to the eigenvalue 4. The minus signs and zeros after the decimal point on the diagonal of D are due to the fact that the computed eigenvalues are approximations to the correct integer values.

PROBLEMS

PART 1

The matrices referred to in each of the next eight problems appear in the exercise set of Section 5.3. In each case find all the eigenvectors.

5.4.1. Problem 5.3.1.

5.4.2. Problem 5.3.2.

5.4.3. Problem 5.3.3.

5.4.4. Problem 5.3.4.

5.4.5. Problem 5.3.5

5.4.6. Problem 5.3.6.

5.4.7. Problem 5.3.7.

5.4.8. Problem 5.3.9.

5.4.9. Find the eigenvalues and eigenvectors of

$$\mathbf{A} = \begin{bmatrix} 0 & 1 \\ -2 & -2 \end{bmatrix}$$

PART 2

5.4.10. If $\mathbf{A}$ is singular, explain why $\mathcal{E}(0) = null(\mathbf{A})$.

5.4.11. Let $\mathbf{A} = \mathbf{u}\mathbf{v}^{\mathrm{T}}, \mathbf{u} \neq \mathbf{0}$. Show that $(\lambda = \mathbf{u}^{\mathrm{T}}\mathbf{v}, \mathbf{x} = \mathbf{u})$ is an eigenpair of $\mathbf{A}$. If $\mathbf{u} \in \mathcal{R}^n, n > 1$, find an eigenvector corresponding to $\lambda = 0$.

5.4.12. Show that the set

$$\left\{ \mathbf{y}_1 = \begin{bmatrix} -1 \\ 1 \\ 0 \\ 0 \\ 0 \end{bmatrix}, \quad \mathbf{y}_2 = \begin{bmatrix} 1 \\ 1 \\ -2 \\ 0 \\ 0 \end{bmatrix}, \quad \mathbf{y}_3 = \begin{bmatrix} 1 \\ 1 \\ 1 \\ -3 \\ 0 \end{bmatrix}, \quad \mathbf{y}_4 = \begin{bmatrix} 1 \\ 1 \\ 1 \\ 1 \\ -4 \end{bmatrix} \right\}$$

is an orthogonal basis for the eigenspace of $\lambda = 0$, an eigenvalue of $\mathbf{J}_5$. Compare with Example 5.4.4.

PART 3

5.4.13. Generalize the result in Problem 5.4.12 for the matrix $\mathbf{J}_n$. Check for $n = 3$ and $n = 4$.

5.4.14. Let $\mathbf{A} = \mathbf{u}\mathbf{v}^{\mathrm{T}}$. If $\mathbf{u}^{\mathrm{T}}\mathbf{v} \neq \mathbf{0}$, show that $\lambda = 0$ is an eigenvalue of $\mathbf{A}$ and that the dimension of $\mathcal{E}(0)$ is $n - 1$. (See Problem 5.4.11.)

5.4.15. Suppose λ is an eigenvalue of $\mathbf{A}$. Show that λ^2 is an eigenvalue of $\mathbf{A}^2$. How are the eigenvectors of $\mathbf{A}$ related to those of $\mathbf{A}^2$?

5.4.16. Generalize the result in Problem 5.4.15 to $\mathbf{A}^n$, where n is a positive integer.

5.4.17. Suppose $\mathbf{P}^2 = \mathbf{P}$. Use the result in Problem 5.4.15 to show that the eigenvalues of $\mathbf{P}$ are either 0 or 1.

5.4.18. Suppose $\mathbf{M}^2 = \mathbf{I}$. Use the result in Problem 5.4.15 to show that the eigenvalues of $\mathbf{M}$ are either -1 or 1.

5.4.19. Show that $\det(\mathbf{J}_n - \lambda\mathbf{I}) = (-\lambda)^{n-1}(n - \lambda)$ by expanding $\det(\mathbf{J}_n - \lambda\mathbf{I})$.

5.4.20. Suppose $\mathbf{T}$ is a matrix whose row sum is constant, that is, for each i, $\sum_{j=1}^{n} t_{ij} = S$, for each i. Show that $(\lambda = S, \ \mathbf{x} = \mathbf{1})$ is an eigenpair.

MATLAB

Use the MATLAB command [X,D] = eig(A) to find the eigenvectors in each of the following problems from Section 5.3.

5.4.21. Problem 5.3.1(*a*).

5.4.22. Problem 5.3.2(*a*)–(*c*).

5.4.23. Problem 5.3.3(*a*)–(*c*).

5.4.24. Problem 5.3.4(*a*)–(*c*).

5.4.25. Problem 5.3.5(*a*), (*b*).

5.4.26. Problem 5.3.6.

5.4.27. Problem 5.3.7.

5.4.28. Problem 5.3.8.

5.4.29. Problem 5.3.9.

5.4.30. Problem 5.3.10.

5.4.31. Problem 5.3.36.

5.4.32. Problem 5.3.37.

5.5 ALGEBRAIC AND GEOMETRIC MULTIPLICITIES OF EIGENVALUES

The dimension of the eigenspace corresponding to a particular eigenvalue is subtly related to the number of repetitions of the eigenvalue as a root of its characteristic equation. This deep and important result is the central theme of this section.

It is a well-known fact of algebra (Theorem 5.2.2) that a polynomial of degree n has n roots. Since the polynomial $p(x) = (2-x)^4$ has only the single root $r = 2$, this theorem can only be true if we count $r = 2$ as a repeated root of $(2-x)^4$, specifically, repeated four times. In general, the number of times $(r-x)$ factors the polynomial is the number of times the root r is counted; this number is called the *algebraic multiplicity* of the root. Write $a(r) = m$ if $(r-x)^m$ factors $p(x)$ and $(r-x)^{m+1}$ does not. For example, if

$$p(x) = (3-x)^3(2-x)(4-x)^2$$

then $a(3) = 3$, $a(2) = 1$, and $a(4) = 2$. Note that the degree of $p(x)$ is six, and this is precisely the sum of the algebraic multiplicities of all the roots $r_1 = 3$, $r_2 = 2$, $r_3 = 4$. In general, the sum of the algebraic multiplicities of each root is the degree of the polynomial; this is implicit in the theorem that a polynomial of degree n has n roots.

If $\lambda = \lambda_0$ is an eigenvalue of $\mathbf{A}$, and the associated eigenspace has dimension s, then write $g(\lambda_0) = s$ and call s the *geometric multiplicity* of λ_0. As an illustration, the eigenvalues 0 and n of $\mathbf{J}_n$ have these multiplicities: $a(0) = g(0) = n-1$ and $a(n) = g(n) = 1$. By definition, then, $g(\lambda) = \dim(\mathcal{E}(\lambda)) = \dim(null(\mathbf{A} - \lambda\mathbf{I}))$. Our aim is to establish the fact that the geometric multiplicity of an eigenvalue can never exceed its algebraic multiplicity, or $g(\lambda) \le a(\lambda)$.

This result is stated and proved in Theorem 5.5.2 to follow. The proof is expedited by two lemmas that are of independent interest and importance.

Lemma 5.1. *For each invertible* $\mathbf{S}$*, the characteristic equations of* $\mathbf{A}$ *and* $\mathbf{S}^{-1}\mathbf{AS}$ *are identical.*

Proof. First note that $\det(\mathbf{S})\det(\mathbf{S}^{-1}) = 1$ because

$$1 = \det(\mathbf{I}) = \det(\mathbf{S}^{-1}\mathbf{S}) = \det(\mathbf{S}^{-1})\det(\mathbf{S})$$

Then, using this fact,

$$\begin{aligned}\det(\mathbf{S}^{-1}\mathbf{AS} - \lambda\mathbf{I}) &= \det(\mathbf{S}^{-1}(\mathbf{A} - \lambda\mathbf{I})S) \\ &= \det(\mathbf{S}^{-1})\det(\mathbf{A} - \lambda\mathbf{I})\det(\mathbf{S}) = \det(\mathbf{A} - \lambda\mathbf{I}) = c(\lambda) \blacksquare\end{aligned}$$

Lemma 5.2. *Suppose* $\mathbf{Ax} = \lambda\mathbf{x}$, $\mathbf{x} \neq \mathbf{0}$ *and* $\mathbf{S}$ *is a nonsingular matrix whose ith column is* $\mathbf{x}$*. Then the ith column of* $\mathbf{S}^{-1}\mathbf{AS}$ *is* $\lambda\mathbf{e}_i$*.*

Proof. Suppose $\mathbf{S} = [\mathbf{s} \ldots \mathbf{x} \ldots \mathbf{s}_n]$, where $\mathbf{s}_i = \mathbf{x}$. Then, since $\mathbf{S}^{-1}\mathbf{S} = \mathbf{I}$, it follows that

$$\mathbf{S}^{-1}\mathbf{S} = \mathbf{S}^{-1}[\mathbf{s}_1 \ldots \mathbf{x} \ldots \mathbf{s}_n] = [\mathbf{S}^{-1}\mathbf{s}_1 \ldots \mathbf{S}^{-1}\mathbf{x} \ldots \mathbf{S}^{-1}\mathbf{s}_n] = \mathbf{I}$$

Therefore, the ith column of $\mathbf{S}^{-1}\mathbf{S}$ is the ith column of $\mathbf{I}$. Thus $\mathbf{S}^{-1}\mathbf{x} = \mathbf{e}_i$. This fact is used in the following argument:

$$\mathbf{S}^{-1}\mathbf{AS} = \mathbf{S}^{-1}\mathbf{A}[\mathbf{s}_1 \ldots \mathbf{x} \ldots \mathbf{s}_n] = \mathbf{S}^{-1}[\mathbf{As}_1 \ldots \mathbf{Ax} \ldots \mathbf{As}_n] \tag{5.5.1}$$

by partitioned multiplication. But, since $\mathbf{Ax} = \lambda\mathbf{x}$,

$$\begin{aligned}\mathbf{S}^{-1}[\mathbf{As}_1 \ldots \mathbf{Ax} \ldots \mathbf{As}_n] &= \mathbf{S}^{-1}[\mathbf{As}_1 \ldots \lambda\mathbf{x} \ldots \mathbf{As}_n] \\ &= [\mathbf{S}^{-1}\mathbf{As}_1 \ldots \lambda\mathbf{S}^{-1}\mathbf{x} \ldots \mathbf{S}^{-1}\mathbf{As}_n] \quad (5.5.2)\end{aligned}$$

again using partitioned multiplication. Because $\mathbf{S}^{-1}\mathbf{x} = \mathbf{e}_i$, Eq. 5.5.1 and Eq. 5.5.2 imply

$$\mathbf{S}^{-1}\mathbf{AS} = [\mathbf{S}^{-1}\mathbf{As}_1 \ldots \lambda\mathbf{e}_i \ldots \mathbf{S}^{-1}\mathbf{As}_n]$$

Thus the ith column of $\mathbf{S}^{-1}\mathbf{AS}$ is $\lambda\mathbf{e}_i = [\mathbf{0} \ldots \lambda \ldots 0]^{\mathrm{T}}$. In expanded form,

$$\mathbf{S}^{-1}\mathbf{AS} = \begin{bmatrix} * & * & \cdots & 0 & \cdots & * & * \\ & & & \vdots & & & \\ * & * & \cdots & \lambda & \cdots & * & * \\ & & & \vdots & & & \\ * & * & \cdots & 0 & \cdots & * & * \end{bmatrix} \leftarrow i\text{th row} \ \blacksquare$$

$$\uparrow$$
$$i\text{th column}$$

Theorem 5.5.1. *If* λ_0 *is an eigenvalue of* $\mathbf{A}$*, then the algebraic multiplicity of* λ_0 *is never less than its geometric multiplicity. That is,*

$$a(\lambda_0) \geq g(\lambda_0) \tag{5.5.3}$$

Proof. Suppose that $g(\lambda_0) = s$ and $\mathbf{x}_1, \mathbf{x}_2, \ldots, \mathbf{x}_s$ are s linearly independent eigenvectors associated with λ_0. It is always possible to define a nonsingular matrix $\mathbf{S}$ whose first s columns are these s vectors. (The last $n - s$ columns, if any, are any $n - s$ vectors $\mathbf{z}_{s+1}, \mathbf{z}_{s+2}, \ldots, \mathbf{z}_n$ chosen so that $\mathbf{S} = [\mathbf{x}_1 \quad \mathbf{x}_2 \quad \ldots \quad \mathbf{x}_s \quad \mathbf{z}_{s+1} \quad \mathbf{z}_{s+2} \quad \ldots \quad \mathbf{z}_n]$ is nonsingular). (See Example 3.2.8 and Theorem 3.2.2.) From Lemma 5.2, with $i = 1, 2, \ldots, s$, it follows that

$$\mathbf{S}^{-1}\mathbf{A}\mathbf{S} = [\lambda_0\mathbf{e}_1 \quad \lambda_0\mathbf{e}_2 \quad \ldots \quad \lambda_0\mathbf{e}_s \quad * \quad \ldots \quad *] = \left[\begin{array}{c|c} \lambda_0\mathbf{I}_s & \mathbf{C} \\ \hline \mathbf{O} & \mathbf{D} \end{array}\right]$$

By Lemma 5.1, $\det(\mathbf{S}^{-1}\mathbf{A}\mathbf{S} - \lambda\mathbf{I}) = \det(\mathbf{A} - \lambda\mathbf{I}) = c(\lambda)$, so that

$$c(\lambda) = \det\left\{\left[\begin{array}{c|c} \lambda_0\mathbf{I}_s & \mathbf{C} \\ \hline \mathbf{O} & \mathbf{D} \end{array}\right] - \lambda\mathbf{I}\right\} = \det\left[\begin{array}{c|c} (\lambda_0 - \lambda)\mathbf{I}_s & \mathbf{C} \\ \hline \mathbf{O} & \mathbf{D} - \lambda\mathbf{I} \end{array}\right] = (\lambda_0 - \lambda)^s q(\lambda)$$

The polynomial $q(\lambda) = \det(\mathbf{D} - \lambda\mathbf{I})$ is of degree $n - s$ and may have λ_0 as a root. Thus, $a(\lambda_0) \geq s = g(\lambda_0)$. ■

Example 5.5.1. As an illustration of Theorem 5.5.1, note that each of the following matrices has the same characteristic equation, $(\lambda - 1)^4 = 0$, and hence $a(1) = 4$. But $g(1)$ ranges from 4 to 1.

$$\begin{bmatrix} 1 & 0 & 0 & 0 \\ 0 & 1 & 0 & 0 \\ 0 & 0 & 1 & 0 \\ 0 & 0 & 0 & 1 \end{bmatrix} \quad \begin{bmatrix} 1 & 1 & 0 & 0 \\ 0 & 1 & 0 & 0 \\ 0 & 0 & 1 & 0 \\ 0 & 0 & 0 & 1 \end{bmatrix} \quad \begin{bmatrix} 1 & 1 & 0 & 0 \\ 0 & 1 & 1 & 0 \\ 0 & 0 & 1 & 0 \\ 0 & 0 & 0 & 1 \end{bmatrix} \quad \begin{bmatrix} 1 & 1 & 0 & 0 \\ 0 & 1 & 1 & 0 \\ 0 & 0 & 1 & 1 \\ 0 & 0 & 0 & 1 \end{bmatrix}$$

Theorem 5.5.2. *Suppose* $\lambda_1, \lambda_2, \ldots, \lambda_k$ *are* k *distinct eigenvalues of* $\mathbf{A}$ *and* $\mathbf{u}_1, \mathbf{u}_2, \ldots, \mathbf{u}_k$ *are corresponding eigenvectors. Then the set* $\{\mathbf{u}_1, \mathbf{u}_2, \ldots, \mathbf{u}_k\}$ *is linearly independent.*

Proof. (By contradiction.) Suppose the eigenvectors are ordered so that $\{\mathbf{u}_1, \mathbf{u}_2, \ldots, \mathbf{u}_m\}$ is linearly independent and $\{\mathbf{u}_1, \mathbf{u}_2, \ldots, \mathbf{u}_{m+1}\}$ is not. Then $\mathbf{u}_{m+1}$ is a linear combination of $\{\mathbf{u}_1, \mathbf{u}_2, \ldots, \mathbf{u}_m\}$. That is,

$$\mathbf{u}_{m+1} = \alpha_1\mathbf{u}_1 + \alpha_2\mathbf{u}_2 + \cdots + \alpha_m\mathbf{u}_m \tag{5.5.4}$$

The essential features of the argument is based on two equalities: first,

$$(\mathbf{A} - \lambda_{m+1}\mathbf{I})\mathbf{u}_{m+1} = \mathbf{0} \tag{5.5.5}$$

by definition of λ_{m+1} and $\mathbf{x}_{m+1}$; and second, for $j < m + 1$,

$$\begin{aligned} (\mathbf{A} - \lambda_m\mathbf{I})\mathbf{u}_j &= \mathbf{A}\mathbf{u}_j - \lambda_m\mathbf{u}_j = \lambda_j\mathbf{u}_j - \lambda_m\mathbf{u}_j \\ &= (\lambda_j - \lambda_m)\mathbf{u}_j \neq \mathbf{0} \end{aligned} \tag{5.5.6}$$

Premultiply Eq. 5.5.4 by $\mathbf{A} - \lambda_{m+1}\mathbf{I}$ and use Eq. 5.5.5 and 5.5.6 to obtain

$$\mathbf{0} = \alpha_1(\lambda_{m+1} - \lambda_1)\mathbf{u}_1 + \alpha_2(\lambda_{m+1} - \lambda_2)\mathbf{u}_2 + \cdots + \alpha_m(\lambda_{m+1} - \lambda_m)\mathbf{u}_m \tag{5.5.7}$$

Since $\mathbf{u}_1, \mathbf{u}_2, \ldots, \mathbf{u}_m$ is linearly independent, the weights in Eq. 5.5.7 are all zero. However $\lambda_{m+1} - \lambda_j \neq 0$, so that $\alpha_1 = \alpha_2 = \cdots = \alpha_k = 0$. Clearly, this contradicts Eq. 5.5.4 because $\mathbf{u}_{m+1} \neq \mathbf{0}$ is an eigenvector. ■

Example 5.5.2. The matrix

$$\mathbf{A} = \begin{bmatrix} 0 & 1 & 0 \\ 0 & 0 & 1 \\ 0 & 1 & 0 \end{bmatrix}$$

has eigenvalues $\lambda_1 = 0$, $\lambda_2 = -1$, and $\lambda_3 = 1$ and corresponding eigenvectors

$$\mathbf{u}_1 = \begin{bmatrix} 1 \\ 0 \\ 0 \end{bmatrix}, \qquad \mathbf{u}_2 = \begin{bmatrix} 1 \\ -1 \\ 1 \end{bmatrix}, \qquad \mathbf{u}_3 = \begin{bmatrix} 1 \\ 1 \\ 1 \end{bmatrix}$$

Theorem 5.5.2 asserts that these vectors are linearly independent. The essential ingredient in the argument is that $(\mathbf{A} - \lambda_i\mathbf{I})\mathbf{u}_j = (\lambda_j - \lambda_i)\mathbf{u}_j$. Here are some illustrative examples of this fact.

$$(\mathbf{A} - \lambda_1\mathbf{I})\mathbf{u}_2 = (\mathbf{A} - 0\mathbf{I})\mathbf{u}_2 = \begin{bmatrix} 0 & 1 & 0 \\ 0 & 0 & 1 \\ 0 & 1 & 0 \end{bmatrix}\begin{bmatrix} 1 \\ -1 \\ 1 \end{bmatrix} = \begin{bmatrix} -1 \\ 1 \\ -1 \end{bmatrix} = (-1-0)\begin{bmatrix} 1 \\ -1 \\ 1 \end{bmatrix}$$

$$(\mathbf{A} - \lambda_2\mathbf{I})\mathbf{u}_3 = (\mathbf{A} + \mathbf{I})\mathbf{u}_3 = \begin{bmatrix} 0 & 1 & 0 \\ 0 & 0 & 1 \\ 0 & 1 & 0 \end{bmatrix}\begin{bmatrix} 1 \\ 1 \\ 1 \end{bmatrix} = \begin{bmatrix} 2 \\ 2 \\ 2 \end{bmatrix} = (1-(-1))\begin{bmatrix} 1 \\ 1 \\ 1 \end{bmatrix}$$

PROBLEMS

PART 1

In each of the next seven problems, find the eigenvalues and their algebraic and geometric multiplicities for each of the matrices given in Section 5.3. Verify Theorem 5.5.2 in each instance where this theorem is applicable.

5.5.1. Problem 5.3.1.

5.5.2. Problem 5.3.2.

5.5.3. Problem 5.3.3.

5.5.4. Problem 5.3.4.

5.5.5. Problem 5.3.5.

5.5.6. Problem 5.3.6.

5.5.7. Problem 5.3.7.

5.5.8. For the matrix **A** of Example 5.5.2, verify $(\mathbf{A} - \lambda_m\mathbf{I})\mathbf{u}_j = (\lambda_j - \lambda_m)\mathbf{u}_j$ $m \neq j$, in all cases not illustrated in this example.

5.5.9. What are the (algebraic) multiplicities of the root r of the polynomials

(*a*) $p(x) = x - r$ (*b*) $p(x) = (x - r)^n$

(*c*) $p(x) = (x - r)^3 g(x)$, $g(x)$ a polynomial in x and $g(r) \neq 0$.

In Problems 5.5.10 and 5.5.11, use the idea outlined in Example 5.4.4 to obtain the characteristic polynomials of the given matrices.

5.5.10 (*a*) $\begin{bmatrix} 1 & 0 & 1 & 0 \\ 0 & 1 & 0 & 1 \\ 1 & 0 & 1 & 0 \\ 0 & 1 & 0 & 1 \end{bmatrix}$ (*b*) $\begin{bmatrix} 0 & 1 & 0 & 1 \\ 1 & 0 & 1 & 0 \\ 0 & 1 & 0 & 1 \\ 1 & 0 & 1 & 0 \end{bmatrix}$ (*c*) $\begin{bmatrix} 1 & 0 & 1 & 0 \\ 1 & 0 & 1 & 0 \\ 0 & 1 & 0 & 1 \\ 0 & 1 & 0 & 1 \end{bmatrix}$

5.5.11 (*a*) $\begin{bmatrix} a & b & a & b \\ b & a & b & a \\ a & b & a & b \\ b & a & b & a \end{bmatrix}$ (*b*) $\begin{bmatrix} a & a & b & b \\ b & a & a & b \\ b & b & a & a \\ a & b & b & a \end{bmatrix}$ (*c*) $\begin{bmatrix} a & b & b & a \\ a & a & b & b \\ b & a & a & b \\ b & b & a & a \end{bmatrix}$

PART 2

5.5.12. Refer to Example 5.5.1 and use 3 and 2 (repeated as often as necessary) as diagonal entries to construct matrices with these properties:
(*a*) $\lambda_1 = \lambda_2 = 3$ and $\lambda_3 = 2$ and $g(3) = 1$.
(*b*) $\lambda_1 = \lambda_2 = 3$ and $\lambda_3 = 2$ and $g(3) = 2$.
(*Hint:* Experiment by placing 1s above the diagonal at various locations.)

5.5.13. Construct a 5×5 matrix with the property that $g(-1) = 2, g(2) = 1$, and $g(0) = 2$. (See Problem 5.5.1 and Example 5.5.1.)

5.5.14. Suppose $(\lambda, \mathbf{x})$ and $(\mu, \mathbf{z})$ are two eigenpairs of $\mathbf{A}$ with $\lambda \neq \mu$. Show that $\mathbf{x} + \mathbf{z}$ is never an eigenvector of $\mathbf{A}$.

PART 3

5.5.15. Suppose $p(x)$ is a polynomial of degree n and $r_1, r_2, \ldots, r_k$ are its distinct roots. Explain why $a(r_1) + a(r_2) + \cdots + a(r_k) = n$.

5.5.16. Suppose $\mathbf{A}$ is $n \times n$, $n \geq 2$, and has rank 1. Explain why $g(0) = n - 1$. If $a(0) = n - 1$ argue why $\mathbf{A}$ has exactly two distinct eigenvalues, where the nonzero eigenvalue is tr($\mathbf{A}$).

5.5.17. Suppose $(\lambda_1, \mathbf{x}_1)$, $(\lambda_2, \mathbf{x}_2), \ldots, (\lambda_k, \mathbf{x}_k)$ are eigenpairs of $\mathbf{A}$ and $\lambda_m \neq \lambda_j$, $m \neq j$. Show that $a_1\mathbf{x}_2 + a_2\mathbf{x}_2 + \cdots + a_k\mathbf{x}_k$ is never an eigenvector of $\mathbf{A}$.

5.6 POLYNOMIALS IN A

It is not always necessary to go through the tedious labor of finding the characteristic equation of $\mathbf{A}$ in order to determine its eigenvalues. There is a class of theorems that avoids direct reference to det($\mathbf{A} - \lambda\mathbf{I}$) by relating the eigenvalues of $\mathbf{A}$ to those of another matrix whose eigenvalues are already known. Theorem 5.6.1, to follow, is of this type; it relates the eigenvalues of polynomials in $\mathbf{A}$ to the eigenvalues of $\mathbf{A}$. It shows, for instance, that if λ is an eigenvalue of $\mathbf{A}$ then the eigenvalues of $\mathbf{A}-k\mathbf{I}$, $\mathbf{A}^2$, $\mathbf{A}^3-2\mathbf{A}+3\mathbf{I}$ are $\lambda-k$, λ^2, and $\lambda^3-2\lambda+3$, respectively. To prepare for this result, examine the following important special cases.

Lemma 5.3. *If λ_0 be an eigenvalue of $\mathbf{A}$ then $\lambda_0 + \alpha$, λ_0^m, and $\alpha\lambda_0$ are eigenvalues of $\mathbf{A} + \alpha\mathbf{I}$, $\mathbf{A}^m$, and $\alpha\mathbf{A}$, respectively.*

Proof. Starting with the defining equation, $\mathbf{Ax_0} = \lambda_0\mathbf{x}_0$, compute

$$(\mathbf{A} + \alpha\mathbf{I})\mathbf{x}_0 = \mathbf{Ax_0} + \alpha\mathbf{x}_0 = \lambda_0\mathbf{x}_0 + \alpha\mathbf{x}_0 = (\lambda_0 + \alpha)\mathbf{x}_0$$

which establishes that $(\lambda_0 + \alpha, \mathbf{x}_0)$ is an eigenpair of $\mathbf{A} + \alpha\mathbf{I}$. Next,

$$(\alpha\mathbf{A})\mathbf{x}_0 = \alpha(\mathbf{A}\mathbf{x}_0) = \alpha(\lambda_0\mathbf{x}_0) = (\alpha\lambda_0)\mathbf{x}_0$$

establishes that $(\alpha\lambda_0, \mathbf{x}_0)$ is an eigenpair of $\alpha\mathbf{A}$. Finally, multiply $\mathbf{A}\mathbf{x}_0 = \lambda_0\mathbf{x}_0$ by $\mathbf{A}$ to obtain

$$\mathbf{A}^2\mathbf{x}_0 = \mathbf{A}(\mathbf{A}\mathbf{x}_0) = \lambda_0\mathbf{A}\mathbf{x}_0 = \lambda_0^2\mathbf{x}_0$$

Hence, $(\lambda_0^2, \mathbf{x}_0)$ is an eigenpair of $\mathbf{A}^2$. If $\mathbf{A}^2\mathbf{x}_0 = \lambda_0^2\mathbf{x}_0$ is multiplied by $\mathbf{A}$, we obtain

$$\mathbf{A}^3\mathbf{x}_0 = \mathbf{A}(\mathbf{A}^2\mathbf{x}_0) = \lambda_0^2\mathbf{A}\mathbf{x}_0 = \lambda_0^3\mathbf{x}_0$$

and, hence, $(\lambda_0^3, \mathbf{x})$ is an eigenpair of $\mathbf{A}^3$. An induction argument shows that $\mathbf{A}^k\mathbf{x}_0 = \lambda_0^k\mathbf{x}_0$, for each integer k. ■

Example 5.6.1. Find the eigenvalues of $\mathbf{A}^2$, where

$$\mathbf{A} = \begin{bmatrix} 1 & 0 \\ 0 & -1 \end{bmatrix}$$

Solution. The eigenvalues of $\mathbf{A}$ are $\lambda_1 = 1$ and $\lambda_2 = -1$. By Lemma 5.3, $\lambda_1^2 = 1 = \lambda_2^2$ is an eigenvalue of $\mathbf{A}^2$. Does this mean $\mathbf{A}^2$ has a repeated eigenvalue, $\mu = 1$? Lemma 5.3 is silent on this issue. In fact, $\mathbf{A}^2 = \mathbf{I}$ and, indeed, $\mu_1 = \mu_2 = 1$.

Example 5.6.2. Find all the eigenvalues of

$$\mathbf{K}_4 = \mathbf{J}_4 - \mathbf{I}_4 = \begin{bmatrix} 0 & 1 & 1 & 1 \\ 1 & 0 & 1 & 1 \\ 1 & 1 & 0 & 1 \\ 1 & 1 & 1 & 0 \end{bmatrix}$$

Solution. Recall Example 5.4.4, which implies that the eigenvalues of $\mathbf{J}_4$ are $\lambda_1 = \lambda_2 = \lambda_3 = 0$ and $\lambda_4 = 4$. Since $\mathbf{K}_4 = \mathbf{J}_4 - \mathbf{I}_4$, it follows from Lemma 5.3 that the eigenvalues of $\mathbf{K}_4$, call them μ_i, are given by $\mu_i = \lambda_i - 1$. That is, $\mu_1 = \mu_2 = \mu_3 = -1$ and $\mu_4 = 3$.

Example 5.6.3. Suppose that λ is an eigenvalue of $\mathbf{A}$ and $\mathbf{A}$ is invertible. Show that λ^{-1} is an eigenvalue of $\mathbf{A}^{-1}$.

Solution. Since $\mathbf{A}$ is invertible, the eigenvalues of $\mathbf{A}$ are nonzero. So $\lambda^{-1}\mathbf{A}^{-1}$ exists. Multiply $\mathbf{A}\mathbf{x} = \lambda\mathbf{x}$ by $\lambda^{-1}\mathbf{A}^{-1}$ to obtain $\mathbf{A}^{-1}\mathbf{x} = \lambda^{-1}\mathbf{x}$. Note once again that if $\mathbf{x}$ is an eigenvector of $\mathbf{A}$, it is an eigenvector of $\mathbf{A}^{-1}$.

The results of Lemma 5.3 can be extended to cover the relationship between the eigenvalues of $\mathbf{A}$ and those of polynomials in $\mathbf{A}$. Study the following theorem.

Theorem 5.6.1. *Suppose* $(\lambda, \mathbf{x})$ *is an eigenpair of* $\mathbf{A}$ *so that* $\mathbf{A}\mathbf{x} = \lambda\mathbf{x}$. *Then the matrix*

$$\mathrm{p}(\mathbf{A}) = a_k\mathbf{A}^n + a_{k-1}\mathbf{A}^{n-1} + \cdots + a_1\mathbf{A} + a_0\mathbf{I} \tag{5.6.1}$$

has the eigenvalue

$$\mathrm{p}(\lambda) = a_k\lambda^k + a_{k-1}\lambda^{k-1} + \cdots + a_1\lambda + a_0 \tag{5.6.2}$$

and $\mathbf{x}$ *is an eigenvector of* $\mathrm{p}(\mathbf{A})$ *corresponding to the eigenvalue* $p(\lambda)$.

Proof. By Lemma 5.3, $\mathbf{A}^m\mathbf{x} = \lambda^m\mathbf{x}$ for each integer m. Hence,

$$\begin{aligned} p(\mathbf{A})\mathbf{x} &= (a_k\mathbf{A}^k + a_{k-1}\mathbf{A}^{k-1} + \cdots + a_1\mathbf{A} + a_0\mathbf{I})\mathbf{x} \\ &= a_k\mathbf{A}^k\mathbf{x} + a_{k-1}\mathbf{A}^{k-1}\mathbf{x} + \cdots + a_1\mathbf{A}\mathbf{x} + a_0\mathbf{I}\mathbf{x} \\ &= (a_k\lambda^k\mathbf{x} + a_{k-1}\lambda^{k-1}\mathbf{x} + \cdots + a_1\lambda\mathbf{x} + a_0\mathbf{x} \\ &= a_k\lambda^k + a_{k-1}\lambda^{k-1} + \cdots + a_1\lambda + a_0)\mathbf{x} = p(\lambda)\mathbf{x} \ \blacksquare \end{aligned}$$

Example 5.6.4. Suppose that $p(x) = 1 + 2x - x^2 + 2x^3$ and

$$\mathbf{A} = \begin{bmatrix} 0 & 1 & 0 & 0 \\ 0 & 0 & 1 & 0 \\ 0 & 0 & 0 & 1 \\ 1 & 0 & 0 & 0 \end{bmatrix}$$

Show that

$$\mathbf{C} = p(\mathbf{A}) = \begin{bmatrix} 1 & 2 & -1 & 2 \\ 2 & 1 & 2 & -1 \\ -1 & 2 & 1 & 2 \\ 2 & -1 & 2 & 1 \end{bmatrix}$$

Find the eigenvalues of $\mathbf{A}$ and, by use of Theorem 5.6.1, those of $\mathbf{C}$.

Solution. The eigenvalues of $\mathbf{A}$ are $\lambda_1 = 1, \lambda_2 = -1, \lambda_3 = i, \lambda_4 = -i$. Therefore, the eigenvalues of $\mathbf{C}$, denoted by μ_i, are the values of the polynomial $p(\lambda) = 1 + 2\lambda - \lambda^2 + 2\lambda^3$ for $\lambda = \lambda_k, k = 1, 2, 3, 4$. Specifically,

$$\begin{aligned} \mu_1 &= p(1) = 1 + 2 - 1 + 2 = 4 \\ \mu_2 &= p(-1) = 1 - 2 - 1 - 2 = -4 \\ \mu_3 &= p(i) = 1 + 2i - i^2 + 2i^3 = 2 \\ \mu_4 &= p(-i) = 1 - 2i - (-i)^2 + (-i)^3 = 2 \end{aligned}$$

Theorem 5.6.1 states that every eigenvector of $\mathbf{A}$ is an eigenvector of $p(\mathbf{A})$, a polynomial in $\mathbf{A}$. Is every eigenvector of $p(\mathbf{A})$ an eigenvector of $\mathbf{A}$? No! This failure is seen even in the case $p(\mathbf{A}) = \mathbf{A}^2$. For example,

$$\mathbf{A} = \begin{bmatrix} 0 & 1 \\ 0 & 0 \end{bmatrix} \qquad \mathbf{A}^2 = \begin{bmatrix} 0 & 0 \\ 0 & 0 \end{bmatrix}$$

Every $\mathbf{x} \in \mathscr{C}^2$ is an eigenvector of $p(\mathbf{A})$ but $\mathbf{A}$ has only one independent eigenvector, $\mathbf{x} = [1 \quad 0]^{\mathrm{T}}$.

A related question can be asked about the eigenvalues of $\mathbf{A}$ and $p(\mathbf{A})$. If μ is an eigenvalue of $p(\mathbf{A})$, is there an eigenvalue λ of $\mathbf{A}$ such that $\mu = p(\lambda)$? The answer to this question is made all the more interesting in view of the negative answer to the parallel question for the eigenvectors of $p(\mathbf{A})$.

Theorem 5.6.2. *Let the characteristic polynomial of* $\mathbf{A}$ *be given by*

$$c_{\mathbf{A}}(\lambda) = (\lambda_1 - \lambda)(\lambda_2 - \lambda)\cdots(\lambda_n - \lambda) \tag{5.6.3}$$

and suppose that $p(\mathbf{A})$ *is defined by Eq. 5.6.1 and* $p(\lambda)$ *by Eq. 5.6.2. Then the characteristic polynomial of* $p(\mathbf{A})$ *is given by*

$$c_{p(\mathbf{A})}(\lambda) = (p(\lambda_1) - \lambda)(p(\lambda_2) - \lambda)\cdots\big(p(\lambda_n) - \lambda\big) \tag{5.6.4}$$

Remark. This theorem is stronger than Theorem 5.6.1 because Eq. 5.6.4 asserts that not only is $p(\lambda)_i$ an eigenvalue of $p(\mathbf{A})$ for each i, but these are the *only* eigenvalues of $p(\mathbf{A})$. The proof is rather lengthy and is omitted.[1]

Corollary 1. *If* λ_i *is an eigenvalue of* $\mathbf{A}$*, then* $p(\lambda_i)$ *is an eigenvalue of* $p(\mathbf{A})$ *and the algebraic multiplicity of* λ_i *is no greater than that of* $p(\lambda_i)$*; that is,* $a(\lambda_i) \le a(p(\lambda_i))$.

Proof. Equation 5.6.4 shows not only that $p(\lambda_i)$ is an eigenvalue of $p(\mathbf{A})$ (since $\big(p(\lambda_i) - \lambda\big)$ is a factor of the characteristic equation of $p(\mathbf{A})$) but it also shows that $\big(p(\lambda_i) - \lambda\big)$ is repeated as a factor of $c_{p(\mathbf{A})}(\lambda)$ at least as often as $(\lambda_i - \lambda)$ is repeated as a factor of $c_{\mathbf{A}}(\lambda)$. Because $p(\lambda_i)$ can equal $p(\lambda_j)$ even though $\lambda_i \ne \lambda_j$, the most that can be asserted is $a(\lambda_i) \le a\big(p(\lambda_i)\big)$. Example 5.6.1 illustrates this case since $1 = a(1) < a\big(p(1)\big) = 2$. ■

Example 5.6.5. Verify that $\mathbf{x}_n = \mathbf{1}$ is an eigenvector of $\mathbf{J}_n$ and $\mathbf{K}_n$ corresponding to the eigenvalues $\lambda = n$ and $\mu = n - 1$, respectively.

Solution. By definition of $\mathbf{J}_n$, $\mathbf{J}_n\mathbf{1} = n\mathbf{1}$. It is equally clear that $\mathbf{K}_n\mathbf{1} = (n-1)\mathbf{1}$. This verifies Theorems 5.6.2 and 5.6.1.

Example 5.6.6. Let $c_{\mathbf{A}}(\lambda)$ be the characteristic polynomial of $\mathbf{A}$. Then the eigenvalues of $\mathbf{B} = c_{\mathbf{A}}(\mathbf{A})$ are all zero.

Solution. By definition, $c_{\mathbf{A}}(\lambda) = (\lambda_1 - \lambda)\cdots(\lambda_n - \lambda)$. From Corollary 1 of Theorem 5.6.2, with $p(\mathbf{x}) = c_{\mathbf{A}}(x)$, the eigenvalues of $\mathbf{B} = c_{\mathbf{A}}(\mathbf{A})$ are given by $\mu_i = c_{\mathbf{A}}(\lambda_i) = 0$. (Incidentally, the zero matrix, $\mathbf{O}_n$, has n zeros as its eigenvalues, but so does every upper triangular matrix with diagonal

---

[1]See Theorem 2.5.2 in P. Lancaster, *Theory of Matrices*, New York: Academic Press, 1969.

entries all zero. However, it is true that $\mathbf{B} = c_{\mathbf{A}}(\mathbf{A}) = \mathbf{O}$ for all square matrices $\mathbf{A}$. This beautiful result is known as the *Cayley-Hamilton theorem.*) (See Section 6.7 and Corollary 1 of Theorem 5.7.2.)

Theorem 5.6.2 can be generalized from polynomials to a remarkably large class of functions that include many of the common functions of calculus. See, for instance, Problem 5.6.6 and the problems in MATLAB.

5.6.1 MATLAB

In MATLAB version 3.5 appears the function of polyvalm (p, A), which computes $p(\mathbf{A})$. Polyvalm assumes that p is a vector whose entries are the coefficients of the polynomial $p(x)$ in descending powers, and $\mathbf{A}$ is a square matrix. Thus, Theorem 5.6.2 is easily verified in specific cases. (See the problems in MATLAB.)

PROBLEMS

PART 1

For each of the next six problems assume

$$\mathbf{A} = \begin{bmatrix} 1 & 2 & 4 \\ 0 & 2 & 0 \\ 0 & 2 & -1 \end{bmatrix}$$

5.6.1. Find the characteristic equation, eigenvalues, and eigenspaces of $\mathbf{A}$.

5.6.2. Verify Theorem 5.6.2 and its corollary for $p(x) = x^2$.

5.6.3. Repeat Problem 5.6.2 for the polynomials $2x$ and $x + 1$.

5.6.4. Repeat Problem 5.6.2 for the polynomial $p_3(x) = x^3 - 2x^2 - x + 2$.

5.6.5. Repeat Problem 5.6.2 for the polynomial $p_3(x) = x^3 - 2x^2 - x + 3$.

5.6.6. Find the characteristic equation and the eigenvalues of $(\mathbf{A}+\mathbf{I})\mathbf{A}^{-1}$ and $\mathbf{A}^{-1}(\mathbf{A}+\mathbf{I})$ and compare with the values of $(x + 1)/x$ at $x = \lambda_1 = -1, x = \lambda_2 = 1$, and $x = \lambda_3 = 2$.

PART 2

5.6.7. An *idempotent* matrix $\mathbf{P}$ is a matrix satisfying $\mathbf{P}^2 = \mathbf{P}$. Use Theorem 5.6.2 to prove that the eigenvalues of $\mathbf{P}$ are 0 or 1. (See Problem 5.4.16.)

5.6.8. Use Theorem 5.6.2 to prove that the eigenvalues of $\mathbf{M}, \mathbf{M}^2 = \mathbf{I}$, are either 1 or -1. (See also Problem 5.4.17.)

5.6.9. The matrix

$$\mathbf{K}_{n+1} = \frac{1}{n}\begin{bmatrix} 0 & 1 & 1 & \cdots & 1 \\ 1 & 0 & 1 & \cdots & 1 \\ 1 & 1 & 0 & & 1 \\ \vdots & \vdots & \vdots & & \vdots \\ 1 & 1 & 1 & & 0 \end{bmatrix}$$

is $(n+1)\times(n+1)$ and is called *doubly stochastic*. It appears in the theory of finite Markov chains. Find the eigenvalues of $\mathbf{K}_{n+1}$ by showing that it is a polynomial in $\mathbf{J}_{n+1}$.

MATLAB

Use polyvalm in each of the following problems.

5.6.10. Verify the answers to Problems 5.6.1–5.6.6.

5.6.11. Verify the work in Example 5.6.4.

In Problems 5.6.12–5.6.14, let $\mathbf{B} = (\frac{1}{4})\mathbf{A}$, where **A** is the matrix in Part 1. The point of these exercises is to suggest that in some circumstances it is possible to define functions of $\mathbf{B}, f(\mathbf{B})$ (such as $e^{\mathbf{B}}$, $\cos \mathbf{B}$, $\sin \mathbf{B}$), for which, among other things, the eigenvalues of $f(\mathbf{B})$ are $f(\lambda)$.

5.6.12. For each eigenvalue λ of **B** compare the eigenvalues of

$$f(\mathbf{B}) = \mathbf{I} + \frac{\mathbf{B}}{1!} + \frac{\mathbf{B}^2}{2!} + \frac{\mathbf{B}^3}{3!} + \frac{\mathbf{B}^4}{4!} + \frac{\mathbf{B}^5}{5!}$$

with the scalars e^{λ}. ($f(\lambda)$ is a fifth-order approximation to e^{λ}.)

5.6.13. For each eigenvalue λ of **B** compare the eigenvalues of

$$f(\mathbf{B}) = \mathbf{I} - \frac{\mathbf{B}^2}{2!} + \frac{\mathbf{B}^4}{4!} + \frac{\mathbf{B}^6}{6!}$$

with the scalars $\cos \lambda$. ($f(\lambda)$ is a seventh-order approximation to $\cos \lambda$.)

5.6.14. For each eigenvalue λ of **B** compare the eigenvalues of

$$f(\mathbf{B}) = \mathbf{B} - \frac{\mathbf{B}^3}{3!} + \frac{\mathbf{B}^5}{5!} + \frac{\mathbf{B}^7}{7!}$$

with the scalars $\sin \lambda$. ($f(\lambda)$ is an eighth-order approximation to $\sin \lambda$.)

5.7 DIAGONALIZABLE MATRICES

The span of all the eigenvectors of **A** is a subspace of $\mathscr{C}^n$. This subspace is at least of dimension 1, since every matrix has at least one eigenvector. Its dimension is no more than n (assuming **A** is $n \times n$) because there can be no more than n linearly independent n-tuples. We are interested in those matrices for which this span is exactly $\mathscr{C}^n$. Clearly this happens if and only if **A** has n linearly independent eigenvectors. A matrix with this property is often called *simple*.[2] Because simple matrices have n linearly independent eigenvectors, they are often described as having a *complete*, or *full*, set of eigenvectors. Matrices that are not simple are *defective*.

Example 5.7.1. The matrix **A** is simple, whereas **B** and **C** are defective.

$$\mathbf{A} = \begin{bmatrix} 2 & 0 & 0 \\ 0 & 2 & 0 \\ 0 & 0 & 2 \end{bmatrix} \qquad \mathbf{B} = \begin{bmatrix} 2 & 1 & 0 \\ 0 & 2 & 0 \\ 0 & 0 & 2 \end{bmatrix} \qquad \mathbf{C} = \begin{bmatrix} 2 & 1 & 0 \\ 0 & 2 & 1 \\ 0 & 0 & 2 \end{bmatrix}$$

Theorem 5.7.1. *If* **A** *has n distinct eigenvalues, then* **A** *is simple.*

---

[2]After Gantmacher, *Theory of Matrices*, Chelsea, 1960; and P. Lancaster and M. Tismenetsky, *The Theory of Matrices*, 2d ed., New York: Academic Press, 1985.

Proof. By Theorem 5.5.2, eigenvectors associated with unequal eigenvalues are linearly independent. Thus, the hypothesis implies that $\mathbf{A}$ has n linearly independent eigenvectors, one from each eigenvalue. ■

A matrix need not have n distinct eigenvalues to be simple; the matrix $\mathbf{A}$ in Example 5.7.1 is one such example. In fact, all diagonal matrices are simple, regardless of whether the eigenvalues are distinct, because the set of unit vectors $\{\mathbf{e}_1, \mathbf{e}_2, \ldots, \mathbf{e}_n\}$ is a complete set of eigenvectors for each diagonal matrix. Now suppose that the eigenvalues of $\mathbf{A}$ are $\lambda_1, \lambda_2, \ldots, \lambda_n$. (If λ_i is a repeated root of $\det(\mathbf{A} - \lambda\mathbf{I})$, then λ_i appears as many times in the list of eigenvalues as $(\lambda_i - \lambda)$ appears as a factor of $\det(\mathbf{A} - \lambda\mathbf{I})$. So, for instance, the list of the eigenvalues of $\mathbf{I}_4$ is 1,1,1,1.) We denote by Λ any diagonal matrix whose diagonal entries are the eigenvalues of $\mathbf{A}$. For the matrix Λ with eigenvalues $\lambda_1, \lambda_2, \ldots, \lambda_n$ (some or all of which may be identical), one such Λ is given by

$$\Lambda = \begin{bmatrix} \lambda_1 & 0 & \cdots & 0 \\ 0 & \lambda_2 & \cdots & 0 \\ \vdots & \vdots & & \vdots \\ 0 & 0 & \cdots & \lambda_n \end{bmatrix} \tag{5.7.1}$$

and $\det(\Lambda - \lambda\mathbf{I}) = (\lambda_1 - \lambda)(\lambda_2 - \lambda)\cdots(\lambda_n - \lambda)$. Every diagonal matrix of eigenvalues of Λ is just a permutation of the diagonal entries of the Λ displayed above. $\mathbf{A}$ is *diagonalizable* if there is a nonsingular matrix $\mathbf{S}$ such that

$$\mathbf{S}^{-1}\mathbf{A}\mathbf{S} = \Lambda \tag{5.7.2}$$

The invertible matrix $\mathbf{S}$ in Eq. 5.7.2 is said to *diagonalize* $\mathbf{A}$. The set of diagonalizable matrices is precisely the set of simple matrices. This is the content of Theorem 5.7.1; however, the heart of the proof appears in Lemma 5.4.

Lemma 5.4. *The (nonzero) columns of* $\mathbf{S}$ *are eigenvectors of* $\mathbf{A}$ *if and only if*

$$\mathbf{A}\mathbf{S} = \mathbf{S}\Lambda \tag{5.7.3}$$

Proof. Let $\mathbf{S} = [\mathbf{x}_1 \quad \mathbf{x}_2 \quad \ldots \quad \mathbf{x}_n]$ and $\Lambda = [\lambda_1\mathbf{e}_1 \quad \lambda_2\mathbf{e}_2 \quad \ldots \quad \lambda_n\mathbf{e}_n]$. Then

$$\mathbf{A}\mathbf{S} = \mathbf{A}[\mathbf{x}_1 \quad \mathbf{x}_2 \quad \ldots \quad \mathbf{x}_n] = [\mathbf{A}\mathbf{x}_1 \quad \mathbf{A}\mathbf{x}_2 \quad \ldots \quad \mathbf{A}\mathbf{x}_n]$$

and

$$\begin{aligned} \mathbf{S}\Lambda &= \mathbf{S}[\lambda_1\mathbf{e}_1 \quad \lambda_2\mathbf{e}_2 \quad \ldots \quad \lambda_n\mathbf{e}_n] = [\lambda_1\mathbf{S}\mathbf{e}_1 \quad \lambda_2\mathbf{S}\mathbf{e}_2 \quad \ldots \quad \lambda_n\mathbf{S}\mathbf{e}_n] \\ &= [\lambda_1\mathbf{x}_1 \quad \lambda_2\mathbf{x}_2 \quad \ldots \quad \lambda_n\mathbf{x}_n] \end{aligned}$$

Hence, $\mathbf{A}\mathbf{S} = \mathbf{S}\Lambda$ if and only if $\mathbf{A}\mathbf{x}_k = \lambda\mathbf{x}_k$ for $k = 1, 2, \ldots, n$. Since $\mathbf{x}_i \neq \mathbf{0}$, Eq. 5.7.3 holds if and only if the columns of $\mathbf{S}$ are eigenvectors of $\mathbf{A}$, regardless of whether the set $\{\mathbf{x}_1, \mathbf{x}_2, \ldots, \mathbf{x}_n\}$ is linearly independent. ■

Theorem 5.7.2. *Suppose* $\mathbf{A}$ *has eigenvalues* $\lambda_1, \lambda_2, \ldots, \lambda_n$ *and corresponding linearly independent eigenvectors* $\mathbf{x}_1, \mathbf{x}_2, \ldots, \mathbf{x}_n$ *. Then* $\mathbf{A}$ *is simple if and only if* $\mathbf{A}$ *is diagonalizable (i.e.,* $\mathbf{S}^{-1}\mathbf{A}\mathbf{S} = \Lambda$, for some $\mathbf{S}$.)

Proof. Since $\{\mathbf{x}_1, \mathbf{x}_2, \ldots, \mathbf{x}_n\}$ are eigenvectors of $\mathbf{A}$, Lemma 5.4 implies that $\mathbf{AS} = \mathbf{\Lambda S}$. So if $\mathbf{A}$ is simple, there are n linearly independent eigenvectors of $\mathbf{A}$, which can be used as the columns of $\mathbf{S}$. Then $\mathbf{S}$ is invertible and $\mathbf{AS} = \mathbf{\Lambda S}$ implies $\mathbf{S}^{-1}\mathbf{AS} = \mathbf{\Lambda}$; that is, $\mathbf{A}$ is diagonalizable. On the other hand, if $\mathbf{A}$ is diagonalizable, $\mathbf{S}^{-1}\mathbf{AS} = \mathbf{\Lambda}$ holds and, therefore, $\mathbf{S}$ is invertible and $\mathbf{AS} = \mathbf{S\Lambda}$. By Lemma 5.4, the columns of $\mathbf{S}$ are eigenvectors of $\mathbf{A}$, and because $\mathbf{S}$ is invertible, the columns of $\mathbf{S}$ are linearly independent. So $\mathbf{A}$ is simple. ■

Theorem 5.7.2 asserts, in essence, that matrices with a complete set of eigenvectors are diagonalizable, and diagonalizable matrices are always simple. This theorem does *not* assert that $\mathbf{S}$ is unique. In fact, there are always infinitely many matrices that diagonalize $\mathbf{A}$; every permutation of the columns of $\mathbf{S}$ results in a matrix that diagonalizes $\mathbf{A}$. For some matrices, the diagonalizing matrices can be quite unrelated. Consider, for instance, $\mathbf{A} = \mathbf{I}$. Since every nonzero vector is an eigenvector of $\mathbf{I}$, $\mathbf{S}$ can be any nonsingular matrix!

Example 5.7.2. Find $\mathbf{S}$ and $\mathbf{\Lambda}$, and verify Theorem 5.7.2 and Eq. 5.7.3 for

$$\mathbf{K}_4 = \begin{bmatrix} 0 & 1 & 1 & 1 \\ 1 & 0 & 1 & 1 \\ 1 & 1 & 0 & 1 \\ 1 & 1 & 1 & 0 \end{bmatrix}$$

Solution. The eigenvalues of $\mathbf{K}_4$ have already been computed in Example 5.6.2; they are $\lambda_1 = \lambda_2 = \lambda_3 = -1$, and $\lambda_4 = 3$. There are three linearly independent eigenvectors associated with $\lambda = -1$:

$$\mathbf{x}_1 = \begin{bmatrix} 1 \\ -1 \\ 0 \\ 0 \end{bmatrix}, \quad \mathbf{x}_2 = \begin{bmatrix} 1 \\ 0 \\ -1 \\ 0 \end{bmatrix}, \quad \mathbf{x}_3 = \begin{bmatrix} 1 \\ 0 \\ 0 \\ -1 \end{bmatrix}$$

Hence, $a(-1) = g(-1) = 3$. The eigenvalue $\lambda_4 = 3$ has the corresponding eigenvector $\mathbf{x}_4 = [1 \quad 1 \quad 1 \quad 1]^{\mathrm{T}}$. So $\mathbf{K}_4$ is simple. Define $\mathbf{S}$ by using the eigenvectors $\mathbf{x}_1, \mathbf{x}_2, \mathbf{x}_3, \mathbf{x}_4$ as the columns of $\mathbf{S}$. So $\mathbf{S} = [\mathbf{x}_1 \quad \mathbf{x}_2 \quad \mathbf{x}_3 \quad \mathbf{x}_4]$, and, after some labor, verify $\mathbf{K}_4\mathbf{S} = \mathbf{S\Lambda}$.

$$\begin{bmatrix} 0 & 1 & 1 & 1 \\ 1 & 0 & 1 & 1 \\ 1 & 1 & 0 & 1 \\ 1 & 1 & 1 & 0 \end{bmatrix}\begin{bmatrix} 1 & 1 & 1 & 1 \\ -1 & 0 & 0 & 1 \\ 0 & -1 & 0 & 1 \\ 0 & 0 & -1 & 1 \end{bmatrix}$$

$$= \begin{bmatrix} 1 & 1 & 1 & 1 \\ -1 & 0 & 0 & 1 \\ 0 & -1 & 0 & 1 \\ 0 & 0 & -1 & 1 \end{bmatrix}\begin{bmatrix} -1 & 0 & 0 & 0 \\ 0 & -1 & 0 & 0 \\ 0 & 0 & -1 & 0 \\ 0 & 0 & 0 & 3 \end{bmatrix}$$

Finally, verify $\mathbf{S}^{-1}\mathbf{K}_4\mathbf{S} = \mathbf{\Lambda}$.

$$\begin{bmatrix} 1 & -3 & 1 & 1 \\ 1 & 1 & -3 & 1 \\ 1 & 1 & 1 & -3 \\ 1 & 1 & 1 & 1 \end{bmatrix}\begin{bmatrix} 1 & 1 & 1 & 1 \\ -1 & 0 & 0 & 1 \\ 0 & -1 & 0 & 1 \\ 0 & 0 & -1 & 1 \end{bmatrix}\begin{bmatrix} 1 & 1 & 1 & 1 \\ -1 & 0 & 0 & 1 \\ 0 & -1 & 0 & 1 \\ 0 & 0 & -1 & 1 \end{bmatrix}$$

$$= \begin{bmatrix} -1 & 0 & 0 & 0 \\ 0 & -1 & 0 & 0 \\ 0 & 0 & -1 & 0 \\ 0 & 0 & 0 & 3 \end{bmatrix}$$

Example 5.7.3. Show that $\mathbf{A}$ is simple implies that $\mathbf{T}^{-1}\mathbf{AT}$ is simple.

Solution. Two approaches come to mind, and both are instructive. The first exploits Theorem 5.7.2 by showing that $\mathbf{T}^{-1}\mathbf{AT}$ is diagonalizable. Since $\mathbf{S}^{-1}\mathbf{AS} = \mathbf{\Lambda}$ implies $\mathbf{A} = \mathbf{S\Lambda S}^{-1}$, it follows that

$$\mathbf{T}^{-1}\mathbf{AT} = \mathbf{T}^{-1}\mathbf{S\Lambda S}^{-1}\mathbf{T} = (\mathbf{S}^{-1}\mathbf{T})^{-1}\mathbf{\Lambda S}^{-1}\mathbf{T}$$

and, thus, $\mathbf{T}^{-1}\mathbf{AT}$ is diagonalized by $\mathbf{T}^{-1}\mathbf{S}$, as is seen from

$$(\mathbf{T}^{-1}\mathbf{S})^{-1}(\mathbf{T}^{-1}\mathbf{AT})(\mathbf{T}^{-1}\mathbf{S}) = \mathbf{S}^{-1}\mathbf{AS} = \mathbf{\Lambda}$$

Alternatively, $\mathbf{T}^{-1}\mathbf{AT}$ can be shown to be simple by finding its n linearly independent eigenvectors. Indeed, its eigenvectors are closely related to the eigenvectors of $\mathbf{A}$. They are, in fact,

$$\mathbf{T}^{-1}\mathbf{x}_1, \mathbf{T}^{-1}\mathbf{x}_2, \ldots, \mathbf{T}^{-1}\mathbf{x}_n$$

where $\mathbf{x}_1, \mathbf{x}_2, \ldots, \mathbf{x}_n$ are eigenvectors of $\mathbf{A}$. To see this, note that $\mathbf{Ax}_k = \lambda_k\mathbf{x}$ holds for each k and, hence

$$\mathbf{T}^{-1}\mathbf{AT}(\mathbf{T}^{-1}\mathbf{x}_k) = \mathbf{T}^{-1}(\mathbf{Ax}_k) = \lambda_k(\mathbf{T}^{-1}\mathbf{x}_k)$$

shows that $\mathbf{T}^{-1}\mathbf{x}_k$ is an eigenvector of $\mathbf{T}^{-1}\mathbf{AT}$ for each k. By hypothesis $\mathbf{A}$ is simple, so $\mathbf{A}$ has n linearly independent eigenvectors. If $\{\mathbf{x}_1, \mathbf{x}_2, \ldots, \mathbf{x}_n\}$ is linearly independent, then so is $\{\mathbf{T}^{-1}\mathbf{x}_1, \mathbf{T}^{-1}\mathbf{x}_2, \ldots, \mathbf{T}^{-1}\mathbf{x}_n\}$, and therefore $\mathbf{T}^{-1}\mathbf{AT}$ has a complete set of eigenvectors.

Example 5.7.4. Prove that if $\mathbf{A}$ is simple, then $\mathbf{A}^{\mathrm{T}}$ is also simple.

Solution. Since $\mathbf{A}$ is simple, it is diagonalizable, so there exists $\mathbf{S}$ such that $\mathbf{S}^{-1}\mathbf{AS} = \mathbf{\Lambda}$. By taking transposes, $\mathbf{S}^{\mathrm{T}}\mathbf{A}^{\mathrm{T}}\mathbf{S}^{-\mathrm{T}} = \mathbf{\Lambda}^{\mathrm{T}} = \mathbf{\Lambda}$. Hence, $\mathbf{A}^{\mathrm{T}}$ is diagonalizable (by $\mathbf{S}^{-\mathrm{T}}$) and is simple.

Example 5.7.5. Let k be a positive integer and $\mathbf{A}$ be a simple matrix that is diagonalized by $\mathbf{S}$. Show that $\mathbf{S}^{-1}\mathbf{A}^k\mathbf{S} = \mathbf{\Lambda}^k$ and, hence, deduce that $\mathbf{A}^k$ is simple and is also diagonalized by $\mathbf{S}$.

Solution. The proof of the general case is based on repeated application o the computations

$$\Lambda^2 = (\mathbf{S}^{-1}\mathbf{A}\mathbf{S})^2 = \mathbf{S}^{-1}\mathbf{A}\mathbf{S}\mathbf{S}^{-1}\mathbf{A}\mathbf{S} = \mathbf{S}^{-1}\mathbf{A}^2\mathbf{S}$$
$$\Lambda^3 = (\mathbf{S}^{-1}\mathbf{A}\mathbf{S})^3 = \mathbf{S}^{-1}\mathbf{A}\mathbf{S}\mathbf{S}^{-1}\mathbf{A}^2\mathbf{S} = \mathbf{S}^{-1}\mathbf{A}^3\mathbf{S}$$

The fact that $\mathbf{A}^k$ is diagonalized by $\mathbf{S}$ shows that every eigenvector of $\mathbf{A}$ is an eigenvector of $\mathbf{A}^k$. Finally, since $\mathbf{A}^k$ is diagonalizable, it is simple. In expanded form,

$$\mathbf{S}^{-1}\mathbf{A}^k\mathbf{S} = \Lambda^k = \begin{bmatrix} \lambda_1^k & 0 & \cdots & 0 \\ 0 & \lambda_2^k & \cdots & 0 \\ \vdots & \vdots & & \vdots \\ 0 & 0 & \cdots & \lambda_n^k \end{bmatrix}$$

This idea can be extended one step further to show that every polynomial in $\mathbf{A}$ is diagonalizable by the same $\mathbf{S}$ that diagonalizes $\mathbf{A}$.

Let $p(x)$ be the polynomial

$$p(x) = a_0 + a_1x + \cdots + a_nx^n \tag{5.7.4}$$

Define the related polynomial in $\mathbf{A}$, $p(\mathbf{A})$, by

$$p(\mathbf{A}) = a_0\mathbf{I} + a_1\mathbf{A} + \cdots + a_n\mathbf{A}^n \tag{5.7.5}$$

Theorem 5.7.3. *With $p(x)$ and $p(\mathbf{A})$ defined by Eqs. 5.7.4 and 5.7.5, if $\mathbf{A}$ is simple, then so is $p(\mathbf{A})$. Moreover,*

$$\mathbf{S}^{-1}p(\mathbf{A})\mathbf{S} = p(\Lambda) = \begin{bmatrix} p(\lambda_1) & 0 & \cdots & 0 \\ 0 & p(\lambda_2) & \cdots & 0 \\ \vdots & \vdots & & \vdots \\ 0 & 0 & \cdots & p(\lambda_n) \end{bmatrix} \tag{5.7.6}$$

Proof. From Example 5.7.5, $\mathbf{S}^{-1}\mathbf{A}^k\mathbf{S} = \Lambda^k$, and therefore,

$$\begin{aligned} \mathbf{S}^{-1}p(\mathbf{A})\mathbf{S} &= \mathbf{S}^{-1}(a_0\mathbf{I} + a_1\mathbf{A} + \cdots + a_n\mathbf{A}^n)\mathbf{S} \\ &= a_0\mathbf{S}^{-1}\mathbf{I}\mathbf{S} + a_1\mathbf{S}^{-1}\mathbf{A}\mathbf{S} + \cdots + a_n\mathbf{S}^{-1}\mathbf{A}^n\mathbf{S} \\ &= a_0\mathbf{I} + a_1\Lambda + \cdots + a_n\Lambda^n = p(\Lambda) \end{aligned}$$

So $p(\mathbf{A})$ is diagonalizable and is therefore simple. ■

The converse of Theorem 5.7.3 is false: $\mathbf{A}$ may be defective and $p(\mathbf{A})$ simple; witness

$$\mathbf{A} = \begin{bmatrix} 0 & 1 \\ 0 & 0 \end{bmatrix} \qquad \mathbf{A}^2 = \begin{bmatrix} 0 & 0 \\ 0 & 0 \end{bmatrix}$$

An interesting corollary to Theorem 5.7.3 is a special case of the remarkable Cayley-Hamilton theorem:

Every matrix satisfies its own characteristic equation.

That is, if $c_{\mathbf{A}}(\lambda)$ is the characteristic equation of $\mathbf{A}$, $c_{\mathbf{A}}(\mathbf{A}) = \mathbf{O}$. The theorem in its most general form is proved in Section 6.7. For simple matrices, Theorem 5.7.3 leads to the following.

Corollary 1. *If* $\mathbf{A}$ *is simple with characteristic equation* $c(\lambda) = 0$ *then* $c(\mathbf{A}) = \mathbf{O}$.

Proof. Use $c(x)$ in place of $p(x)$ in Theorem 5.7.3, Eq. 5.7.6:

$$\mathbf{S}^{-1}c(\mathbf{A})\mathbf{S} = c(\Lambda) = \begin{bmatrix} c(\lambda_1) & 0 & \cdots & 0 \\ 0 & c(\lambda_2) & \cdots & 0 \\ \vdots & \vdots & & \vdots \\ 0 & 0 & \cdots & c(\lambda_n) \end{bmatrix}$$

However, $c(\lambda_k) = 0$ for each k and hence $c(\Lambda) = \mathbf{O}$. Therefore $c(\mathbf{A}) = \mathbf{O}$. ■

Example 5.7.6. A matrix $\mathbf{A}$ is *nilpotent* if for some nonnegative integer k, $\mathbf{A}^k = \mathbf{O}$. Assuming the Cayley-Hamilton theorem, show that $\mathbf{A}$ is nilpotent if and only if all its eigenvalues are zero.

Solution. If $\mathbf{A}^k = \mathbf{O}$ for some nonnegative integer k and $\lambda \neq 0$ is an eigenvalue of $\mathbf{A}$, then $\lambda^k \neq 0$ is an eigenvalue of $\mathbf{A}^k = \mathbf{O}$ contradicting the hypothesis. Now the converse: Suppose all the eigenvalues of $\mathbf{A}$ are zero. So $c(\lambda) = (-\lambda)^n$, and by the Cayley-Hamilton theorem $c(\mathbf{A}) = (-\mathbf{A})^n = \mathbf{O}$.

Example 5.7.6 is interesting because matrices whose eigenvalues are all zero may not display this fact in any simple way. As an illustration, consider

$$\mathbf{A} = \begin{bmatrix} 11 & 11 & 9 \\ -11 & -11 & -9 \\ -1 & -1 & 0 \end{bmatrix}$$

a matrix for which it is not obvious that $\mathbf{A}^3 = \mathbf{O}$ or that $(-\lambda)^3 = 0$ is its characteristic equation.

Example 5.7.7. Let

$$\mathbf{A} = \begin{bmatrix} 1 & 2 & 0 \\ 0 & 2 & 0 \\ 0 & 2 & 1 \end{bmatrix}$$

(*a*) Verify that $c(\lambda) = -\lambda^3 + 4\lambda^2 - 5\lambda + 2$ and that $c(\mathbf{A}) = -\mathbf{A}^3 + 4\mathbf{A}^2 - 5\mathbf{A} + 2\mathbf{I} = \mathbf{O}$.

(*b*) Verify that $\mathbf{A}^{-1}$ is given by $\mathbf{A}^{-1} = \frac{1}{2}\mathbf{A}^2 - 2\mathbf{A} + \frac{5}{2}\mathbf{I}$.

Solution. The determination of the characteristic polynomial is easy. Indeed, so is the following verification:

$$\mathbf{A}^2 = \begin{bmatrix} 1 & 6 & 0 \\ 0 & 4 & 0 \\ 0 & 6 & 1 \end{bmatrix}, \qquad \mathbf{A}^3 = \begin{bmatrix} 1 & 14 & 0 \\ 0 & 8 & 0 \\ 0 & 14 & 1 \end{bmatrix}$$

and, hence, $-\mathbf{A}^3 + 4\mathbf{A}^2 - 5\mathbf{A} + 2\mathbf{I} = \mathbf{O}$. This verifies the Cayley-Hamilton theorem for the given simple matrix $\mathbf{A}$.

Part (*b*) is a consequence of the Cayley-Hamilton theorem, because from $-\mathbf{A}^3 + 4\mathbf{A}^2 - 5\mathbf{A} + 2\mathbf{I} = \mathbf{O}$, it follows that $2\mathbf{I} = \mathbf{A}^3 - 4\mathbf{A}^2 + 5\mathbf{A}$. Hence,

$$\mathbf{I} = (\mathbf{A}^3 - 4\mathbf{A}^2 + 5\mathbf{A})/2 = \mathbf{A}\{(\mathbf{A}^2 - 4\mathbf{A} + 5\mathbf{I})/2\}$$

Thus

$$\mathbf{A}^{-1} = (\mathbf{A}^2 - 4\mathbf{A} + 5\mathbf{I})/2 = \begin{bmatrix} 1 & -1 & 0 \\ 0 & \frac{1}{2} & 0 \\ 0 & -1 & 1 \end{bmatrix}$$

What is noteworthy about Example 5.7.7 is the remarkable fact that the inverse of $\mathbf{A}$ is always a polynomial in $\mathbf{A}$. Indeed, it is a polynomial in $\mathbf{A}$ of degree $n - 1$ or less (assuming the truth of the Cayley-Hamilton theorem). More will be said about this in Section 6.7, but see Problem 5.7.29.

5.7.1 Which A Are Diagonalizable?

As will be shown in Chapter 6, (real) symmetric matrices are among the many classes of simple matrices. Another class of simple matrices is the idempotent matrices, $\mathbf{P}^2 = \mathbf{P}$. (See Problems 5.7.26–5.7.27.) However, in general, there is no better criterion for determining whether a matrix is simple or defective than an examination of the dimension of the eigenspace of each eigenvalue.

If the number of linearly independent eigenvectors corresponding to each eigenvalue is exactly the algebraic multiplicity of that eigenvalue, then the matrix is simple.

To see why, study the proof of the following theorem:

Theorem 5.7.4. $\mathbf{A}$ *is simple if and only if* $a(\lambda_0) = g(\lambda_0)$ *for each eigenvalue* λ_0 *of* $\mathbf{A}$.

Proof. Consider the special case in which

$$c(\lambda) = (\lambda_1 - \lambda)^r(\lambda_2 - \lambda)^s, \qquad r + s = n \tag{5.7.7}$$

Suppose $a(\lambda_1) = g(\lambda_1)$ and $a(\lambda_2) = g(\lambda_2)$. From Eq. 5.7.7, $a(\lambda_1) = r$ and $a(\lambda_2) = s$. By hypothesis, it follows that $g(\lambda_1) = r$ and $g(\lambda_2) = s$. Thus, there are two sets of linearly independent eigenvectors $\{\mathbf{x}_1, \mathbf{x}_2, \ldots, \mathbf{x}_r\}$ and $\{\mathbf{z}_1, \mathbf{z}_2, \ldots, \mathbf{z}_s\}$, the former a basis of the eigenspace of λ_1, the latter a basis of the eigenspace of λ_2. We must now show that $\{\mathbf{x}_1, \ldots, \mathbf{x}_r, \mathbf{z}_1, \ldots, \mathbf{z}_s\}$ is linearly independent, which means that

$$a_1\mathbf{x}_1 + \cdots + a_r\mathbf{x}_r + b_1\mathbf{z}_1 + \cdots + b_s\mathbf{z}_s = \mathbf{0} \tag{5.7.8}$$

implies $a_1 = \cdots = a_r = b_1 = \cdots = b_s = 0$. Toward this end, set

$$\mathbf{x}_0 = a_1\mathbf{x}_1 + \cdots + a_r\mathbf{x}_r \qquad \mathbf{z}_0 = b_1\mathbf{z}_1 + \cdots + b_s\mathbf{z}_s$$

Then, Eq. 5.7.8 is just $\mathbf{x}_0 + \mathbf{z}_0 = \mathbf{0}$. However, $\mathbf{x}_0$ is a vector in the eigenspace of λ_1 and $\mathbf{z}_0$ is a vector in the eigenspace of λ_2, where $\lambda_1 \neq \lambda_2$. By Theorem 5.5.2, $\mathbf{x}_0$ and $\mathbf{z}_0$ are linearly independent and, hence, $\mathbf{x}_0 + \mathbf{z}_0 = \mathbf{0}$ implies $\mathbf{x}_0 = \mathbf{z}_0 = \mathbf{0}$. Because the sets $\{\mathbf{x}_1, \mathbf{x}_2, \ldots, \mathbf{x}_r\}$ and $\{\mathbf{z}_1, \mathbf{z}_2, \ldots, \mathbf{z}_s\}$ are linearly independent (by hypothesis), $\mathbf{x}_0 = \mathbf{0}$ implies that $a_i = 0$ for $i = 1, 2, \ldots, r$ and $\mathbf{z}_0 = \mathbf{0}$ implies $b_j = 0$ for $j = 1, 2, \ldots, s$. Thus, $\mathbf{A}$ is simple.

The converse is far easier. Assume $\mathbf{A}$ is simple and that either $a(\lambda_1) > g(\lambda_1)$ or $a(\lambda_2) > g(\lambda_2)$. (Recall that $a(\lambda_1) \geq g(\lambda_1)$ and $a(\lambda_2) \geq g(\lambda_2)$ from Theorem 5.5.1.) Then $a(\lambda_1) + a(\lambda_2) = r + s = n > g(\lambda_1) + g(\lambda_2)$. Thus, $\mathbf{A}$ does not have n linearly independent eigenvectors and, hence, $\mathbf{A}$ cannot be simple. This is a contradiction. (The general argument is just a more complicated version of the proof of this special case.) ■

Corollary 1. $\mathbf{A}$ *is simple if and only if* $\sum g(\lambda_k) = n$, *this sum taken over the distinct eigenvalues of* $\mathbf{A}$.

Proof. By Theorem 5.7.4, $a(\lambda_k) = g(\lambda_k)$ for each k if and only if $\mathbf{A}$ is simple. Since $\sum a(\lambda_k) = n$ (a restatement of the fact that $\mathbf{A}$ has n eigenvalues counting repetitions), it follows that $n = \sum a(\lambda_k) = \sum g(\lambda_k)$. ■

PROBLEMS

PART 1

5.7.1. Find a basis of eigenvectors for $\mathscr{C}^n$ to show that each of the following matrices is simple.

(*a*) $\begin{bmatrix} \alpha & 1 & 1 \\ 0 & \beta & 1 \\ 0 & 0 & \gamma \end{bmatrix}$, $\alpha \neq \beta \neq \gamma$ (*b*) $\begin{bmatrix} \alpha & 0 & 1 \\ 0 & \alpha & 1 \\ 0 & 0 & \gamma \end{bmatrix}$, $\alpha \neq \gamma$

(*c*) $\begin{bmatrix} 1 & 1 & -1 \\ 1 & 1 & 1 \\ 1 & 1 & 1 \end{bmatrix}$ (*d*) $\mathbf{O}_m$ (*e*) $\mathbf{I}_n$ (*f*) $\begin{bmatrix} \alpha & \beta \\ \beta & \alpha \end{bmatrix}$ (*g*) $\begin{bmatrix} 0 & \beta \\ -\beta & 0 \end{bmatrix}$

5.7.2. Use the eigenvectors found in Problems 5.7.1 (*a*)–(*c*) to construct $\mathbf{S}$ and Λ, and verify $\mathbf{S}^{-1}\mathbf{A}\mathbf{S} = \Lambda$ in each case.

5.7.3. Find $\mathbf{S}$ and verify $\mathbf{S}^{-1}\mathbf{A}\mathbf{S} = \Lambda$ for each of these simple matrices:

(*a*) $\begin{bmatrix} 0 & 1 & 0 \\ 1 & 0 & 0 \\ 0 & 0 & 1 \end{bmatrix}$ (*b*) $\begin{bmatrix} 0 & 0 & 1 \\ 1 & 0 & 0 \\ 0 & 1 & 0 \end{bmatrix}$ (*c*) $\begin{bmatrix} 1 & 0 & 0 \\ 0 & 1 & 0 \\ 0 & 0 & 1 \end{bmatrix}$

5.7.4. Show that

$$\mathbf{C} = \begin{bmatrix} 0 & 1 & 0 \\ 0 & 0 & 1 \\ 1 & -3 & 3 \end{bmatrix}$$

is defective by showing $g(1) = 1$ and $a(1) = 3$.

5.7.5. Show that the following matrices are defective.

(a) $\begin{bmatrix} \alpha & \beta & * \\ 0 & \alpha & * \\ 0 & 0 & \alpha \end{bmatrix}$ $\beta \neq 0$ $\quad (b)$ $\begin{bmatrix} \alpha & 0 & \beta \\ 0 & \alpha & * \\ 0 & 0 & \alpha \end{bmatrix}$ $\beta \neq 0$

(c) $\begin{bmatrix} 1 & 1 & -5/4 \\ 1 & 1 & 1 \\ 1 & 1 & 1 \end{bmatrix}$ $\quad (d)$ $\begin{bmatrix} -\alpha & 1 \\ -\alpha^2 & \alpha \end{bmatrix}$ $\quad (e)$ $\begin{bmatrix} 2\alpha & -\alpha \\ \alpha & 0 \end{bmatrix}$ $\alpha \neq 0$

5.7.6. Find $\mathbf{S}$ and verify $\mathbf{S}^{-1}\mathbf{AS} = \Lambda$ for

$$\mathbf{A} = \begin{bmatrix} \cos\alpha & -\sin\alpha \\ \sin\alpha & \cos\alpha \end{bmatrix}$$

5.7.7. Find a 2×2 defective matrix whose square is simple.

5.7.8. Given

$$A = \begin{bmatrix} 2 & 0 & -1 \\ 0 & 2 & -1 \\ 0 & 0 & 3 \end{bmatrix}$$

$$\mathbf{x}_1 = \begin{bmatrix} 1 \\ 2 \\ 0 \end{bmatrix}, \quad \mathbf{x}_2 = \begin{bmatrix} -3 \\ 1 \\ 0 \end{bmatrix}, \quad \mathbf{x}_3 = \begin{bmatrix} -1 \\ -1 \\ 1 \end{bmatrix}, \quad \mathbf{x}_4 = \begin{bmatrix} 2 \\ 2 \\ 0 \end{bmatrix}$$

set

$$\mathbf{S}_1 = [\mathbf{x}_1 \quad \mathbf{x}_2 \quad \mathbf{x}_3] \qquad \mathbf{S}_2 = [\mathbf{x}_1 \quad \mathbf{x}_3 \quad \mathbf{x}_2]$$

$$\mathbf{S}_3 = [\mathbf{x}_2 \quad \mathbf{x}_3 \quad \mathbf{x}_4] \qquad \mathbf{S}_4 = [\mathbf{x}_4 \quad \mathbf{x}_2 \quad \mathbf{x}_3]$$

and compute the products

(a) $\mathbf{S}_1^{-1}\mathbf{AS}_1$ $\quad (b)$ $\mathbf{S}_2^{-1}\mathbf{AS}_2$ $\quad (c)$ $\mathbf{S}_3^{-1}\mathbf{AS}_3$ $\quad (d)$ $\mathbf{S}_4^{-1}\mathbf{AS}_4$

5.7.9. Set $\mathbf{x}_5 = [2 \quad 3 \quad 1]^T$. For $\mathbf{A}$, $\mathbf{x}_1$, $\mathbf{x}_2$, $\mathbf{x}_3$, $\mathbf{x}_4$ as defined in Problem 5.7.8, set

$$\mathbf{T}_1 = [\mathbf{x}_1 \quad \mathbf{x}_2 \quad \mathbf{x}_5] \qquad \mathbf{T}_2 = [\mathbf{x}_1 \quad \mathbf{x}_3 \quad \mathbf{x}_5] \qquad \mathbf{T}_3 = [\mathbf{x}_1 \quad \mathbf{x}_4 \quad \mathbf{x}_5]$$

Compute

(a) $\mathbf{T}_1^{-1}\mathbf{AT}_1$ $\quad (b)$ $\mathbf{T}_2^{-1}\mathbf{AT}_2$ $\quad (c)$ $\mathbf{T}_3^{-1}\mathbf{AT}_3$

5.7.10. Assuming a_1, a_2, and a_3 are real and not all zero, show that

$$\mathbf{A} = \begin{bmatrix} 0 & -a_3 & a_2 \\ a_3 & 0 & -a_1 \\ -a_2 & a_1 & 0 \end{bmatrix}$$

is simple and find the eigenvalues and corresponding eigenvectors.

5.7.11. Which of the following are simple?

(a) $\mathbf{A} = \begin{bmatrix} -1 & 0 & 2 \\ 1 & 1 & 1 \\ 2 & 0 & -1 \end{bmatrix}$ $\quad (b)$ $\mathbf{A} = \begin{bmatrix} 2 & 0 & 1 \\ 1 & 3 & 1 \\ 1 & 0 & 2 \end{bmatrix}$ $\quad (c)$ $\mathbf{A} = \begin{bmatrix} 2 & 0 & 1 \\ 1 & 1 & 1 \\ 1 & 0 & 2 \end{bmatrix}$

5.7.12. Find $a(1)$ and $g(1)$ and explain why these matrices are defective:

$$(a)\ \mathbf{A} = \begin{bmatrix} 3 & 0 & 2 \\ 1 & 1 & -1 \\ -2 & 0 & -1 \end{bmatrix} \qquad (b)\ \mathbf{A} = \begin{bmatrix} 3 & 0 & 2 \\ 1 & 1 & 1 \\ -2 & 0 & -1 \end{bmatrix}$$

5.7.13. Verify $\mathbf{A}^{-1} = \frac{1}{2}\mathbf{A}^2 - 2\mathbf{A} + \frac{5}{2}\mathbf{I}$ for the matrix $\mathbf{A}$ of Example 5.7.7.

PART 2

5.7.14. If $\mathbf{A}$ is simple, show that $\mathbf{A}^{\mathrm{T}}$ is simple. If $\mathbf{A}$ is also invertible, show that $\mathbf{A}^{-1}$ is simple.

5.7.15. Show by constructing 2×2 examples that $\mathbf{A}$ can be simple and $\mathbf{SA}$ defective. Show by example that $\mathbf{SA}$ can be simple and $\mathbf{A}$ defective.

5.7.16. Interpret the conclusions arrived at in Problem 5.7.15 in terms of the row-equivalent matrices $\mathbf{A}$ and $\mathbf{B}$.

5.7.17. Let

$$\mathbf{A}(r) = \begin{bmatrix} 0 & 1 & 0 \\ 0 & 0 & 1 \\ r^3 & -3r^2 & 3r \end{bmatrix}$$

Show that $a(r) > g(r)$ and hence that $\mathbf{A}(r)$ is defective.

5.7.18. Let

$$\mathbf{A}(r) = \begin{bmatrix} 0 & 1 & 0 \\ 0 & 0 & 1 \\ -r & 1 & r \end{bmatrix}$$

For each fixed r show that

$$\begin{bmatrix} 1 \\ 1 \\ 1 \end{bmatrix}, \quad \begin{bmatrix} 1 \\ -1 \\ 1 \end{bmatrix}, \quad \begin{bmatrix} 1 \\ r \\ r^2 \end{bmatrix}$$

are the eigenvectors of $\mathbf{A}(r)$. Show that $\mathbf{A}(r)$ is simple if $r \neq 1$.

5.7.19. Find the eigenvalues and eigenvectors of

$$\mathbf{D}(s) = \begin{bmatrix} 2-s & s & s-3 \\ 1 & 0 & -1 \\ 0 & 1 & 1 \end{bmatrix}$$

and determine whether $\mathbf{D}(s)$ is simple or defective as a function of s.

5.7.20. Determine whether the following matrix is simple or defective:

$$\mathbf{A} = \begin{bmatrix} 1 & 0 & 1 & 0 \\ 0 & 1 & 0 & 1 \\ 1 & 0 & 1 & 0 \\ 0 & 1 & 0 & 1 \end{bmatrix}$$

5.7.21. Show that an upper (or lower) triangular matrix with at least one nonzero off-diagonal entry and with equal values on its diagonal, is defective. (*Hint:* Show that rank $(\mathbf{A} - \lambda\mathbf{I}) < n$, and compare $g(\lambda)$ with $a(\lambda)$.)

5.7.22. Determine whether the following matrices are simple or defective:

$$(a)\begin{bmatrix} a & b & a & b \\ b & a & b & a \\ a & b & a & b \\ b & a & b & a \end{bmatrix} \quad (b)\begin{bmatrix} a & a & b & b \\ b & a & b & a \\ a & a & b & b \\ b & a & b & a \end{bmatrix} \quad (c)\begin{bmatrix} b & a & a & b \\ a & b & a & b \\ b & a & a & b \\ a & b & a & b \end{bmatrix}$$

(*Hint:* Each is singular, and each has an eigenvector $\mathbf{x} = \mathbf{1} = [1 \quad 1 \quad \ldots \quad 1]^{\mathrm{T}}$.)

5.7.23. Find the eigenvalues of

$$\mathbf{A} = \begin{bmatrix} a & 0 & b \\ c & d & c \\ b & 0 & a \end{bmatrix}$$

(*a*) Show that $\mathbf{A}$ is defective if $c \neq 0$ and $d = a + b$.
(*b*) Show that $\mathbf{A}$ is simple if $d = a - b$. Find $\mathbf{S}$ so that $\mathbf{S}^{-1}\mathbf{AS} = \Lambda$.

PART 3

5.7.24. Suppose $\mathbf{A}$ and $\mathbf{B}$ are simple and have the same set of eigenvectors. Let $\lambda_1, \lambda_2, \ldots, \lambda_n$ be the eigenvalues of $\mathbf{A}$ and $\mu_1, \mu_2, \ldots, \mu_n$ be those of $\mathbf{B}$. Show that $\mathbf{AB} = \mathbf{BA}$ and that the eigenvalues of $\mathbf{AB}$ are $\lambda_1\mu_1, \lambda_2\mu_2, \ldots, \lambda_n\mu_n$ for a suitable ordering of the eigenvalues of $\mathbf{B}$.

5.7.25. Complete the proof of Theorem 5.7.4 assuming that $\mathbf{A}$ has m distinct eigenvalues satisfying the conditions: $a(\lambda_k) = g(\lambda_k) = m_k$ and $\Sigma m_k = n$, $i = 1, 2, \ldots, m$.

5.7.26. Suppose $\mathbf{P}$ is idempotent ($\mathbf{P} = \mathbf{P}$). Show
(*a*) $g(0) = \dim(null(\mathbf{P}))$ and $g(1) = \dim(null(\mathbf{I} - \mathbf{P}))$
(*b*) $col(\mathbf{I} - \mathbf{P}) = null(\mathbf{P})$

5.7.27. Use Problems 5.7.25 and 5.7.26 and $\dim(null(\mathbf{I}-\mathbf{P})) + \operatorname{rank}(\mathbf{I}-\mathbf{P}) = n$ to show that $g(0) + g(1) = n$. Hence, show that idempotent matrices are simple.

5.7.28. If $\mathbf{M}$ satisfies $\mathbf{M}^2 = \mathbf{I}$ then $\mathbf{M}$ is called *involutory*. Show that if $\mathbf{P}$ is idempotent, $2\mathbf{P} - \mathbf{I}$ is involutory. Use this fact to prove that $\mathbf{M}$ is simple.

5.7.29. Assume that $\mathbf{A}$ is simple and invertible with

$$c_{\mathbf{A}}(\lambda) = (-\lambda)^n + a_{n-1}(-\lambda)^{n-1} + \cdots + a_1(-\lambda) + a_0$$

Show that

$$\mathbf{A}^{-1} = \frac{-1}{a_0}\left\{(-\mathbf{A})^{n-1} + a_{n-1}(-\mathbf{A})^{n-2} + \cdots + a_1\mathbf{I}\right\}$$

PART 2 APPLICATIONS

5.8 SIMILARITIES

If there exists a nonsingular matrix $\mathbf{S}$ such that $\mathbf{S}^{-1}\mathbf{BS} = \mathbf{A}$, then $\mathbf{B}$ is said to be *similar* to $\mathbf{A}$. Thus, in particular, a simple matrix is similar to a diagonal matrix of its eigenvalues. The set of all matrices similar to $\mathbf{A}$, which is denoted by $\mathscr{A}$, is the *similarity class* of **A**. $\mathscr{A}$ cannot be empty, because, at the very least, $\mathbf{I}^{-1}\mathbf{A}\mathbf{I} = \mathbf{A}$ shows that **A** is similar to itself and therefore $\mathbf{A} \in \mathscr{A}$. However, **A** may be the only member of $\mathscr{A}$.

Example 5.8.1. Show that the similarity class of the scalar matrix, $a\mathbf{I}$, contains only $a\mathbf{I}$.

Solution. Suppose **B** is similar to $a\mathbf{I}$. Hence for some **S**, $\mathbf{S}^{-1}\mathbf{B}\mathbf{S} = a\mathbf{I}$. Then, solving for **B**, $\mathbf{B} = \mathbf{S}(a\mathbf{I})\mathbf{S}^{-1} = a(\mathbf{S}\mathbf{I}\mathbf{S}^{-1}) = a\mathbf{I}$.

The members of $\mathscr{A}$ are all similar to **A** by definition. In fact, they are also similar to each other. Suppose **B** and **C** belong to $\mathscr{A}$. Then there exist matrices **S** and **T** such that $\mathbf{S}^{-1}\mathbf{B}\mathbf{S} = \mathbf{A}$ and $\mathbf{T}^{-1}\mathbf{C}\mathbf{T} = \mathbf{A}$. Therefore, $\mathbf{S}^{-1}\mathbf{B}\mathbf{S} = \mathbf{T}^{-1}\mathbf{C}\mathbf{T}$. Solving this last equation for **C** leads to

$$\mathbf{C} = \mathbf{T}(\mathbf{S}^{-1}\mathbf{B}\mathbf{S})\mathbf{T}^{-1} = (\mathbf{S}\mathbf{T}^{-1})^{-1}\mathbf{B}(\mathbf{S}\mathbf{T}^{-1})$$

which shows that **B** is similar to **C**. ($\mathbf{S}\mathbf{T}^{-1}$ plays the role of **S** in the definition of similarity).

Example 5.8.2. Prove the following: For each **A**

(*a*) **A** is similar to itself (called *reflexivity*).
(*b*) If **B** is similar to **A**, then **A** is similar to **B** (called *symmetry*).
(*c*) If **C** is similar to **B** and **B** is similar to **A**, then **C** is similar to **A** (called *transitivity*).

Solution. The identity $\mathbf{I}^{-1}\mathbf{A}\mathbf{I} = \mathbf{A}$ furnishes the proof of (*a*). For (*b*), note that $\mathbf{S}^{-1}\mathbf{B}\mathbf{S} = \mathbf{A}$ implies $\mathbf{S}\mathbf{A}\mathbf{S}^{-1} = \mathbf{B}$, and the latter equation is the required statement with $\mathbf{S}^{-1}$ playing the role of **S**. Part (*c*) is left for the exercises.

The three properties listed in Example 5.8.1—reflexivity, symmetry, and transitivity—show that the similarity relationship is an *equivalence relationship*. (Equality, row equivalence of matrices, and congruence of triangles are other examples of equivalence relationships. "$\leq$" is not an equivalence relationship because symmetry fails.) One consequence of the fact that similarity is an equivalence relationship is that similarity classes with a nonempty intersection must be identical. (Why? See Problem 5.8.15.) Thus, the set of all $n \times n$ matrices is partitioned by the property of similarity into mutually exclusive, completely exhaustive sets.

The matrices in a similarity class have the same characteristic polynomials by Lemma 5.1, in Section 5.5, and, hence, have the same eigenvalues, counting algebraic multiplicities. What other properties do they share? Here is an easy argument to show that they all have the same rank.

Example 5.8.3. Show that all matrices in the same similarity class have the same rank.

Solution. Suppose $\mathbf{A}$ and $\mathbf{B}$ belong to the same similarity class. Then they are similar and for some $\mathbf{S}$, $\mathbf{S}^{-1}\mathbf{AS} = \mathbf{B}$. But $\text{rank}(\mathbf{B}) = \text{rank}(\mathbf{S}^{-1}\mathbf{AS}) = \text{rank}(\mathbf{A})$ since the rank is unaltered by pre- or postmultiplication by a nonsingular matrix, by Theorem 2.7.3.

Example 5.8.3 shows that the matrices in a similarity class are either all singular or all nonsingular. A more significant relationship between the matrices in a similarity class is exhibited in the next theorem.

Theorem 5.8.1. *Suppose* $\mathbf{A}$ *is similar to* $\mathbf{B}$ *and* λ_0 *is an eigenvalue of* $\mathbf{A}$ *with* $g_{\mathbf{A}}(\lambda_0) = r$. *Then* λ_0 *is also an eigenvalue of* $\mathbf{B}$ *and* $g_{\mathbf{B}}(\lambda_0) = r$.

Proof. The definition of the geometric multiplicity guarantees that there are r linearly independent eigenvectors of $\mathbf{A}$ corresponding to λ_0. Call them $\{\mathbf{x}_1, \mathbf{x}_2, \ldots, \mathbf{x}_r\}$. Now, consider the set $\{\mathbf{S}^{-1}\mathbf{x}_1, \mathbf{S}^{-1}\mathbf{x}_2, \ldots, \mathbf{S}^{-1}\mathbf{x}_r\}$. First of all, this set is linearly independent because $\mathbf{S}$ is nonsingular and the set $\{\mathbf{x}_1, \mathbf{x}_2, \ldots, \mathbf{x}_r\}$ is linearly independent. Next,

$$\mathbf{B}(\mathbf{S}^{-1}\mathbf{x}_i) = \mathbf{S}^{-1}\mathbf{AS}(\mathbf{S}^{-1}\mathbf{x}_i) = \mathbf{S}^{-1}(\mathbf{A}\mathbf{x}_i) = \lambda_0(\mathbf{S}^{-1}\mathbf{x}_i)$$

shows that $(\lambda_0, \mathbf{S}^{-1}\mathbf{x}_i)$ is an eigenpair of $\mathbf{B}$. ($\mathbf{S}^{-1}\mathbf{x}_i \neq \mathbf{0}$ since $\mathbf{x}_i \neq \mathbf{0}$.) So, $\mathbf{B}$ has at least r eigenvectors corresponding to λ_0. Therefore, $g_{\mathbf{B}}(\lambda_0) \geq g_{\mathbf{A}}(\lambda_0) = r$. By reversing the roles of $\mathbf{A}$ and $\mathbf{B}$, $g_{\mathbf{A}}(\lambda_0) \geq g_{\mathbf{B}}(\lambda_0)$. Thus, $g_{\mathbf{A}}(\lambda_0) = g_{\mathbf{B}}(\lambda_0)$. ■

Example 5.8.4. Show that if $\mathbf{A}$ is diagonalizable and $\mathbf{C}$ defective, then $\mathbf{A}$ cannot be similar to $\mathbf{C}$.

Solution. Suppose that $\mathbf{A}$ were similar to $\mathbf{C}$. Then, since $\mathbf{A}$ is similar to a diagonal matrix, so would be $\mathbf{C}$. But by hypothesis, $\mathbf{C}$ is not.

Example 5.8.5. Suppose $\mathbf{P}$ is idempotent ($\mathbf{P}^2 = \mathbf{P}$). Then all members of the similarity class of $\mathbf{P}$ are idempotent.

Solution. Suppose $\mathbf{B}$ is any member of the similarity class of $\mathbf{P}$. Then there exists a nonsingular $\mathbf{S}$ such that $\mathbf{S}^{-1}\mathbf{BS} = \mathbf{P}$. Then, since $\mathbf{P}^2 = \mathbf{P}$,

$$\mathbf{P}^2 = (\mathbf{S}^{-1}\mathbf{BS})(\mathbf{S}^{-1}\mathbf{BS}) = \mathbf{S}^{-1}\mathbf{B}^2\mathbf{S}$$

implies $\mathbf{S}^{-1}\mathbf{B}^2\mathbf{S} = \mathbf{P}$. By definition, $\mathbf{S}^{-1}\mathbf{BS} = \mathbf{P}$. Hence $\mathbf{B}^2 = \mathbf{B}$.

The *anti-diagonal* of $\mathbf{A}$ is the entries on the "other diagonal" of $\mathbf{A}$: $\{a_{n,1}, a_{n-1,2}, a_{n-2,3}, \ldots, a_{1,n}\}$. The *anti-transpose* of $\mathbf{A}$, written $\mathbf{A}^{\mathrm{S}}$, is the reflection of the entries of $\mathbf{A}$ about its anti-diagonal. For example

$$\begin{bmatrix} 1 & 2 & -1 & 2 \\ 0 & 0 & 1 & -1 \\ 2 & 3 & 0 & 1 \\ 0 & 0 & 0 & 0 \end{bmatrix}^S = \begin{bmatrix} 0 & 1 & -1 & 2 \\ 0 & 0 & 1 & -1 \\ 0 & 3 & 0 & 2 \\ 0 & 2 & 0 & 1 \end{bmatrix}$$

Define $\mathbf{E}_n$ by

$$\mathbf{E}_n = \begin{bmatrix} & & & & 1 \\ & 0 & & 1 & \\ & & \cdot^{\cdot^{\cdot}} & & \\ & 1 & & 0 & \\ 1 & & & & \end{bmatrix} \tag{5.8.1}$$

Example 5.8.6. Show that $\mathbf{A}^{\mathrm{S}}$ is similar to $\mathbf{A}$.

Solution. Clearly $\mathbf{E}^{-1} = \mathbf{E}$. It takes a bit more work to show that $\mathbf{E}^{-1}\mathbf{A}^{\mathrm{S}}\mathbf{E} = \mathbf{A}^{\mathrm{T}}$. (See Problem 5.8.17.) Hence, $\mathbf{A}^{\mathrm{S}}$ is similar to $\mathbf{A}^{\mathrm{T}}$ and, since $\mathbf{A}^{\mathrm{T}}$ is similar to $\mathbf{A}$ (Example 5.7.4), $\mathbf{A}^{\mathrm{S}}$ is similar to $\mathbf{A}$.

Indeed, if $\mathbf{S}^{-1}\mathbf{A}\mathbf{S} = \Lambda$, then $\mathbf{S}^{\mathrm{T}}\mathbf{A}^{\mathrm{T}}\mathbf{S}^{-\mathrm{T}} = \Lambda$ and, therefore, using $\mathbf{E}^{-1} = \mathbf{E}$,

$$\mathbf{S}^{\mathrm{T}}(\mathbf{E}\mathbf{A}^{\mathrm{S}}\mathbf{E})\mathbf{S}^{-\mathrm{T}} = \mathbf{S}^{\mathrm{T}}\mathbf{A}^{\mathrm{T}}\mathbf{S}^{-\mathrm{T}} = \Lambda \tag{5.8.2}$$

Now, $\mathbf{E}\mathbf{S}^{\mathrm{T}}\mathbf{E} = \mathbf{S}^{\mathrm{S}}$. Hence, if Eq. 5.8.2 is multiplied on the right and left by $\mathbf{E}$, we obtain

$$\mathbf{E}\mathbf{S}^{\mathrm{T}}(\mathbf{E}\mathbf{A}^{\mathrm{S}}\mathbf{E})\mathbf{S}^{-\mathrm{T}}\mathbf{E} = (\mathbf{E}\mathbf{S}^{\mathrm{T}}\mathbf{E})\mathbf{A}^{\mathrm{S}}(\mathbf{E}\mathbf{S}^{-\mathrm{T}}\mathbf{E}) = \mathbf{S}^{\mathrm{S}}\mathbf{A}^{\mathrm{S}}\mathbf{S}^{-\mathrm{S}} = \mathbf{E}\Lambda\mathbf{E} = \Lambda^{\mathrm{S}}$$

That is, $\mathbf{S}^{\mathrm{S}}\mathbf{A}^{\mathrm{S}}\mathbf{S}^{-\mathrm{S}} = \Lambda^{\mathrm{S}}$.

PROBLEMS

PART 1

5.8.1. Verify the conclusion of Example 5.8.7.

5.8.2. Show that

$$\mathbf{A} = \begin{bmatrix} 0 & 1 \\ 0 & 0 \end{bmatrix} \qquad \mathbf{B} = \begin{bmatrix} 1 & 0 \\ 0 & 0 \end{bmatrix}$$

cannot be similar, by verifying that $\mathbf{AS} = \mathbf{SB}$ implies that $\mathbf{S}$ is singular.

5.8.3. Find a nonsingular $\mathbf{S}$ such that $\mathbf{S}^{-1}\mathbf{AS} = \mathbf{B}$ where

$$\mathbf{A} = \begin{bmatrix} 0 & 1 \\ 0 & 0 \end{bmatrix} \qquad \mathbf{B} = \begin{bmatrix} 0 & 0 \\ 1 & 0 \end{bmatrix}$$

5.8.4. Explain why Example 5.8.3 shows that all members of $\mathcal{A}$ are either singular or nonsingular. Offer an example of two singular, nonsimilar matrices.

PART 2

5.8.5. If $\mathbf{A}$ is similar to $\mathbf{B}$ and $\mathbf{A}^{-1}$ exists, show that $\mathbf{B}^{-1}$ exists and prove that $\mathbf{A}^{-1}$ is similar to $\mathbf{B}^{-1}$ by computing $(\mathbf{S}^{-1}\mathbf{AS})^{-1}$.

5.8.6. Prove the transitivity of similarities, Part (*c*) of Example 5.8.2.

5.8.7. Suppose $\mathbf{A} \in \mathcal{A}$ and $\mathbf{A} \in \mathcal{B}$. Show that $\mathcal{A} = \mathcal{B}$.

5.8.8. If $\mathbf{A}$ is similar to $\mathbf{B}$, show that $p(\mathbf{A})$ is similar to $p(\mathbf{B})$ for every polynomial $p(x)$.

5.8.9. If $\mathbf{B}^{-1}$ exists, show that $\mathbf{AB}$ is similar to $\mathbf{BA}$ by using $\mathbf{S} = \mathbf{B}^{-1}$.

5.8.10. If $\mathbf{A}_1$ is similar to $\mathbf{A}_2$ and $\mathbf{B}_1$ is similar to $\mathbf{B}_2$, show that

$$\left[\begin{array}{c|c} \mathbf{A}_1 & \mathbf{O} \\ \hline \mathbf{O} & \mathbf{B}_1 \end{array}\right]$$

is similar to

$$\left[\begin{array}{c|c} \mathbf{A}_2 & \mathbf{O} \\ \hline \mathbf{O} & \mathbf{B}_2 \end{array}\right]$$

5.8.11. If $\mathbf{A}$ is similar to an involutary matrix $\mathbf{M}$ ($\mathbf{M}^2 = \mathbf{I}$), show that $\mathbf{A}$ is also involutary.

5.8.12. If $\mathbf{A}$ is similar to a nilpotent matrix $\mathbf{N}$ of order k, that is, $\mathbf{N}^k = \mathbf{O}$, $\mathbf{N}^j \neq \mathbf{O}$ for all $j < k$, show that $\mathbf{A}$ is nilpotent of order k.

PART 3

Let the diagonal matrix $\mathbf{D}(v) = \text{diag}[v_1, v_2, \ldots, v_n]$ be defined by

$$\mathbf{D}(v) = \begin{bmatrix} v_1 & & \cdots & 0 \\ 0 & v_2 & \cdots & 0 \\ \vdots & \vdots & & \vdots \\ 0 & 0 & \cdots & v_n \end{bmatrix}$$

Suppose $v_i \neq 0$ for each i so that $\mathbf{D}^{-1}(v) = \text{diag}[v_1^{-1}, v_2^{-1}, \ldots, v_n^{-1}]$ exists. Problems 5.8.13, 5.8.14, and 5.8.16 use this notation.

5.8.13. Verify the following identity:

$$\mathbf{D}^{-1}(v)\mathbf{A}\mathbf{D}(v) = \begin{bmatrix} a_{11} & (v_2/v_1)a_{12} & \cdots & (v_n/v_1)a_{1n} \\ (v_1/v_2)a_{21} & a_{22} & \cdots & (v_n/v_2)a_{2n} \\ \vdots & \vdots & & \vdots \\ (v_1/v_n)a_{n1} & (v_2/v_n)a_{n2} & \cdots & a_{nn} \end{bmatrix}$$

5.8.14. Let $\mathbf{A} = (a_{ij})$ and $v_i = \rho^i$. Use the result of Problem 5.8.13 to show that $\mathbf{D}^{-1}\mathbf{A}\mathbf{D} = (\rho^{j-i}a_{ij})$.

5.8.15. If $\mathbf{A}$ is similar to $\mathbf{B}$, show that $\dim(\textit{null}(\mathbf{A})) = \dim(\textit{null}(\mathbf{B}))$.

5.8.16. Let $\mathbf{P}$ be the elementary row matrix that permutes rows i and j. Show that $\mathbf{P}^{-1} = \mathbf{P}$, that is, that $\mathbf{P}$ is involutary. Now show that $\mathbf{P}\mathbf{D}_v\mathbf{P}$ interchanges v_i with v_j. Explain why repeated use of this argument shows that two diagonal matrices are similar if the diagonal entries of one are a rearrangement of the diagonal entries of the other.

5.8.17. Refer to Example 5.8.6 and Eq. 5.8.1.

(*a*) Show that $\mathbf{E} = \mathbf{E}^{\mathrm{S}} = \mathbf{E}^{-1}$.

(*b*) Describe the effect of $\mathbf{EA}$ on the rows of $\mathbf{A}$ and $\mathbf{AE}$ on the columns of $\mathbf{A}$.

(*c*) Show that $\mathbf{E}\mathbf{A}^{\mathrm{S}}\mathbf{E} = \mathbf{A}^{\mathrm{T}}$, that $\mathbf{E}\mathbf{A}^{\mathrm{T}}\mathbf{E} = \mathbf{A}^{\mathrm{S}}$, and that $(\mathbf{A}^{\mathrm{S}})^{\mathrm{T}} = (\mathbf{A}^{\mathrm{T}})^{\mathrm{S}}$. Hence, writing $(\mathbf{A}^{\mathrm{S}})^{\mathrm{T}} = \mathbf{A}^{\mathrm{ST}}$, show that $\mathbf{EAE} = \mathbf{A}^{\mathrm{ST}}$.

(*d*) Show that $\mathbf{A}^{\mathrm{S}}$ is similar to $\mathbf{A}^{\mathrm{T}}$.

5.9 CIRCULANTS

An interesting and important class of simple matrices are the so-called circulants.[3] *Circulants* are polynomials in the matrix $\mathbf{C}_n$,

$$\mathbf{C}_n = \begin{bmatrix} 0 & 1 & 0 & \cdots & 0 & 0 \\ 0 & 0 & 1 & \cdots & 0 & 0 \\ \vdots & \vdots & \vdots & & \vdots & \vdots \\ 0 & 0 & 0 & \cdots & 0 & 1 \\ 1 & 0 & 0 & \cdots & 0 & 0 \end{bmatrix} \tag{5.9.1}$$

Theorem 5.9.1. *For each n,* $\mathbf{C}_n$ *is simple and has characteristic polynomial*

$$c(\lambda) = (-1)^n(\lambda^n - 1) \tag{5.9.2}$$

Proof. Expand $\det(\mathbf{C}_n - \lambda\mathbf{I})$ by cofactors of the first column:

$$\det(\mathbf{C}_n - \lambda\mathbf{I}) = \det\begin{bmatrix} -\lambda & 1 & 0 & \cdots & 0 & 0 \\ 0 & -\lambda & 1 & \cdots & 0 & 0 \\ \vdots & \vdots & \vdots & & \vdots & \vdots \\ 0 & 0 & 0 & \cdots & -\lambda & 1 \\ 1 & 0 & 0 & \cdots & 0 & -\lambda \end{bmatrix}$$

$$= (-\lambda)\det\begin{bmatrix} -\lambda & 1 & \cdots & 0 & 0 \\ 0 & -\lambda & \cdots & 0 & 0 \\ \vdots & \vdots & & \vdots & \vdots \\ 0 & 0 & \cdots & 0 & -\lambda \end{bmatrix}$$

$$-(-1)^n \det\begin{bmatrix} 1 & 0 & \cdots & 0 & 0 \\ -\lambda & 1 & \cdots & 0 & 0 \\ \vdots & \vdots & & \vdots & \vdots \\ 0 & 0 & \cdots & -\lambda & 1 \end{bmatrix} = (-1)^n\lambda^n - (-1)^n \quad \blacksquare$$

The characteristic equation is $\lambda^n - 1 = 0$, and this equation has n distinct roots $\omega, \omega^2, \ldots, \omega^n = 1$, where

$$\omega = \cos(2\pi/n) + i\sin(2\pi/n) = e^{2\pi i/n}$$

and

$$\omega^k = \cos(2\pi k/n) + i\sin(2\pi k/n) = e^{2\pi ik/n}$$

(See Section 5.2.) Thus,

$$c(\lambda) = (1 - \lambda)(\omega - \lambda)\cdots(\omega^{n-1} - \lambda) \tag{5.9.3}$$

---

[3] Philip J. Davis's excellent monograph *Circulant Matrices* (New York: Wiley-Interscience, 1979) provides an extensive presentation with many applications. See also Section 5.12.

Now define $\mathbf{W}_n$ by

$$\mathbf{W}_n = \begin{bmatrix} a_0 & a_1 & a_2 & \cdots & a_{n-2} & a_{n-1} \\ a_{n-1} & a_0 & a_1 & \cdots & a_{n-3} & a_{n-2} \\ a_{n-2} & a_{n-1} & a_0 & \cdots & a_{n-4} & a_{n-3} \\ \vdots & \vdots & \vdots & & \vdots & \vdots \\ a_1 & a_2 & a_3 & \cdots & a_{n-1} & a_0 \end{bmatrix} \tag{5.9.4}$$

Matrices $\mathbf{W}_n$ are called *circulants,* because of the way the rows of $\mathbf{W}_n$ are related. Now set

$$p(x) = a_0 + a_1 x + \cdots + a_{n-1}x^{n-1} \tag{5.9.5}$$

Theorem 5.9.2. *$\mathbf{W}_n = p(\mathbf{C}_n)$ and, therefore, $\mathbf{W}_n$ is simple. Moreover, the characteristic equation of $\mathbf{W}_n$ is*

$$c(\lambda) = (p(1) - \lambda)(p(\omega) - \lambda)\cdots(p(\omega^{n-1}) - \lambda) \tag{5.9.6}$$

Proof. Compute the various powers of $\mathbf{C}_n$ by observing that the columns of $\mathbf{C}_n$ and its powers are permutations of unit vectors. That is,

$$\begin{aligned} \mathbf{C}_n &= [\mathbf{e}_n \quad \mathbf{e}_1 \quad \mathbf{e}_2 \quad \ldots \quad \mathbf{e}_{n-1}] \\ \mathbf{C}_n^2 &= [\mathbf{e}_{n-1} \quad \mathbf{e}_n \quad \mathbf{e}_1 \quad \ldots \quad \mathbf{e}_{n-2}] \\ &\vdots \\ \mathbf{C}_n^{n-1} &= [\mathbf{e}_2 \quad \mathbf{e}_3 \quad \mathbf{e}_4 \quad \ldots \quad \mathbf{e}_n \quad \mathbf{e}_1] \end{aligned}$$

It is now easy to verify that

$$p(\mathbf{C}_n) = a_0\mathbf{I} + a_1\mathbf{C}_n + \cdots + a_{n-1}\mathbf{C}_n^{n-1} = \mathbf{W}_n \tag{5.9.7}$$

Finally, the characteristic equation of $\mathbf{W}_n$ is derived by applying Theorem 5.6.2. (Note that the coefficients of $p(x)$ are given by the entries in the first row of $\mathbf{W}_n$.) ∎

Example 5.9.1. Use Theorem 5.9.2 to find the eigenvalues of the circulant

$$\mathbf{W}_3 = \begin{bmatrix} 1 & 2 & 1 \\ 1 & 1 & 2 \\ 2 & 1 & 1 \end{bmatrix}$$

Solution. The coefficients of the first row of $\mathbf{W}_3$, read from left to right, define $p(x) = 1 + 2x + x^2 = (1+x)^2$. The eigenvalues of $\mathbf{C}_3$ are the three third roots of unity

$$\begin{aligned} \omega &= \lambda_1 = -\frac{1}{2} + i\frac{\sqrt{3}}{2} \\ \omega^2 &= \lambda_2 = -\frac{1}{2} - i\frac{\sqrt{3}}{2} \\ \omega^3 &= \lambda_3 = 1 \end{aligned}$$

(See Example 5.2.3(*a*).) Hence, the three eigenvalues of $\mathbf{W}_3$ are given by $(1 + \lambda_k)^2$, $k = 1, 2, 3$:

$$\mu_1 = (1 + \lambda_1)^2 = \tfrac{1}{2}(-1 + i\sqrt{3})$$

$$\mu_2 = (1 + \lambda_2)^2 = \tfrac{1}{2}(-1 - i\sqrt{3})$$

$$\mu_3 = (1 + \lambda_3)^2 = 4$$

Example 5.9.2. Use Theorem 5.9.2 to find the eigenvalues of the circulant,

$$\mathbf{W}_4 = \begin{bmatrix} a & b & a & b \\ b & a & b & a \\ a & b & a & b \\ b & a & b & a \end{bmatrix}$$

Solution. The entries in the first row of $\mathbf{W}_4$ define $p(x)$:

$$p(x) = a + bx + ax^2 + bx^3 = (x^2 + 1)(a + bx).$$

From Theorem 5.9.2, it follows that the eigenvalues of $\mathbf{W}_4$ are given by $p(\lambda_1)$, $p(\lambda_2)$, $p(\lambda_3)$, and $p(\lambda_4)$, where the λ_i are the four fourth roots of unity. (See Example 5.2.3(*b*).) That is, $\omega = \lambda_1 = i$, $\omega^2 = \lambda_2 = -1$, $\omega^3 = \lambda_3 = -i$, and $\lambda_4 = 1$. Thus the eigenvalues of $\mathbf{W}_4$ are

$$\begin{aligned} \mu_1 &= p(i) = 0, \\ \mu_2 &= p(-1) = 2(a - b) \\ \mu_3 &= p(-i) = 0, \\ \mu_4 &= p(1) = 2(a + b) \end{aligned}$$

These values can be checked by substitution into $\det(\mathbf{W}_4 - \mu_i\mathbf{I}_4)$.

The next topic is the construction of the n linearly independent eigenvectors of $\mathbf{C}_n$. Let $\rho \neq 0$ be an arbitrary parameter. Consider the vector $\mathbf{u} = [1 \quad \rho \quad \rho^2 \quad \ldots \quad \rho^{n-1}]^{\mathrm{T}}$ and the product $\mathbf{C}_n\mathbf{u}$

$$\mathbf{C}_n\mathbf{u} = \begin{bmatrix} 0 & 1 & 0 & \cdots & 0 & 0 \\ 0 & 0 & 1 & \cdots & 0 & 0 \\ \vdots & \vdots & \vdots & & \vdots & \vdots \\ 0 & 0 & 0 & \cdots & 0 & 1 \\ 1 & 0 & 0 & \cdots & 0 & 0 \end{bmatrix} \begin{bmatrix} 1 \\ \rho^1 \\ \vdots \\ \rho^{n-1} \end{bmatrix} = \begin{bmatrix} \rho^1 \\ \rho^2 \\ \vdots \\ 1 \end{bmatrix} = \rho \begin{bmatrix} 1 \\ \rho^1 \\ \vdots \\ \rho^{-1} \end{bmatrix}$$

Thus $(\rho, \mathbf{u})$ is an eigenpair of $\mathbf{C}_n$ if $\rho^{-1} = \rho^{n-1}$. But $\rho^{-1} = \rho^{n-1}$ implies that ρ is an nth root of unity. Therefore, since the eigenvalues are distinct, a complete set of eigenvectors of $\mathbf{C}_n$ is given by setting $\rho = \omega^k$

$$\mathbf{u}_k = \begin{bmatrix} 1 \\ \omega^k \\ \vdots \\ (\omega^k)^{n-1} \end{bmatrix}, \qquad k = 1, 2, \ldots, n$$

That is,

$$\mathbf{u}_n = \mathbf{1}, \qquad \mathbf{u}_1 = \begin{bmatrix} 1 \\ \omega \\ \vdots \\ \omega^{n-1} \end{bmatrix}, \qquad \mathbf{u}_2 = \begin{bmatrix} 1 \\ \omega^2 \\ \vdots \\ \omega^{2n-2} \end{bmatrix}, \qquad \cdots \qquad \mathbf{u}_{n-1} = \begin{bmatrix} 1 \\ \omega^{n-1} \\ \vdots \\ \omega^{(n-1)^2} \end{bmatrix} \tag{5.9.8}$$

These vectors are also the eigenvectors of $\mathbf{W}_n$, because every eigenvector of $\mathbf{A}$ is an eigenvector of every polynomial in $\mathbf{A}$ (Theorem 5.6.1). The n scalars $p(\omega^k)$, $k = 1, 2, \ldots, n$, are its corresponding eigenvalues. The upshot of this is that the entries in a given eigenvector of $p(\mathbf{C}_n)$ are simply the successive powers of the eigenvalue of $\mathbf{C}_n$ associated with this eigenvector. Therefore, it is unnecessary to find the eigenvalues of $\mathbf{W}_n = \mathrm{p}\,(\mathbf{C}_n)$ if only the eigenvectors of $\mathbf{W}_n$ are needed.

Example 5.9.3. Find a linearly independent set of four eigenvectors of any 4×4 circulant.

Solution. The eigenvectors are determined by using the eigenvalues of $\mathbf{C}_4$; therefore, the eigenvalues of the circulant are irrelevant. The eigenvalues of $\mathbf{C}_4$ are the four fourth roots of unity: $i, -1, -i$, and 1, and hence, the eigenvectors are given by Eq. 5.9.8:

$$\mathbf{u}_1 = \begin{bmatrix} 1 \\ i \\ -1 \\ -i \end{bmatrix}, \qquad \mathbf{u}_2 = \begin{bmatrix} 1 \\ -1 \\ 1 \\ -1 \end{bmatrix}, \qquad \mathbf{u}_3 = \begin{bmatrix} 1 \\ -i \\ -1 \\ i \end{bmatrix}, \qquad \mathbf{u}_4 = \begin{bmatrix} 1 \\ 1 \\ 1 \\ 1 \end{bmatrix}$$

Let $\mathbf{S} = \mathbf{V}_n(\omega)$ be the matrix whose columns are the eigenvectors of $\mathbf{W}_n$,

$$\mathbf{V}_n(\omega) = \begin{bmatrix} 1 & 1 & \cdots & 1 \\ 1 & \omega & \cdots & \omega^{n-1} \\ \vdots & & & \\ 1 & \omega^{n-1} & \cdots & \omega^{(n-1)^2} \end{bmatrix} \tag{5.9.9}$$

Since $\mathbf{S}^{-1}$ diagonalizes the simple matrix $\mathbf{W}_n$, it follows that

$$\mathbf{V}_n(\omega)^{-1} p(\mathbf{C}_n) \mathbf{V}_n(\omega) = \begin{bmatrix} p(1) & 0 & \cdots & 0 \\ 0 & p(\omega) & \cdots & 0 \\ \vdots & \vdots & & \vdots \\ 0 & 0 & \cdots & p(\omega^{n-1}) \end{bmatrix}$$

The matrices, $\mathbf{V}_n(\omega)$, are special cases of *Vandermonde matrices* and are intimately connected with the theory of finite Fourier transforms, a topic of extensive engineering and biological importance. (See Problem 5.9.13.)

PROBLEMS

PART 1

5.9.1. Find all the eigenvalues and eigenvectors of the matrices
(*a*) $\mathbf{C}_1$ (*b*) $\mathbf{C}_2$ (*c*) $\mathbf{C}_3$

5.9.2. Let $\omega = -1/2 + i\sqrt{3}/2$. Compute ω^2, ω^{-1}, ω^{-2}, ω^4, and ω^{-4}. Verify the following identities:
(*a*) $1 + \omega + \omega^2 = 0$ (*b*) $1 + \omega^2 + \omega^4 = 0$
(*c*) $1 + \omega^{-1} + \omega^{-2} = 0$ (*d*) $1 + \omega^{-2} + \omega^{-4} = 0$ (*e*) $1\omega\omega^2 = 1$.

5.9.3. Use the results of Problem 5.9.2 to show that $\mathbf{V}_3(\omega)$, as defined in Eq. 5.9.9, is invertible and that its inverse is $\mathbf{V}_3(\omega^{-1})/3$.

5.9.4. Verify that $\mathbf{V}_4(\omega^{-1})/4$ is the inverse of $\mathbf{V}_4(\omega)$.

PART 2

5.9.5. Verify that $\mathbf{I}_n + \mathbf{C}_n + \mathbf{C}_n^2 + \cdots + \mathbf{C}_n^{n-1} = \mathbf{J}_n$ and find the eigenvalues and eigenvectors of $\mathbf{J}_n$ by use of Theorem 5.9.8. (*Hint:* It may help to note the identity $(1 + x + x^2 + \cdots + x^{n-1})(1 - x) = 1 - x^n$).)

PART 3

5.9.6. Show that $\mathbf{C}_n^{\mathrm{T}}$ and $\mathbf{C}_n^{-1}$ are circulants.

5.9.7. Show that a polynomial in a circulant is a circulant.

5.9.8. Suppose $\mathbf{W}_n$ is an invertible circulant. Prove that $\mathbf{W}_n^{-1}$ is a circulant.

5.9.9. Show that $\det(\mathbf{C}_n) = \omega\omega^2 \cdots \omega^{n-1} = (-1)^{n-1}$.

5.9.10. Suppose $p(x) = a_0 + a_1 x + \cdots + a_{n-1}x^{n-1}$. Show that

$$na_0 = p(1) + p(\omega) + p(\omega^2) + \cdots + p(\omega^{n-1})$$

by using the fact that $\mathrm{tr}(\mathbf{W}_n)$ is the sum of the eigenvalues of $\mathbf{W}_n$.

5.9.11. Show that the Vandermonde matrix $\mathbf{V}_n(\omega)$ is invertible and that its inverse is $\mathbf{V}_n(\omega^{-1})/n$.

5.9.12. Call $\mathbf{V}_n(\omega)\mathbf{x} = \mathbf{y}$ the *Finite Fourier transform* of $\mathbf{x} = [x_1 \ x_2 \ \ldots \ x_n]^{\mathrm{T}}$. Suppose $\mathbf{y} = [\mathbf{y}_1 \ \mathbf{y}_2 \ \ldots \ \mathbf{y}_n]^{\mathrm{T}}$. Define the *inverse finite Fourier transform* of $\mathbf{y}$ as $\mathbf{Fy} = \mathbf{x}$. Use the result in Problem 5.9.11 to show that $\mathbf{V}_n^{-1}(\omega)/n = \mathbf{F}$ and that

$$x_k = \frac{1}{n}\sum_{j=0}^{n-1} y_{j+1}e^{-2\pi i(k-1)j/n}$$

where k is an integer satisfying $1 \le k \le n-1$ and $i = \sqrt{-1}$.

5.9.13. Define the matrices $\mathbf{C}_n(r)$ and $\mathbf{W}_n(r)$ as follows:

$$\mathbf{C}_n(r) = \begin{bmatrix} 0 & 1 & 0 & \cdots & 0 & 0 \\ 0 & 0 & 1 & \cdots & 0 & 0 \\ \vdots & \vdots & \vdots & & \vdots & \vdots \\ 0 & 0 & 0 & \cdots & 0 & 1 \\ r & 0 & 0 & \cdots & 0 & 0 \end{bmatrix} \qquad \mathbf{W}_n(r) = \begin{bmatrix} a_0 & a_1 & \cdots & a_{n-2} & a_{n-1} \\ ra_{n-1} & a_0 & \cdots & a_{n-3} & a_{n-2} \\ \vdots & \vdots & & \vdots & \vdots \\ ra_1 & ra_2 & \cdots & ra_{n-1} & a_0 \end{bmatrix}$$

Show that $\mathbf{W}_n(r)$ is a polynomial in $\mathbf{C}_n(r)$ and find its eigenvalues.

5.9.14. Refer to Section 5.8 for the definition of anti-transpose. Show that $\mathbf{W}^{\mathrm{S}} = \mathbf{W}$ for every circulant. (*Hint*: Show that $\mathbf{C}_n^{\mathrm{S}} = \mathbf{C}_n$.)

5.10 THE SOLUTION OF LINEAR DIFFERENCE EQUATIONS

When we model phenomena that evolve over time, we expect our theory to predict future events. In Section 0.1.6, for example, we asked whether a colony of beetles, subject to prescribed birth and death rates, would ultimately become extinct. This deterministic, discrete model of population growth is due to H. Bernardelli, P. H. Leslie, and E. G. Leslie.

5.10.1 Modeling Population Dynamics

A census is taken each year beginning with year $t = 0$ and continuing through $t = 1, 2, \ldots, m$. At time $t = k$, let x_k be the number of females under one year of age, y_k be the number of females between 1 and 2 years old, and z_k represent the number in the third and last year of life. We call $\mathbf{p}_k = [x_k \quad y_k \quad z_k]^{\mathrm{T}}$ the *population distribution* vector at time $t = k$. When the colony is surveyed again, one year later, at time $t = k + 1$, the census will show this relationship between survivors in each age category:

$$x_{k+1} = 4y_k + 6z_k \qquad y_{k+1} = \tfrac{1}{2}x_k \qquad z_{k+1} = \tfrac{1}{3}y_k$$

These "difference equations" are the results of the hypotheses on the birth and death rates assumed for this population of beetles. For example, x_{k+1} is the sum of the number of offspring borne by females in the second and third years of their lives. These equations are represented by

$$\mathbf{p}_{k+1} = \begin{bmatrix} 0 & 4 & 6 \\ \tfrac{1}{2} & 0 & 0 \\ 0 & \tfrac{1}{3} & 0 \end{bmatrix} \mathbf{p}_k, \qquad k = 0, 1, \ldots, m \tag{5.10.1}$$

The *initial distribution* is the population at the time of the first census and is given by the *initial* vector $\mathbf{p}_0 = [100 \quad 50 \quad 25]^{\mathrm{T}}$. Given the initial population vector $\mathbf{p}_0$, Eq. 5.10.1 can be iterated to yield $\mathbf{p}_k$ for every integer k. Such calculations, though interesting and important, do not provide a theory which would answer such questions as: Which initial population vectors, if any, lead to extinction of the population? To see what is required for a complete analysis, note that Eq. 5.10.1 implies

$$\mathbf{p}_k = \begin{bmatrix} 0 & 4 & 6 \\ \tfrac{1}{2} & 0 & 0 \\ 0 & \tfrac{1}{3} & 0 \end{bmatrix}^k \mathbf{p}_0, \qquad k = 0, 1, \ldots, m \tag{5.10.2}$$

Now questions about the long-term behavior of the population can be stated in terms of the behavior of

$$\mathbf{P}^k = \begin{bmatrix} 0 & 4 & 6 \\ \tfrac{1}{2} & 0 & 0 \\ 0 & \tfrac{1}{3} & 0 \end{bmatrix}^k$$

for large k. In view of the enormous complexity of matrix multiplication, how can we hope to determine $\mathbf{P}^k$ except by computer computation in specific numerical cases? It is the resolution of this question that makes up the material of this section.

5.10.2 First-Order Difference Equations

Consider the following system of *linear first-order difference equations*,

$$\mathbf{x}_k = \mathbf{A}\mathbf{x}_{k-1}, \qquad \mathbf{x}_0 = \mathbf{a}, \qquad k = 1, 2, \ldots \tag{5.10.3}$$

Clearly, $\mathbf{x}_1 = \mathbf{A}\mathbf{a}$, $\mathbf{x}_2 = \mathbf{A}\mathbf{x}_1 = \mathbf{A}(\mathbf{A}\mathbf{a}) = \mathbf{A}^2\mathbf{a}$, and, in general,

$$\mathbf{x}_k = \mathbf{A}^k\mathbf{a}, \qquad k = 1, 2, \ldots \tag{5.10.4}$$

Equation 5.10.4 shows why the solution of Eq. 5.10.3 depends on a knowledge of how the entries in $\mathbf{A}^k$ depend on $\mathbf{A}$ and k. If $\mathbf{A}$ is diagonalizable then it is possible to circumvent the direct computation of $\mathbf{A}^k$. Consider the following analysis:

Suppose $\mathbf{A}$ is simple. Then $\mathbf{A}$ has n linearly independent eigenvectors $\{\mathbf{u}_1, \mathbf{u}_2, \ldots, \mathbf{u}_n\}$ and, as usual, set $\mathbf{S} = [\mathbf{u}_1 \quad \mathbf{u}_2 \quad \ldots \quad \mathbf{u}_n]$. Then $\mathbf{A}$ is diagonalized by $\mathbf{S}$. Thus, from $\mathbf{S}^{-1}\mathbf{A}\mathbf{S} = \Lambda$, it follows that $\mathbf{A} = \mathbf{S}\Lambda\mathbf{S}^{-1}$ and hence that $\mathbf{A}^2 = (\mathbf{S}\Lambda\mathbf{S}^{-1})(\mathbf{S}\Lambda\mathbf{S}^{-1}) = \mathbf{S}\Lambda^2\mathbf{S}^{-1}$. In the same way, $\mathbf{A}^3 = \mathbf{S}\Lambda^3\mathbf{S}^{-1}$ and, in general, $\mathbf{A}^k = \mathbf{S}\Lambda^k\mathbf{S}^{-1}$. Substituting this expression for $\mathbf{A}^k$ into Eq. 5.10.4 yields

$$\mathbf{x}_k = (\mathbf{S}\Lambda^k\mathbf{S}^{-1})\mathbf{a}, \qquad k = 1, 2, \ldots \tag{5.10.5}$$

Now set $\mathbf{c} = [c_1 \quad c_2 \quad \ldots \quad c_n]^{\mathrm{T}} = \mathbf{S}^{-1}\mathbf{a}$. Then $\mathbf{S}\mathbf{c} = \mathbf{a}$ or, equivalently,

$$\mathbf{a} = c_1\mathbf{u}_1 + c_2\mathbf{u}_2 + \cdots + c_n\mathbf{u}_n \tag{5.10.6}$$

Consider

$$\mathbf{x}_k = \mathbf{S}\Lambda^k\mathbf{S}^{-1}\mathbf{a} = \mathbf{S}\Lambda^k\mathbf{c} = \mathbf{S}\begin{bmatrix} \lambda_1^k & & 0 \\ & \ddots & \\ 0 & & \lambda_n^k \end{bmatrix}\begin{bmatrix} c_1 \\ \vdots \\ c_n \end{bmatrix}$$

$$= \mathbf{S}(c_1\lambda_1^k\mathbf{e}_1 + c_2\lambda_2^k\mathbf{e}_2 + \cdots + c_n\lambda_n^k\mathbf{e}_n)$$

$$= (c_1\lambda_1^k\mathbf{S}\mathbf{e}_1 + c_2\lambda_2^k\mathbf{S}\mathbf{e}_2 + \cdots + c_n\lambda_n^k\mathbf{S}\mathbf{e}_n) \tag{5.10.7}$$

But, $\mathbf{S}\mathbf{e}_i = \mathbf{u}_i$ and, therefore, Eq. 5.10.7 leads to

$$\mathbf{x}_k = c_1\lambda_1^k\mathbf{u}_1 + c_2\lambda_2^k\mathbf{u}_2 + \cdots + c_n\lambda_n^k\mathbf{u}_n, \qquad \mathbf{c} = \mathbf{S}^{-1}\mathbf{a} \tag{5.10.8}$$

Put somewhat differently but to the same end, let

$$\mathbf{y}_k = \mathbf{S}^{-1}\mathbf{x}_k, \qquad k = 1, 2, \ldots \tag{5.10.9}$$

Then, using $\mathbf{c} = \mathbf{S}^{-1}\mathbf{a}$ and substituting Eq. 5.10.9 into Eq. 5.10.3, yields

$$\mathbf{y}_k = \mathbf{S}^{-1}\mathbf{A}\mathbf{S}\mathbf{y}_{k-1} = \Lambda\mathbf{y}_{k-1}, \qquad \mathbf{y}_0 = \mathbf{c} \tag{5.10.10}$$

Now Eq. 5.10.10 yields in turn

$$\mathbf{y}_k = \Lambda^k\mathbf{c}, \qquad \mathbf{c} = \mathbf{S}^{-1}\mathbf{a} \tag{5.10.11}$$

The system of Eq. 5.10.11 is said to be "uncoupled" because the components of $\mathbf{y}_k$ can be determined independently of each other.

Equations 5.10.8 and 5.10.11 represent the same solution, as is seen by noting that $\mathbf{S}\mathbf{y}_k = \mathbf{x}_k$, but the derivation of Eq. 5.10.11 shows why the technique for the solution of Eq. 5.10.3 is a "change of variable" method, from $\mathbf{x}_k$ to $\mathbf{y}_k = \mathbf{S}^{-1}\mathbf{x}_k$. Here are a few illustrative examples.

Example 5.10.1. Use Eq. 5.10.8 and Eq. 5.10.11 to find the solution of

$$\mathbf{x}_k = \begin{bmatrix} 2 & 6 \\ 2 & -2 \end{bmatrix} \mathbf{x}_{k-1}, \qquad \mathbf{x}_0 = \mathbf{a} = \begin{bmatrix} 1 \\ 1 \end{bmatrix}$$

Solution. The eigenvalues of $\mathbf{A}$ are $\lambda_1 = -4$ and $\lambda_2 = 4$, and the corresponding eigenvectors are

$$\mathbf{u}_1 = \begin{bmatrix} 1 \\ -1 \end{bmatrix}, \qquad \mathbf{u}_2 = \begin{bmatrix} 3 \\ 1 \end{bmatrix}$$

Both Eq. 5.10.8 and Eq. 5.10.11 require the determination of $\mathbf{c} = \mathbf{S}^{-1}\mathbf{a}$, which is most easily obtained by solving the inhomogeneous system

$$\mathbf{S}\mathbf{c} = \begin{bmatrix} 1 & 3 \\ -1 & 1 \end{bmatrix} \mathbf{c} = \mathbf{a} = \begin{bmatrix} 1 \\ 1 \end{bmatrix}$$

Thus

$$\mathbf{c} = \begin{bmatrix} -\tfrac{1}{2} \\ \tfrac{1}{2} \end{bmatrix}$$

and from Eq. 5.10.11,

$$\mathbf{y}_k = \Lambda^k \mathbf{c} = \begin{bmatrix} -4 & 0 \\ 0 & 4 \end{bmatrix}^k \begin{bmatrix} -\tfrac{1}{2} \\ \tfrac{1}{2} \end{bmatrix} = \frac{-(4)^k}{2} \begin{bmatrix} (-1)^k \\ -1 \end{bmatrix} \tag{5.10.12}$$

Now, from Eq. 5.10.9,

$$\mathbf{x}_k = [\mathbf{u}_1 \quad \mathbf{u}_2]\mathbf{y}_k = \begin{bmatrix} 1 & 3 \\ -1 & 1 \end{bmatrix} \mathbf{y}_k = -\frac{(4)^k}{2} \begin{bmatrix} 1 & 3 \\ -1 & 1 \end{bmatrix} \begin{bmatrix} (-1)^k \\ -1 \end{bmatrix}$$

$$= -\frac{(4)^k}{2} \begin{bmatrix} (-1)^k - 3 \\ -(-1)^k - 1 \end{bmatrix} = \frac{(4)^k}{2} \begin{bmatrix} -(-1)^k + 3 \\ (-1)^k + 1 \end{bmatrix} \tag{5.10.13}$$

Finally, writing $k = 2r$ for k even and $k = 2r - 1$ for k odd, it follows that

$$\mathbf{x}_{2r} = (2)^{4r} \begin{bmatrix} 1 \\ 1 \end{bmatrix}, \qquad \mathbf{x}_{2r-1} = (2)^{4r-1} \begin{bmatrix} 1 \\ 0 \end{bmatrix}, \qquad r = 1, 2, \ldots$$

Equations 5.10.8 and 5.10.11 were derived under the assumption that $\mathbf{A}$ is simple. The next theorem shows that this assumption may be replaced by the weaker hypothesis that the starting value, $\mathbf{x}_0 = \mathbf{a}$, is in the span of the eigenvectors of $\mathbf{A}$. In fact, Corollary 1 of Theorem 5.10.1 provides an alternative derivation of Eq. 5.5.8.

Theorem 5.10.1. *Suppose the eigenpairs of* $\mathbf{A}$ *are* $(\lambda_1, \mathbf{u}_1), (\lambda_2, \mathbf{u}_2), \ldots, (\lambda_m, \mathbf{u}_m)$, *and that*

$$\mathbf{a} = c_1\mathbf{u}_1 + c_2\mathbf{u}_2 + \cdots + c_m\mathbf{u}_m \tag{5.10.14}$$

Then for each $k \geq 1$,

$$\mathbf{x}_k = c_1\lambda_1^k\mathbf{u}_1 + c_2\lambda_2^k\mathbf{u}_2 + \cdots + c_m\lambda_m^k\mathbf{u}_m \tag{5.10.15}$$

satisfies $\mathbf{x}_k = \mathbf{A}\mathbf{x}_{k-1}, \mathbf{x}_0 = \mathbf{a}$.

Proof. To show that $\mathbf{x}_k$ (given by Eq. 5.10.15) solves $\mathbf{x}_n = \mathbf{A}\mathbf{x}_{n-1}$, $\mathbf{x}_0 = \mathbf{a}$, first verify that Eq. 5.10.15 reduces to $\mathbf{x}_0 = \mathbf{a}$ for $k = 0$. Multiply Eq. 5.10.15 by $\mathbf{A}$ and then simplify by using $\mathbf{A}\mathbf{u}_i = \lambda_i\mathbf{u}$. This yields $\mathbf{x}_{k+1} = \mathbf{A}\mathbf{x}_k$. ■

Corollary 1. *If* $\mathbf{A}$ *is simple, then for each* $\mathbf{a}$, *the function defined by Eq. 5.10.14 and Eq. 5.10.15 is a solution of* $\mathbf{x}_k = \mathbf{A}\mathbf{x}_{k-1}, \mathbf{x}_0 = \mathbf{a}$ *for all* $k \geq 1$.

Proof. The eigenvectors of a simple matrix span $\mathscr{C}^n$. ■

Example 5.10.2. Find $\mathbf{a}_k = \mathbf{A}^k\mathbf{a}$ for each k, given

$$\mathbf{A} = \begin{bmatrix} 0 & 1 \\ 1 & 1 \end{bmatrix}, \qquad \mathbf{a} = \begin{bmatrix} 0 \\ 1 \end{bmatrix}$$

Solution. The characteristic equation of $\mathbf{A}$ is $\lambda^2 - \lambda - 1 = 0$, so the eigenvalues are $\lambda_1 = (1 + \sqrt{5})/2$ and $\lambda_2 = (1 - \sqrt{5})/2$. The eigenvectors are computed directly from $(\mathbf{A} - \lambda\mathbf{I})\mathbf{x} = \mathbf{0}$ and are

$$\mathbf{u}_1 = \begin{bmatrix} 1 \\ \dfrac{1 + \sqrt{5}}{2} \end{bmatrix}, \qquad \mathbf{u}_2 = \begin{bmatrix} 1 \\ \dfrac{1 - \sqrt{5}}{2} \end{bmatrix}$$

Hence,

$$\mathbf{a} = \frac{\sqrt{5}}{5}\begin{bmatrix} 1 \\ \dfrac{1 + \sqrt{5}}{2} \end{bmatrix} - \frac{\sqrt{5}}{5}\begin{bmatrix} 1 \\ \dfrac{1 - \sqrt{5}}{2} \end{bmatrix}$$

expresses $\mathbf{a}$ as a linear combination of the eigenvectors of $\mathbf{A}$. Thus, from Theorem 5.10.1, Eq. 5.10.15 leads immediately to

$$\begin{aligned} \mathbf{a}_k &= \begin{bmatrix} a_k \\ a_{k+1} \end{bmatrix} = \mathbf{A}^k\mathbf{a} \\ &= \frac{1}{\sqrt{5}}\left(\frac{1 + \sqrt{5}}{2}\right)^k \begin{bmatrix} 1 \\ \dfrac{1 + \sqrt{5}}{2} \end{bmatrix} - \frac{1}{\sqrt{5}}\left(\frac{1 - \sqrt{5}}{2}\right)^k \begin{bmatrix} 1 \\ \dfrac{1 - \sqrt{5}}{2} \end{bmatrix} \end{aligned} \tag{5.10.16}$$

Clearly, the first entry of $\mathbf{a}_k$ is given by

$$a_k = \frac{1}{\sqrt{5}}\left(\frac{1+\sqrt{5}}{2}\right)^k - \frac{1}{\sqrt{5}}\left(\frac{1-\sqrt{5}}{2}\right)^k, \qquad k = 0, 1, \ldots \quad (5.10.17)$$

Remarkably, the sequence $\{a_k; k = 0, 1, \ldots\}$ is the sequence of integers generated by adding two consecutive terms to obtain the next:

$$0, 1, 1, 2, 3, 5, \ldots, a_k = a_{k-1} + a_{k-2}, \ldots \quad (5.10.18)$$

The sequence in Eq. 5.10.18 dates back to the time of Pythagoras and is commonly known as the (classical) *Fibonacci sequence*. (See Section 5.12.)

5.10.3 The Power Method for the Dominant Eigenvalue

Determining the characteristic polynomial of **A** and then computing its roots is generally a poor method for finding the eigenvalues of **A**. For one thing, the coefficients of the characteristic polynomial are extremely sensitive to variations in the entries of **A**. Theorem 5.10.1 leads to an alternative method, valid under rather modest hypotheses.

Suppose **a** is given and is a linear combination of some of the eigenvectors of **A**. Using the notation of Theorem 5.10.1: suppose

$$\mathbf{a} = c_1\mathbf{u}_1 + c_2\mathbf{u}_2 + \cdots + c_n\mathbf{u}_n$$

then

$$\mathbf{A}^k\mathbf{a} = c_1\lambda_1^k\mathbf{u}_1 + c_2\lambda_2^k\mathbf{u}_2 + \cdots + c_n\lambda_n^k\mathbf{u}_n \quad (5.10.19)$$

Suppose the eigenvalues of **A** are real, $|\lambda_1| > |\lambda_m|$ for $m = 1, 2, \ldots, n$, and that $c_1 \neq 0$. Set $\mathbf{a}_k = \mathbf{A}^k\mathbf{a}$. Then Eq. 5.10.19 takes the form

$$\mathbf{a}_k = \mathbf{A}^k\mathbf{a} = \lambda_1^k\left(c_1\mathbf{u}_1 + c_2(\lambda_2^k/\lambda_1^k)\mathbf{u}_2 + \cdots + c_n(\lambda_n^k/\lambda_1^k)\mathbf{u}_n\right) \quad (5.10.20)$$

By hypothesis, $|\lambda_m/\lambda_1| < 1$. Hence, for k "large," $|\lambda_m/\lambda_1|^k$ is near zero, and thus $\mathbf{a}_k$ is approximately $\lambda_1^k c_1\mathbf{u}_1$, and $\mathbf{a}_{k+1}$ is approximately $\lambda_1^{k+1}c_1\mathbf{u}_1$. Now let $\cong$ stand for the phrase "is approximately equal to," and consider the *Rayleigh quotient*:

$$\sigma_k = \frac{\mathbf{a}_k^T\mathbf{A}\mathbf{a}_k}{\|\mathbf{a}_k\|^2} = \frac{\langle \mathbf{a}_k, \mathbf{A}\mathbf{a}_k\rangle}{\|\mathbf{a}_k\|^2} = \frac{\langle \mathbf{a}_k, \mathbf{a}_{k+1}\rangle}{\|\mathbf{a}_k\|^2} \quad (5.10.21)$$

Then using the approximation given above for $\mathbf{a}_k$ and $\mathbf{a}_{k+1}$ in Eq. 5.10.21 leads to the approximation, $\sigma_k \cong \lambda_1$. This method for approximating the "dominant" eigenvalue is known as the *power method*.

Example 5.10.3. Find an approximation to $\mathbf{u}_1 = [1 \quad (1+\sqrt{5})/2]^T$ and $\lambda_1 = \sqrt{5}/5$ for matrix **A** of Example 5.10.2.

Solution. Take as the initial approximation $\mathbf{a} = [1 \quad 1]^T$. Then successive terms in the sequence $\mathbf{Aa}, \mathbf{A}^2\mathbf{a}, \ldots$ are

$$\mathbf{a}_1 = \mathbf{Aa} = \begin{bmatrix} 1 \\ 2 \end{bmatrix}, \qquad \mathbf{a}_2 = \mathbf{A}^2\mathbf{a} = \begin{bmatrix} 2 \\ 3 \end{bmatrix}, \qquad \mathbf{a}_3 = \mathbf{A}^3\mathbf{a} = \begin{bmatrix} 3 \\ 5 \end{bmatrix},$$

$$\ldots, \mathbf{a}_8 = \mathbf{A}^8\mathbf{a} = \begin{bmatrix} 34 \\ 55 \end{bmatrix}, \qquad \mathbf{a}_9 = \mathbf{A}^9\mathbf{a} = \begin{bmatrix} 55 \\ 89 \end{bmatrix}$$

Now, $\mathbf{A}^9\mathbf{a} = \mathbf{a}_9 \cong \lambda_1\mathbf{a}_8 = \lambda_1\mathbf{A}^8\mathbf{a}$ leads to $\lambda_1 \cong 1.6180 \cong (1 + \sqrt{5})/2$. Also, $\left\|\mathbf{a}_9\right\|^2 = 4{,}181$ and $\langle \mathbf{a}_8, \mathbf{a}_9 \rangle = 6{,}765$. Hence, from Eq. 5.10.17, $\sigma_9 = 1.6180 \cong \lambda_1$

The power method of approximating the "dominant" eigenvalue λ_1 may fail if any of these conditions obtain:

1. The initial guess $\mathbf{a}$ has no component in the direction of $\mathbf{u}_1$. For instance, the matrix $\mathbf{J}_2$ has eigenvalues $\lambda_1 = 2$ and $\lambda_2 = 0$ and corresponding eigenvectors $\mathbf{u}_1 = [1 \quad 1]^T$, $\mathbf{u}_2 = [1 \quad -1]^T$. If the initial guess is $\mathbf{a} = \mathbf{u}_2$, then $\mathbf{Aa} = \mathbf{0}$ and, hence, $\mathbf{A}^k\mathbf{a} = \mathbf{0}$, for all $k \geq 1$.
2. The eigenvalues of $\mathbf{A}$ are repeated or have the same magnitude. (See Problem 5.10.14.)
3. The eigenvalues of $\mathbf{A}$ are complex. (See Problem 5.10.16.)

5.10.4 MATLAB

Example 5.10.4. Solve the system representing the population distribution of the beetle colony in Sections 0.1.6 and 5.10.1.

Solution. The population distribution is given by the system in Eq. 5.10.1:

$$\mathbf{p}_{k+1} = \mathbf{Pp}_k = \begin{bmatrix} 0 & 4 & 0 \\ \tfrac{1}{2} & 0 & 0 \\ 0 & \tfrac{1}{3} & 0 \end{bmatrix} \mathbf{p}_k, \qquad \mathbf{p}_0 = \begin{bmatrix} 100 \\ 50 \\ 25 \end{bmatrix}$$

Then [X,D] = eig(P) returns the pair

```
X =                                      D =
    1.0000    1.0000    1.0000               1.6180    1.0000    1.0000
    0.3090   -0.5000   -0.8090               0        -1.0000    0
    0.0637    0.1667    0.4363               0         0        -0.6180
```

and C = P^50*[100 50 25]′, B = S*D^50*inv(S)*[100 50 25]′ returns

```
C = B =
    1.0 e^12*
        4.4619
        1.3788
        0.2841
```

The total population at $t = 50$ is $X = x_{50} + y_{50} + z_{50} = 6.1248e^{12}$. Then $x_{50}/X = 0.729$, $y_{50}/x = 0.225$, and $z_{50}/X = 0.046$ give the proportions of one-, two-, and three-year-old beetles. These ratios are the same for all $t > 50$, at least to four places of accuracy. Thus, although the population of beetles grows without bound, the proportion of females in the various age categories stabilizes. (See MATLAB Problems 5.10.18 and 5.10.19.)

PROBLEMS

PART 1

5.10.1. Find $\mathbf{x}_k$ given

$$\mathbf{x}_k = \begin{bmatrix} 2 & -2 \\ -1 & 1 \end{bmatrix} \mathbf{x}_{k-1}$$

for each $\mathbf{x}_0$:

$(a)\ \mathbf{x}_0 = \begin{bmatrix} 1 \\ 1 \end{bmatrix}$ $(b)\ \mathbf{x}_0 = \begin{bmatrix} -1 \\ 1 \end{bmatrix}$ $(c)\ \mathbf{x}_0 = \begin{bmatrix} 0 \\ 1 \end{bmatrix}$ $(d)\ \mathbf{x}_0 = \begin{bmatrix} 1 \\ 0 \end{bmatrix}$

5.10.2. Same $\mathbf{x}_0$ as in Problem 5.10.1, except $\mathbf{A}$ is given by:

$(a)\ \mathbf{A} = \begin{bmatrix} 2 & 2 \\ 1 & 1 \end{bmatrix}$ $(b)\ \mathbf{A} = \begin{bmatrix} 1 & 1 \\ 1 & 1 \end{bmatrix}$ $(c)\ \mathbf{A} = \begin{bmatrix} 1 & 3 \\ 1 & -1 \end{bmatrix}$

$(d)\ \mathbf{A} = \begin{bmatrix} 2 & 1 \\ 2 & 3 \end{bmatrix}$

5.10.3. Find $\mathbf{x}_k$ given $\mathbf{x}_k = \mathbf{A}\mathbf{x}_{k-1}$ and $\mathbf{x}_0$ for the system with

$$\mathbf{A} = \begin{bmatrix} 7 & 2 & -3 \\ 4 & 6 & -4 \\ 5 & 2 & -1 \end{bmatrix}$$

$(a)\ \mathbf{x}_0 = \begin{bmatrix} 1 \\ 0 \\ 0 \end{bmatrix}$ $(b)\ \mathbf{x}_0 = \begin{bmatrix} 0 \\ 1 \\ 0 \end{bmatrix}$ $(c)\ \mathbf{x}_0 = \begin{bmatrix} 0 \\ 0 \\ 1 \end{bmatrix}$

5.10.4. Repeat Problem 5.10.3 for

$(a)\ \mathbf{x}_0 = \begin{bmatrix} 1 \\ 1 \\ 0 \end{bmatrix}$ $(b)\ \mathbf{x}_0 = \begin{bmatrix} 1 \\ 1 \\ 1 \end{bmatrix}$ $(c)\ \mathbf{x}_0 = \begin{bmatrix} 1 \\ -1 \\ 1 \end{bmatrix}$

5.10.5. Find $\mathbf{x}_k$ given $\mathbf{x}_k = \mathbf{A}\mathbf{x}_{k-1}$ and $\mathbf{x}_0$ for the system with

$$\mathbf{A} = \begin{bmatrix} 1 & 0 & 0 \\ 0 & 0 & 2 \\ 0 & 2 & 0 \end{bmatrix}$$

$(a)\ \mathbf{x}_0 = \begin{bmatrix} 1 \\ 0 \\ 0 \end{bmatrix}$ $(b)\ \mathbf{x}_0 = \begin{bmatrix} 0 \\ 1 \\ 0 \end{bmatrix}$ $(c)\ \mathbf{x}_0 = \begin{bmatrix} 0 \\ 0 \\ 1 \end{bmatrix}$

5.10.6. Repeat Problem 5.10.5 for

$$(a)\ \mathbf{x}_0 = \begin{bmatrix} 1 \\ 1 \\ 0 \end{bmatrix} \qquad (b)\ \mathbf{x}_0 = \begin{bmatrix} 1 \\ 1 \\ 1 \end{bmatrix} \qquad (c)\ \mathbf{x}_0 = \begin{bmatrix} 1 \\ -1 \\ 1 \end{bmatrix}$$

5.10.7. Find $\mathbf{x}_k$ given $\mathbf{x}_k = \mathbf{A}\mathbf{x}_{k-1}$ and $\mathbf{x}_0$ for the system with

$$\mathbf{A} = \begin{bmatrix} 1 & 0 & 0 \\ 0 & 0 & 2 \\ 0 & 2 & 0 \end{bmatrix}$$

$$(a)\ \mathbf{x}_0 = \begin{bmatrix} 1 \\ 0 \\ 0 \end{bmatrix} \qquad (b)\ \mathbf{x}_0 = \begin{bmatrix} 0 \\ 1 \\ 0 \end{bmatrix} \qquad (c)\ \mathbf{x}_0 = \begin{bmatrix} 0 \\ 0 \\ 1 \end{bmatrix}$$

5.10.8. Repeat Problem 5.10.7 for

$$(a)\ \mathbf{x}_0 = \begin{bmatrix} 1 \\ 1 \\ 0 \end{bmatrix} \qquad (b)\ \mathbf{x}_0 = \begin{bmatrix} 1 \\ 1 \\ 1 \end{bmatrix} \qquad (c)\ \mathbf{x}_0 = \begin{bmatrix} 1 \\ -1 \\ 1 \end{bmatrix}$$

5.10.9. Find $\mathbf{x}_k$ given $\mathbf{x}_k = \mathbf{A}\mathbf{x}_{k-1}$ and $\mathbf{x}_0$ for the system with

$$\mathbf{A} = \begin{bmatrix} 4 & -3 \\ 2 & -1 \end{bmatrix}$$

$$(a)\ \mathbf{x}_0 = \begin{bmatrix} 1 \\ 0 \end{bmatrix} \qquad (b)\ \mathbf{x}_0 = \begin{bmatrix} 0 \\ 1 \end{bmatrix} \qquad (c)\ \mathbf{x}_0 = \begin{bmatrix} 0 \\ 0 \end{bmatrix}$$

5.10.10. Repeat Problem 5.10.9 for

$$(a)\ \mathbf{x}_0 = \begin{bmatrix} 1 \\ 1 \end{bmatrix} \qquad (b)\ \mathbf{x}_0 = \begin{bmatrix} -1 \\ 1 \end{bmatrix} \qquad (c)\ \mathbf{x}_0 = \begin{bmatrix} 1 \\ -1 \end{bmatrix}$$

5.10.11. Find $\mathbf{x}_k$ given

$$\mathbf{x}_k = \begin{bmatrix} 0 & 1 & 1 \\ 1 & 0 & 1 \\ 1 & 1 & 0 \end{bmatrix} \mathbf{x}_{k-1}, \qquad \mathbf{x}_0 = \begin{bmatrix} 1 \\ 0 \\ 1 \end{bmatrix}$$

PART 2

5.10.12. If $\mathbf{y}_k = \mathbf{A}\mathbf{y}_{k-1}$ and $\mathbf{z}_k = \mathbf{A}\mathbf{z}_{k-1}$, show that

$$a\mathbf{y}_k + b\mathbf{z}_k = \mathbf{A}(a\mathbf{y}_{k-1} + b\mathbf{z}_{k-1})$$

for all scalars a and b.

5.10.13. Derive Eq. 5.10.16.

5.10.14. Show that the eigenvalues of

$$\mathbf{A} = \begin{bmatrix} 1 & 2 \\ 4 & -1 \end{bmatrix}$$

are $\lambda_1 = 3$ and $\lambda_2 = -3$, with corresponding eigenvectors $\mathbf{u}_1 = [1 \quad 1]^T$ and $\mathbf{u}_2 = [1 \quad -1]^T$. Starting with the initial guess $\mathbf{x}_0 = [0 \quad 1]^T$, show that $\mathbf{A}^k\mathbf{x}_0$ does not converge. Explain.

5.10.15. Use Eq. 5.10.17 to establish Eq. 5.10.18.

PART 3

5.10.16. Suppose $\mathbf{A}$ has only complex eigenvalues. Explain why any real initial guess can never lead to $\mathbf{x}_{k+1} \cong \lambda_1 \mathbf{x}_k$.

5.10.17. Suppose $\{\mathbf{u}_1, \mathbf{u}_2, \ldots, \mathbf{u}_m\}$ is a set of eigenvectors of $\mathbf{A}$ given and for some $\mathbf{b}$

$$\mathbf{b} = c_1\mathbf{u}_1 + c_2\mathbf{u}_2 + \cdots + c_n\mathbf{u}_n$$

Use the argument given in Theorem 5.10.1 to show that the solution of $\mathbf{Ax} = \mathbf{b}$ can be written as

$$\mathbf{x} = c_1\lambda_1^{-1}\mathbf{u}_1 + c_2\lambda_2^{-1}\mathbf{u}_2 + \cdots + c_n\lambda_n^{-1}\mathbf{u}_n$$

MATLAB

5.10.18. Refer to the notation of Example 5.10.4. Compute $\mathbf{P}^{25}\mathbf{p}_0$, $\mathbf{P}^{60}\mathbf{p}_0$, and $\mathbf{P}^{75}\mathbf{p}_0$. For each of these population distribution vectors, compute x_t/X, y_t/X, and z_t/X, and compare these ratios with those obtained in Example 5.10.4.

5.10.19. Repeat Problem 5.10.18 for the initial distributions

(*a*) $\mathbf{p}_0 = [1 \quad 1 \quad 1]^{\mathrm{T}}$ (*b*) $\mathbf{p}_0 = [1 \quad 0 \quad 0]^{\mathrm{T}}$

(*c*) $\mathbf{p}_0 = [0 \quad 1 \quad 0]^{\mathrm{T}}$ (*d*) $\mathbf{p}_0 = [1 \quad 2 \quad 4]^{\mathrm{T}}$

5.11 SYSTEMS OF LINEAR DIFFERENTIAL EQUATIONS

The initial-value problem of finding functions $x_1(t)$ and $x_2(t)$ that solve the system of differential equations

$$\begin{aligned} x_1'(t) &= 2x_1(t) - 2x_2(t) \\ x_2'(t) &= -x_1(t) + x_2(t) \end{aligned} \tag{5.11.1}$$

and meet the initial conditions

$$x_1(0) = 3, \qquad x_2(0) = 0 \tag{5.11.2}$$

is a special case of the general initial-value problem for constant-coefficient, linear differential systems,

$$\mathbf{x}'(t) = \mathbf{Ax}(t), \qquad \mathbf{x}(0) = \mathbf{x}_0 \tag{5.11.3}$$

In the system in Eq. 5.11.3, $\mathbf{A}$ is an $n \times n$ matrix of constants, and $\mathbf{x}$ and $\mathbf{x}'$ are given by

$$\mathbf{x}(t) = \begin{bmatrix} x_1(t) \\ x_2(t) \\ \vdots \\ x_n(t) \end{bmatrix} \qquad \mathbf{x}'(t) = \begin{bmatrix} x_1'(t) \\ x_2'(t) \\ \vdots \\ x_n'(t) \end{bmatrix} \tag{5.11.4}$$

The function $\mathbf{x}(t)$ is a solution of the system in Eq. 5.11.3 if it satisfies $\mathbf{x}'(t) = \mathbf{Ax}(t)$ for all t, and $\mathbf{x}(0) = \mathbf{x}_0$.

Example 5.11.1. Verify that the functions

$$\mathbf{y}(t) = \begin{bmatrix} 1 \\ 1 \end{bmatrix} \qquad \mathbf{z}(t) = \begin{bmatrix} 2 \\ -1 \end{bmatrix} e^{3t}$$

satisfy the differential system in Eq. 5.11.1 for all t.

Solution. The verification is simply a matter of substitution.

$$\mathbf{Ay}(t) = \begin{bmatrix} 2 & -2 \\ -1 & 1 \end{bmatrix} \begin{bmatrix} 1 \\ 1 \end{bmatrix} = \mathbf{0} = \mathbf{y}'(t)$$

and

$$\mathbf{z}(t) = \begin{bmatrix} 2 & -2 \\ -1 & 1 \end{bmatrix} \begin{bmatrix} 2 \\ -1 \end{bmatrix} e^{3t} = \begin{bmatrix} 6 \\ -3 \end{bmatrix} e^{3t} = 3 \begin{bmatrix} 2 \\ -1 \end{bmatrix} e^{3t} = \mathbf{z}'(t)$$

Neither function in Example 5.11.1 satisfies the initial condition, $\mathbf{x}(0) = [3 \quad 0]^T$. However, if $\mathbf{y}(t)$ and $\mathbf{z}(t)$ are solutions of the system $\mathbf{x}' = \mathbf{Ax}$, then $(\mathbf{y}+\mathbf{z})' = \mathbf{y}' + \mathbf{z}'$, and $\mathbf{A}(\mathbf{y}+\mathbf{z}) = \mathbf{Ay} + \mathbf{Az} = \mathbf{y}' + \mathbf{z}'$ shows that $\mathbf{y}+\mathbf{z}$ is also a solution. But $\mathbf{y}(0) + \mathbf{z}(0) = [3 \quad 0]^T$ and, therefore, $\mathbf{y}(t) + \mathbf{z}(t)$ is a solution that satisfies the given initial conditions.

The method of solution of the general initial value problem is remarkably similar to that used in solving the difference system $\mathbf{x}_k = \mathbf{Ax}_{k-1}, \mathbf{x}_0 = \mathbf{a}$. Compare the following theorem with Theorem 5.10.1.

Theorem 5.11.1. *Suppose the eigenpairs of* $\mathbf{A}$ *are* $(\lambda_1, \mathbf{u}_1), (\lambda_2, \mathbf{u}_2), \ldots, (\lambda_m, \mathbf{u}_m)$ *and that*

$$\mathbf{x}_0 = c_1\mathbf{u}_1 + c_2\mathbf{u}_2 + \cdots + c_m\mathbf{u}_m \tag{5.11.5}$$

Then for each t,

$$\mathbf{x}(t) = c_1\mathbf{u}_1 e^{\lambda_1 t} + c_2\mathbf{u}_2 e^{\lambda_2 t} + \cdots + c_m\mathbf{u}_m e^{\lambda_m t} \tag{5.11.6}$$

is a solution of $\mathbf{x}'(t) = \mathbf{Ax}(t)$ *such that* $\mathbf{x}(0) = \mathbf{x}_0$.

Proof. Start with the function $\mathbf{x}(t)$ given by Eq. 5.11.6 and compare $\mathbf{Ax}(t)$ with $\mathbf{x}'(t)$:

$$\mathbf{x}'(t) = c_1\mathbf{u}_1\lambda_1 e^{\lambda_1 t} + c_2\mathbf{u}_2\lambda_2 e^{\lambda_2 t} + \cdots + c_m\mathbf{u}_m\lambda_m e^{\lambda_m t} \tag{5.11.7}$$

$$\mathbf{Ax}(t) = c_1\mathbf{Au}_1 e^{\lambda_1 t} + c_2\mathbf{Au}_2 e^{\lambda_2 t} + \cdots + c_m\mathbf{Au}_m e^{\lambda_m t} \tag{5.11.8}$$

Thus, $\mathbf{Ax}$ and $\mathbf{x}'$ are identical because $\mathbf{Au}_i = \lambda_i\mathbf{u}_i$. Finally, at $t = 0$, Eq. 5.11.6 reduces to $\mathbf{x}(0) = \mathbf{x}_0$. ■

Theorem 5.11.1 does not require that $\mathbf{A}$ be simple. Instead, the crucial assumption is that the initial vector $\mathbf{x}_0$ be in the span of the eigenvectors of $\mathbf{A}$. However, if $\mathbf{A}$ is simple then $\mathbf{A}$ has a complete set of eigenvectors, and the following corollary obtains:

Corollary 1. *If* $\mathbf{A}$ *is simple, then for every* $\mathbf{x}_0$, *the function given by Eq. 5.11.6* $(m = n)$ *satisfies the initial-value problem* $\mathbf{x}' = \mathbf{Ax}, \mathbf{x}(0) = \mathbf{x}_0$.

Proof. The hypothesis in Eq. 5.11.5 is always satisfied. ■

The function $\mathbf{x}(t)$ defined by Eq. 5.11.6 is called a *general solution* of $\mathbf{x}'(t) = \mathbf{Ax}(t)$ if every initial-value problem, $\mathbf{x}'(t) = \mathbf{Ax}(t), \mathbf{x}(0) = \mathbf{x}_0$, has a solution obtainable from $\mathbf{x}(t)$ by some choice of the weights c_i. Thus, the corollary asserts that for simple matrices, $\mathbf{x}(t)$ is a general solution. If $\mathbf{A}$ is defective, the solution $\mathbf{x}(t)$ will fail to satisfy the initial condition when $\mathbf{x}_0$ is not in the span of the eigenvectors of $\mathbf{A}$. The following three examples illustrate some of the possibilities.

Example 5.11.2. Find the solution to the initial-value problem

$$\mathbf{x}' = \begin{bmatrix} 1 & 1 \\ 0 & 1 \end{bmatrix} \mathbf{x}, \qquad \mathbf{x}(0) = \begin{bmatrix} 2 \\ 0 \end{bmatrix}$$

Solution. The coefficient matrix has the characteristic equation $(1-\lambda)^2 = 0$ with the sole independent eigenvector $\mathbf{u} = [1 \quad 0]^{\mathrm{T}}$. However, $\mathbf{x}(0) = 2\mathbf{u}$ shows that $\mathbf{x}(0)$ is in the span of the eigenvectors and, hence, $\mathbf{x}(t) = 2e^t[1 \quad 0]^{\mathrm{T}}$ is the required solution.

Example 5.11.3. Solve the initial-value problem

$$\mathbf{x}' = \begin{bmatrix} 2 & 1 & 0 \\ 2 & 1 & 0 \\ 0 & 0 & 1 \end{bmatrix} \mathbf{x}, \qquad \mathbf{x}(0) = \mathbf{x}_0 = \begin{bmatrix} 1 \\ 0 \\ 2 \end{bmatrix}$$

Solution. The eigenvalues are $\lambda_1 = 0$, $\lambda_2 = 1$, $\lambda_3 = 3$, and the corresponding eigenvectors are

$$\mathbf{u}_1 = \begin{bmatrix} 1 \\ -2 \\ 0 \end{bmatrix}, \qquad \mathbf{u}_2 = \begin{bmatrix} 0 \\ 0 \\ 1 \end{bmatrix}, \qquad \mathbf{u}_3 = \begin{bmatrix} 1 \\ 1 \\ 0 \end{bmatrix}$$

Thus, a general solution is

$$\mathbf{x}(t) = c_1 \begin{bmatrix} 1 \\ -2 \\ 0 \end{bmatrix} + c_2 \begin{bmatrix} 0 \\ 0 \\ 1 \end{bmatrix} e^t + c_3 \begin{bmatrix} 1 \\ 1 \\ 0 \end{bmatrix} e^{3t}$$

From the equation $\mathbf{Sc} = \mathbf{x}_0$, $\mathbf{c} = [\tfrac{1}{3} \quad 2 \quad \tfrac{2}{3}]^{\mathrm{T}}$. Hence, the solution of the initial-value problem is

$$\mathbf{x}(t) = \frac{1}{3} \begin{bmatrix} 1 \\ -2 \\ 0 \end{bmatrix} + 2 \begin{bmatrix} 0 \\ 0 \\ 1 \end{bmatrix} e^t + \frac{2}{3} \begin{bmatrix} 1 \\ 1 \\ 0 \end{bmatrix} e^{3t}$$

The solution $\mathbf{x}(t)$ given by Eq. 5.11.6 may suffer from the awkwardness of having complex scalars as its entries, even if $\mathbf{A}$ and $\mathbf{x}_0$ are real. However, if $\mathbf{A}$ has real entries, a real solution can always be constructed from Eq. 5.11.6 by invoking the familiar Euler formulas relating the exponential function of a complex argument to trigonometric functions with real arguments. (See Problem 5.11.13.)

If $\mathbf{A}$ is defective, then it is possible for $\mathbf{x}' = \mathbf{A}\mathbf{x}$, $\mathbf{x}(0) = \mathbf{x}_0$ not to have a solution of the form Eq. 5.11.16. This is the case precisely when $\mathbf{x}_0$ is not in the span of the eigenvectors of $\mathbf{A}$. A change in the initial condition for the system given in Example 5.11.2 provides an example.

Example 5.11.4. Find the solution to the initial-value problem

$$\mathbf{x}' = \begin{bmatrix} 1 & 1 \\ 0 & 1 \end{bmatrix} \mathbf{x}, \qquad \mathbf{x}(0) = \begin{bmatrix} 0 \\ 1 \end{bmatrix}$$

Solution. The unique solution can be obtained by elementary methods common to the theory of differential equations (see Problem 5.11.20). Here is the result:

$$\mathbf{x}(t) = \begin{bmatrix} t \\ 1 \end{bmatrix} e^t$$

A complete theory of $\mathbf{x}' = \mathbf{A}\mathbf{x}$ requires a deeper study of defective matrices than we are prepared to give here. Fortunately, many of the physical problems that give rise to linear, constant coefficient systems of differential equations result in symmetric coefficient matrices, and, as we show in Chapter 6, symmetric matrices are simple.

PROBLEMS

PART 1

5.11.1. Find the solutions of the following initial-value problems by first finding a general solution and then determining the arbitrary constants.

$$\mathbf{A} = \begin{bmatrix} 2 & -2 \\ -1 & 1 \end{bmatrix}$$

$(a)\ \mathbf{x}_0 = \begin{bmatrix} 1 \\ 1 \end{bmatrix}$ $(b)\ \mathbf{x}_0 = \begin{bmatrix} -1 \\ 1 \end{bmatrix}$ $(c)\ \mathbf{x}_0 = \begin{bmatrix} 0 \\ 1 \end{bmatrix}$ $(d)\ \mathbf{x}_0 = \begin{bmatrix} 1 \\ 0 \end{bmatrix}$

5.11.2. Repeat Problem 5.11.1, except

$(a)\ \mathbf{A} = \begin{bmatrix} 2 & 2 \\ 1 & 1 \end{bmatrix}$ $(b)\ \mathbf{A} = \begin{bmatrix} 1 & 1 \\ 1 & 1 \end{bmatrix}$ $(c)\ \mathbf{A} = \begin{bmatrix} 1 & 3 \\ 1 & -1 \end{bmatrix}$

$(d)\ \mathbf{A} = \begin{bmatrix} 2 & 1 \\ 2 & 3 \end{bmatrix}$

5.11.3. Repeat Problem 5.11.1, except

$$\mathbf{A} = \begin{bmatrix} 7 & 2 & -3 \\ 4 & 6 & -4 \\ 5 & 2 & -1 \end{bmatrix}$$

$(a)\ \mathbf{x}_0 = \begin{bmatrix} 1 \\ 0 \\ 0 \end{bmatrix}$ $(b)\ \mathbf{x}_0 = \begin{bmatrix} 0 \\ 1 \\ 0 \end{bmatrix}$ $(c)\ \mathbf{x}_0 = \begin{bmatrix} 0 \\ 0 \\ 1 \end{bmatrix}$

5.11.4. Repeat Problem 5.11.3 with these initial conditions:

$$(a)\ \mathbf{x}_0 = \begin{bmatrix} 1 \\ 1 \\ 0 \end{bmatrix} \qquad (b)\ \mathbf{x}_0 = \begin{bmatrix} 1 \\ 1 \\ 1 \end{bmatrix} \qquad (c)\ \mathbf{x}_0 = \begin{bmatrix} 1 \\ -1 \\ 1 \end{bmatrix}$$

5.11.5. Repeat Problem 5.11.1, except

$$\mathbf{A} = \begin{bmatrix} 1 & 0 & 0 \\ 0 & 0 & 2 \\ 0 & -2 & 0 \end{bmatrix}$$

$$(a)\ \mathbf{x}_0 = \begin{bmatrix} 1 \\ 0 \\ 0 \end{bmatrix} \qquad (b)\ \mathbf{x}_0 = \begin{bmatrix} 0 \\ 1 \\ 0 \end{bmatrix} \qquad (c)\ \mathbf{x}_0 = \begin{bmatrix} 0 \\ 0 \\ 1 \end{bmatrix}$$

5.11.6. Repeat Problem 5.11.5 with these initial conditions:

$$(a)\ \mathbf{x}_0 = \begin{bmatrix} 1 \\ 1 \\ 0 \end{bmatrix} \qquad (b)\ \mathbf{x}_0 = \begin{bmatrix} 1 \\ 1 \\ 1 \end{bmatrix} \qquad (c)\ \mathbf{x}_0 = \begin{bmatrix} 1 \\ -1 \\ 1 \end{bmatrix}$$

5.11.7. Repeat Problem 5.11.1, except

$$\mathbf{A} = \begin{bmatrix} 1 & 0 & 0 \\ 0 & 0 & 2 \\ 0 & 2 & 0 \end{bmatrix}$$

$$(a)\ \mathbf{x}_0 = \begin{bmatrix} 1 \\ 0 \\ 0 \end{bmatrix} \qquad (b)\ \mathbf{x}_0 = \begin{bmatrix} 0 \\ 1 \\ 0 \end{bmatrix} \qquad (c)\ \mathbf{x}_0 = \begin{bmatrix} 0 \\ 0 \\ 1 \end{bmatrix}$$

5.11.8. Repeat Problem 5.11.7 with these initial conditions:

$$(a)\ \mathbf{x}_0 = \begin{bmatrix} 1 \\ 1 \\ 0 \end{bmatrix} \qquad (b)\ \mathbf{x}_0 = \begin{bmatrix} 1 \\ 1 \\ 1 \end{bmatrix} \qquad (c)\ \mathbf{x}_0 = \begin{bmatrix} 1 \\ -1 \\ 1 \end{bmatrix}$$

5.11.9. Repeat Problem 5.11.1, except

$$\mathbf{A} = \begin{bmatrix} 4 & -3 & -2 \\ 2 & -1 & -2 \\ 3 & -3 & -1 \end{bmatrix}$$

$$(a)\ \mathbf{x}_0 = \begin{bmatrix} 1 \\ 0 \\ 0 \end{bmatrix} \qquad (b)\ \mathbf{x}_0 = \begin{bmatrix} 0 \\ 1 \\ 0 \end{bmatrix} \qquad (c)\ \mathbf{x}_0 = \begin{bmatrix} 0 \\ 0 \\ 1 \end{bmatrix}$$

5.10.10. Repeat Problem 5.11.9 with these initial conditions:

$$(a)\ \mathbf{x}_0 = \begin{bmatrix} 1 \\ 1 \\ 0 \end{bmatrix} \qquad (b)\ \mathbf{x}_0 = \begin{bmatrix} 1 \\ 1 \\ 1 \end{bmatrix} \qquad (c)\ \mathbf{x}_0 = \begin{bmatrix} 1 \\ -1 \\ 1 \end{bmatrix}$$

5.11.11. Find a general solution of

$$\mathbf{x}' = \begin{bmatrix} 0 & 1 & 1 \\ 1 & 0 & 1 \\ 1 & 1 & 0 \end{bmatrix} \mathbf{x}$$

PART 2

5.11.12. Formulate an analog of Theorem 5.11.1 if the initial condition is given as $\mathbf{x}(t_0) = \mathbf{x}_0$. (*Hint:* Make the change of variables $\tau = t - t_0$.)

5.11.13. Suppose $\mathbf{A}$ is real and $\mathbf{x}(t)$ is a solution of $\mathbf{x}' = \mathbf{A}\mathbf{x}$. Show that $\mathrm{Re}(\mathbf{x}(t))$ and $\mathrm{Im}(\mathbf{x}(t))$ are two real solutions.

5.11.14. Suppose $\mathbf{A}$ is real with eigenvalue λ_1 and corresponding eigenvectors $\mathbf{u}_1$. Show that $(\overline{\lambda}_1 = \lambda_2, \overline{\mathbf{u}}_1 = \mathbf{u}_2)$ is an eigenpair.

5.11.15. Use the results of Problems 5.11.13 and 5.11.14 to write out $\mathrm{Re}(\mathbf{x})$ and $\mathrm{Im}(\mathbf{x})$ for $\mathbf{x}$ given by Eq. 5.11.6 applied to

$$\mathbf{x}' = \begin{bmatrix} 1 & 1 \\ -1 & 1 \end{bmatrix} \mathbf{x}, \qquad \mathbf{x}_0 = \begin{bmatrix} 1 \\ 1 \end{bmatrix}$$

5.11.16. Show that the initial-value problem

$$\mathbf{x}' = \begin{bmatrix} 1 & 1 \\ 0 & 1 \end{bmatrix} \mathbf{x}, \qquad \mathbf{x}_0 = \begin{bmatrix} 0 \\ 1 \end{bmatrix}$$

has no solution of the form given in Eq. 5.11.6.

5.11.17. Find vector $\mathbf{v}$ such that $\mathbf{x}(t) = (t\mathbf{u} + \mathbf{v})e^t$ ($\mathbf{u}$ an eigenvector of $\mathbf{A}$) is a solution of the initial-value problem given in Problem 5.11.16.

PART 3

5.11.18. Assume $\mathbf{A} = \mathbf{S}\Lambda\mathbf{S}^{-1}$ where, as usual, $\mathbf{S} = [\mathbf{u}_1 \;\; \mathbf{u}_2 \;\; \ldots \;\; \mathbf{u}_n]$ is a matrix of linearly independent eigenvectors of $\mathbf{A}$, and Λ is the diagonal matrix of corresponding eigenvalues. Make the change of variable $\mathbf{y} = \mathbf{S}^{-1}\mathbf{x}$ in the system $\mathbf{x}' = \mathbf{A}\mathbf{x}$ and show that the resulting system has uncoupled variables. Solve the resulting system and, thus, rederive Corollary 1 of Theorem 5.11.1.

5.11.19. Under the assumptions of Problem 5.11.18, solve the system $\mathbf{x}'' = \mathbf{A}\mathbf{x}$. Recall the solutions of the second order scalar equation, $\mathbf{y}'' = a^2 y$, $a^2 > 0$, are $\mathrm{K}_1 e^{at}$ and $\mathrm{K}_2 e^{-at}$.

5.11.20. Define the exponential of a diagonal matrix Λ as follows:

$$\exp(\Lambda) = \mathbf{I} + \Lambda + \frac{\Lambda^2}{2!} + \frac{\Lambda^3}{3!} + \cdots + \frac{\Lambda^n}{n!} + \cdots$$

Show that the diagonal entries of $\exp(\Lambda)$ are e^{λ_i}. With this in mind, argue that $\exp(\Lambda t)$ is a solution of $\mathbf{y}'(t) = \Lambda\mathbf{y}(t)$.

5.11.21. Suppose $\mathbf{A}$ is simple. Use the ideas in Problems 5.11.20 to formulate a definition of $\exp(\mathbf{A}t)$. Show that $\mathbf{x}t) = \exp(\mathbf{A}t)\mathbf{x}_0$ is a solution of $\mathbf{x}' = \mathbf{A}\mathbf{x}, \mathbf{x}(0) = \mathbf{x}_0$. Compare with Eq. 5.11.6.

5.11.22. Suppose the components of $\mathbf{x}$ in Example 5.11.4 are $x_1(t)$ and $x_2(t)$. Show that $x_2'(t) = x_2(t)$ and, hence, that $x_2(t) = k_2 e^t$. Now show that $x_1'(t) = x_1(t) + k_2 e^t$. Next show that the solution of this equation is given by $x_1(t) = k_1 t e^t + k_2 e^t$. Verify the conclusion given in Example 5.11.4.

5.12 COMPANION MATRICES AND THE nTH-ORDER LINEAR EQUATIONS

The theories of the nth-order linear differential and difference equation can be cast as special cases in the theory of systems of equations. The matrix of coefficients in both cases are called *companion matrices* and the resulting systems *companion systems*.

The general $n \times n$ companion matrix[4] is

$$\mathbf{C}_n = \begin{bmatrix} 0 & 1 & 0 & \cdots & 0 \\ 0 & 0 & 1 & \cdots & 0 \\ \vdots & \vdots & \vdots & & \vdots \\ 0 & 0 & 0 & \cdots & 1 \\ -c_0 & -c_1 & -c_2 & \cdots & -c_{n-1} \end{bmatrix} \tag{5.12.1}$$

(The notation $\mathbf{C}_n$ has appeared already in Section 5.9. In that context, $-c_0 = 1$ and $c_i = 0, i > 0$. No confusion should result from this more general usage.) In this section, $\mathbf{C}_n$ refers exclusively to the matrix defined in Eq. 5.12.1. Here are three examples illustrating how $\mathbf{C}_n$ arises. The change of variables that takes an nth-order equation to its companion system can be motivated by physical considerations, as in the first example.

Example 5.12.1. A particle moves so that its distance s as a function of time t is given by the equation $s''(t) - \alpha s'(t) - \beta s(t) = 0$. Set $v(t) = s'(t)$ and $a(t) = v'(t)$. Then v and a are the velocity and acceleration of the particle, respectively. Since

$$a(t) = s''(t) = \alpha s'(t) + \beta s(t) = \alpha v'(t) + \beta s(t)$$

the variables s and $v = s'$ satisfy the companion system

$$\begin{bmatrix} s \\ v \end{bmatrix}' = \begin{bmatrix} v \\ a \end{bmatrix} = \begin{bmatrix} 0 & 1 \\ \beta & \alpha \end{bmatrix} \begin{bmatrix} s \\ v \end{bmatrix}$$

Example 5.12.2. Let $y^{(n)}$ represent the nth derivative of y. Consider the third-order, constant-coefficient differential equation

$$y^{(3)} + c_2 y^{(2)} + c_1 y^{(1)} + c_0 y = 0$$

Let $x_1 = y, x_2 = y^{(1)}$, and $x_3 = y^{(2)}$. Then from

$$y^{(3)} = -c_2 y^{(2)} - c_1 y^{(1)} - c_0 y$$

it follows that

$$x_1^{(1)} = y^{(1)} = x_2 \qquad x_2^{(1)} = y^{(2)} = x_3$$
$$x_3^{(1)} = -c_2 x_3 - c_1 x_2 - c_0 x_1$$

---

[4]Some authors call the simlar matrix $\mathbf{C}^{ST} = \mathbf{ECE}$ a companion matrix. (See Section 5.8, in particular, the material following Example 5.8.5 and Problem 5.8.17.)

These simultaneous equations have the form $\mathbf{x}' = \mathbf{C}_3\mathbf{x}$. Explicitly,

$$\mathbf{x}'(t) = \begin{bmatrix} 0 & 1 & 0 \\ 0 & 0 & 1 \\ -c_0 & -c_1 & -c_2 \end{bmatrix} \mathbf{x}(t)$$

where $\mathbf{x}(t) = [x_1(t) \quad x_2(t) \quad x_3(t)]^{\mathrm{T}}$, and $\mathbf{C}_3$ is a companion matrix.

Example 5.12.3. The difference equation

$$y_{n+3} = 2y_{n+2} - y_{n+1} + y_n$$

is a third-order equation analogous to the third-order differential equation $y^{(3)} = 2y^{(2)} - y^{(1)} + y$. Set $\mathbf{y}_n = [y_n \quad y_{n+1} \quad y_{n+2}]^{\mathrm{T}}$. Then $\mathbf{y}_n$ satisfies the companion system

$$\mathbf{y}_{n+1} = \begin{bmatrix} 0 & 1 & 0 \\ 0 & 0 & 1 \\ 1 & -1 & 2 \end{bmatrix} \mathbf{y}_n$$

Theorem 5.12.1. *The characteristic polynomial of the companion matrix* $\mathbf{C}_n$ *is*

$$c(\lambda) = (-1)^n(\lambda^n + c_{n-1}\lambda^n + \cdots + c_0) \qquad (5.12.2)$$

Moreover, if μ *is an eigenvalue,* $\mathbf{u} = [1 \quad \mu \quad \mu^2 \quad \ldots \quad \mu^{n-1}]^{\mathrm{T}}$ *is a corresponding eigenvector with geometric multiplicity* 1 *(that is,* $g(\mu) = 1$*).*

Proof. Suppose $(\mu, \mathbf{u} = [u_1 \quad u_2 \quad \ldots \quad u_n]^{\mathrm{T}})$ is an eigenpair of $\mathbf{C}_n$. Set

$$\nu = -c_0u_1 - c_1u_2 - \cdots - c_{n-1}u_n$$

Then, it follows that

$$\mathbf{C}_n\mathbf{u} = \begin{bmatrix} 0 & 1 & 0 & \cdots & 0 \\ 0 & 0 & 1 & \cdots & 0 \\ \vdots & \vdots & \vdots & & \vdots \\ 0 & 0 & 0 & \cdots & 1 \\ -c_0 & -c_1 & -c_2 & \cdots & -c_{n-1} \end{bmatrix} \begin{bmatrix} u_1 \\ u_2 \\ \vdots \\ u_n \end{bmatrix} = \begin{bmatrix} u_2 \\ u_3 \\ \vdots \\ \nu \end{bmatrix} = \mu \begin{bmatrix} u_1 \\ u_2 \\ \vdots \\ u_n \end{bmatrix}$$

Thus, $u_2 = \mu u_1, u_3 = \mu u_2, \ldots, u_n = \nu = \mu u_{n-1}$ by equating rows 1 through $n-1$ of $\mathbf{C}_n\mathbf{u}$ and $\mu\mathbf{u}$. From the last row,

$$\nu = -c_0u_1 - c_1u_2 - \cdots - c_{n-1}u_n = \mu u_n$$

First, note that it is not possible for u_1 to be zero. For if it were, then $u_i = 0$ for all i, and, therefore, it would follow that $\mathbf{u} = \mathbf{0}$. Since $u_1 \neq 0$, choose $u_1 = 1$. Then, it is necessary and sufficient for $u_2 = \mu, u_3 = \mu^2, \ldots, u_n = \mu^{n-1}$ in order that $(\mu,\mathbf{u})$ be an eigenpair of $\mathbf{A}$. Finally, using

$$\mathbf{u} = \begin{bmatrix} 1 \\ \mu \\ \vdots \\ \mu^{n-1} \end{bmatrix} \tag{5.12.3}$$

verify that $\mathbf{C}_n\mathbf{u} = \mu\mathbf{u}$ for

$$\mu^n + c_{n-1}\mu^{n-1} + \cdots + c_1\mu + c_0 = 0.$$

Since fixing μ determines the eigenvector up to the multiplicative constant, it follows that the geometric multiplicity of each eigenvalue is 1. ■

Given an arbitrary *monic* polynomial

$$p(x) = x^n + c_{n-1}x^n + \cdots + c_1x + c_0$$

Theorem 5.12.1 provides the means for constructing a matrix whose eigenvalues are the zeros of $p(x)$. (Indeed, MATLAB solves the equation $p(x) = 0$ by constructing the companion matrix and finding its eigenvalues!)

Corollary 1. *A companion matrix is simple if and only if it has distinct eigenvalues.*

Proof. In view of the fact that a matrix with n distinct eigenvalues is simple, it is only necessary to establish that the converse holds. Since $g(\lambda) = 1$ for companion matrices, $\mathbf{C}_n$ has n linearly independent eigenvectors, one for each eigenvalue. ■

There are a number of other corollaries to this theorem that deserve mention. These are stated informally and the proofs are reserved for the problem set. First, for every set of n complex numbers, there is a companion matrix whose characteristic equation has these numbers as roots. (Except for the coefficient of λ^n, the characteristic polynomial is completely arbitrary.) Second, the characteristic equation of $\mathbf{C}_n$ is the auxiliary equation of $y^{(n)} + c_{n-1}y^{(n-1)} + \cdots + c_0y = 0$. (Recall from the theory of linear differential equations with constant coefficients that $y_p(t) = e^{mt}$ is a solution of the given equation if and only if m satisfies the auxiliary equation.) Third, as shown in Section 5.9, the theory of the circulant is based on an analysis of polynomials in the special companion matrix in which $a_0 = -1$ and $a_i = 0$ for $i \neq 0$. Here are some illustrations.

Example 5.12.4. Find the general solution of $y^{(3)} - y = 0$.

Solution. From the elementary theory of differential equations, the general solution is given by

$$y(t) = K_1 + K_2e^{-t} + K_3e^t \tag{5.12.4}$$

This solution can also be obtained by the methods of this section. Consider the companion system

$$\mathbf{y}'(t) = \begin{bmatrix} 0 & 1 & 0 \\ 0 & 0 & 1 \\ 0 & 1 & 0 \end{bmatrix} \mathbf{y}(t)$$

The characteristic equation is $c(\lambda) = \lambda^3 - \lambda = 0$, so the eigenvalues are $\lambda_1 = 0$, $\lambda_2 = -1$, and $\lambda_3 = 1$. The eigenvectors are

$$\mathbf{u}_1 = \begin{bmatrix} 1 \\ 0 \\ 0 \end{bmatrix}, \qquad \mathbf{u}_2 = \begin{bmatrix} 1 \\ -1 \\ 1 \end{bmatrix}, \qquad \mathbf{u}_3 = \begin{bmatrix} 1 \\ 1 \\ 1 \end{bmatrix}$$

as expected from Eq. 5.9.8. The companion system has the general solution

$$y(t) = c_1 \begin{bmatrix} 1 \\ 0 \\ 0 \end{bmatrix} + c_2 e^{-t} \begin{bmatrix} 1 \\ -1 \\ 1 \end{bmatrix} + c_3 e^{t} \begin{bmatrix} 1 \\ 1 \\ 1 \end{bmatrix} \tag{5.12.5}$$

by Theorem 5.12.1. The first component of this solution is the required general solution. Compare with the general solution given in Eq. 5.12.4.

Example 5.12.5. Find the solution of the initial-value problem

$$\mathbf{y}'(t) = \begin{bmatrix} 0 & 1 & 0 \\ 0 & 0 & 1 \\ 0 & 1 & 0 \end{bmatrix} \mathbf{y}(t), \qquad \mathbf{y}(0) = \begin{bmatrix} 0 \\ 0 \\ 1 \end{bmatrix}$$

Solution. From Eq. 5.12.5,

$$\mathbf{y}(0) = c_1 \begin{bmatrix} 1 \\ 0 \\ 0 \end{bmatrix} + c_2 \begin{bmatrix} 1 \\ -1 \\ 1 \end{bmatrix} + c_3 \begin{bmatrix} 1 \\ 1 \\ 1 \end{bmatrix} = \begin{bmatrix} 1 & 1 & 1 \\ 0 & -1 & 1 \\ 0 & 1 & 1 \end{bmatrix} \mathbf{c} = \begin{bmatrix} 0 \\ 0 \\ 1 \end{bmatrix}$$

which leads to $\mathbf{c} = [c_1 \;\; c_2 \;\; c_3]^{\mathrm{T}} = [-1 \;\; \tfrac{1}{2} \;\; \tfrac{1}{2}]^{\mathrm{T}}$ and, hence,

$$\mathbf{y}(t) = -\begin{bmatrix} 1 \\ 0 \\ 0 \end{bmatrix} + \frac{e^{-t}}{2} \begin{bmatrix} 1 \\ -1 \\ 1 \end{bmatrix} + \frac{e^{t}}{2} \begin{bmatrix} 1 \\ 1 \\ 1 \end{bmatrix}$$

The connection between the nth-order differential equation and the system of first-order differential equations obtained by the variable change $x_1 = y$, $x_2 = y^{(1)}, \ldots, x_{n-1} = y^{(n-1)}$ is summarized in the next theorem. First let us stipulate the following notational conventions:

$$\mathbf{y}(t) = \begin{bmatrix} y \\ y^{(1)} \\ \vdots \\ y^{(n-2)} \\ y^{(n-1)} \end{bmatrix} \qquad \mathbf{z}(t) = \begin{bmatrix} y^{(1)} \\ y^{(2)} \\ \vdots \\ y^{(n-1)} \\ z \end{bmatrix} \tag{5.12.6}$$

Theorem 5.12.2. *The nth-order equation*

$$y^{(n)} + c_{n-1}y^{(n-1)} + \cdots + c_0 y = 0 \tag{5.12.7}$$

has the solution $\mathbf{y}(t)$ *if and only if the companion system*

$$\mathbf{y}'(t) = \mathbf{C}_n\mathbf{y}(t) \tag{5.12.8}$$

has the solution $\mathbf{y}(t) = [y \quad y^{(1)} \quad y^{(2)} \quad \ldots \quad y^{(n-1)}]^{\mathrm{T}}$.

Proof. The argument is analogous to the one given for Theorem 5.12.1. Define

$$z(t) = -c_{n-1}y^{(n-1)} - \cdots - c_0 y$$

In view of this definition of $z(t)$ and the definitions of $\mathbf{y}(t)$ and $\mathbf{z}(t)$ in Eq. 5.12.6, it follows that $\mathbf{C}_n\mathbf{y}(t) = \mathbf{z}(t)$. Now suppose $y(t)$ is a solution of Eq. 5.12.7. Then $z(t) = y^{(n)}$ and, hence, $\mathbf{z}(t) = \mathbf{y}'(t)$. Thus, $\mathbf{y}$ solves the companion system $\mathbf{C}_n\mathbf{y} = \mathbf{y}'$.

Next, suppose the converse: assume $\mathbf{y}$ is a solution of Eq. 5.12.8. Then since $\mathbf{y}' = \mathbf{C}_n\mathbf{y}$ and $\mathbf{z} = \mathbf{C}_n\mathbf{y}$, it follows that $\mathbf{y}' = \mathbf{z}$. Equating the last entries of $\mathbf{y}'$ and $\mathbf{z}$, it follows that $y^{(n)} = -c_{n-1}y^{(n-1)} - \cdots - c_0 y$. ■

An interesting sidelight to Theorem 5.12.2 is the observation that the entries in $\mathbf{y}(t)$ are the various derivatives of $y(t)$. In Example 5.12.4, for instance, the derivative of the general solution of $y^{(3)} - y = 0$ is given by the second component of Eq. 5.12.5; namely, $y'(t) = -c_2e^{-t} + c_3e^{t}$.

5.12.1 Fibonacci Series

The second-order difference equation

$$g_{n+1} = g_n + g_{n-1} \qquad g_0 = a \qquad g_1 = b$$

defines the sequence

$$a, a + b, 2a + b, 3a + 2b, \ldots$$

a *generalized Fibonacci sequence*. The special case $a = 0$, $b = 1$ defines the classical Fibonacci sequence. (See Example 5.10.2.) The companion system for the generalized Fibonacci sequence is given by

$$\mathbf{g}_n = \mathbf{G}\mathbf{g}_{n-1} = \begin{bmatrix} 0 & 1 \\ 1 & 1 \end{bmatrix}\mathbf{g}_{n-1}, \qquad \mathbf{g}_0 = \begin{bmatrix} a \\ b \end{bmatrix} \tag{5.12.9}$$

The matrix $\mathbf{G}$ is the matrix of the system in Example 5.10.2. Hence, a general solution of Eq. 5.12.9 is given by

$$\mathbf{g}_n = c_1\left(\frac{1+\sqrt{5}}{2}\right)^n \begin{bmatrix} 1 \\ \dfrac{1+\sqrt{5}}{2} \end{bmatrix} + c_2\left(\frac{1-\sqrt{5}}{2}\right)^n \begin{bmatrix} 1 \\ \dfrac{1-\sqrt{5}}{2} \end{bmatrix} \tag{5.12.10}$$

Since we must have $\mathbf{g}_0 = [a \quad b]^T$, the parameters c_1, c_2 in Eq. 5.12.10 are determined by setting $n = 0$. (The details are left as an exercise, Problem 5.12.18.) Writing $\mathbf{g}_n = [g_n \quad g_{n+1}]^T$, we find

$$\begin{aligned} g_n &= \frac{1}{\sqrt{5}}\left(\frac{1+\sqrt{5}}{2}\right)^n \left(b + a(1+\sqrt{5})/2\right) \\ &\quad - \frac{1}{\sqrt{5}}\left(\frac{1-\sqrt{5}}{2}\right)^n \left(b + a(1-\sqrt{5})/2\right) \end{aligned} \qquad (5.12.11)$$

5.12.2 MATLAB

For any polynomial $p(x)$, compan(p) produces the transpose of the anti-transpose of the companion matrix $\mathbf{C}_n$. For example, let $p(x) = x^3 - 2x^2 + x - 1$. Then after entering p = [1 − 2 1 − 1], the command C = compan(p) produces

$$\begin{matrix} 2 & -1 & 1 \\ 1 & 0 & 0 \\ 0 & 1 & 0 \end{matrix}$$

Note that E*C*E = C^{ST} produces the companion matrix as defined in this section. (See Eq. 5.8.1 and Example 5.8.6.)

PROBLEMS

PART 1

In each of the next three problems, construct the companion system; find its characteristic equation, eigenvalues, and eigenvectors; and solve the system. From the solution of the system, determine the solution of the given difference equation.

5.12.1. $y_{n+1} = y_n - y_{n-1}, y_0 = 1, y_1 = 0.$

5.12.2. $y_{n+1} = 2y_n - y_{n-1}, y_0 = 1, y_1 = 1.$

5.12.3. $y_{n+1} = y_n, y_0 = 1.$

In each of the next five problems construct the companion system; find its characteristic equation, eigenvalues, and eigenvectors; and solve the system. From the solution of the system, determine the solution of the given differential equation and its first two derivatives.

5.12.4. $y'' = y' + y, y(0) = 0, y'(0) = 1.$

5.12.5. $y'' = y', y(0) = 1, y'(0) = 0.$

5.12.6. $y'' = y, y(0) = 1, y'(0) = 0.$

5.12.7. $y'' = y, y(0) = 0, y'(0) = 1.$

5.12.8. $y^{(3)} = y, y(0) = 0, y'(0) = 1, y''(0) = 0.$

Find the companion matrix whose characteristic equation has the given roots. (Recall that $a(5) = 3$ means that the root $\lambda = 5$ is repeated three times.)

5.12.9. $a(0) = 2, a(1) = 3$, $\mathbf{A}$ is 5×5.

5.12.10. $a(-1) = 1, a(1) = 2$, $\mathbf{A}$ is 3×3.

PART 2

5.12.11. Find the companion systems for

$$(a)\ y^{(n)} = y^{(n-1)} + y^{(n-2)} + \cdots + y$$
$$(b)\ y_n = y_{n-1} + y_{n-2} + \cdots + y.$$

Compare the answers to (a) and (b).

5.12.12. Find the companion matrix whose characteristic equation has the roots

$$(a)\ a(0) = n - 1,\ a(n) = 1,\ \mathbf{A} \text{ is } n \times n$$
$$(b)\ a(0) = 1,\ a(n) = n - 1,\ \mathbf{A} \text{ is } n \times n$$
$$(c)\ a(1) = n,\ \mathbf{A} \text{ is } n \times n$$

5.12.13. Explain why a companion matrix is simple if and only if it has distinct eigenvalues.

5.12.14. Show that none of the following are companion matrices:
$(a)\ \mathbf{C}_n^2 \qquad (b)\ \mathbf{C}_n + k\mathbf{I},\ k \neq 0 \qquad (c)\ k\mathbf{C}_n,\ k \neq 1$

5.12.15. Find a matrix whose eigenvalues are $r_1, r_2, \ldots, r_n$.

5.12.16. Show that the auxiliary equation of Eq. 5.12.7 is the characteristic equation of Eq. 5.12.8.

PART 3

5.12.17. Suppose $\mathbf{C}_n'$ and $\mathbf{C}_n''$ are each companion matrices of size n. Show that $\tilde{\mathbf{C}}_n = a_1\mathbf{C}_n' + a_2\mathbf{C}_n''$, $a_1 + a_2 = 1$ is a companion matrix. If λ is a common eigenvalue of $\mathbf{C}_n'$ and $\mathbf{C}_n''$, show that it is an eigenvalue of $\tilde{\mathbf{C}}_n$ as well. Does this hypothesis imply that $\mathbf{C}_n'$, $\mathbf{C}_n''$, and $\tilde{\mathbf{C}}_n$ have a common eigenvector?

5.12.18. Fill in the details in the derivation of Eq. 5.12.11 from Eqs. 5.12.19 and 5.12.20.

5.12.19. Derive Eq. 5.12.10.

5.12.20. Show that

$$\mathbf{b}_k = \begin{bmatrix} 0 & 1 \\ 1 & 1 \end{bmatrix} \mathbf{b}_{k-1}, \quad \mathbf{b}_0 = \begin{bmatrix} 1 \\ 0 \end{bmatrix}$$

has the solution

$$\mathbf{b}_k = \frac{1}{\sqrt{5}}\left(\frac{1+\sqrt{5}}{2}\right)^{k+1} \begin{bmatrix} 1 \\ \dfrac{1+\sqrt{5}}{2} \end{bmatrix} - \frac{1}{\sqrt{5}}\left(\frac{1-\sqrt{5}}{2}\right)^{k+1} \begin{bmatrix} 1 \\ \dfrac{1-\sqrt{5}}{2} \end{bmatrix}$$

5.12.21. Use the result in Problems 5.12.17 and 5.12.20 and Eq. 5.8.10 to derive Eq. 5.12.11. (*Hint:* Show that $a\mathbf{a}_k + b\mathbf{b}_k$ solves Eq. 5.12.9.)

5.12.22. Refer to the notation of Problem 5.8.13. Let

$$\mathbf{A} = \begin{bmatrix} 0 & a_{12} & 0 & \cdots & 0 \\ 0 & 0 & a_{23} & \cdots & 0 \\ \vdots & \vdots & \vdots & \ddots & \vdots \\ 0 & 0 & 0 & \cdots & a_{(n-1),n} \\ \alpha_1 & \alpha_2 & \alpha_3 & \cdots & \alpha_{n-1} \end{bmatrix}$$

Find $\mathbf{D}(v)$ such that $\mathbf{D}(v)^{-1}\mathbf{A}\mathbf{D}(v)$ is a companion matrix and find $c_{\mathbf{A}}(\lambda)$.

5.12.23. Refer to Example 5.8.7 and Eq. 5.8.1 and Problems 5.8.17 and 5.12.22. Let

$$\mathbf{A} = \begin{bmatrix} \alpha_1 & \alpha_2 & \alpha_3 & \cdots & \alpha_{n-1} & \alpha_n \\ a_{21} & 0 & 0 & \cdots & 0 & 0 \\ 0 & a_{32} & 0 & \cdots & 0 & 0 \\ \vdots & \vdots & \vdots & & \vdots & \vdots \\ 0 & 0 & 0 & \cdots & a_{n,n-1} & 0 \end{bmatrix}$$

and assume $\mathbf{a}_{k,k-1} \neq 0$ for $k = 2, 3, \ldots, n$. Find $\mathbf{D}(v)$ such that $\mathbf{D}(v)^{-1}(\mathbf{A}^{\mathrm{T}})^{\mathrm{S}}\mathbf{D}(v)$ is a companion matrix. Find $c_{\mathbf{A}}(\lambda)$.

CHAPTER 6

UNITARY SIMILARITIES AND SCHUR'S THEOREM

Defective matrices lack a complete set of eigenvectors and, because of this, are not diagonalizable by a similarity transformation. This chapter attempts to remedy this deficiency by means of Schur's theorem, a result that applies to all matrices, defective or simple, and that is almost as effective as the diagonalization theorem for analyzing the structure of **A**. Schur's theorem is stated and proved in Section 6.3; some applications appear in the succeeding sections.

Most of the material in this chapter is a natural extension of the ideas developed in Chapter 5, pitched at a somewhat more theoretical level.

6.1 THE HERMITIAN INNER PRODUCT

At the heart of Schur's theorem is a similarity transformation that uses a matrix **U**, often containing complex entries. Suppose $\mathbf{U} = (u_{ij})$. Set $\bar{\mathbf{U}} = (\bar{u}_{ij})$ and define $\mathbf{U}^{\mathrm{H}} = (\bar{\mathbf{U}})^{\mathrm{T}}$. ($\mathbf{U}^{\mathrm{H}}$ is the *hermitian transpose* of **U**.) Then, as we shall see, the existence of **U** with the property that $\mathbf{U}^{\mathrm{H}}\mathbf{U} = \mathbf{I}$ is a crucial ingredient of Schur's theorem. If **U** is a square matrix with only real entries, then **U** is orthogonal (why?). As an example of a matrix **U** such that $\mathbf{U}^{\mathrm{H}}\mathbf{U} = \mathbf{I}$ and **U** is not orthogonal, consider

$$\mathbf{U} = \frac{1}{\sqrt{2}}\begin{bmatrix} i & i \\ 1 & -1 \end{bmatrix}, \qquad \mathbf{U}^{\mathrm{H}} = \frac{1}{\sqrt{2}}\begin{bmatrix} -i & 1 \\ -i & -1 \end{bmatrix}$$

The definition of the *hermitian inner product* was given in Section 4.2.2, and we repeat it here:

$$\langle \mathbf{x}, \mathbf{y} \rangle = \bar{x}_1 y_1 + \bar{x}_2 y_2 + \cdots + \bar{x}_n y_n = \mathbf{x}^{\mathrm{H}} \mathbf{y} \tag{6.1.1}$$

Then, as in the real case,

$$\|\mathbf{x}\|^2 = \langle \mathbf{x}, \mathbf{x} \rangle = |x_1|^2 + |x_2|^2 + \cdots + |x_n|^2 \geq 0 \tag{6.1.2}$$

Clearly, if $\mathbf{x}$ and $\mathbf{y}$ are real vectors, $x_i = \bar{x}_i$, and Eqs. 6.1.1 and 6.1.2 reduce to their euclidean counterparts. And finally, $\|\mathbf{x}\| = 0$ if and only if $\mathbf{x} = \mathbf{0}$.

Some slight changes occur in the various identities involving inner products; the most important of these are tabulated in Theorem 6.1.1:

Theorem 6.1.1. *For vectors* $\mathbf{x}$ *and* $\mathbf{y}$ *in* $\mathscr{C}^n$ *and (complex) scalars* k,

$$(a)\ \overline{\langle \mathbf{x}, \mathbf{y} \rangle} = \langle \mathbf{y}, \mathbf{x} \rangle \qquad (b)\ \langle k\mathbf{x}, \mathbf{y} \rangle = \bar{k}\langle \mathbf{x}, \mathbf{y} \rangle \qquad (c)\ \langle \mathbf{x}, k\mathbf{y} \rangle = k\langle \mathbf{x}, \mathbf{y} \rangle$$
$$(d)\ \langle \mathbf{y}, a_1\mathbf{x}_1 + a_2\mathbf{x}_2 + \cdots + a_n\mathbf{x}_n \rangle = a_1\langle \mathbf{y}, \mathbf{x}_1 \rangle + a_2\langle \mathbf{y}, \mathbf{x}_2 \rangle + \cdots + a_n\langle \mathbf{y}, \mathbf{x}_n \rangle$$

Proof. Each of these identities is straightforward, and the arguments are left to the problems. ■

An important consequence of the definition of hermitian inner product is that the notion of orthogonality and the Gram-Schmidt method carries over from $\mathscr{R}^n$ to $\mathscr{C}^n$ without formal change. All that is needed is to define the relation "$\mathbf{x}$ is orthogonal to $\mathbf{y}$" as meaning $\mathbf{x}^{\mathrm{H}}\mathbf{y} = \mathbf{0}$ and repeat all the arguments given in Chapter 4 for this extension of the meaning of orthogonality. Two more differences between the euclidean and the hermitian inner products and norms should be mentioned. First, vectors $\mathbf{x}$ that satisfy $\mathbf{A}\mathbf{x} = \mathbf{0}$ are not necessarily orthogonal to the rows of $\mathbf{A}$. Second, the proof of the Schwarz inequality (Theorem 4.2.2) for hermitian inner products is not a trivial generalization of the argument given for the real inner product.

Theorem 6.1.2. *(The Schwarz Inequality). For the hermitian inner product and norm*

$$|\mathbf{y}^{\mathrm{H}}\mathbf{x}| = |\mathbf{x}^{\mathrm{H}}\mathbf{y}| \leq \|\mathbf{x}\|\,\|\mathbf{y}\| \tag{6.1.3}$$

Proof. Recall that $\langle \mathbf{x}, \mathbf{y} \rangle = \overline{\langle \mathbf{y}, \mathbf{x} \rangle}$ and therefore $|\ \mathbf{x}^{\mathrm{H}}\mathbf{y}\ | = |\ \mathbf{y}^{\mathrm{H}}\mathbf{x}\ |$. Let α be any complex number, and consider

$$0 \leq \|\mathbf{x} - \alpha\mathbf{y}\|^2 = (\mathbf{x} - \alpha\mathbf{y})^{\mathrm{H}}(\mathbf{x} - \alpha\mathbf{y}) = \|\mathbf{x}\|^2 - \alpha\mathbf{x}^{\mathrm{H}}\mathbf{y} - \bar{\alpha}\mathbf{y}^{\mathrm{H}}\mathbf{x} + |\alpha|^2\|\mathbf{y}\|^2 \tag{6.1.4}$$

Since this inequality is valid for all complex α, it is true for the (clever) choice $\alpha = \mathbf{y}^{\mathrm{H}}\mathbf{x}/\|y\|^2$, $\mathbf{y} \neq \mathbf{0}$. (*Note:* If $\|\mathbf{y}\| = 0$, Eq 6.1.3 holds trivially, so we may assume that $\mathbf{y} \neq \mathbf{0}$ and, hence, that α is defined.) Substitute the preceding expression for α into Eq. 6.1.4 and obtain

$$0 \le \|\mathbf{x}\|^2 - \frac{\mathbf{y}^H\mathbf{x}}{\|\mathbf{y}\|^2}(\mathbf{x}^H\mathbf{y}) - \frac{\overline{\mathbf{y}^H\mathbf{x}}}{\|\mathbf{y}\|^2}(\mathbf{y}^H\mathbf{x}) + \frac{|\mathbf{y}^H\mathbf{x}|^2}{\|\mathbf{y}\|^4}\|\mathbf{y}\|^2$$

$$= \|\mathbf{x}\|^2 - \frac{|\mathbf{x}^H\mathbf{y}|^2}{\|\mathbf{y}\|^2} - \frac{|\mathbf{y}^H\mathbf{x}|^2}{\|\mathbf{y}\|^2} + \frac{|\mathbf{x}^H\mathbf{y}|^2}{\|\mathbf{y}\|^2} = \|\mathbf{x}\|^2 - \frac{|\mathbf{y}^H\mathbf{x}|^2}{\|\mathbf{y}\|^2}$$

Hence, the theorem follows upon taking square roots. ■

Corollary 1. $\|\mathbf{x} + \mathbf{y}\| \le \|\mathbf{x}\| + \|\mathbf{y}\|$

Proof. By Eq. 6.1.4 with $\alpha = -1$,

$$0 \le \|\mathbf{x} + \mathbf{y}\|^2 = \|\mathbf{x}\|^2 + \mathbf{x}^H\mathbf{y} + \mathbf{y}^H\mathbf{x} + \|\mathbf{y}\|^2 \tag{6.1.5}$$

Now $\mathbf{x}^H\mathbf{y} = \overline{\mathbf{y}^H\mathbf{x}}$. Hence, $\mathbf{x}^H\mathbf{y} + \mathbf{y}^H\mathbf{x} = 2\mathrm{Re}(\mathbf{x}^H\mathbf{y}) \le 2\|\mathbf{x}^H\mathbf{y}\|$, by Theorem 5.2.1(*f*). Substituting this inequality into Eq. 6.1.5 leads to

$$0 \le \|\mathbf{x} + \mathbf{y}\|^2 = \|\mathbf{x}\|^2 + 2\|\mathbf{x}^H\mathbf{y}\| + \|\mathbf{y}\|^2 = (\|\mathbf{x}\| + \|\mathbf{y}\|)^2$$

from which the conclusion follows. ■

6.1.1 MATLAB

MATLAB computes the hermitian norm when the command norm(x,2) is given and computes the hermitian transpose in response to A′.

PROBLEMS

PART 1

6.1.1. Compute the (hermitian) norms of the vectors:

$(a)\ \begin{bmatrix} 1 \\ i \\ 1 \end{bmatrix} \quad (b)\ \begin{bmatrix} 1 \\ 1+i \\ -1 \end{bmatrix} \quad (c)\ \begin{bmatrix} 2-i \\ 1+i \\ 0 \end{bmatrix}$

6.1.2. Compute the (hermitian) inner products of the vectors:

$(a)\ \left\langle \begin{bmatrix} i \\ 1 \end{bmatrix}, \begin{bmatrix} i \\ -1 \end{bmatrix} \right\rangle \quad (b)\ \left\langle \begin{bmatrix} i \\ -1 \end{bmatrix}, \begin{bmatrix} i \\ 1 \end{bmatrix} \right\rangle \quad (c)\ \left\langle \begin{bmatrix} i \\ i \end{bmatrix}, \begin{bmatrix} 1 \\ -1 \end{bmatrix} \right\rangle$

$(d)\ \left\langle \begin{bmatrix} 1 \\ -1 \end{bmatrix}, \begin{bmatrix} i \\ i \end{bmatrix} \right\rangle$

6.1.3. Verify the Schwarz inequality for each of the pairs of vectors in Problem 6.1.2.

PART 2

6.1.4. Prove Theorem 6.1.1.

6.1.5. Given $\mathbf{u} = [1 \quad i \quad -1]^{\mathrm{T}}$, find by inspection $\mathbf{y}_1 \neq \mathbf{0}$ so that $\mathbf{u}^{\mathrm{H}}\mathbf{y}_1 = 0$. Given $\mathbf{x} = [1 \quad 1 \quad 1]^{\mathrm{T}}$, find scalars α and β so that $\mathbf{y}_2 = \mathbf{x} - \beta\mathbf{y}_1 - \alpha\mathbf{u}$ is orthogonal to $\mathbf{y}_1$ and $\mathbf{u}$.

6.1.6. Use the Gram-Schmidt method or inspection to form an orthonormal basis for $\mathscr{C}^3$ that contains a multiple of $\mathbf{u}_1 = [1+i \quad 0 \quad 1-i]^{\mathrm{T}}$.

6.1.7. Derive the Gram-Schmidt method using hermitian inner products and norms in place of its euclidean counterparts. Are any changes in the arguments necessary?

6.1.8. Show that:

(a) $\mathbf{A}^{\mathrm{H}} = \overline{(\mathbf{A}^{\mathrm{T}})}$ $\quad (b)$ $(\mathbf{A}^{\mathrm{H}})^{\mathrm{H}} = \mathbf{A}$ $\quad (c)$ $(\overline{\mathbf{A}})^{\mathrm{H}} = \mathbf{A}^{\mathrm{T}}$ $\quad (d)$ $(\mathbf{A}^{\mathrm{T}})^{\mathrm{H}} = \overline{\mathbf{A}}$

6.1.9. Prove that $\langle \mathbf{Ax}, \mathbf{y} \rangle = \langle \mathbf{x}, \mathbf{A}^{\mathrm{H}}\mathbf{y} \rangle$.

6.1.10. Show that $\mathbf{A}^{\mathrm{H}}\mathbf{A}$ is a diagonal matrix where

$$\mathbf{A} = \begin{bmatrix} 1 & 1 & -1 \\ i & 0 & 2i \\ -1 & 1 & 1 \end{bmatrix}$$

Is $\mathbf{AA}^{\mathrm{H}}$ a diagonal matrix?

6.1.11. Repeat Problem 6.1.10 for the matrix

$$\mathbf{V} = \begin{bmatrix} \frac{1}{\sqrt{3}} & \frac{1}{\sqrt{2}} & \frac{-1}{\sqrt{6}} \\ \frac{i}{\sqrt{3}} & 0 & \frac{2i}{\sqrt{6}} \\ \frac{-1}{\sqrt{3}} & \frac{1}{\sqrt{2}} & \frac{1}{\sqrt{6}} \end{bmatrix}$$

6.1.12. Does the Schwarz inequality for the hermitian inner product, Eq. 6.1.3, lead to the Schwarz inequality for the euclidean inner product when all the vectors are real?

6.1.13. Show that $\det(\mathbf{A}^{\mathrm{H}}) = \overline{\det(\mathbf{A})}$.

MATLAB

6.1.14. Use norm(x,2) to answer Problem 6.1.1.

6.1.15. Use MATLAB commands to answer Problem 6.1.10.

6.1.16. Use MATLAB commands to answer Problem 6.1.11.

6.2 UNITARY MATRICES

Recall that an orthogonal matrix is a real, square matrix whose columns form an orthonormal set. That is, $\mathbf{Q} = [\mathbf{q}_1 \quad \mathbf{q}_2 \quad \dots \quad \mathbf{q}_n]$ is orthogonal if and only if $\mathbf{q}_i^{\mathrm{T}}\mathbf{q}_j = \delta_{ij}$. Alternatively, the orthogonality of $\mathbf{Q}$ can be defined by the identity $\mathbf{Q}^{\mathrm{T}}\mathbf{Q} = \mathbf{I}$. (See Section 4.3.) The natural generalization of an orthogonal matrix to matrices with complex entries requires the replacement of the real inner product with the hermitian inner product. The square matrix $\mathbf{U}$ is *unitary* if its columns form an orthonormal set with respect to the hermitian inner product. Suppose

$\mathbf{U} = [\mathbf{u}_1 \quad \mathbf{u}_2 \quad \ldots \quad \mathbf{u}_n]$. If the columns of $\mathbf{U}$ are mutually orthogonal and have unit norm, then, by the definition of matrix multiplication, $\mathbf{U}^{\mathrm{H}}\mathbf{U} = (\mathbf{u}_i^{\mathrm{H}}\mathbf{u}_j) = (\delta_{ij}) = \mathbf{I}$. Hence, $\mathbf{U}^{-1} = \mathbf{U}^{\mathrm{H}}$, and the definition of unitary matrix is equivalent to the equations

$$\mathbf{U}^{\mathrm{H}}\mathbf{U} = \mathbf{U}\mathbf{U}^{\mathrm{H}} = \mathbf{I} \tag{6.2.1}$$

Note, as expected, orthogonal matrices are real, unitary matrices. The matrix

$$\mathbf{U} = \frac{1}{\sqrt{2}}\begin{bmatrix} 1 & i \\ i & 1 \end{bmatrix}$$

is an example of a matrix that is unitary but not orthogonal because the term *orthogonal* is customarily reserved for real matrices only.

Example 6.2.1. Show that if $\mathbf{U}$ and $\mathbf{V}$ are unitary, so are

(*a*) $\mathbf{UV}$ (*b*) $\mathbf{U}^{\mathrm{H}}$ (*c*) $\mathbf{U}^{\mathrm{T}}$ (*d*) $\overline{\mathbf{U}}$

Solution. For (*a*), $(\mathbf{UV})^{\mathrm{H}}(\mathbf{UV}) = \mathbf{V}^{\mathrm{H}}\mathbf{U}^{\mathrm{H}}\mathbf{UV} = \mathbf{I}$. The remaining parts follow just as easily.

As in the case of orthogonal matrices, unitary matrices preserve norms and inner products in the hermitian sense. First note that

$$\langle \mathbf{Ax},\mathbf{y}\rangle = (\mathbf{Ax})^{\mathrm{H}}\mathbf{y} = \mathbf{x}^{\mathrm{H}}(\mathbf{A}^{\mathrm{H}}\mathbf{y}) = \langle \mathbf{x},\mathbf{A}^{\mathrm{H}}\mathbf{y}\rangle$$

Then

$$\langle \mathbf{Ux},\mathbf{Uy}\rangle = \langle \mathbf{x},\mathbf{U}^{\mathrm{H}}\mathbf{Uy}\rangle = \langle \mathbf{x},\mathbf{y}\rangle \tag{6.2.2}$$

from which it follows that

$$\|\mathbf{Ux}\|^2 = \langle \mathbf{Ux},\mathbf{Ux}\rangle = \langle \mathbf{x},\mathbf{U}^{\mathrm{H}}\mathbf{Ux}\rangle = \langle \mathbf{x},\mathbf{x}\rangle = \|\mathbf{x}\|^2 \tag{6.2.3}$$

In fact, Eq. 6.2.2 is necessary and sufficient for $\mathbf{U}$ to be unitary.

Theorem 6.2.1. $\mathbf{U}$ *is unitary if and only if* $\langle \mathbf{Ux},\mathbf{Uy}\rangle = \langle \mathbf{x},\mathbf{y}\rangle$ *for every* $\mathbf{x}$ *and* $\mathbf{y}$.

Proof. The *only if* part has already been proved. So suppose that for each $\mathbf{x}$ and $\mathbf{y}$, Eq. 6.2.2 holds. The following argument establishes that $\mathbf{U}$ must be unitary. Since $\langle \mathbf{x},\mathbf{y}\rangle = \langle \mathbf{x},\mathbf{U}^{\mathrm{H}}\mathbf{Uy}\rangle$ for all $\mathbf{x}$ and $\mathbf{y}$, this equality holds for $\mathbf{x} = \mathbf{e}_i$ and $\mathbf{y} = \mathbf{e}_j$. But $\delta_{ij} = \langle \mathbf{e}_i,\mathbf{e}_j\rangle = \langle \mathbf{e}_i, \mathbf{U}^{\mathrm{H}}\mathbf{U}\mathbf{e}_j\rangle$ implies that $\mathbf{U}^{\mathrm{H}}\mathbf{U}$ has δ_{ij} in the (i,j) position. (Recall that $\mathbf{U}^{\mathrm{H}}\mathbf{U}\mathbf{e}_j$ is the jth column of $\mathbf{U}^{\mathrm{H}}\mathbf{U}$.) ■

In fact, one can actually prove an apparently stronger theorem, namely, that Eq. 6.2.3 implies $\mathbf{U}$ is unitary. This proof is left for Problem 6.2.15.

Theorem 6.2.2. *If* $\mathbf{U}$ *is unitary and* λ *is an eigenvalue of* $\mathbf{U}$, *then* $|\lambda| = 1$ *and* $|\det(\mathbf{U})| = 1$.

Proof. On the one hand, $\mathbf{Ux} = \lambda\mathbf{x}$ implies

$$\langle \mathbf{Ux}, \mathbf{Ux} \rangle = \langle \lambda\mathbf{x}, \lambda\mathbf{x} \rangle = \lambda\bar{\lambda}\langle \mathbf{x}, \mathbf{x} \rangle = |\lambda|^2\|\mathbf{x}\|$$

On the other hand, $\langle \mathbf{Ux}, \mathbf{Ux} \rangle = \|\mathbf{x}\|^2$. Hence, $|\lambda|^2\|\mathbf{x}\|^2 = \|\mathbf{x}\|^2$. Since $\|\mathbf{x}\|^2 \neq 0$, $|\lambda| = 1$ follows. Since det(**U**) is the product of its eigenvalues, $|\det(\mathbf{A})| = 1$ is a consequence of $|\lambda| = 1$. ■

Now consider similarity transformations in which the diagonalizing matrix **S**, denoted here by **U**, is unitary. If **A** and **B** are related by an equation of the form $\mathbf{U}^{\mathrm{H}}\mathbf{AU} = \mathbf{B}$, and **U** is unitary, **B** is called *unitarily similar* to **A**. The relationship $\mathbf{U}^{\mathrm{H}}\mathbf{AU}$ is a *unitary transformation*. Since $\mathbf{U}^{\mathrm{H}}\mathbf{AU} = \mathbf{B}$ implies $\mathbf{UBU}^{\mathrm{H}} = \mathbf{A}$, and $\mathbf{U}^{\mathrm{H}}$ is unitary, **A** is unitarily similar to **B** if **B** is unitarily similar to **A**. Of course, **A** is unitarily similar to itself (choose $\mathbf{U} = \mathbf{I}$). And finally, if **A** is unitarily similar to **B** and **B** to **C**, then **A** is unitarily similar to **C** (why?). Unitary transformations are special cases of similarity transformations, and for this reason all results that hold for similarity transformations hold for unitary transformations as well. (See Problem 6.2.19.)

PROBLEMS

PART 1

6.2.1. Show that the following matrices are unitary and verify Eq. 6.2.2.

$$(a)\ \begin{bmatrix} 0 & i \\ i & 0 \end{bmatrix} \qquad (b)\ \begin{bmatrix} 0 & i \\ -i & 0 \end{bmatrix} \qquad (c)\ \frac{1}{\sqrt{2}}\begin{bmatrix} 1 & i \\ i & 1 \end{bmatrix}$$

6.2.2. Suppose that **Q** is orthogonal. Show that $e^{i\alpha}\mathbf{Q}$ is unitary.

6.2.3. Prove parts (*b*), (*c*), and (*d*) of Example 6.2.1.

6.2.4. If **U** is unitary and $\mathbf{U}^{\mathrm{H}} = \mathbf{U}$, show that det(**U**)= 1 or −1.

6.2.5. Construct a 3 × 3 unitary matrix that is neither orthogonal nor a multiple of an orthogonal matrix. (*Hint:* The matrix in Problem 6.2.1(*c*) is a 2 × 2 example.)

PART 2

6.2.6. Find conditions on the real scalars α and β so that

$$\mathbf{U} = \begin{bmatrix} 0 & \alpha & 0 & i\beta \\ \alpha & 0 & i\beta & 0 \\ 0 & i\beta & 0 & \alpha \\ i\beta & 0 & \alpha & 0 \end{bmatrix}$$

is unitary. (Do so by computing det(**U**) and, alternatively, by finding the eigenvalue corresponding to the eigenvector $\mathbf{u} = \mathbf{1}$.)

6.2.7. Repeat Problem 6.2.6 for the matrix

$$\mathbf{V} = \begin{bmatrix} 0 & 0 & \gamma & i\delta \\ 0 & 0 & i\delta & \gamma \\ \gamma & i\delta & 0 & 0 \\ i\delta & \gamma & 0 & 0 \end{bmatrix}$$

6.2.8. If **U** is unitary, show that

$$\mathbf{V} = \begin{bmatrix} \mathbf{I} & \mathbf{O} \\ \mathbf{O} & \mathbf{U} \end{bmatrix}$$

is also unitary.

6.2.9. Prove that $\mathbf{U}^{-1}$ is unitary if **U** is unitary.

6.2.10. Prove that **U** is unitary implies that $\mathbf{U}^{\mathrm{H}}$, $\mathbf{U}^{\mathrm{T}}$, and $\mathbf{\bar{U}}$ are also unitary.

6.2.11. Prove that $\mathbf{U}^m$ is unitary if **U** is unitary and m is a positive integer.

6.2.12. Find **UV** for the matrices exhibited in Problems 6.2.6 and 6.2.7 and show without reference to Example 6.2.1 that this product is unitary, assuming α, β, γ, and δ are properly chosen.

PART 3

6.2.13. Assume $\|\mathbf{Ux}\| = \|\mathbf{x}\|$ for all **x**. Expand $\|\mathbf{U}(\mathbf{x}+\mathbf{y})\|^2$ using this assumption and thereby deduce that $\mathrm{Re}\langle \mathbf{Ux}, \mathbf{Uy}\rangle = \mathrm{Re}\langle \mathbf{x}, \mathbf{y}\rangle$ for all **x** and **y**.

6.2.14. Repeat Problem 6.2.13 using $\|\mathbf{U}(\mathbf{x}-\mathbf{y})\|^2$ to deduce $\mathrm{Im}\langle \mathbf{Ux}, \mathbf{Uy}\rangle = \mathrm{Im}\langle \mathbf{x}, \mathbf{y}\rangle$.

6.2.15. Assume $\|\mathbf{Ux}\| = \|\mathbf{x}\|$ for all **x**. Show that $\mathbf{U}^{\mathrm{H}}\mathbf{U} = \mathbf{I}$ by using the results of Problems 6.2.13 and 6.2.14.

6.2.16. Show that $\|\mathbf{Ux}\| = \|\mathbf{x}\|$ for all **x** implies $\|\mathbf{U}^{\mathrm{H}}\mathbf{x}\| = \|\mathbf{x}\|$ for all **x**.

6.2.17. Let ω be either of the complex cubic roots of unity, $\omega = (-1 \pm i\sqrt{3})/2$. Show $\omega^3 = 1$, $|\omega| = 1$, and $1 + \omega + \omega^2 = 0$. Find restrictions on a, b, and c such that the following matrix is unitary:

$$\mathbf{V} = \frac{1}{\sqrt{3}} \begin{bmatrix} a & b & c \\ a & b\omega^2 & c\omega \\ a & b\omega & c\omega^2 \end{bmatrix}$$

6.2.18. Prove that **A** unitarily similar to **B** and **B** unitarily similar to **C** implies **A** is unitarily similar to **C**.

6.2.19. Let $\mathcal{A}$ represent the class of all matrices unitarily similar to **A** and $\mathcal{B}$ the class unitarily similar to **B**. Show that:

(*a*) $\mathcal{A}$ is not empty.

(*b*) If $\mathbf{A} \in \mathcal{B}$, then $\mathcal{A} = \mathcal{B}$.

(*c*) If $\mathbf{B} \in \mathcal{A}$ and $\mathbf{C} \in \mathcal{A}$, then **B** and **C** are unitarily similar.

(*d*) If $\mathcal{A}$ and $\mathcal{B}$ contain a matrix in common, then $\mathcal{A} = \mathcal{B}$.

6.2.20. Set $\omega = \cos(2\pi/n) + i\sin(2\pi/n)$ and, following Section 5.9, define the Vandermonde matrix

$$\mathbf{V}_n(\omega) = \begin{bmatrix} 1 & 1 & \cdots & 1 \\ 1 & \omega & \cdots & \omega^{n-1} \\ \vdots & & & \\ 1 & \omega^{n-1} & \cdots & \omega^{(n-1)^2} \end{bmatrix}$$

Show that $\mathbf{V}_n(\omega)/\sqrt{n}$ is unitary.

6.3 SCHUR'S THEOREM

In Chapter 5 we studied simple matrices and found extensive applications to the theory of differential and difference equations. The tool that made this possible was the diagonalization theorem for simple matrices, namely, that there exists a nonsingular $\mathbf{S}$ such that $\mathbf{S}^{-1}\mathbf{AS} = \Lambda$. No such theorem is possible for defective matrices (by definition), but we can prove a theorem of I. Schur in which the diagonal matrix Λ is replaced by an upper triangular matrix $\mathbf{T}$. Besides providing a tool for the study of defective matrices, Schur's theorem is useful in the analysis of a variety of important simple matrices. This section is devoted to its proof.

Theorem 6.3.1. *(Schur's Theorem). For any square matrix* $\mathbf{A}$*, there exists a unitary matrix* $\mathbf{U}$ *and an upper triangular matrix* $\mathbf{T}$ *such that*

$$\mathbf{U}^{\mathrm{H}}\mathbf{AU} = \mathbf{T} \tag{6.3.1}$$

Proof. The proof is by induction. Suppose $\mathbf{A}$ is $n \times n$ and the theorem is true for all $(n-1)\times(n-1)$ matrices. Let $(\lambda, \mathbf{u})$ be an eigenpair of $\mathbf{A}$. If $\|\mathbf{u}\| \neq 1$, set $\mathbf{v} = \mathbf{u}/\|\mathbf{u}\|$ and note that $(\lambda, \mathbf{v})$ is also an eigenpair of $\mathbf{A}$. Hence, we may assume, to begin with, that $\|\mathbf{u}\| = 1$. Now, it is always possible to find $n-1$ vectors $\mathbf{y}_2, \mathbf{y}_3, \ldots, \mathbf{y}_n$ such that the set $\{\mathbf{u}, \mathbf{y}_2, \ldots, \mathbf{y}_n\}$ is orthonormal. (This can be done, for example, by first finding a basis for $\mathscr{C}^n$ containing $\mathbf{u}$ and then using the Gram-Schmidt method with $\mathbf{u}$ as the initial vector; see Section 4.5.) Next define $\mathbf{U} = [\mathbf{u} \quad \mathbf{y}_2 \quad \cdots \quad \mathbf{y}_n]$ and verify $\mathbf{U}^{-1} = \mathbf{U}^{\mathrm{H}}$. By repeating the argument given in the proof of Lemma 5.2, Section 5.4, using $\mathbf{U}$ in place of $\mathbf{S}$, derive

$$\mathbf{U}^{\mathrm{H}}\mathbf{AU} = \begin{bmatrix} \lambda & \mathbf{c}^{\mathrm{T}} \\ \mathbf{0} & \mathbf{B} \end{bmatrix}$$

The vectors $\mathbf{0}$ and $\mathbf{c}$ have $n-1$ entries, and $\mathbf{B}$ is $(n-1) \times (n-1)$. By the induction hypothesis, there exists a unitary matrix $\mathbf{V}$ such that $\mathbf{V}^{\mathrm{H}}\mathbf{BV} = \mathbf{T}$, $\mathbf{T}$ upper triangular. Define $\mathbf{W}$ as follows:

$$\mathbf{W} = \begin{bmatrix} 1 & \mathbf{0}^{\mathrm{T}} \\ \mathbf{0} & \mathbf{V} \end{bmatrix}$$

and verify that $\mathbf{W}$ is unitary: indeed, it is a special case of Problem 6.2.8. From Example 6.2.1, it follows that $\mathbf{UW}$ is also unitary. Now verify

$$(\mathbf{UW})^{\mathrm{H}}\mathbf{A}(\mathbf{UW}) = \mathbf{W}^{\mathrm{H}}(\mathbf{U}^{\mathrm{H}}\mathbf{AU})\mathbf{W} = \begin{bmatrix} 1 & \mathbf{0}^{\mathrm{T}} \\ \mathbf{0} & \mathbf{V} \end{bmatrix}^{\mathrm{H}} \begin{bmatrix} \lambda & \mathbf{c}^{\mathrm{T}} \\ \mathbf{0} & \mathbf{B} \end{bmatrix} \begin{bmatrix} 1 & \mathbf{0}^{\mathrm{T}} \\ \mathbf{0} & \mathbf{V} \end{bmatrix}$$

$$= \begin{bmatrix} \lambda & \mathbf{c}^{\mathrm{T}}\mathbf{V}^{\mathrm{H}} \\ \mathbf{0} & \mathbf{V}^{\mathrm{H}}\mathbf{BV} \end{bmatrix} = \begin{bmatrix} \lambda & \mathbf{c}^{\mathrm{T}}\mathbf{V}^{\mathrm{H}} \\ \mathbf{0} & \mathbf{T} \end{bmatrix}$$

The last matrix in this string of equalities is upper triangular. Thus, $\mathbf{UW}$ is the unitary matrix that "upper triangularizes" $\mathbf{A}$. To complete the induction, note that the theorem is trivial if $\mathbf{A}$ is 1×1 or 2×2. ■

Since the preceding proof is constructive, examples will illustrate the various points in the argument.

Example 6.3.1. Construct $\mathbf{U}$ so that $\mathbf{U}^{\mathrm{H}}\mathbf{A}\mathbf{U}$ is upper triangular, where

$$\mathbf{A} = \begin{bmatrix} 2 & -1 & 0 \\ -6 & 2 & 1 \\ 2 & -3 & 2 \end{bmatrix}$$

Solution. First note that $\det(\mathbf{A}) = 0$, so that $\lambda = 0$ is an eigenvalue. A corresponding eigenvector is $\mathbf{u} = [1 \quad 2 \quad 2]^{\mathrm{T}}$. Now construct an orthonormal basis for $\mathcal{R}^3$. (Since the eigenvalues and eigenvectors are real, the proof of Theorem 6.3.1 can be illustrated without resorting to hermitian inner products.) There are many such bases; we pick one that avoids working with square roots:

$$\mathbf{u} = \frac{1}{3}\begin{bmatrix} 1 \\ 2 \\ 2 \end{bmatrix}, \qquad \mathbf{y}_1 = \frac{1}{3}\begin{bmatrix} -2 \\ -1 \\ 2 \end{bmatrix}, \qquad \mathbf{y}_2 = \frac{1}{3}\begin{bmatrix} -2 \\ 2 \\ -1 \end{bmatrix}$$

The matrix with these vectors as columns is a unitary matrix (which happens to be orthogonal), $\mathbf{U} = [\mathbf{u} \quad \mathbf{y}_1 \quad \mathbf{y}_2]$. After some computations,

$$\mathbf{U}^{\mathrm{H}}\mathbf{A}\mathbf{U} = \begin{bmatrix} 0 & 3 & 0 \\ 0 & 0 & -3 \\ 0 & 3 & 6 \end{bmatrix} \tag{6.3.2}$$

Now let $\mathbf{B}$ be the 2×2 submatrix in the lower-right-hand corner of $\mathbf{U}^{\mathrm{H}}\mathbf{A}\mathbf{U}$. Then

$$\mathbf{B} = \begin{bmatrix} 0 & -3 \\ 3 & 6 \end{bmatrix} \tag{6.3.3}$$

and both eigenvalues of $\mathbf{B}$ are 3 (so that $a(3) = 2$), and an eigenvector of unit length is given by $\mathbf{z} = [1 \quad -1]^{\mathrm{T}}/\sqrt{2}$. An orthonormal basis for $\mathcal{R}^2$ containing $\mathbf{z}$ can be obtained by inspection:

$$\mathbf{z} = \frac{1}{\sqrt{2}}\begin{bmatrix} 1 \\ -1 \end{bmatrix}, \qquad \mathbf{w} = \frac{1}{\sqrt{2}}\begin{bmatrix} 1 \\ 1 \end{bmatrix}$$

Define a unitary matrix $\mathbf{V}$ with these orthonormal vectors as columns:

$$\mathbf{V} = \frac{1}{\sqrt{2}}\begin{bmatrix} 1 & 1 \\ -1 & 1 \end{bmatrix}$$

Then

$$\mathbf{V}^{\mathrm{H}}\mathbf{B}\mathbf{V} = \begin{bmatrix} 3 & -6 \\ 0 & 3 \end{bmatrix}$$

and setting

$$\mathbf{W} = \left[\begin{array}{c|c} 1 & 0 \quad 0 \\ \hline 0 & \\ 0 & \mathbf{V} \end{array}\right] = \left[\begin{array}{c|cc} 1 & 0 & 0 \\ \hline 0 & 3 & -6 \\ 0 & 0 & 3 \end{array}\right]$$

leads to

$$\mathbf{W}^{H}(\mathbf{U}^{H}\mathbf{A}\mathbf{U})\mathbf{W} = (\mathbf{U}\mathbf{W})^{H}\mathbf{A}(\mathbf{U}\mathbf{W}) = \begin{bmatrix} 0 & \frac{3}{\sqrt{2}} & \frac{3}{\sqrt{2}} \\ 0 & 3 & -6 \\ 0 & 0 & 3 \end{bmatrix} \tag{6.3.4}$$

The triangularizing unitary matrix is given by

$$\mathbf{U}\mathbf{W} = \frac{1}{3\sqrt{2}}\begin{bmatrix} \sqrt{2} & 0 & -4 \\ 2\sqrt{2} & -3 & 1 \\ 2\sqrt{2} & 3 & 1 \end{bmatrix}$$

Corollary 1. *If* $\mathbf{U}^{H}\mathbf{A}\mathbf{U} = \mathbf{T}$, *then the eigenvalues of* $\mathbf{A}$ *are the diagonal entries of* $\mathbf{T}$.

Proof. The eigenvalues of **A** and **T** are identical because **A** and **T** are similar. The diagonal entries of **T** are its eigenvalues because **T** is upper triangular. ■

It is instructive to work through an example in which **A** is simple. We shall discover that Schur's theorem does *not necessarily* provide the diagonalization of **A**.

Example 6.3.2. Apply Schur's theorem to the simple matrix

$$\mathbf{A} = \begin{bmatrix} 0 & 1 \\ 3 & 2 \end{bmatrix}$$

Solution. The arithmetic is left to the reader; following are the various intermediate stages. Corresponding to $\lambda = -1$ is the eigenvector of unit norm: $\mathbf{x} = [\sqrt{2}/2 \quad \sqrt{2}/2]^{T}$. Hence,

$$\mathbf{U} = \frac{\sqrt{2}}{2}\begin{bmatrix} 1 & 1 \\ -1 & 1 \end{bmatrix}$$

and it follows that

$$\mathbf{T} = \mathbf{U}^{H}\mathbf{A}\mathbf{U} = \begin{bmatrix} -1 & -2 \\ 0 & 3 \end{bmatrix}$$

The second eigenvalue of **A** can be read from the diagonal entries of **T**; namely, $\lambda = 3$. The second column of **U** is not an eigenvector of **A**. In fact, this matrix, though diagonalizable, is not diagonalizable by unitary matrices. More will be said about this phenomenon in Sections 6.5 and 6.6. (See also Problem 6.3.12 in the following problem set.)

6.3.1 Schur Decomposition in MATLAB

MATLAB provides two commands related to Schur's theorem. The output from these commands appears in two different guises. First, if **A** is a real matrix *with real eigenvalues,* or if **A** has complex entries, then T = schur(A) produces an upper triangular matrix whose diagonal entries are the eigenvalues of **A**. The command [T,U] = schur(A) produces both T and the unitary matrix U such that U′*A*U = T. (Recall that in MATLAB, U′ corresponds to $\mathbf{U}^H$.) A second form of Schur's theorem is returned if **A** is real and has complex eigenvalues. If, for example, $c = a + ib$ is an eigenvalue, then so is $\bar{c} = a - ib$; in this case, MATLAB presents a modified form of the matrix T in which there is a 2×2 block, placed symmetrically along the diagonal, whose eigenvalues are c and $\bar{c}$. These points can be made clear by example.

Example 6.3.3. Enter A = [0 1 0 0; 0 0 1 0; 0 0 0 1; −3 4 −4 4]. The eigenvalues of this matrix are 3, 1, i and $-i$.

Enter schur(A)

ans =

3.0000	1.8138	−1.6913	6.1220
0	0.2261	−1.1371	0.6811
0	0.9244	−0.2261	1.9124
0	0	0	1.0000

The 2×2 matrix

$$\mathbf{B} = \begin{bmatrix} 0.2261 & -1.1371 \\ 0.9244 & -0.2261 \end{bmatrix}$$

which appears about the diagonal of **A**, has eigenvalues i and $-i$, as is easily verified by invoking eig(B).

Example 6.3.4. Enter A = [0 1 0 0; 0 0 1 0; 0 0 0 1; 2 −3 −1 3]. The eigenvalues of this matrix are 2, 1, 1 and −1.

Enter schur(A)

ans =

2.0000	1.3988	−3.2585	1.5193
0	1.0000	−1.8391	0.8575
0	0.0000	1.0000	0.0000
0	0	0	−1.0000

The answer is upper triangular, as expected from Schur's theorem.

PROBLEMS

PART 1

The next five problems relate to the various matrices and vectors that appear in Example 6.3.1.

6.3.1. Verify Eq. 6.3.2.

6.3.2. Verify Eq. 6.3.3.

6.3.3. Verify Eq. 6.3.4.

6.3.4. Find the characteristic equation of

$$\mathbf{B} = \begin{bmatrix} 0 & 3 \\ -3 & 6 \end{bmatrix}$$

and verify that its eigenvalues are both 3 and an eigenvector of unit length is $\mathbf{z} = [1 \quad -1]^T/\sqrt{2}$.

6.3.5. Show that the characteristic equation of

$$\mathbf{A} = \begin{bmatrix} 2 & -1 & 0 \\ -6 & 2 & 1 \\ 2 & -3 & 2 \end{bmatrix}$$

is $\lambda(3-\lambda)^2 = 0$ and that $(\lambda = 0,\ \mathbf{u} = [1 \quad 2 \quad 2]^T)$ is an eigenpair.

The matrices and vectors in Problems 6.3.6 to 6.3.10 relate to Example 6.3.2.

6.3.6. Find the characteristic equation, eigenvalues, and eigenvectors of the matrix

$$\mathbf{A} = \begin{bmatrix} 0 & 1 \\ 3 & 2 \end{bmatrix}$$

6.3.7. Verify that

$$\mathbf{A} = \frac{\sqrt{2}}{2}\begin{bmatrix} 1 & 1 \\ -1 & 1 \end{bmatrix}$$

is unitary and triangularizes the matrix of Problem 6.3.6.

6.3.8. For the matrices in Problems 6.3.6 and 6.3.7, verify that

$$\mathbf{U}^H\mathbf{A}\mathbf{U} = \begin{bmatrix} -1 & -2 \\ 0 & 3 \end{bmatrix}$$

6.3.9. Do Example 6.3.2 using the eigenvalue $\lambda = 3$.

6.3.10. Diagonalize $\mathbf{A}$ by $\mathbf{S}^{-1}\mathbf{A}\mathbf{S} = \Lambda$, where the columns of $\mathbf{S}$ are the eigenvectors of $\mathbf{A}$.

6.3.11. Use Schur's theorem to triangularize the matrices

$(a)\ \begin{bmatrix} 0 & 1 \\ -4 & 4 \end{bmatrix} \quad (b)\ \begin{bmatrix} 1 & 1 \\ 1 & 1 \end{bmatrix} \quad (c)\ \begin{bmatrix} 0 & 1 \\ -1 & 0 \end{bmatrix} \quad (d)\ \begin{bmatrix} 0 & 1 \\ 1 & 0 \end{bmatrix}$

PART 2

6.3.12. Demonstrate that there cannot exist a unitary matrix $\mathbf{U}$ such that $\mathbf{U}^H\mathbf{A}\mathbf{U}$ is diagonal for the matrix

$$\mathbf{A} = \begin{bmatrix} 0 & 1 \\ 3 & 2 \end{bmatrix}$$

(*Hint:* Show that there is no orthogonal set of eigenvectors of $\mathbf{A}$.)

6.3.13. Suppose $\mathbf{Q}$ is orthogonal and $\mathbf{A}$ is symmetric. Show that $\mathbf{Q}^T\mathbf{A}\mathbf{Q} = \mathbf{T}$, where $\mathbf{T}$ is upper triangular, implies $\mathbf{T}$ is diagonal.

6.3.14. Triangularize

$$\mathbf{A} = \begin{bmatrix} -1 & * & * & * \\ 0 & 1 & * & * \\ 0 & 0 & 1 & 1 \\ 0 & 0 & 1 & 1 \end{bmatrix}$$

by using the eigenvalue $\lambda = 0$. Do the same using $\lambda = 2$. These are the eigenvalues of the lower-right-hand 2×2 submatrix.

PART 3

6.3.15. Suppose $\mathbf{A}$ has k linearly independent eigenvectors corresponding to the eigenvalues λ_0. Show how to construct a unitary matrix $\mathbf{U}$ such that

$$\mathbf{U}^{\mathrm{H}}\mathbf{A}\mathbf{U} = \begin{bmatrix} \lambda_0\mathbf{I} & \mathbf{O} \\ \mathbf{O} & \mathbf{T} \end{bmatrix}$$

where $\mathbf{T}$ is upper triangular. This accomplishes in one step what would require k steps using Schur's theorem.

6.4 HERMITIAN MATRICES

Real symmetric matrices form the most important class of matrices with applications to the physical sciences. Natural generalizations of these matrices, consistent[1] with the hermitian inner product, are those satisfying the relationship $\mathbf{A}^{\mathrm{H}} = \mathbf{A}$. These matrices are called *hermitian,* and it is obvious that every real symmetric matrix is hermitian. The diagonal of every hermitian matrix must be real since $\bar{a}_{ii} = a_{ii}$ is required if $\mathbf{A}^{\mathrm{H}} = \mathbf{A}$. $\mathbf{A}$ is called *skew-hermitian* if $\mathbf{A}^{\mathrm{H}} = -\mathbf{A}$. The diagonal entries of a skew-hermitian matrix must be purely imaginary since $\bar{a}_{ii} = -a_{ii}$ implies $\mathrm{Re}(a_{ii}) = 0$.

Example 6.4.1. Consider the matrices

$$(a)\begin{bmatrix} 2 & i \\ i & -1 \end{bmatrix} \quad (b)\begin{bmatrix} 2 & i \\ -i & -1 \end{bmatrix} \quad (c)\begin{bmatrix} 2 & 1 \\ 1 & -1 \end{bmatrix} \quad (d)\begin{bmatrix} 0 & i \\ i & 0 \end{bmatrix}$$

The first is symmetric but not hermitian. The second is hermitian but not symmetric, and the third is hermitian and symmetric. The last is clearly skew-hermitian and symmetric.

Example 6.4.2. If $\mathbf{A}$ is skew-hermitian, show that $i\mathbf{A}$ is hermitian.

Solution. It follows from $(i\mathbf{A})^{\mathrm{H}} = -i\mathbf{A}^{\mathrm{H}}$ and $\mathbf{A}^{\mathrm{H}} = -\mathbf{A}$ that $(i\mathbf{A})^{\mathrm{H}} = i\mathbf{A}$. Since the diagonal entries of a hermitian matrix are real, this result is another proof that the diagonal entries of a skew-hermitian matrix are pure imaginary.

The seemingly innocuous hypothesis $\mathbf{A}^{\mathrm{H}} = \mathbf{A}$ yields a wealth of conclusions. First, all the eigenvalues of a hermitian matrix are real. This is remarkable, particularly in view of the difficulty of finding the characteristic equation of $\mathbf{A}$. Incidentally, even knowing the characteristic equation does not immediately make evident whether or not the eigenvalues of $\mathbf{A}$ are real! Second, and perhaps more important, hermitian matrices are simple. Since real symmetric matrices are hermitian, this proves that real symmetric matrices are also simple.

---

[1] In this sense, $\langle \mathbf{Ax},\mathbf{y}\rangle = \langle \mathbf{x},\mathbf{Ay}\rangle$.

Theorem 6.4.1. *If* $\mathbf{A}$ *is hermitian, its eigenvalues are real and there exists a unitary matrix* $\mathbf{U}$ *such that* $\mathbf{U}^{\mathrm{H}}\mathbf{A}\mathbf{U} = \Lambda$.

Proof. By Schur's theorem, there exists a unitary matrix $\mathbf{U}$ such that $\mathbf{U}^{\mathrm{H}}\mathbf{A}\mathbf{U} = \mathbf{T}$, where $\mathbf{T}$ is upper triangular. Because $\mathbf{A}$ is hermitian, so is $\mathbf{T}$. But $\mathbf{T}^{\mathrm{H}} = \mathbf{T}$ for triangular matrices implies that $\mathbf{T}$ is diagonal and real. ∎

Corollary 1. *If* $\mathbf{A}$ *is hermitian, it is simple.*

Proof. This follows from the definition of simple matrices and Theorem 6.4.1. ∎

Corollary 2. *If* $\mathbf{A}$ *is hermitian, then there exists an orthonormal set of eigenvectors spanning* $\mathscr{C}^n$.

Proof. The columns of $\mathbf{U}$ form the orthonormal basis for $\mathscr{C}^n$. ∎

Corollary 3. *If* $\mathbf{A}$ *is real symmetric, then there exists a real orthonormal set of eigenvectors spanning* $\mathscr{R}^n$.

Proof. Because the eigenvalues of a hermitian matrix are real and a real symmetric matrix is hermitian, the determination of the eigenvectors of $\mathbf{A}$ involves solving the real homogeneous system $(\mathbf{A} - \lambda\mathbf{I})\mathbf{x} = \mathbf{0}$. Hence, in the proof of Schur's theorem, all the computations may be restricted to the set of real n-tuples. ∎

Corollary 3 asserts that a real symmetric matrix $\mathbf{A}$ has a set of orthonormal eigenvectors that spans $\mathscr{R}^n$. It does not imply that *every* set of linearly independent eigenvectors of $\mathbf{A}$ is orthogonal. In some cases, however, the eigenvectors of $\mathbf{A}$ are automatically orthogonal.

Theorem 6.4.2. *If* $\mathbf{A}$ *is hermitian with eigenpairs* $(\lambda,\mathbf{u})$ *and* $(\mu,\mathbf{v})$*, and* $\lambda \neq \mu$*, then* $\mathbf{u}$ *and* $\mathbf{v}$ *are orthogonal.*

Proof. The proof is easy and very instructive. Because λ is real (Theorem 6.4.1), $(\mathbf{A}\mathbf{u})^{\mathrm{H}}\mathbf{v} = (\lambda\mathbf{u})^{\mathrm{H}}\mathbf{v} = \lambda\mathbf{u}^{\mathrm{H}}\mathbf{v}$. Also,

$$(\mathbf{A}\mathbf{u})^{\mathrm{H}}\mathbf{v} = \mathbf{u}^{\mathrm{H}}(\mathbf{A}^{\mathrm{H}}\mathbf{v}) = \mathbf{u}^{\mathrm{H}}(\mathbf{A}\mathbf{v}) = \mu\mathbf{u}^{\mathrm{H}}\mathbf{v}.$$

Therefore, $\lambda\mathbf{u}^{\mathrm{H}}\mathbf{v} = \mu\mathbf{u}^{\mathrm{H}}\mathbf{v}$, and this implies $(\lambda - \mu)\mathbf{u}^{\mathrm{H}}\mathbf{v} = 0$. By hypothesis $\lambda \neq \mu$, it follows that $\mathbf{u}^{\mathrm{H}}\mathbf{v} = 0$. ∎

Corollary 1. *If* $\mathbf{A}$ *is hermitian with distinct eigenvalues, then the corresponding eigenvectors are mutually orthogonal.*

Proof. This corollary is obvious from Theorem 6.4.2. ∎

Example 6.4.3. Verify that the eigenvalues of

$$\mathbf{A} = \begin{bmatrix} 3 & -2 & 0 \\ -2 & 0 & 0 \\ 0 & 0 & -3 \end{bmatrix}$$

are real and that the eigenvectors are mutually orthogonal.

Solution. Since $c(\lambda) = (\lambda + 3)(\lambda + 1)(\lambda - 4)$, this confirms the reality of the eigenvalues of $\mathbf{A}$. A set of eigenpairs is listed:

$$\left(\lambda_1 = 4,\ \mathbf{u}_1 = \begin{bmatrix} 2 \\ -1 \\ 0 \end{bmatrix}\right), \qquad \left(\lambda_2 = -1,\ \mathbf{u}_2 = \begin{bmatrix} 1 \\ 2 \\ 0 \end{bmatrix}\right),$$

$$\left(\lambda_3 = -3,\ \mathbf{u}_3 = \begin{bmatrix} 0 \\ 0 \\ 1 \end{bmatrix}\right)$$

These eigenvectors are mutually orthogonal.

The work in the previous example was simplified because the eigenvalues of $\mathbf{A}$ are distinct and, hence, orthogonal by Theorem 6.4.2. If an eigenvalue is repeated, pairs of eigenvectors corresponding to this root may not be orthogonal, as the next example illustrates.

Example 6.4.4. Find a set of orthogonal eigenvectors

$$\mathbf{J}_4 = \begin{bmatrix} 1 & 1 & 1 & 1 \\ 1 & 1 & 1 & 1 \\ 1 & 1 & 1 & 1 \\ 1 & 1 & 1 & 1 \end{bmatrix}$$

Solution. This is a familiar example (see, for instance, Example 5.4.4). The characteristic polynomial is $c(\lambda) = (-\lambda)^3(4 - \lambda)$, and for $\lambda = 0$, a linearly independent set of eigenvectors is

$$\left\{ \mathbf{u}_1 = \begin{bmatrix} -1 \\ 1 \\ 0 \\ 0 \end{bmatrix},\ \mathbf{u}_2 = \begin{bmatrix} -1 \\ 0 \\ 1 \\ 0 \end{bmatrix},\ \mathbf{u}_3 = \begin{bmatrix} -1 \\ 0 \\ 0 \\ 1 \end{bmatrix} \right\} \tag{6.4.1}$$

For $\lambda = 4$, an eigenvector is $\mathbf{v} = [1 \quad 1 \quad 1 \quad 1]^{\mathrm{T}}$. Note that $\mathbf{v}^{\mathrm{H}}\mathbf{u}_i = 0$ for all i, as predicted by Theorem 6.4.2. However, the eigenvectors corresponding to $\lambda = 0$ are not mutually orthogonal. It is possible to use the Gram-Schmidt method to find an orthogonal basis for the eigenspace of $\lambda = 0$ or, as is easy to do in this example, to construct this basis by inspection. Take $\mathbf{w}_1 = \mathbf{u}_1$ and note that every eigenvector corresponding to $\lambda = 0$ must have the sum of entries zero.

$$\mathbf{w}_1 = \mathbf{u}_1 = \begin{bmatrix} -1 \\ 1 \\ 0 \\ 0 \end{bmatrix}, \qquad \mathbf{w}_2 = \begin{bmatrix} 1 \\ 1 \\ -2 \\ 0 \end{bmatrix}, \qquad \mathbf{w}_3 = \begin{bmatrix} 1 \\ 1 \\ 1 \\ -3 \end{bmatrix}$$

is an orthogonal basis. Note that $\mathbf{v}^{\mathrm{H}}\mathbf{w}_i = 0$.

Example 6.4.5. Find a hermitian matrix with eigenvalues 0,6,−6, and corresponding eigenvectors

$$\mathbf{u}_1 = \begin{bmatrix} i \\ 0 \\ 1 \end{bmatrix}, \qquad \mathbf{u}_2 = \begin{bmatrix} -i \\ i \\ 1 \end{bmatrix}, \qquad \mathbf{u}_3 = \begin{bmatrix} i \\ 2i \\ -1 \end{bmatrix}$$

Solution. The given eigenvectors are mutually orthogonal but not of unit norm. This is remedied by dividing each vector by its norm and defining $\mathbf{U}$ as the matrix with these unit eigenvectors:

$$\mathbf{U} = \begin{bmatrix} \frac{i}{\sqrt{2}} & \frac{-i}{\sqrt{3}} & \frac{i}{\sqrt{6}} \\ 0 & \frac{i}{\sqrt{3}} & \frac{2i}{\sqrt{6}} \\ \frac{1}{\sqrt{2}} & \frac{1}{\sqrt{3}} & \frac{-1}{\sqrt{6}} \end{bmatrix}$$

Then $\mathbf{A}$ is given by $\mathbf{A} = \mathbf{U}\Lambda\mathbf{U}^{\mathrm{H}}$. After some computation,

$$\mathbf{U}\Lambda\mathbf{U}^{\mathrm{H}} = \begin{bmatrix} \frac{i}{\sqrt{2}} & \frac{-i}{\sqrt{3}} & \frac{i}{\sqrt{6}} \\ 0 & \frac{i}{\sqrt{3}} & \frac{2i}{\sqrt{6}} \\ \frac{1}{\sqrt{2}} & \frac{1}{\sqrt{3}} & \frac{-1}{\sqrt{6}} \end{bmatrix} \begin{bmatrix} 0 & 0 & 0 \\ 0 & 6 & 0 \\ 0 & 0 & -6 \end{bmatrix} \begin{bmatrix} \frac{-i}{\sqrt{2}} & 0 & \frac{1}{\sqrt{2}} \\ \frac{i}{\sqrt{3}} & \frac{-i}{\sqrt{3}} & \frac{1}{\sqrt{3}} \\ \frac{-i}{\sqrt{6}} & \frac{-2i}{\sqrt{6}} & \frac{-1}{\sqrt{6}} \end{bmatrix}$$

$$= \begin{bmatrix} 1 & -4 & -i \\ -4 & -2 & 4i \\ i & -4i & 1 \end{bmatrix} = \mathbf{A}.$$

It is natural to ask whether there exists a hermitian matrix with a prescribed set of n orthogonal eigenvectors and their corresponding real eigenvalues. The answer is yes and the proof easy; it is left for Problem 6.4.23.

Example 6.4.6. Suppose $\mathbf{A}$ is $m \times n$ but otherwise arbitrary. Show that the eigenvalues of $\mathbf{A}^{\mathrm{H}}\mathbf{A}$ are nonnegative.

Solution. Let $(\sigma, \mathbf{u})$ be an eigenpair of $\mathbf{A}^{\mathrm{H}}\mathbf{A}$. Then $\mathbf{A}^{\mathrm{H}}\mathbf{A}\mathbf{u} = \sigma\mathbf{u}$ and, because $\mathbf{u}^{\mathrm{H}}\mathbf{A}^{\mathrm{H}}\mathbf{A}\mathbf{u} = \|\mathbf{A}\mathbf{u}\|^2$, it follows that

$$\|\mathbf{Au}^2\| = (\mathbf{Au})^{\mathrm{H}}(\mathbf{Au}) = \mathbf{u}^{\mathrm{H}}\mathbf{A}^{\mathrm{H}}\mathbf{Au} = \sigma\mathbf{u}^{\mathbf{H}}\mathbf{u} = \sigma\|\mathbf{u}\|^2$$

Therefore, $\sigma = \|\mathbf{Au}\|^2/\|\mathbf{u}\|^2 \geq 0$.

PROBLEMS

PART 1

6.4.1. Find the eigenvalues, eigenvectors, and spectral radius of

$$(a)\ \begin{bmatrix} 0 & i \\ -i & 0 \end{bmatrix} \qquad (b)\ \begin{bmatrix} i & -4 \\ 1 & -2i \end{bmatrix} \qquad (c)\ \begin{bmatrix} i & -2 \\ 2 & -2i \end{bmatrix}$$

6.4.2. Find a set of orthonormal eigenvectors of

$$(a)\ \mathbf{J}_3 = \begin{bmatrix} 1 & 1 & 1 \\ 1 & 1 & 1 \\ 1 & 1 & 1 \end{bmatrix} \qquad (b)\ \mathbf{K}_3 = \begin{bmatrix} 0 & 1 & 1 \\ 1 & 0 & 1 \\ 1 & 1 & 0 \end{bmatrix} \qquad (c)\ \mathbf{A} = \begin{bmatrix} 0 & -1 & 1 \\ -1 & 0 & -1 \\ 1 & -1 & 0 \end{bmatrix}$$

6.4.3. Show that det(**A**) is real if **A** is hermitian.

6.4.4. If **A** is hermitian and **u** is an eigenvector of **A** corresponding to the eigenvalue λ, show that $\mathbf{u}^{\mathrm{H}}\mathbf{A} = \lambda\mathbf{u}^{\mathrm{H}}$.

6.4.5. If **A** is hermitian with n zero eigenvalues, show that $\mathbf{A} = \mathbf{O}$.

6.4.6. If **A** and **B** are hermitian, what hypotheses, if any, are required to show that **AB** is hermitian?

6.4.7. Show that $\mathbf{TT}^{\mathrm{H}} = \mathbf{T}^{\mathrm{H}}\mathbf{T}$ implies **T** is diagonal if

$$\mathbf{T} = \begin{bmatrix} t_{11} & t_{12} \\ 0 & t_{22} \end{bmatrix} \quad \text{or} \quad \mathbf{T} = \begin{bmatrix} t_{11} & t_{12} & t_{13} \\ 0 & t_{22} & t_{23} \\ 0 & 0 & t_{33} \end{bmatrix}$$

6.4.8. Show that $\mathbf{A}^{\mathrm{H}}\mathbf{A}$ and $\mathbf{AA}^{\mathrm{H}}$ are hermitian for all $\mathbf{A}_{m \times n}$.

6.4.9. Show that $\mathbf{A}^m, \mathbf{A}^{-1}, \bar{\mathbf{A}}, \mathbf{A}^{\mathrm{T}}$, and $\mathbf{A}^{\mathrm{H}}$ are all hermitian if **A** is hermitian.

6.4.10. For what constants k is $k\mathbf{A}$ hermitian if **A** is hermitian?

6.4.11. For what constants k is $k\mathbf{A}$ skew-hermitian if **A** is skew-hermitian?

6.4.12. For what constants k is $k\mathbf{A}$ hermitian if **A** is skew-hermitian?

6.4.13. For what constants k is $k\mathbf{A}$ skew-hermitian if **A** is hermitian?

6.4.14. If $p(x)$ is a polynomial with real coefficients and **A** is hermitian, show that $p(\mathbf{A})$ is hermitian.

PART 2

6.4.15. Construct a real symmetric matrix with eigenvectors

$$\begin{bmatrix} 1 \\ -1 \\ -1 \end{bmatrix}, \quad \begin{bmatrix} 2 \\ 1 \\ 1 \end{bmatrix}, \quad \begin{bmatrix} 0 \\ -1 \\ 1 \end{bmatrix}$$

and corresponding eigenvalues:

(a) 0,1,2 $\quad (b)$ 1,1,2 $\quad (c)$ $\lambda_1 = \lambda_2 = \lambda_3$ $\quad (d)$ $\lambda, \lambda + 1, \lambda - 1$

6.4.16. If **A** is real symmetric and **B** is real skew-symmetric, show that $\mathbf{H} = \mathbf{A} + i\mathbf{B}$ is hermitian and $\mathbf{G} = i\mathbf{A} + \mathbf{B}$ is skew-hermitian.

6.4.17. If $\mathbf{H}$ is hermitian, show that there is a real symmetric matrix $\mathbf{A}$ and a real skew-symmetric matrix $\mathbf{B}$ such that $\mathbf{H} = \mathbf{A} + i\mathbf{B}$. (*Hint:* Use the result from Problem 6.4.16.)

6.4.18. Show that the eigenvalues of a skew-hermitian matrix are imaginary and that such matrices have a complete set of orthonormal eigenvectors.

6.4.19. Show that $\mathbf{U} = (i\mathbf{I} - \mathbf{H})(i\mathbf{I} + \mathbf{H})^{-1}$ is unitary if $\mathbf{H}$ is hermitian. ($\mathbf{U}$ is called the *Cayley transform* of $\mathbf{H}$.) Verify this conclusion for the hermitian matrix

$$\begin{bmatrix} 2 & i \\ -i & -1 \end{bmatrix}$$

6.4.20. Show that $\mathbf{H} = i(\mathbf{I} - \mathbf{U})(\mathbf{I} + \mathbf{U})^{-1}$ is hermitian if $\mathbf{U}$ is unitary and -1 is not an eigenvalue of $\mathbf{U}$. ($\mathbf{H}$ is sometimes called the *inverse Cayley transform* of $\mathbf{U}$.)

6.4.21. Substitute $\mathbf{H}$ as defined in Problem 6.4.20 in the formula for $\mathbf{U}$ given in Problem 6.4.19. Substitute $\mathbf{U}$ as defined in Problem 6.4.19 in the formula for $\mathbf{H}$ given in Problem 6.4.20. The result explains the term *inverse Cayley transform* of $\mathbf{U}$.

6.4.22. Show that every matrix $\mathbf{A}$ is the sum of a hermitian and skew-hermitian matrix, and these matrices are uniquely determined by $\mathbf{A}$. [*Hint:* Consider $(\mathbf{A} + \mathbf{A}^{\mathrm{H}})/2$ and $(\mathbf{A} - \mathbf{A}^{\mathrm{H}})/2$.]

PART 3

6.4.23. Suppose $\{\mathbf{u}_1, \mathbf{u}_2, \ldots, \mathbf{u}_n\}$ is an orthonormal set. Suppose the scalars $\lambda_1, \lambda_2, \ldots, \lambda_n$ are real. Show that there exists a matrix $\mathbf{H}$ with the property that $\mathbf{H}\mathbf{u}_i = \lambda_i\mathbf{u}$ for each i. Moreover, show that every $\mathbf{H}$ with the property that $\mathbf{H}\mathbf{u}_i = \lambda_i\mathbf{u}_i$ is hermitian. (*Hint:* Consider $\mathbf{U} = [\mathbf{u}_1 \ \ \mathbf{u}_2 \ \ \ldots \ \ \mathbf{u}_n]$ and $\Lambda = \mathrm{diag}[\lambda_1, \lambda_2, \ldots, \lambda_n]$.

6.4.24. Suppose $\mathbf{H}$ is hermitian. Let $(\lambda, \mathbf{u})$ be an eigenpair of $\mathbf{H}$. Verify $(\mathbf{H}\mathbf{u})^{\mathrm{H}}\mathbf{u} = \bar{\lambda}\|\mathbf{u}\|^2$ and $(\mathbf{H}\mathbf{u})^{\mathrm{H}}\mathbf{u} = \lambda\|\mathbf{u}\|^2$. Then show that the eigenvalues of $\mathbf{H}$ are real without resorting to Schur's theorem.

6.4.25. Show that $\mathrm{tr}(\mathbf{A}^{\mathrm{H}}\mathbf{A}) = 0$ implies that the eigenvalues of $\mathbf{A}^{\mathrm{H}}\mathbf{A}$ are zero.

6.4.26. Assume $\mathbf{A}$ is square and show that $\mathrm{tr}(\mathbf{A}^{\mathrm{H}}\mathbf{A}) = 0$ implies $\mathbf{A} = \mathbf{0}$. (*Hint:* Problem 6.4.25 and the fact that $\mathbf{A}^{\mathrm{H}}\mathbf{A}$ is hermitian.)

6.5 NORMAL MATRICES

For each simple matrix $\mathbf{A}$ there exists a nonsingular matrix $\mathbf{S}$ such that

$$\mathbf{S}^{-1}\mathbf{A}\mathbf{S} = \Lambda \tag{6.5.1}$$

where Λ is the diagonal matrix of eigenvalues of $\mathbf{A}$. The columns of $\mathbf{S}$ form a basis for $\mathscr{C}^n$ and are the eigenvectors of $\mathbf{A}$ corresponding to the ordering of the eigenvalues in Λ. If the set of eigenvectors of $\mathbf{A}$ can be selected so that they form an orthonormal basis for $\mathscr{C}^n$, then the invertible matrix $\mathbf{S}$ in Eq. 6.5.1 can be replaced by the unitary matrix $\mathbf{U}$, and Eq. 6.5.1 becomes

$$\mathbf{U}^{\mathrm{H}}\mathbf{A}\mathbf{U} = \Lambda \tag{6.5.2}$$

As we showed in Section 6.4, Eq. 6.5.2 is always possible if $\mathbf{A}$ is hermitian. It is also evident that this equation can hold for some $\mathbf{A}$ that are not hermitian, for instance, $\mathbf{A} = i\mathbf{I}$. ($\mathbf{U} = \mathbf{I}$ in this case.) A matrix that satisfies Eq. 6.5.2 is *normal*. Thus, a normal matrix is one for which there exists an orthonormal basis of eigenvectors for $\mathscr{C}^n$. Can normal matrices be characterized by properties that do not require an explicit knowledge of **U** or **Λ**? The answer is yes and surprisingly simple: **A** is normal if and only if $\mathbf{A}^H\mathbf{A} = \mathbf{A}\mathbf{A}^H$. This is the content of Theorem 6.5.1, and in preparation for its proof, consider the following example and lemma. (Often $\mathbf{A}^H\mathbf{A} = \mathbf{A}\mathbf{A}^H$ is taken as the definition of normal, and then one proves that a matrix is normal if and only if its eigenvectors are an orthonormal basis for $\mathscr{C}^n$.)

One last remark should be made. Although every unitary similarity is a similarity (in the sense of Section 5.8), not every similarity is a unitary similarity. Moreover, not all diagonalizable matrices are normal. Indeed, this is the point of Example 6.3.2.

Example 6.5.1. Assume that **A** is normal. Show that the following are also normal:

(*a*) $k\mathbf{A}$ (*b*) $\mathbf{A}^m$, m a positive integer (*c*) $\mathbf{A}^H$ (*d*) **U** unitary
(*e*) $\mathbf{U}^H\mathbf{A}\mathbf{U}$, if **U** is unitary (*f*) $p(\mathbf{A})$, where $p(x)$ is a polynomial in x.

Solution. Parts (*a*) through (*e*) offer no challenge and are left for the exercises. For Part (*f*), suppose $\mathbf{V}^H\mathbf{A}\mathbf{V} = \Lambda$ for some unitary matrix **V**. Then $\mathbf{V}^H p(\mathbf{A})\mathbf{V} = p(\mathbf{V}^H\mathbf{A}\mathbf{V}) = p(\Lambda)$, a diagonal matrix.

Write the general upper triangular matrix **T** and its hermitian transpose, $\mathbf{T}^H$, in the expanded forms

$$\mathbf{T} = \begin{bmatrix} t_{11} & t_{12} & \cdots & t_{1n} \\ 0 & t_{22} & \cdots & t_{2n} \\ \vdots & \vdots & & \vdots \\ 0 & 0 & \cdots & t_{nn} \end{bmatrix}, \qquad \mathbf{T}^H = \begin{bmatrix} \bar{t}_{11} & 0 & \cdots & 0 \\ \bar{t}_{12} & \bar{t}_{22} & \cdots & 0 \\ \vdots & \vdots & & \vdots \\ \bar{t}_{1n} & \bar{t}_{2n} & \cdots & \bar{t}_{nn} \end{bmatrix}$$

Lemma 6.1. *If* **T** *is upper triangular and commutes with* $\mathbf{T}^H$, *then* **T** *is diagonal.*

Proof. The proofs in the cases where **T** is 2 × 2 and 3 × 3 were presented as Problem 6.4.7. The proof for the $n \times n$ case can be effected by induction on n (see Problem 6.5.19) or by an extension of the argument for the 4 × 4 case, as is now shown.

By hypothesis, $\mathbf{T}^H\mathbf{T} = \mathbf{T}\mathbf{T}^H$:

$$\mathbf{T}^H\mathbf{T} = \begin{bmatrix} \bar{t}_{11} & 0 & 0 & 0 \\ \bar{t}_{12} & \bar{t}_{22} & 0 & 0 \\ \bar{t}_{13} & \bar{t}_{23} & \bar{t}_{33} & 0 \\ \bar{t}_{14} & \bar{t}_{24} & \bar{t}_{34} & \bar{t}_{44} \end{bmatrix} \begin{bmatrix} t_{11} & t_{12} & t_{13} & t_{14} \\ 0 & t_{22} & t_{23} & t_{24} \\ 0 & 0 & t_{33} & t_{34} \\ 0 & 0 & \cdots & t_{44} \end{bmatrix}$$

$$\mathbf{T}\mathbf{T}^H = \begin{bmatrix} t_{11} & t_{12} & t_{13} & t_{14} \\ 0 & t_{22} & t_{23} & t_{24} \\ 0 & 0 & t_{33} & t_{34} \\ 0 & 0 & \cdots & t_{44} \end{bmatrix} \begin{bmatrix} \bar{t}_{11} & 0 & 0 & 0 \\ \bar{t}_{12} & \bar{t}_{22} & 0 & 0 \\ \bar{t}_{13} & \bar{t}_{23} & \bar{t}_{33} & 0 \\ \bar{t}_{14} & \bar{t}_{24} & \bar{t}_{34} & \bar{t}_{44} \end{bmatrix}$$

Corresponding diagonal entries of $\mathbf{T}^{\mathrm{H}}\mathbf{T}$ and $\mathbf{T}\mathbf{T}^{\mathrm{H}}$ are equal by hypothesis. For the first diagonal entries, this leads to the equation

$$|t_{11}|^2 = |t_{11}|^2 + |t_{12}|^2 + |t_{13}|^2 + |t_{14}|^2 \tag{6.5.3}$$

Hence, $0 = t_{12} = t_{13} = t_{14}$. The second diagonal entries lead to

$$|t_{12}|^2 + |t_{22}|^2 = |t_{22}|^2 + |t_{23}|^2 + |t_{24}|^2 \tag{6.5.4}$$

Using $t_{12} = 0$ in Eq. 6.5.4 leads to $0 = t_{23} = t_{24}$. Finally, by equating the third diagonal entry in both products, there follows

$$|t_{13}|^2 + |t_{23}|^2 + |t_{33}|^2 = |t_{33}|^2 + |t_{34}|^2 \tag{6.5.5}$$

The fact that $0 = t_{13} = t_{23}$ leads to $0 = t_{34}$. Thus, $\mathbf{T}$ is diagonal. ■

Theorem 6.5.1. $\mathbf{A}$ *is normal if and only if it commutes with* $\mathbf{A}^{\mathrm{H}}$, *that is,*

$$\mathbf{A}^{\mathrm{H}}\mathbf{A} = \mathbf{A}\mathbf{A}^{\mathrm{H}} \tag{6.5.6}$$

Proof. Suppose $\mathbf{A}$ is normal. Then there exists a unitary matrix $\mathbf{U}$ such that $\mathbf{U}^{\mathrm{H}}\mathbf{A}\mathbf{U} = \Lambda$, from which $\mathbf{U}^{\mathrm{H}}\mathbf{A}^{\mathrm{H}}\mathbf{U} = \Lambda^{\mathrm{H}}$ follows. Then,

$$(\mathbf{U}^{\mathrm{H}}\mathbf{A}^{\mathrm{H}}\mathbf{U})(\mathbf{U}^{\mathrm{H}}\mathbf{A}\mathbf{U}) = \mathbf{U}^{\mathrm{H}}\mathbf{A}^{\mathrm{H}}\mathbf{A}\mathbf{U} = \Lambda^{\mathrm{H}}\Lambda$$

and

$$(\mathbf{U}^{\mathrm{H}}\mathbf{A}\mathbf{U})(\mathbf{U}^{\mathrm{H}}\mathbf{A}^{\mathrm{H}}\mathbf{U}) = \mathbf{U}^{\mathrm{H}}\mathbf{A}\mathbf{A}^{\mathrm{H}}\mathbf{U} = \Lambda\Lambda^{\mathrm{H}}$$

However, diagonal matrices commute, so from $\Lambda\Lambda^{\mathrm{H}} = \Lambda^{\mathrm{H}}\Lambda$ it follows that $\mathbf{A}^{\mathrm{H}}\mathbf{A} = \mathbf{A}\mathbf{A}^{\mathrm{H}}$.

Now for the converse. Suppose $\mathbf{A}\mathbf{A}^{\mathrm{H}} = \mathbf{A}^{\mathrm{H}}\mathbf{A}$. By Schur's theorem, there exists a unitary matrix $\mathbf{U}$ such that $\mathbf{U}^{\mathrm{H}}\mathbf{A}\mathbf{U} = \mathbf{T}$, $\mathbf{T}$ upper triangular. Then by taking hermitian transposes, $\mathbf{U}^{\mathrm{H}}\mathbf{A}^{\mathrm{H}}\mathbf{U} = \mathbf{T}^{\mathrm{H}}$. Hence,

$$(\mathbf{U}^{\mathrm{H}}\mathbf{A}^{\mathrm{H}}\mathbf{U})(\mathbf{U}^{\mathrm{H}}\mathbf{A}\mathbf{U}) = \mathbf{U}^{\mathrm{H}}\mathbf{A}^{\mathrm{H}}\mathbf{A}\mathbf{U} = \mathbf{T}^{\mathrm{H}}\mathbf{T}$$

and

$$(\mathbf{U}^{\mathrm{H}}\mathbf{A}\mathbf{U})(\mathbf{U}^{\mathrm{H}}\mathbf{A}^{\mathrm{H}}\mathbf{U}) = \mathbf{U}^{\mathrm{H}}\mathbf{A}\mathbf{A}^{\mathrm{H}}\mathbf{U} = \mathbf{T}\mathbf{T}^{\mathrm{H}}$$

Since $\mathbf{A}^{\mathrm{H}}\mathbf{A} = \mathbf{A}\mathbf{A}^{\mathrm{H}}$, it follows that $\mathbf{T}^{\mathrm{H}}\mathbf{T} = \mathbf{T}\mathbf{T}^{\mathrm{H}}$. By Lemma 6.1, $\mathbf{T}$ is diagonal. So $\mathbf{A}$ is normal. ■

Equation 6.5.6 is sometimes used to define normal matrices. Then Theorem 6.5.1 shows that normal matrices are unitarily diagonalizable.

Example 6.5.2. Show that

$$\mathbf{A} = \begin{bmatrix} 1 & 2 & 0 \\ 0 & 1 & 2 \\ 2 & 0 & 1 \end{bmatrix}$$

is normal without finding an orthogonal set of eigenvectors.

Solution. The use of Theorem 6.5.1 makes this otherwise tedious problem trivial, for it is easy to verify

$$\mathbf{AA}^{\mathrm{H}} = \mathbf{A}^{\mathrm{H}}\mathbf{A} = \begin{bmatrix} 3 & 2 & 2 \\ 2 & 4 & 2 \\ 2 & 2 & 5 \end{bmatrix} \tag{6.5.7}$$

In Problem 6.5.1 the reader is invited to find the orthonormal set of eigenvectors of **A**.

Example 6.5.3. Theorem 6.5.1 implies that all hermitian, skew-hermitian, and unitary matrices are normal.

Example 6.5.4. Theorem 6.5.1 also implies that real symmetric, real skew-symmetric, and orthogonal matrices are normal.

Example 6.5.5. Show by example that some complex symmetric matrices are defective, some normal, and some simple but not normal.

Solution. Complex symmetric matrices are neither real symmetric nor hermitian and therefore do not fit in any class previously shown to be normal. Consider these examples:

$$\mathbf{A}_1 = \begin{bmatrix} i & 1 \\ 1 & -i \end{bmatrix}, \qquad \mathbf{A}_2 = \begin{bmatrix} 1 & i \\ i & 1 \end{bmatrix}, \qquad \mathbf{A}_3 = \begin{bmatrix} 6 & 2i \\ 2i & 1 \end{bmatrix}$$

All are symmetric, and none real, but $\mathbf{A}_1$ is defective, $\mathbf{A}_2$ is normal, and $\mathbf{A}_3$ is simple but not normal. The explanations are easy. The eigenvalues of $\mathbf{A}_1$ are both zero but $\operatorname{rank}(\mathbf{A}_1) = 1$, so $\mathbf{A}_1$ is defective. On the other hand, $\mathbf{A}_2^{\mathrm{H}}\mathbf{A}_2 = \mathbf{A}_2\mathbf{A}_2^{\mathrm{H}}$. In fact, the eigenpairs of $\mathbf{A}_2$ are

$$\left(\lambda_i = 1 + i,\ \mathbf{u}_1 = \begin{bmatrix} 1 \\ 1 \end{bmatrix}\right); \qquad \left(\lambda_2 = 1 - i,\ \mathbf{u}_2 = \begin{bmatrix} 1 \\ -1 \end{bmatrix}\right)$$

and the eigenvectors are orthogonal. Finally, the eigenpairs of $\mathbf{A}_3$ are

$$\left(\lambda_1 = 5,\ \mathbf{u}_1 = \begin{bmatrix} 2i \\ -1 \end{bmatrix}\right); \qquad \left(\lambda_2 = 2,\ \mathbf{u}_2 = \begin{bmatrix} 1 \\ 2i \end{bmatrix}\right)$$

Since these eigenvectors correspond to distinct eigenvalues but are not orthogonal, $\mathbf{A}_3$ is not normal. However, since $\mathbf{A}_3$ has a complete set of eigenvectors, it is simple.

Example 6.5.6. Suppose $\mathbf{C} = \mathbf{A} + i\mathbf{B}$ is a symmetric matrix, and **A** and **B** are real matrices. Show that **C** is normal if and only if $\mathbf{AB} = \mathbf{BA}$. (See also Corollary 2 of Theorem 6.6.2.)

Solution. Since **C** is symmetric, so are **A** and **B**. Now we compute

$$\begin{aligned} \mathbf{C}^{\mathrm{H}}\mathbf{C} &= (\mathbf{A} + i\mathbf{B})^{\mathrm{H}}(\mathbf{A} + i\mathbf{B}) = \mathbf{A}^2 - \mathbf{B}^2 - i\mathbf{BA} + i\mathbf{AB} \\ \mathbf{CC}^{\mathrm{H}} &= (\mathbf{A} + i\mathbf{B})(\mathbf{A} + i\mathbf{B})^{\mathrm{H}} = \mathbf{A}^2 - \mathbf{B}^2 + i\mathbf{BA} - i\mathbf{AB} \end{aligned}$$

Thus, $\mathbf{C}^{\mathrm{H}}\mathbf{C} - \mathbf{CC}^{\mathrm{H}} = -2i(\mathbf{BA} - \mathbf{AB}) = \mathbf{O}$ if and only if $\mathbf{AB} = \mathbf{BA}$.

PROBLEMS

PART 1

6.5.1. Find $\mathbf{U}$ so that $\mathbf{U}^{\mathrm{H}}\mathbf{AU}$ is diagonal for the matrix of Example 6.5.2.

6.5.2. Verify that the matrix of Example 6.5.2 is normal by confirming Eq. 6.5.7.

6.5.3. Apply Theorem 6.5.1 to verify each part of Example 6.5.3.

6.5.4. Show that $\mathbf{A}_1$, given in Example 6.5.5, is defective.

6.5.5. Verify that $\lambda_1 = 1+i,\ \lambda_2 = -1+i$ are the eigenvalues of $\mathbf{A}_2$, given in Example 6.5.5, and that $\mathbf{A}_2$ is normal.

6.5.6. Verify that $\lambda_1 = 5,\ \lambda_2 = 2$ are the eigenvalues of $\mathbf{A}_3$ in Example 6.5.5. Explain in detail why is $\mathbf{A}_3$ not hermitian. Why is $\mathbf{A}_3$ not normal?

6.5.7. If $\mathbf{A}$ is symmetric, show that $\mathbf{A}^{\mathrm{H}}\mathbf{A} = \bar{\mathbf{A}}\mathbf{A}$ and $\mathbf{A}\mathbf{A}^{\mathrm{H}} = \mathbf{A}\bar{\mathbf{A}}$. Does it follow that $\mathbf{A}\bar{\mathbf{A}} = \bar{\mathbf{A}}\mathbf{A}$? Explain. (Consider $\mathbf{A}_1$ of Example 6.5.5.)

PART 2

6.5.8. Assume that $\mathbf{A}$ is normal. Show that $k\mathbf{A}$, $\bar{\mathbf{A}}$, and $\mathbf{A}^n$ are also normal.

6.5.9. Show that $\mathbf{U}^{\mathrm{H}}\mathbf{AU}$ is normal if $\mathbf{U}$ is unitary and $\mathbf{A}$ is normal.

6.5.10. Assume that $\mathbf{A}$ is normal and $\mathbf{A}^{-1}$ exists. Show that $\mathbf{A}^k$ is normal for all integers k. (Define $\mathbf{A}^0 = \mathbf{I}$.)

6.5.11. Show that $\mathbf{A}$ is normal if and only if $\mathbf{A}^{\mathrm{H}}$ is normal.

6.5.12. Show that unitary matrices are normal.

6.5.13. Show that all circulants are normal by using the result in Problem 6.5.12. (*Hint:* Refer to Section 5.8 and show that $\mathbf{C}_n$ is normal.)

6.5.14. Why are $\mathbf{A}^{\mathrm{H}}\mathbf{A}$ and $\mathbf{A}\mathbf{A}^{\mathrm{H}}$ normal for every square $\mathbf{A}$?

6.5.15. Under what circumstances is the rank one matrix $\mathbf{u}\mathbf{v}^{\mathrm{H}}$ normal?

6.5.16. Suppose $\mathbf{A}$ is a real scalar matrix and $\mathbf{B}$ is real and symmetric. Explain why $\mathbf{C} = \mathbf{A} + i\mathbf{B}$ is normal.

6.5.17. Suppose $\mathbf{A}$ is real and symmetric. Show that (*a*) $\mathbf{A} + i\mathbf{A}^{-1}$ and (*b*) $p(\mathbf{A}) + iq(\mathbf{A})$ are normal, where p and q are polynomials.

PART 3

6.5.18. If $\mathbf{A}$ is normal, show that $c(\mathbf{A}) = \mathbf{O}$, where $c(\lambda)$ is the characteristic equation of $\mathbf{A}$.

6.5.19. If $\mathbf{T}^{\mathrm{H}}\mathbf{T} = \mathbf{T}\mathbf{T}^{\mathrm{H}}$ implies that $\mathbf{T}$ is diagonal for every upper triangular matrix of size n, show that the same conclusion is true for every upper triangular matrix of size $n+1$.

6.5.20. Show that the Vandermonde matrices, $\mathbf{V}_n(\omega)/n$, are normal. (See Eq. 5.9.9 and Problem 5.9.14.)

6.6 SOME CHARACTERIZATIONS OF NORMAL MATRICES

Recall what is known about the problem of diagonalizing $\mathbf{A}$ by transformations $\mathbf{S}^{-1}\mathbf{AS}$. First of all, there are some matrices that cannot be diagonalized by any such $\mathbf{S}$. These are the defective matrices. Next, $\mathbf{A}$ is diagonalizable if and only if $\mathbf{A}$ has n linearly independent eigenvectors; these are the simple matrices. All normal matrices are diagonalizable by special $\mathbf{S}$, namely, unitary matrices $\mathbf{U}$. In this case, $\mathbf{S}^{-1} = \mathbf{U}^{\mathrm{H}}$. There are some matrices that are simple but not normal. So if the class of simple matrices is denoted by $\mathcal{S}$ and the class of normal matrices by $\mathcal{U}$, we have $\mathcal{U} \subset \mathcal{S}$. The class $\mathcal{U}$ comprises a large collection of important special matrices, among which are the hermitian and unitary matrices as well as polynomials in these matrices. (A skew-hermitian matrix is a multiple of a hermitian matrix and is therefore a polynomial in a hermitian matrix.) The matrix

$$\mathbf{A} = \begin{bmatrix} 1 & 2 & 0 \\ 0 & 1 & 2 \\ 2 & 0 & 1 \end{bmatrix} \tag{6.6.1}$$

is not an obvious representative of any of the above sets but is normal. (It is, in fact, a polynomial in an orthogonal matrix; see Problem 6.6.7.) In fact, all normal matrices are composed of combinations of hermitian and skew-hermitian matrices in the sense described by Theorem 6.6.2.

The first theorem that follows shows that normal matrices that are not hermitian must have at least one complex eigenvalue, for those with real eigenvalues are hermitian.

Theorem 6.6.1. *If* $\mathbf{A}$ *is normal with real eigenvalues, then* $\mathbf{A}$ *is hermitian.*

Proof. Since $\mathbf{U}^{\mathrm{H}}\mathbf{A}\mathbf{U} = \Lambda$ for some unitary $\mathbf{U}$ and real diagonal Λ, then

$$(\mathbf{U}^{\mathrm{H}}\mathbf{A}\mathbf{U})^{\mathrm{H}} = \mathbf{U}^{\mathrm{H}}\mathbf{A}^{\mathrm{H}}\mathbf{U} = \Lambda^{\mathbf{H}} = \Lambda$$

Thus, $\mathbf{U}^{\mathrm{H}}\mathbf{A}\mathbf{U} = \mathbf{U}^{\mathrm{H}}\mathbf{A}^{\mathrm{H}}\mathbf{U}$ and, hence, $\mathbf{A} = \mathbf{A}^{\mathrm{H}}$. ■

Corollary 1. *If* $\mathbf{A}$ *is normal with purely imaginary eigenvalues, then* $\mathbf{A}$ *is skew-hermitian.*

Proof. If $\mathbf{A}$ has imaginary eigenvalues, $i\mathbf{A}$ has real eigenvalues and is normal because it is a scalar times a normal matrix. Hence, $i\mathbf{A}$ is hermitian and, therefore, $\mathbf{A} = -i(i\mathbf{A})$ is skew-hermitian. ■

Corollary 2. *If* $\mathbf{A}$ *is real, normal, and not symmetric, it must have at least two nonreal eigenvalues, and all its complex eigenvalues come in complex conjugate pairs.*

Proof. The eigenvalues of $\mathbf{A}$ cannot all be real because if they were, $\mathbf{A}$ would be hermitian and, hence, symmetric by Theorem 6.6.1. This contradicts the hypothesis. Therefore, $\mathbf{A}$ has at least one nonreal eigenvalue. But since the characteristic equation of $\mathbf{A}$ has only real coefficients, its roots must come in complex conjugate pairs. ■

Theorem 6.6.2. $\mathbf{A}$ *is normal if and only if there exist hermitian matrices* $\mathbf{H}_1$ *and* $\mathbf{H}_2$ *such that* $\mathbf{A} = \mathbf{H}_1 + i\mathbf{H}_2$, *and* $\mathbf{H}_1\mathbf{H}_2 = \mathbf{H}_2\mathbf{H}_1$.

Proof. Assume $\mathbf{H}_1$ and $\mathbf{H}_2$ are hermitian and commute. Then $\mathbf{A} = \mathbf{H}_1 + i\mathbf{H}_2$ implies that

$$\mathbf{A}^{\mathrm{H}} = (\mathbf{H}_1 + i\mathbf{H}_2)^{\mathrm{H}} = \mathbf{H}_1^{\mathrm{H}} - i\mathbf{H}_2^{\mathrm{H}} = \mathbf{H}_1 - i\mathbf{H}_2$$

Thus,

$$\mathbf{A}^{\mathrm{H}}\mathbf{A} = (\mathbf{H}_1 - i\mathbf{H}_2)(\mathbf{H}_1 + i\mathbf{H}_2) = \mathbf{H}_1^2 + \mathbf{H}_2^2 + i\mathbf{H}_1\mathbf{H}_2 - i\mathbf{H}_2\mathbf{H}_1 = \mathbf{H}_1^2 + \mathbf{H}_2^2$$

By the same analysis, $\mathbf{A}\mathbf{A}^{\mathrm{H}} = \mathbf{H}_1^2 + \mathbf{H}_2^2$. Hence, $\mathbf{A}^{\mathrm{H}}\mathbf{A} = \mathbf{A}\mathbf{A}^{\mathrm{H}}$.

Conversely, assume $\mathbf{A}$ is normal. Then, $\mathbf{U}^{\mathrm{H}}\mathbf{A}\mathbf{U} = \Lambda$. Write $\Lambda = \Lambda_1 + i\Lambda_2$, where Λ_1 and Λ_2 are real. Then

$$\mathbf{A} = \mathbf{U}(\Lambda_1 + i\Lambda_2)\mathbf{U}^{\mathrm{H}} = \mathbf{U}\Lambda_1\mathbf{U}^{\mathrm{H}} + i\mathbf{U}\Lambda_2\mathbf{U}^{\mathrm{H}}$$

But $\mathbf{H}_1 = \mathbf{U}\Lambda_1\mathbf{U}^{\mathrm{H}}$ and $\mathbf{H}_2 = \mathbf{U}\Lambda_2\mathbf{U}^{\mathrm{H}}$ are easily seen to be hermitian. Finally, $\mathbf{H}_1\mathbf{H}_2 = \mathbf{U}\Lambda_1\Lambda_2\mathbf{U}^{\mathrm{H}} = \mathbf{U}\Lambda_2\Lambda_1\mathbf{U}^{\mathrm{H}} = \mathbf{H}_2\mathbf{H}_1$. ■

Corollary 1. $\mathbf{A}$ *is real and normal if and only if there exists a real symmetric matrix* $\mathbf{A}_S$ *and a real skew-symmetric matrix* $\mathbf{A}_A$ *such that*

$$\mathbf{A} = \mathbf{A}_S + \mathbf{A}_A \quad \text{and} \quad \mathbf{A}_S\mathbf{A}_A = \mathbf{A}_A\mathbf{A}_S \tag{6.6.2}$$

Proof. First assume that $\mathbf{A}$ is real and normal. From Theorem 6.6.2, $\mathbf{A} = \mathbf{H}_1 + i\mathbf{H}_2$ and $\mathbf{A}^{\mathrm{H}} = \mathbf{A}^{\mathrm{T}} = \mathbf{H}_1 - i\mathbf{H}_2$. Therefore, $\mathbf{A} + \mathbf{A}^{\mathrm{T}} = 2\mathbf{H}_1$ and $\mathbf{A} - \mathbf{A}^{\mathrm{T}} = 2i\mathbf{H}_2$. Clearly, $\mathbf{A}_S = 2\mathbf{H}_1$ is real and symmetric. Also, $\mathbf{A}_A = 2i\mathbf{H}_2$ is real and skew-symmetric, because $(2i\mathbf{H}_2)^{\mathrm{T}} = (\mathbf{A} - \mathbf{A}^{\mathrm{T}})^{\mathrm{T}} = -(\mathbf{A} - \mathbf{A}^{\mathrm{T}})$. Thus, $\mathbf{A}$ is the sum of real symmetric and real skew-symmetric matrices. By Theorem 6.6.2 and hypothesis, $\mathbf{H}_1\mathbf{H}_2 = \mathbf{H}_2\mathbf{H}_1$. Therefore, $\mathbf{A}_S = 2\mathbf{H}_1$ and $\mathbf{A}_A = 2i\mathbf{H}_2$ commute.

Now the converse. Assume that $\mathbf{A}_S$ and $\mathbf{A}_A$ are real matrices, satisfying $\mathbf{A}_S\mathbf{A}_A = \mathbf{A}_A\mathbf{A}_S$, with $\mathbf{A}_S$ symmetric and $\mathbf{A}_A$ skew-symmetric. Define $\mathbf{A} = \mathbf{A}_S + \mathbf{A}_A = \mathbf{A}_S + i(\mathbf{A}_A/i)$. Clearly, $\mathbf{A}$ is real. Now, since $\mathbf{A}_S$ is real symmetric, it is hermitian. Since $\mathbf{A}_A$ is skew-symmetric, $(\mathbf{A}_A/i)^{\mathrm{H}} = -\mathbf{A}_A^{\mathrm{T}}/i = \mathbf{A}_A/i$; thus, $\mathbf{A}_A/i$ is hermitian. By Theorem 6.6.2, $\mathbf{A} = \mathbf{A}_S + i(\mathbf{A}_A/i)$ is normal. ■

Corollary 2. *If* $\mathbf{C}$ *is symmetric, it is normal if and only if its real and imaginary parts commute.*

Proof. A proof was given in Example 6.5.6. As a corollary to Theorem 6.6.2, it follows by noting that $\mathbf{C} = \mathbf{A} + i\mathbf{B}$ and that $\mathbf{A} = \mathbf{H}_1$ and $\mathbf{B} = \mathbf{H}_2$ are real symmetric and therefore hermitian. ■

Example 6.6.1. Show that every real 2×2 normal matrix is either a symmetric matrix or a real multiple of an orthogonal matrix.

Solution. The argument uses Corollary 1 as follows: Suppose $\mathbf{A}$ is normal. Then $\mathbf{A} = \mathbf{A}_S + \mathbf{A}_A$ for some real symmetric $\mathbf{A}_S$ and real skew-symmetric

$\mathbf{A}_A$. The most general real symmetric and real skew-symmetric 2×2 matrices are

$$\mathbf{A}_S = \begin{bmatrix} a & b \\ b & c \end{bmatrix}, \qquad \mathbf{A}_A = \begin{bmatrix} 0 & d \\ -d & 0 \end{bmatrix} \tag{6.6.3}$$

If $d = 0$, then $\mathbf{A} = \mathbf{A}_S$ and, therefore, $\mathbf{A}$ is real symmetric. If $d \neq 0$, then $\mathbf{A}_S\mathbf{A}_A = \mathbf{A}_A\mathbf{A}_S$ implies $b = 0$ and $a = c$, because

$$\mathbf{A}_S\mathbf{A}_A = \begin{bmatrix} a & b \\ b & c \end{bmatrix}\begin{bmatrix} 0 & d \\ -d & 0 \end{bmatrix} = \begin{bmatrix} -bd & ad \\ -cd & bd \end{bmatrix}$$

$$\mathbf{A}_A\mathbf{A}_S = \begin{bmatrix} 0 & d \\ -d & 0 \end{bmatrix}\begin{bmatrix} a & b \\ b & c \end{bmatrix} = \begin{bmatrix} bd & cd \\ -ad & -bd \end{bmatrix}$$

Therefore,

$$\mathbf{A} = \begin{bmatrix} a & 0 \\ 0 & a \end{bmatrix} + \begin{bmatrix} 0 & d \\ -d & 0 \end{bmatrix} = \begin{bmatrix} a & d \\ -d & a \end{bmatrix}$$

and $\mathbf{A}$ is a multiple of an orthogonal matrix.

PROBLEMS

PART 1

For the next five problems, confirm that the given matrix is normal by verifying that $\mathbf{AA}^{\mathrm{H}} = \mathbf{A}^{\mathrm{H}}\mathbf{A}$. If $\mathbf{A}$ is real with real eigenvalues, find only real eigenvectors.

6.6.1. $\begin{bmatrix} 1 & 2 & 0 \\ 0 & 1 & 2 \\ 2 & 0 & 1 \end{bmatrix}$

6.6.2. $\begin{bmatrix} 1 & 1 & 1 \\ 1 & 1 & 1 \\ 1 & 1 & 1 \end{bmatrix}$

6.6.3. $\begin{bmatrix} 1 & -1 & 1 \\ 1 & 1 & -1 \\ -1 & 1 & 1 \end{bmatrix}$

6.6.4. $\begin{bmatrix} i & -i & 1 \\ 1 & i & -i \\ -i & 1 & i \end{bmatrix}$

6.6.5. $\begin{bmatrix} b \\ a \end{bmatrix}[b \quad a]$, $\quad$ a and b real

PART 2

6.6.6. Show that an idempotent matrix ($\mathbf{P}^2 = \mathbf{P}$) is normal if and only if $\mathbf{P}^{\mathrm{H}} = \mathbf{P}$. (*Hint:* Use Theorem 6.6.1.)

6.6.7. Show that the matrix $\mathbf{A}$ of Eq. 6.6.1 is a circulant. (See Section 5.9.) Use this fact to show that $\mathbf{A}$ is a polynomial in an orthogonal matrix and must therefore be normal.

6.7 MATRICES SATISFY THEIR OWN CHARACTERISTIC EQUATIONS

The theorem whose assertion is the title of this section is known as the *Cayley-Hamilton theorem*. This remarkable theorem has many proofs, perhaps the simplest of which uses the identity $\mathbf{AA}^+ = \det(\mathbf{A})\mathbf{I}$, where $\mathbf{A}^+$ is the adjoint of $\mathbf{A}$. (See Theorem 1.7.1.) Following is a sketch of this argument.

The expression $\mathbf{AA}^+ = \det(\mathbf{A})\mathbf{I}$ holds for all square matrices, so it certainly holds for $\mathbf{A} - \lambda\mathbf{I}$. That is,

$$(\mathbf{A} - \lambda\mathbf{I})(\mathbf{A} - \lambda\mathbf{I})^+ = \det(\mathbf{A} - \lambda\mathbf{I})\mathbf{I} = c(\lambda)\mathbf{I}$$

Now the entries of $(\mathbf{A} - \lambda\mathbf{I})^+$ are polynomials of degree $n - 1$ or less in λ. (See Problem 6.7.5.) Hence, $(\mathbf{A} - \lambda\mathbf{I})^+$ can be written as a polynomial in λ of degree $n - 1$ with matrix coefficients. Suppose, then, that

$$(\mathbf{A} - \lambda\mathbf{I})^+ = \mathbf{A}_0 + \mathbf{A}_1\lambda + \mathbf{A}_2\lambda^2 + \cdots + \mathbf{A}_{n-1}\lambda^{n-1} \tag{6.7.1}$$

defines the coefficient matrices $\mathbf{A}_0, \mathbf{A}_1, \ldots, \mathbf{A}_{n-1}$. Then

$$\begin{aligned} c(\lambda)\mathbf{I} &= (\mathbf{A} - \lambda\mathbf{I})(\mathbf{A} - \lambda\mathbf{I})^+ \\ &= (\mathbf{A} - \lambda\mathbf{I})(\mathbf{A}_0 + \mathbf{A}_1\lambda + \mathbf{A}_2\lambda^2 + \cdots + \mathbf{A}_{n-1}\lambda^{n-1}) \\ &= \mathbf{AA}_0 + (\mathbf{AA}_1 - \mathbf{A}_0)\lambda + \cdots + (\mathbf{AA}_{n-1} - \mathbf{A}_{n-2})\lambda^{n-1} - \mathbf{A}_{n-1}\lambda^n \end{aligned} \tag{6.7.2}$$

But $c(\lambda) = a_0 - a_1\lambda + \cdots + a_{n-1}(-\lambda)^{n-1} + (-\lambda)^n$ implies

$$c(\lambda)\mathbf{I} = a_0\mathbf{I} - a_1\mathbf{I}\lambda + \cdots + a_{n-1}\mathbf{I}(-\lambda)^{n-1} + \mathbf{I}(-\lambda)^n \tag{6.7.3}$$

Therefore, equating these two expressions of $c(\lambda)\mathbf{I}$, Eqs. 6.7.2 and 6.7.3,

$$\mathbf{AA}_0 + (\mathbf{AA}_1 - \mathbf{A}_0)\lambda + \cdots - \mathbf{A}_{n-1}\lambda^n = a_0\mathbf{I} - a_1\mathbf{I}\lambda + \cdots + a_{n-1}\mathbf{I}(-\lambda)^{n-1} + \mathbf{I}(-\lambda)^n$$

Since this is an identity in λ, the coefficients of λ^k on each side are the same. This leads to the following $n + 1$ identities:

(0)	$\mathbf{AA}_0 = a_0\mathbf{I}$	from the constant term
(1)	$\mathbf{AA}_1 - \mathbf{A}_0 = -a_1\mathbf{I}$	from the linear term
(2)	$\mathbf{AA}_2 - \mathbf{A}_1 = a_2\mathbf{I}$	from the coefficients of λ^2
	$\vdots$	$\vdots$
$(n-1)$	$\mathbf{AA}_{n-1} - \mathbf{A}_{n-2} = (-1)^{n-1}a_{n-1}\mathbf{I}$	from the coefficients of λ^{n-1}
(n)	$-\mathbf{A}_{n-1} = (-1)^n\mathbf{I}$	from the coefficients of λ^n

If the ith equation is multiplied by $\mathbf{A}^i (i \geq 1)$ and the resulting identities (0) through (n) are then added, there is cancellation of all the terms on the left, and this sum is $\mathbf{O}$. The right-hand side sums to

$$c(\mathbf{A}) = a_0\mathbf{I} - a_1\mathbf{A} + \cdots + a_{n-1}(-\mathbf{A})^{n-1} + (-\mathbf{A})^n$$

Hence, $c(\mathbf{A}) = \mathbf{O}$.

In keeping with the spirit of this chapter, we offer an alternative proof based on Schur's theorem. The following two examples are guides to the argument. In both cases the matrices are upper triangular.

Example 6.7.1. Show that $\mathbf{T}$ satisfies its own characteristic equation, $c(\lambda) = (2 - \lambda)(1 - \lambda)^2$, where

$$\mathbf{T} = \begin{bmatrix} 2 & 1 & 1 \\ 0 & 1 & 2 \\ 0 & 0 & 1 \end{bmatrix}$$

Solution. Evaluate $c(\mathbf{T}) = (2\mathbf{I} - \mathbf{T})(\mathbf{I} - \mathbf{T})^2$ by direct substitution:

$$c(\mathbf{T}) = \left[\begin{array}{c:cc} 0 & -1 & -1 \\ 0 & 1 & -2 \\ 0 & 0 & 1 \end{array}\right] \begin{bmatrix} -1 & -1 & -1 \\ 0 & 0 & -2 \\ 0 & 0 & 1 \end{bmatrix} \begin{bmatrix} -1 & -1 & -1 \\ 0 & 0 & -2 \\ 0 & 0 & 0 \end{bmatrix}$$

$$= \left[\begin{array}{cc:c} 0 & 0 & 1 \\ 0 & 0 & -4 \\ 0 & 0 & 1 \end{array}\right] \begin{bmatrix} -1 & -1 & -1 \\ 0 & 0 & -1 \\ 0 & 0 & 0 \end{bmatrix} = \begin{bmatrix} 0 & 0 & 0 \\ 0 & 0 & 0 \\ 0 & 0 & 0 \end{bmatrix}$$

Example 6.7.2. Show that $\mathbf{T}$ satisfies its own characteristic equation, $c(\lambda) = (2 - \lambda)(1 - \lambda)(-1 - \lambda)$, where

$$\mathbf{T} = \begin{bmatrix} 2 & -1 & 1 \\ 0 & -1 & 3 \\ 0 & 0 & 1 \end{bmatrix}$$

Solution. By direct substitution,

$$c(\mathbf{T}) = (2\mathbf{I} - \mathbf{T})(\mathbf{I} - \mathbf{T})(-\mathbf{I} - \mathbf{T})$$

$$= \left[\begin{array}{c:cc} 0 & -1 & -1 \\ 0 & -3 & -3 \\ 0 & 0 & -1 \end{array}\right] \begin{bmatrix} -3 & 1 & -1 \\ 0 & 0 & -3 \\ 0 & 0 & -2 \end{bmatrix} \begin{bmatrix} -1 & 1 & -1 \\ 0 & 2 & -3 \\ 0 & 0 & 0 \end{bmatrix}$$

$$= \left[\begin{array}{cc:c} 0 & 0 & 5 \\ 0 & 0 & 15 \\ 0 & 0 & 2 \end{array}\right] \begin{bmatrix} -1 & 1 & -1 \\ 0 & 2 & -2 \\ 0 & 0 & 0 \end{bmatrix} = \begin{bmatrix} 0 & 0 & 0 \\ 0 & 0 & 0 \\ 0 & 0 & 0 \end{bmatrix}$$

The important point to observe in each of these examples is the manner in which zero columns enter the premultipliers: after each multiplication, a new column of zeros appears in the leftmost factor. This is true in all cases and is at the heart of the proof that upper triangular matrices satisfy their own characteristic equations.

Lemma 6.2. *The product of a matrix whose first $k-1$ columns are zero and an upper triangular matrix with a zero in the kth diagonal entry is a matrix whose first k columns are zero.*

Proof. The proof is actually a simple consequence of matrix multiplication. If the premultiplier has $k-1$ columns of zeros, then the product has at least this many. That the product has, in fact, k or more columns of zeros is most easily seen by the following display:

$$\left[\begin{array}{cccc|cccc} 0 & 0 & \cdots & 0 & * & * & \cdots & * \\ 0 & 0 & \cdots & 0 & * & * & \cdots & * \\ \vdots & \vdots & & \vdots & \vdots & \vdots & & \vdots \\ 0 & 0 & \cdots & 0 & * & * & \cdots & * \\ \hline 0 & 0 & \cdots & 0 & * & * & \cdots & * \\ \vdots & \vdots & & \vdots & \vdots & \vdots & & \vdots \\ 0 & 0 & \cdots & 0 & * & * & \cdots & * \end{array}\right] \cdot \left[\begin{array}{cccc|cccc} a & * & \cdots & * & * & * & \cdots & * \\ 0 & b & \cdots & * & * & * & \cdots & * \\ \vdots & \vdots & & \vdots & \vdots & \vdots & & \vdots \\ 0 & 0 & \cdots & c & * & * & \cdots & * \\ \hline 0 & 0 & \cdots & 0 & 0 & * & \cdots & * \\ \vdots & \vdots & & \vdots & \vdots & \vdots & & \vdots \\ 0 & 0 & \cdots & 0 & 0 & 0 & \cdots & * \end{array}\right] \leftarrow \text{Row } k$$

Column $k-1$ ↑ Column k ↑

$$= \left[\begin{array}{cccc|cccc} 0 & 0 & \cdots & 0 & 0 & * & \cdots & * \\ 0 & 0 & \cdots & 0 & 0 & * & \cdots & * \\ \vdots & \vdots & & \vdots & \vdots & \vdots & & \vdots \\ 0 & 0 & \cdots & 0 & 0 & * & \cdots & * \\ \hline 0 & 0 & \cdots & 0 & 0 & * & \cdots & * \\ \vdots & \vdots & & \vdots & \vdots & \vdots & & \vdots \\ 0 & 0 & \cdots & 0 & 0 & 0 & \cdots & 0 \end{array}\right] \leftarrow \text{Row } k \quad \blacksquare$$

Column k ↑

This lemma and the two illustrative examples show how to proceed with the proof of the Cayley-Hamilton theorem for upper triangular matrices.

Lemma 6.3. *If* $\mathbf{T}$ *is upper triangular with characteristic equation* $c(\lambda)$, *then* $c(\mathbf{T}) = \mathbf{O}$.

Proof. Suppose the eigenvalues of $\mathbf{T}$ are $\lambda_1, \lambda_2, \ldots, \lambda_n$ and

$$\mathbf{T} = \begin{bmatrix} \lambda_1 & t_{12} & \cdots & t_{1n} \\ 0 & \lambda_2 & \cdots & t_{2n} \\ \vdots & \vdots & & \vdots \\ 0 & 0 & \cdots & \lambda_n \end{bmatrix}$$

Now consider $c(\mathbf{T}) = (\lambda_1\mathbf{I} - \mathbf{T})(\lambda_2\mathbf{I} - \mathbf{T})\ldots(\lambda_n\mathbf{I} - \mathbf{T})$. The first column of the leftmost matrix, $(\lambda_1\mathbf{I} - \mathbf{T})$, is a column of zeros. The second factor, $(\lambda_2\mathbf{I} - \mathbf{T})$, has a zero in the (2, 2) position. By Lemma 6.2, the product $(\lambda_1\mathbf{I}-\mathbf{T})(\lambda_2\mathbf{I}-\mathbf{T})$ has as its first two columns zeros. Proceed in this manner, column by column, until the last factor on the right, $(\lambda_n \mathbf{I} - \mathbf{T})$, clears the last column of the product to a column of zeros. ■

Theorem 6.7.1. *(Cayley-Hamilton). Suppose* $\mathbf{A}$ *has characteristic polynomial* $c(\lambda)$. *Then for* $\mathbf{A}$ *simple or defective,* $c(\mathbf{A}) = \mathbf{O}$.

Proof. The argument is a duplicate of the proof for simple matrices using Lemma 6.3 in place of $c(\mathbf{\Lambda}) = \mathbf{0}$. By Schur's theorem, $\mathbf{U}^H\mathbf{A}\mathbf{U} = \mathbf{T}$ and, hence, $\mathbf{U}^H c(\mathbf{A})\mathbf{U} = c(\mathbf{T})$. The eigenvalues of $\mathbf{A}$ are the eigenvalues of $\mathbf{T}$, and by Lemma 6.3, $c(\mathbf{T}) = \mathbf{O}$. Thus, $c(\mathbf{A}) = \mathbf{U}^H\mathbf{O}\mathbf{U} = \mathbf{O}$.

PROBLEMS

PART 1

6.7.1. Verify Lemmas 6.2 and 6.3 by performing the indicated multiplications from the left to the right:

$$\begin{bmatrix} 0 & 2 & -1 & -2 \\ 0 & 1 & 3 & 1 \\ 0 & 0 & -3 & 0 \\ 0 & 0 & 0 & 1 \end{bmatrix} \begin{bmatrix} 4 & 1 & -1 & 2 \\ 0 & 0 & -1 & 0 \\ 0 & 0 & 2 & 0 \\ 0 & 0 & 0 & 1 \end{bmatrix} \begin{bmatrix} 6 & 1 & -1 & 0 \\ 0 & 1 & 3 & 1 \\ 0 & 0 & 0 & 1 \\ 0 & 0 & 0 & -1 \end{bmatrix} \begin{bmatrix} 0 & 2 & 1 & 2 \\ 0 & 1 & 3 & 1 \\ 0 & 0 & 3 & 1 \\ 0 & 0 & 0 & 0 \end{bmatrix}$$

6.7.2. Verify the Cayley-Hamilton theorem for the following matrices:

$$(a)\ \begin{bmatrix} \cos\tau & \sin\tau \\ -\sin\tau & \cos\tau \end{bmatrix} \quad (b)\ \begin{bmatrix} 0 & 1 \\ 2 & 1 \end{bmatrix} \quad (c)\ \begin{bmatrix} 1 & 1 \\ 1 & 1 \end{bmatrix} \quad (d)\ \begin{bmatrix} 1 & 1 \\ 2 & 1 \end{bmatrix}$$

PART 2

6.7.3. Verify Lemma 6.2 for the product,

$$\begin{bmatrix} 0 & 1 \\ 0 & 1 \end{bmatrix} \begin{bmatrix} 1 & 1 \\ 0 & 0 \end{bmatrix}$$

Is Lemma 6.2 applicable if the order of the factors in this product is reversed? Is the product still $\mathbf{O}$?

6.7.4. Offer a proof of the theorem: *A matrix with only zero eigenvalues satisfies the equation* $\mathbf{A}^n = \mathbf{O}$. Does this imply $\mathbf{A} = \mathbf{O}$?

PART 3

6.7.5. Explain why $(\mathbf{A} - \lambda\mathbf{I})^+$ is a polynomial in λ with matrix coefficients. (*Hint:* First show that the entries of $(\mathbf{A} - \lambda\mathbf{I})^+$ are polynomials in λ by using the definition of cofactor. Next determine the degrees of these polynomial entries.)

MATLAB

6.7.6. Let $\mathbf{A}$ be a square matrix chosen at random. Use polyvalm (p,A) to verify the Cayley-Hamilton theorem. (*Hint:* Set p = poly(A).)

CHAPTER 7

UNITARY SIMILARITIES CONTINUED

7.1 INVARIANT SUBSPACES

A vector subspace $\mathcal{S}$ of $\mathcal{C}^n$ is an *invariant subspace* of $\mathbf{A}_{n\times n}$ if $\mathbf{x} \in \mathcal{S}$ implies $\mathbf{Ax} \in \mathcal{S}$. Put somewhat differently, $\mathcal{S}$ is an invariant subspace of $\mathbf{A}$ if $\mathcal{S}$ is "closed" with respect to the multiplication of members of $\mathcal{S}$ by $\mathbf{A}$. This idea can be expressed symbolically by the formalism $\mathbf{A}\mathcal{S} \subseteq \mathcal{S}$. The eigenspace $\mathcal{E}(\lambda_0)$ of $\mathbf{A}$ corresponding to the eigenvalue λ_0 is one example of an invariant subspace of $\mathbf{A}$ since if $\mathbf{x} \in \mathcal{E}(\lambda_0)$, then $\mathbf{Ax} = \lambda_0\mathbf{x}$ shows that $\mathbf{Ax} \in \mathcal{E}(\lambda_0)$. Clearly, $\mathcal{C}^n$ and $\{0_n\}$ are invariant subspaces of every $\mathbf{A}_n$.

Example 7.1.1. Let $\mathbf{x}$ be a fixed vector in $\mathcal{C}^n$ and $\mathbf{A}$ be any $n \times n$ matrix. Show that $\mathcal{S} = span\{\mathbf{x}, \mathbf{Ax}, \mathbf{A}^2\mathbf{x}, \ldots, \mathbf{A}^{n-1}\mathbf{x}\}$ is an invariant subspace of $\mathbf{A}$.

Solution. Suppose $\mathbf{y} \in \mathcal{S}$. Then there are weights $a_0, a_1, \ldots, a_{n-1}$ such that $\mathbf{y} = a_0\mathbf{x} + a_1\mathbf{Ax} + \cdots + a_{n-1}\mathbf{A}^{n-1}\mathbf{x}$. Hence, after multiplying through by $\mathbf{A}$,

$$\mathbf{Ay} = a_0\mathbf{Ax} + a_1\mathbf{A}^2\mathbf{x} + \cdots + a_{n-1}\mathbf{A}^n\mathbf{x} \tag{7.1.1}$$

Since the set $\mathcal{T} = \{\mathbf{x}, \mathbf{Ax}, \mathbf{A}^2\mathbf{x}, \ldots, \mathbf{A}^{n-1}\mathbf{x}, \mathbf{A}^n\mathbf{x}\}$ contains $n + 1$ n-tuples, it is a linearly dependent set. Thus, there is a dependency relationship

$$b_0\mathbf{x} + b_1\mathbf{Ax} + b_2\mathbf{A}^2\mathbf{x} + \cdots + b_n\mathbf{A}^n\mathbf{x} = 0 \tag{7.1.2}$$

in which not all the b_is are zero. Now b_n cannot be zero, for then Eq. 7.1.2 would imply that $\mathcal{S}$ is a linearly dependent set. So, from Eq. 7.1.2,

$$\mathbf{A}^n\mathbf{x} = -\left(\frac{b_0}{b_n}\right)\mathbf{x} - \left(\frac{b_1}{b_n}\right)\mathbf{Ax} - \cdots - \left(\frac{b_{n-1}}{b_n}\right)\mathbf{A}^{n-1}\mathbf{x} \tag{7.1.3}$$

Substituting this expression into Eq. 7.1.1 shows that $\mathbf{Ay} \in \mathcal{S}$.

Example 7.1.2. Show that $null(\mathbf{A})$ is an invariant subspace of $\mathbf{A}$.

Solution. Let $\mathcal{S} = null(\mathbf{A})$. By definition, if $\mathbf{x} \in null(\mathbf{A})$, then $\mathbf{Ax} = \mathbf{0}$. But $\mathbf{0}$ is a member of every vector space. Hence, $\mathbf{Ax} \in \mathcal{S}$.

Example 7.1.3. Show that $col(\mathbf{A})$ is an invariant subspace of $\mathbf{A}$.

Solution. Let $\mathcal{S} = col(\mathbf{A})$. Since $\mathbf{Ay} \in col(\mathbf{A})$ for every $\mathbf{y}$, $\mathbf{Ay} \in \mathcal{S}$ for those particular $\mathbf{y}$ already belonging to $col(\mathbf{A})$.

Although every eigenspace of $\mathbf{A}$ is an invariant subspace of $\mathbf{A}$, the converse is false; witness Examples 7.1.2 and 7.1.3. However, it is true that every nontrivial invariant subspace of $\mathbf{A}$ contains an eigenvector of $\mathbf{A}$. Indeed, this is the central result of this section.

Theorem 7.1.1. *If $\mathcal{S} \neq \{\mathbf{0}\}$ is an invariant subspace of $\mathbf{A}$, there exists an eigenvector of $\mathbf{A}$ belonging to $\mathcal{S}$.*

Proof. Let $\{\mathbf{y}_1,\mathbf{y}_2,\ldots,\mathbf{y}_r\}$ be a basis for $\mathcal{S}$. Consider the vectors $\mathbf{Ay}_1,\mathbf{Ay}_2,\ldots,\mathbf{Ay}_r$. Then, because $\mathcal{S}$ is an invariant subspace of $\mathbf{A}$, $\mathbf{Ay}_i$ belongs to $\mathcal{S}$ for each $i \leq r$. Thus, for each i there is a set of weights $\{g_{1i},g_{2i},\ldots,g_{ri}\}$ such that

$$\mathbf{Ay}_i = g_{1i}\mathbf{y}_1 + g_{2i}\mathbf{y}_2 + \cdots + g_{ri}\mathbf{y}_r, \tag{7.1.4}$$

Set $\mathbf{Y} = [\mathbf{y}_1 \ \ \mathbf{y}_2 \ \ \ldots \ \ \mathbf{y}_r]$ and $\mathbf{g}_i = [g_{1i} \ g_{2i} \ \ldots \ g_{ri}]^{\mathrm{T}}$. Then Eq. 7.1.4 may be written

$$\mathbf{Ay}_i = \mathbf{Yg}_i, \qquad \text{for } i = 1,2,\ldots,r \tag{7.1.5}$$

Set $\mathbf{G} = [\mathbf{g}_1 \ \ \mathbf{g}_2 \ \ \ldots \ \ \mathbf{g}_r]$. Then the r systems given in Eq. 7.1.5 have the matrix form

$$\mathbf{AY} = \mathbf{YG} \tag{7.1.6}$$

Now $\mathbf{G}$ is $r \times r$ and has an eigenpair, say $(\mu,\mathbf{g})$, so that $\mathbf{Gg} = \mu\mathbf{g}$. Therefore, by premultiplication of $\mathbf{Gg} = \mu\mathbf{g}$ by $\mathbf{Y}$,

$$\mathbf{YGg} = \mu\mathbf{Yg} \tag{7.1.7}$$

Hence, postmultiplying Eq. 7.1.6 by $\mathbf{g}$ and using Eq. 7.1.7, it follows that $\mathbf{A}(\mathbf{Yg}) = \mathbf{YGg} = \mu(\mathbf{Yg})$. Therefore, if $\mathbf{Yg} \neq \mathbf{0}, \mathbf{Yg} \in \mathcal{S}$ and is an eigenvector of $\mathbf{A}$. But $\mathbf{g} \neq \mathbf{0}$, and $\mathbf{Y}$ has linearly independent columns. Hence, $\mathbf{Yg} \neq \mathbf{0}$. ■

PROBLEMS

PART 1

7.1.1. Let

$$\mathbf{A} = \begin{bmatrix} 1 & -1 & 2 \\ 1 & -2 & 1 \\ 0 & 1 & -1 \end{bmatrix}, \qquad \mathbf{y}_1 = \begin{bmatrix} 2 \\ 1 \\ 0 \end{bmatrix}, \qquad \mathbf{y}_2 = \begin{bmatrix} 4 \\ 1 \\ 2 \end{bmatrix}$$

Define $\mathbf{Y} = [\mathbf{y}_1 \quad \mathbf{y}_2]$ and verify the steps in the proof of Theorem 7.1.1 as follows:

(*a*) Find $\mathbf{G}$ such that $\mathbf{AY} = \mathbf{YG}$.

(*b*) Find the eigenvectors of $\mathbf{G}$ and show by direct computation that $\mathbf{Yg}$ is an eigenvector of $\mathbf{A}$ if $\mathbf{g}$ is an eigenvector of $\mathbf{G}$.

7.1.2. If $\mathcal{S}$ is an invariant subspace of $\mathbf{A}$, is $\mathcal{S}$ an invariant subspace of $\mathbf{A}^2$? Of $\mathbf{A}^m$, for m a positive integer?

7.1.3. Repeat Problem 7.1.2 for $\alpha\mathbf{A}^k + \beta\mathbf{A}^m$, with α and β arbitrary scalars.

7.1.4. Repeat Problem 7.1.2 for $p(\mathbf{A})$, with $p(x)$ an arbitrary polynomial.

7.1.5. Let $\mathcal{S}$ be a one-dimensional invariant subspace of $\mathbf{A}$. Show that every nonzero vector in $\mathcal{S}$ is an eigenvector of $\mathbf{A}$.

7.2 IF AB = BA

Two arbitrary matrices rarely commute; if they do, special note is made of it. For instance, $\mathbf{A}^{-1}\mathbf{A} = \mathbf{A}\mathbf{A}^{-1}, \mathbf{IA} = \mathbf{AI}, \mathbf{OA} = \mathbf{AO}$, and, most interesting, the case $p(\mathbf{A})q(\mathbf{A}) = q(\mathbf{A})p(\mathbf{A})$, where $p(x)$ and $q(x)$ are arbitrary polynomials. The commutation of operators plays a role in quantum mechanics. Two "observables" that commute are observables that can, in principle, be measured simultaneously with infinite precision. Thus, observables for which the Heissenberg principle excludes simultaneous exact measurements do not commute. It is natural to speculate whether for fixed $\mathbf{A}$ it is possible to find those $\mathbf{B}$ such that $\mathbf{A}$ and $\mathbf{B}$ commute. As we shall see, if $\mathbf{A}$ and $\mathbf{B}$ are simple, one criterion is that a set of n linearly independent eigenvectors be shared by both matrices. Ideas of this type are explored in this section.

Theorem 7.2.1. *If* $\mathbf{AB} = \mathbf{BA}$, *then* $\mathbf{A}$ *and* $\mathbf{B}$ *have a common eigenvector for each eigenvalue of* $\mathbf{B}$ *and each eigenvalue of* $\mathbf{A}$.

Proof. Let λ_b be an eigenvalue of $\mathbf{B}$, and let $\{\mathbf{x}_1, \mathbf{x}_2, \ldots, \mathbf{x}_r\}$ be a basis for the eigenspace $\mathscr{E}_B(\lambda_b)$ of $\mathbf{B}$ corresponding to λ_b. Although none of the vectors $\mathbf{x}_i$, $1 \le i \le r$, need be eigenvectors of $\mathbf{A}$, some linear combination must be. To see this, first note that if $\mathbf{Ax}_i = \mathbf{0}$, then $(0, \mathbf{x}_i)$ is an eigenpair of $\mathbf{A}$. Since, by hypothesis, $\mathbf{x}_i$ is an eigenvector of $\mathbf{B}$, the proof is done. So assume that $\{\mathbf{Ax}_1, \mathbf{Ax}_2, \ldots, \mathbf{Ax}_r\}$ is a set of nonzero vectors. Now, because $\mathbf{AB} = \mathbf{BA}$,

$$\mathbf{B}(\mathbf{Ax}_i) = \mathbf{A}(\mathbf{Bx}_i) = \lambda_b \mathbf{Ax}_i, \qquad i = 1, 2, \ldots, r$$

Therefore, $\mathbf{Ax}_i \in \mathscr{E}_B(\lambda_b)$. But this means that $\mathscr{E}_B(\lambda_b)$ is an invariant subspace of $\mathbf{A}$. Hence, $\mathscr{E}_B(\lambda_b)$ contains an eigenvector of $\mathbf{A}$, by Theorem 7.1.1. This is a common eigenvector of $\mathbf{A}$ and $\mathbf{B}$. A similar argument holds with the roles of $\mathbf{A}$ and $\mathbf{B}$ reversed. ■

Since $\mathbf{IB} = \mathbf{BI}$ for arbitrary $\mathbf{B}$, it is easy to construct examples of commuting $\mathbf{A}$ and $\mathbf{B}$ that share no more than one (linearly independent) eigenvector; pick a $\mathbf{B}$ with one distinct eigenvalue λ and for which $g(\lambda) = 1$:

$$\mathbf{B} = \begin{bmatrix} \lambda & 1 & 0 \\ 0 & \lambda & 1 \\ 0 & 0 & \lambda \end{bmatrix}$$

On the other hand, the following corollary exhibits a most dramatic contrast to the preceding remark.

Corollary 1. *If* $\mathbf{AB} = \mathbf{BA}$ *and* $\mathbf{B}$ *has* n *distinct eigenvalues, then* $\mathbf{A}$ *is simple and* $\mathbf{A}$ *and* $\mathbf{B}$ *have a common set of* n *linearly independent eigenvectors.*

Proof. For each distinct eigenvalue of $\mathbf{B}$, apply Theorem 7.2.1 and hence conclude that $\mathbf{A}$ and $\mathbf{B}$ share n linearly independent eigenvectors. This means, of course, that $\mathbf{A}$ and $\mathbf{B}$ are both simple. ■

$\mathbf{A}$ and $\mathbf{B}$ are said to be *simultaneously diagonalizable* if there exists a matrix $\mathbf{S}$ such that both $\mathbf{S}^{-1}\mathbf{AS}$ and $\mathbf{S}^{-1}\mathbf{BS}$ are diagonal matrices. Clearly, if $\mathbf{A}$ and $\mathbf{B}$ share a set of n linearly independent eigenvectors, then $\mathbf{A}$ and $\mathbf{B}$ are simultaneously diagonalizable by the matrix $\mathbf{S}$ whose columns are the common eigenvectors.

Conversely, if $\mathbf{A}$ and $\mathbf{B}$ are simultaneously diagonalizable, the columns of $\mathbf{S}$ provide a common set of linearly independent eigenvectors; thus the following equivalent formulation of Corollary 1.

Corollary 2. *If* $\mathbf{AB} = \mathbf{BA}$ *and* $\mathbf{B}$ *has* n *distinct eigenvalues, then* $\mathbf{A}$ *is simple and* $\mathbf{A}$ *and* $\mathbf{B}$ *are simultaneously diagonalizable.*

Example 7.2.1. If $\mathbf{AB} = \mathbf{BA}$ and $\mathbf{B}$ has n distinct eigenvalues, show that every pair of matrices in the set $\{\mathbf{A},\mathbf{B},\mathbf{AB},\mathbf{A}+\mathbf{B}\}$ are simultaneously diagonalizable. Find the eigenvalues of $\mathbf{AB}$ and $\mathbf{A}+\mathbf{B}$ in terms of the eigenvalues of $\mathbf{A}$ and $\mathbf{B}$.

Solution. By Corollary 2, there exists an invertible $\mathbf{S}$ such that $\mathbf{S}^{-1}\mathbf{AS} = \Lambda_1$ and $\mathbf{S}^{-1}\mathbf{BS} = \Lambda_2$. Then

$$\mathbf{S}^{-1}\mathbf{ABS} = \mathbf{S}^{-1}\mathbf{ASS}^{-1}\mathbf{BS} = \Lambda_1\Lambda_2$$

and

$$\mathbf{S}^{-1}(\mathbf{A}+\mathbf{B})\mathbf{S} = \mathbf{S}^{-1}\mathbf{AS} + \mathbf{S}^{-1}\mathbf{BS} = \Lambda_1 + \Lambda_2$$

But both $\Lambda_1\Lambda_2$ and $\Lambda_1 + \Lambda_2$ are diagonal matrices; hence, $\mathbf{A}$, $\mathbf{B}$, $\mathbf{AB}$, and $\mathbf{A}+\mathbf{B}$ are simultaneously diagonalizable. The eigenvalues of $\mathbf{AB}$ and $\mathbf{A}+\mathbf{B}$ are the diagonal entries of $\Lambda_1\Lambda_2$ and $\Lambda_1 + \Lambda_2$. We can be more explicit. Suppose that $(\lambda_i,\mathbf{x}_i)$ and $(\mu_i,\mathbf{x}_i)$ are eigenpairs of $\mathbf{A}$ and $\mathbf{B}$, respectively. Assume that $\mathbf{x}_i$ is the ith column of $\mathbf{S}$. Then $\lambda_i\mu_i$ are the eigenvalues of $\mathbf{AB}$, and $\lambda_i + \mu_i$ are the eigenvalues of $\mathbf{A}+\mathbf{B}$.

Example 7.2.2. Suppose **A** and **B** are simultaneously diagonalizable. Show that **AB** = **BA**.

Solution. By hypothesis, there exists **S** such that $\mathbf{S}^{-1}\mathbf{AS} = \Lambda_1$ and $\mathbf{S}^{-1}\mathbf{BS} = \Lambda_2$. Then $\mathbf{S}^{-1}\mathbf{ASS}^{-1}\mathbf{BS} = \mathbf{S}^{-1}\mathbf{ABS} = \Lambda_1\Lambda_2$. But diagonal matrices commute, so that

$$\Lambda_1\Lambda_2 = \Lambda_2\Lambda_1 = \mathbf{S}^{-1}\mathbf{BSS}^{-1}\mathbf{AS} = \mathbf{S}^{-1}\mathbf{BAS}$$

Hence, $\mathbf{S}^{-1}\mathbf{ABS} = \mathbf{S}^{-1}\mathbf{BAS}$, and this implies that **AB** = **BA**.

If **A** and **B** are simple and **AB** = **BA**, then **A** and **B** are simultaneously diagonalizable. The proof of this theorem is somewhat involved and not presented here. The proofs of two weaker theorems are outlined in Part 3 of the following problem set.

Example 7.2.3. Let

$$\mathbf{A} = \begin{bmatrix} 4 & 1 & -1 \\ -2 & -1 & 0 \\ 10 & 2 & -3 \end{bmatrix}, \qquad \mathbf{B} = \begin{bmatrix} -1 & -1 & 1 \\ 6 & 4 & -2 \\ -6 & -2 & 4 \end{bmatrix}$$

Show that **AB** = **BA** and find a set of linearly independent eigenvectors common to **A** and **B**.

Solution. Verify

$$\mathbf{AB} = \begin{bmatrix} 4 & 1 & -1 \\ -2 & -1 & 0 \\ 10 & 2 & -3 \end{bmatrix}\begin{bmatrix} -1 & -1 & 1 \\ 6 & 4 & -2 \\ -6 & -2 & 4 \end{bmatrix} = \begin{bmatrix} 8 & 2 & -2 \\ -4 & -2 & 0 \\ 20 & 4 & -6 \end{bmatrix} = \mathbf{BA}$$

Suppose the eigenvalues of **A** are denoted by λ_i and those of **B** by $\mu_i, i = 1,2,3$. After some labor:

1. A common eigenvector is $\mathbf{u}_1 = [1 \quad -1 \quad 2]^{\mathrm{T}}$, corresponding to the eigenvalues $\lambda_1 = 1, \mu_1 = 2$. Here is the verification:

$$\begin{bmatrix} 4 & 1 & -1 \\ -2 & -1 & 0 \\ 10 & 2 & -3 \end{bmatrix}\begin{bmatrix} 1 \\ -1 \\ 2 \end{bmatrix} = \begin{bmatrix} 1 \\ -1 \\ 2 \end{bmatrix}, \qquad \begin{bmatrix} -1 & -1 & 1 \\ 6 & 4 & -2 \\ -6 & -2 & 4 \end{bmatrix}\begin{bmatrix} 1 \\ -1 \\ 2 \end{bmatrix} = 2\begin{bmatrix} 1 \\ -1 \\ 2 \end{bmatrix}$$

2. $\lambda_2 = -1$ and $\mu_2 = 2$, and the common eigenvector is $\mathbf{u}_2 = [0 \quad 1 \quad 1]^{\mathrm{T}}$:

$$\begin{bmatrix} 4 & 1 & -1 \\ -2 & -1 & 0 \\ 10 & 2 & -3 \end{bmatrix}\begin{bmatrix} 0 \\ 1 \\ 1 \end{bmatrix} = -\begin{bmatrix} 0 \\ 1 \\ 1 \end{bmatrix}, \qquad \begin{bmatrix} -1 & -1 & 1 \\ 6 & 4 & -2 \\ -6 & -2 & 4 \end{bmatrix}\begin{bmatrix} 0 \\ 1 \\ 1 \end{bmatrix} = 2\begin{bmatrix} 0 \\ 1 \\ 1 \end{bmatrix}$$

3. $\lambda_3 = 0$ and $\mu_3 = 3$, and the common eigenvector is $\mathbf{u}_3 = [1 \quad -2 \quad 2]^T$:

$$\begin{bmatrix} 4 & 1 & -1 \\ -2 & -1 & 0 \\ 10 & 2 & -3 \end{bmatrix}\begin{bmatrix} 1 \\ -2 \\ 2 \end{bmatrix} = \begin{bmatrix} 0 \\ 0 \\ 0 \end{bmatrix}, \qquad \begin{bmatrix} -1 & -1 & 1 \\ 6 & 4 & -2 \\ -6 & -2 & 4 \end{bmatrix}\begin{bmatrix} 1 \\ -2 \\ 2 \end{bmatrix} = 3\begin{bmatrix} 1 \\ -2 \\ 2 \end{bmatrix}$$

Example 7.2.4. Show that $\mathbf{C}$ is simple and commutes with $\mathbf{A}$ and $\mathbf{B}$ of Example 7.2.3, where $\mathbf{C}$ is given by

$$\mathbf{C} = \begin{bmatrix} 7 & 2 & -2 \\ -12 & -3 & 4 \\ 12 & 4 & -3 \end{bmatrix}$$

Also show that not all eigenvectors of $\mathbf{C}$ are eigenvectors of $\mathbf{A}$.

Solution. Verify

$$\mathbf{CA} = \begin{bmatrix} 7 & 2 & -2 \\ -12 & -3 & 4 \\ 12 & 4 & -3 \end{bmatrix}\begin{bmatrix} 4 & 1 & -1 \\ -2 & -1 & 0 \\ 10 & 2 & -3 \end{bmatrix} = \begin{bmatrix} 4 & 1 & -1 \\ -2 & -1 & 0 \\ 10 & 2 & -3 \end{bmatrix} = \mathbf{AC}$$

$$\mathbf{CB} = \begin{bmatrix} 7 & 2 & -2 \\ -12 & -3 & 4 \\ 12 & 4 & -3 \end{bmatrix}\begin{bmatrix} -1 & -1 & 1 \\ 6 & 4 & -2 \\ -6 & -2 & 4 \end{bmatrix} = \begin{bmatrix} 17 & 5 & -5 \\ -30 & -8 & 10 \\ 30 & 10 & -8 \end{bmatrix} = \mathbf{BC}$$

The eigenvectors $\mathbf{u}_1, \mathbf{u}_2, \mathbf{u}_3$ of Example 7.2.3 are also eigenvectors of $\mathbf{C}$. This verification is left for the exercises (Problem 7.2.2). However,

$$\begin{bmatrix} 7 & 2 & -2 \\ -12 & -3 & 4 \\ 12 & 4 & -3 \end{bmatrix}\begin{bmatrix} -1 \\ 3 \\ 0 \end{bmatrix} = \begin{bmatrix} -1 \\ 3 \\ 0 \end{bmatrix}$$

shows that $\mathbf{u}_4 = [-1 \quad 3 \quad 0]^T$ is an eigenvector of $\mathbf{C}$ corresponding to the eigenvalue $\nu = 1$; it is not an eigenvector of $\mathbf{A}$ but is an eigenvector of $\mathbf{B}$. This happens because $g_{\mathbf{C}}(1) = 2$. Not all vectors in this two-dimensional eigenspace, $\mathscr{E}_{\mathbf{C}}(1)$, can be eigenvectors of the matrices that commute with $\mathbf{C}$, since the eigenspaces of $\mathbf{A}$ are one-dimensional.

7.2.1 The Characteristic Equations of AB and BA

Now consider an incidental question that seems quite natural in the context of this section. For $\mathbf{A}_{m\times n}$ and $\mathbf{B}_{n\times m}$, $m \le n$, both $\mathbf{AB}$ and $\mathbf{BA}$ exist and are square matrices. What can be deduced about the relationships between the eigenvalues and eigenvectors of $\mathbf{AB}$ and $\mathbf{BA}$? There is reason to hope for some connections because, in the special case $n = m$ and invertible $\mathbf{B}$,

$$\mathbf{AB} = (\mathbf{B}^{-1}\mathbf{B})\mathbf{AB} = \mathbf{B}^{-1}(\mathbf{BA})\mathbf{B}$$

shows that $\mathbf{AB}$ is similar to $\mathbf{BA}$. On the other hand, if *both* $\mathbf{A}$ and $\mathbf{B}$ are singular, then $\mathbf{AB}$ need not be similar to $\mathbf{BA}$, as the following example shows.

Example 7.2.5. Define **A** and **B** as follows:

$$\mathbf{A} = \begin{bmatrix} 0 & 1 \\ 0 & 0 \end{bmatrix}, \quad \mathbf{B} = \begin{bmatrix} 1 & 0 \\ 0 & 0 \end{bmatrix}$$

Then

$$\mathbf{AB} = \begin{bmatrix} 0 & 1 \\ 0 & 0 \end{bmatrix}\begin{bmatrix} 1 & 0 \\ 0 & 0 \end{bmatrix} = \begin{bmatrix} 0 & 0 \\ 0 & 0 \end{bmatrix}, \qquad \mathbf{BA} = \begin{bmatrix} 1 & 0 \\ 0 & 0 \end{bmatrix}\begin{bmatrix} 0 & 1 \\ 0 & 0 \end{bmatrix} = \begin{bmatrix} 0 & 1 \\ 0 & 0 \end{bmatrix}$$

The eigenvalues are $\lambda_1 = \lambda_2 = 0$ for both **AB** and **BA**. Clearly, **AB** is simple, and **BA** is defective. But a simple matrix cannot be similar to a defective matrix.

It is the zero eigenvalues that are the source of the subtlety in the relationship between **AB** and **BA**. For eigenvalues that are not zero, the situation is as simple as one might hope for:

Theorem 7.2.2. *For* $\mathbf{A}_{m\times n}$ *and* $\mathbf{B}_{n\times m}$, *if* $(\lambda_0 \neq 0, \mathbf{u})$ *is an eigenpair of* **AB** *with* $g_{\mathbf{AB}}(\lambda_0) = r$, *then* $(\lambda_0, \mathbf{Bu})$ *is an eigenpair of* **BA** *and* $g_{\mathbf{BA}}(\lambda_0) = r$.

Proof. By hypothesis, $\mathbf{ABu} = \lambda_0\mathbf{u}$. Hence, multiplying through by **B**,

$$\mathbf{B(AB)u} = \mathbf{(BA)(Bu)} = \mathbf{B}(\lambda_0\mathbf{u}) = \lambda_0(\mathbf{Bu})$$

shows that $(\lambda_0, \mathbf{Bu})$ is an eigenpair of **BA** *provided* $\mathbf{Bu} \neq \mathbf{0}$. But if $\mathbf{Bu} = \mathbf{0}$, it would follow that $\mathbf{ABu} = \mathbf{A0} = \mathbf{0}$. Hence, $(0, \mathbf{u})$ would be an eigenpair of **AB**, and this contradicts $\lambda_0 \neq 0$. Now consider the geometric multiplicity of λ_0. Suppose $g_{\mathbf{AB}}(\lambda_0) = r, g_{\mathbf{BA}}(\lambda_0) = s$, and that $\{\mathbf{u}_1, \mathbf{u}_2, \ldots, \mathbf{u}_r\}$ is a linearly independent set of eigenvectors of **AB** corresponding to the nonzero eigenvalue λ_0. The set $\{\mathbf{Bu}_1, \mathbf{Bu}_2, \ldots, \mathbf{Bu}_r\}$ is, as seen above, a set of eigenvectors for **BA**. Suppose

$$a_1\mathbf{Bu}_1 + a_2\mathbf{Bu}_2 + \cdots + a_r\mathbf{Bu}_r = \mathbf{0}$$

Then premultiplying this equation by **A** leads to

$$\begin{aligned} \mathbf{A0} = \mathbf{0} &= a_1\mathbf{ABu}_1 + a_2\mathbf{ABu}_2 + \cdots + a_r\mathbf{ABu}_r \\ &= a_1\lambda_0\mathbf{u}_1 + a_2\lambda_0\mathbf{u}_2 + \cdots + a_r\lambda_0\mathbf{u}_r \\ &= \lambda_0(a_1\mathbf{u}_1 + a_2\mathbf{u}_2 + \cdots + a_r\mathbf{u}_r) \end{aligned}$$

Since $\lambda_0 \neq 0$ by hypothesis, it follows that

$$\mathbf{0} = a_1\mathbf{u}_1 + a_2\mathbf{u}_2 + \cdots + a_r\mathbf{u}_r$$

But the assumption that $\{\mathbf{u}_1, \mathbf{u}_2, \ldots, \mathbf{u}_r\}$ is linearly independent implies that all the weights are zero and, therefore, that $\{\mathbf{Bu}_1, \mathbf{Bu}_2, \ldots, \mathbf{Bu}_r\}$ is linearly independent. Hence, $s = g_{\mathbf{BA}}(\lambda_0) \geq r$. By reversing the roles of **AB** and **BA**, we deduce that $r \geq s$. Hence, $r = s$. ■

The proof breaks down if $\lambda_0 = 0$ is the eigenvalue in question. However, if either **A** or **B** is nonsingular, then **AB** is similar to **BA** and, therefore, $g_{\mathbf{AB}}(0) =$

$g_{\mathbf{BA}}(0)$. Indeed, assuming **A** is singular and **B** is nonsingular, then rank(**A**) = rank(**BA**) = rank(**AB**), and hence

$$\begin{aligned} g_{\mathbf{AB}}(0) &= n - \text{rank}(\mathbf{AB}) = n - \text{rank}(\mathbf{A}) \\ &= n - \text{rank}(\mathbf{BA}) = g_{\mathbf{BA}}(0) \end{aligned} \tag{7.2.1}$$

The following, interesting theorem, valid for every **A** and **B** for which **AB** and **BA** are defined, has an elegant, ingenious proof.

Theorem 7.2.3. *Suppose* **A** *is $m \times n$ and* **B** *is $n \times m$. Let $c_{\mathbf{AB}}(\lambda)$ and $c_{\mathbf{BA}}(\lambda)$ be the characteristic polynomials of* **AB** *and* **BA** *respectively. Then*

$$\lambda^{n-m} c_{\mathbf{AB}}(\lambda) = c_{\mathbf{BA}}(\lambda) \tag{7.2.2}$$

Proof. Since $c_{\mathbf{AB}}(\lambda)$ is a polynomial of degree m and $c_{\mathbf{BA}}(\lambda)$ is a polynomial of degree n, **AB** need not be similar to **BA**. However, consider the following partitioned multiplication:

$$\begin{bmatrix} \mathbf{I} & \mathbf{A} \\ \mathbf{O} & \mathbf{I} \end{bmatrix}^{-1} \begin{bmatrix} \mathbf{AB} & \mathbf{O} \\ \mathbf{B} & \mathbf{O} \end{bmatrix} \begin{bmatrix} \mathbf{I} & \mathbf{A} \\ \mathbf{O} & \mathbf{I} \end{bmatrix} = \begin{bmatrix} \mathbf{I} & -\mathbf{A} \\ \mathbf{O} & \mathbf{I} \end{bmatrix} \begin{bmatrix} \mathbf{AB} & \mathbf{O} \\ \mathbf{B} & \mathbf{O} \end{bmatrix} \begin{bmatrix} \mathbf{I} & \mathbf{A} \\ \mathbf{O} & \mathbf{I} \end{bmatrix} = \begin{bmatrix} \mathbf{O} & \mathbf{O} \\ \mathbf{B} & \mathbf{BA} \end{bmatrix}$$

This shows that

$$\mathbf{C} = \begin{bmatrix} \mathbf{AB} & \mathbf{O} \\ \mathbf{B} & \mathbf{O} \end{bmatrix} \qquad \mathbf{D} = \begin{bmatrix} \mathbf{O} & \mathbf{O} \\ \mathbf{B} & \mathbf{BA} \end{bmatrix}$$

are similar, and hence their characteristic equations are identical. But $c_{\mathbf{C}}(\lambda) = \lambda^n c_{\mathbf{AB}}(\lambda)$ and $c_{\mathbf{D}}(\lambda) = \lambda^m c_{\mathbf{BA}}(\lambda)$, from which the conclusion is immediate. ■

Corollary 1. *If $n = m$, then $c_{\mathbf{AB}}(\lambda) = c_{\mathbf{BA}}(\lambda)$.*

Theorem 7.2.4. *Suppose* **A** *is $m \times m$ and* **B** *is $n \times m$ and* **AB** *is simple. Then* **BA** *is simple if and only if* rank(**AB**) = rank(**BA**).

Proof. Let $\{\lambda_1, \lambda_2, \ldots, \lambda_k\}$ be the distinct, nonzero eigenvalues of **BA**. By Theorem 3.5.2, $n = \text{rank}(\mathbf{BA}) + \dim(null(\mathbf{BA}))$. Set $g_{\mathbf{BA}}(0) = 0$ if $\lambda = 0$ is not an eigenvalue of **BA**. Then $\dim(null(\mathbf{BA})) = g_{\mathbf{BA}}(0)$ whether 0 is an eigenvalue of **BA** or not. Hence, with this convention,

$$n = \text{rank}(\mathbf{BA}) + g_{\mathbf{BA}}(0) \tag{7.2.3}$$

Similarly,

$$m = \text{rank}(\mathbf{AB}) + g_{\mathbf{AB}}(0) \tag{7.2.4}$$

So subtracting Eq. 7.2.4 from Eq. 7.2.3 results in

$$n - m = \text{rank}(\mathbf{BA}) - \text{rank}(\mathbf{AB}) + g_{\mathbf{BA}}(0) - g_{\mathbf{AB}}(0) \tag{7.2.5}$$

Now define s by

$$s = g_{\mathbf{BA}}(0) + g_{\mathbf{BA}}(\lambda_1) + g_{\mathbf{BA}}(\lambda_2) + \cdots + g_{\mathbf{BA}}(\lambda_k) \tag{7.2.6}$$

However, by Theorem 7.2.2, $g_{\mathbf{AB}}(\lambda_i) = g_{\mathbf{BA}}(\lambda_i)$ for $i = 1,2,\ldots,k$. Hence, Eq. 7.2.6 can be written

$$s = g_{\mathbf{BA}}(0) + \left(g_{\mathbf{AB}}(0) + g_{\mathbf{AB}}(\lambda_1) + g_{\mathbf{AB}}(\lambda_2) + \cdots + g_{\mathbf{AB}}(\lambda_k)\right) - g_{\mathbf{AB}}(0) \tag{7.2.7}$$

However, since **AB** is simple, it follows from Corollary 1 of Theorem 5.7.3 that

$$m = g_{\mathbf{AB}}(0) + g_{\mathbf{AB}}(\lambda_1) + g_{\mathbf{AB}}(\lambda_2) + \cdots + g_{\mathbf{AB}}(\lambda_k)$$

so that Eq. 7.2.7 becomes

$$s = g_{\mathbf{BA}}(0) - g_{\mathbf{AB}}(0) + m \qquad (7.2.8)$$

Substituting Eq. 7.2.8 into Eq. 7.2.5 leads to

$$n - m = \text{rank}(\mathbf{BA}) - \text{rank}(\mathbf{AB}) + s - m$$

so that we have, finally,

$$n - s = \text{rank}(\mathbf{BA}) - \text{rank}(\mathbf{AB}) \qquad (7.2.9)$$

By Corollary 1 of Theorem 5.7.3, $n = s$ if and only if **BA** is simple. Thus, $n = s$ if and only if rank(**BA**) − rank(**AB**) = 0. ■

Corollary 1. *If* rank(**BA**) = rank(**AB**), *then* **BA** *and* **AB** *are both simple or both defective.*

Proof. If **BA** (or **AB**) is simple, then the theorem implies that the other is also. ■

Corollary 2. *If* rank(**BA**) ≠ rank(**AB**), *then either* **BA** *or* **AB** *or both are defective.*

Proof. If **BA** or **AB** is simple, then by the theorem, the other is defective. ■

Example 7.2.6. Show that $\mathbf{uv}^{\mathrm{T}} \neq \mathbf{O}$ is defective if and only if $\mathbf{u}^{\mathrm{T}}\mathbf{v} = [0]$.

Solution. Since $\text{rank}(\mathbf{uv}^{\mathrm{T}}) \leq \text{rank}(\mathbf{u}) = 1$, $\text{rank}(\mathbf{uv}^{\mathrm{T}}) = 1$ because only the zero matrix has rank zero. But $\text{rank}(\mathbf{u}^{\mathrm{T}}\mathbf{v}) = \text{rank}([0]) = 0$ by hypothesis. Hence, by Theorem 7.2.4, $\mathbf{uv}^{\mathrm{T}}$ is defective. Thus, for example,

$$\mathbf{uv}^{\mathrm{T}} = \begin{bmatrix} 1 \\ 1 \\ 1 \\ 1 \end{bmatrix} [1 \quad -1 \quad 1 \quad -1] = \begin{bmatrix} 1 & -1 & 1 & -1 \\ 1 & -1 & 1 & -1 \\ 1 & -1 & 1 & -1 \\ 1 & -1 & 1 & -1 \end{bmatrix}$$

is defective since $\mathbf{u} \cdot \mathbf{v} = 0$.

PROBLEMS

PART 1

7.2.1. Verify the various computations given in Example 7.2.3.
7.2.2. Repeat Problem 7.2.1 for the matrices in Example 7.2.4.

PART 2

7.2.3. Suppose **A** is $r \times 2r$, and rank(**A**) = r. Let **N** be a matrix whose r columns are linearly independent solutions of $\mathbf{Ax} = \mathbf{O}$. Find conditions for which **NA** is defective.

PART 3

7.2.4. Suppose $\mathbf{AB} = \mathbf{BA}$ and $\mathbf{B}$ has n distinct eigenvalues. If $\mathbf{B}$ is hermitian show that $\mathbf{A}$ is hermitian and that $\mathbf{A}$ and $\mathbf{B}$ are simultaneously diagonalizable by a unitary matrix.

7.2.5. Suppose $\mathbf{A}$ and $\mathbf{B}$ are simple and $\lambda = \lambda_0$ is the only distinct eigenvalue of $\mathbf{A}$. Show that $\mathbf{A}$ and $\mathbf{B}$ are simultaneously diagonalizable.

7.2.6. The matrix $\mathbf{C}$ is *block diagonal* if

$$\mathbf{C} = \begin{bmatrix} \mathbf{C}_1 & & & \\ & \mathbf{C}_2 & & \mathbf{O} \\ & & \ddots & \\ & \mathbf{O} & & \mathbf{C}_k \end{bmatrix} \tag{7.2.6}$$

and $\mathbf{C}_1, \mathbf{C}_2, \ldots, \mathbf{C}_k$ are square matrices. Every diagonal matrix Λ is block diagonal in the trivial sense that $\mathbf{C}_i = [\lambda_i]$. A more interesting partition of Λ into block diagonal form is

$$\Lambda = \begin{bmatrix} \lambda_1\mathbf{I}_1 & & & \\ & \lambda_2\mathbf{I}_2 & & \mathbf{O} \\ & & \ddots & \\ & \mathbf{O} & & \lambda_k\mathbf{I}_k \end{bmatrix} \tag{7.2.7}$$

where $\lambda_i \neq \lambda_j$ if $i \neq j$. The size of each identity block is the algebraic multiplicity of the eigenvalue that is its scalar multiplicative factor.

(*a*) Suppose $\mathbf{U}^H\mathbf{AU} = \Lambda$, and $\mathbf{U}^H\mathbf{BU} = \mathbf{C}$. If $\mathbf{AB} = \mathbf{BA}$ show that $\Lambda\mathbf{C} = \mathbf{C}\Lambda$.

(*b*) Show that if $\mathbf{C}$ commutes with the diagonal matrix $\mathbf{A}$, then $\mathbf{C}$ is in the block diagonal form of Eq. 7.2.6 and the size of $\mathbf{C}_i$ is the size of $\lambda_i\mathbf{I}_i$.

(*c*) Suppose $\mathbf{C}$ is in the block diagonal form of Eq. 7.2.6. Show that $\mathbf{C}$ is normal if and only if each $\mathbf{C}_i$ is normal. (*Hint:* Show that the unitary diagonalizing matrix can be constructed in block diagonal form.)

(*d*) Given $\mathbf{A}$ and $\mathbf{B}$ normal, with $\mathbf{AB} = \mathbf{BA}$ and Λ and $\mathbf{C}$ defined as in part (*a*), show that there exists a unitary matrix $\mathbf{V}$ such that $\mathbf{V}^H\mathbf{CV} = \Lambda_{\mathbf{B}}$ and $\mathbf{V}^H\Lambda\mathbf{V} = \Lambda$.

(*e*) Prove: If $\mathbf{A}$ and $\mathbf{B}$ are normal and commute, there is a unitary matrix that simultaneously diagonalizes $\mathbf{A}$ and $\mathbf{B}$. (*Hint:* Consider the unitary matrix $\mathbf{UV}$, where $\mathbf{U}$ and $\mathbf{V}$ are defined as in parts (*a*) and (*d*).)

7.2.7. Use Theorem 7.2.4 to prove: If $\mathbf{AB}$ is invertible, then $\mathbf{AB}$ and $\mathbf{BA}$ are both simple or both defective.

7.2.8. If $\text{rank}(\mathbf{AB}) = 0$, show that $\mathbf{BA}$ is defective if and only if $\mathbf{BA} \neq \mathbf{O}$.

7.3 GERSCHGORIN'S THEOREM

The eigenvalue-eigenvector equation $\mathbf{Ax} = \lambda\mathbf{x}$ provides a simple estimate for the location of the eigenvalues, which is particularly useful in numerical analysis and is often a convenient tool for theoretical work. It leads, for example, to a simple proof that the spectral radius of a stochastic matrix is 1. (See Example 7.3.3.) The main theorem in this section was published in the 1930s and is known as *Gerschgorin's Theorem,* after the discoverer.

To fix ideas, suppose that $\mathbf{A}$ is $n \times n$ and is given by

$$\mathbf{A} = \begin{bmatrix} a_{11} & a_{12} & \cdots & a_{1n} \\ a_{21} & a_{22} & \cdots & a_{2n} \\ \vdots & \vdots & & \vdots \\ a_{n1} & a_{n2} & \cdots & a_{nn} \end{bmatrix}$$

The row and column sums play a major role in the forthcoming theory. Denote the sum of the absolute values of the entries in the *i*th row by r_i and the corresponding sum of the *j*th column by c_j. That is, for each i and j, $1 \leq i, j \leq n$,

$$r_i = |a_{i1}| + |a_{i2}| + \cdots + |a_{in}| = \sum_{k=1}^{n} |a_{ik}| \tag{7.3.1}$$

$$c_j = |a_{1j}| + |a_{2j}| + \cdots + |a_{nj}| = \sum_{k=1}^{n} |a_{kj}| \tag{7.3.2}$$

Thus, for instance, $r_i = c_i = n$ for $\mathbf{J}_n$ and $|k|$ for $k\mathbf{I}$. The row and column sums of $\mathbf{A}$ are generally quite fragile; they are altered by elementary row or column operations and by similarities. The sums of the absolute values of the off-diagonal entries in the *i*th row and *j*th column are given by

$$r_i' = r_i - |a_{ii}| \qquad \text{and} \qquad c_j' = c_j - |a_{jj}|$$

respectively.

The set of z such that $|z - a| \leq r$ is a closed disk in the complex plane with center at a and radius r. Figure 7.1 shows two such disks. The leftmost has the origin as center and radius 1; the points in the disk and on its circumference satisfy $|z| \leq 1$. The disk on the right is defined by the inequality $|z - i| \leq 2$. Now define the *Gerschgorin disks* (of $\mathbf{A}$) as the set of λs such that

$$|\lambda - a_{ii}| \leq r_i', \qquad i = 1,2,\ldots,n \tag{7.3.3}$$

and call r_i' the *Gerschgorin radii*.

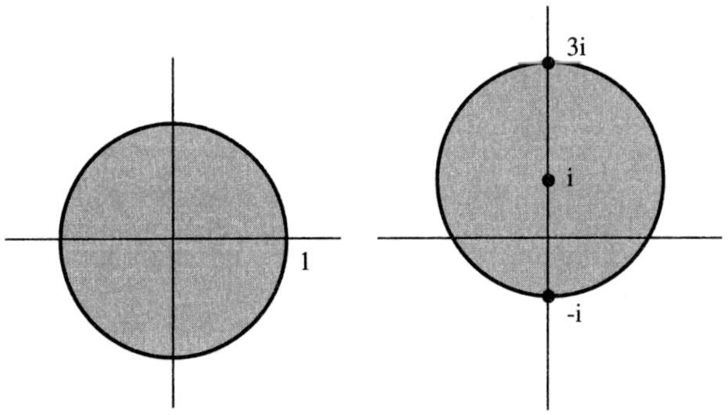

FIGURE 7-1
Closed disks in the complex plane.

Example 7.3.1. Find the Gerschgorin radii and disks for the matrix

$$\mathbf{A} = \begin{bmatrix} 0 & 0 & -1 & 2 \\ 1 & 2 & 1 & -1 \\ 0 & 0 & 1 & 1 \\ 1 & 1 & 0.5 & -1 \end{bmatrix}$$

Solution. The values of the various radii are $r_1' = 3, r_2' = 3, r_3' = 1$, and $r_4' = 2.5$. Thus, the Gerschgorin disks are $|\lambda| \le 3, |\lambda - 2| \le 3, |\lambda - 1| \le 1$, and $|\lambda + 1| \le 2.5$.

Theorem 7.3.1. *The eigenvalues of* **A** *lie in union of the Gerschgorin disks,*

$$|\lambda - a_{ii}| \le r_i', \qquad i = 1,2,\ldots,n \tag{7.3.4}$$

Proof. Suppose $(\lambda_0, \mathbf{u} = [u_1 \ u_2 \ \ldots \ u_n]^{\mathrm{T}})$ is an eigenpair of **A**. Suppose u_m has the largest absolute value of all the entries in **u**, so that $|u_m| = \max\{|u_1|, |u_2|, \ldots, |u_n|\}$. The mth equation in the system $(\mathbf{A} - \lambda_0\mathbf{I})\mathbf{u} = \mathbf{0}$ is

$$(a_{mm} - \lambda_0)u_m = -\sum_{j=1}^{n}{}' a_{mj}u_j \tag{7.3.5}$$

where $\sum_{j=1}^{n}{}' a_{mj}u_j$ omits the term $a_{mm}u_m$, since this term already appears in the left-hand side of Eq. 7.3.5. Since $|u_m| \ge |u_j|$ for all j and $\mathbf{u} \ne \mathbf{0}$, Eq. 7.3.5 implies

$$|a_{mm} - \lambda_0| \le \sum_{j=1}^{n}{}' \frac{|a_{mj}||u_j|}{|u_m|} \le \sum_{j=1}^{n}{}' |a_{mj}| = r_i'$$

Thus, for each eigenvalue λ, there is some i for which $|\lambda - a_{ii}| \le r_i'$. Put equivalently, the set of eigenvalues of **A** lie in the union of the Gerschgorin disks of **A**. ■

A slight weakening of the conclusion of Theorem 7.3.1 is used repeatedly in applications and is based on the fact that $|\lambda - a_{ii}| \le r_i'$ implies the milder assertion $|\lambda| \le r_i' + |a_{ii}| = r_i$. (Recall that for all complex numbers a and b, $|a + b| \le |a| + |b|$.) Set

$$r_{\max} = \max\{r_1, r_2, \ldots, r_n\}$$

and recall that the spectral radius of **A**, denoted by $\rho(\mathbf{A})$, is the magnitude of the eigenvalue with greatest modulus.

Corollary 1. *Using the preceding notation and terminology, the eigenvalues of* **A** *lie in the disk*

$$|\lambda| \le r_{\max} \tag{7.3.6}$$

and therefore $\rho(\mathbf{A}) \le r_{\max}$.

Proof. Equation 7.3.6 is a weakened version of Eq. 7.3.4. $\rho(A) \le r_{\max}$ follows since $r_{\max} \ge r_i$ for all i. ■

Applied to Example 7.3.1, Corollary 1 asserts that all the eigenvalues of the matrix of that example have moduli no more than 5. Following is an example of a similar type.

Example 7.3.2. Find the Gerschgorin disks and thus estimate the spectral radius of

$$\mathbf{A} = \begin{bmatrix} 2 & 0 & 1 \\ 1 & 2 & 0 \\ 0 & 1 & 2 \end{bmatrix}$$

Solution. The sum of the absolute values of the off-diagonal entries r_i' is 1 for each row. Also, the diagonal entries are all 2; hence the three Gerschgorin disks are the same, $|\lambda - 2| \leq 1$. Thus, all the eigenvalues of $\mathbf{A}$ lie in $1 \leq |\lambda| \leq 3$, and $1 \leq \rho(\mathbf{A}) \leq 3$. Because all the eigenvalues have moduli greater than 1, it follows that $\mathbf{A}$ is nonsingular. In fact, the eigenvalues of $\mathbf{A}$ are $(3 \pm i\sqrt{3})/2$ and 3, and all three eigenvalues have modulus 3.

Example 7.3.3. A matrix $\mathbf{S}$ is said to be a *stochastic matrix* if it contains only nonnegative entries and each row sum is 1. It is easy to verify that (1, **1**) is an eigenpair of $\mathbf{S}$. Since $r_i = 1$ for all i, $r_{\max} = 1$ and, by Corollary 1, $\rho(\mathbf{A}) = 1$. Show that if λ is an eigenvalue of $\mathbf{S}$ and $a_{ii} \neq 0$ for all i, then $|\lambda| = 1$, implies $\lambda = 1$.

Solution. This is a beautiful application of Gerschgorin's theorem. Since $r_i = 1$ for all i, the Gerschgorin disks of Eq. 7.3.3 become

$$|\lambda - a_{ii}| \leq r_i' = 1 - a_{ii}, \qquad i = 1, 2, \ldots, n$$

The unit circle $|\lambda| = 1$ and the closed disk $|\lambda - a_{ii}| \leq 1 - a_{ii}$ are sketched in Fig. 7.2. As is shown in the figure, only $\lambda = 1$ can satisfy both $|\lambda| = 1$

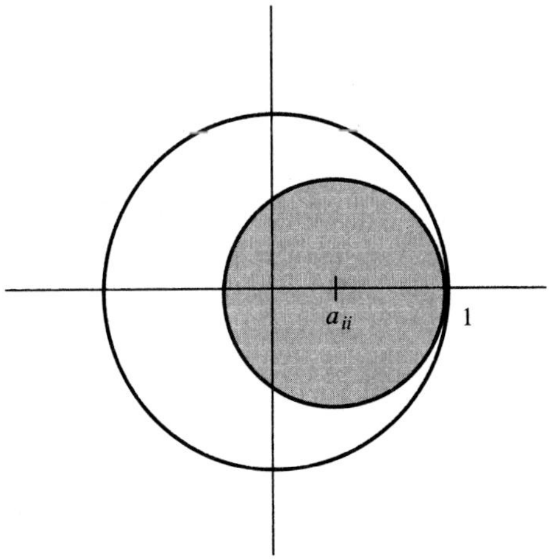

FIGURE 7-2
The disk $|\lambda - a_{ii}| \leq 1 - a_{ii}$ and the circle $|\lambda| = 1$.

and $|\lambda - a_{ii}| \leq 1 - a_{ii}$, if $a_{ii} > 0$ for all i. If $a_{ii} = 0$, then one or more of the Gerschgorin disks are $|\lambda| \leq 1$.

Gerschgorin's theorem implies two further results. The first is based on the fact that similar matrices have the same eigenvalues. The second applies Gerschgorin's theorem to a new class of matrices. Preliminary to the first theorem, define the following diagonal matrix:

$$\mathbf{D}(\nu) = \begin{bmatrix} \nu_1 & 0 & \cdots & 0 \\ 0 & \nu_2 & \cdots & 0 \\ \vdots & & \ddots & \\ 0 & 0 & \cdots & \nu_n \end{bmatrix}, \qquad \text{where } \nu_i \neq 0 \text{ for all } i \tag{7.3.7}$$

Theorem 7.3.2. *Let $\{\nu_1, \nu_2, \ldots, \nu_n\}$ be any set of n positive numbers. Then the eigenvalues of* **A** *lie in the union of the disks*

$$|\lambda - a_{ii}| \leq \frac{1}{\nu_i}\left[\sum_{j=1}^{n}{}' \nu_j |a_{ij}|\right], \qquad i = 1,2,\ldots,n \tag{7.3.8}$$

Note that the summation of Eq. 7.3.8 omits the term $\nu_i a_{ii}$.

Proof. Let $\mathbf{D}(\nu)$ be defined as in Eq. 7.3.7. Then $\mathbf{D}^{-1}(\nu) = \mathbf{D}(\nu^{-1})$ exists. The matrix $\mathbf{D}^{-1}\mathbf{AD}$ is similar to **A** and therefore has the same eigenvalues as **A**. In expanded form,

$$\mathbf{D}^{-1}\mathbf{AD} = \begin{bmatrix} (\nu_1/\nu_1)a_{11} & (\nu_2/\nu_1)a_{12} & \cdots & (\nu_n/\nu_1)a_{1n} \\ (\nu_1/\nu_2)a_{21} & (\nu_2/\nu_2)a_{22} & \cdots & (\nu_n/\nu_2)a_{2n} \\ \vdots & \vdots & & \vdots \\ (\nu_1/\nu_n)a_{n1} & (\nu_2/\nu_n)a_{2n} & \cdots & (\nu_n/\nu_n)a_{nn} \end{bmatrix} \tag{7.3.9}$$

The proof is completed by applying Gerschgorin's theorem to $\mathbf{D}^{-1}\mathbf{AD}$. ■

Example 7.3.4. Find an upper bound to the spectral radius of

$$\mathbf{A} = \begin{bmatrix} 1 & 3 \\ 4 & 2 \end{bmatrix}$$

Solution. A direct application of Corollary 1 yields the upper bound $\rho(\mathbf{A}) \leq 6$, since $r_1 = 4, r_2 = 6$, and therefore $r_{\max} = 6$. However, utilizing Theorem 7.3.2 and setting $\nu = \nu_1/\nu_2$, it follows that

$$\mathbf{D}^{-1}\mathbf{AD} = \begin{bmatrix} 1 & 3/\nu \\ 4\nu & 2 \end{bmatrix}$$

Hence, $|\lambda| \leq 1 + 3/\nu$ or $|\lambda| \leq 2 + 4\nu$. A better estimate than $\rho(\mathbf{A}) \leq 6$ can be obtained by selecting ν so that $1 + 3/\nu = 2 + 4\nu$. This leads to $\nu = 3/4$. Then $|\lambda| \leq 2 + 4\ (3/4) = 5$. Indeed, the eigenvalues of **A** are $\lambda_1 = -2$ and $\lambda_2 = 5$. Thus, no better estimate is possible in this example.

A matrix is *strictly diagonally dominant* if for each i, $|a_{ii}| > r_i'$. The inequality $|a_{ii} - \lambda| \le r_i'$ implies $|\lambda| \ge |a_{ii}| - r_i' > 0$. Define s_i by

$$s_i = |a_{ii}| - r_i' \tag{7.3.10}$$

and

$$s_{\min} = \min\{s_1, s_2, \ldots, s_n\}$$

So **A** is strictly diagonally dominant implies that $|\lambda| \ge s_{\min} > 0$ must hold for each eigenvalue of **A** and, therefore, **A** is nonsingular.

Example 7.3.5. The matrix

$$\mathbf{A} = \begin{bmatrix} 2 & 1 & 0 \\ 1 & 2 & 0 \\ 0 & 1 & 2 \end{bmatrix}$$

is nonsingular because it is strictly diagonally dominant.

Example 7.3.6. Suppose the diagonal entries of **A** are positive and **A** is strictly diagonally dominant. Show that the eigenvalues of **A** must have positive real parts.

Solution. The hypothesis specifies the Gerschgorin disks in this manner: Since $a_{ii} > r' \ge 0, |\lambda - a_{ii}| \le r' < a_{ii}$ is a disk with its center on the positive axis and with radius less than the distance from the center to the origin. See Fig. 7.3. All points in such a disk, and therefore all the eigenvalues of **A**, have positive real parts.

Theorem 7.3.3. **A** *is strictly diagonally dominant if and only if* $s_{\min} > 0$. *Moreover, if* **A** *is strictly diagonally dominant, then* $|\det(\mathbf{A})| \ge s_{\min}^n$ *and* **A** *is nonsingular.*

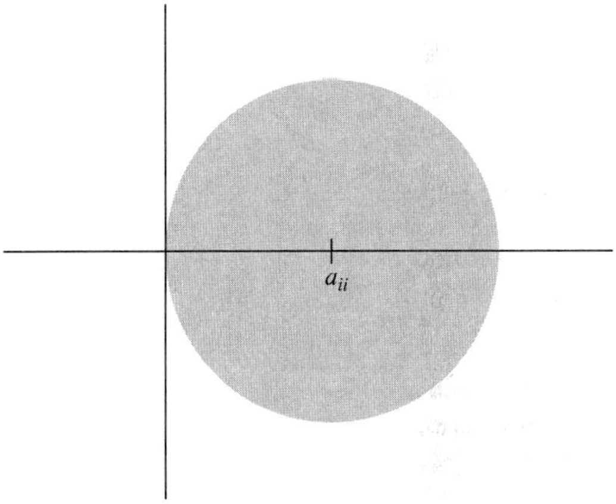

FIGURE 7-3
The open disk $|\lambda - a_{ii}| < a_{ii}$.

Proof. The first assertion is a trivial consequence of the meaning of strict diagonal dominance and $s_{\min}$. If **A** is strictly diagonally dominant, both latter assertions of the theorem follow from the fact that det(**A**) is the product of its eigenvalues and $|\lambda| \geq s_{\min}$. ■

The fact that strictly diagonally dominant matrices are nonsingular is sometimes referred to as the *Levy-Desplanques-Hadamard theorem*. The scalar matrices $k\mathbf{I}$ show that $|\det(\mathbf{A})| = s_{\min}^n$ is possible. Note that the hypothesis of "strict" diagonal dominance cannot be relaxed to read $|a_{ii}| \geq r_i'$, a hypothesis called *diagonal dominance*. The matrix $\mathbf{J}_2$ is diagonally dominant but is singular. The converse of the Levy-Desplanques-Hadamard theorem is false, as shown by the matrix

$$\begin{bmatrix} 1 & 1 \\ 0.9 & 1 \end{bmatrix}$$

which is not strictly diagonally dominant but is nonsingular.

7.3.1 Bounds on the Roots of Polynomials

The various forms of Gerschgorin's theorem have been applied to companion matrices to establish bounds on the location of the zeros of polynomials.[1] Here are two illustrations; the outline of two more are left for the problem set.

Recall that the characteristic equation of the companion matrix

$$\mathbf{C}_n = \begin{bmatrix} 0 & 1 & 0 & \cdots & 0 \\ 0 & 0 & 1 & \cdots & 0 \\ \vdots & \vdots & \vdots & & \vdots \\ 0 & 0 & 0 & \cdots & 1 \\ -a_0 & -a_1 & -a_2 & \cdots & -a_{n-1} \end{bmatrix}$$

is $\lambda^n + a_{n-1}\lambda^{n-1} + \cdots + a_1\lambda + a_0 = 0$. Thus, the zeros of

$$p(z) = z^n + a_{n-1}z^{n-1} + \cdots + a_1 z + a_0$$

are the eigenvalues of $\mathbf{C}_n$. Hence, theorems that bear on the location of the eigenvalues of $\mathbf{C}_n$, describe restrictions on the roots of $p(z)$. In particular, applying Gerschgorin's theorem, Corollary 1, to $\mathbf{C}_n^{\mathrm{T}}$ implies a theorem of Cauchy:

The zeros of $p(z) = z^n + a_{n-1}z^{n-1} + \cdots + a_1 z + a_0$ *lie in the disk* $|z| \leq \max\{|a_0|, 1 + |a_1|, \ldots, 1 + |a_{n-1}|\}$.

A generalization of this theorem due to Ballieu, and sometimes called the *Ballieu-Cauchy* theorem, is based on precisely the same idea but applied to the similar

---

[1]See Howard E. Bell, "Gerschgorin's Theorem and the Zeros of Polynomials," *Amer. Math. Monthly* 72, no. 3, 1965 pp. 292–295.

matrix $\mathbf{D}^{-1}\mathbf{C}_n\mathbf{D}$. Using Eq. 7.3.9 with $\nu_n = 1$,

$$\mathbf{D}^{-1}\mathbf{C}_n\mathbf{D} = \begin{bmatrix} 0 & \nu_2\nu_1^{-1} & 0 & \cdots & 0 \\ 0 & 0 & \nu_3\nu_2^{-1} & \cdots & 0 \\ \vdots & & & & \\ 0 & 0 & 0 & \cdots & \nu_{n-1}^{-1} \\ -a_0\nu_1 & -a_1\nu_2 & -a_2\nu_3 & \cdots & -a_{n-1} \end{bmatrix} \tag{7.3.11}$$

Thus, for any set of positive scalars $\nu_i, i = 1,2,\ldots,n-1$,

$$|z| \le \max\{|a_0\nu_1|, \frac{\nu_{i+1}}{\nu_i} + |a_i\nu_{i+1}|\} \tag{7.3.12}$$

Gerschgorin's theorem has been studied in great detail, and a number of interesting and important extensions have been made. One of the more striking illustrations is this: The disks $|\lambda - a_{ii}| \le r_i'$ generally overlap. In the event that a Gerschgorin disk is disjoint from the remaining disks, it has been proved that there must be an eigenvalue of $\mathbf{A}$ in such a disk.

PROBLEMS

PART 1

7.3.1. Find $s_{\min}$ for the matrix $k\mathbf{I}$. Show that $|\det(k\mathbf{I})| = s_{\min}^n$.

7.3.2. Find the Gerschgorin disks for the matrices

(*a*) $\begin{bmatrix} 4 & 3 & 2 \\ 2 & 4 & 3 \\ 3 & 2 & 4 \end{bmatrix}$ (*b*) Λ_n (*c*) $\mathbf{J}_n$ (*d*) $\begin{bmatrix} i & 1 \\ -i & 0 \end{bmatrix}$ (*e*) $\begin{bmatrix} \cos\varphi & \sin\varphi \\ -\sin\varphi & \cos\varphi \end{bmatrix}$

7.3.3. Determine an upper bound for the spectral radius of each matrix in Problem 7.3.2.

7.3.4. Verify that the matrix in Example 7.3.5 is strictly diagonally dominant, find $s_{\min}$, and compare $|\det(\mathbf{A})|$ with $s_{\min}^3$.

PART 2

7.3.5. Use the fact that $\mathbf{A}^{\mathrm{T}}$ has the same characteristic equation as $\mathbf{A}$ to formulate a Gerschgorin theorem for column sums.

7.3.6. Let $a_{\max} = \max\{|a_{ij}|; i,j = 1,2,\ldots,n\}$ and $r_{\max} = \max\{r_1,r_2,\ldots,r_n\}$.
(*a*) Show that $r_{\max} \le n a_{\max}$. (*b*) Show that $\rho(\mathbf{A}) \le n a_{\max}$.

7.3.7. Show that $|\det(\mathbf{A})| \le r_{\max}^n$.

7.3.8. Show that $\mathbf{P}^2 = \mathbf{P}, \mathbf{P} \ne \mathbf{I}$ cannot be strictly diagonally dominant.

7.3.9. Show that the sum of Eq. 7.3.5, can also be written

$$-\sum_{j=1}^{n}{}' a_{mj}u_j = \sum_{j=1}^{n}(\delta_{mj} - 1)a_{mj}u_j$$

7.3.10. Suppose $\mathbf{A}$ given and $\mathbf{D}(r)$ is the diagonal matrix defined in Eq. 7.3.7 with $\nu_i = r_i = |a_{i1}| + |a_{i2}| + \cdots + |a_{in}| = \sum_{k=1}^n |a_{ik}|$. Define $\mathbf{B} = \mathbf{D}(r^{-1})\mathbf{A}$.

Show that the sums of the absolute values in each row of **B** is 1. Hence, using the result of Problem 7.3.7, show that det(**B**) $\le 1 = \det(\mathbf{A})/r_1 r_2 \ldots r_n$. Use this to prove the following upper bound: det(**A**) $\le r_1 r_2 \ldots r_n$.

7.3.11. Consider the *triadiagonal* matrix

$$\begin{bmatrix} d & e & & & & \\ e & d & e & & & \\ & e & d & e & 0 & \\ & & & \ddots & & \\ & 0 & & e & d & e \\ & & & & e & d \end{bmatrix}$$

For what values of e can we be assured that the given matrix is nonsingular?

PART 3

7.3.12. Suppose $p(z) = a_n z^n + a_{n-1} z^{n-1} + \cdots + a_1 z + a_0$. Use Eq. 7.3.12 with $\nu_i^{-1} = a_i$ to establish bounds on the zeros of $p(z)$ due to Kojima:

$$|z| \le \max\left\{\left|\frac{a_0}{a_1}\right|, 2\left|\frac{a_1}{a_2}\right|, \ldots, 2\left|\frac{a_{n-1}}{a_n}\right|\right\}$$

7.3.13. (*a*) Find the inverse of the companion matrix $\mathbf{C}_n$.

(*b*) Let $\mathbf{D} = \mathbf{D}(\nu)$, where $\nu_i = \rho^{i-1}$, and compute the similar matrix $\mathbf{D}\mathbf{C}_n^{-1}\mathbf{D}^{-1}$.

(*c*) Apply Gerschgorin's theorem to deduce the following bounds on the zeros of $p(z)$:

$$|z| \le \max\left\{\frac{|a_0| + |a_i|\rho^i}{|a_0|\rho.}\right\}$$

7.3.14. Assume that $p(0) \ne 0$ for $p(z)$ given in Problem 7.3.12.

(*a*) Show that the zeros of $z^n p(1/z)$ are the reciprocals of the zeros of $p(z)$.

(*b*) Let $M = \max\{|a_1\rho|, |a_2\rho^2|, \ldots, |a_n\rho^n|\}$. Use the bounds on the zeros of $p(z)$ given by part (*c*) of Problem 7.3.13 to prove the following lower bound on the zeros of $p(z)$ due to Landau and Markovitch: The zeros of $p(z)$ satisfy

$$|z| \ge \frac{|a_0|\rho}{|a_0| + M}$$

for each fixed positive ρ.

7.4 THE FROBENIUS MATRIX NORM

The length of a line segment provides the motivation for the definition of (euclidean) norm for vectors. There are no intuitively plausible models to suggest a "natural" definition of matrix norm. Indeed, many definitions are possible; in fact, an extensive, abstract theory of norms has been developed not only for vectors and matrices, but for the general context of *normed linear spaces*. We have no intention of exploring this advanced theory; rather, we choose a definition that is plausible, easy to evaluate, and useful in practice.

To this end, define the *Frobenius norm* of the square matrix $\mathbf{A}$, written $\|\mathbf{A}\|$, as the square root of the sum of the squares of the absolute values of the entries of $\mathbf{A}$. That is,

$$\|\mathbf{A}\|^2 = \sum |a_{ij}|^2 \tag{7.4.1}$$

(Summations without upper and lower limits are sums over all values of the indices.) If $\mathbf{A} = [\mathbf{a}_1 \ \ \mathbf{a}_2 \ \ \ldots \ \ \mathbf{a}_n]$, then

$$\begin{aligned} \|\mathbf{A}\|^2 &= \sum |a_{ij}|^2 = \mathbf{a}_1^{\mathrm{H}}\mathbf{a}_1 + \mathbf{a}_2^{\mathrm{H}}\mathbf{a}_2 + \cdots + \mathbf{a}_n^{\mathrm{H}}\mathbf{a}_n \\ &= \|\mathbf{a}_1\|^2 + \|\mathbf{a}_2\|^2 + \cdots + \|\mathbf{a}_n\|^2 \end{aligned} \tag{7.4.2}$$

Thus, $\|\mathbf{A}\|^2$ is the sum of squares of the hermitian norms of its columns. A compact way of expressing these two equivalent formulations of the norm of $\mathbf{A}$ is given in the following example.

Example 7.4.1. Show that $\|\mathbf{A}\|^2 = \mathrm{tr}(\mathbf{A}^{\mathrm{H}}\mathbf{A})$ and $\|\mathbf{A}\|^2 \geq \sum |a_{ii}|^2$.

Solution. Equation 7.4.2 and the definition of trace yield $\mathrm{tr}(\mathbf{A}^{\mathrm{H}}\mathbf{A}) = \mathbf{a}_1^{\mathrm{H}}\mathbf{a}_1 + \mathbf{a}_2^{\mathrm{H}}\mathbf{a}_2 + \cdots + \mathbf{a}_n^{\mathrm{H}}\mathbf{a}_n$. Clearly, $\sum |a_{ii}|^2 \leq \sum |a_{ij}|^2$.

Example 7.4.2. Compute the norms of the following matrices:

(*a*) $\mathbf{I}_n$ (*b*) $\mathbf{J}_n$ (*c*) $\mathbf{U}$ is unitary
(*d*) $\mathbf{D}$ is diagonal (*e*) $\mathbf{O}_n$ (*f*) $\mathbf{x}_n$

Solution. The definition of matrix norm applied to $\mathbf{I}_n$ and $\mathbf{J}_n$ yields $\|\mathbf{I}_n\| = \sqrt{n}$ and $\|\mathbf{J}_n\| = n$, respectively. Applied to $\mathbf{D} = [\ldots \ \ d_i\mathbf{e}_i \ \ \ldots]$, the definition yields $\|\mathbf{D}\|^2 = \sum |d_i|^2$. If $\mathbf{U}$ is unitary, $\|\mathbf{U}\|^2 = \mathrm{tr}(\mathbf{U}^{\mathrm{H}}\mathbf{U}) = \mathrm{tr}(\mathbf{I}) = n$. Clearly, $\|\mathbf{O}\| = 0$. Finally $\|\mathbf{x}\|^2$, either as a vector or matrix, is $\sum |x_i|^2$.

Example 7.4.3. Show that $\|\mathbf{Ax}\| \leq \|\mathbf{A}\|\|\mathbf{x}\|$.

Solution. The expression $\|\mathbf{Ax}\|$ represents a hermitian vector norm. Since the entries of $\mathbf{Ax}$ are $\mathbf{a}_i^{\mathrm{T}}\mathbf{x}$, the Schwarz inequality leads to

$$\begin{aligned} \|\mathbf{Ax}\|^2 &= |\mathbf{a}_1^{\mathrm{T}}\mathbf{x}|^2 + |\mathbf{a}_2^{\mathrm{T}}\mathbf{x}|^2 + \cdots + |\mathbf{a}_n^{\mathrm{T}}\mathbf{x}|^2 \\ &\leq \|\mathbf{a}_1\|^2\|\mathbf{x}\|^2 + \|\mathbf{a}_2\|^2\|\mathbf{x}\|^2 + \cdots + \|\mathbf{a}_n\|^2\|\mathbf{x}\|^2 = \|\mathbf{A}\|^2\|\mathbf{x}\|^2 \end{aligned}$$

where the last equality is a consequence of Eq. 7.4.2.

In order that a norm capture some of the essential ingredients of a measure of "size," we demand that $\|\mathbf{A}\|$ be nonnegative, and zero if and only if $\mathbf{A} = \mathbf{O}$. In fact, $\|\mathbf{A}\|$ satisfies a good deal more.

Theorem 7.4.1. *For all scalars k and matrices* **A** *and* **B**,

(*a*) $\|k\mathbf{A}\| = |k|\|\mathbf{A}\|$ (*b*) $\|\mathbf{A}\| \geq 0$ (*c*) $\|\mathbf{A}\| = 0$ *if and only if* $\mathbf{A} = \mathbf{O}$
(*d*) $\|\mathbf{A} + \mathbf{B}\| \leq \|\mathbf{A}\| + \|\mathbf{B}\|$ (*e*) $\|\mathbf{AB}\| \leq \|\mathbf{A}\|\|\mathbf{B}\|$

Proof. Properties (*a*)–(*c*) are obvious from the definition. Property (*d*) follows from Eq. 7.4.2 and the corresponding result for vectors, $\|\mathbf{x} + \mathbf{y}\|^2 \leq \|\mathbf{x}\|^2 + \|\mathbf{y}\|^2$. (See Corollary 1 of Theorem 6.1.2.)

$$\begin{aligned} \|\mathbf{A} + \mathbf{B}\|^2 &= \|\mathbf{a}_1 + \mathbf{b}_1\|^2 + \|\mathbf{a}_2 + \mathbf{b}_2\|^2 + \cdots + \|\mathbf{a}_n + \mathbf{b}_n\|^2 \\ &\leq \|\mathbf{a}_1\|^2 + \|\mathbf{b}_1\|^2 + \|\mathbf{a}_2\|^2 + \|\mathbf{b}_2\|^2 + \cdots + \|\mathbf{a}_n\|^2 + \|\mathbf{b}_n\|^2 \\ &= \|\mathbf{A}\|^2 + \|\mathbf{B}\|^2 \end{aligned}$$

The last inequality, (*e*), is proved by noting that

$$\mathbf{AB} = \mathbf{A}[\mathbf{b}_1 \ \ \mathbf{b}_2 \ \ \ldots \ \ \mathbf{b}_n] = [\mathbf{Ab}_1 \ \ \mathbf{Ab}_2 \ \ \ldots \ \ \mathbf{Ab}_n]$$

and therefore, from Eq. 7.4.2,

$$\begin{aligned} \|\mathbf{AB}\|^2 &= \|\mathbf{Ab}_1\|^2 + \|\mathbf{Ab}_2\|^2 + \cdots + \|\mathbf{Ab}_n\|^2 \\ &\leq \|\mathbf{A}\|^2\left(\|\mathbf{b}_1\|^2 + \|\mathbf{b}_2\|^2 + \cdots + \|\mathbf{b}_n\|^2\right) = \|\mathbf{A}\|^2\|\mathbf{B}\|^2 \ \blacksquare \end{aligned}$$

A few other elementary observations are in order. Note that $\|\mathbf{A}\| = \|\overline{\mathbf{A}}\| = \|\mathbf{A}^{\mathrm{T}}\| = \|\mathbf{A}^{\mathrm{H}}\|$. A slightly more complicated procedure is required to prove $\|\mathbf{AB}\| = \|\mathbf{BA}\|$, and this is left for the exercise set. (See Problems 7.4.12 and 7.4.13.)

Theorem 7.4.2. *If* **U** *is unitary, then* $\|\mathbf{A}\| = \|\mathbf{UA}\| = \|\mathbf{AU}\|$.

Proof. Verify the chain of equalities

$$\|\mathbf{UA}\|^2 = \mathrm{tr}\left[(\mathbf{UA})^{\mathrm{H}}(\mathbf{UA})\right] = \mathrm{tr}(\mathbf{A}^{\mathrm{H}}\mathbf{U}^{\mathrm{H}}\mathbf{UA}) = \mathrm{tr}(\mathbf{A}^{\mathrm{H}}\mathbf{A}) = \|\mathbf{A}\|^2$$

and

$$\|\mathbf{AU}\| = \|(\mathbf{AU})^{\mathrm{H}}\| = \|\mathbf{U}^{\mathrm{H}}\mathbf{A}^{\mathrm{H}}\| = \|\mathbf{A}^{\mathrm{H}}\| = \|\mathbf{A}\|$$

The latter equalities follow from $\|\mathbf{C}^{\mathrm{H}}\| = \|\mathbf{C}\|$ and the fact that $\mathbf{U}^{\mathrm{H}}$ is unitary and, hence, for every **C**, $\|\mathbf{U}^{\mathrm{H}}\mathbf{C}\| = \|\mathbf{C}\|$. ■

Corollary 1. *If* **A** *and* **B** *are unitarily similar, then* $\|\mathbf{A}\| = \|\mathbf{B}\|$

Proof. By hypothesis, there exists a unitary matrix **U** such that $\mathbf{U}^{\mathrm{H}}\mathbf{AU} = \mathbf{B}$. By Theorem 7.4.2, $\|\mathbf{B}\| = \|\mathbf{U}^{\mathrm{H}}\mathbf{AU}\| = \|\mathbf{A}\|$. ■

Corollary 2. *If* **A** *is normal with eigenvalues* $\lambda_1, \lambda_2, \ldots, \lambda_n$, *then*

$$\|\mathbf{A}\|^2 = |\lambda_1|^2 + |\lambda_2|^2 + \cdots + |\lambda_n|^2$$

Proof. By Corollary 1 and $\mathbf{U}^{\mathrm{H}}\mathbf{AU} = \Lambda$. ■

Corollary 2 suggests a strong connection between the norm of **A** and its eigenvalues. Indeed, by Schur's theorem, we have $\mathbf{U}^{\mathrm{H}}\mathbf{A}\mathbf{U} = \mathbf{T}$ for some unitary matrix **U** and some upper triangular matrix **T**. The eigenvalues of **A** are displayed along the diagonal of **T**. Hence, by Corollary 1 and the definition of the Frobenius norm,

$$\|\mathbf{A}\|^2 = \|\mathbf{T}\|^2 = \sum_{i=1}^{n} |\lambda_i|^2 + \sum_{i<j}^{n} |t_{ij}^2| \tag{7.4.3}$$

Equation 7.4.3 yields a number of interesting conclusions, which are stated in the following theorem and its corollaries.

Theorem 7.4.3. *Let $\lambda_1, \lambda_2, \ldots, \lambda_n$ be the eigenvalues of* **A**. *Then*

$$\|\mathbf{A}\|^2 \geq \sum_{i=1}^{n} |\lambda_i|^2 \tag{7.4.4}$$

and, hence, $\rho(\mathbf{A}) \leq \|\mathbf{A}\|$. Equality holds in Eq. 7.4.4 if and only if **A** *is normal.*

Proof. The inequality follows from Eq. 7.4.3 by discarding the nonnegative sum of the squares of the off-diagonal entries of **T**. From $|\lambda|^2 \leq \Sigma|\lambda_i|^2 \leq \|\mathbf{A}\|^2$ for every λ, and the fact that $\rho(\mathbf{A}) = |\lambda|$ for the eigenvalue of largest modulus, it follows that $\rho^2(\mathbf{A}) \leq \|\mathbf{A}\|^2$. Finally, equality holds in Eq. 7.4.4 if and only if **T** is diagonal. But **T** is diagonal if and only if **A** is normal. ■

Corollary 1. *Set* $a_{\max} = \max\{|a_{ij}|;\ i, j = 1, 2, \ldots, n\}$. *Then*

$$\|\mathbf{A}\| \leq n a_{\max} \text{ and } |\det(\mathbf{A})|^{1/n} \leq n^{1/2} a_{\max}$$

Proof. The definition of $\|\mathbf{A}\|$ yields $\|\mathbf{A}\| \leq n a_{\max}$, since there are n^2 terms in the sum Eq. 7.4.1. Now the geometric mean of any set of nonnegative numbers is never greater than the arithmetic mean of these numbers. That is,

$$(p_1 p_2 \ldots p_n)^{1/n} \leq \frac{p_1 + p_2 + \cdots + p_n}{n}$$

Let $p_i = |\lambda_i|^2$. Then

$$|\det(\mathbf{A})|^2 = |\lambda_1|^2|\lambda_2|^2 \ldots |\lambda_n|^2 \leq \left[(|\lambda_1|^2 + |\lambda_2|^2 + \cdots + |\lambda_n|^2)/n\right]^n$$

$$\leq \left[\frac{1}{n}\|\mathbf{A}\|^2\right]^n \leq \left[\frac{1}{n} n^2 a_{\max}^2\right]^n = (n a_{\max}^2)^n \quad ■$$

Arguments similar to the ones just offered can be used to deduce inequalities on the real and imaginary parts of λ. For this purpose, write **A** as the sum of a hermitian and skew-hermitian matrix, namely,

$$\mathbf{A} = ½(\mathbf{A} + \mathbf{A}^{\mathrm{H}}) + ½(\mathbf{A} - \mathbf{A}^{\mathrm{H}})$$

For convenience, set $\mathbf{A}_H = \frac{1}{2}(\mathbf{A}+\mathbf{A}^{\mathrm{H}})$ and $\mathbf{A}_S = \frac{1}{2}(\mathbf{A}-\mathbf{A}^{\mathrm{H}})$. Clearly, $\mathbf{A}_H$ is hermitian and $\mathbf{A}_S$ is skew-hermitian. These matrices have real and purely imaginary eigenvalues, respectively.

Theorem 7.4.4. *If the eigenvalues of* $\mathbf{A}$ *are* $\lambda_1, \lambda_2, \ldots, \lambda_n$, *then*

$$(a)\ \|\mathbf{A}_H\|^2 \geq \sum_{i=1}^{n} \left(\mathrm{Re}(\lambda_i)\right)^2 \qquad (b)\ \|\mathbf{A}_S\|^2 \geq \sum_{i=1}^{n} \left(\mathrm{Im}(\lambda_i)\right)^2$$

Proof. For some unitary matrix $\mathbf{U}$, $\mathbf{U}^{\mathrm{H}}\mathbf{A}\mathbf{U} = \mathbf{T}$, and $\mathbf{U}^{\mathrm{H}}\mathbf{A}^{\mathrm{H}}\mathbf{U} = \mathbf{T}^{\mathrm{H}}$. Hence, $\mathbf{A}_H = \frac{1}{2}\mathbf{U}^{\mathrm{H}}(\mathbf{T} + \mathbf{T}^{\mathrm{H}})\mathbf{U}$. So,

$$\|\mathbf{A}_H\| = \tfrac{1}{2}\|\mathbf{U}^{\mathrm{H}}(\mathbf{T} + \mathbf{T}^{\mathrm{H}})\mathbf{U}\| = \tfrac{1}{2}\|\mathbf{T} + \mathbf{T}^{\mathrm{H}}\|$$

The diagonal entries of $\mathbf{T} + \mathbf{T}^{\mathrm{H}}$ are $2\,\mathrm{Re}(\lambda_i)$. (Note that $\mathbf{T} + \mathbf{T}^{\mathrm{H}}$ is not triangular and its diagonal entries are not its eigenvalues.) Now invoke Example 7.4.1 to prove (a). The proof for (b) is accomplished by using $\mathbf{A}_S$ in place of $\mathbf{A}_H$ and the observation that the diagonal entries of $\mathbf{T} - \mathbf{T}^{\mathrm{H}}$ are $(2i)\mathrm{Im}(\lambda_i)$. ■

The inequalities in (a) and (b) of Theorem 7.4.4 can be used to deduce bounds on $|\mathrm{Re}(\lambda)|$ and $|\mathrm{Im}(\lambda)|$ in terms of the maximum entry in $\mathbf{A}_H$ and $\mathbf{A}_S$, in much the same way that the bounds were deduced in Corollary 1 of Theorem 7.4.3. These deductions are set as Problem 7.4.16. A more interesting inequality is given in the next corollary. First define $e_{\max} = \max(|a_{ij} - a_{ji}|/2)$, the maximum taken over all i and j.

Corollary 1. *Suppose* $\mathbf{A}$ *is real. Then* $|\mathrm{Im}(\lambda_i)| \leq e_{\max}\sqrt{n(n-1)/2}$

Proof. If $\mathbf{A}$ is real, then $\mathbf{A}_S = \frac{1}{2}(\mathbf{A} - \mathbf{A}^{\mathrm{T}})$ and its entries are $(a_{ij} - a_{ji})/2$. But then, by Theorem 7.4.4,

$$\sum_{i=1}^{n} \left(\mathrm{Im}(\lambda_i)\right)^2 \leq \|\mathbf{A}_S\|^2 = \sum_{i \neq j} (a_{ij} - a_{ji})^2/4 \leq n(n-1)e_{\max}^2$$

The factor $n(n-1)$ arises because there are exactly this many off-diagonal entries. Finally, because $\mathbf{A}$ is real, its eigenvalues come in complex conjugate pairs. For each fixed k, $(\mathrm{Im}(\lambda_k))^2 = (\mathrm{Im}(\bar{\lambda}_k))^2$. Hence,

$$2\left(\mathrm{Im}(\lambda_k)\right)^2 \leq \sum_{i=1}^{n} \left(\mathrm{Im}(\lambda_i)\right)^2 \leq n(n-1)e_{\max}^2$$

The assertion now follows by taking roots. ■

If Corollary 1 of Theorem 7.4.4 is applied to real symmetric matrices, then, since $e_{\max} = 0$, it follows that $|\mathrm{Im}(\lambda_i)| \leq 0$. That is, $\mathrm{Im}(\lambda_i) = 0$, and thus the eigenvalues of a real symmetric matrix are real—not the most expeditious proof of this theorem!

7.4.1 The Frobenius Norm in MATLAB

Suppose $\mathbf{A}$ is $m \times n$. The command norm(A,'fro') returns the scalar

$$\left[\sum |a_{ij}|^2\right]^{1/2}$$

the sum extended over all indices i, j. Note that norm(x,'fro') returns $\|\mathbf{x}\|$ and norm(A,'fro') returns $\|\mathbf{A}\|$ if $\mathbf{A}$ is a square matrix.

PROBLEMS

PART 1

7.4.1. Find the frobenius norms of these matrices:

(*a*) $\begin{bmatrix} \cos\tau & \sin\tau \\ \sin\tau & \sin\tau \end{bmatrix}$ (*b*) $\begin{bmatrix} \cos\tau & \sin\tau \\ -\sin\tau & \sin\tau \end{bmatrix}$ (*c*) $\begin{bmatrix} i & -i \\ 1 & 0 \end{bmatrix}$ (*d*) $[a]$

7.4.2. For each matrix in Problem 7.4.1 compute $\|\mathbf{A}^2\|$ and $\|\mathbf{A}\|^2$ and compare the two.

7.4.3. Let $M = \|\mathbf{A}\|$. Show that $\mathbf{A}/M$ has norm 1 if $\mathbf{A} \neq \mathbf{O}$.

PART 2

7.4.4. Prove Parts (*a*)–(*c*) of Theorem 7.4.1.

7.4.5. Complete the proof of Part (*e*) of Theorem 7.4.1.

7.4.6. Let $(\lambda, \mathbf{x})$ be an eigenpair of A. Use the result in Example 7.4.3 to show that $|\lambda| \leq \|\mathbf{A}\|$.

7.4.7. Suppose $\mathbf{D}$ is a diagonal matrix with nonzero diagonal entries $a, a^2, \ldots, a^n$. Compute $\|\mathbf{D}^{-1}\mathbf{A}\mathbf{D}\|^2$.

7.4.8. Use Theorem 7.4.4 to show that a hermitian matrix has only real eigenvalues and a skew-hermitian matrix has only pure imaginary eigenvalues.

7.4.9. If $\mathbf{P} \neq \mathbf{O}$ is idempotent ($\mathbf{P}^2 = \mathbf{P}$), show that $1 \leq \|\mathbf{P}\|$. Is equality possible?

7.4.10. If $\mathbf{M}$ is involutory ($\mathbf{M}^2 = \mathbf{I}$), show that $\sqrt{n} \leq \|\mathbf{M}\|$. Is equality possible?

7.4.11. Find a 2×2 example of a simple matrix $\mathbf{A}$ for which $\|\mathbf{A}\|^2 > \sum_{i=1}^{n} \|\lambda_i\|^2$.

PART 3

7.4.12. Show that tr(**ABC**) = tr(**BCA**). (*Hint:* tr(**EF**) = tr(**FE**).)

7.4.13. Show that $\|\mathbf{AB}\| = \|\mathbf{BA}\|$ by using $\|\mathbf{AB}\|^2 = \mathrm{tr}[(\mathbf{AB})^{\mathrm{H}}(\mathbf{AB})]$ and the result of Problem 7.4.12.

7.4.14. Suppose $\|\mathbf{A}\| = M$, and $\mathbf{A}$ is invertible. Show that $\|\mathbf{A}^{-1}\| \geq n/M$. Find matrices for which $\|\mathbf{A}^{-1}\| = n/M$.

7.4.15. Prove: If $\mathbf{P}$ is idempotent, then $\|\mathbf{P}\|^2 \geq \mathrm{rank}(\mathbf{P})$.

7.4.16. Let $\sigma = \max|\mathrm{Re}(\lambda_i)|$ and $\tau = \max|\mathrm{Im}(\lambda_i)|$, the maxima taken over all the eigenvalues of $\mathbf{A}$. Show that $\sigma \leq \|\mathbf{A}_H\|$ and $\tau \leq \|\mathbf{A}_S\|$, where $\mathbf{A}_H$ and $\mathbf{A}_S$ are defined as in Theorem 7.4.1.

MATLAB

Compute the norms of the matrices in Problems 7.4.17–7.4.19 by using the command norm(A,'fro').

7.4.17. (*a*) $\begin{bmatrix} \cos\pi/4 & \sin\pi/4 \\ \sin\pi/4 & \sin\pi/4 \end{bmatrix}$ (*b*) $\begin{bmatrix} i & -i \\ 1 & 0 \end{bmatrix}$ (*c*) $[1+i]$

7.4.18. (*a*) $\mathbf{I}_5$ (*b*) $\mathbf{J}_5$

7.4.19. For $\mathbf{u} = [1 \quad -1 \quad 1]^{\mathrm{T}}$ and $\mathbf{v} = [2 \quad 0 \quad -3]$:

(*a*) $\mathbf{u}$ (*b*) $\mathbf{v}$ (*c*) $\mathbf{u}\mathbf{v}^{\mathrm{T}}$

7.4.20. Let

$$\mathbf{A} = \begin{bmatrix} 1 & 0 & -1 \\ 0 & 1 & 2 \\ 1 & 1 & 0 \end{bmatrix}$$

Use the command [Q,R] = qr(A) to find the **QR** factorization of **A** and eig(A) to find the eigenvalues of **A**.

7.4.21. For the matrix in Problem 7.4.20, find

(*a*) $\|\mathbf{A}\|$ (*b*) $\|\mathbf{Q}\|$, $\|\mathbf{R}\|$, and $\|\mathbf{Q}\|\,\|\mathbf{R}\|$ (*c*) $\sum|\lambda_i|^2$ (*d*) $|\det(\mathbf{A})|^{1/3}$

7.4.22. Verify $|\det(\mathbf{A})|^{1/n} \le n^{1/2}a_{\max}$ for the matrix of Problem 7.4.20.

7.4.23. Verify $\|\mathbf{A}\|^2 \ge \sum|\lambda_i|^2$ for the matrix of Problem 7.4.20.

7.5 THE LIMIT OF $\mathbf{A}^m$ FOR $\rho(\mathbf{A}) \ne 1$

Exactly four cases arise for the limit of a^m as $m \to \infty$. If $|a| < 1$, then $a^m \to 0$; if $|a| > 1$, then $\lim(a^m)$ does not exist; if $a = 1$, then, of course, $a^m \to 1$; and finally, if $|a| = 1$ but $a \ne 1$, then $\lim(a^m)$ does not exist. The situation for square matrices is at least this complicated for two reasons: First, the powers of the scalar matrix $a\mathbf{I}$ behave precisely as the powers of the scalar a. Second, if $\mathbf{A}$ is diagonal with entries $d_1, d_2, \ldots, d_n$, then $\mathbf{A}^m$ is the diagonal matrix with entries $d_1^m, d_2^m, \ldots, d_n^m$, and $\lim(\mathbf{A}^m)$ depends on n separate scalar limits. In this section we treat the case analogous to $|a| \ne 1$, by finding a necessary and sufficient condition for $\lim(\mathbf{A}^m) = \mathbf{O}$.

Let $\mathbf{A}_1, \mathbf{A}_2, \ldots, \mathbf{A}_m$ be a sequence of $n \times n$ matrices whose entries we denote by $\mathbf{A}_m = (a_{ij}^{(m)})$. This sequence is said to converge if the n^2 scalar limits, $\lim_{m\to\infty} a_{ij}^{(m)}$ exist. Set $\lim_{m\to\infty} a_{ij}^{(m)} = a_{ij}^{(\infty)}$ and define $\mathbf{A}_\infty = (a_{ij}^{(\infty)})$. Write

$$\lim(\mathbf{A}_m) = \mathbf{A}_\infty \tag{7.5.1}$$

to indicate that $\lim_{m\to\infty} a_{ij}^{(m)} = a_{ij}^{(\infty)}$ exists for each i and j. (It is often convenient to write $\mathbf{A}_m \to \mathbf{A}_\infty$ to express Eq. 7.5.1.) The following example illustrates the care that must be taken in transferring results from the scalar theory to the theory of matrix limits.

Example 7.5.1. Suppose

$$\mathbf{A} = \begin{bmatrix} 1 & 1 \\ 0 & 0 \end{bmatrix}, \qquad \mathbf{B} = \begin{bmatrix} 1 & 0 \\ 1 & 0 \end{bmatrix}$$

Then $\mathbf{A}^2 = \mathbf{A}$ and $\mathbf{B}^2 = \mathbf{B}$, so that $\mathbf{A}^m \to \mathbf{A}$ and $\mathbf{B}^m \to \mathbf{B}$. However,

$$\mathbf{AB} = \begin{bmatrix} 1 & 1 \\ 0 & 0 \end{bmatrix}\begin{bmatrix} 1 & 0 \\ 1 & 0 \end{bmatrix} = \begin{bmatrix} 2 & 0 \\ 0 & 0 \end{bmatrix}$$

and $(\mathbf{AB})^m$ diverges, because

$$(\mathbf{AB})^m = \begin{bmatrix} 2^m & 0 \\ 0 & 0 \end{bmatrix}$$

The upshot of this is: Although $\lim(ab)^m$ converges to $\lim(a^m)\lim(b^n)$ if $\lim(a^m)$ and $\lim(b^n)$ exist, this is not the case for $\lim(\mathbf{AB})^m$.

Example 7.5.2. Let $\mathbf{A}_m = \mathbf{A}^m$. Determine whether $\lim(\mathbf{A}^m)$ exists for each of the following matrices, and if it does, find the limit.

$(a)\ \begin{bmatrix} -1 & 0 \\ 0 & 1 \end{bmatrix} \qquad (b)\ \begin{bmatrix} 0 & 3 & 6 \\ 0 & 0 & 2 \\ 0 & 0 & 0 \end{bmatrix} \qquad (c)\ \mathbf{J}_n/n \qquad (d)\ \begin{bmatrix} \frac{1}{2} & a \\ 0 & \frac{1}{2} \end{bmatrix}$

Solution. (a) $\mathbf{A}^m$ diverges because $a_{11}^{(m)} = (-1)^m$. (b) $\mathbf{A}^m \to \mathbf{O}$ because $\mathbf{A}^m = \mathbf{O}$ for $m \geq 3$. For part (c), use $(\mathbf{J}_n/n)^m = \mathbf{J}_n/n$ to deduce that $(\mathbf{J}_n/n)^m \to \mathbf{J}_n/n$. Part (d) is more complicated. Compute the explicit expression for the entries of $\mathbf{A}^m$ and find

$$\mathbf{A}^m = \begin{bmatrix} \frac{1}{2} & a \\ 0 & \frac{1}{2} \end{bmatrix}^m = \begin{bmatrix} (\frac{1}{2})^m & m(\frac{1}{2})^{m-1}a \\ 0 & (\frac{1}{2})^m \end{bmatrix} \to \mathbf{O}$$

because $m(\frac{1}{2})^m \to 0$ as $m \to \infty$.

If $\mathbf{A}_m \to \mathbf{A}_\infty$, then $\mathbf{CA}_m \to \mathbf{CA}_\infty$ and $\mathbf{A}_m\mathbf{B} \to \mathbf{A}_\infty\mathbf{B}$. On the other hand, if $\lim(\mathbf{A}_m)$ does not exist, then $\lim(\mathbf{CA}_m)$ and $\lim(\mathbf{A}_m\mathbf{B})$ also do not exist if $\mathbf{C}$ and $\mathbf{B}$ are *nonsingular*. (See Problems 7.5.4, 7.5.5, and 7.5.6.) Hence, if $\mathbf{A}$ is simple, $\mathbf{A} = \mathbf{S}^{-1}\Lambda\mathbf{S}$ and therefore, $\lim(\mathbf{A}^m)$ exists if and only if $\lim(\Lambda^m)$ exists. Moreover, $\lim(\Lambda^m)$ can contain only zeros and ones on its diagonal since these are the only possible limits of λ^m. The situation is far more subtle if $\mathbf{A}$ is defective.

Example 7.5.3. Determine the choice of parameters a and t for which $\lim(\mathbf{A}^m)$ exists, and find this limit given

$$\mathbf{A} = \begin{bmatrix} 1 & a \\ 0 & t \end{bmatrix}, \qquad a \neq 0$$

Solution. Compute

$$\mathbf{A}^m = \begin{bmatrix} 1 & a \\ 0 & t \end{bmatrix}^m = \begin{bmatrix} 1 & a^{(m)} \\ 0 & t^m \end{bmatrix}$$

where

$$a^{(m)} = a(1 + t + t^2 + \cdots + t^{m-1})$$

Thus, if $|t| \geq 1$, $\lim(\mathbf{A}^m)$ diverges since $a \neq 0$. If, however, $|t| < 1$, then

$$a^{(m)} = a(1 + t + t^2 + \cdots + t^{m-1}) \to a(1 - t)^{-1}$$

Hence, for all $|t| < 1$ and for all a (even $a = 0$),

$$\mathbf{A}_\infty = \lim(\mathbf{A}^m) = \begin{bmatrix} 1 & a(1-t)^{-1} \\ 0 & 0 \end{bmatrix}$$

With these preliminaries to guide us, we can now begin a more detailed analysis of $\lim(\mathbf{A}^m)$. First define a general upper triangular matrix $\mathbf{T}$ and a related matrix $\mathbf{S}(\sigma)$, constructed from $\mathbf{T}$ by altering some of its nonzero entries. Specifically, let $\mathbf{T}$ and $\mathbf{S}(\sigma)$, σ nonnegative, be given by

$$\mathbf{T} = \begin{bmatrix} \lambda_1 & t_{12} & t_{13} & & t_{1n} \\ 0 & \lambda_2 & t_{23} & \cdots & t_{2n} \\ \vdots & \vdots & \vdots & & \vdots \\ 0 & 0 & 0 & \cdots & t_{n-1,n} \\ 0 & 0 & 0 & \cdots & \lambda_n \end{bmatrix}, \qquad \mathbf{S}(\sigma) = \begin{bmatrix} \sigma & |t_{12}| & |t_{13}| & \cdots & |t_{1n}| \\ 0 & \sigma & |t_{23}| & \cdots & |t_{2n}| \\ \vdots & \vdots & \vdots & & \vdots \\ 0 & 0 & 0 & \cdots & |t_{n-1,n}| \\ 0 & 0 & 0 & \cdots & \sigma \end{bmatrix}$$

respectively. Now consider $\mathbf{S}(\sigma)$. First, $\mathbf{S}(\sigma) = \sigma\mathbf{I} + \mathbf{S}(0)$, where $\mathbf{S}(0)$ is $\mathbf{S}(\sigma)$ evaluated at $\sigma = 0$. Since $\mathbf{S}^m(0) = \mathbf{O}$ for all $m \geq n$, by Lemma 6.3 of Section 6.7;[2] and $\mathbf{I}$ commutes with all matrices, $(\sigma\mathbf{I} + \mathbf{S}(0))^m$ may be expanded by the binomial theorem to yield

$$\mathbf{S}^m(\sigma) = \sigma^m\mathbf{I} + \sum_{k=1}^{n-1} C\binom{m}{k}\sigma^{m-k}\mathbf{S}^k(0) \tag{7.5.2}$$

where $C\binom{m}{k}$ is the usual binomial coefficient. Thus, as $m \to \infty$,

$$\lim_{m\to\infty}\left(\mathbf{S}^m(\sigma)\right) = \lim_{m\to\infty}(\sigma^m)\mathbf{I} + \sum_{k=1}^{n-1}\mathbf{S}^k(0)\left[\lim_{m\to\infty}\left(C\binom{m}{k}\sigma^{m-k}\right)\right] \tag{7.5.3}$$

Lemma 7.1. $\mathbf{S}^m(\sigma) \to \mathbf{O}$ *if and only if* $\sigma < 1$.

Proof. The right-hand side of Eq. 7.5.3 is a sum of n terms, each of which tends to 0 as m tends to infinity because $C\binom{m}{k}\sigma^{m-k} \to 0$ for $\sigma < 1$. (See Problem 7.5.7.) If $\sigma > 1$, then $\lim(\sigma^m)\mathbf{I}$ diverges. Finally, if $\sigma = 1$, the diagonal entries of $\mathbf{S}^m(\sigma)$ are all 1s, and hence $\mathbf{S}^m(\sigma)$ cannot tend to $\mathbf{O}$. ■

Example 7.5.4. It is instructive to work through the steps in the preceding argument for a specific example. Consider $\mathbf{T}$ and $\mathbf{S}(\sigma)$ defined as follows:

$$\mathbf{T} = \begin{bmatrix} 0.1 & 3 & -2 \\ 0 & 0.2 & 1 \\ 0 & 0 & 0.1 \end{bmatrix}, \qquad \mathbf{S}(0.2) = \begin{bmatrix} 0.2 & 3 & 2 \\ 0 & 0.2 & 1 \\ 0 & 0 & 0.2 \end{bmatrix}$$

---

[2] $\mathbf{S}^m(0) = \mathbf{O}$ also follows by direct computation, or by the fact that the characteristic equation of $\mathbf{S}(0)$ is $(-\lambda)^n = 0$ and, hence, by the Cayley-Hamilton theorem, $(-\mathbf{S}(0))^n = \mathbf{O}$.

Now apply the binomial theorem to $\mathbf{S}^m(0.2)$, $m \geq 3$.

$$\mathbf{S}^m(0.2) = \left[(0.2)\begin{bmatrix}1&0&0\\0&1&0\\0&0&1\end{bmatrix} + \begin{bmatrix}0&3&2\\0&0&1\\0&0&0\end{bmatrix}\right]^m = (0.2)^m\begin{bmatrix}1&0&0\\0&1&0\\0&0&1\end{bmatrix}$$

$$+m(0.2)^{m-1}\begin{bmatrix}0&3&2\\0&0&1\\0&0&0\end{bmatrix} + \frac{m(m-1)}{2}(0.2)^{m-2}\begin{bmatrix}0&3&2\\0&0&1\\0&0&0\end{bmatrix}^2 +$$

$$\cdots + \begin{bmatrix}0&3&2\\0&0&1\\0&0&0\end{bmatrix}^m$$

Because $\mathbf{S}(0)^m = \mathbf{O}$ for all $m \geq 3$, it follows that

$$\mathbf{S}^m(0.2) = (0.2)^m\begin{bmatrix}1&0&0\\0&1&0\\0&0&1\end{bmatrix} + m(0.2)^{m-1}\begin{bmatrix}0&3&2\\0&0&1\\0&0&0\end{bmatrix}$$

$$+\frac{m(m-1)}{2}(0.2)^{m-2}\begin{bmatrix}0&0&8\\0&0&0\\0&0&0\end{bmatrix}$$

Since

$$\lim_{m\to\infty}(0.2)^m = \lim_{m\to\infty}\left[m(0.2)^{m-1}\right] = \lim_{m\to\infty}\left\{\frac{m(m-1)}{2}(0.2)^{m-2}\right\} = 0$$

it follows that $\mathbf{S}^m(0.2) \to \mathbf{O}$.

Lemma 7.2. $\mathbf{T}^m \to \mathbf{O}$ *if and only if* $\rho(\mathbf{T}) < 1$.

Proof. As usual, the (i, j) entries of $\mathbf{T}^m$ and $\mathbf{S}^m(\sigma)$ are denoted by $t_{ij}^{(m)}$ and $s_{ij}^{(m)}$, respectively. Consider $m = 2$. Set $\sigma = \rho(\mathbf{T})$. By definition of $\mathbf{S}(\sigma)$, $t_{ij} \leq |s_{ij}|$. Then

$$\begin{aligned}|t_{ij}^{(2)}| &= |t_{i1}t_{1j} + t_{i2}t_{2j} + \cdots + t_{in}t_{nj}|\\ &\leq |t_{i1}||t_{1j}| + |t_{i2}||t_{2j}| + \cdots + |t_{in}||t_{nj}|\\ &= s_{i1}s_{1j} + s_{i2}s_{2j} + \cdots + s_{in}s_{ij} = s_{ij}^{(2)}\end{aligned}$$

Use $|t_{ij}^{(2)}| \leq s_{ij}^{(2)}$ and the definition $\mathbf{T}^3 = \mathbf{T}^2\mathbf{T}$ to prove that $|t_{ij}^{(3)}| \leq s_{ij}^{(3)}$ and, by repeating this argument, to establish that $|t_{ij}^{(m)}| \leq s_{ij}^{(m)}$ for all positive integers m. Hence, $t_{ij}^{(m)} \to 0$ if $s_{ij}^{(m)} \to 0$. But $s_{ij}^{(m)} \to 0$ if and only if $\sigma = \rho(\mathbf{T}) < 1$, by Lemma 7.1. Conversely, if $t_{ij}^{(m)} \to 0$, then, since $t_{ii}^{(m)} = t_{ii}^m$, $t_{ii}^m \to 0$, which implies that $|t_{ii}| < 1$. Hence, $\rho(\mathbf{T}) < 1$. ■

We are now in a position to establish the main result of this section, the proof that $\mathbf{A}^m \to \mathbf{O}$ if and only if the spectral radius of $\mathbf{A}$ is less than 1. The proof makes use of Schur's theorem and Lemma 7.2.

Theorem 7.5.1. *For every square matrix* $\mathbf{A}$, $\mathbf{A}^m \to \mathbf{O}$ *if and only if* $\rho(\mathbf{A}) < 1$.

Proof. By Schur's theorem, there exists an upper triangular matrix $\mathbf{T}$ and a unitary matrix $\mathbf{U}$ such that $\mathbf{UTU}^{\mathrm{H}} = \mathbf{A}$. Hence, $\mathbf{UT}^m\mathbf{U}^{\mathrm{H}} = \mathbf{A}^m$, and thus $\mathbf{A}^m \to \mathbf{O}$ if and only if $\mathbf{T}^m \to \mathbf{O}$. Lemma 7.2 completes the argument, since $\rho(\mathbf{A}) = \rho(\mathbf{T})$. ■

The geometric series

$$\mathbf{I} + \mathbf{A} + \mathbf{A}^2 + \cdots + \mathbf{A}^m + \cdots +$$

converges if the sequence of its partial sums converge, that is, if $\lim(\mathbf{I}+\mathbf{A}+\mathbf{A}^2+\cdots+\mathbf{A}^{m-1})$ exists. This is the direct extension of the definition of convergence of scalar geometric series and its analysis follows from the same algebraic identity (see Eq. 7.5.4 in the following corollary).

Corollary 1. *The geometric series converges if and only if the spectral radius of* $\mathbf{A}$ *is less than* 1. *Moreover, if the series converges, it does so to* $(\mathbf{I} - \mathbf{A})^{-1}$.

Proof. If the matrix series converges, then for each i and j, the scalar series

$$a_{ij}^{(1)} + a_{ij}^{(2)} + a_{ij}^{(3)} + \cdots + a_{ij}^{(m)} + \cdots +$$

must also converge. (Recall that $a_{ij}^{(m)}$ is the (i, j) entry of $\mathbf{A}^m$.) Hence, from the scalar theory of convergence, $a_{ij}^{(m)} \to 0$, and therefore, by definition, $\mathbf{A}^m \to \mathbf{O}$ as $m \to \infty$. Hence, by Theorem 7.5.1, $\rho(\mathbf{A}) < 1$. For the converse, note that $p(\mathbf{A}) < 1$ implies that $\mathbf{I}-\mathbf{A}$ is nonsingular because $\lambda = 1$ cannot be an eigenvalue of $\mathbf{A}$. Next consider the identity

$$(\mathbf{I} + \mathbf{A} + \mathbf{A}^2 + \cdots + \mathbf{A}^{m-1})(\mathbf{I} - \mathbf{A}) = \mathbf{I} - \mathbf{A}^m \tag{7.5.4}$$

Postmultiply both sides by $(\mathbf{I} - \mathbf{A})^{-1}$ and rearrange terms to deduce

$$\mathbf{I} + \mathbf{A} + \mathbf{A}^2 + \cdots + \mathbf{A}^{m-1} - (\mathbf{I} - \mathbf{A})^{-1} = -\mathbf{A}^m(\mathbf{I} - \mathbf{A})^{-1} \tag{7.5.5}$$

Because $\rho(\mathbf{A}) < 1$, $\mathbf{A}^m \to \mathbf{O}$ follows from Theorem 7.5.1. Thus, the right-hand side of Eq. 7.5.5 tends to $\mathbf{O}$. Therefore,

$$(\mathbf{I} + \mathbf{A} + \mathbf{A}^2 + \cdots + \mathbf{A}^{m-1} - (\mathbf{I} - \mathbf{A})^{-1}) \to \mathbf{O}$$

from which it follows that

$$\lim(\mathbf{I} + \mathbf{A} + \mathbf{A}^2 + \cdots + \mathbf{A}^{m-1}) = (\mathbf{I} - \mathbf{A})^{-1} \ ■$$

Example 7.5.5. Suppose that $\rho(\mathbf{T}) < 1$. Show that

$$\mathbf{A}^m = \begin{bmatrix} \mathbf{I} & \mathbf{C} \\ \mathbf{O} & \mathbf{T} \end{bmatrix}^m \to \begin{bmatrix} \mathbf{I} & \mathbf{C}(\mathbf{I} - \mathbf{T})^{-1} \\ \mathbf{O} & \mathbf{O} \end{bmatrix}$$

Proof. It is easy to establish that

$$\mathbf{A}^m = \begin{bmatrix} \mathbf{I} & \mathbf{C} \\ \mathbf{O} & \mathbf{T} \end{bmatrix}^m = \begin{bmatrix} \mathbf{I} & \mathbf{C}^{(m)} \\ \mathbf{O} & \mathbf{T}^m \end{bmatrix}$$

where $\mathbf{C}^{(m)} = \mathbf{C}(\mathbf{I} + \mathbf{T} + \mathbf{T}^2 + \cdots + \mathbf{T}^{m-1})$. Hence, $\mathbf{C}^{(m)} \to \mathbf{C}(\mathbf{I} - \mathbf{T})^{-1}$ by Corollary 1 of Theorem 7.5.1. Also, since $\rho(\mathbf{T}) < 1$ by hypothesis, $\mathbf{T}^m \to \mathbf{O}$ by Lemma 7.2. Thus,

$$\mathbf{A}^m = \begin{bmatrix} \mathbf{I} & \mathbf{C}^{(m)} \\ \mathbf{O} & \mathbf{T}^m \end{bmatrix} \to \begin{bmatrix} \mathbf{I} & \mathbf{C}(\mathbf{I} - \mathbf{T})^{-1} \\ \mathbf{O} & \mathbf{O} \end{bmatrix}$$

PROBLEMS

PART 1

For the matrices listed in Problems 7.5.1–7.5.3, compute $\mathbf{A}^k$ explicitly. For which matrices does $\lim(\mathbf{A}^k)$ exist? What is the limit matrix $\mathbf{A}_\infty$?

7.5.1. (*a*) $\begin{bmatrix} 1 & 0 \\ 0 & 0 \end{bmatrix}$ (*b*) $\begin{bmatrix} 0 & 1 \\ 0 & 0 \end{bmatrix}$ (*c*) $\begin{bmatrix} 1 & 1 \\ 0 & 0 \end{bmatrix}$ (*d*) $\begin{bmatrix} 1 & 1 \\ 0 & 1 \end{bmatrix}$ (*e*) $\begin{bmatrix} \frac{1}{2} & 1 \\ 0 & \frac{1}{2} \end{bmatrix}$

(*f*) $\begin{bmatrix} 0 & 1 \\ 1 & 0 \end{bmatrix}$ (*g*) $\begin{bmatrix} 0 & 1 & 0 \\ 1 & 0 & 0 \\ 0 & 0 & 1 \end{bmatrix}$

7.5.2. (*a*) $\begin{bmatrix} \frac{1}{2} & \frac{1}{2} \\ \frac{1}{2} & \frac{1}{2} \end{bmatrix}$ (*b*) $\begin{bmatrix} \frac{3}{2} & 1 \\ 0 & \frac{1}{2} \end{bmatrix}$ (*c*) $\begin{bmatrix} a & b \\ 1-a & 1-b \end{bmatrix}$ (*d*) $\begin{bmatrix} -1 & 0 \\ 0 & 0 \end{bmatrix}$

7.5.3. (*a*) $\left[\begin{array}{ccc|cc} 1 & 0 & 0 & 0 & 0 \\ 0 & 1 & 0 & 0 & 0 \\ 0 & 0 & 1 & 0 & 0 \\ \hline 0 & 0 & 0 & 0 & 1 \\ 0 & 0 & 0 & 1 & 0 \end{array}\right]$ (*b*) $\begin{bmatrix} a & 0 & 0 & 0 & 0 \\ 0 & b & 0 & 0 & 0 \\ 0 & 0 & c & 0 & 0 \\ 0 & 0 & 0 & d & 0 \\ 0 & 0 & 0 & 0 & e \end{bmatrix}$

7.5.4. Show that $\lim(\mathbf{A}^m)$ diverges but $\lim(\mathbf{C}\mathbf{A}^m)$ exists for $\mathbf{A}$ and $\mathbf{C}$:

$$\mathbf{A} = \begin{bmatrix} -1 & 0 \\ 0 & 1 \end{bmatrix}, \qquad \mathbf{C} = \begin{bmatrix} 0 & 1 \\ 0 & 1 \end{bmatrix}$$

7.5.5. Show that $\lim(\mathbf{A}^m\mathbf{C})$ diverges for $\mathbf{A}$ and $\mathbf{C}$ of Problem 7.5.4.

PART 2

7.5.6. Prove that $\lim(\mathbf{C}\mathbf{A}_m)$ and $\lim(\mathbf{A}_m\mathbf{B})$ diverge if $\lim(\mathbf{A}_m)$ diverges and C and B are nonsingular.

7.5.7. Invoke L'Hôpital's rule to show that $C\binom{m}{k}\sigma^{m-k} \to 0$ if $|\sigma| < 1$.

7.5.8. Show that

$$\left[\begin{array}{cccc|cc} 0 & 0 & 0 & 1 & 0 & 0 \\ 0 & 0 & 0.5 & 0 & 0.5 & 0 \\ 0 & 0.5 & 0 & 0 & 0 & 0.5 \\ 0.5 & 0 & 0 & 0 & 0.5 & 0 \\ \hline 0 & 0 & 0 & 0 & 1 & 0 \\ 0 & 0 & 0 & 0 & 0 & 1 \end{array}\right]^m \to \left[\begin{array}{cccc|cc} 0 & 0 & 0 & 0 & 1 & 0 \\ 0 & 0 & 0 & 0 & \frac{2}{3} & \frac{1}{3} \\ 0 & 0 & 0 & 0 & \frac{1}{3} & \frac{2}{3} \\ 0 & 0 & 0 & 0 & 1 & 0 \\ \hline 0 & 0 & 0 & 0 & 1 & 0 \\ 0 & 0 & 0 & 0 & 0 & 1 \end{array}\right]$$

(*Hint:* First show that

$$\mathbf{A}^m = \begin{bmatrix} \mathbf{T} & \mathbf{C} \\ \mathbf{O} & \mathbf{I} \end{bmatrix}^m \rightarrow \begin{bmatrix} \mathbf{O} & (\mathbf{I}-\mathbf{T})^{-1}\mathbf{C} \\ \mathbf{O} & \mathbf{I} \end{bmatrix}$$

by modifying the ideas used in Example 7.5.5 to fit this problem.)

7.5.9. Write out the steps of the proof of Lemma 7.2 using $\mathbf{T}$ and $\mathbf{S}(0.2)$ of Example 7.5.4.

7.6 THE LIMIT OF $\mathbf{A}^m$ FOR $\rho(\mathbf{A}) = 1$

Although the complete analysis of $\lim(\mathbf{A}^m)$ for $\rho(\mathbf{A}) = 1$ is more difficult and the conclusion more subtle than that for $\rho(\mathbf{A}) < 1$, it is possible to draw some inferences about the limit matrix, if it exists, from the general properties of limits. For instance, suppose we assume that $\lim(\mathbf{A}^m) = \mathbf{A}_\infty$. Then $\mathbf{A}_\infty$ is idempotent; that is, $\mathbf{A}_\infty^2 = \mathbf{A}_\infty$. To see why, note that $\lim(\mathbf{A}^{2m}) = \mathbf{A}_\infty$ and $\lim(\mathbf{A}^{2m}) = \lim^2(\mathbf{A}^m) = \mathbf{A}_\infty^2$. Hence, $\mathbf{A}_\infty$ is simple, and its eigenvalues are 0s and 1s. (In the case in which $\rho(\mathbf{A}) < 1$, $\mathbf{A}_\infty = \mathbf{O}$, and this result is trivial. The same can be said for the special case $\mathbf{A} = [a]$ because for the scalar limit, $a^m \rightarrow a_\infty$, a_∞ must be either 0 or 1.) That $\mathbf{A}_\infty$ is idempotent is a result of great importance to the theory of finite Markov processes. (See Section 7.7.) Further conclusions can also be deduced in this manner; these are left for the exercises (Problem 7.6.10).

For the remainder of this section, assume that all matrices denoted by $\mathbf{T}$, with or without subscripts, are upper triangular; that $\mathbf{T}(0)$ is upper triangular with zero diagonal entries; and that $\mathbf{U}$ is unitary. We show first that if $\mathbf{A}$ has an eigenvalue $\lambda_0 \neq 1$ and $|\lambda_0| = 1$, then $\lim(\mathbf{A}^m)$ must diverge.

Lemma 7.3. *Suppose λ_0 is an eigenvalue of $\mathbf{A}$ such that $|\lambda_0| = 1$ but $\lambda_0 \neq 1$. Then $\lim(\mathbf{A}^m)$ does not exist.*

Proof. By Schur's theorem, $\mathbf{A}^m = \mathbf{U}\mathbf{T}^m\mathbf{U}^{\mathrm{H}}$. Now $\mathbf{T}^m$ has λ_0^m on its diagonal. However, $\lim(\lambda_o^m)$ does not exist, because $\lambda_0 \neq 1$ and $|\lambda_0| = 1$. It follows that $\lim(\mathbf{T}^m)$ cannot exist, and then it follows that neither can $\lim(\mathbf{A}^m)$. ■

In view of Lemma 7.3, there is no loss in assuming that all the eigenvalues with modulus 1 have the value 1. There must be at least one such eigenvalue, by hypothesis. The following two lemmas divide the proof into smaller, more manageable pieces. Lemma 7.4 examines the situation in which all the eigenvalues of $\mathbf{A}$ are equal to 1.

Lemma 7.4. *Suppose $\mathbf{A}$ has eigenvalues $\lambda_i = 1$ for all i. Then $\lim_{m\rightarrow\infty}(\mathbf{A}^m)$ exists if and only if $\mathbf{A}$ is simple.*

Proof. First the trivial case: If $\mathbf{A}$ is simple, then $\mathbf{A} = \mathbf{I}$, and there is nothing to prove.

Now the converse: Suppose that $\mathbf{A}$ is defective. We prove that $\lim(\mathbf{A}^m)$ cannot exist. By Schur's theorem, there exist $\mathbf{U}$ such that $\mathbf{U}^{\mathrm{H}}\mathbf{A}\mathbf{U} = \mathbf{T}$. $\mathbf{T}$ has 1s on its diagonal and cannot be diagonal since **A** is defective. Hence, $\mathbf{T} = \mathbf{I} + \mathbf{T}(0)$ and $\mathbf{T}(0) \neq \mathbf{O}$. Following the analysis in Section 7.5, the binomial expansion

$$\mathbf{U}^{\mathrm{H}}\mathbf{A}^{m}\mathbf{U} = \mathbf{T}^{m} = [\mathbf{I} + \mathbf{T}(0)]^{m} = \mathbf{I} + \sum_{k=1}^{n-1} C\binom{m}{k}\mathbf{T}^{k}(0) \tag{7.6.1}$$

is valid for all $m \geq n$. Since $\mathbf{T}(0) \neq \mathbf{O}$, it has at least one nonzero off-diagonal entry, say $t_{ij}^{(1)} = t_{ij}$, and therefore, from Eq. 7.6.1, the (i, j)th entry in $\mathbf{T}^{m}$ is given by

$$t_{ij}^{(m)} = mt_{ij}^{(1)} + C\binom{m}{2}t_{ij}^{(2)} + \cdots + C\binom{m}{n-1}t_{ij}^{(n-1)} \tag{7.6.2}$$

Equation 7.6.2 shows that $t_{ij}^{(m)} \to \infty$. (See Problem 7.6.7.) Hence, $\lim(\mathbf{A}^{m}) = \mathbf{U}\left(\lim(\mathbf{T}^{m})\right)\mathbf{U}^{\mathrm{H}}$ does not exist. ■

Lemma 7.5. *If $\lambda = 1$ is an eigenvalue of **A** with geometric multiplicity r, then there is a unitary matrix **U** such that*

$$\mathbf{U}^{\mathrm{H}}\mathbf{A}\mathbf{U} = \mathbf{T} = \left[\begin{array}{c|c} \mathbf{I}_r & \mathbf{C} \\ \hline \mathbf{O} & \mathbf{T}_1 \end{array}\right] \tag{7.6.3}$$

Proof. This is a slightly refined version of Schur's theorem. By hypothesis, there are r linearly independent eigenvectors of **A** corresponding to the eigenvalue 1. Orthonormalize this set and use these orthonormal eigenvectors for the first r columns of **U**. The remaining $n - r$ columns of **U** are obtained by completing an orthonormal basis for $\mathscr{C}^{n}$. Equation 7.6.3 then follows. Note that we do not exclude the possibility that there may be more than r eigenvalues with value 1; that is, we make no assumptions about the algebraic multiplicity of the eigenvalue $\lambda = 1$. ■

Theorem 7.6.1. *Suppose **A** has spectral radius $\rho(\mathbf{A}) = 1$. Then $\lim(\mathbf{A}^{m})$ exists if and only if*

1. $\lambda = 1$ *is the only eigenvalue of modulus 1, and*
2. $a(1) = g(1)$.

Proof. Suppose that $\rho(\mathbf{A}) = 1$. Then there is an eigenvalue of **A**, say λ_0, such that $|\lambda_0| = 1$. There are two theorems to prove. The first assumes $\lim(\mathbf{A}^{m})$ exists. Then $\lambda_0 \neq 1$ contradicts Lemma 7.3. Hence, $\lambda_0 = 1$. Next suppose that the geometric multiplicity of $\lambda_0 = 1$ is less than its algebraic multiplicity. To be specific, set $a(1) = s$, $g(1) = r < s$. By Lemma 7.5,

$$\mathbf{U}^{\mathrm{H}}\mathbf{A}\mathbf{U} = \mathbf{T} = \left[\begin{array}{c|c} \mathbf{I}_r & \mathbf{C} \\ \hline \mathbf{O} & \mathbf{T}_1 \end{array}\right] \tag{7.6.4}$$

Now $\mathbf{T}_1$ has at least one diagonal entry equal to 1, since $a(1) = s > r$. So

$$\mathbf{T}_1 = \left[\begin{array}{c|c} \mathbf{T}_2 & \mathbf{D} \\ \hline \mathbf{O} & \mathbf{T}_3 \end{array}\right] \tag{7.6.5}$$

where $\mathbf{T}_2$ has only 1s on its diagonal. Moreover, $\mathbf{T}_2$ is defective; for if it were not, it would be possible to find another eigenvector corresponding to $\lambda = 1$ that is not a linear combination of the previous s eigenvectors. Then $g(1)$ would exceed r, contradicting the hypothesis. If Eq. 7.6.5 is substituted into Eq. 7.6.4,

$$\mathbf{U}^{\mathrm{H}}\mathbf{A}^m\mathbf{U} = \mathbf{T}^m = \left[\begin{array}{c|c|c} \mathbf{I}_r & \mathbf{E} & \mathbf{F} \\ \hline \mathbf{O} & \mathbf{T}_2 & \mathbf{D} \\ \hline \mathbf{O} & \mathbf{O} & \mathbf{T}_3 \end{array}\right]^m = \left[\begin{array}{c|c|c} \mathbf{I}_r & * & * \\ \hline \mathbf{O} & \mathbf{T}_2^m & * \\ \hline \mathbf{O} & \mathbf{O} & \mathbf{T}_3^m \end{array}\right] \tag{7.6.6}$$

results. Applying Lemma 7.4 to the above representation of $\mathbf{T}^m$, implies that $\lim(\mathbf{T}_2^m)$ must not exist since it is defective and has only 1s as its eigenvalues. Thus, $\mathbf{A}^m$ must also diverge, contradicting the assumption.

Now the converse. Here are the assumptions: There is at least one eigenvalue equal to 1, say $\lambda_1 = 1$. Every eigenvalue with modulus 1 has value 1, and all other eigenvalues, if there are any, have modulus less than 1; and $a(1) = g(1)$. (To fix ideas, set $a(1) = r$.) The representation for $\mathbf{T}$ given by Eq. 7.6.4 still holds, except that each diagonal entry in $\mathbf{T}_1$ has modulus less than 1. But this is exactly Example 7.5.5, and therefore,

$$\mathbf{U}^{\mathrm{H}}\mathbf{A}^m\mathbf{U} = \mathbf{T}^m \to \begin{bmatrix} \mathbf{I}_r & \mathbf{C}(\mathbf{I} - \mathbf{T})^{-1} \\ \mathbf{O} & \mathbf{O} \end{bmatrix} \quad \blacksquare$$

Corollary 1. *Under the hypothesis of Theorem 7.6.1 and the notation of Eq. 7.6.3,* $\mathbf{A}^m \to \mathbf{A}_\infty$*, where* $\mathbf{A}_\infty$ *is idempotent with* $\mathrm{rank}(\mathbf{A}_\infty) = g(1) = r$.

Proof. Because

$$\mathbf{A}_\infty = \mathbf{U}\begin{bmatrix} \mathbf{I}_r & \mathbf{C}(\mathbf{I} - \mathbf{T})^{-1} \\ \mathbf{O} & \mathbf{O} \end{bmatrix}\mathbf{U}^{\mathrm{H}}$$

it follows that $(\mathbf{A}_\infty)^2 = \mathbf{A}_\infty$. $\mathrm{Rank}(\mathbf{A}_\infty) = r$ is obvious. $\blacksquare$

PROBLEMS

PART 1

7.6.1. Use Theorem 7.6.1 to determine for which of the following matrices $\lim(\mathbf{A}^m)$ exists. When this limit exists, use Corollary 1 of Theorem 7.6.1 to find the limit.

(*a*) $\begin{bmatrix} 1 & 0 \\ 0 & 0 \end{bmatrix}$ (*b*) $\begin{bmatrix} 1 & 1 \\ 0 & 0 \end{bmatrix}$ (*c*) $\begin{bmatrix} 1 & 1 \\ 0 & 1 \end{bmatrix}$ (*d*) $\begin{bmatrix} 0 & 1 \\ 1 & 0 \end{bmatrix}$ (*e*) $\begin{bmatrix} 0 & 1 & 0 \\ 1 & 0 & 0 \\ 0 & 0 & 1 \end{bmatrix}$

7.6.2. Repeat Problem 7.6.1 for the matrices

$$(a)\begin{bmatrix} \frac{1}{2} & \frac{1}{2} \\ \frac{1}{2} & \frac{1}{2} \end{bmatrix} \qquad (b)\begin{bmatrix} -1 & 0 \\ 0 & 0 \end{bmatrix} \qquad (c)\begin{bmatrix} a & b \\ 1-a & 1-b \end{bmatrix}$$

7.6.3. Repeat Problem 7.6.1 for the matrix

$$\mathbf{A} = \left[\begin{array}{ccc|cc} 1 & 0 & 0 & 0 & 0 \\ 0 & 1 & 0 & 0 & 0 \\ 0 & 0 & 1 & 0 & 0 \\ \hline 0 & 0 & 0 & 0 & 1 \\ 0 & 0 & 0 & 1 & 0 \end{array}\right]$$

7.6.4. Lemma 7.4 asserts that $\lim(\mathbf{A}^m)$ diverges, where

$$\mathbf{A} = \begin{bmatrix} 1 & 1 & 0 & 0 & 0 \\ 0 & 1 & 0 & 0 & 0 \\ 0 & 0 & 1 & 0 & 0 \\ 0 & 0 & 0 & 1 & 0 \\ 0 & 0 & 0 & 0 & 1 \end{bmatrix}$$

because it is defective. Verify that $\mathbf{A}$ is indeed defective and, by finding $\mathbf{A}^m$ explicitly, verify that at least one entry in $\mathbf{A}^m$ must tend to ∞.

7.6.5. For matrix $\mathbf{A}$ of Problem 7.6.4, find $t_{12}^{(m)}$ by use of Eq. 7.6.1.

PART 2

7.6.6. Prove: If $\mathbf{A}$ and $\mathbf{B}$ are similar and $\lim(\mathbf{A}^m)$ exists, then $\lim(\mathbf{B}^m)$ exists.

7.6.7. Equation 7.6.2 asserts the equality

$$t_{ij}^{(m)} = mt_{ij}^{(1)} + C\binom{m}{2}t_{ij}^{(2)} + \cdots + C\binom{m}{n-1}t_{ij}^{(n-1)}$$

Show that $t_{ij}^{(m)} \to \infty$ if $t_{ij}^{(1)}$ $(= t_{ij})$ is not zero. (*Hint:* $t_{ij}^{(m)}$ is a polynomial of degree at least 1 in m.)

PART 3

7.6.8. Show that the convergence of $\sum a_m\|\mathbf{A}\|^m$ implies the convergence of $\sum a_m\mathbf{A}^m$.

7.6.9. If $\lim \mathbf{A}^k = \mathbf{A}_\infty$, show that $\mathbf{A}\mathbf{A}_\infty = \mathbf{A}_\infty$ and, hence, that the columns of $\mathbf{A}_\infty$ are either $\mathbf{O}$ or an eigenvector of $\mathbf{A}$ corresponding to $\lambda = 1$.

7.7 DISCRETE MARKOV PROCESSES

The theory of Markov processes is a branch of probability theory that makes extensive use of the ideas introduced in Section 7.6. In Section 0.1.7 we offered one illustration of this theory. Here we present another.[3]

---

[3]Both illustrations are variations on examples presented in Martin Pearl, *Matrix Theory and Finite Mathematics*, New York: McGraw-Hill, 1973.

Example 7.7.1. A mouse is placed in one of the rooms of the maze sketched in Fig. 7.4. This mouse has previously been conditioned to leave the room at the sound of a bell. If there is a choice of exits, as there is in rooms 2, 3, and 4, the mouse will choose an exit at random. The openings in rooms 5 and 6 are entrances; there are no exits from these rooms. If the mouse is initially placed in room 2, what is the probability p that it will ever enter room 5? We denote by a_{ij} the probability that the mouse will enter room i from room j at the sound of the bell. The matrix $\mathbf{A} = (a_{ij})$ is called the transition matrix for this problem. A little thought shows that

$$\mathbf{A} = \begin{bmatrix} 0 & 0 & 0 & \frac{1}{2} & 0 & 0 \\ 0 & 0 & \frac{1}{2} & 0 & 0 & 0 \\ 0 & \frac{1}{2} & 0 & 0 & 0 & 0 \\ 1 & 0 & 0 & 0 & 0 & 0 \\ 0 & \frac{1}{2} & 0 & \frac{1}{2} & 1 & 0 \\ 0 & 0 & \frac{1}{2} & 0 & 0 & 1 \end{bmatrix}$$

Let $\mathbf{A}^m = (a_{ij}^{(m)})$. Then the probability that the mouse will be in room i after m steps, assuming the mouse starts in room j, is $a_{ij}^{(m)}$. (This is a consequence of the theory of conditional probability and the definition of matrix multiplication. We choose not to prove this result.) Now, once the mouse is in room 5, it can never leave. (Room 5 is known as an *absorbing state*.) So $a_{52}^{(\infty)} = \lim(a_{52}^{(m)})$ as $m \to \infty$ is the probability the mouse will ever enter room 5, given it started in room 2. We shall see later on that

$$\mathbf{A}_\infty = \lim_{m\to\infty} (\mathbf{A}^m) = \begin{bmatrix} 0 & 0 & 0 & 0 & 0 & 0 \\ 0 & 0 & 0 & 0 & 0 & 0 \\ 0 & 0 & 0 & 0 & 0 & 0 \\ 0 & 0 & 0 & 0 & 0 & 0 \\ 1 & \frac{2}{3} & \frac{1}{3} & 1 & 1 & 0 \\ 0 & \frac{1}{3} & \frac{2}{3} & 0 & 0 & 1 \end{bmatrix}$$

and $p = \frac{2}{3}$. (See Example 7.7.5.)

We begin the general theory by introducing two new terms; transition matrices and probability vectors. A *transition matrix* $\mathbf{A}$ is a square matrix with

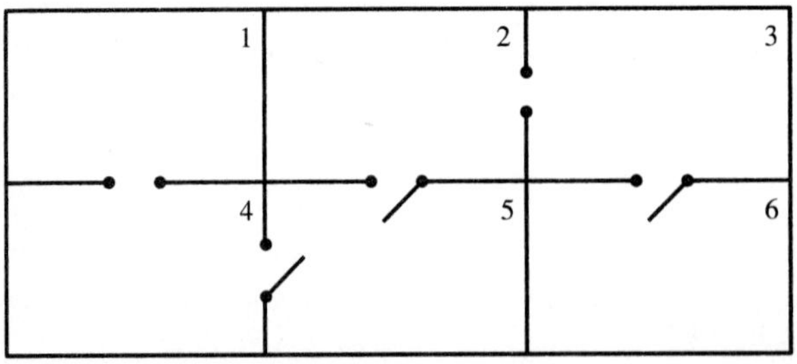

FIGURE 7-4
The maze for Example 7.7.1.

nonnegative entries whose columns sum to 1. (We write $\mathbf{A} \geq \mathbf{O}$ when $\mathbf{A}$ is nonnegative and $\mathbf{A} > \mathbf{O}$ when $\mathbf{A}$ has only positive entries.) Hence, $0 \leq a_{ij} \leq 1$ for each i and j and

$$\sum_{i=1}^{n} a_{ij} = 1, \qquad \text{for each } j = 1,2,\ldots,n$$

The transpose of **A** is a stochastic matrix. (See Example 7.3.3.) A square matrix with nonnegative entries is called a *nonnegative matrix*. Thus, **A** is a transition matrix if and only if **A** is nonnegative and $\mathbf{1}^{\mathrm{T}}\mathbf{A} = \mathbf{1}^{\mathrm{T}}$. (Why?) This necessary and sufficient condition makes it easy to prove that $\mathbf{A}^k$ is a transition matrix for every nonnegative integer k. The argument is inductive. Suppose $\mathbf{A}^{k-1}$ is a transition matrix. Then

$$\mathbf{1}^{\mathrm{T}}\mathbf{A}^k = (\mathbf{1}^{\mathrm{T}}\mathbf{A})\mathbf{A}^{k-1} = \mathbf{1}^{\mathrm{T}}\mathbf{A}^{k-1} = \mathbf{1}^{\mathrm{T}}$$

shows that $\mathbf{A}^k$ is also a transition matrix. We are assuming that **A** is a transition matrix, so that the induction process begins with $k = 1$.

A *probability vector* **p** is a column vector whose entries are nonnegative and sum to 1. Let

$$\mathbf{p} = \begin{bmatrix} p_1 \\ p_2 \\ \vdots \\ p_n \end{bmatrix}$$

Note that a nonnegative vector **p** is a probability vector if and only if $\mathbf{1}^{\mathrm{T}}\mathbf{p} = 1$; a result resembling the criterion used to decide whether or not a nonnegative matrix is a transition matrix.

Theorem 7.7.1. *If* **A** *is a transition matrix and* **p** *is a probability vector, then* **Ap** *is also a probability vector.*

Proof. It is obvious that the entries of **Ap** are nonnegative. We need to show that $\mathbf{1}^{\mathrm{T}}(\mathbf{Ap}) = 1$. But $\mathbf{1}^{\mathrm{T}}(\mathbf{Ap}) = (\mathbf{1}^{\mathrm{T}}\mathbf{A})\mathbf{p} = \mathbf{1}^{\mathrm{T}}\mathbf{p} = 1$. ∎

Example 7.7.2. The following are transition matrices:

(*a*) J_n/n (*b*) $(J_n - I_n)/(n-1)$ (*c*) **I**

$$(d)\ \mathbf{A} = \begin{bmatrix} 0 & 2/3 & 0 & 0 & 0 & 0 & 0 \\ 1/3 & 0 & 2/3 & 0 & 0 & 0 & 0 \\ 0 & 1/3 & 0 & 2/3 & 0 & 0 & 0 \\ 0 & 0 & 1/3 & 0 & 2/3 & 0 & 0 \\ 0 & 0 & 0 & 1/3 & 0 & 0 & 0 \\ 2/3 & 0 & 0 & 0 & 0 & 1 & 0 \\ 0 & 0 & 0 & 0 & 1/3 & 0 & 1 \end{bmatrix}$$

Theorem 7.7.2. *If* $\mathbf{A}$ *is a transition matrix, then* $\rho(\mathbf{A}) = 1$. *Moreover, the only eigenvalue with absolute value* 1 *is* $\lambda = 1$.

Proof. The matrices $\mathbf{A}$ and $\mathbf{A}^{\mathrm{T}}$ are similar and hence have the same eigenvalues (including geometric multiplicities). However, $\mathbf{A}^{\mathrm{T}}$ is a stochastic matrix, and we have proved this theorem for stochastic matrices in Example 7.3.6. ■

Since $\mathbf{A}$ and $\mathbf{A}^{\mathrm{T}}$ have the same eigenvalues, there is an eigenpair $(1, \mathbf{p})$ of $\mathbf{A}$ so that $\mathbf{Ap} = \mathbf{p}$. If $\mathbf{p} \geq \mathbf{0}$ and the sum of its entries is 1, then $\mathbf{p}$ is called a *stationary vector* of $\mathbf{A}$. It is not at all obvious that stationary vectors exist; it may be, for instance, that every eigenvector of $\mathbf{A}$ corresponding to $\lambda = 1$ has a negative entry!

Stationary vectors arise in the study of $\lim(\mathbf{p}_k) = \lim(\mathbf{A}^k\mathbf{p}_0) = \mathbf{A}_\infty\mathbf{p}_0$, as is made clear in the next theorem.

Theorem 7.7.3. *If* $\mathbf{A}$ *is a transition matrix and* $\lim(\mathbf{A}^m) = \mathbf{A}_\infty$, *then* $\mathbf{A}_\infty$ *is a transition matrix whose columns are stationary vectors of* $\mathbf{A}$.

Proof. Since $\rho(\mathbf{A}) = 1$ and $\mathbf{A} \geq 0$, we know from Theorem 7.5.1 that $\mathbf{A}_\infty \geq \mathbf{O}$. Also, since $\mathbf{1}^{\mathrm{T}} = \mathbf{1}^{\mathrm{T}}\mathbf{A}^m$, it follows that $\mathbf{1}^{\mathrm{T}} = \mathbf{1}^{\mathrm{T}}\lim(\mathbf{A}^m) = \mathbf{1}^{\mathrm{T}}\mathbf{A}_\infty$ and, hence, that $\mathbf{A}_\infty$ is a transition matrix. So the columns of $\mathbf{A}_\infty$ are probability vectors. Now $\mathbf{A}_\infty = \lim(\mathbf{A}^{m+1}) = \mathbf{A}\lim(\mathbf{A}^m) = \mathbf{A}\mathbf{A}_\infty$ shows that the columns of $\mathbf{A}_\infty$ satisfy $\mathbf{Ap} = \mathbf{p}$. Hence, these columns are stationary vectors. ■

Example 7.7.3. The transition matrix

$$\mathbf{A} = \begin{bmatrix} \frac{1}{2} & \frac{1}{4} & \frac{1}{3} \\ \frac{1}{2} & \frac{1}{4} & \frac{1}{3} \\ 0 & \frac{1}{2} & \frac{1}{3} \end{bmatrix}$$

has eigenpair $(1, \mathbf{u})$, where $\mathbf{u} = [4 \quad 4 \quad 3]^{\mathrm{T}}$. Since no entry of $\mathbf{u}$ is negative, we can normalize $\mathbf{u}$ by dividing by the sum of its entries. This yields the stationary vector

$$\mathbf{p} = \frac{1}{11}\begin{bmatrix} 4 \\ 4 \\ 3 \end{bmatrix}$$

It is possible to show by direct computation[4] that

$$\mathbf{A}^{50} \simeq \mathbf{A}_\infty = \frac{1}{11}\begin{bmatrix} 4 & 4 & 4 \\ 4 & 4 & 4 \\ 3 & 3 & 3 \end{bmatrix}$$

[4] See Section 7.7.1

which confirms that the columns of $\mathbf{A}_\infty$ are stationary vectors of $\mathbf{A}$. Finally, let $\mathbf{p}_0 = [p_1 \quad p_2 \quad p_3]^{\mathrm{T}}$. Then the sequence
$\mathbf{p}_0, \mathbf{p}_1 = \mathbf{A}\mathbf{p}_0, \mathbf{p}_2 = \mathbf{A}^2\mathbf{p}_0, \mathbf{p}_3 = \mathbf{A}^3\mathbf{p}_0, \ldots, \mathbf{p}_k = \mathbf{A}^k\mathbf{p}_0 \to \mathbf{A}_\infty\mathbf{p}_0$

$$= \frac{1}{11}\begin{bmatrix} 4 & 4 & 4 \\ 4 & 4 & 4 \\ 3 & 3 & 3 \end{bmatrix} \mathbf{p}_0 = \frac{1}{11}\begin{bmatrix} 4p_1 + 4p_2 + 4p_3 \\ 4p_1 + 4p_2 + 4p_3 \\ 3p_1 + 3p_2 + 3p_3 \end{bmatrix} = \frac{1}{11}\begin{bmatrix} 4 \\ 4 \\ 3 \end{bmatrix} = \mathbf{p}$$

The rather startling conclusion that $\lim(\mathbf{p}_k)$ is a stationary vector—at least in some circumstances—prompts a more detailed study of $\mathbf{A}_\infty$. The next theorem is a step in this direction.

Theorem 7.7.4. *Suppose* $\mathbf{A} > \mathbf{O}$ *is a transition matrix. Then* $k\mathbf{1}$ *are the only eigenvectors of* $\mathbf{A}^{\mathrm{T}}$ *corresponding to* $\lambda = 1$.

Proof. For convenience we prove this theorem for the stochastic matrix $\mathbf{S} = \mathbf{A}^{\mathrm{T}}$. Suppose $(1, \mathbf{x})$ is an eigenpair of $\mathbf{S}$. Let $\mathbf{x} = [x_1 \quad x_2 \quad \ldots \quad x_n]^{\mathrm{T}}$. Suppose $|x_m| \geq |x_i|$ for all i, and consider the mth equation in the system $\mathbf{Sx} = 1\mathbf{x}$:

$$\sum_{i=1}^{m} s_{mi}x_i = x_m \tag{7.7.1}$$

Since $x_m \neq 0$ (for otherwise $\mathbf{x}$ would be $\mathbf{0}$), Eq. 7.7.1 implies

$$\sum_{i=1}^{m} s_{mi}\frac{x_i}{x_m} = 1 \tag{7.7.2}$$

From Eq. 7.2.2,

$$1 = \left|\sum_{i=1}^{m} s_{mi}\frac{x_i}{x_m}\right| \leq \sum_{i=1}^{m} s_{mi}\left|\frac{x_i}{x_m}\right| \leq \sum_{i=1}^{m} s_{mi} = 1 \tag{7.7.3}$$

from which we deduce that the two inequalities are equalities; that is,

$$1 = \left|\sum_{i=1}^{m} s_{mi}\frac{x_i}{x_m}\right| = \sum_{i=1}^{m} s_{mi}\left|\frac{x_i}{x_m}\right| = \sum_{i=1}^{m} s_{mi} \tag{7.7.4}$$

Since every $s_{mi} > 0$, the third of the three equalities in Eq. 7.7.4 implies that $|x_i/x_m| = 1$. From the second equality it follows that x_i/x_m is a positive multiple of some complex number c. That is, $x_i/x_m = t_ic, t_i > 0$. But then $1 = |x_i/x_m| = t_i|c|$ implies $t_i = 1/|c|$ for each i. Therefore, $x_i = x_mc/|c|$. Thus, $\mathbf{x} = (x_mc/|c|)\mathbf{1}$. ■

A significant improvement of this theorem is possible. If $\mathbf{A}^r$ contains only positive entries, $\mathbf{A}$ is said to be *regular*. If $\mathbf{A}^r$ is used in place of $\mathbf{A}$ in the theorem, then the eigenspace $\mathscr{E}(1)$ of $\mathbf{A}^r$ is one-dimensional. This leads to the important corollary and theorem that follow.

Corollary 1. *If* $\mathbf{A}$ *is a regular transition matrix, then the eigenspace associated with* $\lambda = 1$ *is one-dimensional.*

Proof. Since every eigenvector of $\mathbf{A}$ is an eigenvector of $\mathbf{A}^r$, there cannot be two or more linearly independent eigenvectors associated with the eigenvalue 1. ■

Theorem 7.7.5. *If* $\mathbf{A}$ *is a regular transition matrix, then* $\mathbf{A}_\infty$ *exists and is a transition matrix of rank* 1.

Proof. The hypotheses of Theorem 7.6.1 are satisfied with $a(1) = g(1) = 1$. Hence, $\mathbf{A}_\infty$ exists. Corollary 1 of Theorem 7.6.1 establishes that $\text{rank}(\mathbf{A}_\infty) = 1$. Finally, $\mathbf{A}_\infty$ is a transition matrix, from Theorem 7.7.3. ■

Theorem 7.7.6. *If* $\mathbf{A}$ *is a regular transition matrix, then* $\mathbf{A}_\infty = \mathbf{p}\mathbf{1}^{\mathrm{T}}$, *where* $\mathbf{p}$ *is the unique stationary vector of* $\mathbf{A}$.

Proof. From Theorem 7.7.3 we know that the columns of $\mathbf{A}_\infty$ are stationary vectors of $\mathbf{A}$. From Theorem 7.7.5 we know that $\mathbf{A}_\infty$ has rank 1. Hence, the columns of $\mathbf{A}_\infty$ are identical. So $\mathbf{A}_\infty = [\mathbf{p}\ \mathbf{p}\ \ldots\ \mathbf{p}] = \mathbf{p}\mathbf{1}^{\mathrm{T}}$. By Corollary 1 of Theorem 7.7.4, we conclude that $\mathbf{p}$ is the only stationary vector of $\mathbf{A}$. ■

Corollary 1. *Suppose* $\mathbf{A}$ *is a regular transition matrix and* $\mathbf{p}_0$ *is a probability vector. Define* $\mathbf{p}_k = \mathbf{A}\mathbf{p}_{k-1}$. *Then* $\lim(\mathbf{p}_k) = \mathbf{p}$, *where* $\mathbf{p}$ *is the unique stationary vector of* $\mathbf{A}$.

Proof. Since $\mathbf{p}_k = \mathbf{A}^k\mathbf{p}_0$, it follows from Theorem 7.7.6 that $\lim(\mathbf{p}_k) = \lim(\mathbf{A}^k)\mathbf{p}_0 = \mathbf{A}_\infty\mathbf{p}_0 = (\mathbf{p}\mathbf{1}^{\mathrm{T}})\mathbf{p}_0 = \mathbf{p}(\mathbf{1}^{\mathrm{T}}\mathbf{p}_0) = \mathbf{p}1 = \mathbf{p}$. ■

Note that $\mathbf{A}$ of Example 7.7.3 has the property that $\mathbf{A}^2 > \mathbf{O}$; so $\mathbf{A}$ is regular. The transition matrix in Example 7.7.2 (*d*) is not regular.

Example 7.7.4. Verify Theorem 7.7.5 for the transition matrices (*a*) $\mathbf{J}_n/n$ and (*b*) $(\mathbf{J}_n - \mathbf{I}_n)(n-1)^{-1}$, $n > 2$.

Proof. (*a*) This example is easy. Since $(\mathbf{J}_n/n)^2 = \mathbf{J}_n/n$, $\lim(\mathbf{J}_n/n)^k = \mathbf{J}_n/n$. Thus, each column of $\mathbf{J}_n/n$ is $\mathbf{1}/n$, and this is the sole stationary vector. (*b*) This example is considerably more difficult. Consider the following expansion by the binomial theorem:

$$(\mathbf{I}_n - \mathbf{J}_n)^m = \mathbf{I}_n + \sum_{i=1}^{m} C\binom{m}{i}(-1)^i\mathbf{J}_n^i \tag{7.7.5}$$

Now use $(\mathbf{J}_n/n)^i = \mathbf{J}_n/n$ to simplify Eq. 7.7.5:

$$\begin{aligned}(\mathbf{I}_n - \mathbf{J}_n)^m &= \mathbf{I}_n + (\mathbf{J}_n/n)\sum_{i=1}^{m} C\binom{m}{i}(-1)^i n^i \\ &= \mathbf{I}_n + (\mathbf{J}_n/n)[(1-n)^m - 1]\end{aligned} \tag{7.7.6}$$

Hence,

$$(\mathbf{J}_n - \mathbf{I}_n)^m (n-1)^{-m} = (1-n)^{-m}\mathbf{I}_n + (\mathbf{J}_n/n)(1-(1-n)^{-m})$$

and it follows that $\lim[(\mathbf{J}_n - \mathbf{I}_n)^m (n-1)^{-m}] = \mathbf{J}_n/n$, for $n > 2$. (For $n = 2$, $(\mathbf{J}_n - \mathbf{I}_n)(n-1)^{-1} = \mathbf{J}_2 - \mathbf{I}_2$; this matrix is not regular, and the limit fails to exist.) ■

The transition matrix that models the game introduced in Section 0.1.7 is not regular. This is obvious by inspection:

$$\mathbf{A} = \begin{bmatrix} 0 & 2/3 & 0 & 0 & 0 & 0 & 0 \\ 1/3 & 0 & 2/3 & 0 & 0 & 0 & 0 \\ 0 & 1/3 & 0 & 2/3 & 0 & 0 & 0 \\ 0 & 0 & 1/3 & 0 & 2/3 & 0 & 0 \\ 0 & 0 & 0 & 1/3 & 0 & 0 & 0 \\ 2/3 & 0 & 0 & 0 & 0 & 1 & 0 \\ 0 & 0 & 0 & 0 & 1/3 & 0 & 1 \end{bmatrix} \tag{7.7.7}$$

Nonetheless, $\lim(\mathbf{A}^m)$ does exist. We analyze this limit by considering the more general transition matrix

$$\mathbf{A} = \begin{bmatrix} \mathbf{B} & \mathbf{O} \\ \mathbf{C} & \mathbf{I}_r \end{bmatrix} \tag{7.7.8}$$

We assume that $\mathscr{E}(1) = r$, so that 1 is not an eigenvalue of $\mathbf{B}$. Thus, it follows from $\rho(\mathbf{A}) = 1$ that $\rho(\mathbf{B}) < 1$. Hence, $\mathbf{B}^m \to \mathbf{O}$, and $\mathbf{B}^{(m)} = \mathbf{I} + \mathbf{B} + \mathbf{B}^2 + \cdots + \mathbf{B}^{k-1} \to (\mathbf{I} - \mathbf{B})^{-1}$ is a consequence of Theorem 7.5.1 and its corollary. Thus,

$$\mathbf{A}_\infty = \lim \begin{bmatrix} \mathbf{B} & \mathbf{O} \\ \mathbf{C} & \mathbf{I}_r \end{bmatrix}^m = \lim \begin{bmatrix} \mathbf{B}^m & \mathbf{O} \\ \mathbf{C}\mathbf{B}^{(m)} & \mathbf{I}_r \end{bmatrix} = \begin{bmatrix} \mathbf{O} & \mathbf{O} \\ \mathbf{C}(\mathbf{I} - \mathbf{B})^{-1} & \mathbf{I}_r \end{bmatrix}$$

Note that $\mathrm{rank}(\mathbf{A}_\infty) = r = \mathscr{E}(1)$. Note also that the standard unit vectors displayed as the last r columns of $\mathbf{A}$ (and $\mathbf{A}_\infty$) are stationary vectors, as is every convex combination of these vectors. We apply these results to Eq. 7.7.7 in the subsection to follow.

7.7.1 MATLAB

Enter the transition matrix $\mathbf{A}$ given in Eq. 7.7.7. Then, rounding to two decimal places,

Enter A^{50}

ans =

$$\begin{matrix} 0.00 & 0 & 0.00 & 0 & 0.00 & 0 & 0 \\ 0 & 0.00 & 0 & 0.00 & 0 & 0 & 0 \\ 0.00 & 0 & 0.00 & 0 & 0.00 & 0 & 0 \\ 0 & 0.00 & 0 & 0.00 & 0 & 0 & 0 \\ 0.00 & 0 & 0.00 & 0 & 0.00 & 0 & 0 \\ 0.98 & 0.95 & 0.89 & 0.76 & 0.51 & 1 & 0 \\ 0.01 & 0.05 & 0.11 & 0.24 & 0.49 & 0 & 1 \end{matrix} \tag{7.7.9}$$

Now enter B and C as follows:

```
B = [0   ⅔  0   0   0   0   0;
⅓   0   ⅔   0   0   0   0;
0   ⅓   0   ⅔   0   0   0;
0   0   ⅓   0   ⅔   0   0;
0   0   0   ⅓   0   0   0 ]

C = [ ⅔  0  0  0  0  0;0  0  0  0  ⅓ ]
```

Then

```
Enter C * inv(eye(5) - B)
ans =
        0.98  0.95  0.89  0.76  0.51
        0.02  0.50  0.11  0.24  0.49
```
(7.7.10)

which are the last two rows of A^{50}, excluding columns 6 and 7.

Example 7.7.5. Enter the matrix **A** of Example 7.7.1:

$$\mathbf{A} = \begin{bmatrix} 0 & 0 & 0 & \frac{1}{2} & 0 & 0 \\ 0 & 0 & \frac{1}{2} & 0 & 0 & 0 \\ 0 & \frac{1}{2} & 0 & 0 & 0 & 0 \\ 1 & 0 & 0 & 0 & 0 & 0 \\ 0 & \frac{1}{2} & 0 & \frac{1}{2} & 1 & 0 \\ 0 & 0 & \frac{1}{2} & 0 & 0 & 1 \end{bmatrix}$$

Then eig(A) reveals that the eigenvalues of **A** are $\lambda_1 = \lambda_2 = 1$, $\lambda_3 = 0.5$, $\lambda_4 = -0.5$, $\lambda_5 = \sqrt{2}/2$, and $\lambda_6 = -\sqrt{2}/2$. We conjecture from the computation of A^50 that

$$\mathbf{A}_\infty = \begin{bmatrix} 0 & 0 & 0 & 0 & 0 & 0 \\ 0 & 0 & 0 & 0 & 0 & 0 \\ 0 & 0 & 0 & 0 & 0 & 0 \\ 0 & 0 & 0 & 0 & 0 & 0 \\ 1 & \frac{2}{3} & \frac{1}{3} & 1 & 1 & 0 \\ 0 & \frac{1}{3} & \frac{2}{3} & 0 & 0 & 1 \end{bmatrix}$$

Hence, $a_{52}^{(\infty)} = 2/3$.

PROBLEMS

PART 1

7.7.1. Show that every 2×2 transition matrix is simple.

7.7.2. Find a 3×3 transition matrix that is defective.

7.7.3. If **A** and **B** are transition matrices, show that **AB** is also a transition matrix.

7.7.4. Suppose $\mathbf{A} \geq \mathbf{O}$ and the sum of each column is c. Show that $\mathbf{A}/c$ is a transition matrix.

7.7.5. Let $\mathbf{W}_n > \mathbf{O}$ be a circulant. Find r so that $\mathbf{A} = \mathbf{W}_n/r$ is a transition matrix. Show that $\mathbf{A}^{\mathrm{T}}$ is also a transition matrix, and find $\mathbf{A}_\infty$.

7.7.6. Suppose $\mathbf{S}$ is a symmetric, regular transition matrix. Find $\mathbf{S}_\infty$.

7.7.7. Suppose $\mathbf{Q}$ is an orthogonal transition matrix. Show that $\mathbf{Q} = \mathbf{I}$.

7.7.8. Suppose $\mathbf{A}$ and $\mathbf{B}$ are transition matrices. Show that $a\mathbf{A} + b\mathbf{B}$ is a transition matrix if $a \geq 0$ and $b \geq 0$ and $a + b = 1$.

7.7.9. Construct a 3×3 defective transition matrix. Show that every 2×2 transition matrix is simple.

PART 2

7.7.10. Suppose $\mathbf{A}$ is a transition matrix and $\mathbf{p} = [p_1\ p_2\ \ldots\ p_n]^{\mathrm{T}}$ is a probability vector. Show that $p_1\mathbf{I} + p_2\mathbf{A} + \cdots + p_n\mathbf{A}^{n-1}$ is a transition matrix.

7.7.11. Let $\mathbf{C}_n$ be a companion matrix (Eq. 5.12.1) in which the last row is positive with sum 1. Show that $\mathbf{A} = \mathbf{C}_n^{\mathrm{T}}$ is a regular transition matrix and determine $\mathbf{A}_\infty$. (See Section 5.12.)

7.7.12. Let $\mathbf{M}$ be a magic square of size $n > 2$. (See Section 0.0.1.) Show that $\mathbf{1}^{\mathrm{T}}\mathbf{M} = M\mathbf{1}^{\mathrm{T}}$, where $M = n(n^2 + 1)/2$ is the common row and column sum. (*Hint:* The sum of all the entries in $\mathbf{M}$ must be nM. Now let $\mathbf{A} = \mathbf{M}/M$ and $\mathbf{B} = \mathbf{A}^{\mathrm{T}}$. Find $\mathbf{A}_\infty$ and $\mathbf{B}_\infty$.

7.7.13. For the transition matrix $\mathbf{A}$ in Eq. 7.7.8, show that $\rho(\mathbf{B}) < 1$.

MATLAB

7.7.14. Verify that $\lim((\mathbf{J}_n - \mathbf{I}_n)^m (n-1)^{-m}) = \mathbf{J}_n/n$ for $n = 3$ and $n = 4$.

7.7.15. (Refer to Problem 7.7.12.) Enter magic(7) and verify that $\mathbf{1}^{\mathrm{T}}\mathbf{M} = 175\ \mathbf{1}^{\mathrm{T}}$. Compute $\mathbf{M}^{100}$.

7.7.16. For the companion matrix $\mathbf{C}_4$ whose last row is $[\ \frac{1}{2}\ \ \frac{1}{4}\ \ \frac{1}{8}\ \ \frac{1}{8}]$, show that $\mathbf{A}^{\mathrm{T}} = \mathbf{C}_4$ is a regular transition matrix, and compute $\mathbf{A}_\infty$ approximately.

7.7.17. Verify the computations given and suggested in Example 7.7.5.

CHAPTER

8

QUADRATIC FORMS

8.1 INTRODUCTION

The theory of matrices is a branch of an extensive discipline called *linear algebra*. All our experiences with matrices confirm the appropriateness of the term *linear* in describing the behavior of $\mathbf{A}$. For example, $\mathbf{A}(\alpha\mathbf{x}+\beta\mathbf{y}) = \alpha\mathbf{A}\mathbf{x}+\beta\mathbf{A}\mathbf{y}$ for all α and β is the demonstration that $\mathbf{A}$ is a linear operator. It is all the more surprising, therefore, that the theory of matrices should play a central role in the study of the quadratic functions $\mathbf{x}^{\mathrm{T}}\mathbf{A}\mathbf{x}$. Indeed, if $\mathbf{A}$ is symmetric, the expression $\mathbf{x}^{\mathrm{T}}\mathbf{A}\mathbf{x}$ is a quadratic function (of the n components of $\mathbf{x}$) that appears in many guises, theoretical and applied. Following is a sampling. (See also Example 0.1.5.)

8.1.1 The Theory of Small Oscillations

The description of the motion of mechanical systems can be analyzed by studying $\mathbf{M}\mathbf{y}'' + \mathbf{S}\mathbf{y} = \mathbf{0}$, which in turn leads to a study of the quadratic function $\mathbf{y}^{\mathrm{T}}\mathbf{S}\mathbf{y}$. (See Section 8.7.)

8.1.2 Central Conics

A central conic in n dimensions is a quadratic function of the form

$$\sum_{i=1}^{n} a_{ii}x_i^2 + \sum_{i<j} 2a_{ij}x_ix_j$$

This function can be written $\mathbf{x}^{\mathrm{T}}\mathbf{A}\mathbf{x}$, where $\mathbf{A} = (a_{ij})$. We study $\mathbf{A}$ to determine the nature of the graph of $y = \mathbf{x}^{\mathrm{T}}\mathbf{A}\mathbf{x}$. See Section 8.6.1.

8.1.3 A Sufficient Condition for Relative Maximum and Minimum

The Taylor series expansion of $f(\mathbf{x})$ about the point $\mathbf{x} = \mathbf{x}_0$ is given by

$$f(\mathbf{x}_0) + \nabla f(\mathbf{x}_0)^{\mathrm{T}}(\mathbf{x} - \mathbf{x}_0) + (\mathbf{x} - \mathbf{x}_0)^{\mathrm{T}}\mathbf{H}(\mathbf{x} - \mathbf{x}_0) + \cdots$$

where $\mathbf{H} = (h_{ij})$ is real symmetric and

$$h_{ij} = \frac{\partial^2 f(x_0)}{\partial x_i \partial x_j}$$

If $\nabla f(\mathbf{x}_0) = \mathbf{0}$, then $f(\mathbf{x})$ has an extreme point at $\mathbf{x}_0$. It is the quadratic term $(\mathbf{x}-\mathbf{x}_0)^{\mathrm{T}}\mathbf{H}(\mathbf{x}-\mathbf{x}_0)$ that can (under suitable conditions) distinguish between relative maxima and relative minima.

8.1.4 The Power Method for the Approximation of the Dominant Eigenvalue

This method of approximation begins with an initial vector $\mathbf{a}_0$. The sequence $\mathbf{a}_k = \mathbf{A}^k\mathbf{a}_0$ is then generated. Under certain carefully prescribed conditions, the Rayleigh quotient,

$$\sigma_k = \frac{\mathbf{a}_k^{\mathrm{T}}\mathbf{A}\mathbf{a}_k}{\|\mathbf{a}_k\|^2}$$

provides an approximation to the eigenvalue of $\mathbf{A}$ with largest modulus. (See Section 5.10.)

8.1.5 The Hausdorff Theory of Moments

The Hausdorff theory of moments is an advanced theory concerned with the representation of $f(x)$ given the infinite sequence of moments (definite integrals)

$$\int_a^b f(x)x^m\,dx = \alpha_m, \qquad m = 0,1,2,\ldots$$

Associated with this sequence of moments is the sequence of symmetric matrices $\mathbf{A} = (a_{i+j})$. The "positive definiteness" of these matrices is a key element in the theory.

Statistics and numerical analysis are two other fields where functions of the form $\mathbf{x}^{\mathrm{T}}\mathbf{A}\mathbf{x}$ appear with some frequency. In this chapter, we explore some properties of $\mathbf{A}$ that are relevant to applications.

8.2 QUADRATIC FORMS

The expressions

$$\begin{aligned} q_1 &= x_1x_2 + x_2^2 + x_1x_3 \\ q_2 &= x_1^2 + x_2^2 \\ q_3 &= x_1x_2 \end{aligned}$$

are examples of quadratic functions of 3, 2, and 2 variables, respectively. These functions are known as *real quadratic forms*. The general case in n variables may be written

$$q(\mathbf{x}) = \sum_{i=1}^{n} a_{ii}x_i^2 + \sum_{i<j} 2a_{ij}x_ix_j \tag{8.2.1}$$

where the scalars a_{ij} are real. The matrix of the form given in Eq. 8.2.1 is the $n \times n$ real symmetric matrix

$$\mathbf{A} = \begin{bmatrix} a_{11} & a_{12} & & a_{1n} \\ a_{12} & a_{22} & \cdots & a_{2n} \\ & \vdots & \ddots & \vdots \\ a_{1n} & a_{2n} & \cdots & a_{nn} \end{bmatrix}$$

and it follows that

$$q(\mathbf{x}) = \mathbf{x}^{\mathrm{T}}\mathbf{A}\mathbf{x} = <\mathbf{x}, \mathbf{A}\mathbf{x}> = <\mathbf{A}\mathbf{x}, \mathbf{x}> \tag{8.2.2}$$

The matrix of the form q is constructed from the weights in Eq. 8.2.1, and each real symmetric matrix defines a quadratic form by Eq. 8.2.2. Also, for each $\mathbf{x} \in \mathcal{R}^n$, $q(\mathbf{x})$ is a real number, the *value* of the form. Thus, $q(\mathbf{x})$ may be viewed as a real-valued quadratic function of n variables with no linear or constant terms.

Example 8.2.1 Find the matrix of the quadratic forms

(*a*) $q_1(\mathbf{x}) = x_1^2 + 2x_1x_2 + 4x_1x_3$

(*b*) $q_2(\mathbf{x}) = \dfrac{x_1^2}{4} + \dfrac{x_2^2}{9}$

(*c*) $q_3(\mathbf{x}) = ax_1^2 + 2cx_1x_2 + bx_2^2$

Solution. It is easy to verify the following products:

(*a*) $[x_1 \quad x_2 \quad x_3]\begin{bmatrix} 1 & 1 & 2 \\ 1 & 0 & 0 \\ 2 & 0 & 0 \end{bmatrix}\begin{bmatrix} x_1 \\ x_2 \\ x_3 \end{bmatrix} = x_1^2 + 2x_1x_2 + 4x_1x_3$

(*b*) $[x_1 \quad x_2]\begin{bmatrix} 1/4 & 0 \\ 0 & 1/9 \end{bmatrix}\begin{bmatrix} x_1 \\ x_2 \end{bmatrix} = \dfrac{x_1^2}{4} + \dfrac{x_2^2}{9}$

(*c*) $[x_1 \quad x_2]\begin{bmatrix} a & c \\ c & b \end{bmatrix}\begin{bmatrix} x_1 \\ x_2 \end{bmatrix} = ax_1^2 + 2cx_1x_2 + bx_2^2$

For any nonsingular matrix $\mathbf{S}$, $\mathbf{x} = \mathbf{S}\mathbf{y}$ defines $\mathbf{x}$ and $\mathbf{y}$ in terms of the entries of $\mathbf{S}$. This "change of variables" transforms a quadratic form in $\mathbf{x}$ into a quadratic form in $\mathbf{y}$:

$$\mathbf{x}^{\mathrm{T}}\mathbf{A}\mathbf{x} = (\mathbf{S}\mathbf{y})^{\mathrm{T}}\mathbf{A}(\mathbf{S}\mathbf{y}) = \mathbf{y}^{\mathrm{T}}(\mathbf{S}^{\mathrm{T}}\mathbf{A}\mathbf{S})\mathbf{y} = \mathbf{y}^{\mathrm{T}}\mathbf{B}\mathbf{y} \tag{8.2.3}$$

where $\mathbf{B} = \mathbf{S}^{\mathrm{T}}\mathbf{A}\mathbf{S}$. ($\mathbf{B}$ is symmetric and is the matrix of the form in $\mathbf{y}$.)

The relationship $\mathbf{S}^T\mathbf{AS} = \mathbf{B}$ is called a *congruence*. Congruences are equivalence relationships because, first of all, $\mathbf{A}$ is congruent to itself ($\mathbf{I}^T\mathbf{AI} = \mathbf{A}$). Second, if $\mathbf{A}$ is congruent to $\mathbf{B}$, then $\mathbf{B}$ is congruent to $\mathbf{A}$ by use of $\mathbf{S}^{-1}$. Finally, if $\mathbf{S}^T\mathbf{AS} = \mathbf{B}$ and $\mathbf{T}^T\mathbf{BT} = \mathbf{C}$, then $(\mathbf{ST})^T\mathbf{A}(\mathbf{ST}) = \mathbf{C}$ shows that congruences are transitive. These are the criteria that define an equivalence relationship.

If $\mathbf{D}$ is a diagonal matrix, then the form $\mathbf{x}^T\mathbf{Dx}$ is said to be a *diagonal form*. If $\mathbf{S}^T\mathbf{AS} = \mathbf{D}$, then $\mathbf{S}$ is said to *diagonalize the form*. It turns out that, except for $\mathbf{O}$, every real symmetric matrix is congruent to infinitely many diagonal forms. (Of course, if $\mathbf{O}$ is congruent to $\mathbf{B}$, then $\mathbf{B} = \mathbf{O}$.) The importance of diagonal forms is that they represent combinations of squares; there are no cross-product terms. For example, the conics $a^2x^2 \pm b^2y^2 = 1$ are far easier to classify and graph than $ax^2 + cxy + by^2 = 1$. (See Sections 0.1.5. and 8.6.1.)

Suppose $\mathbf{A}$ is real symmetric. Then there exists a real orthogonal matrix $\mathbf{Q}$ (whose columns are linearly independent orthonormal eigenvectors of $\mathbf{A}$) such that $\mathbf{Q}^{-1}\mathbf{AQ} = \mathbf{\Lambda}$. Since $\mathbf{Q}^{-1} = \mathbf{Q}^T, \mathbf{Q}^{-1}\mathbf{AQ} = \mathbf{Q}^T\mathbf{AQ} = \mathbf{\Lambda}$, $\mathbf{A}$ is always congruent to a diagonal matrix of its real eigenvalues. The fact that a unitary similarity is also a congruence is very useful but only incidental to the theory of congruences. Our main interest is in the effects of the change of variable $\mathbf{x} = \mathbf{Sy}$ on $\mathbf{x}^T\mathbf{Ax}$. We require $\mathbf{S}$ to be nonsingular but not necessarily orthogonal.

Theorem 8.2.1. *Suppose $\mathbf{A}$ is the matrix of the quadratic form $q(\mathbf{x})$ and $\lambda_1 rm, \lambda_2, \ldots, \lambda_n$ are the eigenvalues of $\mathbf{A}$. Then there exists a real orthogonal matrix $\mathbf{Q}$ such that for $\mathbf{y}$ defined by $\mathbf{x} = \mathbf{Qy}$,*

$$q(\mathbf{x}) = q(\mathbf{Qy}) = \hat{q}(\mathbf{y}) = \lambda_1 y_1^2 + \lambda_2 y_2^2 + \cdots + \lambda_n y_n^2 \tag{8.2.4}$$

Proof. The right-hand side of Eq. 8.2.4 is simply $\mathbf{y}^T\mathbf{\Lambda y}$. ∎

Corollary 1. *If $\mathbf{A}$ is the matrix of the quadratic form $q(\mathbf{x})$ and $\mathbf{B}$ is a real symmetric matrix such that $q(\mathbf{x}) = \mathbf{x}^T\mathbf{Bx}$ for all $\mathbf{x} \in \mathcal{R}^n$, then $\mathbf{A} = \mathbf{B}$.*

Proof. By definition $q(\mathbf{x}) = \mathbf{x}^T\mathbf{Ax}$, so that for all $\mathbf{x} \in \mathcal{R}^n$, $\mathbf{x}^T\mathbf{Ax} = \mathbf{x}^T\mathbf{Bx}$. Hence, $\mathbf{x}^T(\mathbf{A}-\mathbf{B})\mathbf{x} = 0$. By Theorem 8.2.1, there exists an orthogonal $\mathbf{Q}$ that diagonalizes $\mathbf{A} - \mathbf{B}$. So, defining $\mathbf{y} = \mathbf{Q}^{-1}\mathbf{x}$, we have $\mathbf{Qy} = \mathbf{x}$, and therefore

$$0 = \mathbf{x}^T(\mathbf{A} - \mathbf{B})\mathbf{x} = (\mathbf{Qy})^T(\mathbf{A} - \mathbf{B})\mathbf{Qy} = \lambda_1 y_1^2 + \lambda_2 y_2^2 + \cdots + \lambda_n y_n^2$$

Now choose $\mathbf{y} = \mathbf{e}_i$ and deduce that $0 = \lambda_i$ for each i. However, a real symmetric matrix with all its eigenvalues zero is the zero matrix. That is, $\mathbf{A} - \mathbf{B} = \mathbf{O}$. ∎

Corollary 1 is a uniqueness theorem; it asserts that there is just one real symmetric matrix associated with the form $q(\mathbf{x})$. It is for this reason that $\mathbf{A}$ is called *the* matrix of the form $q(\mathbf{x})$. By contrast, if the requirement that $\mathbf{B}$

be symmetric is dropped, then it is possible for $\mathbf{x}^T\mathbf{A}\mathbf{x} = \mathbf{x}^T\mathbf{B}\mathbf{x}$ to hold without $\mathbf{A} = \mathbf{B}$. For example,

$$q(\mathbf{x}) = 2x_1x_2 = [x_1 \quad x_2]\begin{bmatrix} 0 & \tfrac{1}{2} \\ \tfrac{1}{2} & 0 \end{bmatrix}\begin{bmatrix} x_1 \\ x_2 \end{bmatrix} = [x_1 \quad x_2]\begin{bmatrix} 0 & 2 \\ 0 & 0 \end{bmatrix}\begin{bmatrix} x_1 \\ x_2 \end{bmatrix}$$

Define the diagonal matrices $\mathbf{\Lambda}$ and $\mathbf{D}$ as follows:

$$\mathbf{\Lambda} = \begin{bmatrix} \lambda_1 & 0 & & 0 \\ 0 & \lambda_2 & \cdots & 0 \\ \vdots & \vdots & \ddots & \vdots \\ 0 & 0 & \cdots & \lambda_n \end{bmatrix} \qquad \mathbf{D} = \begin{bmatrix} d_1 & 0 & & 0 \\ 0 & d_2 & \cdots & 0 \\ \vdots & \vdots & \ddots & \vdots \\ 0 & 0 & \cdots & d_n \end{bmatrix}$$

Suppose that $\mathbf{Q}^T\mathbf{A}\mathbf{Q} = \mathbf{\Lambda}$. Then $\mathbf{D}\mathbf{Q}^T\mathbf{A}\mathbf{Q}\mathbf{D} = \mathbf{D}\mathbf{\Lambda}\mathbf{D} = \mathbf{D}^2\mathbf{\Lambda}$ is also a diagonal matrix, and

$$(\mathbf{D}\mathbf{Q}^T)\mathbf{A}(\mathbf{Q}\mathbf{D}) = \mathbf{D}\mathbf{\Lambda}\mathbf{D} = \mathbf{D}^2\mathbf{\Lambda} = \begin{bmatrix} d_1^2\lambda_1 & 0 & & 0 \\ 0 & d_2^2\lambda_2 & \cdots & 0 \\ \vdots & \vdots & \ddots & \vdots \\ 0 & 0 & \cdots & d_n^2\lambda_n \end{bmatrix} \tag{8.2.5}$$

But $(\mathbf{Q}\mathbf{D})^T = \mathbf{D}\mathbf{Q}^T$, and Eq. 8.2.5 shows that $\mathbf{A}$ is congruent to $\mathbf{D}^2\mathbf{\Lambda}$; hence, every real symmetric $\mathbf{A} \neq \mathbf{O}$ is congruent to infinitely many diagonal matrices. (If $\mathbf{S}^T\mathbf{A}\mathbf{S} = \mathbf{B}$ for all $\mathbf{S}$, then $\mathbf{A} = \mathbf{B} = \mathbf{O}$. See Problem 8.2.12.)

We now turn our attention to the problem of standardizing diagonal forms. By choosing

$$d_i = \begin{cases} 1/|\lambda_i|^{1/2} & \text{if } \lambda_i \neq 0 \\ 1 & \text{if } \lambda_i = 0 \end{cases} \tag{8.2.6}$$

one can find a diagonal matrix of 1s, -1s, and 0s congruent to $\mathbf{A}$. In Section 8.8 it is shown that the number of 1s, -1s, and 0s are invariants of the quadratic form under a congruence equivalence relationship.

There are two canonical forms $\mathbf{x}^T\mathbf{A}\mathbf{x}$; the first is given by the (algebraic) weighted sum of squares, with the eigenvalues of $\mathbf{A}$ as the weights (see Eq. 8.2.4). The second is given as part of the next theorem.

Theorem 8.2.2. *Suppose* rank($\mathbf{A}$) $= r$, *and* $\mathbf{A}$ *is real symmetric with p positive eigenvalues. Then there exists a nonsingular* $\mathbf{T}$ *such that for* $\mathbf{x} = \mathbf{T}\mathbf{z}$

$$q(\mathbf{x}) = q(\mathbf{T}\mathbf{z}) = \tilde{q}(\mathbf{z}) = z_1^2 + \cdots + z_p^2 - (z_{p+1}^2 + \cdots + z_r^2) \tag{8.2.7}$$

Proof. The change of variables $\mathbf{x} = \mathbf{Q}\mathbf{y}$ transforms $q(\mathbf{x})$ into the canonical form of Eq. 8.2.4. If $\mathbf{z}$ is defined by $\mathbf{y} = \mathbf{D}\mathbf{z}$, where $\mathbf{D}$ is given by Eq. 8.2.6, then $\mathbf{x} = \mathbf{D}\mathbf{Q}\mathbf{z}$ leads to Eq. 8.2.7. Since the rank of $\mathbf{A}$ is r, there are r nonzero eigenvalues of $\mathbf{A}$. By definition of p, $r - p$ is the number of negative eigenvalues of $\mathbf{A}$. Thus, the subscript on the z with a minus one coefficient in Eq. 8.2.7 runs from $p + 1$ to r. ■

8.2.1 Hermitian Forms

Although we will confine ourselves to real quadratic forms for most of this chapter, there is a natural and convenient generalization to forms in which $\mathbf{x} \in \mathcal{C}^n$. A *hermitian form* is an expression $\mathbf{x}^H\mathbf{A}\mathbf{x}$ in which $\mathbf{A}$ is hermitian. If $\mathbf{A}$ is a hermitian matrix, it is not difficult to see that for each $\mathbf{x} \in \mathcal{C}^n$, $q(\mathbf{x}) = \mathbf{x}^H\mathbf{A}\mathbf{x} = (\mathbf{A}\mathbf{x})^H\mathbf{x}$ is real:

$$\overline{q(\mathbf{x})} = <\overline{\mathbf{A}\mathbf{x},\mathbf{x}}> = <\mathbf{x},\mathbf{A}\mathbf{x}> = <\mathbf{A}^H\mathbf{x},\mathbf{x}> = (\mathbf{A}\mathbf{x})^H\mathbf{x} = q(\mathbf{x})$$

But $\overline{q(\mathbf{x})} = q(\mathbf{x})$ shows that $q(\mathbf{x})$ is real for all $\mathbf{x} \in \mathcal{C}^n$. (See also Problems 8.2.13 and 8.2.14 and Section 4.3.2.)

Most theorems in this chapter are stated for real symmetric $\mathbf{A}$ and orthogonal $\mathbf{Q}$. In fact, most can be translated by the following dictionary into theorems for hermitian forms:

For $\mathbf{x} \in \mathcal{R}^n$	$\rightarrow$	For $\mathbf{x} \in \mathcal{C}^n$
$\mathbf{A}$ is real symmetric	$\rightarrow$	$\mathbf{A}$ is hermitian
$\mathbf{Q}$ is orthogonal	$\rightarrow$	$\mathbf{U}$ is unitary
Transpose	$\rightarrow$	Hermitian transpose

PROBLEMS

PART 1

8.2.1. Find the matrix of the following quadratic forms:
(*a*) $q_1 = x_1x_2 + x_2^2 + x_1x_3$
(*b*) $q_2 = x_1^2 + x_2^2$
(*c*) $q_3 = x_1x_2$

8.2.2. Suppose

$$\mathbf{A} = \begin{bmatrix} 3 & 0 & -1 \\ 0 & 1 & 1 \\ -1 & 1 & -2 \end{bmatrix}$$

Express $(\mathbf{x}+\mathbf{y})^T\mathbf{A}(\mathbf{x}+\mathbf{y})$ in terms of $\mathbf{x}$, $\mathbf{y}$, and $\mathbf{A}$.

8.2.3. Suppose $\mathbf{x} = [1 \quad -1 \quad 0]^T$. Find $\mathbf{x}^T\mathbf{A}\mathbf{x}$ for $\mathbf{A}$ of Problem 8.2.2.

8.2.4. For each of the forms in Problem 8.2.1, find the two canonical forms, Eqs. 8.2.4 and 8.2.7, and the transforming matrices $\mathbf{Q}$ and $\mathbf{T}$, respectively.

PART 2

8.2.5. Find a complex symmetric 2×2 nonzero matrix all of whose eigenvalues are zero. (*Hint:* Let the off-diagonal entries be i.)

8.2.6. Which theorem implies that a real symmetric matrix can be diagonalized by an orthogonal matrix?

In Problems 8.2.7–8.2.10, assume that $\mathbf{A}$ and $\mathbf{B}$ are real symmetric.

8.2.7. Under what conditions on k, if any, is $k\mathbf{A}$ congruent to $\mathbf{A}$ for all $\mathbf{A}$?

8.2.8. If $\mathbf{A}$ is congruent to $\mathbf{B}$, does it follow that $k\mathbf{A}$ is congruent to $k\mathbf{B}$?

8.2.9. If $\mathbf{A}$ is nonsingular and is congruent to $\mathbf{B}$, show that $\mathbf{A}^{-1}$ is congruent to $\mathbf{B}^{-1}$.

8.2.10. If $\mathbf{S}^T\mathbf{A}\mathbf{S} = \mathbf{B}$ for all $\mathbf{S}$, show that $\mathbf{A} = \mathbf{B} = \mathbf{O}$.

PART 3

8.2.11. Suppose $\mathbf{A}$ is hermitian. Rewrite and prove Theorem 8.2.1 with the real orthogonal matrix $\mathbf{Q}$ replaced by the unitary matrix $\mathbf{U}$.

8.2.12. Prove that Theorem 8.2.2 still holds if the assumption "$\mathbf{A}$ is real symmetric" is replaced by the generalization "$\mathbf{A}$ is hermitian."

8.2.13. Prove that a unitary matrix all of whose eigenvalues are zero is the zero matrix by using the Cayley-Hamilton theorem.

8.2.14. If $\mathbf{A}$ is hermitian and unitarily similar to $\mathbf{B}$, is $\mathbf{A}$ congruent to $\mathbf{B}$?

8.3 DIAGONALIZATION BY COMPLETING THE SQUARE

The problem of classifying conic sections ultimately reduces to finding a diagonal form congruent to $\mathbf{x}^T\mathbf{A}\mathbf{x}$. The unitary similarity $\mathbf{Q}^T\mathbf{A}\mathbf{Q} = \mathbf{\Lambda}$ (where $\mathbf{Q}$ is the orthogonal matrix of normalized eigenvectors of $\mathbf{A}$ and $\mathbf{\Lambda}$ is the real diagonal matrix of the corresponding eigenvalues) is one such congruence. But computing the eigenpairs of $\mathbf{A}$ can be a tedious, time-consuming exercise. Two alternatives that avoid this computation can be easily described. The first, outlined in this section, is an extension to n dimensions of the familiar algorithm for "completing the square." This idea is attributed to Lagrange and is often called *Lagrange's method*. The second method appears in Section 8.5 and is of great theoretical importance.

The point of the following examples is to illustrate the Lagrange method in sufficient detail that all the subtleties and pitfalls of the method may be seen. These examples are also meant to indicate the route a general proof might take, if one were inclined to construct one. The first example presents a case having no subtleties.

Example 8.3.1. Find a diagonal form congruent to the following form:

$$q(\mathbf{x}) = x_1^2 + 2x_1x_2 - x_2^2$$

Solution. The following steps are elementary.

$$q(\mathbf{x}) = x_1^2 + 2x_1x_2 - x_2^2 = (x_1 + x_2)^2 - 2x_2^2$$

If we set $y_1 = x_1 + x_2$ and $y_2 = x_2$, then $q(\mathbf{x}) = y_1^2 - 2y_2^2 = \hat{q}(\mathbf{y})$. The change of variables is given by

$$\mathbf{S}\mathbf{x} = \begin{bmatrix} 1 & 1 \\ 0 & 1 \end{bmatrix} \mathbf{x} = \mathbf{y}$$

The matrix of the given form q is

$$\mathbf{A} = \begin{bmatrix} 1 & 1 \\ 1 & -1 \end{bmatrix}$$

and the congruence is $\mathbf{T}^T\mathbf{A}\mathbf{T}$, where $\mathbf{T} = \mathbf{S}^{-1}$. That is,

$$\begin{bmatrix} 1 & 0 \\ -1 & 1 \end{bmatrix} \mathbf{A} \begin{bmatrix} 1 & -1 \\ 0 & 1 \end{bmatrix} = \begin{bmatrix} 1 & 0 \\ 0 & -2 \end{bmatrix}$$

Example 8.3.2. Find a diagonal form congruent to the following form:

$$q(\mathbf{x}) = x_1^2 + 2x_1x_2 + x_2^2$$

Solution. This example presents the first complication. We find

$$q(\mathbf{x}) = x_1^2 + 2x_1x_2 + x_2^2 = (x_1 + x_2)^2$$

and setting $y_1 = x_1 + x_2$ leads to $\hat{q}(\mathbf{y}) = y_1^2$, a form in only one variable. This is unsatisfactory because the corresponding change of variables,

$$\mathbf{y} = \mathbf{S}\mathbf{x} = \begin{bmatrix} 1 & 1 \\ 0 & 0 \end{bmatrix} \mathbf{x}$$

has $\mathbf{S}$ singular. The remedy is simple. We set $y_2 = x_2$ and write

$$q(\mathbf{x}) = x_1^2 + 2x_1x_2 + x_2^2 = (x_1 + x_2)^2 + 0x_2 = y_1^2 + 0y_2^2$$

Now the change of variables is

$$\mathbf{y} = \mathbf{S}\mathbf{x} = \begin{bmatrix} 1 & 1 \\ 0 & 1 \end{bmatrix} \mathbf{x}$$

and $\mathbf{S}$ is nonsingular. In this example,

$$\mathbf{A} = \begin{bmatrix} 1 & 1 \\ 1 & 1 \end{bmatrix}$$

and the congruence is

$$\begin{bmatrix} 1 & 0 \\ -1 & 1 \end{bmatrix} \mathbf{A} \begin{bmatrix} 1 & -1 \\ 0 & 1 \end{bmatrix} = \begin{bmatrix} 1 & 0 \\ 0 & 0 \end{bmatrix}$$

Example 8.3.3. Find a diagonal form congruent to the following form:

$$q(\mathbf{y}) = 2y_1^2 + 2y_1y_2 + 4y_1y_3 + 2y_2y_3$$

Solution. We have

$$\begin{aligned} q(\mathbf{y}) &= 2y_1^2 + 2y_1y_2 + 4y_1y_3 + 2y_2y_3 \\ &= 2(y_1 + y_2/2 + y_3)^2 - y_2^2/2 - 2y_3^2 - 2y_2y_3 + 2y_2y_3 \\ &= 2(y_1 + y_2/2 + y_3)^2 - y_2^2/2 - 2y_3^2 \end{aligned}$$

Now set $z_1 = 2(y_1 + y_2/2 + y_3)$, $z_2 = y_2$, and $z_3 = y_3$. Then

$$q(\mathbf{y}) = \hat{q}(\mathbf{z}) = 2z_1^2 - z_2^2/2 - 2z_3^2$$

Example 8.3.4. Find a diagonal form congruent to the following form:

$$q(\mathbf{x}) = 2x_1x_2 + 2x_1x_3 + 2x_2x_3$$

Solution. The simple expedient of adding and subtracting x_1^2 won't work for an interesting reason:

$$\begin{aligned} 2x_1x_2 + 2x_1x_3 + 2x_2x_3 &= x_1^2 + 2x_1x_2 + 2x_1x_3 + 2x_2x_3 - x_1^2 \\ &= (x_1 + x_2 + x_3)^2 - x_1^2 - x_2^2 - x_3^2 \end{aligned}$$

and this form is in four variables, $y_4 = x_1 + x_2 + x_3$, $y_1 = x_1$, $y_2 = x_2$, and $y_3 = x_3$. (In this instance $\mathbf{S}$ is 4×3.)

The resolution of this problem is due to Lagrange. We need a preliminary change of variables that introduces x_1^2 without forcing a singular $\mathbf{S}$. Set $y_1 = x_1$, $y_1 + y_2 = x_2$, and $y_3 = x_3$. Then

$$\begin{aligned} 2x_1x_2 + 2x_1x_3 + 2x_2x_3 &= 2y_1(y_1 + y_2) + 2y_1y_3 + 2(y_1 + y_2)y_3 \\ &= 2y_1^2 + 2y_1y_2 + 4y_1y_3 + 2y_2y_3 \end{aligned}$$

This accomplishes our ends; we are now at a stage in which we can proceed with the computations outlined in the earlier examples. Indeed, the form in $\mathbf{y}$ is the form diagonalized in Example 8.3.3.

Of course, these examples do not constitute a proof of the implicit assertion that this technique *always* results in the diagonalization of $\mathbf{A}$. They are meant to explain the ideas needed in the working of specific examples and to suggest the kind of issues a rigorous proof must address.

PROBLEMS

PART 1

8.3.1. Use the method of Lagrange to diagonalize the following forms:
(*a*) $x_1^2 + x_1x_2 + x_1x_3$ (*b*) $x_1^2 + x_1x_2 + 2x_3^2$ (*c*) $x_1^2 + 2x_1x_3 + x_2^2$

8.3.2. Use the method of Lagrange to diagonalize the following forms:
(*a*) $x_1x_2 + x_1x_3$ (*b*) $x_1x_2 + 2x_3^2$ (*c*) $x_1^2 + 2x_2x_3 + x_3^2$

8.3.3. Use the method of Lagrange to find a diagonal matrix congruent to the following matrices:

(*a*) $\begin{bmatrix} 1 & 1 \\ 1 & 0 \end{bmatrix}$ (*b*) $\begin{bmatrix} 1 & 0 & -1 \\ 0 & 1 & 0 \\ -1 & 0 & 1 \end{bmatrix}$ (*c*) $\begin{bmatrix} 0 & 0 & 1 \\ 0 & 1 & 0 \\ 1 & 0 & 0 \end{bmatrix}$

8.4 POSITIVE DEFINITE FORMS

A form q is said to be *positive definite* if $q(\mathbf{x}) > 0$ for all $\mathbf{x} \neq \mathbf{0}$, $\mathbf{x} \in \mathcal{R}^n$.[1] The form is *positive semidefinite* if $q(\mathbf{x}) \geq 0$ for all $\mathbf{x} \in \mathcal{R}$. Therefore, every positive definite form is also semidefinite. If there is an $\mathbf{x}_0 \neq \mathbf{0}$ for which $q(\mathbf{x}_0) = 0$ and for all $\mathbf{x}$, $q(\mathbf{x}) \geq 0$, then the form is *positive semidefinite* and *singular*. The

[1] For hermitian forms, we require that $\mathbf{x}^H\mathbf{A}\mathbf{x} > 0$ for all $\mathbf{x} \neq \mathbf{0} \in \mathcal{C}^n$.

matrix of the form is positive definite (semidefinite) if the form is. (If a form is semidefinite and singular, then the matrix of the form is singular, and this motivates the term *singular* for the form; see Theorem 8.4.2.) The terms *negative definite* and *negative semidefinite* are defined in the obvious way. The form q is *indefinite* if there exist $\mathbf{y}$ and $\mathbf{z}$ such that $q(\mathbf{y}) > 0$ and $q(\mathbf{z}) < 0$.

We shall see that many applications of quadratic forms depend on whether the form is definite or indefinite. Anticipating Theorem 8.6.1, we remark here that a central conic is an ellipse if its form is positive definite and an hyperbola if its form is indefinite.

The definition of *positive definite* is not a particularly useful criterion for determining when a symmetric matrix is positive definite. However, the definition does lead to an algorithm that is efficient and effective. The following two theorems are a start in this direction.

Theorem 8.4.1. *If* $\mathbf{A}$ *and* $\mathbf{B}$ *are congruent and* $\mathbf{A}$ *is positive definite (semidefinite), then* $\mathbf{B}$ *is positive definite (semidefinite).*

Proof. Suppose $\mathbf{A}$ is positive semidefinite. Since $\mathbf{B} = \mathbf{S}^{\mathrm{T}}\mathbf{A}\mathbf{S}$ for some nonsingular $\mathbf{S}$, setting $\mathbf{x} = \mathbf{S}\mathbf{y}$ leads to $\mathbf{y}^{\mathrm{T}}\mathbf{B}\mathbf{y} = \mathbf{y}^{\mathrm{T}}\mathbf{S}^{\mathrm{T}}\mathbf{A}\mathbf{S}\mathbf{y} = \mathbf{x}^{\mathrm{T}}\mathbf{A}\mathbf{x} \geq 0$ for $\mathbf{x} \neq \mathbf{0}$. Now $\mathbf{y} \neq \mathbf{0}$ if and only if $\mathbf{x} \neq \mathbf{0}$ since $\mathbf{S}$ is nonsingular. Therefore, $\mathbf{y}^{\mathrm{T}}\mathbf{B}\mathbf{y} \geq 0$ for all $\mathbf{y} \neq \mathbf{0}$. If $\mathbf{A}$ is positive definite, then $\mathbf{x}^{\mathrm{T}}\mathbf{A}\mathbf{x} > 0$ for all $\mathbf{x} \neq \mathbf{0}$, and this implies $\mathbf{y}^{\mathrm{T}}\mathbf{A}\mathbf{y} > 0$ for all $\mathbf{y} \neq \mathbf{0}$. ■

Theorem 8.4.2. *Suppose* $\mathbf{A}$ *is the matrix of the quadratic form* q. *Then*

(*a*) $\mathbf{A}$ *is positive definite if and only if the eigenvalues of* $\mathbf{A}$ *are positive.*
(*b*) $\mathbf{A}$ *is positive semidefinite if and only if the eigenvalues of* $\mathbf{A}$ *are nonnegative.*
(*c*) $\mathbf{A}$ *is positive semidefinite and singular if and only if the eigenvalues of* $\mathbf{A}$ *are nonnegative and at least one is zero.*
(*d*) $\mathbf{A}$ *is indefinite if and only if at least one eigenvalue of* $\mathbf{A}$ *is positive and at least one is negative.*

Proof. By Theorem 8.2.1, $\mathbf{A}$ is congruent to $\mathbf{\Lambda}$, and hence, for all $\mathbf{y} \neq \mathbf{0}$,

$$q(\mathbf{x}) = q(\mathbf{Q}\mathbf{y}) = \mathbf{y}^{\mathrm{T}}\mathbf{\Lambda}\mathbf{y} = \lambda_1 y_1^2 + \lambda_2 y_2^2 + \cdots + \lambda_n y_n^2 \tag{8.4.1}$$

Therefore, $q(\mathbf{x}) > 0$ if and only if all the eigenvalues of $\mathbf{A}$ are positive. And $q(\mathbf{x}) \geq 0$ if and only if all the eigenvalues of $\mathbf{A}$ are nonnegative. If q is positive semidefinite and singular, then there exists $\mathbf{x}_0 \neq \mathbf{0}$ such that $q(\mathbf{x}_0) = 0$. Define $\mathbf{y}_0 = \mathbf{Q}^{\mathrm{T}}\mathbf{x}_0$. Then $\mathbf{y}_0 \neq \mathbf{0}$ and $\mathbf{y}_0^{\mathrm{T}}\mathbf{\Lambda}\mathbf{y}_0 = 0$. Using Eq. 8.4.1, it follows that at least one eigenvalue of $\mathbf{A}$ must be zero and, therefore, $\mathbf{A}$ is singular. Conversely, if $\mathbf{A}$ is singular and is positive semidefinite, then all the eigenvalues of $\mathbf{A}$ are nonnegative and $\lambda_i = 0$, for some i. Suppose, to be specific, that $\lambda_1 = 0$. Then $\mathbf{y} = \mathbf{e}_1$ leads to $q(\mathbf{Q}\mathbf{e}_1) = 0$, and hence $\mathbf{x}_0 = \mathbf{Q}\mathbf{e}_1$ is a nonzero vector such that $q(\mathbf{x}_0) = \mathbf{0}$. These arguments prove (*a*)–(*c*); the proof of (*d*) is reserved for Problem 8.4.15. ■

Theorem 8.4.3. *If the form q is positive definite and $\mathbf{A} = (a_{ij})$ is the matrix of the form, then:* (*a*) $a_{ii} > 0$, (*b*) $\det(\mathbf{A}) > 0$, (*c*) $a_{ii}a_{jj} > a_{ij}^2$.

Proof. Part (*b*) follows from part (*a*) of Theorem 8.4.2. Since $q(\mathbf{x}) > 0$ for all $\mathbf{x} \neq \mathbf{0}, q(\mathbf{e}_i) = a_{ii} > 0$ establishes (*a*). To prove (*c*), consider the value of q at $x_i\mathbf{e}_i + x_j\mathbf{e}_j$:

$$\begin{aligned} 0 < q(x_i\mathbf{e}_i + x_j\mathbf{e}_j) &= e_i^{\mathrm{T}}\mathbf{A}\mathbf{e}_i x_i^2 + e_i^{\mathrm{T}}\mathbf{A}\mathbf{e}_j x_i x_j + e_i^{\mathrm{T}}\mathbf{A}\mathbf{e}_j x_j^2 + e_j^{\mathrm{T}}\mathbf{A}\mathbf{e}_i x_j x_i \\ &= a_{ii}x_{ii}^2 + 2a_{ij}x_i x_j + a_{jj}x_{jj}^2 \qquad (8.4.2) \end{aligned}$$

The expression $a_{ii}x_{ii}^2 + 2a_{ij}x_ix_j + a_{jj}x_{jj}^2$ is a quadratic form in two variables, and the matrix of this form is

$$\mathbf{B} = \begin{bmatrix} a_{ii} & a_{ij} \\ a_{ij} & a_{jj} \end{bmatrix}$$

Now, Eq. 8.4.2 shows that $\mathbf{B}$ must be positive definite, so $\det(\mathbf{B}) > 0$ by (*b*), and (*c*) follows. ■

The three conditions listed in Theorem 8.4.3 are necessary but not sufficient since it is possible to present an example in which all three conditions are met and the form is indefinite.

Example 8.4.1. Show that all three conditions of Theorem 8.4.3 are satisfied but $\mathbf{A}$ is indefinite, where

$$\mathbf{A} = \begin{bmatrix} 3 & 3 & 3 & 0 \\ 3 & 12 & -6 & 9 \\ 3 & -6 & 6 & -6 \\ 0 & 9 & -6 & 7 \end{bmatrix}$$

Solution. The diagonal entries are positive, and a little computation shows that $\det(\mathbf{A}) = 81$. The six cases involving (*c*) are set as Problem 8.4.1. Finally, $\mathbf{x}^{\mathrm{T}}\mathbf{A}\mathbf{x} = -2$ for $\mathbf{x} = [0 \quad -1 \quad 1 \quad 2]^{\mathrm{T}}$.

Example 8.4.2. Suppose $\mathbf{A}$ is $m \times n$ and $\mathrm{rank}(\mathbf{A}) = n < m$. Show that $\mathbf{A}^{\mathrm{H}}\mathbf{A}$ is positive definite and that $\mathbf{A}\mathbf{A}^{\mathrm{H}}$ is positive semidefinite and singular.

Solution. The matrices $\mathbf{A}^{\mathrm{H}}\mathbf{A}$ and $\mathbf{A}\mathbf{A}^{\mathrm{H}}$ are symmetric, and

$$\mathbf{x}^{\mathrm{H}}\mathbf{A}^{\mathrm{H}}\mathbf{A}\mathbf{x} = <\mathbf{A}\mathbf{x}, \mathbf{A}\mathbf{x}> = \|\mathbf{A}\mathbf{x}\|^2 \geq 0$$

$$\mathbf{x}^{\mathrm{H}}\mathbf{A}\mathbf{A}^{\mathrm{H}}\mathbf{x} = <\mathbf{A}^{\mathrm{H}}\mathbf{x}, \mathbf{A}^{\mathrm{H}}\mathbf{x}> = \|\mathbf{A}^{\mathrm{H}}\mathbf{x}\|^2 \geq 0$$

shows that $\mathbf{A}^{\mathrm{H}}\mathbf{A}$ and $\mathbf{A}\mathbf{A}^{\mathrm{H}}$ are semidefinite. However, if $\mathrm{rank}(\mathbf{A}) = n$, then $\mathbf{A}\mathbf{x} \neq \mathbf{0}$ for $\mathbf{x} \neq \mathbf{0}$ and thus, $\|\mathbf{A}\mathbf{x}\| > 0$ for all $\mathbf{x} \neq \mathbf{0}$. Therefore, $\mathbf{A}^{\mathrm{H}}\mathbf{A}$ is definite. On the other hand, since $m > n$, $\mathbf{A}\mathbf{A}^{\mathrm{H}}$ is $m \times m$ and $\mathrm{rank}(\mathbf{A}\mathbf{A}^{\mathrm{H}}) \leq \mathrm{rank}(\mathbf{A}) = n < m$. Under these circumstances $\mathbf{A}\mathbf{A}^{\mathrm{H}}$ is positive semidefinite and singular.

Example 8.4.3. Show that $\mathbf{J}_n - \mathbf{I}_n$, $n > 1$, is indefinite.

Solution. If $n > 1$, then one of the eigenvalues of $\mathbf{J}_n - \mathbf{I}_n$ is -1 and the others are $n - 1 > 0$. Hence, $\mathbf{J}_n - \mathbf{I}_n$ is indefinite.

Example 8.4.4. Show that the only positive semidefinite unitary matrix is $\mathbf{I}$.

Solution. If λ is an eigenvalue of the unitary matrix $\mathbf{U}$, then $|\lambda| = 1$. (Why?) Since $\mathbf{U}$ is positive semidefinite, its eigenvalues are nonnegative and, therefore, $\lambda = 1$. Because every unitary matrix is simple, $\mathbf{S}^{-1}\mathbf{U}\mathbf{S} = \mathbf{\Lambda}$ for some $\mathbf{S}$. But $\mathbf{\Lambda} = \mathbf{I}$ and, hence, $\mathbf{S}^{-1}\mathbf{U}\mathbf{S} = \mathbf{I}$, and $\mathbf{U} = \mathbf{S}^{-1}\mathbf{I}\mathbf{S} = \mathbf{I}$.

Example 8.4.5. Show that for each $n > 1$, the following matrices are indefinite:

$$\mathbf{E}_n = \begin{bmatrix} & \mathbf{O} & & 1 \\ & & 1 & \\ & \cdot^{\cdot^{\cdot}} & & \\ 1 & & \mathbf{O} & \end{bmatrix}$$

Solution. For each $n > 1$, $\mathbf{E}_n$ is a symmetric orthogonal matrix. By Example 8.4.4, neither $\mathbf{E}_n$ nor $(-\mathbf{E}_n)$ can be positive semidefinite. Hence, $\mathbf{E}_n$ must be indefinite.

PROBLEMS

PART 1

8.4.1. Verify that

$$\mathbf{A} = \begin{bmatrix} 3 & 3 & 3 & 0 \\ 3 & 12 & -6 & 9 \\ 3 & -6 & 6 & -6 \\ 0 & 9 & -6 & 7 \end{bmatrix}$$

satisfies the three conditions in Theorem 8.4.3 but is indefinite.

8.4.2. For what range of ϑ is the matrix

$$\begin{bmatrix} \cos\vartheta & \sin\vartheta \\ \sin\vartheta & \cos\vartheta \end{bmatrix}$$

positive semidefinite? For what range is this matrix indefinite? (*Hint*: Find an expression for the eigenvalues.)

PART 2

8.4.3. Rewrite and prove Theorem 8.4.1 using the hypothesis that $\mathbf{A}$ is negative definite (semidefinite).

8.4.4. Show that $\mathbf{A}$ is positive definite implies that $\mathrm{tr}(\mathbf{A}) > 0$.

8.4.5. Rewrite and prove Theorem 8.4.3 using the hypothesis that $\mathbf{A}$ is indefinite.

8.4.6. Is it possible for a 2×2 indefinite matrix to be singular?

8.4.7. If $\mathbf{A}$ and $\mathbf{B}$ are congruent and $\mathbf{A}$ is indefinite, show that $\mathbf{B}$ is indefinite.

8.4.8. Suppose that $\mathbf{A}$ is an invertible, symmetric matrix. Show that $\mathbf{A}$ is positive definite if and only if $\mathbf{A}^{-1}$ is positive definite.

8.4.9. If $\mathbf{Q}$ is orthogonal and $\mathbf{A}$ is positive definite, show that $\mathbf{Q}^{-1}\mathbf{A}\mathbf{Q}$ is also positive definite. Prove the corresponding theorems, with *semidefinite* and *indefinite* replacing *definite*.

8.4.10. If $\mathbf{P}^{\mathrm{H}} = \mathbf{P} \neq \mathbf{I}$ and $\mathbf{P}^2 = \mathbf{P}$, show that $\mathbf{P}$ is positive semidefinite and singular.

8.4.11. If $\mathbf{M}^2 = \mathbf{I}$ and $\mathbf{M}$ is positive semidefinite, show that $\mathbf{M} = \mathbf{I}$. If $\mathbf{M}$ is real symmetric and $\mathbf{M} \neq \pm\mathbf{I}$, show that $\mathbf{M}$ is indefinite and nonsingular.

PART 3

8.4.12. Show that a symmetric matrix with positive and negative entries on its diagonal is indefinite. Provide a 2×2 example to show that an indefinite matrix need not have positive and negative entries on its diagonal.

8.4.13. If $\mathbf{A}$ is symmetric, show that there exists a constant p such that $\mathbf{A} + k\mathbf{I}$ is positive definite if $k > p$ and is positive semidefinite if $k = p$.

8.4.14. Prove part (*d*) of Theorem 8.4.2: $\mathbf{A}$ is indefinite if and only if at least one eigenvalue of $\mathbf{A}$ is positive and at least one is negative.

8.4.15. If $\mathbf{A}$ is symmetric but not a scalar matrix, show that there exist constants p_1 and p_2 such that $\mathbf{A} + k\mathbf{I}$ is indefinite for $p_1 < k < p_2$.

8.4.16. Suppose $\mathbf{A}$ is symmetric with positive entries and strictly diagonally dominant; that is, for all $i = 1,2,\ldots,n$

$$a_{ii} > a_{1i} + a_{2i} + \cdots + a_{ki} + \cdots + a_{ni}$$

Show that $\mathbf{A}$ is positive definite.

8.4.17. Suppose $p(x)$ is a polynomial and $p(x) > 0$ for all real x. Show that $\mathbf{A}$ is symmetric implies that $p(\mathbf{A})$ is positive definite. If $p(x) \geq 0$, show that $p(\mathbf{A})$ is positive semidefinite. (*Hint:* What are the eigenvalues of $p(\mathbf{A})$?)

8.5 A NECESSARY AND SUFFICIENT CONDITION FOR POSITIVE DEFINITENESS

The most convenient criterion for definiteness can be formulated in terms of the pivots in the row reduction of $\mathbf{A}$ to upper triangular form. We begin the development of this criterion by defining a sequence of submatrices of a symmetric matrix $\mathbf{A}$. If

$$\mathbf{A} = \begin{bmatrix} a_{11} & a_{12} & \cdots & a_{1n} \\ a_{12} & a_{22} & \cdots & a_{2n} \\ \vdots & \vdots & & \vdots \\ a_{1n} & a_{2n} & \cdots & a_{nn} \end{bmatrix}$$

then the *principal leading submatrices* of **A** are the n symmetric matrices

$$\mathbf{A}_1 = [a_{11}], \qquad \mathbf{A}_2 = \begin{bmatrix} a_{11} & a_{12} \\ a_{12} & a_{22} \end{bmatrix}, \ldots, \mathbf{A}_n = \mathbf{A} = \begin{bmatrix} a_{11} & a_{12} & \cdots & a_{1n} \\ a_{12} & a_{22} & \cdots & a_{2n} \\ \vdots & \vdots & & \vdots \\ a_{1n} & a_{2n} & \cdots & a_{nn} \end{bmatrix}$$

The *principal leading minors* of **A** are $\det(\mathbf{A}_k)$, $k = 1,2,\ldots,n$. Note that the principal leading submatrices are symmetric. Now define

$$\mathbf{x}_r = \begin{bmatrix} x_1 \\ x_2 \\ \vdots \\ x_r \end{bmatrix} \in \mathcal{R}^r, \qquad \mathbf{x}_n = \begin{bmatrix} \mathbf{x}_r \\ \mathbf{0}_{n-r} \end{bmatrix} \in \mathcal{R}^n$$

then it follows that

$$\mathbf{x}_n^{\mathrm{T}}\mathbf{A}\mathbf{x}_n = [\mathbf{x}_r^{\mathrm{T}} \quad \mathbf{0}_{n-r}^{\mathrm{T}}] \begin{bmatrix} a_{11} & a_{12} & \cdots & a_{1n} \\ a_{12} & a_{22} & \cdots & a_{2n} \\ \vdots & \vdots & & \vdots \\ a_{1n} & a_{2n} & \cdots & a_{nn} \end{bmatrix} \begin{bmatrix} \mathbf{x}_r \\ \mathbf{0}_{n-r} \end{bmatrix} = \mathbf{x}_r^{\mathrm{T}}\mathbf{A}_r\mathbf{x}_r \tag{8.5.1}$$

Theorem 8.5.1. *The symmetric matrix* **A** *is positive definite if and only if* $\mathbf{A}_k$ *is positive definite for all* $k = 1,2,\ldots,n$.

Proof. Since $\mathbf{A}_n = \mathbf{A}$, the *if* part is trivial. Now consider the converse: If **A** is positive definite, then $\mathbf{A}_k$ is positive definite for each k. But $\mathbf{x}^{\mathrm{T}}\mathbf{A}\mathbf{x} > 0$ for all $\mathbf{x} \neq \mathbf{0}$ immediately implies $\mathbf{x}_r^{\mathrm{T}}\mathbf{A}\mathbf{x}_r > 0$ for all $\mathbf{x}_r \in \mathcal{R}^r$, $\mathbf{x}_r \neq \mathbf{0}_r$, by Eq. 8.5.1. ■

Lemma 8.1. *If* $\det(\mathbf{A}_k) \neq 0$ *for all k, then without the use of row interchanges,* $\mathbf{A} \to \cdots \to \mathbf{U}$,

$$\mathbf{U} = \begin{bmatrix} u_1 & & & * \\ & u_2 & & \\ & & \ddots & \\ \mathbf{O} & & & u_n \end{bmatrix} \tag{8.5.2}$$

where $u_i = a_{11} = \det(\mathbf{A}_1)$ *and* $u_k = \det(\mathbf{A}_k)/\det(\mathbf{A}_{k-1})$, $k > 1$. *Moreover, there exists a lower triangular matrix*

$$\mathbf{L} = \begin{bmatrix} 1 & & & \mathbf{O} \\ & 1 & & \\ & & \ddots & \\ & * & & 1 \end{bmatrix} \tag{8.5.3}$$

such that $\mathbf{LA} = \mathbf{U}$.

Proof. The general proof is more easily understood if the argument is first presented in a special case. So consider the matrix

$$\mathbf{A} = \begin{bmatrix} 1 & 1 & -1 \\ 1 & 4 & -1 \\ -1 & -1 & 3 \end{bmatrix}$$

which has $\det(\mathbf{A}_1) = 1$, $\det(\mathbf{A}_2) = 3$, $\det(\mathbf{A}_3) = 6$. The hypothesis is satisfied, and here is the row reduction:

$$\mathbf{A} = \begin{bmatrix} 1 & 1 & -1 \\ 1 & 4 & -1 \\ -1 & -1 & 3 \end{bmatrix} \to \mathbf{B} = \begin{bmatrix} 1 & 1 & -1 \\ 0 & 3 & 0 \\ -1 & -1 & 3 \end{bmatrix} \to \mathbf{U} = \begin{bmatrix} 1 & 1 & -1 \\ 0 & 3 & 0 \\ 0 & 0 & 2 \end{bmatrix}$$

Note these crucial facts:

1. The principal leading minors are unaltered at each stage of the row reduction. The reason for this is that these minors are subjected to type 3 row operations, operations that leave the values of determinants unchanged. However, the minor M_{11} varies from 11 for **A** to 6 for **U** because type 3 row operations on **A** and **B** are not elementary row operations for the submatrix

$$\begin{bmatrix} 4 & 3 \\ -1 & -1 \end{bmatrix}$$

2. The diagonal entries of **U** are

$$\begin{aligned} a_{11} = u_{11} &= \det(\mathbf{A}_1) = 1 \\ u_2 &= \det(\mathbf{A}_2)/\det(\mathbf{A}_1) = 3 \\ u_3 &= \det(\mathbf{A}_3)/\det(\mathbf{A}_2) = 6/3 = 2 \end{aligned}$$

Now the general proof. Since $\mathbf{A}_1 = a_{11} \neq 0$,

$$\mathbf{A} = \begin{bmatrix} a_{11} & a_{12} & \cdots & a_{1n} \\ a_{12} & a_{22} & \cdots & a_{2n} \\ \vdots & \vdots & & \vdots \\ a_{1n} & a_{n2} & \cdots & a_{nn} \end{bmatrix} \to \cdots \to \begin{bmatrix} a_{11} & * & & * \\ 0 & a_{22}^{(2)} & \cdots & a_{2n}^{(2)} \\ \vdots & \vdots & & \vdots \\ 0 & a_{n2}^{(2)} & \cdots & a_{nn}^{(2)} \end{bmatrix}$$

This diagram uses only type 3 elementary row operations; hence, the values of the principal leading minors are unaltered. (See Problem 8.5.6.) In particular, $\det(A_2) = a_{11}a_{22}^{(2)}$ and $\det(A_2) \neq 0$ implies $a_{22}^{(2)} \neq 0$. Thus, $a_{22}^{(2)}$ may be used as a pivot to obtain

$$\mathbf{A} \to \cdots \to \begin{bmatrix} a_{11} & * & * & \cdots & * \\ 0 & a_{22}^{(2)} & * & \cdots & * \\ 0 & 0 & a_{33}^{(3)} & & * \\ \vdots & \vdots & \vdots & \ddots & \vdots \\ 0 & 0 & a_{3n}^{(3)} & & a_{nn}^{(3)} \end{bmatrix}$$

Likewise, $0 \neq \det(\mathbf{A}_3) = a_{11}a_{22}^{(2)}a_{33}^{(3)}$ implies that $a_{33}^{(3)} \neq 0$, so $a_{33}^{(3)}$ is the next pivot. This argument can be repeated for each step. Hence,

$$\mathbf{A} \to \cdots \to \mathbf{U} = \begin{bmatrix} a_{11} & * & * & \cdots & * \\ 0 & a_{22}^{(2)} & * & \cdots & * \\ 0 & 0 & a_{33}^{(3)} & & * \\ \vdots & \vdots & \vdots & \ddots & \vdots \\ 0 & 0 & 0 & & a_{nn}^{(n)} \end{bmatrix} \tag{8.5.4}$$

From $\det(\mathbf{A}_k) = a_{11}a_{22}^{(2)} \ldots a_{kk}^{(k)}$, it follows that $a_{kk}^{(k)} = \det(\mathbf{A}_k)/\det(\mathbf{A}_{k-1})$ for all $k > 1$. The arrow diagram of Eq. 8.5.4 is equivalent to the assertion that there exists a nonsingular **L** such that **LA** = **U**. To show that **L** has the structure displayed in Eq. 8.5.3, note first of all that **L** is the product of elementary row matrices. Second, each of these elementary row matrices is constructed from **I** by adding a multiple of the *i*th row of **I** to its *j*th row, where $i < j$. Thus, each (elementary row matrix) factor of **L** has 1s on its diagonal and a single nonzero entry below the diagonal. Finally, the product of such matrices is **L** and is lower triangular with 1s as its diagonal entries. ■

Lemma 8.2. *If* **A** *is symmetric and* $\det(\mathbf{A}_k) \neq 0$ *for all* k, *then* $\mathbf{LAL}^{\mathrm{T}} = \mathbf{D}$, *where* **L** *is given by* Eq. 8.5.3 *and* **D** *is given by*

$$\mathbf{D} = \begin{bmatrix} \det(\mathbf{A}_1) & & & \\ & \det(\mathbf{A}_2)/\det(\mathbf{A}_1) & & \mathbf{O} \\ & & \ddots & \\ \mathbf{O} & & & \det(\mathbf{A})/\det(\mathbf{A}_{n-1}) \end{bmatrix} \tag{8.5.5}$$

Proof. By Lemma 8.1, there exist **L** and **U** such that **LA** = **U**. Then, by taking transposes, deduce that $\mathbf{A}^{\mathrm{T}}\mathbf{L}^{\mathrm{T}} = \mathbf{U}^{\mathrm{T}}$; and since **A** is symmetric, $\mathbf{AL}^{\mathrm{T}} = \mathbf{U}^{\mathrm{T}}$, and it follows that $\mathbf{LAL}^{\mathrm{T}} = \mathbf{LU}^{\mathrm{T}}$. However, $\mathbf{LAL}^{\mathrm{T}}$ is symmetric, and therefore so is $\mathbf{LU}^{\mathrm{T}}$. But $\mathbf{LU}^{\mathrm{T}}$ is the product of lower triangular matrices and is, therefore, a lower triangular, symmetric matrix. Hence, $\mathbf{LU}^{\mathrm{T}}$ must be a diagonal matrix. Moreover, since the diagonal entries of **L** are all 1s, the diagonal entries of $\mathbf{LU}^{\mathrm{T}}$ must be the diagonal entries of **U**. Thus, $\mathbf{LAL}^{\mathrm{T}} = \mathbf{D}$. ■

We are now able to state and prove the fundamental theorem alluded to in the title of this section.

Theorem 8.5.2. *The matrix* **A** *of the form* q *is positive definite if and only if* $\det(\mathbf{A}_k) > 0$ *for all* $k = 1, 2, \ldots, n$.

Proof. If all the determinants $\det(\mathbf{A}_k)$ are positive, then by Lemma 8.2, **A** is congruent to **D** and, clearly, **D** is positive definite.

Conversely, suppose that **A** is positive definite. Then by Theorem 8.5.1, so is each leading principal submatrix. Therefore, all the leading principal minors are positive. ■

If **A** is negative definite, then $-\mathbf{A}$ is positive definite, and Theorem 8.5.2 can be used to provide a necessary and sufficient condition that **A** be negative definite. (See Problem 8.5.8.) The analogous theorem for indefinite **A** is less satisfactory because of the possibility that for some k, $\det(\mathbf{A}_k) = 0$.

Theorem 8.5.3. *Suppose* $\det(\mathbf{A}_k) \neq 0$ *for all k. Then* **A** *is indefinite if and only if* **D** *in* Eq. 8.5.5 *is indefinite, and this occurs if and only if* **D** *has both plus and minus terms on its diagonal.*

Proof. Lemma 8.2 is applicable, and hence **D** is congruent to **A**. ■

If q is positive semidefinite, then from Theorem 8.5.1, all $\mathbf{A}_k$ are positive semidefinite and, therefore, $\det(\mathbf{A}_k) \geq 0$ for all k. The converse, however, is false. The matrix

$$\mathbf{A} = \begin{bmatrix} 1 & 1 & -1 \\ 1 & 1 & -1 \\ -1 & -1 & 0 \end{bmatrix}$$

provides a counterexample; $\det(\mathbf{A}_k) \geq 0$ for all k, and yet **A** is indefinite. The problem resides in the failure of Lemma 8.2, which requires $\det(\mathbf{A}_k) \neq 0$. Because

$$\mathbf{A} = \begin{bmatrix} 1 & 1 & -1 \\ 1 & 1 & -1 \\ -1 & -1 & 0 \end{bmatrix} \to \cdots \to \begin{bmatrix} 1 & 1 & -1 \\ 0 & 0 & 0 \\ 0 & 0 & -1 \end{bmatrix}$$

shows that **D** is indefinite and because $\mathbf{LAL}^{\mathrm{T}} = \mathbf{D}$, **A** is also indefinite. Note that this matrix does not satisfy the hypothesis of Theorem 8.5.3.

8.5.1 The Cholesky Decomposition Theorem

If **A** is positive definite, then Theorem 8.5.2 asserts that $\det(\mathbf{A}_k) > 0$ for all k. Hence, it follows from Lemma 8.1 that there is a diagram $\mathbf{A} \to \cdots \to \mathbf{U}$ constructed without the use of row interchanges. Moreover, if **A** is augmented by **I** to form $[\mathbf{A} \quad \mathbf{I}]$, this diagram leads to the diagram

$$[\mathbf{A} \quad \mathbf{I}] \to \cdots \to [\mathbf{U} \quad \mathbf{L}] \tag{8.5.6}$$

where **L** is given by Eq. 8.5.3. (Lemma 8.1 asserts that $\mathbf{LA} = \mathbf{U}$, and thus $\mathbf{L}[\mathbf{A} \quad \mathbf{I}] = [\mathbf{LA} \quad \mathbf{L}] = [\mathbf{U} \quad \mathbf{L}]$. These equations have the diagram interpretation of Eq. 8.5.6.) The importance of Eq. 8.5.6 resides in the fact that the various matrices in the congruence $\mathbf{LAL}^{\mathrm{T}} = \mathbf{D}$ can be read from $[\mathbf{U} \quad \mathbf{L}]$ since *the diagonal entries of* **U** *are the diagonal entries of* **D**. The diagram of Eq. 8.5.6 is an algorithm for computing **L** and **D** that is useful for pedagogic purposes.

Since $\mathbf{L}$ is nonsingular, it follows from $\mathbf{LAL}^{\mathrm{T}} = \mathbf{D}$ that

$$\mathbf{A} = \mathbf{L}^{-1}\mathbf{DL}^{-\mathrm{T}} = (\mathbf{L}^{-1}\mathbf{D}^{1/2})(\mathbf{D}^{1/2}\mathbf{L}^{-\mathrm{T}}) = (\mathbf{L}^{-1}\mathbf{D}^{1/2})(\mathbf{L}^{-1}\mathbf{D}^{1/2})^{\mathrm{T}}$$

where $\mathbf{D}^{1/2}$ is the diagonal matrix whose diagonal entries are the positive square roots of $\mathbf{D}$. Set $\mathbf{W}^{\mathrm{T}} = \mathbf{L}^{-1}\mathbf{D}^{1/2}$ and note that $\mathbf{W}$ is nonsingular and upper triangular and that $\mathbf{A} = \mathbf{W}^{\mathrm{T}}\mathbf{W}$. This factorization of $\mathbf{A}$, called the *Cholesky decomposition of* $\mathbf{A}$, is another necessary and sufficient condition that $\mathbf{A}$ be positive definite:

Theorem 8.5.4. $\mathbf{A}$ *is positive definite if and only if there exists a real nonsingular upper triangular matrix* $\mathbf{W}$ *such that* $\mathbf{A} = \mathbf{W}^{\mathrm{T}}\mathbf{W}$.

Proof. The comments before the statement of this theorem shows that such a factorization of positive definite $\mathbf{A}$ is always possible with $\mathbf{W}^{\mathrm{T}} = \mathbf{L}^{-1}\mathbf{D}^{1/2}$. The converse is equally easy. If $\mathbf{A} = \mathbf{W}^{\mathrm{T}}\mathbf{W}$, then $\mathbf{A}$ is clearly real and symmetric. Since $\mathbf{W}$ is nonsingular, $\mathbf{x}^{\mathrm{T}}\mathbf{Ax} = \mathbf{x}^{\mathrm{T}}\mathbf{W}^{\mathrm{T}}\mathbf{Wx} =< \mathbf{Wx}, \mathbf{Wx} >= \|\mathbf{Wx}\|^2 > 0$, provided $\mathbf{x} \neq \mathbf{0}$. Hence, $\mathbf{A}$ is positive definite. ■

Corollary 1. *Suppose* $\mathbf{B}$ *is positive definite and* $\mathbf{C}$ *is positive semidefinite. Then* $\mathbf{A} = \mathbf{B} + \mathbf{C}$ *is positive definite and* $\det(\mathbf{A}) \geq \det(\mathbf{B})$.

Proof. By Theorem 8.5.4, $\mathbf{B} = \mathbf{W}^{\mathrm{T}}\mathbf{W}$. Set $\mathbf{S} = \mathbf{W}^{-1}$. Then $\mathbf{B} = \mathbf{S}^{-\mathrm{T}}\mathbf{S}^{-1}$, so that $\mathbf{A} = \mathbf{B} + \mathbf{C}$ implies $\mathbf{S}^{\mathrm{T}}\mathbf{AS} = \mathbf{I} + \mathbf{S}^{\mathrm{T}}\mathbf{CS}$. Since $\mathbf{C}$ is positive semidefinite, so is $\mathbf{S}^{\mathrm{T}}\mathbf{CS}$; hence, the eigenvalues of $\mathbf{S}^{\mathrm{T}}\mathbf{CS}$ are nonnegative. Therefore, the eigenvalues of $\mathbf{S}^{\mathrm{T}}\mathbf{AS} = \mathbf{I} + \mathbf{S}^{\mathrm{T}}\mathbf{CS}$ are no less than 1, which implies that $\det(\mathbf{S}^{\mathrm{T}}\mathbf{AS}) \geq 1$ and, hence, that $\mathbf{S}^{\mathrm{T}}\mathbf{AS}$ is positive definite. So $\mathbf{A}$ is positive definite. Now $\det(\mathbf{B}) = \det(\mathbf{S}^{-\mathrm{T}}\mathbf{S}^{-1}) = \left(\det(\mathbf{S})\right)^{-2}$, and therefore

$$1 \leq \det(\mathbf{S}^{\mathrm{T}}\mathbf{AS}) = \det(\mathbf{S})^2\det(\mathbf{A}) = \det(\mathbf{A})/\det(\mathbf{B})$$ ■

8.5.2 MATLAB

If A is entered and is positive definite, MATLAB returns W after the command W = chol(A). Here is an example:

Example 8.5.1. Enter A = [2 −1 0; −1 3 −2; 0 −2 2] and then

W = chol(A) =

1.4159	−0.7071	0
0	1.5811	−1.2649
0	0	0.6325

Note that $\mathbf{W}^{\mathrm{T}}\mathbf{W} = \mathbf{A}$ is now easily verified by W'*W and that $\mathbf{D}$ and $\mathbf{L}$ can be recovered from $\mathbf{W}^{\mathrm{T}} = \mathbf{L}^{-1/2}\mathbf{D}^{1/2}$. In particular, the diagonal entries of $\mathbf{D}$ may be found by entering diag(W*W).

PROBLEMS

PART 1

8.5.1. Use Theorem 8.5.2 to show that the matrix in Example 8.4.1 is indefinite.

8.5.2. Use the diagram of Eq. 8.5.6 to determine whether or not these forms are positive definite:

(*a*) x_1x_2 (*b*) $x_1^2+2x_1x_2+x_2^2$ (*c*) $x_1^2-x_1x_3$ (*d*) $x_1x_2+x_1x_3+x_2x_3$

8.5.3. Use the diagram of Eq. 8.5.4 to determine whether or not these matrices are positive definite:

(*a*) $\begin{bmatrix} 2 & 3 & -2 \\ 3 & 6 & -2 \\ -2 & -2 & 3 \end{bmatrix}$ (*b*) $\begin{bmatrix} 6 & 1 & -4 \\ 1 & 2 & 0 \\ -4 & 0 & 3 \end{bmatrix}$

8.5.4. Use the diagram of Eq. 8.5.6 to determine whether or not these matrices are positive definite:

(*a*) $\begin{bmatrix} 7 & 7 & -4 & 2 \\ 7 & 9 & 5 & 2 \\ 4 & 5 & 10 & 6 \\ 2 & 2 & 6 & 4 \end{bmatrix}$ (*b*) $\begin{bmatrix} 1 & 2 & -1 & 1 \\ 2 & 8 & -6 & 4 \\ -1 & -6 & 6 & -6 \\ 1 & 4 & -6 & 15 \end{bmatrix}$

PART 2

8.5.5. If **A** is 2×2 or 3×3, show that Properties (*a*)–(*c*) of Theorem 8.4.3 imply that **A** is positive definite.

8.5.6. Explain why the leading principal minors of **A** are unaltered by type 3 row operations *applied to* **A**. How might this argument fail for minors that are not leading principal minors?

PART 3

8.5.7. If **A** is negative definite, what can be said about $\det(\mathbf{A}_k)$? (*Hint:* $-\mathbf{A}$ is positive definite.)

8.5.8. Use the result in Problem 8.5.7 to rewrite and prove Theorem 8.5.2 using the hypothesis that **A** is negative definite.

MATLAB

8.5.9. Use chol(A) to determine whether the following matrices are positive definite.

(*a*) $\begin{bmatrix} 2 & 3 & -2 \\ 3 & 6 & -2 \\ -2 & -2 & 3 \end{bmatrix}$ (*b*) $\begin{bmatrix} 6 & 1 & -4 \\ 1 & 2 & 0 \\ -4 & 0 & 3 \end{bmatrix}$

8.5.10. (*a*) $\begin{bmatrix} 7 & 7 & -4 & 2 \\ 7 & 9 & 5 & 2 \\ 4 & 5 & 10 & 6 \\ 2 & 2 & 6 & 4 \end{bmatrix}$ (*b*) $\begin{bmatrix} 1 & 2 & -1 & 1 \\ 2 & 8 & -6 & 4 \\ -1 & -6 & 6 & -6 \\ 1 & 4 & -6 & 15 \end{bmatrix}$

8.6 TWO APPLICATIONS

8.6.1 Conic Sections

The graph of the points satisfying

$$a_{11}x^2 + 2a_{12}xy + a_{22}y^2 + cx + dy + e = 0 \tag{8.6.1}$$

is either (*a*) $\mathcal{R}^2$, (*b*) empty, (*c*) a single point, (*d*) a line, (*e*) two intersecting lines, (*f*) an ellipse, (*g*) a hyperbola, or (*h*) a parabola, depending on the choice of the parameters a, b, c, d, e, and f. Instead of considering the general conic, Eq. 8.6.1, we choose to restrict our attention to the *central conics* defined as the set of points satisfying[2]

$$a_{11}x^2 + 2a_{12}xy + a_{22}y^2 - 1 = 0 \tag{8.6.2}$$

If we set $q(\mathbf{x}) = \mathbf{x}^{\mathrm{T}}\mathbf{A}\mathbf{x}$, where

$$\mathbf{x} = \begin{bmatrix} x \\ y \end{bmatrix}, \qquad \mathbf{A} = \begin{bmatrix} a_{11} & a_{12} \\ a_{12} & a_{22} \end{bmatrix}$$

then Eq. 8.6.2 is $q(\mathbf{x}) = 1$.

If $\mathbf{Q} = [q_1 \quad q_2]$ is an orthogonal matrix of the real eigenvectors of $\mathbf{A}$, then there is a ϑ such that

$$\mathbf{Q} = \begin{bmatrix} \cos\vartheta & -\sin\vartheta \\ \sin\vartheta & \cos\vartheta \end{bmatrix}$$

We find ϑ as follows: Suppose $\mathbf{q}^{\mathrm{T}} = [a \quad b]$. Since $\|\mathbf{q}\|^2 = a^2 + b^2 = 1$, define $\vartheta, 0 \le \vartheta < 2\pi$, by $\cos\vartheta = a$ and $\sin\vartheta = b$. The change of variables $\mathbf{Q}^{-1}\mathbf{x} = \mathbf{y} = [X \quad Y]^{\mathrm{T}}$ may be interpreted as a rotation of the coordinate frame by an angle ϑ. (See Section 3.8.) As we shall see, this rotation will present the conic in one of its standard forms. Note that $\mathbf{Q}^{-1}\mathbf{x} = \mathbf{y}$ converts the form $\mathbf{x}^{\mathrm{T}}\mathbf{A}\mathbf{x}$ into the diagonal form

$$\mathbf{y}^{\mathrm{T}}\mathbf{Q}^{\mathrm{T}}\mathbf{A}\mathbf{Q}\mathbf{y} = \mathbf{y}^{\mathrm{T}}\mathbf{Q}^{-1}\mathbf{A}\mathbf{Q}\mathbf{y} = \mathbf{y}^{\mathrm{T}}\mathbf{\Lambda}\mathbf{y}$$

Thus, in the variables X and Y,

$$q(\mathbf{x}) = q(\mathbf{Q}\mathbf{y}) = \mathbf{y}^{\mathrm{T}}\mathbf{\Lambda}\mathbf{y} = \lambda_1 X^2 + \lambda_2 Y^2 = 1 \tag{8.6.3}$$

The diagonal form of Eq. 8.6.3 is the standard form for a central conic, and the nature of this conic is revealed by the signs of the eigenvalues of $\mathbf{A}$, the matrix of the form of Eq. 8.6.2.

Case 1: A *is singular.*

If $\mathbf{A}$ is singular, one or more of its eigenvalues are zero, and Eq. 8.6.3 describes either the empty set or the graph of two straight lines. Hence, the graph of Eq. 8.6.2 is a pair of lines or the empty set.

---

[2]This restriction eliminates the cases (*a*), (*c*), (*d*), and (*h*).

Case 2: **A** *is negative definite.*

In this case, the eigenvalues of **A** are negative, and Eq. 8.6.3 is impossible for real X and Y. Therefore, the set of points satisfying Eq. 8.6.2 is empty.

Case 3: **A** *is positive definite.*

Both λ_1 and λ_2 are positive, and setting $a^2 = \lambda_1^{-1}$ and $b^2 = \lambda_2^{-1}$ in Eq. 8.6.3 leads to the standard form for the ellipse:

$$\frac{X^2}{a^2} + \frac{Y^2}{b^2} = 1$$

Case 4: **A** *is indefinite.*

One eigenvalue is positive and the other negative, and Eq. 8.6.3 represents a hyperbola. If we suppose $\lambda_1 > 0$ and $\lambda_2 < 0$, then setting $a^2 = \lambda_1^{-1}$ and $b^2 = -\lambda_2^{-1}$ in Eq. 8.6.3 leads to the standard form

$$\frac{X^2}{a^2} - \frac{Y^2}{b^2} = 1$$

On the other hand, if $\lambda_1 < 0$ and $\lambda_2 > 0$, then the hyperbola takes the form

$$\frac{Y^2}{a^2} - \frac{X^2}{b^2} = 1$$

Theorem 8.6.1. *The central conic of* Eq. 8.6.2 *is an ellipse if and only if* **A** *is positive definite. It is a hyperbola if and only if* **A** *is indefinite. The conic is degenerate if and only if* **A** *is singular.*

In spite of the fact that the eigenvalues of **A** are used to distinguish the various types of central conics, explicit knowledge of their values in unnecessary. Any theorem that reveals the "definiteness" of the form $\mathbf{x}^T\mathbf{A}\mathbf{x}$ is sufficient. (However, there is very good reason to want the explicit values of the eigenpairs of **A**. See Problem 8.6.4.)

Example 8.6.1. Show that the conic $x^2 + 4xy + y^2$ is a hyperbola.

Solution. We will apply Lemma 8.2 of Section 8.5. The first step is to row-reduce the matrix of the form as follows:

$$\mathbf{A} = \begin{bmatrix} 1 & 2 \\ 2 & 1 \end{bmatrix} \rightarrow \mathbf{U} = \begin{bmatrix} 1 & 2 \\ 0 & -3 \end{bmatrix}$$

Since $\det(\mathbf{A}_1) = 1$ and $\det(\mathbf{A}) = -3$, Theorem 8.5.3 enables us to conclude that **A** is indefinite. Hence, the form is indefinite and the conic is a hyperbola.

Example 8.6.2. Explain why $2a_{12}xy = 1$, $a_{12} \neq 0$, is a hyperbola.

Solution. The matrix of this form is

$$\mathbf{A} = \begin{bmatrix} 0 & a_{12} \\ a_{12} & 0 \end{bmatrix}$$

and it is easy to see that the eigenvalues of **A** are $\lambda_1 = a_{12}$ and $\lambda_2 = -a_{12}$. Hence, the eigenvalues are of opposite signs and **A** is indefinite.

8.6.2 The Second Derivative Test

Let $\mathbf{x}_0$ be a fixed point in $\mathcal{R}^n$, and suppose $f(\mathbf{x})$ is a real-valued function of $\mathbf{x} \in \mathcal{R}^n$ with continuous second partial derivatives for all $\mathbf{x}$ in the "sphere" $\|\mathbf{x} - \mathbf{x}_0\|^2 \leq r$, $r > 0$. For convenience, denote the various derivatives of f at $\mathbf{x}_0$ by

$$f_i = \frac{\partial f(\mathbf{x}_0)}{\partial x_i}, \qquad f_{ij} = \frac{\partial^2 f(\mathbf{x}_0)}{\partial x_i \partial x_j}$$

The vector $\nabla f(\mathbf{x}_0) = [f_1 \quad f_2 \quad \dots \quad f_n]^{\mathrm{T}}$ is called the *gradient* of f at $\mathbf{x}_0$. The gradient is the multivariable generalization of the derivative of $f(x)$ and reduces to $f'(x_0)$ when $\mathbf{x}_0 \in \mathcal{R}$. Define the symmetric matrix

$$\mathbf{H} = \begin{bmatrix} f_{11} & f_{12} & \cdots & f_{1n} \\ f_{12} & f_{22} & \cdots & f_{2n} \\ & \vdots & & \vdots \\ f_{1n} & f_{2n} & \cdots & f_{nn} \end{bmatrix}$$

called the *Hessian* of f. The quadratic polynomial (in n variables)

$$p_2(\mathbf{x}) = f(\mathbf{x}_0) + \nabla f(\mathbf{x}_0)^{\mathrm{T}}(\mathbf{x} - \mathbf{x}_0) + (\mathbf{x} - \mathbf{x}_0)^{\mathrm{T}}\mathbf{H}(\mathbf{x} - \mathbf{x}_0)$$

is an approximation to f for all $\mathbf{x}$ near $\mathbf{x}_0$ in this sense:

$$\|f(\mathbf{x}) - p_2(\mathbf{x})\| \, \|\mathbf{x} - \mathbf{x}_0\|^{-2} \to 0 \text{ as } \|\mathbf{x} - \mathbf{x}_0\| \to 0 \tag{8.6.4}$$

It is convenient to write $f(\mathbf{x}) - p_2(\mathbf{x}) \simeq \mathbf{0}$ whenever Eq. 8.6.4 holds.

The point $\mathbf{x}_0$ is a *local extremum* if either $f(\mathbf{x}_0) < f(\mathbf{x})$ or $f(\mathbf{x}_0) > f(\mathbf{x})$ for all $\mathbf{x}$ in a sufficiently small sphere about $\mathbf{x}_0$. It is a *local minimum* in the former case, and a *local maximum* in the latter. If $\mathbf{x}_0$ is a local extreme point but is neither a local minimum nor a local maximum, it is called a *saddle point*. A necessary condition for $\mathbf{x}_0$ to be a local extremum is that $\nabla f(\mathbf{x}_0) = \mathbf{0}$. (In one-variable calculus this criterion reduces to the familiar first-derivative test.) Some sufficient conditions for local maxima and minima can be formulated in terms of the quadratic form $\mathbf{y}^{\mathrm{T}}\mathbf{H}\mathbf{y}$.

Theorem 8.6.2. (*The Second-Derivative Test*). *Suppose* $\nabla f(\mathbf{x}_0) = \mathbf{0}$.

(*a*) *If* **H** *is positive definite, then* $\mathbf{x}_0$ *is a local minimum.*
(*b*) *If* **H** *is negative definite, then* $\mathbf{x}_0$ *is a local maximum.*
(*c*) *If* **H** *is indefinite, then* $\mathbf{x}_0$ *is a saddle point.*
(*d*) *If* **H** *is semidefinite and singular, no conclusion is possible.*

Proof. Because $\nabla f(\mathbf{x}_0) = \mathbf{0}$, we can assert that

$$f(\mathbf{x}) - p_2(\mathbf{x}) = f(\mathbf{x}) - f(\mathbf{x}_0) - (\mathbf{x} - \mathbf{x}_0)^{\mathrm{T}}\mathbf{H}(\mathbf{x} - \mathbf{x}_0) \simeq \mathbf{0}$$

Since $\mathbf{H}$ is positive definite, $(\mathbf{x} - \mathbf{x}_0)^{\mathrm{T}}\mathbf{H}(\mathbf{x} - \mathbf{x}_0)$ is positive if $\mathbf{x} \neq \mathbf{x}_0$. Hence, for $\|\mathbf{x} - \mathbf{x}_0\|$ small and not zero, $f(\mathbf{x}) - f(\mathbf{x}_0) > 0$. For these $\mathbf{x}$, $f(\mathbf{x}) > f(\mathbf{x}_0)$, and thus $\mathbf{x}_0$ is a local minimum. Similarly, if $\mathbf{H}$ is negative definite, then $f(\mathbf{x}) < f(\mathbf{x}_0)$ and $\mathbf{x}_0$ is a local maximum.

If $\mathbf{H}$ is indefinite, there exist $\mathbf{y} \neq \mathbf{0}$ and $\mathbf{z} \neq \mathbf{0}$ such that $\mathbf{y}^{\mathrm{T}}\mathbf{H}\mathbf{y} < 0$ and $\mathbf{z}^{\mathrm{T}}\mathbf{H}\mathbf{z} > 0$. Define $\epsilon > 0$ by $\epsilon < r/\|\mathbf{y}\|$ and $\mathbf{x}_1 = \mathbf{x}_0 + \epsilon\mathbf{y}$. Then $0 < \|\mathbf{x}_1 - \mathbf{x}_0\| = \epsilon\|\mathbf{y}\| < r$. So $\mathbf{x}_1$ lies in the disc $\|\mathbf{x}_1 - \mathbf{x}_0\| \leq r$ for every nonzero r. Hence, $f(\mathbf{x}_1) - f(\mathbf{x}_0) > \mathbf{0}$. Similarly, define $\mathbf{x}_2 = \mathbf{x}_0 + \epsilon\mathbf{z}$ and deduce that $f(\mathbf{x}_2) - f(\mathbf{x}_0) < \mathbf{0}$. This shows that $\mathbf{x}_0$ is neither a local maximum nor a local minimum.

Now suppose that $\mathbf{H}$ is semidefinite and singular. To show that no conclusion is possible, we give examples in which $\mathbf{x}_0$ is a local minimum, a local maximum, and a saddle point. Consider the three functions: (*a*) $f(x,y) = x^3 + y^2$, (*b*) $g(x,y) = x^4 + y^2$, and (*c*) $h(x,y) = -x^4 + y^2$. In each case $\mathbf{x}_0 = [x \quad y]^{\mathrm{T}} = \mathbf{0}$ is an extreme point, and the corresponding Hessians are semidefinite and singular. However, $\mathbf{0}$ is a saddle point of f, a local minimum of g, and a local maximum of h. ■

Example 8.6.3. Let $\mathbf{x} = [x \quad y]^{\mathrm{T}}$ and suppose $f(\mathbf{x}) = x^2 + x\sin y + xy + 2y^2$. Show that $\mathbf{x} = \mathbf{0}$ is a relative minimum of f.

Solution. Compute

$$f_1 = 2x + \sin y + y, \qquad f_2 = x\cos y + x + 4y,$$

$$f_{11} = 2, \qquad f_{12} = \cos y + 1, \qquad f_{22} = -x\sin y + 4$$

Since $\nabla f(\mathbf{0}) = \mathbf{0}$, $\mathbf{x}_0 = \mathbf{0}$ is a critical point of f. At $\mathbf{0}$, we have

$$\mathbf{H} = \begin{bmatrix} 2 & 2 \\ 2 & 4 \end{bmatrix} \quad \rightarrow \quad \begin{bmatrix} 2 & 2 \\ 0 & 2 \end{bmatrix}$$

shows that $\mathbf{H}$ is positive definite. Thus, $\mathbf{0}$ is a relative minimum.

PROBLEMS

PART 1

8.6.1. Determine the nature of the following conics:
(*a*) x_1x_2 (*b*) $x_1^2 + 3x_1x_2 + x_2^2$ (*c*) $x_1^2 - x_1x_2$ (*d*) $x_1x_2 + x_2^2$

8.6.2. Find the Hessians of each of the following functions:
(*a*) $xy + e^x$ (*b*) $x + y + z$ (*c*) xy

8.6.3. For each function in Problem 8.6.2, determine all extreme points and decide whether they are relative maxima, minima, or neither.

PART 2

8.6.4. Write the second-derivative test for functions of one variable by using Theorem 8.6.2 and letting $\mathbf{x} \in \mathcal{R}$.

8.6.5. The circle $x^2 + y^2 = 1$ may be written $\mathbf{x}^T\mathbf{I}\mathbf{x} = 1$. Show that

$$\mathbf{x} = \begin{bmatrix} 2 & 0 \\ 0 & 4 \end{bmatrix} \mathbf{y}$$

leads to the ellipse $2X^2 + 4Y^2 = 1$. Hence, conclude that a congruence may not preserve the eccentricity of the conic. If the congruence is also a real unitary similarity, show that the eccentricity of the conic is unaltered.

8.6.6. Derive the equations for the rotation of the graph of $y = f(x)$ through ϑ radians. The matrix of coefficients of these equations is the orthogonal matrix

$$\mathbf{Q} = \begin{bmatrix} \sin\vartheta & -\cos\vartheta \\ \cos\vartheta & \sin\vartheta \end{bmatrix}$$

8.7 SIMULTANEOUS DIAGONALIZATION BY CONGRUENCES

In this section we explore the possibility of finding $\mathbf{T}$ that simultaneously diagonalizes the symmetric matrices $\mathbf{A}$ and $\mathbf{B}$ by a congruence transformation. Specifically, we ask: Under what conditions does $\mathbf{T}$ exist such that $\mathbf{T}^T\mathbf{A}\mathbf{T} = \mathbf{I}$ and $\mathbf{T}^T\mathbf{B}\mathbf{T} = \mathbf{D}$, where $\mathbf{D}$ is diagonal? One motivation for this question is the study of systems of springs and masses. Consider the system shown in Fig. 8.1. The motion of this system is governed by the forces resulting from the extension and compression of the springs according to Hooke's law. Thus, the tension in each spring is

$$T_1 = k_1 x_1$$
$$T_2 = k_2(x_2 - x_1)$$
$$T_3 = k_3(x_3 - x_2)$$

where $k_i > 0$ is the spring constant of the spring S_i, and x_i represents the displacement to the right of the mass m_i from its rest position, so that $x_1 = x_2 = x_3 = 0$ when the springs are neither stretched nor compressed.

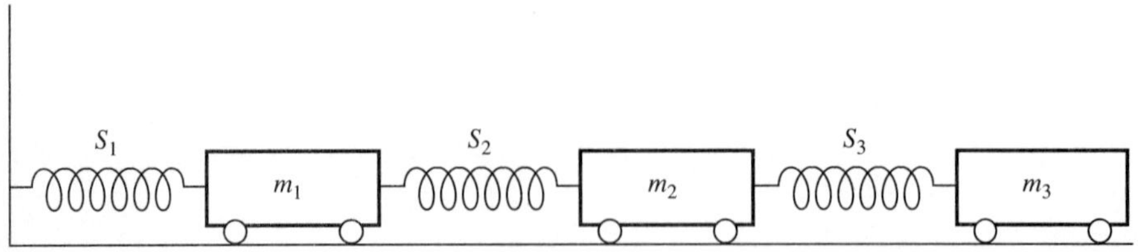

FIGURE 8-1
A spring-mass system.

Newton's second law of motion leads to the three simultaneous second-order differential equations

$$\begin{bmatrix} m_1 & 0 & 0 \\ 0 & m_2 & \\ 0 & 0 & m_3 \end{bmatrix} \mathbf{x}'' + \begin{bmatrix} k_1 + k_2 & -k_2 & 0 \\ -k_2 & k_2 + k_3 & -k_3 \\ 0 & -k_3 & k_3 \end{bmatrix} \mathbf{x} = \mathbf{0} \tag{8.7.1}$$

whose solution describes the displacement of the masses from their equilibrium position as a function of time.

Equation 8.7.1 is a special case of a more general system,

$$\mathbf{M}\mathbf{x}'' + \mathbf{S}\mathbf{x} = \mathbf{0} \tag{8.7.2}$$

where $\mathbf{M}$ and $\mathbf{S}$ are arbitrary positive definite matrices. The system of Eq. 8.7.1 is of this type since $\mathbf{M}$ is a diagonal matrix with positive diagonal entries and $\mathbf{S}$ is positive definite. (The matrix $\mathbf{S}$ in Eq. 8.7.1 is positive definite because its principal leading minors are positive. See also Example 7.3.6 and Problem 8.7.5 in the following problem set.)

There are two related approaches to the solution of Eq. 8.7.2, both of which mimic the ideas used to solve the simpler system $\mathbf{x}' = \mathbf{A}\mathbf{x}$.

First of all, consider the change of variables $\mathbf{x} = \mathbf{T}\mathbf{y}$. Using $\mathbf{x}'' = \mathbf{T}\mathbf{y}''$ in Eq. 8.7.2 leads to $\mathbf{M}\mathbf{T}\mathbf{y}'' + \mathbf{S}\mathbf{T}\mathbf{y} = \mathbf{0}$ and hence, $\mathbf{T}^{\mathrm{T}}\mathbf{M}\mathbf{T}\mathbf{y}'' + \mathbf{T}^{\mathrm{T}}\mathbf{S}\mathbf{T}\mathbf{y} = \mathbf{0}$. Now suppose $\mathbf{T}$ has the property that $\mathbf{T}^{\mathrm{T}}\mathbf{M}\mathbf{T} = \mathbf{I}$ and $\mathbf{T}^{\mathrm{T}}\mathbf{S}\mathbf{T} = \mathbf{D}$, where $\mathbf{D}$ is diagonal. Then

$$\mathbf{T}^{\mathrm{T}}\mathbf{M}\mathbf{T}\mathbf{y}'' + \mathbf{T}^{\mathrm{T}}\mathbf{S}\mathbf{T}\mathbf{y} = \mathbf{y}'' + \mathbf{D}\mathbf{y} = \mathbf{0}$$

and this system is "decoupled." Its solutions are the solutions of the n scalar equations $y_i'' + d_i y_i = 0$. If there were some $d_i < 0$, then the physical system described by Eq. 8.7.2 would have a solution with unbounded growth. This is impossible for unforced physical systems. Hence, it is necessary that $d_i > 0$ for all i, and this is exactly the case if $\mathbf{S}$ is positive definite.

A second technique assumes that there are solutions $\mathbf{x}(t) = \mathbf{u}e^{\lambda t}$. Since $\mathbf{x}'' = \lambda^2\mathbf{u}e^{\lambda t}$, this assumption leads to

$$\mathbf{M}(\mathbf{u}e^{\lambda t})'' + \mathbf{S}\mathbf{u}e^{\lambda t} = e^{\lambda t}(\lambda^2\mathbf{M} + \mathbf{S})\mathbf{u} = \mathbf{0}$$

Therefore, $\mathbf{x}(t) = \mathbf{u}e^{\lambda t}$ is a solution if and only if $\mathbf{u}$ and λ satisfy the algebraic system

$$(\mathbf{S} + \lambda^2\mathbf{M})\mathbf{u} = \mathbf{0} \tag{8.7.3}$$

(This is a generalized version of the eigenvalue-eigenvector problem, $(\mathbf{A} - \lambda\mathbf{I})\mathbf{u} = \mathbf{0}$.) The substitution $\mathbf{u} = \mathbf{T}\mathbf{v}$ transforms Eq. 8.7.3 into the standard eigenvalue-eigenvector problem:

$$\begin{aligned} (\mathbf{S} + \lambda^2\mathbf{M})\mathbf{u} &= (\mathbf{T}^{\mathrm{T}}\mathbf{S} + \lambda^2\mathbf{T}^{\mathrm{T}}\mathbf{M})\mathbf{T}\mathbf{v} = (\mathbf{T}^{\mathrm{T}}\mathbf{S}\mathbf{T} + \lambda^2\mathbf{T}^{\mathrm{T}}\mathbf{M}\mathbf{T})\mathbf{v} \\ &= (\mathbf{D} + \lambda^2\mathbf{I})\mathbf{v} = \mathbf{0} \end{aligned} \tag{8.7.4}$$

provided that $\mathbf{T}$ has the property $\mathbf{T}^{\mathrm{T}}\mathbf{M}\mathbf{T} = \mathbf{I}$ and $\mathbf{T}^{\mathrm{T}}\mathbf{S}\mathbf{T} = \mathbf{D}$. (Note that Eq. 8.7.4 can be obtained directly from $\mathbf{y}'' + \mathbf{D}\mathbf{y} = \mathbf{0}$ by setting $\mathbf{y} = \mathbf{v}e^{\lambda t}$.)

Both approaches ultimately depend on the existence of **T** that simultaneously diagonalizes **M** and **S**. Such **T** always exist, and the proof is based on the construction of the positive semidefinite "square root" of **M**.

Theorem 8.7.1. *If* **M** *is positive semidefinite, then there exists a unique positive semidefinite matrix* $\mathbf{M}^{1/2}$ *such that* $(\mathbf{M}^{1/2})^2 = \mathbf{M}$.

Proof. Since **M** is real symmetric, it is congruent to a diagonal matrix of its eigenvalues; that is, there exists an orthogonal matrix **Q** such that $\mathbf{Q}^T\mathbf{M}\mathbf{Q} = \mathbf{\Lambda}, \mathbf{Q}^T = \mathbf{Q}^{-1}$. Because **M** is positive semidefinite, its eigenvalues are nonnegative; and if $\lambda^{1/2}$ denotes the nonnegative root of λ, then $\mathbf{\Lambda}^{1/2}$ can be defined as follows:

$$\mathbf{\Lambda}^{1/2} = \begin{bmatrix} \lambda_1^{1/2} & & & \mathbf{O} \\ & \lambda_2^{1/2} & & \\ & & \ddots & \\ \mathbf{O} & & & \lambda_n^{1/2} \end{bmatrix} \tag{8.7.5}$$

Now set $\mathbf{M}^{1/2} = \mathbf{Q}\mathbf{\Lambda}^{1/2}\mathbf{Q}^T$. Since **Q** is orthogonal, $\mathbf{Q}^T\mathbf{Q} = \mathbf{I}$, and therefore

$$(\mathbf{M}^{1/2})^2 = (\mathbf{Q}\mathbf{\Lambda}^{1/2}\mathbf{Q}^T)(\mathbf{Q}\mathbf{\Lambda}^{1/2}\mathbf{Q}^T) = \mathbf{Q}\mathbf{\Lambda}\mathbf{Q}^T = \mathbf{M}$$

Clearly, $\mathbf{M}^{1/2} = \mathbf{Q}\mathbf{\Lambda}^{1/2}\mathbf{Q}^T$ is positive semidefinite. The proof that there is only one positive semidefinite root of **M** is more lengthy; it is reserved for Section 8.7.1. ■

Remark. The hypothesis that **M** is positive semidefinite is used to ensure that $\lambda^{1/2} \geq 0$ is possible. The hypothesis that $\mathbf{M}^{1/2}$ is positive semidefinite precludes the possibility of multiple roots of **M**, obtained, for instance, by taking $-\lambda_i^{1/2}$ for some i in Eq. 8.7.5.

Example 8.7.1. Suppose that **M** is positive definite. Set $\mathbf{M}^{-1/2} = (\mathbf{M}^{1/2})^{-1}$. Show that:

(*a*) $(\mathbf{M}^{-1/2})^{-1} = \mathbf{M}^{1/2}$
(*b*) $(\mathbf{M}^{-1/2})\mathbf{M} = \mathbf{M}^{1/2}$
(*c*) $(\mathbf{M}^{1/2})^k = (\mathbf{M}^k)^{1/2}$

for all integers k.

Solution. Consider (*b*). By definition, $\mathbf{M}^{1/2} = \mathbf{Q}\mathbf{\Lambda}^{1/2}\mathbf{Q}^T$. Therefore, $\mathbf{M}^{-1/2} = (\mathbf{Q}\mathbf{\Lambda}^{1/2}\mathbf{Q}^T)^{-1} = \mathbf{Q}\mathbf{\Lambda}^{-1/2}\mathbf{Q}^T$, and it follows that

$$\mathbf{M}^{-1/2}\mathbf{M} = \mathbf{Q}\mathbf{\Lambda}^{-1/2}\mathbf{Q}^T\mathbf{Q}\mathbf{\Lambda}\mathbf{Q}^T = \mathbf{Q}\mathbf{\Lambda}^{1/2}\mathbf{Q}^T = \mathbf{M}^{1/2}$$

The remaining arguments are similar. (See Problem 8.7.6).

Corollary 1. *If* **A** *is symmetric (positive semidefinite) and* **M** *is positive definite, then the matrices* **MA** *and* **AM** *are simple and have n real (nonnegative) eigenvalues.*

Proof. Let $(\lambda,\mathbf{x})$ be an eigenpair of **MA**. Since **M** is positive definite, the positive definite roots $\mathbf{M}^{1/2}$ and $\mathbf{M}^{-1/2}$ exist. Thus, defining $\mathbf{y} = \mathbf{M}^{-1/2}\mathbf{x}$ and using $(\mathbf{MA})\mathbf{x} = \lambda\mathbf{x}$, we have

$$\mathbf{MA}(\mathbf{M}^{1/2}\mathbf{y}) = \lambda(\mathbf{M}^{1/2}\mathbf{y})$$

If this equation is premultiplied by $\mathbf{M}^{-1/2}$, we obtain

$$(\mathbf{M}^{1/2}\mathbf{AM}^{1/2})\mathbf{y} = \lambda\mathbf{y}$$

Now $\mathbf{C} = \mathbf{M}^{1/2}\mathbf{AM}^{1/2}$ is symmetric and hence, simple with real eigenvalues. Moreover, since $\mathbf{M}^{-1/2}\mathbf{CM}^{1/2} = \mathbf{AM}$, **C** is similar to **AM** and hence **AM** is simple. In fact, $(\lambda,\mathbf{x}) = (\lambda,\mathbf{M}^{1/2}\mathbf{y})$, so that every eigenvalue of **A** is an eigenvalue of **C**. Finally, because $\mathbf{AM} = \mathbf{M}^{-1}(\mathbf{MA})\mathbf{M}$, **AM** is similar to **MA**, so that **MA** is also simple with real eigenvalues.

If **A** is positive semidefinite, then since **C** is congruent to **A** (why?), the eigenvalues of **C** (and, therefore, **AM** and **MA**) are nonnegative. ■

Theorem 8.7.2. *If* **M** *is positive definite and* **S** *is symmetric, then there exists a nonsingular matrix* **T** *such that*

$$\mathbf{T}^{\mathrm{T}}\mathbf{MT} = \mathbf{I} \quad \text{and} \quad \mathbf{T}^{\mathrm{T}}\mathbf{ST} = \mathbf{D} \tag{8.7.6}$$

Proof. By Theorem 8.7.1, there exists $\mathbf{M}^{1/2}$ such that $(\mathbf{M}^{1/2})^2 = \mathbf{M}$. Moreover, since $\mathbf{M}^{1/2}$ is positive definite, $\mathbf{M}^{-1/2}$ exists and is symmetric, so that $(\mathbf{M}^{-1/2})^{\mathrm{T}} = \mathbf{M}^{-1/2}$. The symmetric matrix $\mathbf{M}^{-1/2}\mathbf{SM}^{-1/2}$ is unitarily similar to a diagonal matrix of its eigenvalues; that is, there exists an orthogonal matrix **Q** such that $\mathbf{Q}^{\mathrm{T}}(\mathbf{M}^{-1/2}\mathbf{SM}^{-1/2})\mathbf{Q} = \mathbf{D}$. Set $\mathbf{T} = \mathbf{M}^{-1/2}\mathbf{Q}$. Then

$$\mathbf{T}^{\mathrm{T}}\mathbf{MT} = (\mathbf{M}^{-1/2}\mathbf{Q})^{\mathrm{T}}\mathbf{M}(\mathbf{M}^{-1/2}\mathbf{Q}) = \mathbf{Q}^{\mathrm{T}}(\mathbf{M}^{-1/2}\mathbf{MM}^{-1/2})\mathbf{Q} = \mathbf{Q}^{\mathrm{T}}\mathbf{IQ} = \mathbf{Q}^{\mathrm{T}}\mathbf{Q} = \mathbf{I}$$

and

$$\mathbf{T}^{\mathrm{T}}\mathbf{ST} = (\mathbf{M}^{-1/2}\mathbf{Q})^{\mathrm{T}}\mathbf{S}(\mathbf{M}^{-1/2}\mathbf{Q}) = \mathbf{Q}^{\mathrm{T}}(\mathbf{M}^{-1/2}\mathbf{SM}^{-1/2})\mathbf{Q} = \mathbf{D} \ ■$$

Corollary 1. *Suppose* **M** *and* **S** *are positive definite. Then the solutions of the system* $\mathbf{Mx}'' + \mathbf{Sx} = \mathbf{0}$ *are*

$$\mathbf{x}(t) = \sum_{i=1}^{n} y_i\mathbf{T}_{*i} = \sum_{i=1}^{n}\left(\alpha_i \sin\sqrt{d_i}t + \beta_i\cos\sqrt{d_i}t\right)\mathbf{T}_{*i} \tag{8.7.7}$$

where $\mathbf{T}_{*i}$ *is the ith column of* **T**, *and* **T** *satisfies Eq. 8.7.6.*

Proof. Setting $\mathbf{x} = \mathbf{Ty}$ leads to $\mathbf{x}'' = \mathbf{Ty}''$, which in turn leads to

$$\mathbf{0} = \mathbf{Mx}'' + \mathbf{Sx} = \mathbf{MTy}'' + \mathbf{STy}$$

and, therefore, by Eq. 8.7.6

$$\mathbf{T}^{\mathrm{T}}\mathbf{MTy}'' + \mathbf{T}^{\mathrm{T}}\mathbf{STy} = \mathbf{y}'' + \mathbf{Dy} = \mathbf{0}$$

Since **S** is positive definite, **D** is also. Therefore, the diagonal entries of **D** are positive, and the decoupled system $\mathbf{y}'' + \mathbf{Dy} = \mathbf{0}$ has the solutions

$$y_i = \alpha_i \sin \sqrt{d_i}t + \beta \cos \sqrt{d_i}t$$

But $\mathbf{x} = \mathbf{Ty}$ is simply a linear combination of the columns of **T** with weights given by y_i. ■

8.7.1 $\mathbf{M}^{1/2}$ Is Unique

Theorem 8.7.1. (*Continued*) *Suppose* **M** *is positive semidefinite and* $\mathbf{C}^2 = \mathbf{M}$. *Then* $\mathbf{C} = \mathbf{M}^{1/2}$.

Proof. It is convenient to make the following notational stipulations: Suppose rank(**M**)$= r$ and that the positive scalars $\sigma_1, \sigma_2, \ldots, \sigma_r$ are related to the positive eigenvalues of **M** by $\lambda_1 = \sigma_1^2$, $\lambda_2 = \sigma_2^2$, ..., $\lambda_r = \sigma_r^2$. Since **M** is positive semidefinite, there exists an orthogonal matrix **Q** such that $\mathbf{Q}^{\mathrm{T}}\mathbf{MQ} = \mathbf{\Lambda}$; (therefore, since $\mathbf{C}^2 = \mathbf{M}$, $\mathbf{Q}^{\mathrm{T}}\mathbf{C}^2\mathbf{Q} = (\mathbf{Q}^{\mathrm{T}}\mathbf{CQ})(\mathbf{Q}^{\mathrm{T}}\mathbf{CQ}) = \mathbf{\Lambda}$, where

$$\mathbf{\Lambda} = \begin{bmatrix} \mathbf{S}^2 & \mathbf{O} \\ \mathbf{O} & \mathbf{O} \end{bmatrix} \quad \text{and} \quad \mathbf{S} = \begin{bmatrix} \sigma_1 & & & \mathbf{O} \\ & \sigma_2 & & \\ & & \ddots & \\ \mathbf{O} & & & \sigma_r \end{bmatrix}$$

Set $\mathbf{P} = \mathbf{Q}^{\mathrm{T}}\mathbf{CQ}$. Then **P** is positive semidefinite, and

$$\mathbf{P}^{\mathrm{T}}\mathbf{P} = \mathbf{P}^2 = (\mathbf{Q}^{\mathrm{T}}\mathbf{CQ})(\mathbf{Q}^{\mathrm{T}}\mathbf{CQ}) = \mathbf{Q}^{\mathrm{T}}\mathbf{C}^2\mathbf{Q} = \mathbf{\Lambda}^2 = \begin{bmatrix} \mathbf{S}^2 & \mathbf{O} \\ \mathbf{O} & \mathbf{O} \end{bmatrix} \tag{8.7.8}$$

Now we show that

$$\mathbf{P} = \mathbf{\Lambda}^{1/2} = \begin{bmatrix} \mathbf{S} & \mathbf{O} \\ \mathbf{O} & \mathbf{O} \end{bmatrix} \tag{8.7.9}$$

Suppose **P** has columns $\mathbf{p}_i$, $i = 1,2,\ldots,n$. Then $\mathbf{P}^2 = (\mathbf{p}_i^{\mathrm{T}}\mathbf{p}_j)$ and thus, from Eq. 8.7.8, $\mathbf{p}_i^{\mathrm{T}}\mathbf{p}_j = \|\mathbf{p}_i\|^2 = 0$ for all $i > r$. Hence, $\mathbf{p}_{r+1} = \mathbf{p}_{r+2} = \cdots = \mathbf{p}_n = \mathbf{0}$, and therefore, the last $n - r$ columns of **P** are zero columns. Thus,

$$\mathbf{P} = \left[\mathbf{p}_1 \quad \mathbf{p}_2 \quad \ldots \quad \mathbf{p}_r \;\vdots\; \mathbf{0} \quad \ldots \quad \mathbf{0}\right] \tag{8.7.10}$$

Because **P** is symmetric, Eq. 8.7.10 implies that the last $n - r$ rows of **P** are zero rows, and hence,

$$\mathbf{P} = \begin{bmatrix} \mathbf{P}_r & \mathbf{O} \\ \mathbf{O} & \mathbf{O} \end{bmatrix}, \qquad \text{where } \mathbf{P}_r \text{ is } r \times r \tag{8.7.11}$$

By using Eqs. 8.7.8 and 8.7.11, we deduce that

$$\mathbf{P}^2 = \begin{bmatrix} \mathbf{P}_r^2 & \mathbf{O} \\ \mathbf{O} & \mathbf{O} \end{bmatrix} = \begin{bmatrix} \mathbf{S}^2 & \mathbf{O} \\ \mathbf{O} & \mathbf{O} \end{bmatrix} \tag{8.7.12}$$

Therefore, $\mathbf{P}_r^2 = \mathbf{S}^2$, which implies $(\mathbf{P}_r\mathbf{S}^{-1})^{\mathrm{T}}(\mathbf{P}_r\mathbf{S}^{-1}) = \mathbf{I}_r$ and, hence, that $\mathbf{P}_r\mathbf{S}^{-1}$ is an orthogonal matrix. Also, $\mathbf{S}^{-1}$ is positive definite, and $\mathbf{P}_r$ is positive semidefinite since $\mathbf{P}$ is. Hence, by Corollary 1 of Theorem 8.7.1, $\mathbf{P}_r\mathbf{S}^{-1}$ has only nonnegative eigenvalues. It now follows from Example 8.4.4 that $\mathbf{P}_r\mathbf{S}^{-1} = \mathbf{I}_r$ and, hence, that $\mathbf{P}_r = \mathbf{S}$. Therefore, Eq. 8.7.9 holds; that is, $\mathbf{P} = \mathbf{\Lambda}^{1/2}$. However, by definition, $\mathbf{M}^{1/2} = \mathbf{Q}\mathbf{\Lambda}^{1/2}\mathbf{Q}^{\mathrm{T}}$, and $\mathbf{P} = \mathbf{Q}^{\mathrm{T}}\mathbf{C}\mathbf{Q}$. So,

$$\mathbf{M}^{1/2} = \mathbf{Q}\mathbf{\Lambda}^{1/2}\mathbf{Q}^{\mathrm{T}} = \mathbf{Q}\mathbf{P}\mathbf{Q}^{\mathrm{T}} = \mathbf{Q}\mathbf{Q}^{\mathrm{T}}\mathbf{C}\mathbf{Q}\mathbf{Q}^{\mathrm{T}} = \mathbf{C} \quad \blacksquare$$

Remark. If $\mathbf{C}$ is positive definite, then Eq. 8.7.8 becomes $\mathbf{P}^2 = \mathbf{S}^2$, and the steps between Eq. 8.7.9 and Eq. 8.7.12 may be omitted.

PROBLEMS

PART 1

8.7.1. Find the positive definite square root of

$$\mathbf{M} = \begin{bmatrix} 5 & 4 \\ 4 & 5 \end{bmatrix}$$

and verify that $(\mathbf{M}^{1/2})^2 = \mathbf{M}$. Compute $\mathbf{M}^{-1/2}$.

8.7.2. Find a square root of the matrix $\mathbf{M}$ of Problem 8.7.1 that is indefinite.

8.7.3. Find $\mathbf{T}$ that simultaneously diagonalizes

$$\mathbf{M} = \begin{bmatrix} 5 & 4 \\ 4 & 5 \end{bmatrix} \quad \text{and} \quad \mathbf{S} = \begin{bmatrix} 1 & 1 \\ 1 & 1 \end{bmatrix}$$

8.7.4. Solve the generalized eigenvalue-eigenvector problem

$$\left\{ \begin{bmatrix} 5 & 4 \\ 4 & 5 \end{bmatrix} + \lambda \begin{bmatrix} 1 & 1 \\ 1 & 1 \end{bmatrix} \right\} \mathbf{v} = \mathbf{0}$$

8.7.5. If $k_i > 0, i = 1,2,3$, show that

$$\mathbf{S} = \begin{bmatrix} k_1 + k_2 & -k_2 & 0 \\ -k_2 & k_2 + k_3 & -k_3 \\ 0 & -k_3 & k_3 \end{bmatrix}$$

is positive definite by computing the principal leading minors.

PART 2

8.7.6. Prove (*a*) and (*c*) of Example 8.7.1.

8.7.7. Explain why $\mathbf{M}^{1/2}\mathbf{A}\mathbf{M}^{1/2}$ is congruent to $\mathbf{A}$.

PART 3

8.7.8. If **A** is real symmetric and **B** positive definite, show that there are n real eigenpairs $(\lambda_i,\mathbf{u}_i)$ of $\mathbf{B}^{-1/2}\mathbf{A}\mathbf{B}^{-1/2}$.

8.7.9. The pair $(\lambda,\mathbf{x} \neq \mathbf{0})$ such that $(\mathbf{A} - \lambda\mathbf{B})\mathbf{x} = \mathbf{0}$ is called a *generalized eigenpair* of $(\mathbf{A} - \lambda\mathbf{B})\mathbf{x} = \mathbf{0}$. If **A** is real symmetric and **B** positive definite, show that $(\mathbf{A} - \lambda\mathbf{B})\mathbf{x} = \mathbf{0}$ has n generalized eigenpairs $(\lambda_i,\mathbf{x}_i)$, where $\mathbf{x}_i = \mathbf{B}^{-1/2}\mathbf{u}_i$ and $(\lambda_i,\mathbf{u}_i)$ is an eigenpair of $\mathbf{B}^{-1/2}\mathbf{A}\mathbf{B}^{-1/2}$. (See Problem 8.7.8.)

8.7.10. If **A**, **B**, and **C** are positive definite, show that the solutions of $\det(\lambda^2\mathbf{A} + \lambda\mathbf{B} + \mathbf{C}) = 0$ have negative real parts. (*Hint:* Note that $(\lambda^2\mathbf{A} + \lambda\mathbf{B} + \mathbf{C})\mathbf{x} = \mathbf{0}$ has solutions $\lambda_i,\mathbf{x}_i \neq \mathbf{0}$ if and only if $\det(\lambda_i^2\mathbf{A} + \lambda_i\mathbf{B} + \mathbf{C}) = 0$. However, $(\lambda_i^2\mathbf{A}+\lambda_i\mathbf{B}+\mathbf{C})\mathbf{x}_i = \mathbf{0}$ implies $\mathbf{x}_i^T(\lambda_i^2\mathbf{A}+\lambda_i\mathbf{B}+\mathbf{C})\mathbf{x}_i = 0$ and $\mathbf{x}_i^T(\lambda_i^2\mathbf{A}+\lambda_i\mathbf{B}+\mathbf{C})\mathbf{x}_i = 0$ is a quadratic equation in λ_i with positive coefficients.)

8.8 INDEX, RANK, AND SIGNATURE

Matrices similar to **A** must have the same eigenvalues as **A**. This is not true for matrices congruent to **A**. However, congruent matrices have the same number of zero, positive, and negative eigenvalues. These "invariances" under congruence transformations were a discovery of the English mathematician J. J. Sylvester.[3]

Suppose $\text{rank}(\mathbf{A}) = r$. Then the number of zero eigenvalues of **A** is $n - r$ since this is the dimension of the null space of **A**. Let p be the number of positive eigenvalues of **A**; p is called the *index* of the form $\mathbf{x}^T\mathbf{A}\mathbf{x}$ and the index of the matrix **A**. Since $n - p$ is the number of nonpositive eigenvalues, the difference $(n - p) - (n - r) = r - p$ is the number of negative eigenvalues of **A**, and $p - (r - p) = 2p - r$ is the difference between the number of positive and negative eigenvalues. Write $q = 2p - r$ and call q the *signature* of **A** and the form $\mathbf{x}^T\mathbf{A}\mathbf{x}$. In summary,

Size	$n \times n$
Rank	r
Index = number of positive eigenvalues	p
Signature	$q = 2p - r$
Number of zero eigenvalues	$n - r$
Number of negative eigenvalues	$r - p$

The central theorem of this section is that congruent matrices have the same rank, index, and signature. This invariance under congruence transformations is called *Sylvester's law of inertia*. The proof is divided into separate stages. The first result is a lemma about the intersections of spans of linearly independent sets of vectors.

Lemma 8.3. *If* $\{\mathbf{u}_1,\mathbf{u}_2,\ldots,\mathbf{u}_r\}$ *and* $\{\mathbf{v}_1,\mathbf{v}_2,\ldots,\mathbf{v}_s\}$ *are sets of linearly independent vectors in* $\mathcal{R}^n$, *and* $r + s > n$, *then there exists* $\mathbf{y} \neq \mathbf{0}$ *in the span of both* $\{\mathbf{u}_1,\mathbf{u}_2,\ldots,\mathbf{u}_r\}$ *and* $\{\mathbf{v}_1,\mathbf{v}_2,\ldots,\mathbf{v}_s\}$.

---

[3]Published in *Philosophical Magazine* 4 (1852), pp. 138–142.

Proof. Since $\{\mathbf{u}_1,\mathbf{u}_2,\ldots,\mathbf{u}_r,\mathbf{v}_1,\mathbf{v}_2,\ldots,\mathbf{v}_s\}$ contains at least $n+1$ vectors, this set is linearly dependent. Therefore,

$$a_1\mathbf{u}_1 + a_2\mathbf{u}_2 + \cdots + a_r\mathbf{u}_r + b_1\mathbf{v}_1 + b_2\mathbf{v}_2 + \cdots + b_s\mathbf{v}_s = \mathbf{0} \qquad (8.8.1)$$

and not all the weights are zero. Clearly, Eq. 8.8.1 implies

$$a_1\mathbf{u}_1 + a_2\mathbf{u}_2 + \cdots + a_r\mathbf{u}_r = -b_1\mathbf{v}_1 - b_2\mathbf{v}_2 - \cdots - b_s\mathbf{v}_s \qquad (8.8.2)$$

If it were the case that all the weights $a_i = 0$, then Eq. 8.8.2 would imply

$$-b_1\mathbf{v}_1 - b_2\mathbf{v}_2 - \cdots - b_s\mathbf{v}_s = \mathbf{0} \qquad (8.8.3)$$

However, $\{\mathbf{v}_1,\mathbf{v}_2,\ldots,\mathbf{v}_s\}$ is a linearly independent set, and therefore, Eq. 8.8.3 implies that all the weights $b_i = 0$. This contradicts the assumption that Eq. 8.8.1 has at least one nonzero weight. Therefore, at least one weight $a_i \neq 0$, and

$$\mathbf{y} = a_1\mathbf{u}_1 + a_2\mathbf{u}_2 + \cdots + a_r\mathbf{u}_r \neq \mathbf{0}$$

But $\mathbf{y} \in span\{\mathbf{u}_1,\mathbf{u}_2,\ldots,\mathbf{u}_r\}$ by construction, and $\mathbf{y} \in span\{\mathbf{v}_1,\mathbf{v}_2,\ldots,\mathbf{v}_s\}$, from Eq. 8.8.2. ■

Lemma 8.4. *Suppose the real diagonal matrices* **C** *and* **D** *are congruent. Then* **C** *and* **D** *have the same rank, index, and signature.*

Proof. Let **C** and **D** be given by

$$\mathbf{C} = \begin{bmatrix} c_1 & & & \mathbf{O} \\ & c_2 & & \\ & & \ddots & \\ \mathbf{O} & & & c_n \end{bmatrix}, \qquad \mathbf{D} = \begin{bmatrix} d_1 & & & \mathbf{O} \\ & d_2 & & \\ & & \ddots & \\ \mathbf{O} & & & d_n \end{bmatrix}$$

By hypothesis $\mathbf{S}^{\mathrm{T}}\mathbf{DS} = \mathbf{C}$, for some nonsingular matrix **S**. There is no loss in generality in assuming the orderings

$$c_1 \geq c_2 \geq \cdots \geq c_s > 0 \geq c_{s+1} \geq c_{s+2} \geq \cdots \geq c_n \qquad (8.8.4)$$

$$d_1 \geq d_2 \geq \cdots \geq d_p > 0 \geq d_{p+1} \geq d_{p+2} \geq \cdots \geq d_p \qquad (8.8.5)$$

Suppose $\mathbf{S} = [\mathbf{s}_1 \quad \mathbf{s}_2 \quad \ldots \quad \mathbf{s}_n]$. Clearly, $\{\mathbf{e}_1,\mathbf{e}_2,\ldots,\mathbf{e}_p\}$ is linearly independent, and since **S** is invertible, so is the set $\{\mathbf{s}_{s+1},\mathbf{s}_{s+2},\ldots,\mathbf{s}_n\}$. If $p > s$, then $p + (n-s) = n + (p-s) > n$, and therefore, from Lemma 8.3, there exists a $\mathbf{y} \neq \mathbf{0}$ belonging to both $span\{\mathbf{e}_1,\mathbf{e}_2,\ldots,\mathbf{e}_p\}$ and $span\{\mathbf{s}_{s+1},\mathbf{s}_{s+2},\ldots,\mathbf{s}_n\}$. So, for some set of weights,

$$\mathbf{y} = y_1\mathbf{e}_1 + y_2\mathbf{e}_2 + \cdots + y_p\mathbf{e}_p \qquad (8.8.6)$$

and

$$\mathbf{y} = a_{s+1}\mathbf{s}_{s+1} + a_{s+2}\mathbf{s}_{s+2} + \cdots + a_n\mathbf{s}_n \qquad (8.8.7)$$

We compute $\mathbf{y}^{\mathrm{T}}\mathbf{Dy}$ in two ways, first using Eqs. 8.8.6 and 8.8.5:

$$\mathbf{y}^{\mathrm{T}}\mathbf{Dy} = y_1^2 d_1 + y_2^2 d_2 + \cdots + y_p^2 d_p > 0 \qquad (8.8.8)$$

Second, using Eq. 8.8.7, it follows that $\mathbf{y} = \mathbf{Sa}$, where

$$\mathbf{a} = [0 \quad 0 \ldots 0 \quad a_{s+1} \ldots a_n]^{\mathrm{T}}$$

Hence, from Eq. 8.8.4,

$$\mathbf{y}^{\mathrm{T}}\mathbf{D}\mathbf{y} = \mathbf{a}^{\mathrm{T}}\mathbf{S}^{\mathrm{T}}\mathbf{D}\mathbf{S}\mathbf{a} = \mathbf{a}^{\mathrm{T}}\mathbf{C}\mathbf{a} = a_{s+1}^2 c_{s+1} + a_{s+2}^2 c_{s+2} + \cdots + a_n^2 c_n \leq 0 \quad (8.8.9)$$

However, Eqs. 8.8.8 and 8.8.9 are in contradiction, so $p > s$ is false. But $\mathbf{S}^{\mathrm{T}}\mathbf{D}\mathbf{S} = \mathbf{C}$ implies $\mathbf{D} = \mathbf{S}^{-\mathrm{T}}\mathbf{C}\mathbf{S}^{-1}$, and the same argument, reversing the roles of $\mathbf{C}$ and $\mathbf{D}$, implies $p < s$ is also false. Hence, $p = s$. Since rank($\mathbf{C}$) = rank($\mathbf{D}$), the signatures, ranks, and indices of $\mathbf{C}$ and $\mathbf{D}$ are the same. ■

Theorem 8.8.1. *Let* $\mathbf{A}$ *and* $\mathbf{B}$ *be real symmetric and congruent. Then* $\mathbf{A}$ *and* $\mathbf{B}$ *have the same rank, index, and signature.*

Proof. Because $\mathbf{A}$ and $\mathbf{B}$ are real symmetric matrices, orthogonal matrices $\mathbf{U}$ and $\mathbf{V}$ exist such that $\mathbf{U}^{\mathrm{T}}\mathbf{A}\mathbf{U} = \mathbf{\Lambda_A}$ and $\mathbf{V}^{\mathrm{T}}\mathbf{B}\mathbf{V} = \mathbf{\Lambda_B}$. However, since $\mathbf{A}$ and $\mathbf{B}$ are congruent, so are $\mathbf{\Lambda_A}$ and $\mathbf{\Lambda_B}$. By Lemma 8.4 the ranks, indices, and signatures of $\mathbf{\Lambda_A}$ and $\mathbf{\Lambda_B}$ are the same. But, by definition, the index and signature of a real symmetric matrix is precisely the index and signature of the matrix of its eigenvalues. ■

Example 8.8.1. The index, rank, and signature of $x_1^2 + 3x_1x_2 + x_2^2$ is $p = 1$, $r = 2$, and $q = 0$. To see this, examine the matrix of the form

$$\mathbf{A} = \begin{bmatrix} 1 & 3/2 \\ 3/2 & 1 \end{bmatrix} \rightarrow \begin{bmatrix} 1 & 3/2 \\ 0 & -5/4 \end{bmatrix}$$

Clearly, $r = 2$ and $p = 1$. Hence, $q = 2p - r = 0$.

Example 8.8.2. Confirm Theorem 8.8.1 for the matrix

$$\mathbf{A} = \begin{bmatrix} 1 & 3/2 \\ 3/2 & 1 \end{bmatrix}$$

of Example 8.8.1 by finding the eigenvalues of $\mathbf{A}$.

Solution. The eigenvalues of $\mathbf{A}$ are readily computed; they are $\lambda_1 = 5/2$ and $\lambda_2 = -1/2$. Hence, the form $x_1^2 + 3x_1x_2 + x_2^2$ is congruent to the form $5/2 y_1^2 - 1/2 y_2^2$, and the ranks, indices, and signatures of both forms are the same.

PROBLEMS

8.8.1. Find the rank, signature, and index for each of these forms:
(*a*) $x_1x_2 + x_2^2 + x_1x_3$ (*b*) x_1x_2 (*c*) $x_1^2 + x_2^2$

8.8.2. Repeat Problem 8.8.1 for forms represented by the matrices

(*a*) $\begin{bmatrix} 1 & 1 \\ 1 & 0 \end{bmatrix}$ (*b*) $\begin{bmatrix} 1 & 0 & -1 \\ 0 & 1 & 0 \\ -1 & 0 & 1 \end{bmatrix}$ (*c*) $\begin{bmatrix} 0 & 0 & 1 \\ 0 & 1 & 0 \\ 1 & 0 & 0 \end{bmatrix}$ (*d*) $\begin{bmatrix} 1 & 1 & -1 \\ 1 & 1 & -1 \\ -1 & -1 & 0 \end{bmatrix}$

8.8.3. Repeat Problem 8.8.1 for the matrix given in Example 8.4.1.

8.8.4. What are the rank, signature, and index of a positive definite matrix? Of a negative definite matrix?

8.8.5. What are the signature and index of the projector $\mathbf{P}$ ($\mathbf{P}^2 = \mathbf{P}$) given that the rank of $\mathbf{P}$ is r?

8.9 SINGULAR VALUES AND VECTORS

The determination of the rank of $\mathbf{A}$ is a theoretically easy task; it is the number of nonzero rows in the reduced-row-echelon form of $\mathbf{A}$. Experience in numerical computations indicates that this is far from a trivial exercise if some of the rows of $\mathbf{A}$ are "nearly" linearly dependent. One of the main uses of the singular-value decomposition of $\mathbf{A}$ is to provide a numerically sound means for determining rank($\mathbf{A}$).

We begin with some fundamental definitions. First of all, assume that $\mathbf{A}$ is a complex $m \times n$ matrix and rank($\mathbf{A}$) $= r$. Then recall that $\mathbf{A}^H\mathbf{A}$ and $\mathbf{A}\mathbf{A}^H$ are hermitian and positive semidefinite, and that the positive eigenvalues of $\mathbf{A}^H\mathbf{A}$ and $\mathbf{A}\mathbf{A}^H$ are the same and have equal geometric multiplicities. Since $\mathbf{A}^H\mathbf{A}$ is positive semidefinite, $(\mathbf{A}^H\mathbf{A})^{1/2}$ exists, and its eigenvalues are the nonnegative square roots of the eigenvalues of $\mathbf{A}^H\mathbf{A}$. Call the positive eigenvalues of $(\mathbf{A}^H\mathbf{A})^{1/2}$ the *singular values* of $\mathbf{A}$. So if σ is a singular value of $\mathbf{A}$, σ is a positive eigenvalue of $(\mathbf{A}^H\mathbf{A})^{1/2}$ and σ^2 is an eigenvalue of $\mathbf{A}^H\mathbf{A}$ and of $\mathbf{A}\mathbf{A}^H$. The *multiplicity* of the singular value σ is the algebraic (and geometric) multiplicity of σ as an eigenvalue of $(\mathbf{A}^H\mathbf{A})^{1/2}$.

Example 8.9.1. Find the singular values of these matrices:

(*a*) $\mathbf{A} = \begin{bmatrix} 1 & 0 \\ 0 & 0 \\ 1 & 1 \end{bmatrix}$ (*b*) $\mathbf{B} = \begin{bmatrix} 1 & 0 & 0 \\ 0 & 0 & 1 \end{bmatrix}$ (*c*) $\mathbf{A}_n$ positive definite

(*d*) $\mathbf{Q}_n$ real orthogonal

Solution. Since all the matrices are real, the singular values are obtained by computing the eigenvalues of $\mathbf{A}^T\mathbf{A}$.

(*a*) $\mathbf{A}^T\mathbf{A} = \begin{bmatrix} 2 & 1 \\ 1 & 1 \end{bmatrix}$

The eigenvalues of $\mathbf{A}^T\mathbf{A}$ are $(3 \pm \sqrt{5})/2$, and therefore, the singular values of $\mathbf{A}$ are $\sqrt{(3 \pm \sqrt{5})/2}$.

(*b*) $\mathbf{A}^{\mathrm{T}}\mathbf{A} = \begin{bmatrix} 1 & 0 & 0 \\ 0 & 0 & 0 \\ 0 & 0 & 1 \end{bmatrix}$

The eigenvalues of $\mathbf{A}^{\mathrm{T}}\mathbf{A}$ are 1, 1, 0, and the singular values of $\mathbf{A}$ are 1, 1.

(*c*) Since $\mathbf{A}$ is positive definite, its eigenvalues are all positive and $\mathbf{A}^{\mathrm{T}}\mathbf{A} = \mathbf{A}^2$. Thus, the eigenvalues of $\mathbf{A}^{\mathrm{T}}\mathbf{A}$ are the squares of the eigenvalues of A, and the singular values of $\mathbf{A}$ are the eigenvalues of A.

(*d*) Since $\mathbf{Q}^{\mathrm{T}}\mathbf{Q} = \mathbf{I}$, the eigenvalues of $(\mathbf{Q}^{\mathrm{T}}\mathbf{Q})^{1/2}$ are all 1.

Example 8.9.2. Prove the following:

(*a*) The singular values of $\mathbf{A}^{\mathrm{H}}$ are those of $\mathbf{A}$.

(*b*) The singular values of the real symmetric matrix $\mathbf{S}$ are the absolute values of its nonzero eigenvalues.

Solution. The eigenvalues of $(\mathbf{A}^{\mathrm{H}})^{\mathrm{H}}\mathbf{A}^{\mathrm{H}} = \mathbf{A}\mathbf{A}^{\mathrm{H}}$ are those of $\mathbf{A}^{\mathrm{H}}\mathbf{A}$. This establishes (*a*). For (*b*), recall that $\mathbf{S}$ is unitarily similar to a diagonal matrix of its eigenvalues. Since $\mathbf{S}$ is real, the diagonalizing matrix can be chosen with real orthonormal vectors. That is, there exists $\mathbf{Q}$ orthogonal such that $\mathbf{Q}^{\mathrm{T}}\mathbf{S}\mathbf{Q} = \Lambda$ and $\mathbf{Q}^{\mathrm{T}}\mathbf{S}^{\mathrm{T}}\mathbf{Q} = \Lambda$. Hence, $\mathbf{Q}^{\mathrm{T}}\mathbf{S}^{\mathrm{T}}\mathbf{S}\mathbf{Q} = (\mathbf{Q}^{\mathrm{T}}\mathbf{S}^{\mathrm{T}}\mathbf{Q})(\mathbf{Q}^{\mathrm{T}}\mathbf{S}\mathbf{Q}) = \Lambda^2$. It then follows that if $\lambda \neq 0$ is an eigenvalue of $\mathbf{S}$, $|\lambda|$ is an eigenvalue of $(\mathbf{S}^{\mathrm{T}}\mathbf{S})^{1/2}$ and therefore a singular value of $\mathbf{S}$.

Theorem 8.9.1. Rank($\mathbf{A}$) *is the number of singular values of* $\mathbf{A}$.

Proof. First we prove that rank($\mathbf{A}$) = rank($\mathbf{A}^{\mathrm{H}}\mathbf{A}$). If $\mathbf{x} \in null(\mathbf{A})$, then $\mathbf{A}^{\mathrm{H}}\mathbf{A}\mathbf{x} = \mathbf{0}$ shows that $\mathbf{x} \in null(\mathbf{A}^{\mathrm{H}}\mathbf{A})$. Hence, $null(\mathbf{A}) \subseteq null(\mathbf{A}^{\mathrm{H}}\mathbf{A})$. On the other hand, $\mathbf{A}^{\mathrm{H}}\mathbf{A}\mathbf{x} = \mathbf{0}$ implies $\mathbf{x}^{\mathrm{H}}\mathbf{A}^{\mathrm{H}}\mathbf{A}\mathbf{x} = 0$. However, $\mathbf{x}^{\mathrm{H}}\mathbf{A}^{\mathrm{H}}\mathbf{A}\mathbf{x} = \|\mathbf{A}\mathbf{x}\|^2 = 0$ shows that $\mathbf{A}\mathbf{x} = \mathbf{0}$. Hence, $null(\mathbf{A}^{\mathrm{H}}\mathbf{A}) \subseteq null(\mathbf{A})$. Thus, the null spaces of $\mathbf{A}$ and $\mathbf{A}^{\mathrm{H}}\mathbf{A}$ are identical. Since the number of columns of $\mathbf{A}$ and $\mathbf{A}^{\mathrm{H}}\mathbf{A}$ are the same, Eq. 3.5.1 yields rank($\mathbf{A}$) = rank($\mathbf{A}^{\mathrm{H}}\mathbf{A}$).

Now the proof of the theorem is easy. Suppose Λ is the diagonal matrix of eigenvalues of $\mathbf{A}^{\mathrm{H}}\mathbf{A}$. Then, since $\mathbf{A}^{\mathrm{H}}\mathbf{A}$ is symmetric, there exists a unitary matrix $\mathbf{U}$ such that $\mathbf{U}^{\mathrm{H}}\mathbf{A}^{\mathrm{H}}\mathbf{A}\mathbf{U} = \Lambda$. So

$$\text{rank}(\mathbf{A}) = \text{rank}(\mathbf{A}^{\mathrm{H}}\mathbf{A}) = \text{rank}(\mathbf{U}^{\mathrm{T}}\mathbf{A}^{\mathrm{H}}\mathbf{A}\mathbf{U}) = \text{rank}(\Lambda)$$

implies that rank($\mathbf{A}$) is the number of nonzero entries in Λ, which is the number of singular values of $\mathbf{A}$. ■

Theorem 8.9.1 provides a more reliable estimate of rank($\mathbf{A}$) than counting the number of nonzero rows in the rref of $\mathbf{A}$. Caution is most needed in the event that some row of $\mathbf{A}$ is almost a linear combination of other rows of $\mathbf{A}$. (See Section 8.9.2.)

Suppose σ is a singular value of $\mathbf{A}$ repeated k times. Then there exist k linearly independent eigenvectors $\{\mathbf{v}_1,\mathbf{v}_2,\ldots,\mathbf{v}_k\}$ of $\mathbf{A}^{\mathrm{H}}\mathbf{A}$ corresponding to the eigenvalue σ^2. Call each such $\mathbf{v}_i$ a *right singular vector of* $\mathbf{A}$ corresponding to σ and $(\sigma,\mathbf{v}_i)$ a *right singular pair*. Similarly, there exist k linearly independent eigenvectors $\{\mathbf{u}_1,\mathbf{u}_2,\ldots,\mathbf{u}_k\}$ of $\mathbf{A}\mathbf{A}^H$ corresponding to the eigenvalue σ^2 of $\mathbf{A}\mathbf{A}^H$. These eigenvectors are called *left singular vectors of* $\mathbf{A}$ corresponding to the singular value σ, and $(\sigma,\mathbf{u}_i)$ is a *left singular pair*. This terminology is motivated by the fact, to be shown in the next theorem, that $\mathbf{A}\mathbf{v}_i = \sigma\mathbf{u}$, where $\mathbf{u}$ is some left singular vector of $\mathbf{A}$ corresponding to the singular value σ, and also $\mathbf{u}^{\mathrm{H}}\mathbf{A} = \sigma\mathbf{v}^{\mathrm{H}}$, where $\mathbf{v}$ is some right singular vector of $\mathbf{A}$ corresponding to the singular value σ. By definition, if $\mathbf{v}$ is a right singular value of $\mathbf{A}$ corresponding to σ, so is $a\mathbf{v}$ for all nonzero scalars a (similarly for $a\mathbf{u}$).

Theorem 8.9.2. *If* $(\sigma,\mathbf{v})$ *is a right singular pair of* $\mathbf{A}$, *then there exists* $\mathbf{u} \in \mathcal{R}^m$ *such that* $(\sigma,\mathbf{u})$ *is a left singular pair of* $\mathbf{A}$. *Moreover,*

$$(i)\ \mathbf{A}\mathbf{v} = \sigma\mathbf{u} \qquad \text{and} \qquad (ii)\ \mathbf{A}^{\mathrm{H}}\mathbf{u} = \sigma\mathbf{v} \tag{8.9.1}$$

Proof. By definition and hypothesis, $\mathbf{A}^{\mathrm{H}}\mathbf{A}\mathbf{v} = \sigma^2\mathbf{v}$. Define $\mathbf{u}$ by $\mathbf{A}\mathbf{v} = \sigma\mathbf{u}$. Thus, (i) holds by definition of $\mathbf{u}$. By multiplying (i) by $\mathbf{A}^{\mathrm{H}}$, we obtain

$$\mathbf{A}^{\mathrm{H}}\mathbf{A}\mathbf{v} = \mathbf{A}^{\mathrm{H}}(\sigma\mathbf{u}) = \sigma\mathbf{A}^{\mathrm{H}}\mathbf{u}$$

That is, $\mathbf{A}^{\mathrm{H}}\mathbf{A}\mathbf{v} = \sigma\mathbf{A}^{\mathrm{H}}\mathbf{u}$. However, $\mathbf{A}^{\mathrm{H}}\mathbf{A}\mathbf{v} = \sigma^2\mathbf{v}$. Hence, $\sigma\mathbf{A}^{\mathrm{H}}\mathbf{u} = \sigma^2\mathbf{v}$ and (ii) holds. Finally, from $\mathbf{A}^{\mathrm{H}}\mathbf{u} = \sigma\mathbf{v}$ and (i), it follows that

$$\mathbf{A}\mathbf{A}^{\mathrm{H}}\mathbf{u} = \sigma\mathbf{A}\mathbf{v} = \sigma(\sigma\mathbf{u}) = \sigma^2\mathbf{u}$$

and, thus, $(\sigma^2,\mathbf{u})$ is an eigenpair of $\mathbf{A}\mathbf{A}^{\mathrm{H}}$. ■

An analogous theorem holds for left singular vectors.

Theorem 8.9.3. *If* $(\sigma,\mathbf{u})$ *is a left singular pair of* $\mathbf{A}$, *then there exists* $\mathbf{v} \in \mathcal{R}^n$ *such that* $(\sigma,\mathbf{v})$ *is a right singular pair of* $\mathbf{A}$, *and* Eq. 8.9.1 *holds.*

Proof. This is set as Problem 8.9.12. ■

Suppose that $\{\mathbf{v}_1,\mathbf{v}_2,\ldots,\mathbf{v}_k\}$ is a linearly independent set of right singular vectors of $\mathbf{A}$ corresponding to the singular value σ. Since these vectors are also eigenvectors of $\mathbf{A}^{\mathrm{H}}\mathbf{A}$ corresponding to the eigenvalue σ^2, every linear combination of $\{\mathbf{v}_1,\mathbf{v}_2,\ldots,\mathbf{v}_k\}$ is an eigenvector of $\mathbf{A}^{\mathrm{H}}\mathbf{A}$ corresponding to σ^2. Hence, for each choice of real weights $a_i, 1 \le i \le k, (\sigma, a_1\mathbf{v}_1 + a_2\mathbf{v}_2 + \cdots + a_k\mathbf{v}_k)$ is a right singular pair of $\mathbf{A}$. From this observation it follows that $\{\mathbf{v}_1,\mathbf{v}_2,\ldots,\mathbf{v}_k\}$ can be replaced by a set of orthonormal vectors that are also right singular vectors of $\mathbf{A}$ corresponding to σ (by using the Gram-Schmidt method, if necessary). Supposing, then, that $\{\mathbf{v}_1,\mathbf{v}_2,\ldots,\mathbf{v}_k\}$ is a set of orthonormal right singular vectors of $\mathbf{A}$, what can be said about the left singular vectors $\{\mathbf{A}\mathbf{v}_1,\mathbf{A}\mathbf{v}_2,\ldots,\mathbf{A}\mathbf{v}_k\}$?

Theorem 8.9.4. *If* $\{\mathbf{v}_1, \mathbf{v}_2, \ldots, \mathbf{v}_k\}$ *is an orthonormal set of right singular vectors of* $\mathbf{A}$ *corresponding to the singular value* σ, *then* $\{\mathbf{u}_1 = (1/\sigma_1)\mathbf{A}\mathbf{v}_i,\ \mathbf{u}_2 = (1/\sigma_2)\mathbf{A}\mathbf{v}_2, \ldots, \mathbf{u}_k = (1/\sigma_k)\mathbf{A}\mathbf{v}_k\}$ *is a set of orthonormal left singular vectors of* $\mathbf{A}$ *corresponding to* σ.

Proof. By definition $\mathbf{A}^{\mathrm{H}}\mathbf{A}\mathbf{v}_i = \sigma^2\mathbf{v}_i$, and by hypothesis $< \mathbf{v}_i, \mathbf{v}_j > = \delta_{ij}$. Therefore, $< \mathbf{A}\mathbf{v}_i, \mathbf{A}\mathbf{v}_j > = \sigma^2\delta_{ij}$ follows from

$$< \mathbf{A}\mathbf{v}_i, \mathbf{A}\mathbf{v}_j > = < \mathbf{v}_i, \mathbf{A}^{\mathrm{H}}\mathbf{A}\mathbf{v}_j > = < \mathbf{v}_i, \sigma^2\mathbf{v}_j > = \sigma^2 < \mathbf{v}_i, \mathbf{v}_j > = \sigma^2\delta_{ij}$$

On the other hand,

$$\sigma^2\delta_{ij} = < \mathbf{A}\mathbf{v}_i, \mathbf{A}\mathbf{v}_j > = < \sigma\mathbf{u}_i, \sigma\mathbf{u}_j > = \sigma^2 < \mathbf{u}_i, \mathbf{u}_j > .$$

Since $\sigma \neq 0$, $< \mathbf{u}_i, \mathbf{u}_j > = \delta_{ij}$. ■

Example 8.9.3. Find the left and right singular vectors for the matrix

$$\mathbf{A} = \begin{bmatrix} 1 & 0 & -1 \\ 1 & 1 & 1 \end{bmatrix}$$

and verify Theorem 8.9.3.

Solution. First find the eigenpairs of

$$\mathbf{A}^{\mathrm{T}}\mathbf{A} = \begin{bmatrix} 2 & 1 & 0 \\ 1 & 1 & 1 \\ 0 & 1 & 2 \end{bmatrix}$$

These are

$$\left(2, \mathbf{v}_1 = \begin{bmatrix} 1 \\ 0 \\ -1 \end{bmatrix}\right); \quad \left(3, \mathbf{v}_2 = \begin{bmatrix} 1 \\ 1 \\ 1 \end{bmatrix}\right); \quad \left(0, \mathbf{v}_3 = \begin{bmatrix} 1 \\ -2 \\ 1 \end{bmatrix}\right)$$

Hence, the singular values of $\mathbf{A}$ are $\sqrt{2}$ and $\sqrt{3}$. The corresponding right singular vectors are $\mathbf{v}_1$ and $\mathbf{v}_2$, respectively. To determine the left singular vectors, compute $\mathbf{u} = \mathbf{A}\mathbf{v}$:

$$\mathbf{u}_1 = \mathbf{A}\mathbf{v}_1 = \begin{bmatrix} 1 & 0 & -1 \\ 1 & 1 & 1 \end{bmatrix}\begin{bmatrix} 1 \\ 0 \\ -1 \end{bmatrix} = \begin{bmatrix} 2 \\ 0 \end{bmatrix},$$

$$\mathbf{u}_2 = \mathbf{A}\mathbf{v}_2 = \begin{bmatrix} 1 & 0 & -1 \\ 1 & 1 & 1 \end{bmatrix}\begin{bmatrix} 1 \\ 1 \\ 1 \end{bmatrix} = \begin{bmatrix} 0 \\ 3 \end{bmatrix}$$

It is easy to verify that

$$\mathbf{A}\mathbf{A}^{\mathrm{T}} = \begin{bmatrix} 2 & 0 \\ 0 & 3 \end{bmatrix}$$

and trivial to see that $(2, \mathbf{u}_1)$ and $(3, \mathbf{u}_2)$ are eigenpairs of $\mathbf{A}\mathbf{A}^{\mathrm{T}}$.

An orthonormal pair of right singular vectors are

$$\tilde{\mathbf{v}}_1 = \frac{\sqrt{2}}{2}\begin{bmatrix} 1 \\ 0 \\ -1 \end{bmatrix}, \qquad \tilde{\mathbf{v}}_2 = \frac{\sqrt{3}}{3}\begin{bmatrix} 1 \\ 1 \\ 1 \end{bmatrix}$$

Now

$$\tilde{\mathbf{u}}_1 = \sigma^{-1}\mathbf{A}\tilde{\mathbf{v}}_1 = \begin{bmatrix} 1 \\ 0 \end{bmatrix} \quad \text{and} \quad \tilde{\mathbf{u}}_2 = \sigma^{-1}\mathbf{A}\tilde{\mathbf{v}}_2 = \begin{bmatrix} 0 \\ 1 \end{bmatrix}$$

verifies Theorem 8.9.4.

8.9.2 MATLAB Determination of Singular Values and Vectors

There are two MATLAB commands relating to the singular values of $\mathbf{A}_{m\times n}$. First, svd(A) returns a vector whose entries are the singular values of $\mathbf{A}$. (MATLAB takes the position that zero eigenvalues of $\mathbf{A}^{\mathrm{H}}\mathbf{A}$ are singular values of $\mathbf{A}$; hence, svd(A) returns all the eigenvalues of $(\mathbf{A}^{\mathrm{H}}\mathbf{A})^{1/2}$.)

Second, [U,S,V] = svd(A) returns an orthonormal matrix of left singular vectors U, an orthonormal matrix of right singular vectors V, and S, an $m\times n$ matrix whose diagonal comprises the eigenvalues of $(\mathbf{A}^{\mathrm{H}}\mathbf{A})^{1/2}$. As we shall see in the next section, $\mathbf{U}^{\mathrm{H}}\mathbf{A}\mathbf{V} = \mathbf{S}$.

Example 8.9.4. Use [U,S,V] = svd(A) for the matrix $\mathbf{A}$ given in Example 8.9.3 and compute $\mathbf{U}^{\mathrm{H}}\mathbf{A}\mathbf{V}$.

Solution. Enter $\mathbf{A}$. Then

```
[U,S,V] = svd(A)

    U =

        0.0000   -1.0000
        1.0000    0.0000

    S =

        1.7321    0         0
        0         1.4142    0

    V =

        0.5774   -0.7071    0.4082
        0.5774    0.0000   -0.8165
        0.5774    0.7071    0.4082
```

Comparing these values with those in Example 8.9.3, we can see that, in some instances, the singular vectors using MATLAB are the negatives of those computed by hand. (The matrix S was not computed in Example 8.9.3.) Finally,

```
U'*A*V
          ans =
                    1.7321        0   0
                         0   1.4142   0
```

Note that S is U'*A*V and that its diagonal entries are the singular values of **A**.

MATLAB computes rank(**A**) by counting the (positive) singular values of **A**. There are other important uses for svd(A). MATLAB uses the singular values to define a special norm for **A** (the largest singular value is norm(A)) the pseudo-inverse (see Section 8.11), and the condition number of **A**. The condition number is a measure of "the sensitivity of the solution of linear equations to errors in the data." Cond(A) returns the ratio of the largest singular value to the smallest.

PROBLEMS

PART 1

8.9.1. Find the singular values and right and left singular vectors of $\mathbf{x} \neq \mathbf{0}$.

8.9.2. Find the singular values and right and left singular vectors of $\mathbf{J}_4$.

8.9.3. Find the singular values and right and left singular vectors of the orthogonal matrix

$$\begin{bmatrix} \sin\vartheta & -\cos\vartheta \\ \cos\vartheta & \sin\vartheta \end{bmatrix}$$

PART 2

8.9.4. Explain why rank($\mathbf{A}$) $= r$ implies rank($\mathbf{A}^{\mathrm{H}}\mathbf{A}$) $=$ rank($\mathbf{A}\mathbf{A}^{\mathrm{H}}$).

8.9.5. Prove that for nonsingular $\mathbf{A}$, $|\det(\mathbf{A})| = \sigma_1\sigma_2\ldots\sigma_r$.

8.9.6. If σ is a singular value of $\mathbf{A}$, σ^{-1} is a singular value of $\mathbf{A}^{-1}$.

8.9.7. Relate the singular values of $\alpha\mathbf{A}$ to those of $\mathbf{A}$.

8.9.8. If $\mathbf{A} \neq \mathbf{O}$ is real and $n \times n$, show that the spectral radius of $\mathbf{A}$ is the largest singular value of $\mathbf{A}$.

8.9.9. Suppose $\mathbf{Q}$ is real orthogonal. Show that the singular values of $\mathbf{QA}$ are those of $\mathbf{A}$.

8.9.10. Show that the right (left) singular vectors of $\mathbf{A}^{\mathrm{H}}$ are the left (right) singular vectors of $\mathbf{A}$.

8.9.11. Find the singular values and right and left singular vectors of the real orthogonal matrix $\mathbf{Q}$.

8.9.12. Prove Theorem 8.9.3.

8.9.13. If $\mathbf{A}$ and $\mathbf{B}$ are unitarily similar, show that the singular values of $\mathbf{A}$ and $\mathbf{B}$ are the same.

PART 3

8.9.14. Find the singular values and right and left singular vectors of the real symmetric matrix $\mathbf{A}$.

8.9.15. Find the singular values and right and left singular vectors of the positive semidefinite matrix **P**.

8.9.16. Suppose $\mathbf{Q}^{\mathrm{T}}\mathbf{A}\mathbf{Q} = \mathbf{B}$, where **Q** is a real orthogonal matrix and **A** is $n \times n$. Relate the singular values and right and left singular vectors of **B** to those of **A**.

8.9.17. Prove the following analog of Theorem 8.9.2: If $\{\mathbf{u}_i : i = 1,2,\ldots,k\}$ is an orthonormal set of left singular vectors of **A** corresponding to the singular value σ, then $\{\sigma\mathbf{v}_i = \mathbf{A}^{\mathrm{H}}\mathbf{u}_i : i = 1,2,\ldots,k\}$ is a set of orthonormal right singular vectors of **A** corresponding to σ.

MATLAB

Use the commands svd(A) and [U,S,V] = svd(A) in the following problems.

8.9.18. Find the singular values for the following matrices:

(*a*) $\begin{bmatrix} 1 & 0 \\ 0 & 0 \\ 1 & 1 \end{bmatrix}$ (*b*) $\begin{bmatrix} 1 & 0 & 0 \\ 0 & 0 & 1 \end{bmatrix}$ (*c*) $\begin{bmatrix} 1 & 1 & -2 \end{bmatrix}$

(*d*) $\begin{bmatrix} 0 & -1 \\ 1 & 0 \end{bmatrix}$ (*e*) $\begin{bmatrix} 1 & 1 & 1 \\ 1 & 1 & 1 \end{bmatrix}$

8.9.19. For each matrix in Problem 8.9.18, find the right and left singular vectors.

8.10 THE SINGULAR-VALUE DECOMPOSITION OF A

Many of the most important theorems in matrix theory are "decomposition" theorems: the **LU** factorization theorem, the **QR** factorization theorem, the Cholesky decomposition theorem ($\mathbf{A} = \mathbf{W}^{\mathrm{H}}\mathbf{W}$, for positive semidefinite **A**), and even the expression $\mathbf{A} = \mathbf{S}\boldsymbol{\Lambda}\mathbf{S}^{-1}$ (for simple **A**). The SVD (singular-value decomposition) theorem is one more theorem of this type. It is applicable to all matrices and is analogous to but not a generalization of the theorem that expresses simple matrices as $\mathbf{S}\boldsymbol{\Lambda}\mathbf{S}^{-1}$. We begin with a statement of this very useful theorem and reserve the proof to Section 8.10.1.

Theorem 8.10.1. (*The Singular-Value Decomposition of* **A**). *Suppose* **A** *is* $m \times n$. *Then there exist unitary matrices* $\mathbf{U}_{m\times m}$ *and* $\mathbf{V}_{m\times m}$ *such that*

$$\mathbf{A} = \mathbf{U}\mathbf{S}\mathbf{V}^{\mathrm{H}} \tag{8.10.1}$$

where **S** *is an* $m \times n$ *matrix with the singular values of* **A** *displayed along its diagonal and zeros elsewhere.*

Remarks. The proof of Theorem 8.10.1 consists of constructing **S**, **V**, and **U**. Here are the ideas and conclusions relevant to the proof and the construction of **S**, **V**, and **U**. Suppose rank (**A**) $= r$.

1. The matrices $\mathbf{A}^{\mathrm{H}}\mathbf{A}$ and $\mathbf{A}\mathbf{A}^{\mathrm{H}}$ are hermitian and therefore have a complete set of orthonormal eigenvectors. The columns of **U** are the eigenvectors of $\mathbf{A}\mathbf{A}^{\mathrm{H}}$; the columns of **V** are the eigenvectors of $\mathbf{A}^{\mathrm{H}}\mathbf{A}$. It is for this reason that **U** and **V** are $m \times m$ and $n \times n$ unitary matrices, respectively.

2. The columns of $\mathbf{V}$ are ordered so that the first r columns contain the right singular vectors of $\mathbf{A}$, and the remaining columns are eigenvectors corresponding to the zero eigenvalues of $\mathbf{A}^{\mathrm{H}}\mathbf{A}$.
3. For $i = 1,2,\ldots,r$,

$$\mathbf{u}_i = (1/\sigma_i)\mathbf{A}\mathbf{v}_i \tag{8.10.2}$$

defines the ith column of $\mathbf{U}$. The remaining $m - r$ columns of $\mathbf{U}$ are eigenvectors corresponding to the zero eigenvalues of $\mathbf{A}^{\mathrm{H}}\mathbf{A}$. It is part of the proof of Theorem 8.10.1 that $\mathbf{u}_i$ is a left singular vector of $\mathbf{A}$ and that $< \mathbf{u}_i,\mathbf{u}_j >= \delta_{ij}$.
4. The diagonal of the $m \times n$ matrix $\mathbf{S}$ is composed of the singular values of $\mathbf{A}$ and sufficiently many zeros to complete the diagonal. We call $\mathbf{S}$ a *singular-value matrix of* $\mathbf{A}$. Thus, $\mathbf{S}$ has the following form:

$$\mathbf{S} = \begin{bmatrix} \boldsymbol{\Sigma} & \mathbf{O} \\ \mathbf{O} & \mathbf{O} \end{bmatrix} = \begin{bmatrix} \sigma_1 & & & & & & \mathbf{O} \\ & \sigma_2 & & & & & \\ & & \ddots & & & & \\ & & & \sigma_r & & & \\ & & & & 0 & & \\ & \mathbf{O} & & & & 0 & \\ & & & & & & \ddots \end{bmatrix}_{m\times n} \tag{8.10.3}$$

If rank($\mathbf{A}$)$= r = m = n$, then $\mathbf{A}$ is nonsingular and $\mathbf{S} = \boldsymbol{\Sigma}$. If $r = m < n$, then $\mathbf{A}$ has full row rank and $\mathbf{S} = [\boldsymbol{\Sigma} \quad \mathbf{O}]$. On the other hand, if $r = n < m$, then $\mathbf{A}$ has full column rank and

$$\mathbf{S} = \begin{bmatrix} \boldsymbol{\Sigma} \\ \mathbf{O} \end{bmatrix}$$

Corollary 1. *For each matrix* $\mathbf{A}$ *there exist unitary matrices* $\mathbf{U}$ *and* $\mathbf{V}$ *such that*

$$\mathbf{U}^{\mathrm{H}}\mathbf{A}\mathbf{V} = \mathbf{S} \tag{8.10.4}$$

Proof. Equation 8.10.4 follows from Eq. 8.10.1 and the fact that $\mathbf{U}$ and $\mathbf{V}$ are unitary matrices. ■

Corollary 2. *If* $\mathbf{A} \neq \mathbf{O}$ *is positive semidefinite, then* $\mathbf{S} = \boldsymbol{\Lambda}$ *and we may choose* $\mathbf{U} = \mathbf{V}$.

Proof. Positive semidefinite matrices have nonnegative eigenvalues λ_i, and since $\sigma_i = |\lambda_i| = \lambda_i$ for each i, $\mathbf{S} = \boldsymbol{\Lambda}$ for some ordering of the diagonal entries of $\mathbf{S}$. Because $\mathbf{A}^{\mathrm{H}} = \mathbf{A}$, $\mathbf{A}^{\mathrm{H}}\mathbf{A} = \mathbf{A}^2 = \mathbf{A}\mathbf{A}^{\mathrm{H}}$, and because $\mathbf{A}^2$ has the same eigenvectors as $\mathbf{A}$, the right and left singular vectors of $\mathbf{A}$ are the eigenvectors of $\mathbf{A}$ that correspond to its nonzero eigenvalues. Now, by Eq. 8.10.2,

$$\lambda_i\mathbf{u}_i = \sigma_i\mathbf{u}_i = \mathbf{A}\mathbf{v}_i = \sigma_i\mathbf{v}_i$$

so that $\mathbf{u}_i = \mathbf{v}_i$ for $i = 1,2,\ldots,r$. The remaining vectors in **U** and **V** are eigenvectors of **A** corresponding to the eigenvalue 0. We choose the same eigenvectors for **U** as for **V** and arrange that they form an orthonormal set. ■

Example 8.10.1. Find the SVD of

$$\mathbf{A} = \begin{bmatrix} 0 & 4 & 3 \\ 4 & 0 & 0 \\ 3 & 0 & 0 \end{bmatrix}$$

Solution. The eigenpairs of

$$\mathbf{A}^T\mathbf{A} = \begin{bmatrix} 25 & 0 & 0 \\ 0 & 16 & 12 \\ 0 & 12 & 9 \end{bmatrix}$$

are $(25,\mathbf{v}_1)$, $(25,\mathbf{v}_2)$ and $(0,\mathbf{v}_3)$, where

$$\mathbf{v}_1 = \begin{bmatrix} 1 \\ 0 \\ 0 \end{bmatrix}, \quad \mathbf{v}_2 = \begin{bmatrix} 0 \\ 4/5 \\ 3/5 \end{bmatrix}, \quad \mathbf{v}_3 = \begin{bmatrix} 0 \\ 3/5 \\ -4/5 \end{bmatrix}$$

Hence, $\sigma_1 = \sigma_2 = 5$. Setting $\mathbf{V} = [\mathbf{v}_1 \quad \mathbf{v}_2 \quad \mathbf{v}_3]$ leads to

$$\mathbf{V} = \begin{bmatrix} 1 & 0 & 0 \\ 0 & 4/5 & 3/5 \\ 0 & 3/5 & -4/5 \end{bmatrix}$$

Now $\mathbf{u}_3$ is an orthonormal solution of $\mathbf{A}\mathbf{A}^T\mathbf{u}_3 = \mathbf{A}^T\mathbf{A}\mathbf{u}_3 = \mathbf{A}^2\mathbf{u}_3 = \mathbf{0}$, namely, $\mathbf{v}_3$.

$$\mathbf{U} = \begin{bmatrix} \dfrac{\mathbf{A}\mathbf{v}_1}{5} & \dfrac{\mathbf{A}\mathbf{v}_2}{5} & \mathbf{u}_3 \end{bmatrix} = \begin{bmatrix} 0 & 1 & 0 \\ 4/5 & 0 & 3/5 \\ 3/5 & 0 & -4/5 \end{bmatrix}$$

It is easy to verify Eqs. 8.10.1 and 8.10.4.

Example 8.10.2. Find the SVD of $\mathbf{A} = [2 \quad -1 \quad 2]$.

Solution. We compute

$$\mathbf{A}^H\mathbf{A} = \begin{bmatrix} 4 & -2 & 4 \\ -2 & 1 & -2 \\ 4 & -2 & 4 \end{bmatrix}$$

whose eigenpairs are $(9,\mathbf{v}_1)$, $(0,\mathbf{v}_2)$, and $(0,\mathbf{v}_3)$:

$$\mathbf{v}_1 = \frac{1}{3}\begin{bmatrix} 2 \\ -1 \\ 2 \end{bmatrix}, \quad \mathbf{v}_2 = \frac{1}{\sqrt{5}}\begin{bmatrix} 1 \\ 2 \\ 0 \end{bmatrix}, \quad \mathbf{v}_3 = \frac{1}{3\sqrt{5}}\begin{bmatrix} 4 \\ -2 \\ -5 \end{bmatrix}$$

Thus, $\sigma_1 = 3$ is the only (nonzero) singular value. Since $\mathbf{A}\mathbf{A}^T = [9]$, there are no zero eigenvalues, and hence $\mathbf{U} = [\mathbf{A}\mathbf{v}_1/3] = [1]$. Note that Theorem 8.10.1 asserts that $\mathbf{U}$ is 1×1, $\mathbf{S}$ is 1×3, and $\mathbf{V}$ is 3×3. As an easy check:

$$\mathbf{A} = \mathbf{USV}^T = [1][3 \quad 0 \quad 0]\begin{bmatrix} \frac{2}{3} & \frac{1}{\sqrt{5}} & \frac{4/3}{\sqrt{5}} \\ -\frac{1}{3} & \frac{2}{\sqrt{5}} & -\frac{2/3}{\sqrt{5}} \\ \frac{2}{3} & 0 & -\frac{5/3}{\sqrt{5}} \end{bmatrix}^T = [2 \quad -1 \quad 2]$$

Example 8.10.3. Find the SVD of:

(a) $\mathbf{O}_{m \times n}$
(b) $\mathbf{x} \neq \mathbf{0} \in \mathcal{R}^n$
(c) $\mathbf{x}^T, \mathbf{x} \neq \mathbf{0} \in \mathcal{R}^n$
(d) $\mathbf{u}\mathbf{v}^T$, $< \mathbf{u}, \mathbf{v} > \neq 0$, $\mathbf{u}$ and $\mathbf{v} \in \mathcal{R}^n$.

Solution.

(a) We may choose $\mathbf{U} = \mathbf{I}_m$ and $\mathbf{V} = \mathbf{I}_n$. Of course, $\mathbf{S} = \mathbf{O}_{m \times n}$.
(b) First note that $\mathbf{U}$ is $n \times n$, $\mathbf{V}$ is 1×1, and $\mathbf{S}$ is $n \times 1$. Next, $\mathbf{x}^T\mathbf{x} = [\|\mathbf{x}\|^2]$, so that $\mathbf{V} = [1]$ and $\mathbf{S} = [\,\|\mathbf{x}\| \quad 0 \quad \ldots \quad 0\,]^T$. Now $(\|\mathbf{x}\|, \mathbf{x})$ is an eigenpair of $\mathbf{x}\mathbf{x}^T$, so that $\mathbf{u}_1 = \mathbf{x}/\|\mathbf{x}\|$; the remaining columns of $\mathbf{U}$ are orthonormal eigenvectors composing a basis for $\mathcal{E}(0) = null(\mathbf{x}\mathbf{x}^T)$.
(c) Use the results of (b), suitably modified.
(d) Here $\mathbf{A} = \mathbf{u}\mathbf{v}^T$, so that $\mathbf{A}^T\mathbf{A} = \|\mathbf{u}\|^2\mathbf{v}\mathbf{v}^T$. The eigenpairs of $\|\mathbf{u}\|^2\mathbf{v}\mathbf{v}^T$ are $(\|\mathbf{u}\|^2\|\mathbf{v}\|^2, \mathbf{v})$ and $n-1$ eigenpairs corresponding to the eigenvalue 0 of $\|\mathbf{u}\|^2\mathbf{v}\mathbf{v}^T$. Similarly, the eigenpairs of $\mathbf{A}\mathbf{A}^T = \|\mathbf{v}\|^2\mathbf{u}\mathbf{u}^T$ are $(\|\mathbf{u}\|^2\|\mathbf{v}\|^2, \mathbf{u})$ and $n-1$ eigenpairs corresponding to the eigenvalue 0 of $\|\mathbf{v}\|^2\mathbf{u}\mathbf{u}^T$.

Thus,

$$\mathbf{u}\mathbf{v}^T = [\mathbf{u}/\|\mathbf{u}\| \; \mathbf{u}_2 \ldots \mathbf{u}_n]\begin{bmatrix} \|\mathbf{u}\|\,\|\mathbf{v}\| & \mathbf{O} \\ \mathbf{0} & \mathbf{O} \end{bmatrix}[\,\mathbf{v}/\|\mathbf{v}\| \quad \mathbf{v}_2 \quad \ldots \quad \mathbf{v}_n\,]^T$$

Note that $\mathbf{SV}^T = [\|\mathbf{u}\|\mathbf{v} \quad \mathbf{0} \quad \ldots \quad \mathbf{0}]^T$, so that $\mathbf{u}\mathbf{v}^T = \mathbf{USV}^T$ is easy to verify.

Example 8.10.4. Show that $\rho(\mathbf{A})$ is the maximum of the singular values and

$$\|\mathbf{A}\|^2 = \sum \sigma_i^2 \tag{8.10.5}$$

Solution. For $\lambda \neq 0, |\lambda| = \sigma$ and $\rho(\mathbf{A}) = \max\{|\lambda_1|, |\lambda_2|, \ldots, |\lambda_n|\}$ is the largest singular value of **A**, the first assertion is trivial. To prove Eq. 8.10.5, refer to Section 7.4 for the various definitions and theorems. In particular, Theorem 7.4.2 (combined with Eq. 8.10.1) asserts:

$$\|\mathbf{A}\|^2 = \|\mathbf{USV}^{\mathrm{T}}\|^2 = \|\mathbf{S}\|^2 = \sum \sigma_i^2$$

It is interesting to note that $\mathbf{U}^{\mathrm{H}}\mathbf{AV} = \mathbf{S}$ is analogous to the unitary diagonalization of **A**. However, the SVD does not generally reduce to $\mathbf{U}^{\mathrm{H}}\mathbf{AU} = \mathbf{\Lambda}$ even if **A** is normal because the eigenvalues of **A** may not be real, let alone nonnegative. Corollary 2 presents one case in which the SVD is a unitary diagonalization of **A**.

We now present two more applications of Theorem 8.10.1. Both are stated as corollaries. The first regards the solution of $\mathbf{Ax} = \mathbf{b}$.

Corollary 3. *Suppose* **A** *is* $m \times n$ *and real, and* $\operatorname{rank}(\mathbf{A}) = r$. *Then the system* $\mathbf{Ax} = \mathbf{b}$ *is consistent if and only if*

$$< \mathbf{b}, \mathbf{u}_i > = 0 \qquad \text{for } i = r+1, r+2, \ldots, n \tag{8.10.6}$$

Moreover, if $\mathbf{Ax} = \mathbf{b}$ *is consistent and* $\mathbf{U}^{\mathrm{H}}\mathbf{AV} = \mathbf{S}$ *is the* SVD *of* **A**, *then*

$$\mathbf{x}_p = \sum_{i=1}^{r} \frac{< \mathbf{b}, \mathbf{u}_i >}{\sigma_i} \mathbf{v}_i \tag{8.10.7}$$

is a particular solution.

Proof. Using the notation of Theorem 8.10.1, define $\mathbf{y} = \mathbf{V}^{\mathrm{T}}\mathbf{x}$ and replace **x** by **y** in $\mathbf{Ax} = \mathbf{b}$ to obtain $\mathbf{AVy} = \mathbf{b}$, from which it follows (by Eq. 8.10.4) that

$$\mathbf{Sy} = \mathbf{U}^{\mathrm{T}}\mathbf{AVy} = \mathbf{U}^{\mathrm{T}}\mathbf{b} \tag{8.10.8}$$

Thus, $\mathbf{Ax} = \mathbf{b}$ is consistent if and only if $\mathbf{Sy} = \mathbf{U}^{\mathrm{T}}\mathbf{b}$ is consistent. Since the entries of $\mathbf{U}^{\mathrm{T}}\mathbf{b}$ are $< \mathbf{b}, \mathbf{u}_i >$, Eq. 8.10.8 implies

$$< \mathbf{b}, \mathbf{u}_i > /\sigma_i = y_i \qquad \text{for } 1 \leq i \leq r \tag{8.10.9}$$

$$< \mathbf{b}, \mathbf{u}_i > = 0 \qquad \text{for } r+1 \leq i \leq n \tag{8.10.10}$$

Equation 8.10.10 is necessary and sufficient for consistency; $\mathbf{x} = \mathbf{Vy}$ and Eq. 8.10.9 lead to the particular solution of Eq. 8.10.7. ■

Corollary 4. *If* **A** *is* $n \times n$ *then* $\mathbf{AA}^{\mathrm{H}}$ *is unitarily similar to* $\mathbf{A}^{\mathrm{H}}\mathbf{A}$.

Proof. Since $m = n$, **S**, **U**, and **V** are all $n \times n$. Then, from Eq. 8.10.1, $\mathbf{A} = \mathbf{USV}^{\mathrm{H}}$. Hence,

$$\mathbf{AA}^{\mathrm{H}} = (\mathbf{USV}^{\mathrm{T}})(\mathbf{VSU}^{\mathrm{H}}) = \mathbf{US}^2\mathbf{V}^{\mathrm{H}}$$
$$\mathbf{A}^{\mathrm{H}}\mathbf{A} = (\mathbf{USV}^{\mathrm{H}})^{\mathrm{H}}(\mathbf{USV}^{\mathrm{H}}) = (\mathbf{VSU}^{\mathrm{H}})(\mathbf{USV}^{\mathrm{H}}) = \mathbf{VS}^2\mathbf{V}^{\mathrm{H}}$$

Thus, $\mathbf{A}\mathbf{A}^{\mathrm{H}}$ and $\mathbf{A}^{\mathrm{H}}\mathbf{A}$ are unitarily similar to $\mathbf{S}^2$ and, therefore, unitarily similar to each other. ■

8.10.1 The Proof of Theorem 8.10.1

Since $\mathbf{A}^{\mathrm{H}}\mathbf{A}$ and $\mathbf{A}\mathbf{A}^{\mathrm{H}}$ are hermitian and are positive semidefinite matrices, their nonzero eigenvalues are positive and equal, and the positive square roots of these eigenvalues are defined as the singular values of $\mathbf{A}$. The eigenvectors of $\mathbf{A}^{\mathrm{H}}\mathbf{A}$ may be chosen to form an orthonormal basis for $\mathscr{C}^n$. Let

$$\mathbf{V} = [\mathbf{v}_1 \quad \mathbf{v}_2 \quad \dots \quad \mathbf{v}_r \quad \mathbf{v}_{r+1} \quad \dots \quad \mathbf{v}_n] \tag{8.10.11}$$

be the $n \times n$ matrix whose columns are these orthonormal vectors. Suppose that $\mathrm{rank}(\mathbf{A}) = r$. We may assume that the first r columns of $\mathbf{V}$ are eigenvectors associated with the eigenvalues of $\mathbf{A}^{\mathrm{H}}\mathbf{A}$; that is, $\mathbf{A}^{\mathrm{H}}\mathbf{A}\mathbf{v}_i = \sigma_i^2\mathbf{v}_i$, for $i = 1,2,\dots,r$. (These r vectors are the right singular vectors of $\mathbf{A}$ by definition.) The remaining $n - r$ columns in $\mathbf{V}$ are the eigenvectors of $\mathbf{A}^{\mathrm{H}}\mathbf{A}$ corresponding to its zero eigenvalue. Since the columns of $\mathbf{V}$ are orthonormal, $\mathbf{V}$ is unitary. This completes the construction of $\mathbf{V}$.

We now define $\mathbf{U}$ as follows: For $i = 1,2,\dots,r$, set

$$\mathbf{u}_i = (1/\sigma_i)\mathbf{A}\mathbf{v}_i \tag{8.10.12}$$

Next consider any two vectors $\mathbf{u}_i$ and $\mathbf{u}_j$ in this set. From Eq. 8.10.12,

$$\begin{aligned} < \mathbf{u}_i,\mathbf{u}_j > &= (1/\sigma_i)(1/\sigma_j) < \mathbf{A}\mathbf{v}_i,\mathbf{A}\mathbf{v}_j >= (1/\sigma_i)(1/\sigma_j) < \mathbf{v}_i,\mathbf{A}^{\mathrm{H}}\mathbf{A}\mathbf{v}_j > \\ &= (1/\sigma_i)(1/\sigma_j) < \mathbf{v}_i,\sigma_j^2\mathbf{v}_j >= (\sigma_j/\sigma_i) < \mathbf{v}_i,\mathbf{v}_j >= (\sigma_j/\sigma_i)\delta_{ij} \end{aligned}$$

Hence, the set $\{\mathbf{u}_1,\mathbf{u}_2,\dots,\mathbf{u}_r\}$ is orthonormal. These r orthonormal vectors compose the first r columns of $\mathbf{U}$. The remaining $m - r$ columns of $\mathbf{U}$ are orthonormal vectors that form a basis for $null(\mathbf{A}\mathbf{A}^{\mathrm{H}})$, the eigenspace of $\mathbf{A}\mathbf{A}^{\mathrm{H}}$ corresponding to $\lambda = 0$.

Now the last step. Consider

$$\begin{aligned} \mathbf{U}^{\mathrm{H}}\mathbf{A}\mathbf{V} &= \mathbf{U}^{\mathrm{H}}\mathbf{A}[\mathbf{v}_1 \quad \dots \quad \mathbf{v}_r \quad \mathbf{v}_{r+1} \quad \dots \quad \mathbf{v}_n] \\ &= \mathbf{U}^{\mathrm{H}}[\mathbf{A}\mathbf{v}_1 \quad \dots \quad \mathbf{A}\mathbf{v}_r \quad \mathbf{A}\mathbf{v}_{r+1} \quad \dots \quad \mathbf{A}\mathbf{v}_n] \\ &= \mathbf{U}^{\mathrm{H}}[\sigma_1\mathbf{u}_1 \quad \dots \quad \sigma_r\mathbf{u}_r\mathbf{0} \quad \dots \quad \mathbf{0}] \\ &= [\sigma_1\mathbf{U}^{\mathrm{H}}\mathbf{u}_1 \quad \dots \quad \sigma_r\mathbf{U}^{\mathrm{H}}\mathbf{u}_r\mathbf{0} \quad \dots \quad \mathbf{0}] \\ &= [\sigma_1\mathbf{e}_1 \quad \dots \quad \sigma_r\mathbf{e}_r\mathbf{0} \quad \dots \quad \mathbf{0}] \end{aligned}$$

Clearly,

$$\mathbf{S} = [\sigma_1\mathbf{e}_1 \quad \dots \quad \sigma_r\mathbf{e}_r \quad \mathbf{0} \quad \dots \quad \mathbf{0}]$$

is the matrix given in Eq. 8.10.3, the singular-value matrix of $\mathbf{A}$.

8.10.2 MATLAB

The MATLAB command [U,S,V] = svd(A) provides $\mathbf{U}$, $\mathbf{S}$, and $\mathbf{V}$ for each $\mathbf{A}$.

PROBLEMS

PART 1

8.10.1. Find the SVD of

$$\mathbf{A} = \begin{bmatrix} 0 & 1 & 1 & 1 \\ 1 & 0 & 1 & 1 \\ 1 & 1 & 0 & 1 \\ 1 & 1 & 1 & 0 \end{bmatrix}$$

(*Hint:* The eigenvalues of $\mathbf{A}$ are $3, -1, -1, -1$.)

8.10.2. Verify the computations in Example 8.10.2.

8.10.3. Write the SVD theorems for $\mathbf{A}$ positive semidefinite and for $\mathbf{A}$ negative semidefinite.

PART 2

8.10.4. If $\mathbf{A}$ and $\mathbf{B}$ are unitarily similar (that is, $\mathbf{W}^{\mathrm{H}}\mathbf{A}\mathbf{W} = \mathbf{B}$), and $\mathbf{U}\mathbf{B}\mathbf{V}^{\mathrm{H}} = \mathbf{S}$ is the SVD of $\mathbf{B}$, find the SVD of $\mathbf{A}$ in terms of $\mathbf{U}$, $\mathbf{V}$, $\mathbf{W}$, and $\mathbf{S}$.

8.10.5. Given the SVD of the nonsingular matrix $\mathbf{A}$, find the SVD of $\mathbf{A}^{-1}$.

PART 3

8.10.6. Use the SVD theorem to write $\mathbf{A} = \mathbf{U}\mathbf{S}\mathbf{V}^{\mathrm{H}}$, and partition $\mathbf{S}$ and $\mathbf{V}$ as follows:

$$\mathbf{S} = \begin{bmatrix} \mathbf{\Sigma} & \mathbf{O} \\ \mathbf{O} & \mathbf{O} \end{bmatrix} = [\mathbf{S}_1 \quad \mathbf{O}], \qquad \mathbf{V} = [\mathbf{V}_1 \quad \mathbf{V}_2]$$

Show that $\mathbf{S}\mathbf{V}^{\mathrm{H}} = \mathbf{S}_1\mathbf{V}_1^{\mathrm{H}}$.

8.10.7. Use the result from Problem 8.10.6 to establish

$$\mathbf{A} = (\mathbf{U}\mathbf{S}_1\mathbf{U}^{\mathrm{H}})(\mathbf{U}\mathbf{V}_1^{\mathrm{H}})$$

8.10.8. Suppose $\mathbf{A}$ is $m \times n$ with $m \le n$. Set $\mathbf{P} = (\mathbf{A}\mathbf{A}^{\mathrm{H}})^{1/2}$ and show that $\mathbf{P} = \mathbf{U}\mathbf{S}_1\mathbf{U}^{\mathrm{H}}$. Set $\mathbf{W}^{\mathrm{H}} = \mathbf{U}\mathbf{V}_1^{\mathrm{H}}$ and use the result of Problem 8.10.7 to show that $\mathbf{A} = \mathbf{P}\mathbf{W}^{\mathrm{H}}$, where $\mathbf{W}$ is orthonormal and $\mathbf{P}$ is positive semidefinite. (This factorization of $\mathbf{A}$ is called the *polar decomposition theorem*.)

8.10.9. Suppose $\mathbf{A}$ is $m \times n$ with $n \le m$. Apply the result of Problem 8.10.9 to $\mathbf{A}^{\mathrm{H}}$ to deduce the existence of an orthonormal matrix $\mathbf{W}$ and a positive semidefinite matrix $\mathbf{P}$ such that $\mathbf{A} = \mathbf{W}\mathbf{P}$.

8.10.10. Use the polar decomposition theorem to prove: If $\mathbf{A}$ is simple, then there exists a positive definite matrix $\mathbf{P}$ such that $\mathbf{P}^{-1}\mathbf{A}\mathbf{P}$ is normal. Conversely, if there exists a nonsingular matrix $\mathbf{S}$ such that $\mathbf{S}^{-1}\mathbf{A}\mathbf{S}$ is normal, then there exists a positive definite matrix $\mathbf{P}$ such that $\mathbf{P}^{-1}\mathbf{A}\mathbf{P}$ is simple.

8.11 THE PSEUDO-INVERSE

It is possible to generalize the notion of *inverse* so that all matrices, singular or invertible, square or rectangular, have "generalized" inverses. Such generalized inverses have extensive applications in statistics. We present one such application,

Theorem 8.11.3, in Section 8.11.1. We begin with the fundamental existence and uniqueness theorem.

Theorem 8.11.1. *For each $m \times n$ matrix* $\mathbf{A}$, *there exists a unique $n \times m$ matrix* $\mathbf{A}^-$ *satisfying the four properties*

$$\begin{array}{llll} (1) & \mathbf{A}^-\mathbf{A}\mathbf{A}^- = \mathbf{A}^- & (2) & \mathbf{A}\mathbf{A}^-\mathbf{A} = \mathbf{A} \\ (3) & (\mathbf{A}^-\mathbf{A})^{\mathrm{H}} = \mathbf{A}^-\mathbf{A} & (4) & (\mathbf{A}\mathbf{A}^-)^{\mathrm{H}} = \mathbf{A}\mathbf{A}^- \end{array} \tag{8.11.1}$$

Proof. We prove uniqueness first. Suppose $\mathbf{A}^\#$ satisfies the four parts of Eq. 8.11.1. Then, from property (2),

$$\mathbf{A}\mathbf{A}^\# = (\mathbf{A}\mathbf{A}^-\mathbf{A})\mathbf{A}^\# = (\mathbf{A}\mathbf{A}^-)(\mathbf{A}\mathbf{A}^\#)$$

From this equation, and since $\mathbf{A}\mathbf{A}^-$ and $\mathbf{A}\mathbf{A}^\#$ are hermitian by property (4),

$$\begin{aligned} \mathbf{A}\mathbf{A}^\# &= \left((\mathbf{A}\mathbf{A}^-)(\mathbf{A}\mathbf{A}^\#)\right)^{\mathrm{H}} = (\mathbf{A}\mathbf{A}^\#)^{\mathrm{H}}(\mathbf{A}\mathbf{A}^-)^{\mathrm{H}} = (\mathbf{A}\mathbf{A}^\#)(\mathbf{A}\mathbf{A}^-) \\ &= (\mathbf{A}\mathbf{A}^\#\mathbf{A})\mathbf{A}^- = \mathbf{A}\mathbf{A}^- \end{aligned}$$

Similarly, $\mathbf{A}^\#\mathbf{A} = \mathbf{A}^-\mathbf{A}$. Now multiply $\mathbf{A}\mathbf{A}^\# = \mathbf{A}\mathbf{A}^-$ on the left by $\mathbf{A}^\#$ to obtain

$$\mathbf{A}^\# = \mathbf{A}^\#\mathbf{A}\mathbf{A}^\# = \mathbf{A}^\#\mathbf{A}\mathbf{A}^-$$

by property (1). Next multiply $\mathbf{A}^\#\mathbf{A} = \mathbf{A}^-\mathbf{A}$ on the right by $\mathbf{A}^-$ to obtain

$$\mathbf{A}^\#\mathbf{A}\mathbf{A}^- = \mathbf{A}^-\mathbf{A}\mathbf{A}^- = \mathbf{A}^-$$

and this proves that $\mathbf{A}^\# = \mathbf{A}^-$.

Now the existence proof. We construct $\mathbf{A}^-$ in steps. First, recall the SVD theorem (see Section 8.10 and Eq. 8.10.3), which asserts that for each $m \times n$ $\mathbf{A}$, there exist unitary matrices $\mathbf{U}$ and $\mathbf{V}$ and a singular-value matrix $\mathbf{S}$ such that $\mathbf{A} = \mathbf{U}\mathbf{S}\mathbf{V}^{\mathrm{H}}$. In this decomposition theorem, $\mathbf{S}$ is $m \times n$ and is given by

$$\mathbf{S} = \begin{bmatrix} \boldsymbol{\Sigma} & \mathbf{O} \\ \mathbf{O} & \mathbf{O} \end{bmatrix} = \begin{bmatrix} \sigma_1 & & & & & \mathbf{O} \\ & \sigma_2 & & & & \\ & & \ddots & & & \\ & & & \sigma_r & & \\ & & & & 0 & \\ \mathbf{O} & & & & & \ddots \end{bmatrix}_{m\times n} \tag{8.11.2}$$

Define

$$\mathbf{S}^- = \begin{bmatrix} \boldsymbol{\Sigma}^{-1} & \mathbf{O} \\ \mathbf{O} & \mathbf{O} \end{bmatrix} = \begin{bmatrix} \sigma_1^{-1} & & & & & & \mathbf{O} \\ & \sigma_2^{-1} & & & & & \\ & & \ddots & & & & \\ & & & \sigma_r^{-1} & & & \\ & & & & 0 & & \\ & & & & & 0 & \\ \mathbf{O} & & & & & & \ddots \end{bmatrix}_{n\times m} \tag{8.11.3}$$

It is easy to show that $\mathbf{S}^-$ satisfies the four properties of Eq. 8.11.1. By means of $\mathbf{S}^-$ and the SVD theorem, we can now construct $\mathbf{A}^-$ for every $\mathbf{A}$:

$$\mathbf{A}^- = \mathbf{V}\mathbf{S}^-\mathbf{U}^{\mathrm{H}} \tag{8.11.4}$$

We now prove that $\mathbf{V}\mathbf{S}^-\mathbf{U}^{\mathrm{H}}$ satisfies properties (2) and (3) of Eq. 8.11.1; proofs of (1) and (4) are similar and are left for the exercises. To prove (2), recall that $\mathbf{S}\mathbf{S}^-\mathbf{S} = \mathbf{S}$.

$$\mathbf{A}\mathbf{A}^-\mathbf{A} = (\mathbf{U}\mathbf{S}\mathbf{V}^{\mathrm{H}})(\mathbf{V}\mathbf{S}^-\mathbf{U}^{\mathrm{H}})(\mathbf{U}\mathbf{S}\mathbf{V}^{\mathrm{H}}) = \mathbf{U}(\mathbf{S}\mathbf{S}^-\mathbf{S})\mathbf{V}^{\mathrm{H}} = \mathbf{U}\mathbf{S}\mathbf{V}^{\mathrm{H}} = \mathbf{A}$$

For property (3), we use $(\mathbf{S}^-\mathbf{S})^{\mathrm{H}} = \mathbf{S}^-\mathbf{S}$ and $\mathbf{A}^-\mathbf{A} = \mathbf{V}\mathbf{S}^-\mathbf{S}\mathbf{V}^{\mathrm{H}}$:

$$\begin{aligned}(\mathbf{A}^-\mathbf{A})^{\mathrm{H}} &= (\mathbf{V}\mathbf{S}^-\mathbf{U}^{\mathrm{H}}\mathbf{U}\mathbf{S}\mathbf{V}^{\mathrm{H}})^{\mathrm{H}} = (\mathbf{V}\mathbf{S}^-\mathbf{S}\mathbf{V}^{\mathrm{H}})^{\mathrm{H}} \\ &= \mathbf{V}(\mathbf{S}^-\mathbf{S})^{\mathrm{H}}\mathbf{V}^{\mathrm{H}} = \mathbf{V}\mathbf{S}^-\mathbf{S}\mathbf{V}^{\mathrm{H}} = \mathbf{A}^-\mathbf{A} \quad \blacksquare\end{aligned}$$

We call the matrix $\mathbf{A}^-$ the *p-inverse* of $\mathbf{A}$, short for pseudo-inverse. The p-inverse is often called the *generalized* or the *Moore-Penrose inverse* of $\mathbf{A}$.

It is sometimes convenient to rewrite Eq. 8.11.4 in the form

$$\mathbf{V}^{\mathrm{H}}\mathbf{A}^-\mathbf{U} = \mathbf{S}^- \tag{8.11.5}$$

which follows from the fact that $\mathbf{U}$ and $\mathbf{V}$ are unitary.

Although it is always possible to find $\mathbf{A}^-$ from Eq. 8.11.4, it is often more expedient to use various properties of the p-inverse to aid in its discovery. The following corollaries and examples illustrate this point. Note that the proofs of the corollaries are based on Theorem 8.11.1 and not on the construction given in Eq. 8.11.4.

Corollary 1. (*a*) *If* $\mathbf{A}$ *is invertible, then* $\mathbf{A}^{-1} = \mathbf{A}^-$. (*b*) *If* $\mathbf{A}$ *has a right inverse* $\mathbf{B}$ (*that is,* $\mathbf{AB} = \mathbf{I}_m$), *then* $\mathbf{A}^- = \mathbf{B}$. (*c*) *If* $\mathbf{A}$ *has a left inverse* $\mathbf{C}$ (*that is,* $\mathbf{CA} = \mathbf{I}_n$), *then* $\mathbf{A}^- = \mathbf{C}$.

Proof. Consider (*b*). We verify properties (1) and (4) of Eq. 8.11.1:

$$\mathbf{A}^-\mathbf{A}\mathbf{A}^- = \mathbf{BAB} = \mathbf{BI} = \mathbf{B} = \mathbf{A}^-$$

and

$$(\mathbf{A}^-\mathbf{A})^{\mathrm{H}} = (\mathbf{CA})^{\mathrm{H}} - \mathbf{I}_n^{\mathrm{H}} = \mathbf{I}_n = (\mathbf{A}^-\mathbf{A})$$

The remaining arguments are essentially the same. ■

Corollary 2. $(\mathbf{A}^{\mathrm{H}})^- = (\mathbf{A}^-)^{\mathrm{H}}$ *and* $(\mathbf{A}^{\mathrm{T}})^- = (\mathbf{A}^-)^{\mathrm{T}}$. ■

Proof. Here again we illustrate the arguments by selecting only property (2) in Eq. 8.11.1:

$$\mathbf{A}^{\mathrm{H}}(\mathbf{A}^-)^{\mathrm{H}}\mathbf{A}^{\mathrm{H}} = (\mathbf{A}\mathbf{A}^-\mathbf{A})^{\mathrm{H}} = \mathbf{A}^{\mathrm{H}}; \qquad \mathbf{A}^{\mathrm{T}}(\mathbf{A}^-)^{\mathrm{T}}\mathbf{A}^{\mathrm{T}} = (\mathbf{A}\mathbf{A}^-\mathbf{A})^{\mathrm{T}} = \mathbf{A}^{\mathrm{T}} \quad \blacksquare$$

Corollary 3. (*a*) *If* $\mathbf{A}$ *has full column rank, then* $\mathbf{A}^- = (\mathbf{A}^{\mathrm{H}}\mathbf{A})^{-1}\mathbf{A}^{\mathrm{H}}$. (*b*) *If* $\mathbf{A}$ *has full row rank, then* $\mathbf{A}^- = \mathbf{A}^{\mathrm{H}}(\mathbf{A}\mathbf{A}^{\mathrm{H}})^{-1}$.

Proof. For *(a)* we observe that $\mathbf{A}^H\mathbf{A}$ is invertible, so that $(\mathbf{A}^H\mathbf{A})^{-1}\mathbf{A}^H$ is defined. Now for property (1) of Eq. 8.11.1:

$$\left((\mathbf{A}^H\mathbf{A})^{-1}\mathbf{A}^H\right)\mathbf{A}\left((\mathbf{A}^H\mathbf{A})^{-1}\mathbf{A}^H\right) = (\mathbf{A}^H\mathbf{A})^{-1}(\mathbf{A}^H\mathbf{A})(\mathbf{A}^H\mathbf{A})^{-1}\mathbf{A}^H = (\mathbf{A}^H\mathbf{A})^{-1}\mathbf{A}^H$$

Property (3) is equally easy because $\mathbf{A}^-\mathbf{A} = (\mathbf{A}^H\mathbf{A})^{-1}(\mathbf{A}^H\mathbf{A}) = \mathbf{I}$. Again, the proofs of the remaining properties are left for the exercises.

Now suppose that $\mathbf{A}$ has complete row rank. Then $\mathbf{A}^H$ has full column rank, and therefore, from *(a)* with $\mathbf{A}^H$ in place of $\mathbf{A}$,

$$(\mathbf{A}^H)^- = (\mathbf{A}\mathbf{A}^H)^{-1}\mathbf{A}$$

The argument is completed by using Corollary 2, $(\mathbf{A}^H)^- = (\mathbf{A}^-)^H$:

$$(\mathbf{A}^-)^H = (\mathbf{A}^H) = (\mathbf{A}\mathbf{A}^H)^{-1}\mathbf{A}$$

which implies $\mathbf{A}^- = \mathbf{A}^H(\mathbf{A}\mathbf{A}^H)^{-1}$. ∎

Example 8.11.1. Let $\mathbf{x} \neq \mathbf{0} \in \mathcal{R}^n$. Find the p-inverses of $\mathbf{x}$ and $\mathbf{x}^T$.

Solution. We find $\mathbf{x}^-$ by two methods—first, by using Eq. 8.11.4 and the work in Example 8.10.3. From Example 8.10.3,

$$\mathbf{V} = [1], \qquad \mathbf{S} = [\|\mathbf{x}\| \;\; 0 \;\; \dots \;\; 0]^T, \qquad \mathbf{U} = [\mathbf{x}/\|\mathbf{x}\| \;\; \mathbf{u}_2 \;\; \dots \;\; \mathbf{u}_n]$$

So,

$$\mathbf{x}^- = [1]\mathbf{S}^-\mathbf{U}^T = [\|\mathbf{x}\|^{-1} \;\; 0 \;\; \dots \;\; 0]\begin{bmatrix} \mathbf{x}^T/\|\mathbf{x}\| \\ \mathbf{u}_2^T \\ \vdots \\ \mathbf{u}_n^T \end{bmatrix} = \mathbf{x}^T/\|\mathbf{x}\|^2$$

Thus, $\mathbf{x}^- = \mathbf{x}^T/\|\mathbf{x}\|^2$. (Had we been able to guess this conclusion, we would prove it by checking Eq. 8.11.1.)

The second method makes use of the fact that $\mathbf{x}$ has full column rank. By Corollary 3*(a)*, $\mathbf{x}^- = (\mathbf{x}^T\mathbf{x})^{-1}\mathbf{x}^T = \|\mathbf{x}\|^{-2}\mathbf{x}^T$.

Since $\mathbf{x}^T$ has full row rank, and $\|\mathbf{x}^T\| = \|\mathbf{x}\|$, it follows from Corollary 3*(b)*, that $(\mathbf{x}^T)^- = \|\mathbf{x}\|^{-2}\mathbf{x}$.

We now return to the statement and proofs of further corollaries to Theorem 8.11.1.

Corollary 4. $(\mathbf{A}^-)^- = \mathbf{A}$.

Proof. $\mathbf{A}$ and $\mathbf{A}^-$ are interchangeable in Eq. 8.11.1. ∎

Corollary 5. $\mathbf{A}^- = \mathbf{O}$ *if and only if* $\mathbf{A} = \mathbf{O}^T$.

In view of the fact that $\mathbf{A}^-$ is a generalization of $\mathbf{A}^{-1}$, one might hope for a connection between $(\mathbf{AB})^-$ and $\mathbf{B}^-\mathbf{A}^-$. Unfortunately, it is not true in every case that $(\mathbf{AB})^- = \mathbf{B}^-\mathbf{A}^-$. Here is a counterexample:

$$\left(\begin{bmatrix} 1 & 1 \\ 1 & 1 \end{bmatrix}\begin{bmatrix} 1 & 1 \\ -1 & -1 \end{bmatrix}\right)^{-} = \begin{bmatrix} 0 & 0 \\ 0 & 0 \end{bmatrix}^{-} = \mathbf{O}$$

by Corollary 5. On the other hand,

$$\left(\begin{bmatrix} 1 & 1 \\ -1 & -1 \end{bmatrix}\begin{bmatrix} 1 & 1 \\ 1 & 1 \end{bmatrix}\right)^{-} = \begin{bmatrix} 2 & 2 \\ -2 & -2 \end{bmatrix}^{-} \neq \mathbf{O}$$

also by Corollary 5. The following result is the best we choose to do.

Corollary 6. *If* $\mathbf{B}$ *is* $m \times r$ *and* $\mathbf{C}$ *is* $r \times n$ *and* $\operatorname{rank}(\mathbf{B}) = \operatorname{rank}(\mathbf{C}) = r$, *then*

$$(\mathbf{BC})^{-} = \mathbf{C}^{-}\mathbf{B}^{-}$$

Proof. Since $\mathbf{B}$ has a left inverse and $\mathbf{C}$ has a right inverse, these inverses are $\mathbf{B}^{-}$ and $\mathbf{C}^{-}$, respectively (Corollary 1(*b*) and (*c*)). So $\mathbf{B}^{-}\mathbf{B} = \mathbf{I}_r$ and $\mathbf{CC}^{-} = \mathbf{I}_r$. Now verify properties (1)–(4) in Eq. 8.11.1. ∎

Example 8.11.2. Show that $(a\mathbf{A})^{-} = a^{-1}(\mathbf{A}^{-})$.

Solution. The easiest proof is simply to verify that $a^{-1}(\mathbf{A}^{-})$ satisfies the four properties defining the p-inverse of $a\mathbf{A}$.

Example 8.11.3. Let $\mathbf{X}$ and $\mathbf{Y}$ be $m \times m$ and $n \times n$ unitary matrices, respectively. Show that $(\mathbf{XAY})^{-} = \mathbf{Y}^{\mathrm{H}}\mathbf{A}^{-}\mathbf{X}^{\mathrm{H}}$.

Solution. Note that

$$(\mathbf{XAY})\mathbf{Y}^{\mathrm{H}}\mathbf{A}^{-}\mathbf{X}^{\mathrm{H}}(\mathbf{XAY}) = \mathbf{X}(\mathbf{AA}^{-}\mathbf{A})\mathbf{Y} = \mathbf{XAY}$$

This establishes property (2) in Eq. 8.11.1. The rest are equally straightforward.

Example 8.11.4. Find $(\mathbf{uv}^{\mathrm{T}})^{-}$, where $\mathbf{u}^{\mathrm{T}}\mathbf{v} \neq 0$ and $\mathbf{u}, \mathbf{v}^{\mathrm{T}} \in \mathcal{R}^n$, $n > 1$.

Solution. The matrix $\mathbf{uv}^{\mathrm{T}}$ is $n \times n$ and has rank 1, so none of our previous examples or corollaries is applicable. (But see Example 8.11.5.) We resort, therefore, to Eq. 8.11.4 and the work in Example 8.10.3:

$$\mathbf{uv}^{\mathrm{T}} = [\mathbf{u}/\|\mathbf{u}\| \quad \mathbf{u}_2 \quad \ldots \quad \mathbf{u}_n]\begin{bmatrix} \|\mathbf{u}\|\,\|\mathbf{v}\| & \mathbf{O} \\ \mathbf{0} & \mathbf{O} \end{bmatrix}[\mathbf{v}/\|\mathbf{v}\| \quad \mathbf{v}_2 \quad \ldots \quad \mathbf{v}_n]^{\mathrm{T}}$$

From Example 8.11.3 it follows that

$$\begin{aligned}(\mathbf{uv}^{\mathrm{T}})^{-} &= [\mathbf{v}/\|\mathbf{v}\| \quad \mathbf{v}_2 \quad \ldots \quad \mathbf{v}_n]\begin{bmatrix} \|\mathbf{u}\|\,\|\mathbf{v}\| & \mathbf{O} \\ \mathbf{0} & \mathbf{O} \end{bmatrix}^{-}[\mathbf{u}/\|\mathbf{u}\| \quad \mathbf{u}_2 \quad \ldots \quad \mathbf{u}_n]^{\mathrm{T}} \\ &= [\mathbf{v}/\|\mathbf{v}\| \quad \mathbf{v}_2 \quad \ldots \quad \mathbf{v}_n]\begin{bmatrix} \|\mathbf{u}\|^{-1}\|\mathbf{v}\|^{-1} & \mathbf{O} \\ \mathbf{0} & \mathbf{O} \end{bmatrix}[\mathbf{u}/\|\mathbf{u}\| \quad \mathbf{u}_2 \quad \ldots \quad \mathbf{u}_n]^{\mathrm{T}} \\ &= [\mathbf{v}/\|\mathbf{v}\| \quad \mathbf{v}_2 \quad \ldots \quad \mathbf{v}_n]\begin{bmatrix} \mathbf{u}^{\mathrm{T}} \\ \mathbf{0} \end{bmatrix}\|\mathbf{u}\|^{-2}\|\mathbf{v}\|^{-1} = (\mathbf{vu}^{\mathrm{T}})\|\mathbf{u}\|^{-2}\|\mathbf{v}\|^{-2}\end{aligned}$$

We leave as an exercise to verify that

$$(\mathbf{uv}^{\mathrm{T}})^{-} = (\mathbf{vu}^{\mathrm{T}})\|\mathbf{u}\|^{-2}\|\mathbf{v}\|^{-2}$$

by verifying properties (1)–(4) of Theorem 8.11.1.

Setting $\mathbf{u} = \mathbf{v}$ in Example 8.11.4 leads to $(\mathbf{uu}^{\mathrm{T}})^{-} = (\mathbf{uu}^{\mathrm{T}})\|\mathbf{u}\|^{-4}$. In particular, $\mathbf{u} = \mathbf{1}$ leads to $\mathbf{J}_n^{-} = \mathbf{J}_n/n^2$.

Theorem 8.11.2.

(*a*) *If* $\mathbf{A}$ *is normal,* $\mathbf{A}^{-}$ *is normal.*
(*b*) *If* $\mathbf{A}$ *is symmetric,* $\mathbf{A}^{-}$ *is symmetric.*
(*c*) *If* $\mathbf{A}$ *has rank* r, $\mathbf{A}^{-}$ *has rank* r.

Proof. Consider (*a*). By hypothesis $\mathbf{A}$ is normal, so there exists a unitary matrix $\mathbf{U}$ such that $\mathbf{A} = \mathbf{U\Lambda U}^{\mathrm{H}}$. Hence, from Example 8.11.3, $\mathbf{A}^{-} = \mathbf{U\Lambda}^{-}\mathbf{U}^{\mathrm{H}}$. That is, $\mathbf{U}^{\mathrm{H}}\mathbf{A}^{-}\mathbf{U} = \mathbf{\Lambda}^{-}$ shows that $\mathbf{A}^{-}$ is normal. Part (*c*) follows because

$$\operatorname{rank}(\mathbf{A}^{-}) = \operatorname{rank}(\mathbf{US}^{-}\mathbf{U}^{\mathrm{H}}) = \operatorname{rank}(\mathbf{S}^{-}) = \operatorname{rank}(\mathbf{S}) = \operatorname{rank}(\mathbf{A})$$

Part (*b*) is left for the exercises. ■

Example 8.11.5. If $\mathbf{P}$ is a projector, show that $\mathbf{P}^{-} = \mathbf{P}$. (In this chapter, projectors are hermitian matrices such that $\mathbf{P}^2 = \mathbf{P}$.)

Solution. We easily see that $\mathbf{P}^{-}\mathbf{P}\mathbf{P}^{-} = \mathbf{P}^3 = \mathbf{P} = \mathbf{P}^{-}$ and $\mathbf{P}\mathbf{P}^{-}\mathbf{P} = \mathbf{P}^3 = \mathbf{P}$. Clearly, $\mathbf{P}^{-}\mathbf{P} = \mathbf{P}\mathbf{P}^{-} = \mathbf{P}^2 = \mathbf{P}$ completes the verification of Eq. 8.11.1. Since $(\mathbf{uu}^{\mathrm{H}})/\|\mathbf{u}\|^2$ is a projector (why?), $\left((\mathbf{uu}^{\mathrm{H}})/\|\mathbf{u}\|^2\right) = (\mathbf{uu}^{\mathrm{H}})/\|\mathbf{u}\|^2$.

8.11.1 The Solution of $\mathbf{Ax} = \mathbf{b}$

Perhaps the most remarkable theorem in this chapter is the result we are about to state and prove. It is not too much of an exaggeration to assert that this theorem by itself would justify the study of the p-inverse.

Theorem 8.11.3. *For every* $m \times n$ $\mathbf{A}$ *and every* $\mathbf{b} \in \mathscr{C}^n$, *the vector* $\mathbf{x}_m = \mathbf{A}^{-}\mathbf{b}$ *is the least squares solution of* $\mathbf{Ax} = \mathbf{b}$ *having least norm.*

Remarks. (1) *If* $\mathbf{Ax} = \mathbf{b}$ is consistent, then all solutions are least squares solutions in the sense that $\|\mathbf{Ax} - \mathbf{b}\| = 0$. In this case the theorem asserts that $\mathbf{x}_m = \mathbf{A}^{-}\mathbf{b}$ is a solution and is one with least norm. If $\mathbf{Ax} = \mathbf{b}$ has a unique solution, then $\mathbf{A}^{-1}$ exists, and $\mathbf{x}_m = \mathbf{A}^{-}\mathbf{b} = \mathbf{A}^{-1}\mathbf{b}$ makes the conclusion trivial.

(2) The proof is most easily presented by first establishing two lemmas. We do this now.

Lemma 8.5. *The matrix* $\mathbf{P} = \mathbf{AA}^{-}$ *is a projector into* $col(\mathbf{A})$.

Proof. By property (1) of Eq. 8.11.1, $(\mathbf{AA}^-)^2 = \mathbf{AA}^-$ because

$$(\mathbf{AA}^-)^2 = (\mathbf{AA}^-)(\mathbf{AA}^-) = \mathbf{A}(\mathbf{A}^-\mathbf{AA}^-) = \mathbf{AA}^-$$

By property (4) $\mathbf{AA}^-$ is hermitian, and finally, $\mathbf{A}(\mathbf{A}^-\mathbf{b}) \in col(\mathbf{A})$. So $\mathbf{AA}^-$ is a projector[4] into $col(\mathbf{A})$. ∎

Lemma 8.6. *If* $\mathbf{x} \in col(\mathbf{A}^-)$, *then* $\mathbf{x} \in col(\mathbf{A}^H)$.

Proof. Because $\mathbf{x} \in col(\mathbf{A}^-)$, there exists $\mathbf{y}$ such that $\mathbf{A}^-\mathbf{y} = \mathbf{x}$. Hence, by properties (1) and (3) in Eq. 8.11.1,

$$\mathbf{x} = \mathbf{A}^-\mathbf{y} = \mathbf{A}^-\mathbf{AA}^-\mathbf{y} = (\mathbf{A}^-\mathbf{A})^H\mathbf{A}^-\mathbf{y} = \mathbf{A}^H\left((\mathbf{A}^-)^H\mathbf{A}^-\mathbf{y}\right)$$

This shows that $\mathbf{x} \in col(\mathbf{A}^H)$. ∎

We now move to the proof of the theorem. The argument depends on Theorem 4.8.3: If $\mathbf{P}$ is a projector into $col(\mathbf{A})$, then $\|\mathbf{Pb}-\mathbf{b}\| \le \|\mathbf{Ax}_0-\mathbf{b}\|$ for every $\mathbf{x}_0$. Since Lemma 8.5 establishes the fact that $\mathbf{P} = \mathbf{AA}^-$ is a projector into $col(\mathbf{A})$, we have, from Theorem 4.8.3,

$$\|\mathbf{AA}^-\mathbf{b} - \mathbf{b}\| = \|\mathbf{Ax}_m - \mathbf{b}\| \le \|\mathbf{Ax}_0 - \mathbf{b}\|$$

and $\mathbf{x}_m = \mathbf{A}^-\mathbf{b}$ is indeed a least squares solution. We now prove that

$$\|\mathbf{Ax}_m - \mathbf{b}\| = \|\mathbf{Ax}_0 - \mathbf{b}\| \tag{8.11.6}$$

implies that $\|\mathbf{x}_m\| \le \|\mathbf{x}_0\|$. Consider the following:

$$\begin{aligned}\|\mathbf{Ax}_0 - \mathbf{b}\|^2 &= \|\mathbf{Ax}_m - \mathbf{b}\|^2 = \|\mathbf{Ax}_m - \mathbf{Ax}_0 + \mathbf{Ax}_0 - \mathbf{b}\|^2 \\ &\le \|\mathbf{Ax}_m - \mathbf{Ax}_0\|^2 + \|\mathbf{Ax}_0 - \mathbf{b}\|^2\end{aligned}$$

which is possible if and only if $\|\mathbf{Ax}_m-\mathbf{Ax}_0\|^2 = 0$. Thus, we have $\mathbf{A}(\mathbf{x}_m-\mathbf{x}_0) = \mathbf{0}$. Hence, $\mathbf{x}_m - \mathbf{x}_0$ is orthogonal to every vector in $\mathbf{A}^H$. Now, $\mathbf{x}_m = \mathbf{A}^-\mathbf{b}$ means that $\mathbf{x}_m \in col(\mathbf{A}^-)$, and by Lemma 8.6, $\mathbf{x}_m \in col(\mathbf{A}^H)$. Hence, $\mathbf{x}_m$ is orthogonal to $\mathbf{x}_m - \mathbf{x}_0$. By the Pythagorean theorem,

$$\|\mathbf{x}_0\|^2 = \|\mathbf{x}_m - (\mathbf{x}_m - \mathbf{x}_0)\|^2 = \|\mathbf{x}_m\|^2 + \|(\mathbf{x}_m - \mathbf{x}_0)\|^2 > \|\mathbf{x}_m\|^2 \ \blacksquare$$

If $\mathbf{A}$ is real and has full column rank, then $\mathbf{A}^- = (\mathbf{A}^T\mathbf{A})^{-1}\mathbf{A}^T$ by Corollary 3. So the normal equations $\mathbf{A}^T\mathbf{Ax} = \mathbf{A}^T\mathbf{b}$ (see Section 4.9) have the solution $\mathbf{x} = \mathbf{A}^-\mathbf{b}$ because

$$\mathbf{A}^T\mathbf{Ax} = \mathbf{A}^T\mathbf{A}(\mathbf{A}^-\mathbf{b}) = \mathbf{A}^T\mathbf{A}(\mathbf{A}^T\mathbf{A})^{-1}\mathbf{A}^T\mathbf{b} = \mathbf{A}^T\mathbf{b}$$

---

[4]The definition of projector in Chapter 4 assumes that $\mathbf{P}$ is real and symmetric. However, Theorem 4.8.3 holds for $\mathbf{P}$ hermitian as well.

Moreover, if $\mathbf{c}$ is another solution, then $\mathbf{A}^T\mathbf{A}\mathbf{c} = \mathbf{A}^T\mathbf{b}$, and hence

$$\mathbf{c} = (\mathbf{A}^T\mathbf{A})^{-1}\mathbf{A}^T\mathbf{b} = \mathbf{A}^-\mathbf{b}$$

Thus, $\mathbf{A}^-\mathbf{b}$ is the unique solution.

Note also that $\mathbf{P} = \mathbf{A}\mathbf{A}^- = \mathbf{A}(\mathbf{A}^T\mathbf{A})^{-1}\mathbf{A}^T$, which is precisely the projector presented in Theorem 4.9.3(*a*). So, as an illustration of Theorem 8.11.3, we choose an $\mathbf{A}$ that has neither full row nor full column rank.

Example 8.11.6. For $\mathbf{A} = \mathbf{J}_4$, find the least squares solutions of the following systems for $\mathbf{J}_4\mathbf{x} = \mathbf{b}$:

(*a*) $\mathbf{b} = \mathbf{1}_4$ (*b*) $\mathbf{b} = \mathbf{e}_1$

Solution. From Example 8.11.4, with $\mathbf{u} = \mathbf{v} = \mathbf{1}_4$, $\mathbf{J}_4^- = \mathbf{J}_4/4^2$. So for Part (*a*) we have $\mathbf{J}_4^-\mathbf{1}_4 = \mathbf{1}_4/4$, and hence $\|\mathbf{J}_4^-\mathbf{1}_4 - \mathbf{1}_4\| = \frac{3}{4}\|\mathbf{1}_4\| = \frac{3}{2}$. For Part (*b*) $\mathbf{J}_4^-\mathbf{e}_1 = \mathbf{1}_4/16$, and hence

$$\|\mathbf{J}_4^-\mathbf{e}_1 - \mathbf{e}_1\| = \|\mathbf{1}_4/16 - \mathbf{e}_1\| = \frac{\sqrt{57}}{8}$$

8.11.2 MATLAB and the Pseudo-Inverse

The MATLAB command pinv(A) returns $\mathbf{A}^-$. Indeed, pinv(A) is computed by finding the SVD of $\mathbf{A}$.

Example 8.11.7. Let

$$\mathbf{A} = \begin{bmatrix} 1 & 1 & 1 \\ 1 & 1 & 1 \\ 1 & 1 & 1 \\ 1 & 1 & 1 \end{bmatrix}$$

and use pinv(A) to find $\mathbf{A}^-$. Compute:

(*a*) $\mathbf{A}^-\mathbf{1}_4$ and $\|\mathbf{A}^-\mathbf{1}_4\|$.
(*b*) A\ ones(4,1) and norm(A\ ones(4,1),'fro')
(*c*) $\|\mathbf{A}(\mathbf{A}^-\mathbf{1}_4) - \mathbf{1}_4\|$ and norm(A*(A\ ones(4,1)) − ones(4,1),'fro')

Solution. We enter ones(4,3) for $\mathbf{A}$. Then

```
pA = pinv(ones(4, 3))
ans =
     0.0833  0.0833  0.0833  0.0833
     0.0833  0.0833  0.0833  0.0833
     0.0833  0.0833  0.0833  0.0833
```

(*a*) xm = pA*ones(4,1)

```
xm =
      0.3333
      0.3333
      0.3333
```

nxm = norm(xm,'fro')

```
nxm =
      0.5774
```

(*b*) ym = A\ ones(4,1)

```
ym =
      1.0000
      0.0000
      0.0000
```

nym = norm(ym,'fro')

```
nym
      1.0000
```

(Note that xm and ym are solutions of A*x = ones(4,1), but that the norm of xm is smaller than the norm of ym.)

(*c*) Both norms are zero. (Why?)

Example 8.11.8. Let

$$\mathbf{A} = \begin{bmatrix} 1 & 1 & 1 \\ 1 & 1 & 1 \\ 1 & 1 & 1 \\ 1 & 1 & 1 \end{bmatrix}$$

and e1 = [1 0 0 0]'. Compute:

(*a*) $\mathbf{A}^{-}\mathbf{e}_1$ and $\|\mathbf{A}^{-}\mathbf{e}_1\|$

(*b*) A\ e1 and norm(A\ e1,'fro')

(*c*) $\|\mathbf{A}(\mathbf{A}^{-}\mathbf{e}_1) - \mathbf{e}_1\|$ and norm(A*(A\ e1)) − e1,'fro')

Solution. We define pA = pinv(A), so that

(*a*) xm = pA*e1

```
xm =
      0.0833
      0.0833
      0.0833
```

nxm = norm(xm,'fro')

```
nxm =
      0.1443
```

(*b*) ym = pA\ e1

```
ym =
      0.2500
      0.0000
      0.0000
```

nym = norm(ym,'fro')

```
nym
      0.2500
```

(*c*) norm(A*xm-e1,'fro')

```
ans =
      0.8660
```

norm(A*ym-e1,'fro')

```
ans =
      0.8660
```

Thus, the norms of the residuals $\|\mathbf{Ax} - \mathbf{b}\|$ are the same, but pin(A)*e1 has smaller norm than A\ e1.

PROBLEMS

PART 1

8.11.1. If

$$\mathbf{S} = \begin{bmatrix} \boldsymbol{\Sigma} & \mathbf{O} \\ \mathbf{O} & \mathbf{O} \end{bmatrix}$$

show that

$$\mathbf{S}^{-} = \begin{bmatrix} \boldsymbol{\Sigma}^{-1} & \mathbf{O} \\ \mathbf{O} & \mathbf{O} \end{bmatrix}$$

8.11.2. Show that

$$\begin{bmatrix} \mathbf{A} \\ \mathbf{O} \end{bmatrix}^{-} = [\mathbf{A}^{-} \quad \mathbf{O}]$$

8.11.3. Complete the proof of Corollary 1 for the left and right inverses of $\mathbf{A}$.

8.11.4. Complete the proof of Corollary 2 by verifying properties (1), (3), and (4) of Eq. 8.11.1 for the p-inverses of $\mathbf{A}^{\mathrm{H}}$ and $\mathbf{A}^{\mathrm{T}}$.

8.11.5. Complete the proof of Corollary 3 for $\mathbf{A}$ with full column rank and for $\mathbf{A}$ with full row rank.

8.11.6. Complete the proof of Corollary 6.

8.11.7. Verify $\mathbf{x}^{-} = \mathbf{x}^{\mathrm{T}}/\|\mathbf{x}\|^2$, $\mathbf{x} \neq \mathbf{0} \in \mathcal{R}^n$, by using Theorem 8.11.1.

8.11.8. Verify $(a\mathbf{A})^{-} = a^{-1}\mathbf{A}^{-}$ by using Theorem 8.11.1.

8.11.9. Verify $(\mathbf{uv}^{\mathrm{T}})^{-} = (\mathbf{vu}^{\mathrm{T}})/\|\mathbf{u}\|^2\|\mathbf{v}\|^2$ $(\mathbf{u}, \mathbf{v} \neq \mathbf{0} \in \mathcal{R}^n)$ by using Theorem 8.11.1.

8.11.10. Verify $\mathbf{J}_n^{-} = \mathbf{J}_n/n^2$ by using Theorem 8.11.1.

8.11.11. Find $\mathbf{J}_{m\times n}^{-}$.

8.11.12. Complete the verification of properties (1), (3), and (4) of Eq. 8.11.1 for $(\mathbf{XAY})^{-} = \mathbf{Y}^{\mathrm{H}}\mathbf{A}^{-}\mathbf{X}^{\mathrm{H}}$, where $\mathbf{X}$ and $\mathbf{Y}$ are unitary. (See Example 8.11.4.)

8.11.13. If $\mathbf{A}$ is normal, show that for each positive integer k, $(\mathbf{A}^k)^{-} = (\mathbf{A}^{-})^k$.

8.11.14. Complete the proofs of Examples 8.11.2 and 8.11.4.

8.11.15. Complete the proof of Theorem 8.11.2.

8.11.16. Write the general solution $\mathbf{x}_g$ of the system $\mathbf{J}_{3\times 4}\mathbf{x} = \mathbf{1}_4$ as a function of three parameters. Find $\min\|\mathbf{x}_g\|^2$ by calculus and verify that $\min\|\mathbf{x}_g\|^2 = 0.5774$.

PART 2

8.11.17. Prove: If $\mathbf{A}$ is symmetric, so is $\mathbf{A}^{-}$.

8.11.18. Prove: $col(\mathbf{A}^{-}) = col(\mathbf{A}^{\mathrm{H}})$. (*Hint:* Review the proof of Lemma 8.7.)

8.11.19. Prove: If $\mathbf{A}$ is unitarily similar to $\mathbf{B}$, then $\mathbf{A}^{-}$ is unitarily similar to $\mathbf{B}^{-}$.

8.11.20. Suppose $\mathbf{A} = \mathbf{QR}$ is the $\mathbf{QR}$ factorization of the real matrix $\mathbf{A}$. (See Section 4.6.). Show that $\mathbf{A}^{-} = \mathbf{R}^{-1}\mathbf{Q}^{\mathrm{T}}$.

8.11.21. Consider the (possibly inconsistent) system $\mathbf{A}_{m\times n}\mathbf{X}_{n\times q} = \mathbf{B}_{m\times q}$. Show that $\mathbf{A}^{-}\mathbf{B}$ solves $\mathbf{A}^{-}\mathbf{AX} = \mathbf{A}^{-}\mathbf{B}$.

8.11.22. If $\mathbf{U}$ has orthonormal columns or rows, show that $\mathbf{U}^{-} = \mathbf{U}^{\mathrm{H}}$.

8.11.23. Suppose $\mathbf{S}$ is invertible. Which of the four properties in the definition of the p-inverse fails to hold for the conjecture $(\mathbf{SA})^{-} = \mathbf{A}^{-}\mathbf{S}^{-1}$?

MATLAB

Find the p-inverse for each of the following matrices.

8.11.24. $\mathbf{J}_{3\times4}$ and $\mathbf{J}_{4\times2}$.

8.11.25. $\mathbf{x} = [1 \quad -1 \quad 2 \quad 1]$ and $\mathbf{x}^{\mathrm{T}}$.

8.11.26. $\begin{bmatrix} 0 \\ 1 \\ -1 \\ 1 \end{bmatrix} [1 \quad -1 \quad 2 \quad 1]$

8.11.27. $\begin{bmatrix} 1 & -1 & 2 & 1 \\ 2 & -2 & 4 & 2 \\ 0 & 1 & -1 & 1 \end{bmatrix}$

8.11.28. $\begin{bmatrix} 1 & 3 & -1 \\ 0 & -1 & 1 \\ 0 & 0 & 2 \end{bmatrix}$

CHAPTER 9

CONVEX POLYHEDRONS AND SYSTEMS OF LINEAR INEQUALITIES

9.1 INTRODUCTION

The purpose of this chapter is to connect the geometry of linear algebra to the study of systems of linear inequalities. Such systems are at the heart of one of the most important applications of linear algebra, the solution of linear optimization problems.

The geometry of linear algebra begins with a study of lines and planes and their connections to affine and vector spaces. This analysis is essentially a generalization of ordinary analytic geometry to n dimensions. (See Chapter 3, especially Section 3.7.) From lines and planes in n dimensions, it is a simple step to hyperplanes, half-spaces and their intersections, and then the study of convex polyhedrons. The solution sets of systems of linear inequalities are convex polyhedrons, and this is partly the reason for our interest in them.

Systems of linear inequalities have a much richer geometric content than do systems of linear equalities. For example, the solution set of

$$\begin{aligned} x + y &= 1 \\ x - y &= -\tfrac{1}{2} \end{aligned}$$

is the point (½, ¾). By contrast, the solution set of

$$x + y \le 1 \qquad x \ge 0, y \ge 0$$
$$x - y \ge -½$$

is the interior of the quadrilateral with vertices (0,0), (0, ½), (1,0), and (¼, ¾).

This chapter concludes with five sections devoted to an introduction to the *simplex method,* a relatively recent technique for the solution of systems of linear inequalities and the class of optimization problems known as linear programs.

9.2 CONVEX SETS

This section is concerned with convexity, a concept laden with geometric content and practical applications. One of the most important applications is discussed later in this chapter, in the sections devoted to the exposition of the theory of linear programming. We will develop the theory of convex sets in a way that parallels our approach to affine spaces. (See Section 3.7.1.)

A *convex combination* $\{\mathbf{x}_1, \mathbf{x}_2, \ldots, \mathbf{x}_k\}$, $\mathbf{x}_i \in \mathcal{R}^n$ is a linear combination

$$a_1\mathbf{x}_1 + a_2\mathbf{x}_2 + \cdots + a_k\mathbf{x}_k \tag{9.2.1}$$

subject to the restrictions

$$a_1 + a_2 + \cdots + a_k = 1, \qquad a_i \ge 0, i = 1,2,\ldots,k \tag{9.2.2}$$

Thus, a convex combination is an affine combination with nonnegative weights.

Definition 9.1. *A set of vectors $\mathcal{K} \subseteq \mathcal{R}^n$ is a convex set if, for each scalar α and β, $\alpha \ge 0$, $\beta \ge 0$, and $\alpha + \beta = 1$,*

$$\mathbf{x} \in \mathcal{K} \text{ and } \mathbf{y} \in \mathcal{K} \text{ implies } \alpha\mathbf{x} + \beta\mathbf{y} \in \mathcal{K}$$

Theorem 9.2.1. *The set $\mathcal{K}$ is convex if, for each γ, $0 \le \gamma \le 1$,*

$$\mathbf{x} \in \mathcal{K} \text{ and } \mathbf{y} \in \mathcal{K} \text{ implies } (1-\gamma)\mathbf{x} + \gamma\mathbf{y} \in \mathcal{K}$$

Proof. Set $\beta = 1 - \gamma$. ■

In $\mathcal{R}^2$, the latter form of the convexity condition has a straightforward geometric interpretation: A set is convex if, whenever it contains two points it also contains the line segment joining these points. This is the geometric definition of convexity in $\mathcal{R}^n$ as well. In Fig. 9.1, we display a variety of convex sets in two and three dimensions.

Every vector and affine space is a convex set. Thus, all lines, planes, and hyperplanes are convex sets, and so are the sets $\mathcal{R}^n$ and $\{\mathbf{0}_n\}$.

Example 9.2.1. Show that the hyperplane $\mathbf{a}^T\mathbf{x} = b$ is convex.

Solution. Since a hyperplane is an affine space, it is a convex set, and the proof is done. Nevertheless, it is good drill to study the following alternative

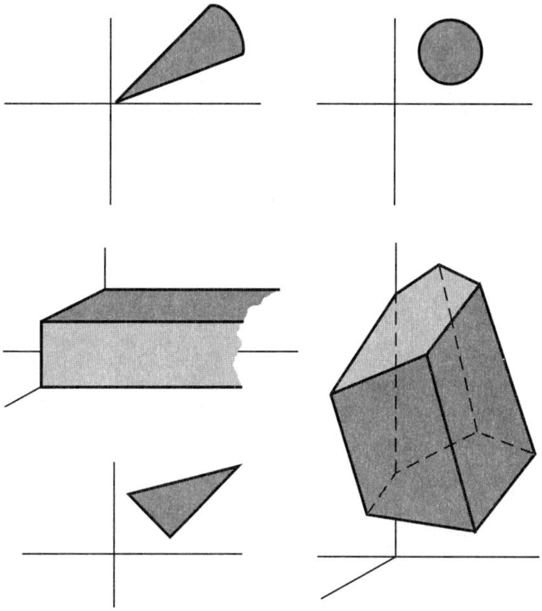

FIGURE 9-1
Convex sets.

argument based directly on the definition of convex set. Let $\mathbf{y}$ and $\mathbf{z}$ be points on the hyperplane; that is, $\mathbf{a}^{\mathrm{T}}\mathbf{y} = b$ and $\mathbf{a}^{\mathrm{T}}\mathbf{z} = b$. Then

$$\mathbf{a}^{\mathrm{T}}\big((1-\gamma)\mathbf{y} + \gamma\mathbf{z}\big) = (1-\gamma)\mathbf{a}^{\mathrm{T}}\mathbf{y} + \gamma\mathbf{a}^{\mathrm{T}}\mathbf{z} = (1-\gamma)b + \gamma b = b$$

for all γ and, hence, certainly for those γ, $0 \le \gamma \le 1$.

A vector $\mathbf{x}$ is *nonnegative* if each entry of $\mathbf{x}$ is nonnegative; this is represented as $\mathbf{x} \ge \mathbf{0}$. By extension, $\mathbf{x} \ge \mathbf{b}$ means that $\mathbf{x} - \mathbf{b} \ge \mathbf{0}$.

Example 9.2.2. Show that the set of all $\mathbf{x}$, $\mathbf{Ax} \ge \mathbf{b}$, is a convex set.

Solution. Suppose $\mathbf{Ay} \ge \mathbf{b}$ and $\mathbf{Az} \ge \mathbf{b}$. Then, provided that $0 \le \gamma \le 1$,

$$\mathbf{A}\big((1-\gamma)\mathbf{y} + \gamma\mathbf{z}\big) = (1-\gamma)\mathbf{Ay} + \gamma\mathbf{Az} \ge (1-\gamma)\mathbf{b} + \gamma\mathbf{b} = \mathbf{b}$$

In contrast to the argument in Example 9.2.2, if $\gamma \notin [0,1]$, then the crucial inequality in the proof does not follow.

Recall that the set of all linear combinations of a fixed set of vectors is a vector space called the *span* of the vectors, and that the set of all affine combinations is an affine space. We now state and prove the analogous result for convex combinations.

Theorem 9.2.2. *The set of all convex combinations of* $\{\mathbf{x}_1, \mathbf{x}_2, \ldots, \mathbf{x}_k\}$ *is a convex set.*

Proof. Let $\mathbf{y}$ and $\mathbf{z}$ be convex combinations of $\{\mathbf{x}_1, \mathbf{x}_2, \ldots, \mathbf{x}_k\}$. So for some sets of nonnegative weights $\{\alpha_1, \alpha_2, \ldots, \alpha_k\}$ and $\{\beta_1, \beta_2, \ldots, \beta_k\}$ satisfying $\alpha_1 + \alpha_2 + \cdots + \alpha_k = \beta_1 + \beta_2 + \cdots + \beta_k = 1$,

$$\mathbf{y} = \alpha_1\mathbf{x}_1 + \alpha_2\mathbf{x}_2 + \cdots + \alpha_k\mathbf{x}_k, \qquad \mathbf{z} = \beta_1\mathbf{x}_1 + \beta_2\mathbf{x}_2 + \cdots + \beta_k\mathbf{x}_k$$

Assume $\alpha + \beta = 1$ and compute

$$\alpha\mathbf{y} + \beta\mathbf{z} = (\alpha\alpha_1 + \beta\beta_1)\mathbf{x}_1 + \cdots + (\alpha\alpha_k + \beta\beta_k)\mathbf{x}_k$$

Clearly, $\alpha\alpha_i + \beta\beta_i \geq 0$, so we need only verify that the sum of the weights is 1. This is done as follows:

$$\sum_{i=1}^{k}(\alpha\alpha_i + \beta\beta_i) = \alpha\sum_{i=1}^{k}\alpha_i + \beta\sum_{i=1}^{k}\beta_i = \alpha + \beta = 1 \; \blacksquare$$

One major class of convex sets suggested by Theorem 9.2.2 is analogous to the span of a finite set of vectors.

Definition 9.2. *The convex hull of* $\{\mathbf{x}_1, \mathbf{x}_2, \ldots, \mathbf{x}_k\}$ *is the set of all convex combinations of these vectors.*

Example 9.2.3. Show that the convex hull of $\{\mathbf{x}_1, \mathbf{x}_2\}$ corresponds to the line segment L joining $\mathbf{x}_1$ to $\mathbf{x}_2$, where $\mathbf{x}_1$ and $\mathbf{x}_2$ represent the points (1,2) and (2,1), respectively.

Solution. Geometrically, the (closed) line segment L joining (1,2) to (2,1) is a convex set because if $\mathbf{u}$ and $\mathbf{v}$ are points on L, then the line segment joining $\mathbf{u}$ to $\mathbf{v}$ is a subset of L. Analytically, the convex hull of $\mathbf{x}_1 = [1 \quad 2]^T$ and $\mathbf{x}_2 = [2 \quad 1]^T$ is the set of all vectors of the form $\mathbf{y} = (1 - \gamma)\mathbf{x}_1 + \gamma\mathbf{x}_2$, $0 \leq \gamma \leq 1$. But each such $\mathbf{y}$ corresponds to a point on L, by elementary considerations of vector algebra.

Theorem 9.2.3. *The intersection of two convex sets* $\mathcal{H}_1$ *and* $\mathcal{H}_2$ *is either convex or empty.*

Proof. Suppose the intersection $\mathcal{H} = \mathcal{H}_1 \cap \mathcal{H}_2$ is not empty. Let $\mathbf{y}$ and $\mathbf{z}$ belong to $\mathcal{H}$. Then both points lie in the convex sets $\mathcal{H}_1$ and $\mathcal{H}_2$. Hence, the line segment joining $\mathbf{y}$ and $\mathbf{z}$ belongs to $\mathcal{H}_1$ and $\mathcal{H}_2$ and, therefore, to $\mathcal{H}$. Hence, $\mathcal{H}$ is convex. $\blacksquare$

The convex hulls of various sets of vectors are given in Fig. 9.2. Recall that the set of all $\mathbf{x}$ satisfying the equation $\mathbf{a}^T\mathbf{x} = b$ is called a *hyperplane*. Lines in two-dimensional space and planes in three-dimensional space are examples of hyperplanes. The sets $\mathbf{a}^T\mathbf{x} \leq b$ and $\mathbf{a}^T\mathbf{x} \geq b$ are called *half-spaces*. Clearly, a hyperplane is the boundary of half-spaces. All of these sets are convex.

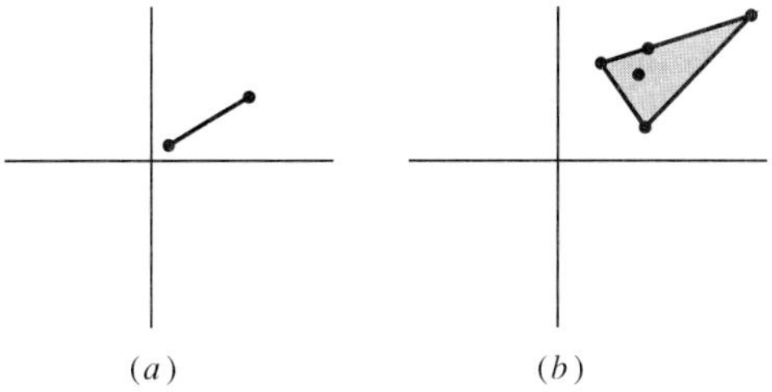

FIGURE 9-2
(*a*) Convex hull of two points. (*b*) Convex hull of five points.

Example 9.2.4. Sketch the half-space $\mathbf{a}^T\mathbf{x} \geq 1$, where $\mathbf{a} = [1 \quad -2]^T$.

Solution. The hyperplane $x - 2y = 1$ is $\mathbf{a}^T\mathbf{x} = 1$ and is the boundary of the half-space $\mathbf{a}^T\mathbf{x} \geq 1$. The half-space is sketched in Fig. 9.3.

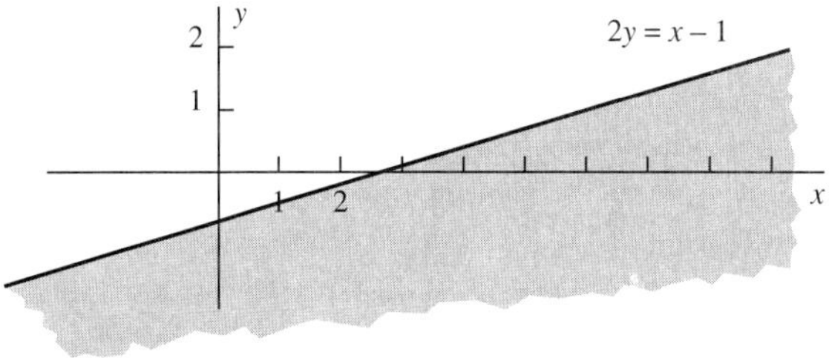

FIGURE 9-3
The half-space $[1 \quad -2]\begin{bmatrix} x \\ y \end{bmatrix}^T \geq 1$.

Note that the origin is not contained in the half-space $\mathbf{a}^T\mathbf{x} \geq 1$ of Example 9.2.4. It is evident from the sketch that $\mathbf{a}^T\mathbf{x} \leq 1$ is also a half-space. The general argument follows from the trivial observation that $(-\mathbf{a})^T\mathbf{x} \geq -1$ implies $\mathbf{a}^T\mathbf{x} \leq 1$. Systems that contain inequality and equality constraints are also convex sets. One example of sufficient importance to warrant a specific reference is stated as the next theorem.

Theorem 9.2.4. *The set of all solutions of* $\mathbf{Ax} = \mathbf{b}$, $\mathbf{x} \geq \mathbf{0}$, *is a convex set.*

Proof. The set of all solutions of $\mathbf{Ax} = \mathbf{b}$ is an affine space and is therefore a convex set. The set of vectors satisfying $\mathbf{x} \geq \mathbf{0}$ is also a convex set because it is the intersection of the half-spaces $\mathbf{e}_i^T\mathbf{x} \geq 0$. The intersection of these sets is the set of all nonnegative solutions of $\mathbf{Ax} = \mathbf{b}$ and is convex or empty by Theorem 9.2.3. ■

The nonempty intersection of finitely many half-spaces is a convex set called a *convex polyhedron*. Bounded convex polyhedrons are called *convex polytopes*. Note that the hyperplane $\mathbf{a}^T\mathbf{x} = b$ is a convex polyhedron because it is the intersection of the two half-spaces, $\mathbf{a}^T\mathbf{x} \leq b$ and $\mathbf{a}^T\mathbf{x} \geq b$. Figure 9.4 illustrates examples of convex polyhedrons and polytopes in two- and three-dimensional space. Here is an example of a convex polytope defined by the intersection of five half-spaces in $\mathcal{R}^2$.

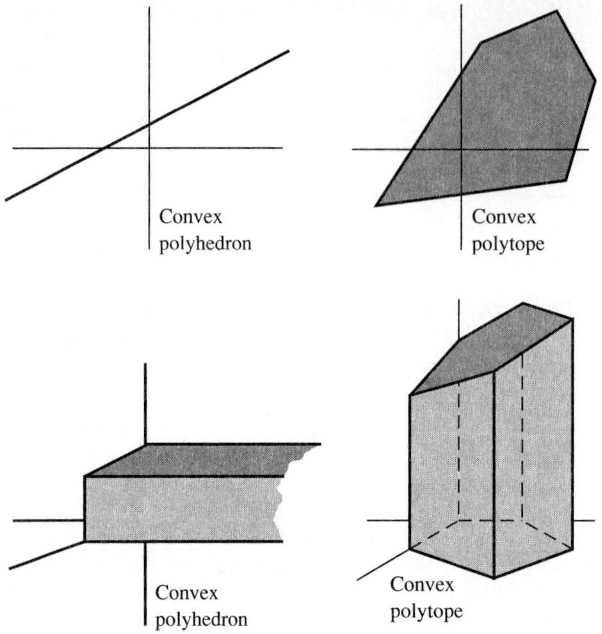

FIGURE 9-4
Convex polyhedrons and convex polytopes in two- and three-dimensional space.

Example 9.2.5. Sketch the convex polyhedron defined by the inequalities $x \geq 0,\ y \geq 0,\ y \leq x+1,\ y \geq x$, and $y \leq -x+2$.

Solution.

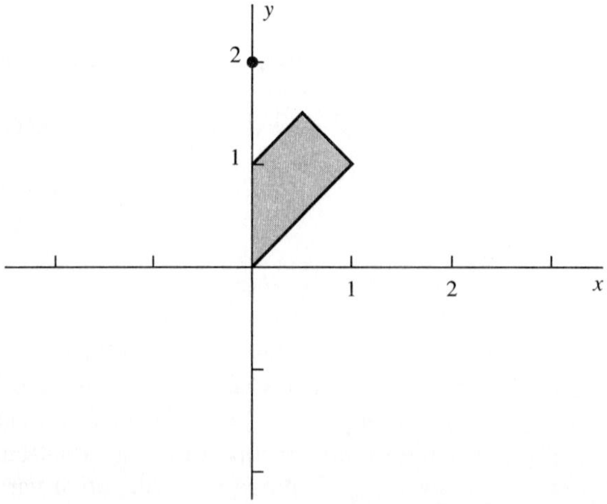

PROBLEMS

PART 1

9.2.1. Sketch the convex hulls of these sets:

(a) $\left\{\begin{bmatrix}1\\2\end{bmatrix}, \begin{bmatrix}-1\\0\end{bmatrix}\right\}$ (b) $\left\{\begin{bmatrix}1\\2\end{bmatrix}, \begin{bmatrix}-1\\0\end{bmatrix}, \begin{bmatrix}1\\-1\end{bmatrix}\right\}$

(c) $\left\{\begin{bmatrix}0\\0\end{bmatrix}, \begin{bmatrix}1\\0\end{bmatrix}, \begin{bmatrix}0\\1\end{bmatrix}\right\}$ (d) $\left\{\begin{bmatrix}-1\\0\end{bmatrix}, \begin{bmatrix}1\\0\end{bmatrix}, \begin{bmatrix}0\\1\end{bmatrix}, \begin{bmatrix}0\\-1\end{bmatrix}\right\}$

9.2.2. Sketch the convex set defined by $2x - y \leq 1, x + y \leq 1, y \geq 1$.

9.2.3. Sketch the convex set defined by $2x - y \leq 1, y \geq 1$. Compare the result with the answer to Problem 9.2.2.

9.2.4. Is $\mathbf{a}^T\mathbf{x} < b$ a convex set? Explain.

PART 2

9.2.5. Prove that every vector and affine space is a convex set.

9.2.6. Show by example that the union of two convex sets need not be convex.

9.2.7. Show that the set consisting of a single point satisfies the definition of a convex set.

9.2.8. Is the complement of a set with a single point a convex set?

PART 3

9.2.9. Construct an example of a nonempty intersection of infinitely many half-spaces that is not a convex polytope.

9.2.10. Does the statement "the empty set is convex" contradict the definition of convex set?

9.2.11. Suppose that $\mathcal{K} \subseteq \mathcal{R}^n$ is the convex set of all nonnegative vectors in $\mathcal{R}^n$. Show that $\mathcal{K}$ cannot contain any affine space other than those with a single point.

9.3 SYSTEMS OF INEQUALITIES IN STANDARD FORM

This section begins the systematic study of linear inequalities. The first issue that arises is a minor but annoying difficulty: A system containing a mix of inequalities and equations is not readily amenable to a general notation. For instance, the system

$$\begin{aligned} 2x_2 \quad\quad\quad + x_4 &= 2 \\ x_1 + \ x_2 \quad\quad\quad + x_4 &\leq 3 \qquad x_1 \geq 0, x_2 \geq 0, x_3 \geq 0 \\ -x_1 - 2x_2 + x_3 \quad\quad &\geq 1 \end{aligned}$$

is not a special case of either $\mathbf{Ax} = \mathbf{b}$, $\mathbf{Ax} \geq \mathbf{b}$, or $\mathbf{Ax} \leq \mathbf{b}$. We can circumvent this notational awkwardness by introducing auxiliary variables (called *slacks*) into the given system and making appropriate changes of variable. Indeed, the purpose of this section is to show how a general system of inequalities and equations can be transformed into an "equivalent" system of equations in nonnegative variables of the form $\mathbf{Ax} = \mathbf{b}$, $\mathbf{x} \geq \mathbf{0}$, called the *standard form*. (The simplex method for solving linear optimization problems begins with the assumption that the problem is formulated as a system of equations in nonnegative variables. See Sections 9.6–9.10.) We illustrate the basic technique with two simple examples and then proceed to the general case.

Example 9.3.1. Put $-3 \leq x \leq 4$ into standard form.

Solution. The inequality $-3 \leq x$ is a lower bound on x. By defining $x_1 = 3 + x$, the lower bound inequality is replaced by $x_1 \geq 0$. In terms of x_1, the constraint $x \leq 4$ becomes $x_1 \leq 7$. Inequality constraints that are not lower bounds are transformed into equalities by the introduction of slacks. In this case, define s_1 so that $x_1 + s_1 = 7$. Then, since $x_1 \leq 7$, it follows that $s_1 \geq 0$. In terms of the new variables x_1 and s_1, the system $-3 \leq x \leq 4$ becomes an equality constraint in nonnegative variables:

$$x_1 + s_1 = 7, \qquad x_1 \geq 0, s_1 \geq 0 \tag{9.3.1}$$

Each solution of Eq. 9.3.1 determines a solution of $-3 \leq x \leq 4$ via $x = x_1 - 3$. Conversely, each x for which $-3 \leq x \leq 4$ holds determines x_1 and s_1 satisfying Eq. 9.3.1.

This example illustrates two crucial points: First, inequalities of the form $l \leq x$ are separated from the remaining constraints and are transformed into the nonnegative variable x_i by substitutions of the form $x_i = x - l$. Second, all other inequality constraints are transformed into equalities by the introduction of nonnegative slacks, including upper bound constraints $x \leq u$. Here is a second example.

Example 9.3.2. Convert the system $x_1 + x_2 \leq 3$, $x_1 \leq 0$, and $x_2 \geq 1$ into standard form.

Solution. The lower bound, $x_2 \geq 1$, is transformed into $x_3 \geq 0$ by the substitution $x_3 = x_2 - 1$, so that $x_1 + x_2 \leq 3$ becomes $x_1 + x_3 \leq 2$. We introduce two nonnegative slacks, one for each of the remaining inequalities, $x_1 + x_3 \leq 2$ and $x_1 \leq 0$. This leads to the following equivalent system:

$$\begin{aligned} x_1 + x_3 + s_1 &= 2 \\ x_1 + s_2 &= 0 \end{aligned} \qquad x_3 \geq 0, s_1 \geq 0, s_2 \geq 0 \tag{9.3.2}$$

The constraints $x_3 \geq 0$, $s_1 \geq 0$, and $s_2 \geq 0$ are called *sign restrictions* to distinguish them from the remaining equality constraints. A further simplification of Eq. 9.3.2 is possible because x_1 is not among the set of sign-restricted variables but does appear in a constraint. (Indeed, the failure of x_1 to appear as sign-restricted is the reason that Eq. 9.3.2 is not yet in the form $\mathbf{Ax} = \mathbf{b}$, $\mathbf{x} \geq \mathbf{0}$.) The unrestricted variable x_1 can be eliminated from the set of equality constraints by solving for x_1 in the second constraint to obtain $x_1 = -s_2$, and then substituting $-s_2$ for x_1 in the first constraint. The system is in standard form and now reads

$$x_3 + s_1 - s_2 = 2 \qquad x_3 \geq 0, s_1 \geq 0, s_2 \geq 0 \tag{9.3.3}$$

Bear in mind that each solution of Eq. 9.3.3 leads to a solution of the given system by the variable changes $x_1 = -s_2$ and $x_2 = x_3 + 1$.

With these examples behind us, we can now consider the general case. Suppose we have a system whose constraints are a mixture of $\mathbf{a}^T\mathbf{x} \leq \mathbf{b}$, $\mathbf{a}^T\mathbf{x} \geq \mathbf{b}$, and $\mathbf{a}^T\mathbf{x} = \mathbf{b}$. That is, each constraint is one of the varieties

$$a_{i1}x_1 + a_{i2}x_2 + \cdots + a_{in}x_n \begin{cases} \leq b_i \\ = b_i \\ \geq b_i \end{cases} \tag{9.3.4}$$

for $i = 1, 2, \ldots, m$. Geometrically, the set of all $\mathbf{x}$ that simultaneously satisfy Eq. 9.3.4 is an intersection of half-spaces and hyperplanes and is therefore a (possibly empty) convex polyhedron. If $x_i \geq b_i$ is one of the constraints in the set of Eq. 9.3.4, we say x_i is *bounded below;* this inequality is called a *lower bound constraint*. For each lower bound constraint, make the change of variable $y_i = x_i - b_i$ and substitute y_i for x_i in every constraint in which x_i appears. By this means, every lower bound constraint becomes a sign restricted variable $y_i \geq 0$. From this point on, the set of nonnegative sign-restricted variables is separated from the set of constraints. The body of constraints now contains (possibly) *upper bound constraints* $x_i \leq b_i$, equality constraints, and inequality constraints in *more than* one variable.

Now convert all upper bound and inequality constraints into equality constraints by the introduction of slack variables. For each inequality of the form

$$a_{i1}x_1 + a_{i2}x_2 + \cdots + a_{in}x_n \leq b_i \tag{9.3.5}$$

define the slack s_i by

$$s_i = b_i - (a_{i1}x_1 + a_{i2}x_2 + \cdots + a_{in}x_n) \tag{9.3.6}$$

Then Eqs. 9.3.5 and 9.3.6 imply $s_i \geq 0$ and

$$a_{i1}x_1 + a_{i2}x_2 + \cdots + a_{in}x_n + s_i = b_i \tag{9.3.7}$$

replaces Eq. 9.3.5. Conversely, if $s_i \geq 0$ and Eq. 9.3.7 holds, then Eq. 9.3.5 follows. The nonnegative variable s_i is adjoined to the set of sign-restricted variables.

If a constraint is of the form

$$a_{i1}x_1 + a_{i2}x_2 + \cdots + a_{in}x_n \geq b_i$$

simply multiply through by -1 and treat the new inequality as in Eq. 9.3.5.

By repeated use of these techniques, each inequality can be replaced by an equality constraint and a nonnegative slack. Thus, a mixed system of inequalities and equalities can always be converted to the system $\mathbf{Ax} = \mathbf{b}$ along with a set of nonnegative sign restrictions—some originally present, some introduced as slacks, and some resulting from the change of variables introduced for lower bound constraints. There remains one more situation to consider. Suppose x_i does not appear in the set of sign restrictions but appears in at least one constraint. Such a variable is called *unrestricted*. (Of course, x_i is implicitly restricted by each constraint in which it appears! The use of the term *unrestricted* in this context is meant to convey the fact that x_i is not in the set of sign restrictions.) For instance, suppose x_1 is unrestricted and appears in the ith constraint:

$$a_{i1}x_1 + a_{i2}x_2 + \cdots + a_{in}x_n = b_i$$

We solve for x_1:

$$x_1 = -\frac{1}{a_{i1}}\left[b_i - (a_{i2}x_2 + \cdots + a_{in}x_n)\right]$$

and use this equation to eliminate x_1 from the other constraints. After all these transformations are effected, and the variables renamed where necessary, we have an equivalent system of equality constraints in nonnegative variables of the form

$$\mathbf{Ax} = \mathbf{b}, \qquad \mathbf{x} \geq \mathbf{0} \tag{9.3.8}$$

(There is no loss in generality in assuming that $\mathbf{b} \geq \mathbf{0}$, for if any b_i were negative, the ith equation in Eq. 9.3.8 could be multiplied by -1 resulting in $-b_i \geq 0$. When it is convenient, we shall make this assumption.) Finally, if $\mathbf{A}$ is $m \times n$ and rank($\mathbf{A}$) $= m$, then the system in Eq. 9.3.8 is now in standard form, regardless of whether $\mathbf{b} \geq \mathbf{0}$. (If rank($\mathbf{A}$) $< m$, then row operations can be used to eliminate redundant equations, so that the assumption that $\mathbf{A}$ has full row rank is not an essential restriction.) The following examples are further illustrations of the conversion of a general system into standard form.

Example 9.3.3. Convert the following system into standard form:

$$\begin{aligned} 2x_2 \qquad\quad + x_4 &= 2 \qquad (x_i \geq 0,\ i \neq 4) \\ x_1 + \ x_2 \qquad\quad + x_4 &\leq 3 \\ -x_1 - 2x_2 + x_3 \qquad\quad &\geq 1 \end{aligned} \tag{9.3.9}$$

Solution. (This system appeared at the beginning of this section.) There are three constraints; the second and the third require slacks. Let x_5 and x_6 be the slacks for these inequalities. Then the system becomes

$$\begin{aligned} 2x_2 \qquad\quad + x_4 \qquad\qquad &= 2 \qquad (x_i \geq 0,\ i \neq 4) \\ x_1 + \ x_2 \qquad\quad + x_4 + x_5 \qquad &= 3 \\ -x_1 - 2x_2 + x_3 \qquad\qquad\quad - x_6 &= 1 \end{aligned}$$

Since x_4 is unrestricted, the first constraint can be used to eliminate x_4 from the system by substituting $x_4 = 2 - 2x_2$ into the second equation. After collecting terms, the following system in nonnegative variables is obtained:

$$\begin{aligned} x_1 - x_2 \qquad + x_5 \qquad &= 1 \\ -x_1 - 2x_2 + x_3 \qquad - x_6 &= 1 \end{aligned} \tag{9.3.10}$$

By inspection, $x_1 = 1,\ x_2 = 2,\ x_3 = 6,\ x_5 = 2,\ x_6 = 0$ is a solution to Eq. 9.3.10 in nonnegative variables (but by no means the only one), and Eq. 9.3.9 has the corresponding solution $\mathbf{x} = [1 \quad 2 \quad 6 \quad -2]^{\mathrm{T}}$.

Example 9.3.4. (*The Brewer's Resource Allocation Problem.*) See Section 0.1.2.) Put the following inequality constraints in nonnegative variables into standard form:

$$\begin{aligned} 2x + y + z &\le 10 \\ x \quad\ \ + z &\le 5 \end{aligned} \tag{9.3.11}$$

Solution. In the formulation of this problem, the variables x, y, and z represent production amounts and are therefore nonnegative. Hence, the introduction of the slacks $s_1 = 10 - 2x + y + z$ and $s_2 = 5 - x - z$ suffices to put, Eq. 9.3.11 in standard form:

$$\begin{aligned} 2x + y + z + s_1 \qquad &= 10 \qquad x, y, z, s_1, s_2 \ge 0 \\ x \quad\ \ + z \qquad + s_2 &= 5 \end{aligned} \tag{9.3.12}$$

It may happen that the elimination of unrestricted variables results in a set of sign-restricted variables and no equality constraints. Then Eq. 9.3.8 reduces to $\mathbf{x} \ge \mathbf{0}$. The solution is the set of all $\mathbf{x} \ge \mathbf{0}$ with all the defining equations.

PROBLEMS

PART 1

Put the systems of inequalities and equality constraints given in Problems 9.3.1–9.3.8 into standard form.

9.3.1. $-2 \le x \le 3$
$-1 \le y \le 1$
$x + y = 2$

9.3.2. $x + y + z \le 1$
$x \ge 0,\ y \ge 0$

9.3.3. $x + y \le 1$
$x \ge 0$

9.3.4. $x \ge 1,\ y \ge 2$
$x \ge 0$

9.3.5. $-2 \le x + y \le 2$

9.3.6. $-2 \le x + y \le 2$
$x \le 0$

9.3.7. $x + y + z = 1$
$x - y = 2$
$x \le 0, \qquad y \ge 0,\ z \ge 0$

9.3.8. $x + y + z \ge 1$
$x - y \le 2$
$x \le 0,\ y \ge 0,\ z \ge 0$

9.3.9. Eliminate the obvious redundant inequalities and transform the resulting system into standard form:

$$x + y + z \le 2, \qquad x \ge 0,\ y \ge 0,\ z \ge 0, \qquad x \ge -2,\ y \ge -1,\ -1 \le z \le 1$$

PART 2

9.3.10. Can the system $\mathbf{Ax} = \mathbf{b}$ be put in standard form? Explain.

9.3.11. What is the standard form for the system $\mathbf{x} \geq \mathbf{0}$?

9.3.12. Show that the standard form for the system $\mathbf{Ax} \leq \mathbf{b},\ \mathbf{x} \geq \mathbf{0}$ is

$$[\mathbf{A} \quad \mathbf{I}]\begin{bmatrix} \mathbf{x} \\ \mathbf{s} \end{bmatrix} = \mathbf{b}, \qquad \begin{bmatrix} \mathbf{x} \\ \mathbf{s} \end{bmatrix} \geq \mathbf{0}$$

9.3.13. Show that the standard form for the system $\mathbf{Ax} \geq \mathbf{b},\ \mathbf{x} \geq \mathbf{0}$ is

$$[\mathbf{A} \quad -\mathbf{I}]\begin{bmatrix} \mathbf{x} \\ \mathbf{s} \end{bmatrix} = \mathbf{b}, \qquad \begin{bmatrix} \mathbf{x} \\ \mathbf{s} \end{bmatrix} \geq \mathbf{0}$$

9.3.14. Show that the standard form for the system $\mathbf{Ax} = \mathbf{b},\ \mathbf{Dx} \leq \mathbf{d},\ \mathbf{x} \geq \mathbf{0}$ is

$$\left[\begin{array}{c|c} \mathbf{A} & \mathbf{O} \\ \hline \mathbf{D} & \mathbf{I} \end{array}\right]\begin{bmatrix} \mathbf{x} \\ \mathbf{s} \end{bmatrix} = \begin{bmatrix} \mathbf{b} \\ \mathbf{d} \end{bmatrix}, \qquad \begin{bmatrix} \mathbf{x} \\ \mathbf{s} \end{bmatrix} \geq \mathbf{0}$$

9.3.15. Find the standard form for the system $\mathbf{Ax} = \mathbf{b},\ \mathbf{Dx} \geq \mathbf{d}$.

9.3.16. Show that the standard form for the system $\mathbf{Ax} = \mathbf{b},\ \mathbf{x} \geq \mathbf{c}$ is $\mathbf{Ay} = \mathbf{d},\ \mathbf{y} \geq \mathbf{0}$, where $\mathbf{y} = \mathbf{x} - \mathbf{c}$ and $\mathbf{d} = \mathbf{b} - \mathbf{Ac}$.

9.4 BASIC FEASIBLE SOLUTIONS OF $\mathbf{Ax} = \mathbf{b},\ \mathbf{x} \geq \mathbf{0}$

A solution of $\mathbf{Ax} = \mathbf{b}$ that satisfies the nonnegative condition $\mathbf{x} \geq \mathbf{0}$ is called a *feasible solution*. The set of all feasible solutions is either empty or a convex set in $\mathcal{R}^n$, and is denoted by $\mathcal{K}$. When $\mathcal{K}$ is nonempty, the standard system $\mathbf{Ax} = \mathbf{b},\ \mathbf{x} \geq \mathbf{0}$ is called *feasible*. (Note that a standard system can be *infeasible* either because $\mathbf{Ax} = \mathbf{b}$ is inconsistent or because, although $\mathbf{Ax} = \mathbf{b}$ is consistent, there are no nonnegative solutions.) We shall assume that $\mathbf{Ax} = \mathbf{b}$ is consistent; the question, then, is whether there are any nonnegative solutions. For convenience, assume also that $\mathbf{A}$ has full row rank, so there are no redundant equations in the system $\mathbf{Ax} = \mathbf{b}$. Geometrically, $\mathbf{Ax} = \mathbf{b},\ \mathbf{x} \geq \mathbf{0}$ is a convex polyhedron that has feasible solutions if this convex set is nonempty.

A solution (feasible or not) of $\mathbf{Ax} = \mathbf{b}$ is said to use the ith column of $\mathbf{A}$ if $x_i > 0$. Thus, if $\mathbf{A} = [\mathbf{A}_{*1} \quad \mathbf{A}_{*2} \quad \ldots \quad \mathbf{A}_{*n}]$ and $\mathbf{x}$ uses columns $\mathbf{A}_{*1}, \mathbf{A}_{*2}, \ldots, \mathbf{A}_{*k}$, then

$$\mathbf{Ax} = \mathbf{A}_{*1}x_1 + \mathbf{A}_{*2}x_2 + \cdots + \mathbf{A}_{*k}x_k$$

Example 9.4.1. The standard system

$$\mathbf{Ax} = \begin{bmatrix} 1 & 0 & 1 & 2 \\ 0 & 1 & 1 & 2 \end{bmatrix}\mathbf{x} = \begin{bmatrix} 1 \\ 1 \end{bmatrix}, \qquad \mathbf{x} \geq \mathbf{0}$$

has a feasible solution, $\mathbf{x}_1 = [1 \quad 1 \quad 0 \quad 0]^T$, and this solution uses columns 1 and 2 of $\mathbf{A}$. The vector $\mathbf{x}_2 = [\tfrac{1}{2} \quad \tfrac{1}{2} \quad \tfrac{1}{2} \quad 0]^T$ is also a feasible solution and uses columns 1, 2, and 3.

Definition 9.3. *A basic feasible solution* (BFS) *of* $\mathbf{Ax} = \mathbf{b},\ \mathbf{x} \geq \mathbf{0}$ *is a feasible solution that uses a linearly independent set of columns of* $\mathbf{A}$.

The feasible solution $\mathbf{x}_1$ in Example 9.4.1 uses a linearly independent set of columns of $\mathbf{A}$ and is therefore a BFS. On the other hand, $\mathbf{x}_2$ uses three columns of $\mathbf{A}$, and three 2-tuples are always linearly dependent. BFSs are important for their geometric interpretation as special points of $\mathcal{K}$. Consider the standard system $\mathbf{Ax} = \mathbf{b},\ \mathbf{x} \geq \mathbf{0}$, and suppose $\mathcal{K}$ is the convex polyhedron of its feasible solutions. Then every BFS corresponds to a vertex (corner) of $\mathcal{K}$, and every vertex of $\mathcal{K}$ corresponds to a BFS. The proof of this remarkable geometric connection between BFSs and vertices of $\mathcal{K}$ requires a fairly extensive discussion of the algebraic conditions under which a point in a convex set is a vertex. This analysis is undertaken in Section 9.6. For the time being, we will take this theorem on faith. Nevertheless, it is reassuring to work a few examples to substantiate this claim.

Example 9.4.2. Consider the system

$$\begin{bmatrix} 1 & 1 & 1 \\ 0 & 1 & -1 \end{bmatrix} \mathbf{x} = \begin{bmatrix} 3 \\ 0 \end{bmatrix}$$

in nonnegative variables. Show that $\mathbf{x}_2 = [3 \quad 0 \quad 0]^T$ and $\mathbf{x}_3 = [0 \quad 3/2 \quad 3/2]^T$ are basic feasible solutions and that $\mathbf{x}_1 = [1 \quad 1 \quad 1]^T$ is a nonbasic feasible solution. Let $\mathcal{K}$ be the set of feasible solutions. Show that $\mathbf{x}_2$ and $\mathbf{x}_3$ correspond to vertices of $\mathcal{K}$ and that $\mathbf{x}_1$ does not.

Solution. We can easily verify that each vector is a feasible solution; that $\mathbf{x}_1$ is not a BFS, since it uses three columns of $\mathbf{A}$; and that $\mathbf{x}_2$ and $\mathbf{x}_3$ use linearly independent columns of $\mathbf{A}$ and are therefore BFSs. What is more interesting is the connection between these solutions and the set of vertices of $\mathcal{K}$. Figure 9.5 shows clearly that $\mathbf{x}_1$, $\mathbf{x}_2$, and $\mathbf{x}_3$ are points in $\mathcal{K}$, and that only the latter two correspond to vertices.

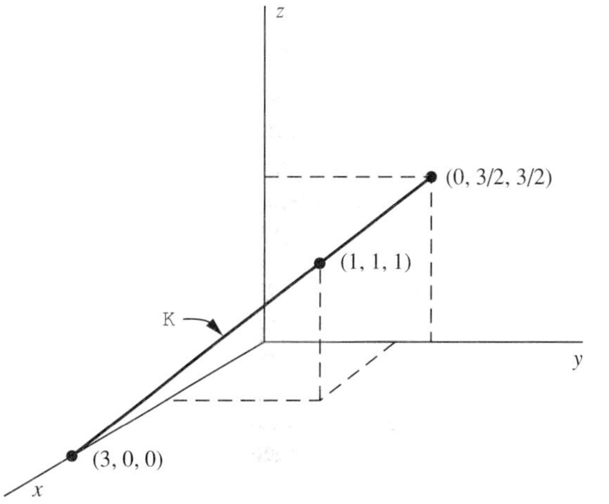

FIGURE 9-5
The line of feasible solutions, $\mathcal{K}$, of the system

$$\begin{bmatrix} 1 & 1 & 1 \\ 0 & 1 & -1 \end{bmatrix} \mathbf{x} = \begin{bmatrix} 3 \\ 0 \end{bmatrix}$$

in nonnegative variables.

Example 9.4.3. Find all the BFSs of the system $x + y + z = 3$, $x \geq 0$, $y \geq 0$, $z \geq 0$. Sketch $\mathcal{K}$ and verify that the BFSs correspond one-to-one with the set of vertices of $\mathcal{K}$.

Solution. Since $\mathbf{A} = [1 \quad 1 \quad 1]$ is a row matrix, every BFS must use one column of $\mathbf{A}$. This leads immediately to the conclusion that there are only three BFSs, which are $\mathbf{x}_1 = [3 \quad 0 \quad 0]^T$, $\mathbf{x}_2 = [0 \quad 3 \quad 0]^T$, and $\mathbf{x}_3 = [0 \quad 0 \quad 3]^T$. The sketch of $\mathcal{K}$ is given in Fig. 9.6.

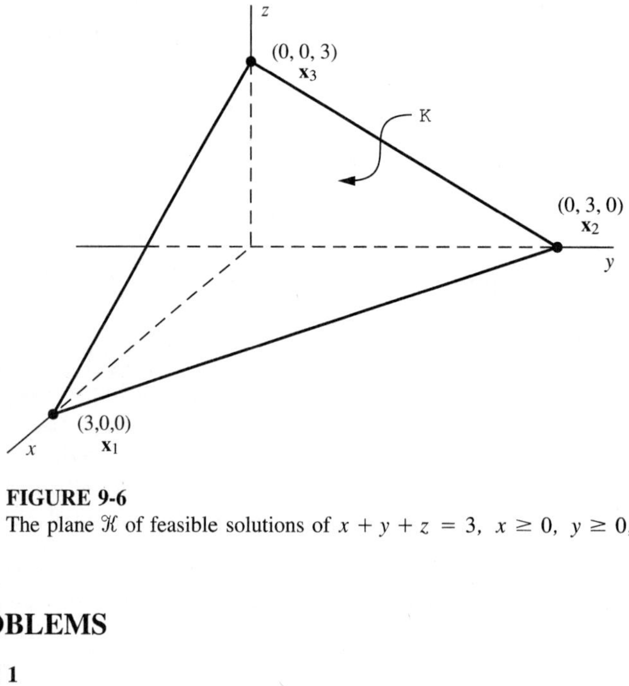

FIGURE 9-6
The plane $\mathcal{K}$ of feasible solutions of $x + y + z = 3$, $x \geq 0$, $y \geq 0$, $z \geq 0$.

PROBLEMS

PART 1

Sketch the convex polyhedron $\mathcal{K}$ of feasible solutions for each of the following 10 systems, and identify the vertices of $\mathcal{K}$.

9.4.1. $-2 \leq x \leq 3$, $-1 \leq y \leq 1$, $x + y = 2$

9.4.2. $x + y + z \leq 1$, $x \geq 0$, $y \geq 0$

9.4.3. $x + y \geq 1$, $x \geq 0$

9.4.4. $x \geq 1$, $y \geq 2$, $x \geq 0$

9.4.5. $-2 \leq x + y \leq 2$

9.4.6. $-2 \leq x + y \leq 2$, $x \leq 0$

9.4.7. $x + y + z = 1$, $x - y = 2$, $x \leq 0$

9.4.8. $x + y + z \geq 1$, $x - y \leq 2$, $x \leq 0, y \geq 0, z \geq 0$

9.4.9. $-1 \leq x + y \leq 3$, $x \geq 0$, $y \geq 0$

9.4.10. $2x + y \leq 4$, $x \geq 0$, $y \geq 0$

PART 2

Each of the following four problems refer to Part 1. Convert the system to standard form and find all the BFSs. Plot the BFSs in the space of the original variables and compare with the vertices of $\mathcal{H}$, where $\mathcal{H}$ is the set of feasible solutions in the original variables.

9.4.11. Problem 9.4.6 **9.4.12.** Problem 9.4.8

9.4.13. Problem 9.4.9 **9.4.14.** Problem 9.4.10

9.4.15. Sketch the set of feasible solutions of $2x + y = 4,\ x \geq 0,\ y \geq 0$, and find all its BFSs. Identify the vertices of $\mathcal{H}$ and show that the BFSs correspond to these points.

9.4.16. Sketch the set of feasible solutions of $x + y + z = 3$ for $x \geq 0,\ y \geq 0$, and z unrestricted. Identify the vertices of $\mathcal{H}$. Although the feasible solutions $[3\ \ 0\ \ 0]^T$ and $[0\ \ 3\ \ 0]^T$ use linearly independent columns of $\mathbf{A} = [1\ \ 1\ \ 1]$, show that these points are not vertices of $\mathcal{H}$.

PART 3

In Problems 9.4.17 and 9.4.18, rank($\mathbf{A}$) $= m$, $\mathbf{A}$ is $m \times n$, and $\mathbf{A}\mathbf{x}_k = \mathbf{b},\ \mathbf{x}_k \geq \mathbf{0}$.

9.4.17. Suppose $\mathbf{x}_k$ uses $k < m$ columns of $\mathbf{A}$. Is $\mathbf{x}_k$ a BFS?

9.4.18. Suppose $\mathbf{x}_k$ uses $k = m$ columns of $\mathbf{A}$. Is $\mathbf{x}_k$ a BFS?

9.4.19. If $\mathbf{x}_k$ uses no columns of $\mathbf{A}$, show that $\mathbf{x}_k = \mathbf{b} = \mathbf{0}$.

9.4.20. If $\mathbf{x}_k$ and $\mathbf{y}_k$ are BFSs, is $(1 - \alpha)\mathbf{x}_k + \alpha\mathbf{y}_k,\ 0 < \alpha < 1$, a solution? A feasible solution? A BFS?

9.4.21. If $\mathbf{x}_k$ is a BFS using only the first column of $\mathbf{A}$, what is $\mathbf{b}$?

9.4.22. Show that the system $\mathbf{A}\mathbf{x} \leq \mathbf{b},\ \mathbf{b} \geq \mathbf{0},\ \mathbf{x} \geq \mathbf{0}$ is always feasible. The standard form for this system may be written

$$[\mathbf{A}\ \mathbf{I}]\begin{bmatrix}\mathbf{x}\\ \mathbf{s}\end{bmatrix} = \mathbf{b}, \qquad \begin{bmatrix}\mathbf{x}\\ \mathbf{s}\end{bmatrix} \geq \mathbf{0} \tag{9.4.1}$$

(See Problem 9.3.12) Explain why $\mathbf{x}_k = \begin{bmatrix}\mathbf{0}\\ \mathbf{b}\end{bmatrix}$ is a BFS of Eq. 9.4.1. To what feasible solution in the original variables does $\mathbf{x}_k$ correspond?

9.4.23. Show by example that an analysis similar to the preceding one is not possible for the system $\mathbf{A}\mathbf{x} \geq \mathbf{b},\ \mathbf{b} \geq \mathbf{0},\ \mathbf{x} \geq \mathbf{0}$. (*Hint:* Consider the 1×1 system $ax \geq b$.)

9.4.24. Show that Definition 9.3 can be stated as follows: $\mathbf{x}_k$ is a BFS if it is a feasible solution not using a dependent set of columns of $\mathbf{A}$. Now give a plausible explanation of why $\mathbf{x} = \mathbf{0}$ is a BFS if it is a feasible solution.

9.5 A FUNDAMENTAL THEOREM

If the point $\mathbf{x}_k$ lies in the convex set $\mathcal{H}$, and $\mathcal{H}$ contains at least two distinct points, then a line segment can be drawn in $\mathcal{H}$ containing $\mathbf{x}_k$. The importance of this simple fact is evident from the observation that if $\mathcal{H}$ is the set of feasible solutions of $\mathbf{A}\mathbf{x} = \mathbf{b},\ \mathbf{x} \geq \mathbf{0}$, then the feasible solution $\mathbf{x}_k$ is on a line (or line segment) of feasible solutions. This line may be bounded or unbounded depending on the shape of $\mathcal{H}$ (various cases are sketched in Fig. 9.7). The goal of this section is to provide an algorithm for the determination of this line and from this generate BFSs from feasible solutions. The fundamental theorem alluded to in the title of this section is this algorithm.

Every line segment containing $\mathbf{x}_k \in \mathcal{H}$ is of the form $\mathbf{x}_k + \lambda\mathbf{a}$ for some $\mathbf{a}$ and

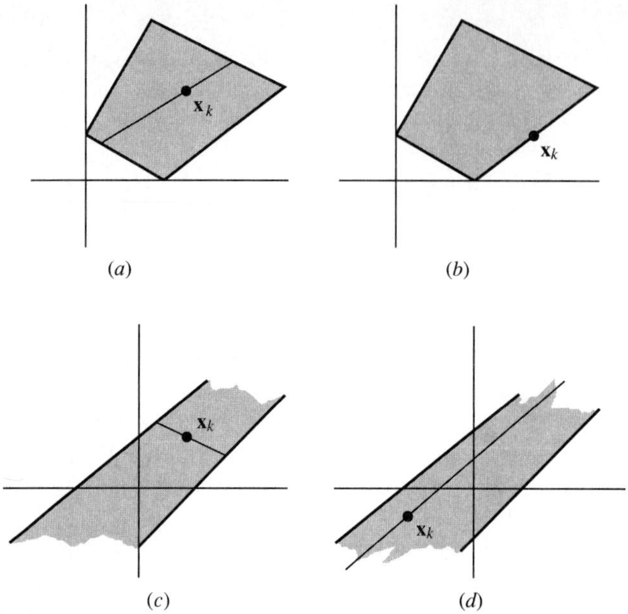

FIGURE 9-7
Lines or segments containing the feasible solution $\mathbf{x}_k$ for various convex polyhedra.

λ. For what $\mathbf{a}$ and for what λ is $\mathbf{x}_k + \lambda_{\mathbf{a}} \in \mathcal{K}$? To make these ideas somewhat more specific, let us assume that the convex set $\mathcal{K}$ is the set of all feasible solutions of $\mathbf{Ax} = \mathbf{b},\ \mathbf{x} \geq \mathbf{0}$. (Not all the cases illustrated in Fig. 9.7 obtain in these circumstances. For instance, it should be obvious that (*c*) is not a result of solving $\mathbf{Ax} = \mathbf{b},\ \mathbf{x} \geq \mathbf{0}$ for any $\mathbf{A}$ and $\mathbf{b}$.)

If $\mathbf{x}_k + \lambda\mathbf{a}$ is a feasible solution, then $\mathbf{A}(\mathbf{x}_k + \lambda\mathbf{a}) = \mathbf{Ax}_k + \lambda\mathbf{Aa} = \mathbf{b}$ and $\mathbf{x}_k + \lambda\mathbf{a} \geq \mathbf{0}$ must hold. Since $\mathbf{Ax}_k = \mathbf{b}$, it follows that $\lambda\mathbf{Aa} = \mathbf{0}$. Therefore, to find a line segment containing $\mathbf{x}_k$ lying in $\mathcal{K}$, we select $\mathbf{a} \in null(\mathbf{A}),\ \mathbf{a} \neq \mathbf{0}$, if possible. For such $\mathbf{a}$, the system of inequalities $\mathbf{x}_k + \lambda\mathbf{a} \geq \mathbf{0}$ is always consistent for some λ, since $\lambda = 0$ and $\mathbf{x}_k \in \mathcal{K}$ imply that $\mathbf{x}_k + \lambda\mathbf{a} \geq \mathbf{0}$. The crucial question is this: Does there exist $\mathbf{a} \neq \mathbf{0},\ \mathbf{Aa} = \mathbf{0}$ such that $\mathbf{x}_k + \lambda\mathbf{a} \geq \mathbf{0}$ *for λ in a nondegenerate interval, $-\epsilon < \lambda < \epsilon, \epsilon > 0$*? The next example points to two alternatives arising from different choices of $\mathbf{x}_k$.

Example 9.5.1. The standard problem

$$\mathbf{Ax} = \begin{bmatrix} 1 & 0 & 1 & 2 \\ 0 & 1 & 1 & 2 \end{bmatrix} \mathbf{x} = \begin{bmatrix} 1 \\ 1 \end{bmatrix}, \qquad \mathbf{x} \geq \mathbf{0}$$

has the feasible solution $\mathbf{x}_k = [1 \quad 1 \quad 0 \quad 0]$, and $\mathbf{a} = [0 \quad 0 \quad -2 \quad 1]^{\mathrm{T}}$ satisfies $\mathbf{Aa} = \mathbf{0}$. The line

$$\mathbf{x}_k + \lambda\mathbf{a} = \begin{bmatrix} 1 \\ 1 \\ 0 \\ 0 \end{bmatrix} + \lambda \begin{bmatrix} 0 \\ 0 \\ -2 \\ 1 \end{bmatrix} \geq \mathbf{0}$$

is feasible if and only if $\lambda = 0$. In this case $\mathbf{x}_k + \lambda\mathbf{a} = \mathbf{x}_k$, and the line degenerates into a point. On the other hand, $\mathbf{a} = [1 \quad 1 \quad -1 \quad 0]^{\mathrm{T}}$ is another solution of $\mathbf{Aa} = \mathbf{0}$, but now

$$\mathbf{x}_k + \lambda\mathbf{a} = \begin{bmatrix} 1 \\ 1 \\ 0 \\ 0 \end{bmatrix} + \lambda \begin{bmatrix} 1 \\ 1 \\ -1 \\ 0 \end{bmatrix} \geq \mathbf{0}$$

for all λ, $-1 \leq \lambda \leq 0$, and no other λ. The vectors $\mathbf{x}_k + \lambda\mathbf{a}$ represent a bounded line segment.

The next theorem asserts that under certain circumstances, it is always possible to select solutions of $\mathbf{Ax} = \mathbf{0}$ whose nonzero entries correspond to a subset of the nonzero entries of $\mathbf{x}_k$. Put in other words, such an $\mathbf{a}$ uses a subset of the columns used by $\mathbf{x}_k$. (Recall that a vector $\mathbf{y}$ "uses" the ith column of $\mathbf{A}$ if $y_i \neq 0$.) There will always be a nontrivial $\mathbf{a}$ solving $\mathbf{Ax} = \mathbf{0}$ and using a subset of the columns used by $\mathbf{x}_k$ if $\mathbf{x}_k$ is *not* a BFS of $\mathbf{Ax} = \mathbf{b}$, $\mathbf{x} \geq \mathbf{0}$. This fact is the content of the next theorem, a result so important to the theory that we call it *the fundamental theorem*.

Theorem 9.5.1. (*The Fundamental Theorem*). *Suppose $\mathbf{x}_k$ is a feasible solution of $\mathbf{Ax} = \mathbf{b}$, $\mathbf{x} \geq \mathbf{0}$ that uses a linearly dependent set of columns of $\mathbf{A}$, so $\mathbf{x}_k$ is not a* BFS. *Then there exists an $\mathbf{a} \neq \mathbf{0}$, that uses a subset of the columns of $\mathbf{A}$ used by $\mathbf{x}_k$, and there exist scalars λ_- and λ_+, such that $\lambda_- < 0$, $\lambda_+ > 0$, and*

$$\mathbf{x}(\lambda) = \mathbf{x}_k + \lambda\mathbf{a} \tag{9.5.1}$$

is a feasible solution for all λ, $\lambda_- \leq \lambda \leq \lambda_+$.

Remark. Since λ_- is negative and λ_+ is positive, $\lambda = 0$ is in the interior of the interval $[\lambda_-, \lambda_+]$. This implies that $\mathbf{x}_k$ lies in the interior of the line segment of feasible solutions $\mathbf{x}(\lambda)$. Specifically, $\mathbf{x}_k = \mathbf{x}(0)$.

Proof. For convenience, assume that $\mathbf{x}$ uses only the first k columns of $\mathbf{A}_{m\times n}$. Assume that these columns are linearly dependent. Then there is a dependency relationship among these k columns. Let this relationship by given by

$$a_1\mathbf{A}_{*1} + a_2\mathbf{A}_{*2} + \cdots + a_k\mathbf{A}_{*k} = \mathbf{0} \tag{9.5.2}$$

where not all the weights are zero, and $\mathbf{a} = [a_1 \quad \ldots \quad a_k \quad 0 \quad \ldots \quad 0]^{\mathrm{T}}$ denotes the vector of weights. Then $\mathbf{a}$ uses a subset of the columns used by $\mathbf{x}_k$, and $\mathbf{Aa} = \mathbf{0}$, by Eq. 9.5.2. Define $\mathbf{x}(\lambda)$ by the expression

$$\mathbf{x}(\lambda) = \mathbf{x}_k + \lambda\mathbf{a} = \begin{bmatrix} x_1 \\ \vdots \\ x_k \\ 0 \\ \vdots \\ 0 \end{bmatrix} + \lambda \begin{bmatrix} a_1 \\ \vdots \\ a_k \\ 0 \\ \vdots \\ 0 \end{bmatrix}$$

There are three cases to consider. First, it may happen that all $a_i \geq 0$. In such a circumstance, $\lambda \geq -x_i/a_i$ must hold for all $a_i > 0$ in order for $\mathbf{x}(\lambda)$ to be feasible. (Not all $a_i = 0$, for then $\mathbf{a} = \mathbf{0}$, contradicting the hypothesis.) We satisfy all these requirements by defining λ_- by

$$\lambda_- = \max\{-x_i/a_i; a_i > 0\} \tag{9.5.3}$$

Note that $\lambda_- < 0$, since x_i and a_i are both positive. Then $\mathbf{x}(\lambda)$ is a feasible solution for each λ, $\lambda_- \leq \lambda < \infty$.

Second, if $a_i \leq 0$ for all i, then we define λ_+ by

$$\lambda_+ = \min\{-x_i/a_i; a_i < 0\} \tag{9.5.4}$$

Note that $\lambda_+ > 0$. This guarantees that $\mathbf{x}(\lambda)$ is a feasible solution for all λ, $-\infty < \lambda \leq \lambda_+$.

Finally, suppose that some a_i are negative and some positive. By the same analysis, $\mathbf{x}(\lambda)$ is a feasible solution for all λ, if $\lambda_- \leq \lambda \leq \lambda_+$. Here λ_- and λ_+ are defined by Eqs. 9.5.3 and 9.5.4, respectively.

By construction, λ_- is strictly negative (or is $-\infty$), and λ_+ is strictly positive (or is $+\infty$). Hence, the interval $[\lambda_-, \lambda_+]$ is nondegenerative and contains 0 in its interior in all three cases. ■

Example 9.5.2. Find a line passing through the point (2,1,1) and remaining within the convex set of solutions $\mathcal{K}$ of

$$\begin{bmatrix} 1 & 0 & -1 \\ 0 & 1 & 2 \end{bmatrix} \mathbf{x} = \begin{bmatrix} 1 \\ 3 \end{bmatrix}, \qquad \mathbf{x} \geq \mathbf{0}$$

Solution. The vector $\mathbf{x}_k = [2 \quad 1 \quad 1]^{\mathrm{T}}$ is clearly in $\mathcal{K}$ and uses all three columns of $\mathbf{A}$. Thus, any nontrivial solution of $\mathbf{Ax} = \mathbf{0}$ suffices for $\mathbf{a}$. The dependency relationship

$$(-1)\begin{bmatrix} 1 \\ 0 \end{bmatrix} + (2)\begin{bmatrix} 0 \\ 1 \end{bmatrix} + (-1)\begin{bmatrix} -1 \\ 2 \end{bmatrix} = \begin{bmatrix} 0 \\ 0 \end{bmatrix}$$

among the columns of $\mathbf{A}$ leads to

$$\mathbf{a} = \begin{bmatrix} -1 \\ 2 \\ -1 \end{bmatrix}$$

Now consider

$$\mathbf{x}(\lambda) = \begin{bmatrix} 2 \\ 1 \\ 1 \end{bmatrix} + \lambda \begin{bmatrix} -1 \\ 2 \\ -1 \end{bmatrix} \geq \mathbf{0}$$

This vector inequality is equivalent to the three inequalities $2 - \lambda \geq 0$, $1 - \lambda \geq 0$, and $1 + 2\lambda \geq 0$. Hence, $\mathbf{x}(\lambda)$ is a feasible solution for all λ in the interval $-\frac{1}{2} \leq \lambda \leq 1$. The line segment $\mathbf{x}(\lambda)$, $-\frac{1}{2} \leq \lambda \leq 1$, and the three points

$$\mathbf{x}(-\tfrac{1}{2}) = \begin{bmatrix} \frac{5}{2} \\ 0 \\ \frac{3}{2} \end{bmatrix}, \qquad \mathbf{x}(1) = \begin{bmatrix} 1 \\ 3 \\ 0 \end{bmatrix}, \qquad \mathbf{x}(0) = \begin{bmatrix} 2 \\ 1 \\ 1 \end{bmatrix}$$

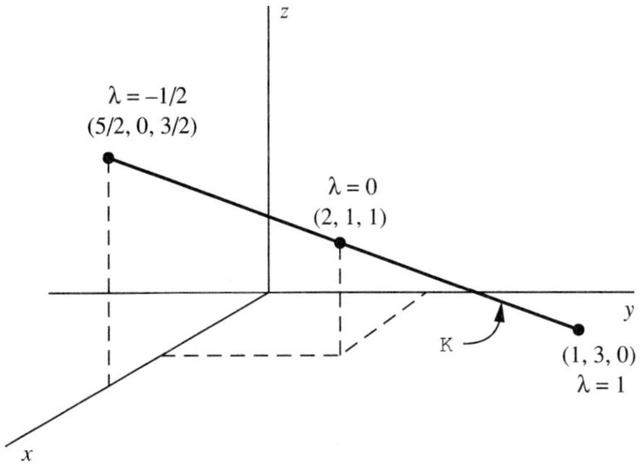

FIGURE 9-8
The line $\mathcal{K}$ of feasible solutions containing the BFSs

$$\mathbf{x}(-\tfrac{1}{2}) = \begin{bmatrix} \tfrac{5}{2} \\ 0 \\ \tfrac{3}{2} \end{bmatrix}, \qquad \mathbf{x}(1) = \begin{bmatrix} 1 \\ 3 \\ 0 \end{bmatrix}$$

are sketched in Fig. 9.8. The vectors $\mathbf{x}(-\tfrac{1}{2})$ and $\mathbf{x}(1)$ represent points at the boundary of the convex set of feasible solutions. This is so because if λ were not in the interval $[-\tfrac{1}{2}, 1]$, $\mathbf{x}(\lambda)$ would be infeasible. Note that $\mathbf{x}(-\tfrac{1}{2})$ and $\mathbf{x}(1)$ use fewer columns than $\mathbf{x}(0)$.

Example 9.5.3. Repeat Example 9.5.2 for the system

$$\begin{bmatrix} 1 & 0 & -1 & 1 & 2 \\ 0 & 1 & 2 & -1 & 1 \end{bmatrix} \mathbf{x} = \begin{bmatrix} 4 \\ 2 \end{bmatrix}, \qquad \mathbf{x} \geq \mathbf{0}$$

starting with the feasible solution $\mathbf{x}_k = [1 \quad 2 \quad 0 \quad 1 \quad 1]^{\mathrm{T}}$.

Solution. The given feasible solution uses columns 1, 2, 4, and 5. These columns of **A** form a linearly dependent set. Search for a dependency relationship among only these columns by solving

$$a_1 \begin{bmatrix} 1 \\ 0 \end{bmatrix} + a_2 \begin{bmatrix} 0 \\ 1 \end{bmatrix} + a_3 \begin{bmatrix} 1 \\ -1 \end{bmatrix} + a_4 \begin{bmatrix} 1 \\ -1 \end{bmatrix} + a_5 \begin{bmatrix} 2 \\ 1 \end{bmatrix} = \begin{bmatrix} 0 \\ 0 \end{bmatrix}$$

One solution, discovered by inspection, is

$$(2) \begin{bmatrix} 1 \\ 0 \end{bmatrix} + (1) \begin{bmatrix} 0 \\ 1 \end{bmatrix} + (-1) \begin{bmatrix} 2 \\ 1 \end{bmatrix} = \begin{bmatrix} 0 \\ 0 \end{bmatrix}$$

Hence,

$$\mathbf{x}(\lambda) = \begin{bmatrix} 1 \\ 2 \\ 0 \\ 1 \\ 1 \end{bmatrix} + \lambda \begin{bmatrix} 2 \\ 1 \\ 0 \\ 0 \\ -1 \end{bmatrix}$$

This is equivalent to the three inequalities $1 + 2\lambda \geq 0$, $2 + \lambda \geq 0$, and $1 - \lambda \geq 0$. Thus, $-\frac{1}{2} \leq \lambda \leq 1$, and for each such λ, $\mathbf{x}(\lambda)$ is a feasible solution. The endpoints,

$$\mathbf{x}(-\tfrac{1}{2}) = \begin{bmatrix} 0 \\ \frac{3}{2} \\ 0 \\ 1 \\ \frac{3}{2} \end{bmatrix}, \qquad \mathbf{x}(1) = \begin{bmatrix} 3 \\ 3 \\ 0 \\ 1 \\ 0 \end{bmatrix}$$

are feasible solutions using three columns of $\mathbf{A}$. The feasible solution $\mathbf{x} = [1 \quad 2 \quad 0 \quad 1 \quad 1]^T$ uses four columns of $\mathbf{A}$.

Corollary 1. *Under the hypothesis of the theorem, if λ_- and λ_+ are both finite, then $\mathbf{x}(\lambda_-)$ and $\mathbf{x}(\lambda_+)$ are feasible solutions that use a proper subset of the columns used by $\mathbf{x} = \mathbf{x}(0)$.*

Proof. When λ takes either of the values λ_- or λ_+, at least one of the entries of $\mathbf{x}(\lambda)$ vanishes. Since no zero entry of $\mathbf{x}(\lambda)$ is made nonzero by any choice of λ, the proof is complete. ■

Corollary 2. *Assume that the convex set of feasible solutions $\mathcal{H}$ of $\mathbf{Ax} = \mathbf{b}$, $\mathbf{x} \geq \mathbf{0}$, is nonempty. Then $\mathcal{H}$ is a polytope if and only if $\mathbf{Ax} = \mathbf{0}$, $\mathbf{x} \geq \mathbf{0}$, has only the trivial feasible solution $\mathbf{x} = \mathbf{0}$.*

Proof. (Recall that a polytope is a bounded polyhedron.) Let $\mathbf{x}_k$ be a feasible solution of $\mathbf{Ax} = \mathbf{b}$, $\mathbf{x} \geq \mathbf{0}$. Such a solution exists by hypothesis. If $\mathbf{a} \neq \mathbf{0}$ is a nonnegative solution of $\mathbf{Ax} = \mathbf{0}$, then $\mathbf{x}_k + \lambda\mathbf{a}$ is feasible for all $0 \leq \lambda$. Hence, $\mathcal{H}$ must be unbounded. This proves that if $\mathcal{H}$ is bounded, $\mathbf{0}$ is the only feasible solution of $\mathbf{Ax} = \mathbf{0}$, $\mathbf{x} \geq \mathbf{0}$.

Now for the converse. Suppose that $\mathcal{H}$ is unbounded. Then there must be a line in $\mathcal{H}$ that is unbounded. Such a line has the equation $\mathbf{x}_k + \lambda\mathbf{a}$ for some feasible solution $\mathbf{x}_k$, some $\mathbf{a} \neq \mathbf{0}$, and all $\lambda \geq 0$. Since $\mathbf{Ax}_k = \mathbf{b}$ and $\mathbf{A}(\mathbf{x}_k + \lambda\mathbf{a}) = \mathbf{b}$, it follows that $\mathbf{Aa} = \mathbf{0}$. Since $\mathbf{x}_k + \lambda\mathbf{a} \geq \mathbf{0}$ for all $\lambda \geq 0$, no entry in $\mathbf{a}$ can be negative. So $\mathbf{a}$ is a nontrivial, feasible solution of the homogeneous system $\mathbf{Ax} = \mathbf{0}$, $\mathbf{x} \geq \mathbf{0}$. ■

Example 9.5.4. Sketch the path traced by $\mathbf{x}(\lambda)$ in Corollary 1 for system $[1 \quad 1 \quad 1]\mathbf{x} = 3$, $\mathbf{x} \geq \mathbf{0}$, when $\mathbf{x}_k = [1 \quad 1 \quad 1]^T$. (Here $\mathbf{A} = [1 \quad 1 \quad 1]$.)

Solution. The feasible solution $\mathbf{x}$ uses columns 1, 2, and 3 of $\mathbf{A}$. There are many dependency relationships possible among these three columns. Choose $2\mathbf{A}_{*1} - \mathbf{A}_{*2} - \mathbf{A}_{*3} = \mathbf{0}$, which translates into $2 - 1 - 1 = 0$ for this $\mathbf{A}$. So

$$\mathbf{x}(\lambda) = \mathbf{x}_k + \lambda\mathbf{a} = \begin{bmatrix} 1 \\ 1 \\ 1 \end{bmatrix} + \lambda \begin{bmatrix} 2 \\ -1 \\ -1 \end{bmatrix} = \begin{bmatrix} 1 + 2\lambda \\ 1 - \lambda \\ 1 - \lambda \end{bmatrix}$$

and $\mathbf{x}(\lambda) \geq 0$ for λ in the interval $-\frac{1}{2} \leq \lambda \leq 1$. For $\lambda = -\frac{1}{2}$, $\mathbf{x}(-\frac{1}{2}) = [0 \quad \frac{3}{2} \quad \frac{3}{2}]^T$ is a feasible solution that is not a vertex. On the other hand, for $\lambda = 1$, $\mathbf{x}(1) = [3 \quad 0 \quad 0]^T$, and this is a vertex of $\mathcal{H}$. Set $\mathbf{z}_k = \mathbf{x}(-\frac{1}{2}) = [0 \quad \frac{3}{2} \quad \frac{3}{2}]^T$. Then $\mathbf{z}_k$ uses a linearly dependent set of columns, and along similar lines,

$$\mathbf{z}(\lambda) = \mathbf{z}_k + \lambda\mathbf{a} = \begin{bmatrix} 0 \\ \frac{3}{2} \\ \frac{3}{2} \end{bmatrix} + \lambda \begin{bmatrix} 0 \\ 1 \\ -1 \end{bmatrix} = \begin{bmatrix} 0 \\ \frac{3}{2} + \lambda \\ \frac{3}{2} - \lambda \end{bmatrix}$$

therefore, $-\frac{3}{2} \leq \lambda \leq \frac{3}{2}$. Two more extreme points are obtained by selecting $\lambda = -\frac{3}{2}$ and $\lambda = \frac{3}{2}$, namely $\mathbf{z}(-\frac{3}{2}) = [0 \quad 0 \quad 3]^T$ and, finally, $\mathbf{z}(\frac{3}{2}) = [0 \quad 3 \quad 0]^T$. See Fig. 9.9.

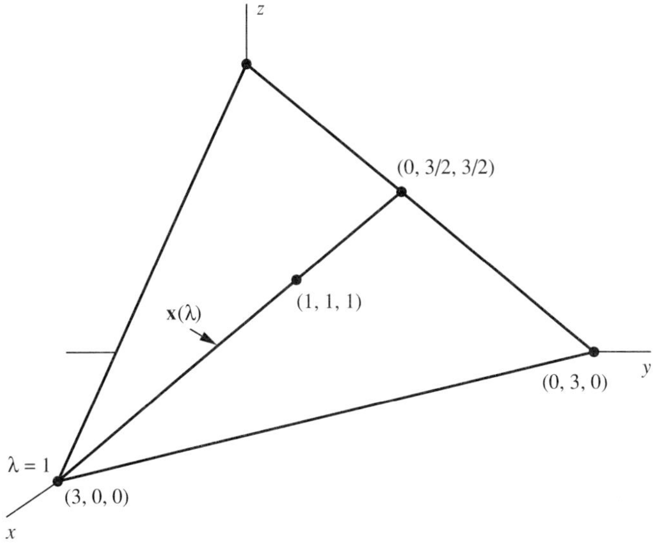

FIGURE 9-9
The line segment of feasible solutions containing (1,1,1) and terminating in the vertex (3,0,0) and the boundary point $(0, \frac{3}{2}, \frac{3}{2})$.

PROBLEMS

PART 1

The system $\mathbf{Ax} = \mathbf{b}$, $\mathbf{x} \geq \mathbf{0}$, is to be assumed for Problems 9.5.1 – 9.5.4. The matrix $\mathbf{A}$ is given by

$$\mathbf{A} = \begin{bmatrix} 1 & 0 & -2 & 1 & -1 \\ 0 & 1 & 1 & 0 & 0 \\ -1 & 0 & 2 & 2 & 1 \end{bmatrix}$$

For each $\mathbf{b}$ and each feasible solution $\mathbf{x}_k$, find $\mathbf{a}$ (if possible) so that $\mathbf{x}(\lambda) = \mathbf{x}_k + \lambda\mathbf{a}$ is a feasible solution of $\mathbf{Ax} = \mathbf{b}$, $\mathbf{x} \geq \mathbf{0}$ for all λ in some nontrivial interval $[a,b]$ containing 0. Find the smallest a and the largest b for which this is possible. Determine the columns used by $\mathbf{x}(\lambda)$ for each λ.

9.5.1. Let $\mathbf{b} = [1 \quad 1 \quad 2]^T$ and $\mathbf{x} = [1 \quad 1 \quad 0 \quad 1 \quad 1]^T$.
9.5.2. Let $\mathbf{b} = [0 \quad 2 \quad 3]^T$ and $\mathbf{x} = [1 \quad 1 \quad 1 \quad 1 \quad 0]^T$.
9.5.3. Let $\mathbf{b} = [2 \quad 0 \quad 1]^T$ and $\mathbf{x} = [1 \quad 0 \quad 0 \quad 1 \quad 0]^T$.
9.5.4. Let $\mathbf{b} = [-1 \quad 2 \quad 1]^T$ and $\mathbf{x} = [1 \quad 1 \quad 1 \quad 0 \quad 0]^T$.
9.5.5. Show that $\lambda \geq 0$ if $a > 0$ and

$$\begin{bmatrix} 0 \\ 0 \\ * \end{bmatrix} + \lambda \begin{bmatrix} a \\ * \\ * \end{bmatrix} \geq \mathbf{0}$$

9.5.6. Show that $\lambda = 0$ if $a > 0$ and $b < 0$ and

$$\begin{bmatrix} 0 \\ 0 \\ * \end{bmatrix} + \lambda \begin{bmatrix} a \\ b \\ * \end{bmatrix} \geq \mathbf{0}$$

PART 2

9.5.7. Sketch a convex polytope in $\mathcal{K} \subseteq \mathcal{R}^2$ and identify three points $\mathbf{x}_1$, $\mathbf{x}_2$, and $\mathbf{x}_3$ each in $\mathcal{K}$ and with these properties:
(*a*) $\mathbf{x}_1 + \lambda\mathbf{a} \in \mathcal{K},\ \mathbf{a} \neq \mathbf{0},\ -\epsilon < \lambda < \epsilon$, for some $\epsilon > 0$
(*b*) $\mathbf{x}_2 + \lambda\mathbf{a} \in \mathcal{K},\ \mathbf{a} \neq \mathbf{0},\ 0 < \lambda < \epsilon$, for some $\epsilon > 0$ and $\mathbf{x}_2 - \lambda\mathbf{a} \notin \mathcal{K}$
(*c*) For some $\mathbf{a}$, $\mathbf{x}_3 + \lambda\mathbf{a} \notin \mathcal{K}$ for all $\lambda \neq 0$
9.5.8. Refer to Example 9.5.4. Beginning with $\mathbf{x}_k = [1 \quad 1 \quad 1]^T$, sketch the path traced by $\mathbf{x}(\lambda) = \mathbf{x}_k + \lambda\mathbf{a}$ in Eq. 9.5.1 by using these choices for $\mathbf{a}$:
(*a*) $\mathbf{a} = [1 \quad -1 \quad 0]^T$ (*b*) $\mathbf{a} = [0 \quad -1 \quad 1]^T$ (*c*) $\mathbf{a} = [1 \quad 0 \quad -1]^T$
9.5.9. Repeat Problem 9.5.8, except begin with the feasible solution $\mathbf{x}_k = [\tfrac{1}{2} \quad 2 \quad \tfrac{1}{2}]^T$

PART 3

9.5.10. Suppose

$$\mathbf{x}(\lambda) = \begin{bmatrix} \mathbf{x} \\ \mathbf{0} \end{bmatrix} + \lambda \begin{bmatrix} \mathbf{0} \\ \mathbf{a} \end{bmatrix} \quad \text{and} \quad \begin{bmatrix} \mathbf{x} \\ \mathbf{0} \end{bmatrix} \geq \mathbf{0}$$

(*a*) Show that $\mathbf{x}(\lambda) \geq \mathbf{0}$ for all $\lambda \geq 0$ if and only if $\mathbf{a} \geq \mathbf{0}$.
(*b*) Show that $\mathbf{x}(\lambda) \geq \mathbf{0}$ for all $\lambda \leq 0$ if and only if $\mathbf{a} \leq \mathbf{0}$.
(*c*) Show that $\mathbf{x}(\lambda) \geq \mathbf{0}$ only for $\lambda = 0$, if $\mathbf{a}$ has positive and negative entries.
9.5.11. Let $\mathbf{a}$ be arbitrary and $\mathbf{x} > \mathbf{0}$. Find $\epsilon > 0$ so that $\mathbf{x} + \lambda\mathbf{a} \geq \mathbf{0}$ for all λ, $-\epsilon \leq \lambda \leq \epsilon$.
9.5.12. Show: If $\mathcal{K}$ is an unbounded, convex polyhedron and $\mathbf{x}$ is any point of $\mathcal{K}$, then there is an $\mathbf{a} \neq \mathbf{0}$ such that $\mathbf{x} + \lambda\mathbf{a} \in \mathcal{K}$ for all $\lambda \geq 0$.

9.6 STANDARD LINEAR PROGRAMS

The problem of finding an $\mathbf{x}$ that minimizes $z(\mathbf{x}) = \mathbf{c}^T\mathbf{x}$, for $\mathbf{x}$ in a convex polyhedron $\mathcal{K}$, is called a *linear program* (LP), and the linear function $\mathbf{c}^T\mathbf{x}$ is called the *objective function*. If $\mathbf{x}_0 \in \mathcal{K}$ has the property

$$z(\mathbf{x}_0) \leq z(\mathbf{x}) \tag{9.6.1}$$

for all $\mathbf{x} \in \mathcal{H}$, then $\mathbf{x}_0$ is called an *optimal feasible solution*. We write $z_{\min} = z(\mathbf{x}_0)$ and call $z_{\min}$ the *optimal value* of the objective function. The brewer's resource allocation problem, of Section 0.1.2 is a typical example of a linear program. If for *each M* there is a feasible solution $\mathbf{x}_M$ such that $z(\mathbf{x}_M) \le M$, then the objective function is said to be *unbounded below* on $\mathcal{H}$. (For the objective function to be unbounded below, it is necessary for $\mathcal{H}$ to be an unbounded polyhedron. The converse is false, as can easily be seen by choosing $z(\mathbf{x}) = 0$.)

The convex sets over which we attempt to find the minimum of $z(\mathbf{x})$ arise as the set of feasible solutions of systems to equations in nonnegative variables:

$$\begin{aligned} \text{minimize:} \quad & z(\mathbf{x}) = \mathbf{c}^{\mathrm{T}}\mathbf{x} \\ \text{subject to:} \quad & \mathbf{A}\mathbf{x} = \mathbf{b}, \ \mathbf{x} \ge \mathbf{0} \end{aligned} \tag{9.6.2}$$

The LP given in Eq. 9.6.2 is called a standard linear program or SLP. It is convenient to consider only SLP's. This is no loss of generality, because every LP can be converted into an SLP by the methods of Section 9.3.

Example 9.6.1. *(Brewer's Problem).* Convert the following LP into an SLP:

$$\begin{aligned} \text{maximize:} \quad & w(x_1, x_2, x_3) = 2x_1 + 3x_2 + 4x_3 \\ \text{subject to:} \quad & \left.\begin{aligned} 2x_1 + x_2 + x_3 &\le 10 \\ x_1 \qquad + x_3 &\le 5 \end{aligned}\right\} \quad x_1 \ge 0, \ x_2 \ge 0, \ x_3 \ge 0 \end{aligned}$$

Solution. The introduction of two slacks, one for each inequality constraint, and the conversion of maximization to minimization is all that is needed here. The equivalent SLP is

$$\begin{aligned} \text{minimize:} \quad & \hat{z}(x_1,x_2,x_3,s_1,s_2) = -w(x_1,x_2,x_3,s_1,s_2) \\ & \qquad = -2x_1 - 3x_2 - 4x_3 + 0s_1 + 0s_2 \\ \text{subject to:} \quad & \left.\begin{aligned} 2x_1 + x_2 + x_3 + s_1 \qquad &= 10 \\ x_1 + x_2 \qquad\qquad + s_2 &= 5 \end{aligned}\right\} \quad \begin{aligned} & x_i \ge 0, \ i = 1, 2, 3 \\ & s_1 \ge 0, \ s_2 \ge 0 \end{aligned} \end{aligned}$$

If the constraints and sign restrictions in an LP imply an empty feasibility set, the LP is called *infeasible* and is discarded; otherwise the LP is called *feasible*. The next theorem shows that an optimal solution can always be found among the set of BFSs of an SLP. The proof is constructive, interesting, and worth detailed study.

Theorem 9.6.1. *Suppose a* SLP *has an optimal feasible solution,* $\mathbf{x}_0$. *Then there also exists an optimal* BFS, $\mathbf{x}_f$.

Proof. If $\mathbf{x}_0$ uses a linearly independent set of columns of $\mathbf{A}$, then $\mathbf{x}_0$ is a BFS by definition and there is nothing to prove. So assume that $\mathbf{x}_0$ uses a linearly dependent set of columns. By Theorem 9.5.1, $\mathbf{x}(\lambda) = \mathbf{x}_0 + \lambda\mathbf{a}$, $\lambda_- \le \lambda \le \lambda_+$, is a line segment of feasible solutions. Moreover, since either λ_- or λ_+ or both are finite, one or both of $\mathbf{x}(\lambda_-)$ or $\mathbf{x}(\lambda_+)$ is a feasible solution using fewer columns than $\mathbf{x}_0$. Remarkably, $z(\mathbf{a}) = 0$ along this line of feasible solutions! To see this, first recall that λ_- is negative and λ_+ is positive. Next verify that $z\{\mathbf{x}(\lambda)\} = z(\mathbf{x}_0) + \lambda z(\mathbf{a})$. If $z(\mathbf{a}) < 0$, choose a positive λ such that $\lambda < \lambda_+$.

Then $z\{\mathbf{x}(\lambda)\} = z\{(\mathbf{x}_0) + \lambda z(\mathbf{a}) < z(\mathbf{x}_0)$, contradicting the assumption that $\mathbf{x}_0$ is an optimum. Similarly, if $z(\mathbf{a}) > 0$, choose a negative λ such that $\lambda > \lambda_-$ to obtain a contradiction. So $z(\mathbf{a}) = 0$. For ease of reference, suppose λ_+ is finite. Then it follows that $z\{\mathbf{x}(\lambda)\} = z(\mathbf{x}_0)$ for all λ, $0 \le \lambda \le \lambda_+$; therefore, $\mathbf{x}(\lambda_+)$ is an optimal feasible solution. But $\mathbf{x}(\lambda_+)$ uses fewer columns than $\mathbf{x}_0$. If $\mathbf{x}(\lambda_+)$ is a BFS, we are done. If not, set $\mathbf{x}_0 = \mathbf{x}(\lambda_+)$. Now repeat the above analysis to obtain optimal solutions using still fewer columns until $\mathbf{x}_0$ uses a linearly independent set of columns. If necessary, the algorithm will produce an optimal solution using one column of **A**, which is guaranteed to be a linearly independent set. This optimal solution is a BFS. ■

The proof just given has an interesting geometric interpretation. Suppose $\mathcal{K}$ is a convex polyhedron in three-dimensional-space. (Although not particularly subtle, a cube will do quite well as an example.) Suppose $\mathbf{x}_0$ is a point in the interior of this polyhedron. The line segment $\mathbf{x}(\lambda)$ terminates at the boundary of $\mathcal{K}$, which is either a face of $\mathcal{K}$ (a square), an edge of $\mathcal{K}$, or a vertex of $\mathcal{K}$ (See Fig. 9.10.) If the line terminates at a face, the new optimal solution lies in a two-dimensional polyhedron. A line segment containing $\mathbf{x}_0$ now terminates on the boundary of this polyhedron, which is either an edge or a vertex of $\mathcal{K}$. If it is at an edge, the next line segment must terminate at a vertex. Thus, at the end of at most three applications of this technique, an optimal solution is found at a vertex of $\mathcal{K}$.

The importance of this theorem is easy to understand. Instead of requiring a search for an optimal solution over the infinitely many vectors in $\mathcal{K}$, it is necessary to examine the value of z only at the finite number of vertices of $\mathcal{K}$. In fact, the most powerful method of finding an optimal solution, the simplex method, is based precisely on this idea. The next four sections elaborate the details of this method. Here are two examples that reinforce the ideas behind the proof of Theorem 9.6.1.

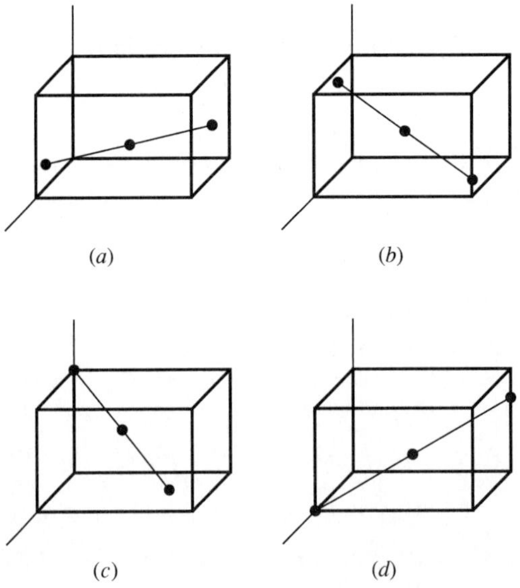

(*a*) (*b*) (*c*) (*d*)

FIGURE 9-10
The line segment $\mathbf{x}(\lambda)$ containing $\mathbf{x}_0$.

Example 9.6.2. Evaluate $z(\mathbf{x})$ at each of the BFSs of the SLP:

$$\text{minimize:} \quad z(\mathbf{x}) = -x_1 + x_2 + x_3 - x_4$$

$$\text{subject to:} \quad \begin{bmatrix} 1 & 0 & 1 & 2 \\ 0 & 1 & -1 & 1 \end{bmatrix} \mathbf{x} = \begin{bmatrix} 4 \\ 2 \end{bmatrix}, \qquad \mathbf{x} \geq \mathbf{0}$$

Solution. The simplest way to find all the BFSs of this SLP is to set two variables equal to zero and solve the resulting 2×2 systems, and then set three variables equal to zero and solve the resulting 2×1 systems.

There are six possible ways of setting two variables at zero, one of which leads to the infeasible solution $x_2 = x_4 = 0$, $x_3 = -2$. Of the remaining five that are feasible, three lead to identical solutions, so in all there are three distinct BFSs:

$$\mathbf{x}_1 = \begin{bmatrix} 4 \\ 2 \\ 0 \\ 0 \end{bmatrix}, \qquad \mathbf{x}_2 = \begin{bmatrix} 0 \\ 0 \\ 0 \\ 2 \end{bmatrix}, \qquad \mathbf{x}_3 = \begin{bmatrix} 0 \\ 6 \\ 4 \\ 0 \end{bmatrix}$$

Hence, $z(\mathbf{x}_1) = z(\mathbf{x}_2) = -2 \leq z(\mathbf{x}_3) = 10$. Thus, from Theorem 9.6.1 it follows that $\mathbf{x}_1$ and $\mathbf{x}_2$ are optimum solutions and $z_{\min}(\mathbf{x}) = -2$.

There are four 2×1 systems but only one is consistent; $x_1 = x_2 = x_3 = 0$, $x_4 = 2$ This feasible solution is $\mathbf{x}_2$ (a solution using one column of $\mathbf{A}$), already computed as one of the solutions of the 2×2 systems.

Example 9.6.3. Show that $\mathbf{x}_0 = [2 \quad 1 \quad 0 \quad 1]^{\mathrm{T}}$ is an optimal solution of the SLP given in Example 9.6.2, and derive a BFS from it using the ideas in the proof of Theorem 9.6.1.

Solution. The minimum value of the objective function given in Example 9.6.2 is -2. Since $z(\mathbf{x}_0) = -2$, $\mathbf{x}_0 \geq \mathbf{0}$, and $\mathbf{A}\mathbf{x}_0 = \mathbf{b}$, $\mathbf{x}_0$ is an optimal feasible solution. Since $\mathbf{x}_0$ uses columns 1, 2, and 4 of $\mathbf{A}$, there is a dependency relationship among these columns:

$$2\begin{bmatrix} 1 \\ 0 \end{bmatrix} + \begin{bmatrix} 0 \\ 1 \end{bmatrix} + (-1)\begin{bmatrix} 2 \\ 1 \end{bmatrix} = \mathbf{0}$$

Hence, $\mathbf{a} = [2 \quad 1 \quad 0 \quad -1]^{\mathrm{T}}$. (One of the crucial steps in the proof of Theorem 9.6.1 is that $z(\mathbf{a}) = 0$ is a consequence of $\mathbf{x}_0$ being an optimal solution. This is confirmed by the computation $z(\mathbf{a}) = -(2) + 1 + 0 - (-1) = 0$.) The next step is finding λ_- and λ_+ from the equation for the line segment of feasible solutions:

$$\mathbf{x}_0 + \lambda\mathbf{a} = \begin{bmatrix} 2 \\ 1 \\ 0 \\ 1 \end{bmatrix} + \lambda \begin{bmatrix} 2 \\ 1 \\ 0 \\ -1 \end{bmatrix} \geq \mathbf{0}$$

From this system $2 + 2\lambda \geq 0,\ 1 + \lambda \geq 0, 0 + 0\lambda = 0$, and $1 - \lambda \geq 0$, and these inequalities imply that $-1 \leq \lambda \leq 1$. $\mathbf{x}_1$ is obtained when $\lambda = 1$, and $\mathbf{x}_2$ is obtained when $\lambda = -1$. These are two of the three BFSs obtained in Example 9.6.2.

PROBLEMS

PART 1

9.6.1. (*a*) Find all the BFSs of the following SLP:

$$\text{minimize:} \quad z(\mathbf{x}) = x + y + z$$
$$\text{subject to:} \quad x + y + z = 3, \quad x \geq 0,\ y \geq 0,\ z \geq 0$$

(*b*) Evaluate $z(\mathbf{x})$ at each BFS found in (*a*) and determine all the optimal BFSs. Are there optimal feasible solutions that are not BFSs?

9.6.2. Repeat Problem 9.6.1 for the SLP

$$\text{minimize:} \quad z(\mathbf{x}) = x - y$$
$$\text{subject to:} \quad x + y + z = 3, \quad x \geq 0,\ y \geq 0,\ z \geq 0$$

9.6.3. Repeat Problem 9.6.1 for the SLP

$$\text{minimize:} \quad z(\mathbf{x}) = x + y + z$$
$$\text{subject to:} \quad x + y - z = 3, \quad x \geq 0,\ y \geq 0,\ z \geq 0$$

9.6.4. Repeat Problem 9.6.1 for the SLP

$$\text{minimize:} \quad z(\mathbf{x}) = x + y + z$$
$$\text{subject to:} \quad x - y = 3, \quad x \geq 0,\ y \geq 0,\ z \geq 0$$

9.6.5. Assume that $\mathbf{x}_0 = [2 \quad 1 \quad 1]^{\mathrm{T}}$ is an optimal feasible solution of:

$$\text{minimize :} \quad z(\mathbf{x}) = x + y + z$$
$$\text{subject to :} \quad \begin{bmatrix} 1 & 0 & -1 \\ 0 & 1 & 2 \end{bmatrix} \mathbf{x} = \begin{bmatrix} 1 \\ 3 \end{bmatrix}$$

Find an optimal BFS by applying the technique of Theorem 9.6.1 to $\mathbf{x}_0$. How many optimal BFSs does this method yield? Are there any other optimal solutions?

PART 2

9.6.6. Suppose $\mathbf{x}_0$ is an optimal feasible solution of the LP: maximize $z(\mathbf{x}) = \mathbf{c}^{\mathrm{T}}\mathbf{x}$ subject to $\mathbf{A}\mathbf{x} = \mathbf{b},\ \mathbf{x} \geq \mathbf{0}$. Show that $\mathbf{x}_0$ is an optimal feasible solution of the SLP: minimize $w(\mathbf{x}) = -z(\mathbf{x}),\ \mathbf{A}\mathbf{x} = \mathbf{b},\ \mathbf{x} \geq \mathbf{0}$.

9.6.7. Suppose that the SLP; minimize $z(\mathbf{x}) = \mathbf{c}^{\mathrm{T}}\mathbf{x}$ subject to $\mathbf{A}\mathbf{x} = \mathbf{b},\ \mathbf{x} \geq \mathbf{0}$, has a feasible solution $\mathbf{x}_1$. Suppose $\mathbf{a} \geq \mathbf{0}$ is a solution of $\mathbf{A}\mathbf{x} = \mathbf{0}$ and that $z(\mathbf{a}) < 0$. By considering $z(\mathbf{x}_1 + \lambda\mathbf{a})$, show that the given SLP must be unbounded below.

9.6.8. Use the conclusion of Problem 9.6.7 to argue that the question of whether or not an SLP has an optimal feasible solution or is unbounded below does not depend on the choice of $\mathbf{b}$ in the system of constraints $\mathbf{A}\mathbf{x} = \mathbf{b}$.

PART 3

9.6.9. Show that the set of optimal feasible solutions of a (feasible) SLP is a convex set.

9.6.10. Explain why a feasibility set (of an SLP) that is a polytope must have an optimal feasible solution for all objective functions. On the other hand, show that a feasibility set that is not a polytope may not have an SLP that is unbounded below. (*Hint:* Choose a very simple objective function.)

9.7 INITIAL AND CANONICAL TABLEAUX

The problem of finding feasible solutions of $\mathbf{Ax} = \mathbf{b},\ \mathbf{x} \geq \mathbf{0}$ is far more difficult than solving $\mathbf{Ax} = \mathbf{b}$. Solutions obtained by row reductions are usually not feasible even for a feasible SLP. Moreover, because the SLP may be infeasible, a random search for feasible solutions may be futile. And this is not the only difficulty. Although we know from Theorem 9.6.1 that optimum solutions can be found among the BFSs of an SLP, there may be far too many BFSs to examine them all, for optimality, even if we had a method of finding them. There are potentially $C\binom{n}{m} = n!/m!(n-m)!$ different BFSs for $\mathbf{A}$ with size $m \times n$, which is an exceedingly large number for even modestly-sized, realistic SLPs. (The symbol $C\binom{50}{25}$ represents the number of ways of selecting 25 objects out of a set of 50 and is an integer larger than 3×10^{14}.) In view of these pessimistic considerations, it is all the more remarkable that an efficient method exists for testing an SLP for feasibility and discovering an optimal solution when it exists. This technique is known as the *simplex method.*

There are two steps in the simplex method. The first, called *phase* 1, determines if the SLP is feasible and if it is, provides a BFS. (The details are presented in Section 9.9.) The second step, *phase* 2, begins with a BFS, $\mathbf{x}_f$, and proceeds to find a new BFS, $\mathbf{x}_g$, such that $z(\mathbf{x}_g) \leq z(\mathbf{x}_f)$. The method stops after a finite number of steps, either by showing that the objective function is unbounded below (i.e., there is no minimum value of the objective function on $\mathcal{K}$) or by finding an optimal BFS. Phase 2 is presented in Section 9.8; in this section, we present some important preliminaries.

Consider the following representative SLP: For $x_i \geq 0$,

$$\text{minimize} \quad z(\mathbf{x}) = c_1x_1 + c_2x_2 + \cdots + c_7x_7 - z_0 \tag{9.7.1}$$

subject to the constraints

$$\begin{aligned} x_1 \qquad\quad +a_{14}x_4 + a_{15}x_5 + a_{16}x_6 + a_{17}x_7 &= b_1 \\ x_2 \quad +a_{24}x_4 + a_{25}x_5 + a_{26}x_6 + a_{27}x_7 &= b_2 \\ x_3 + a_{34}x_4 + a_{35}x_5 + a_{36}x_6 + a_{37}x_7 &= b_3 \end{aligned} \tag{9.7.2}$$

The *initial tableau* is the elaborately labeled matrix

Basic variables	x_1	x_2	x_3	x_4	x_5	x_6	x_7	$-z$	**b**
x_1	1	0	0	a_{14}	a_{15}	a_{16}	a_{17}	0	b_1
x_2	0	1	0	a_{24}	a_{25}	a_{25}	a_{26}	0	b_2
x_3	0	0	1	a_{34}	a_{35}	a_{36}	a_{37}	0	b_3
$-z$	c_1	c_2	c_3	c_4	c_5	c_6	c_7	1	z_0

(9.7.3)

The headings are self-explanatory except for the column labeled $-z$. The $-z$ column provides an interpretation of the last row. If the objective function is viewed as the equation

$$c_1x_1 + c_2x_2 + \cdots + c_7x_7 - z = z_0 \tag{9.7.4}$$

then the last row is the detached form of Eq. 9.7.3, in which $z(\mathbf{x})$ appears as the variable $-z$. Of course, Eq. 9.7.4 is just a rearrangement of Eq. 9.7.1.

The entries a_{ij} are *input-output coefficients,* the c_i terms are the *cost coefficients,* and b_i are the *right-hand-side constants.* The variables heading the columns containing the unit vectors $\mathbf{e}_1, \mathbf{e}_2, \mathbf{e}_3$ are called *basic variables.* In the initial tableau given in Eq. 9.7.3, the basic variables are x_1, x_2, x_3, and these are listed in the first column. The *free* variables are the nonbasic variables; in Eq. 9.7.3 these are x_4, x_5, x_6, x_7. A *basic solution* is the vector obtained by solving Eq. 9.7.3 assuming $x_4 = x_5 = x_6 = x_7 = 0$, namely, $\mathbf{x} = [b_1 \quad b_2 \quad b_3 \quad 0 \quad 0 \quad 0 \quad 0]^{\mathrm{T}}$. Clearly, $\mathbf{x}$ is a BFS if and only if $\mathbf{b} \geq \mathbf{0}$. If any entry of $\mathbf{b}$ is negative, $\mathbf{x}$ is not feasible, and a different set of basic variables is selected. The result of phase 1, however, is either no feasible solution or a set of basic and free variables resulting in a feasible solution. One more preliminary step is required before phase 2 of the simplex method can begin: The initial tableau must be transformed into a tableau in which the cost coefficients of the basic variables are all zero. This is done by adding suitable multiples of the first three rows to the cost coefficient row. The resulting tableau is called a *canonical tableau* and has the form:

Basic variables	x_1	x_2	x_3	x_4	x_5	x_6	x_7	$-z$	$\mathbf{b}$
x_1	1	0	0	a_{14}	a_{15}	a_{16}	a_{17}	0	b_1
x_2	0	1	0	a_{24}	a_{25}	a_{25}	a_{26}	0	b_2
x_3	0	0	1	a_{34}	a_{35}	a_{36}	a_{37}	0	b_3
$-z$	0	0	0	$\bar{c}_4$	$\bar{c}_5$	$\bar{c}_6$	$\bar{c}_7$	1	$\bar{z}_0$

(9.7.5)

Note that the change from the initial to the canonical tableau alters only the $-z$ row. The cost coefficients $\bar{c}_i$ are called *relative cost coefficients* (relative to the choice of basic variables), and the process of clearing the cost coefficients of the basic variables to zero is known as *pricing out* or *updating* the cost coefficients. The pricing out of the cost coefficients results in an altered form of the objective function in the $-z$ row:

$$\bar{c}_4x_4 + \bar{c}_5x_5 + \bar{c}_6x_6 + \bar{c}_7x_7 - z(x) = \bar{z}_0 \tag{9.7.6}$$

(For convenience, we have assumed that the basic variables are x_1, x_2, x_3. As the next example shows, only a slight notational modification is required when the basic variables are not the first variables in the system.) If the SLP is presented in the form of Eq. 9.7.5 and if we assume $\mathbf{b}$ is nonnegative, then the solution

$$\mathbf{x}_f = [b_1 \quad b_2 \quad b_3 \quad 0 \quad 0 \quad 0 \quad 0]^{\mathrm{T}} \tag{9.7.7}$$

is said to be a BFS *relative to the tableau* of Eq. 9.7.5, and $z(\mathbf{x}_f) = -\bar{z}_0$.

Summarizing, a tableau is *canonical* if it satisfies these criteria:

1. The right-hand-side constants are nonnegative.
2. The matrix **A** contains the columns $\mathbf{e}_1, \mathbf{e}_2, \ldots, \mathbf{e}_m$ in some order.
3. The last row, labeled $-z$, contains zeros in the columns of the basic variables (i.e., the cost coefficients of the basic variables have been priced out).

Example 9.7.1. Find the initial and canonical tableaux associated with the following SLP, and find the BFS associated with these tableaux:

$$\text{minimize:} \quad z(\mathbf{x}) = -2x_1 + 4x_2 + 2x_3 + 3x_4 + 3x_5$$

$$\text{subject to:} \quad \left.\begin{aligned} 2x_2 \quad + x_4 \quad &= 2 \\ x_1 + x_2 \quad + x_5 &= 3 \\ x_2 + 2x_2 - x_3 \quad &= -1 \end{aligned}\right\} x_i \geq 0$$

Solution. The right-hand-side constant in the third constraint is -1, so the first step is to multiply the third equation by -1. Then the initial tableau is given by

Basic variables	x_1	x_2	x_3	x_4	x_5	$-z$	**b**
x_4	0	2	0	1	0	0	2
x_5	1	1	0	0	1	0	3
x_3	-1	-2	1	0	0	0	1
$-z$	-2	4	2	3	3	1	0

The input-output coefficients are simply the entries of the coefficient matrix, and the column headed **b** is self-explanatory. The basic variables are those heading the columns $\mathbf{e}_1$, $\mathbf{e}_2$, and $\mathbf{e}_3$ and are listed under the heading *basic variable*. (Note that x_4 is listed first because it heads the column containing $\mathbf{e}_1$, and x_5 is listed second because it heads the column containing $\mathbf{e}_2$. Also note that, in this example, $z_0 = 0$.)

To update the cost coefficients relative to the present basis, it is necessary to use the appropriate elementary row operations to clear c_3, c_4, and c_5. Thus, -3 times row 1, -3 times row 2, and -2 times row 3 are added to the cost coefficient row. This results in the canonical tableau:

Basic variables	x_1	x_2	x_3	x_4	x_5	$-z$	**b**
x_4	0	2	0	1	0	0	2
x_5	1	1	0	0	1	0	3
x_3	-1	-2	1	0	0	0	1
$-z$	-3	-1	0	0	0	1	-17

(9.7.8)

Since the basic variables are x_4, x_5, and x_3, the free variables are x_1 and x_2. These are set zero to find a BFS, and this results in the BFS $\mathbf{x}_f = [0 \;\; 0 \;\; 1 \;\; 2 \;\; 3]^{\mathrm{T}}$. The objective row is the detached form of $-3x_1 - x_2 - z(\mathbf{x}) = -17$. Hence, $z(\mathbf{x}_f) = 17$. The objective function can also be evaluated from the detached form given in the initial tableau:

$$-2x_1 + 4x_2 + 2x_3 + 3x_4 + 3x_5 - z(\mathbf{x}) = 0$$

The arithmetic is now somewhat more involved. We find

$$-2x_1 + 4x_2 + 2x_3 + 3x_4 + 3x_5 - z(x_f) = 0 + 0 + 2 + 6 + 9 - z(x_f) = 0$$

which confirms the value of z at $\mathbf{x}_f$ as 17.

Example 9.7.2. Find the initial and canonical tableaux for the brewer's problem, Example 9.6.1.

Solution. The initial tableau is already in canonical form because the cost coefficients of the slack variables are always zero. Specifically, the canonical tableau is given by

Basic variables	x_1	x_2	x_3	s_1	s_2	$-z$	**b**
s_1	2	1	1	1	0	0	10
s_2	1	0	1	0	1	0	5
$-z$	−2	−3	−4	0	0	1	0

The BFS associated with this tableau is $\mathbf{x}_f = [0 \;\; 0 \;\; 0 \;\; 10 \;\; 5]^{\mathrm{T}}$ and $z(\mathbf{x}_f) = 0$. This means that the brewer can achieve a zero profit by producing no beer, a conclusion evident from the start. But, as we shall see, this trivial observation is an important first step.

PROBLEMS

PART 1

9.7.1. Consider the initial tableau:

Basic variables	x_1	x_2	x_3	x_4	x_5	$-z$	**b**
*	0	2	0	1	0	0	2
*	1	1	0	0	1	0	3
*	−1	−2	1	0	0	0	1
$-z$	1	5	2	3	3	1	0

Convert this tableau to canonical form relative to the following basic variables:
(*a*) $\{\mathbf{x}_1, \mathbf{x}_2, \mathbf{x}_3\}$ (*b*) $\{\mathbf{x}_1, \mathbf{x}_2, \mathbf{x}_4\}$ (*c*) $\{\mathbf{x}_1, \mathbf{x}_2, \mathbf{x}_5\}$
(*d*) $\{\mathbf{x}_3, \mathbf{x}_2, \mathbf{x}_5\}$ (*e*) $\{\mathbf{x}_3, \mathbf{x}_1, \mathbf{x}_4\}$ (*f*) $\{\mathbf{x}_4, \mathbf{x}_1, \mathbf{x}_5\}$
Is the resulting BFS associated with the canonical form feasible?

9.7.2. Repeat Problem 9.7.1 for the tableau

Basic variables	x_1	x_2	x_3	x_4	x_5	$-z$	**b**
*	-3	2	0	1	0	0	2
*	-1	1	0	0	1	0	3
*	1	-2	1	0	0	0	1
$-z$	-2	-1	0	0	0	1	-17

9.7.3. Find the initial tableau for the SLP, minimize $z = x + y$ subject to the constraints $2x - y \leq 1,\ y \leq 2$, in nonnegative variables.

PART 2

9.7.4. Convert the following tableau into a canonical tableau by suitable elementary row operations. (The column headed x_2, for example, must be the vector $\mathbf{e}_1$.) For what range of b is the basic solution associated with this tableau feasible?

Basic variables	x_1	x_2	x_3	x_4	x_5	$-z$	**b**
x_2	0	2	0	1	0	0	b
x_1	1	1	0	0	1	0	3
x_3	-1	-2	1	0	0	0	1
$-z$	1	5	2	3	3	1	0

9.7.5. As in the preceding problem, for what range of b is the basic solution associated with the following tableau feasible?

Basic variables	x_1	x_2	x_3	x_4	x_5	$-z$	**b**
x_2	0	2	0	1	0	0	2
x_1	1	1	0	0	1	0	b
x_3	-1	-2	1	0	0	0	1
$-z$	1	5	2	3	3	1	0

9.7.6. As in the preceding two problems, for what range of b is the basic solution associated with the following tableau feasible?

Basic variables	x_1	x_2	x_3	x_4	x_5	$-z$	**b**
x_2	0	2	0	1	0	0	2
x_1	1	1	0	0	1	0	3
x_3	-1	-2	1	0	0	0	b
$-z$	1	5	2	3	3	1	0

9.7.7. Introduce slacks into the LP, minimize $z(\mathbf{x})$ subject to $\mathbf{Ax} \le \mathbf{b}$, $\mathbf{b} \ge \mathbf{0}$, $\mathbf{x} \ge \mathbf{0}$, thus converting this LP into an SLP. Show that the initial tableau associated with this SLP is a canonical tableau.

PART 3

9.7.8. Let $\mathbf{x}_f$ be the BFS defined by the tableau in Eq. 9.7.5. Show that $z(\mathbf{x}_f)$ is the same, whether obtained from Eq. 9.7.5 or Eq. 9.7.3.

9.7.9. If an SLP is feasible and the cost coefficients before pricing out are all nonnegative, show that $z_{\min}(\mathbf{x}) \ge 0$. Give an example to show that $z_{\min}(\mathbf{x}) > 0$ is possible.

9.8 THE SIMPLEX METHOD: PHASE 2

Phase 2 of the simplex method assumes that the tableau for the SLP is in canonical form and that a permutation of some the columns of $\mathbf{A}_{m\times n}$ results in the identity matrix $\mathbf{I}_m$. If these conditions are met, then a BFS can be obtained by setting the free variables all to zero and identifying the basic variables with the corresponding entries of $\mathbf{b}$. The value of the objective function is $-z_0$. If we assume, as usual, that the basic variables appear as the first m variables, the canonical tableau of Eq. 9.7.5 generalizes easily:

Basic variables	x_1	x_2	$\cdots$	x_m	x_{m+1}	$\cdots$	x_s	$\cdots$	x_n	$-z$	$\mathbf{b}$
x_1	1	0	$\cdots$	0	$a_{1,m+1}$	$\cdots$	a_{1s}	$\cdots$	a_{1n}	0	b_1
x_2	0	1	$\cdots$	0	$a_{2,m+1}$	$\cdots$	a_{2s}	$\cdots$	a_{2n}	0	b_2
	$\vdots$										
x_m	0	0	$\cdots$	1	$a_{m,m+1}$	$\cdots$	a_{ms}	$\cdots$	a_{mn}	0	b_m
$-z$	0	0	$\cdots$	0	$\bar{c}_{m+1}$	$\cdots$	$\bar{c}_s$	$\cdots$	$\bar{c}_n$	1	$\bar{z}_0$

(9.8.1)

The tableau of Eq. 9.8.1 will arise, for example, if the LP $\mathbf{Ax} \le \mathbf{b}$, $\mathbf{x} \ge \mathbf{0}$ is transformed into an SLP by the introduction of m slacks. The set of constraints can be written in partitioned matrix form:

$$[\mathbf{A}\quad \mathbf{I}]\begin{bmatrix}\mathbf{x}\\ \mathbf{s}\end{bmatrix} = \mathbf{b}, \qquad \begin{bmatrix}\mathbf{x}\\ \mathbf{s}\end{bmatrix} \ge \mathbf{0}$$

Theorem 9.8.1. *If all the relative cost coefficients in a canonical tableau are nonnegative, then the* BFS $\mathbf{x}_f = [b_1 \quad b_2 \quad \ldots \quad b_m \quad 0 \quad \ldots \quad 0]^{\mathrm{T}}$, *is an optimal feasible solution.*

Proof. The objective function takes the form

$$\overline{c}_{m+1}x_{m+1} + \overline{c}_{m+2}x_{m+2} + \cdots + \overline{c}_n x_n + z_0 = z(\mathbf{x}) \qquad (9.8.2)$$

Because we have assumed that $\overline{c}_k \ge 0$, Eq 9.8.2 implies that $z(\mathbf{x}) \ge z_0$ *for all feasible solutions*. But $z(\mathbf{x}_f) = z_0$, where $\mathbf{x}_f$ is the BFS implied by the tableau. So for each feasible $\mathbf{x}$, Eq. 9.8.2 leads to $z(\mathbf{x}_f) \le z(\mathbf{x})$. Hence, $\mathbf{x}_f$ is an optimal solution and simultaneously a BFS. ■

In view of Theorem 9.8.1, the case in which at least one relative cost coefficient, say $\overline{c}_s$, is negative is all that remains to consider. The pivot is chosen from column s, and elementary row operations are applied so that column s becomes a unit vector. One implication of the fact that the pivot is chosen from the sth column is that x_s will be a new basic variable. In these circumstances we call x_s an *entering variable*. There are m potential choices for the pivot—any of the nonzero input-output coefficients in the sth column, $a_{1s}, a_{2s}, \ldots, a_{ms}$. Suppose a_{is} is chosen as the pivot. (The criterion for this choice is discussed in the subsection to follow.) Then, after a sequence of elementary row operations, column s becomes $\mathbf{e}_i$; the relative cost coefficient c_s of x_s is priced out; x_s enters the set of basic variables; and x_i is driven out. The variable x_i is called the *exiting variable*. To clarify these ideas, consider the following examples.

Example 9.8.1. For the tableau of Eq. 9.7.8 select a_{21} as the pivot, and verify that x_1 is the entering variable and x_5 is the exiting variable. Update the cost coefficients for the new set of basic variables, and find the resulting BFS and the value of the objective function.

Solution. The following diagram, devoid of most column and row labels, shows the results of the elementary row operations when the pivot is a_{21}:

$$\begin{array}{c} x_4 \\ x_5 \\ x_3 \\ \\ \end{array}\left[\begin{array}{ccccc:c} 0 & 2 & 0 & 1 & 0 & 2 \\ 1 & 1 & 0 & 0 & 1 & 3 \\ -1 & -2 & 1 & 0 & 0 & 1 \\ \hdashline -3 & -1 & 0 & 0 & 0 & -17 \end{array}\right] \rightarrow$$

$$\cdots \rightarrow \begin{array}{c} x_4 \\ x_1 \\ x_3 \\ \\ \end{array}\left[\begin{array}{ccccc:c} 0 & 2 & 0 & 1 & 0 & 2 \\ 1 & 1 & 0 & 0 & 1 & 3 \\ 0 & -1 & 1 & 0 & 1 & 4 \\ \hdashline 0 & 2 & 0 & 0 & 3 & -8 \end{array}\right]$$

The tableau obtained from the last matrix in this diagram is

Basic variables	x_1	x_2	x_3	x_4	x_5	**b**
x_4	0	2	0	1	0	2
x_1	1	1	0	0	1	3
x_3	0	−1	1	0	1	4
$-z$	0	2	0	0	3	−8

(9.8.3)

A number of interesting conclusions can be drawn from this tableau. First and most important, it is canonical. (Contrast this with Example 9.8.2, to follow.) Second, $\mathbf{x}_f = [3 \quad 0 \quad 4 \quad 2 \quad 0]^{\mathrm{T}}$ is a BFS, and since the updated cost coefficients are all nonnegative, $\mathbf{x}_f$ is an optimal solution, by Theorem 9.8.1. The exiting variable is x_5, and the entering variable is x_1. Finally, the minimum value of the objective function is $z_{\min}(\mathbf{x}_f) = -(-8) = 8$.

Example 9.8.2. Redo Example 9.8.1, choosing a_{22} as the pivot.

Solution. The row operations are straightforward:

$$\begin{matrix} x_4 \\ x_5 \\ x_3 \\ \\ \end{matrix} \left[\begin{array}{ccccc|c} 0 & 2 & 0 & 1 & 0 & 2 \\ 1 & 1 & 0 & 0 & 1 & 3 \\ -1 & -2 & 1 & 0 & 0 & 1 \\ \hline -3 & -1 & 0 & 0 & 0 & -17 \end{array}\right] \rightarrow$$

$$\cdots \rightarrow \begin{matrix} x_4 \\ x_2 \\ x_3 \\ \\ \end{matrix} \left[\begin{array}{ccccc|c} -2 & 0 & 0 & 1 & 0 & -4 \\ 1 & 1 & 0 & 0 & 1 & 3 \\ 0 & 0 & 1 & 0 & 1 & 7 \\ \hline -2 & 0 & 0 & 0 & 3 & -14 \end{array}\right]$$

The value of the objective function dropped from 17 to 14, but the resulting tableau is not canonical, unlike Example 9.8.1, because $\mathbf{b} = -4$. One consequence of this fact is that the basic solution associated with the tableau is not feasible, for now $\mathbf{x}_f = [0 \quad 3 \quad 7 \quad -4 \quad 0]^{\mathrm{T}}$.

Example 9.8.3. The canonical tableau of the SLP representing the brewer's problem (Example 9.7.1) is given by

$$\begin{matrix} s_1 \\ s_2 \\ \\ \end{matrix} \left[\begin{array}{ccccc|c} 2 & 1 & 1 & 1 & 0 & 10 \\ 1 & 0 & 1 & 0 & 1 & 5 \\ \hline -2 & -3 & -4 & 0 & 0 & 0 \end{array}\right]$$

In this case choose the pivot $a_{23} = 1$. This choice implies that x_3 is the entering variable and s_2 is the exiting variable.

$$\begin{matrix} s_1 \\ s_2 \\ \\ \end{matrix} \left[\begin{array}{ccccc|c} 2 & 1 & 1 & 1 & 0 & 10 \\ 1 & 0 & 1 & 0 & 1 & 5 \\ \hline -2 & -3 & -4 & 0 & 0 & 0 \end{array}\right] \rightarrow \cdots \rightarrow \begin{matrix} s_1 \\ x_3 \\ \\ \end{matrix} \left[\begin{array}{ccccc|c} 1 & 1 & 0 & 1 & -1 & 5 \\ 1 & 0 & 1 & 0 & 1 & 5 \\ \hline 2 & -3 & 0 & 0 & 4 & 20 \end{array}\right]$$

The next pivot is forced on us since there is only one negative cost coefficient, $\overline{c}_2 = -3$, and column 2 has only one nonzero input-output coefficient, a_{12}. Then s_1 exits the basic set of variables, and x_2 enters.

$$\begin{matrix} s_1 \\ x_3 \\ \\ \end{matrix} \left[\begin{array}{ccccc|c} 1 & 1 & 0 & 1 & -1 & 5 \\ 1 & 0 & 1 & 0 & 1 & 5 \\ \hline 2 & -3 & 0 & 0 & 4 & 20 \end{array}\right] \rightarrow \cdots \rightarrow \begin{matrix} x_2 \\ x_3 \\ \\ \end{matrix} \left[\begin{array}{ccccc|c} 1 & 1 & 0 & 1 & -1 & 5 \\ 1 & 0 & 1 & 0 & 1 & 5 \\ \hline 5 & 0 & 0 & 3 & 1 & 35 \end{array}\right]$$

In this case, our choice of pivots resulted in two successive canonical tableaux, and in each tableau the objective value diminished from a high of 0 through the intermediate value -20 to a low of -35. The last tableau has nonnegative relative cost coefficients, so the associated basic feasible solution is optimal. Thus, an optimum BFS solution is $\mathbf{x}_f = [0 \quad 5 \quad 5 \quad 0 \quad 0]^{\mathrm{T}}$ and $z(\mathbf{x}_f) = -35$. (In terms of the original variables in the brewer's problem, the maximum profit is \$35 dollars, obtained by canceling production of Brand X (corresponding to $x_1 = 0$) and producing five kegs of Brand X-lite and Brand Y.

When Theorem 9.8.1 is applicable, we say that the simplex method terminates by the *optimal stopping criterion*. The next example illustrates a case in which the unboundedness of the objective function is detected by the simplex method.

Example 9.8.4. Use the pivot a_{31} to remove x_3 from the set of basic variables, and enter x_1 for the SLP represented by the canonical tableau

Basic variables	x_1	x_2	x_3	x_4	x_5	**b**
x_4	-3	2	0	1	0	2
x_5	-1	1	0	0	1	3
x_3	1	-2	1	0	0	1
$-z$	-2	-1	0	0	0	-17

Solution. The row reductions are illustrated by the diagram

$$\left[\begin{array}{rrrrr|r} -3 & 2 & 0 & 1 & 0 & 2 \\ -1 & 1 & 0 & 0 & 1 & 3 \\ 1 & -2 & 1 & 0 & 0 & 1 \\ \hline -2 & -1 & 0 & 0 & 0 & -17 \end{array}\right] \rightarrow \cdots \rightarrow \left[\begin{array}{rrrrr|r} 0 & -4 & 3 & 1 & 0 & 0 \\ 0 & -1 & 1 & 0 & 1 & 4 \\ 1 & -2 & 1 & 0 & 0 & 1 \\ \hline 0 & -5 & 2 & 0 & 0 & -15 \end{array}\right] \qquad (9.8.4)$$

The BFS is $\mathbf{x}_f = [1 \quad 0 \quad 0 \quad 5 \quad 4]^{\mathrm{T}}$ and $z(\mathbf{x}_f) = 15$, all of which can be read from the canonical tableau obtained from the rightmost matrix in Eq. 9.8.4:

Basic variables	x_1	x_2	x_3	x_4	x_5	**b**
x_4	0	-4	3	1	0	5
x_5	0	-1	1	0	1	4
x_1	1	-2	1	0	0	1
$-z$	0	-5	2	0	0	-15

(9.8.5)

The SLP represented by this tableau is:

$$\begin{aligned} &\text{minimize:} && z(\mathbf{x}) = -5x_2 + 2x_3 + 15 \\ &\text{subject to:} && \begin{bmatrix} 0 & -4 & 3 & 1 & 0 \\ 0 & -1 & 1 & 0 & 1 \\ 1 & -2 & 1 & 0 & 0 \end{bmatrix} \mathbf{x} = \begin{bmatrix} 5 \\ 4 \\ 1 \end{bmatrix}, \qquad \mathbf{x} \geq \mathbf{0} \end{aligned}$$

Suppose we denote the columns of the coefficient matrix given above by $\mathbf{A}_{*1} = \mathbf{e}_1$, $\mathbf{A}_{*2}$, $\mathbf{A}_{*3}$, $\mathbf{A}_{*4} = \mathbf{e}_1$, and $\mathbf{A}_{*5} = \mathbf{e}_2$. Clearly,

$$2\mathbf{A}_{*1} + \mathbf{A}_{*2} + 4\mathbf{A}_{*4} + \mathbf{A}_{*5} = \mathbf{0}$$

Thus, $\mathbf{a} = [2 \quad 1 \quad 0 \quad 4 \quad 1]^T$ is a solution of $\mathbf{Ax} = \mathbf{0}$, $\mathbf{x} \geq \mathbf{0}$. The value of z at $\mathbf{x}_f + \lambda\mathbf{a}$ is given by $z(\mathbf{x}_f + \lambda_{\mathbf{a}}) = 15 - 5\lambda$. Now

$$\mathbf{x} + \lambda\mathbf{a} = \begin{bmatrix} 1 \\ 0 \\ 0 \\ 5 \\ 4 \end{bmatrix} + \lambda \begin{bmatrix} 2 \\ 1 \\ 0 \\ 4 \\ 1 \end{bmatrix}$$

is a feasible solution for all $\lambda \geq 0$. Thus, $z(\mathbf{x}_f + \lambda\mathbf{a}) = 15 - 5\lambda$ tends to $-\infty$ as λ tends to ∞, which is the definition of z unbounded below.

Theorem 9.8.2. *If the relative cost coefficient $\overline{c}_{m+1} < 0$ and $a_{i,m+1} \leq 0$ for all $i = 1, 2, \ldots, m$, then the objective function is unbounded below.*

Proof. Suppose the basic variables are $x_1, x_2, \ldots, x_m$. Then generalizing from Eq. 9.8.5, the vector

$$\mathbf{a} = [-a_{1j} \quad -a_{2j} \quad \ldots \quad -a_{mj} \quad 1 \quad 0 \quad \ldots \quad 0]^T \geq \mathbf{0}$$

is a feasible solution of $\mathbf{Ax} = \mathbf{0}$, $\mathbf{x} \geq \mathbf{0}$. (That is, $\mathbf{Aa} = \mathbf{0}$ and $\mathbf{a} \geq \mathbf{0}$.) Then $\mathbf{x}_f + \lambda\mathbf{a}$ is always a solution of $\mathbf{Ax} = \mathbf{b}$. Moreover, because $\mathbf{a} \geq \mathbf{0}$, $\mathbf{x}_f + \lambda\mathbf{a}$ is always a feasible solution of $\mathbf{Ax} = \mathbf{b}$, $\mathbf{x} \geq \mathbf{0}$, for all $\lambda \geq 0$. The value of the objective function is $z(\mathbf{x}_f + \lambda\mathbf{a}) = z_0 + \lambda\overline{c}_{m+1}$. By hypothesis, $\overline{c}_{m+1} < 0$. Thus, $z(\mathbf{x}_f + \lambda_{\mathbf{a}})$ can be made smaller than any preassigned value M by choosing λ sufficiently large. That is, $z(\mathbf{x}_f + \lambda\mathbf{a}) \to -\infty$ as $\lambda \to \infty$. ■

When Theorem 9.8.2 is applicable, we say that the simplex method is terminated by the *unboundedness stopping criterion*.

The fundamental theorem in the theory of the simplex method is that after a finite number of steps, the simplex method terminates by either the optimal or the unboundedness stopping criteria.

The proof of this important theorem is complicated by the existence of "degenerate" SLPs. In these LPs it is possible for the simplex method to generate a finite number of BFSs in which the objective function remains constant and in which the first and last BFSs are identical. In this circumstance, the simplex method simply cycles endlessly through these solutions. Space considerations prohibit a discussion of these "degenerate" cases and how they are circumvented in theory and in practice. Suffice it to say that realistic LPs never exhibit degeneracy, and in any case, implementations of the simplex algorithm are designed to avoid cycling.

9.8.1 The Choice of Pivots

The choice of the pivot is at the heart of the simplex algorithm. So far we have shown only that the pivot will be selected from the input-output coefficients in a column whose relative cost coefficient is negative. (If there is no relative cost coefficient that is negative, then Theorem 9.8.1 asserts that the BFS associated with the tableau is optimal, and the simplex algorithm stops.) Suppose $\overline{c}_s < 0$ in the tableau

Basic variables	x_1	x_2	$\cdots$	x_m	x_{m+1}	$\cdots$	x_s	$\cdots$	x_n	$-z$	**b**	**Ratios**
x_1	1	0	$\cdots$	0	$a_{1,m+1}$	$\cdots$	a_{1s}	$\cdots$	a_{1n}	0	b_1	b_1/a_{1s}
x_2	0	1	$\cdots$	0	$a_{2,m+1}$	$\cdots$	a_{2s}	$\cdots$	a_{2n}	0	b_2	b_2/a_{2s}
	$\vdots$											
x_m	0	0	$\cdots$	1	$a_{m,m+1}$	$\cdots$	a_{ms}	$\cdots$	a_{mn}	0	b_m	b_m/a_{ms}
$-z$	0	0	$\cdots$	0	$\overline{c}_{m+1}$	$\cdots$	$\overline{c}_s$	$\cdots$	$\overline{c}_n$	1	$\overline{z}_0$	

Step 2 in the simplex method requires the computation of the ratios b_i/a_{is}, for those $a_{is} > 0$. (No ratio is computed for negative a_{is}.) These are tabulated in the last column. There are two cases:

Case 1: None of the input-output coefficients in column s are positive; thus, no ratios are computed. Since $\overline{c}_s < 0$, the unboundedness criteria are met, and the given SLP is unbounded below.

Case 2: There is at least one positive input-output coefficient in column s. Then the column of ratios has at least one entry, and since it has at most m, there is a minimum, nonnegative ratio. *This minimum ratio is denoted by ϑ, and if it occurs in row i, the pivot is* $a_{is} > 0$. Together, the negative relative cost coefficient and the nonnegative input-output coefficient define the pivot entry.

Again, suppose $\overline{c}_s < 0$. Define

$$\vartheta = \min\{b_i/a_{is},\ \text{for } a_{is} > 0\} \qquad i = 1, 2, \ldots, m \tag{9.8.6}$$

and suppose this minimum is attained for $i = k$. (In the event of a tie, say $\vartheta = b_i/a_{is} = b_j/a_{js}$, either a_{is} or a_{js} may be used as the pivot.) The determination of ϑ is called the *minimum ratio test*. The importance of this test is that the pivot selected by this method results in a canonical tableau. To see why, consider the following abbreviated form of the previous tableau, and suppose $\vartheta = b_2/a_{24}$. Then a_{24} is the pivot, and the following diagram results:

$$\begin{array}{c} x_1 \\ x_2 \\ x_3 \\ \\ \end{array} \left[\begin{array}{ccccccc|c} 1 & 0 & 0 & a_{14} & * & * & * & b_1 \\ 0 & 1 & 0 & a_{24} & * & * & * & b_2 \\ 0 & 0 & 1 & a_{34} & * & * & * & b_3 \\ \hline 0 & 0 & 0 & \overline{c}_4 & * & * & * & -z_0 \end{array}\right] \rightarrow$$

$$\cdots \rightarrow \begin{array}{c} x_1 \\ x_4 \\ x_3 \\ \\ \end{array} \left[\begin{array}{ccccccc|c} 1 & * & 0 & 0 & * & * & * & b_1 - a_{14}\vartheta \\ 0 & * & 0 & 1 & * & * & * & \vartheta \\ 0 & * & 1 & 0 & * & * & * & b_3 - a_{34}\vartheta \\ \hline 0 & * & 0 & 0 & * & * & * & -z_0 - \overline{c}_4\vartheta \end{array}\right]$$

If $a_{i4} \leq 0$, then $b_i - a_{i4}\vartheta$ is nonnegative because b_i and ϑ are nonnegative.

If $a_{i4} > 0$, then $b_i - a_{i4}\vartheta$ is nonnegative because $\vartheta \le b_i/a_{i4}$ for all i, by definition of ϑ. So the tableau is canonical. The new value of the objective function is $-(-z_0 - \overline{c}_4\vartheta) = z_0 + \overline{c}_4\vartheta$, which is not greater than z_0, since $\overline{c}_4 < 0$ and $\vartheta \ge 0$. Finally, the original basic set of $\{x_1, x_2, x_3\}$ is replaced by the set $\{x_1, x_4, x_3\}$.

Note that the rightmost tableau is canonical because of the minimum ratio test, not because $\overline{c}_4 < 0$. Also, $z(\mathbf{x})$ cannot increase because $\overline{c}_4$ and ϑ are nonnegative, not because ϑ is picked by the minimum ratio test.

Example 9.8.5. Find an optimal BFS and the minimum value of the objective function for the LP

$$\text{maximize:} \qquad \hat{z}(\mathbf{x}) = 2x_1 + x_2 - 19$$

$$\text{subject to:} \qquad \left.\begin{aligned} -3x_1 + 7x_2 &\le 2 \\ -x_1 + x_2 &\le 3 \\ x_1 - 2x_2 &\le 1 \end{aligned}\right\} \qquad x_1 \ge 0,\ y_2 \ge 0$$

Solution. Introduce a slack for each of the inequality constraints, and convert the maximization of $\hat{z}$ to the minimization of $-z = -2x_1 - x_2 + 19$. This results in the canonical tableau

Basic variables	x_1	x_2	s_1	s_2	s_3	**b**
s_1	−3	7	1	0	0	2
s_2	−1	1	0	1	0	3
s_3	1	−2	0	0	1	1
$-z$	−2	−1	0	0	0	−19

(9.8.7)

The elementary row operations determined by the minimum ratio test results in this diagram:

$$\begin{matrix} s_1 \\ s_2 \\ s_3 \\ \\ \end{matrix}\left[\begin{array}{rrrrr|r} -3 & 7 & 1 & 0 & 0 & 2 \\ -1 & 1 & 0 & 1 & 0 & 3 \\ \boxed{1} & -2 & 0 & 0 & 1 & 1 \\ \hline -2 & -1 & 0 & 0 & 0 & -19 \end{array}\right] \begin{matrix} \text{ratio} \\ - \\ - \\ 1 = \vartheta \\ \\ \end{matrix} \rightarrow$$

$$\cdots \rightarrow \begin{matrix} s_1 \\ s_2 \\ x_1 \\ \\ \end{matrix}\left[\begin{array}{rrrrr|r} 0 & \boxed{1} & 1 & 0 & 3 & 5 \\ 0 & -1 & 0 & 1 & 1 & 4 \\ 1 & -2 & 0 & 0 & 1 & 1 \\ \hline 0 & -5 & 0 & 0 & 2 & -17 \end{array}\right] \begin{matrix} \text{ratio} \\ 5 = \vartheta \\ - \\ - \\ \\ \end{matrix} \rightarrow$$

$$\cdots \rightarrow \begin{matrix} x_2 \\ s_2 \\ x_1 \\ \\ \end{matrix}\left[\begin{array}{rrrrr|r} 0 & 1 & 1 & 0 & 3 & 5 \\ 0 & 0 & 1 & 1 & 4 & 9 \\ 1 & 0 & 2 & 0 & 7 & 11 \\ \hline 0 & 0 & 5 & 0 & 2 & 8 \end{array}\right]$$

The basic variables in the last tableau are $x_2 = 5$, $s_2 = 9$, $x_1 = 11$; the optimal BFS is given by $\mathbf{x}_f = [11 \quad 5 \quad 0 \quad 2 \quad 0]^T$, and the optimal value of the objective function is $z = -8$. These answers are for the variables in the SLP that was derived from the original problem. In terms of the original variables, $\mathbf{x} = [11 \quad 5]^T$ is an optimal feasible solution, and the maximum value of $\hat{z}$ is 8. This is easily verified from the definition of $\hat{z}$.

PROBLEMS

PART 1

9.8.1. Use the pivot a_{12} in the tableau in Eq. 9.7.8 to enter the variable x_2 into the basic set. What variable exits the basic set? Is the resulting tableau canonical? Is the corresponding BFS optimal?

9.8.2. Redo Example 9.8.3 using the pivot $a_{12} = 1$ as the first pivot instead of a_{23} used in the example. Is the resulting tableau canonical? Is the corresponding BFS optimal? What is the value of z after the tableau is updated?

9.8.3. Repeat Problem 9.8.2. except use the input-output coefficient $a_{11} = 2$ as the first pivot.

9.8.4. Repeat Problem 9.8.2 except use the input-output coefficient $a_{21} = 1$ as the first pivot.

9.8.5. Redo Example 9.8.4 using a_{12} as the first pivot. Does the resulting tableau terminate by the unboundedness stopping criterion?

PART 2

9.8.6. Let $\mathcal{K}$ denote the set of feasible solutions of an SLP. If $\mathcal{K}$ is unbounded, can the SLP have an optimal solution?

9.8.7. Under what circumstances will the value of the objective function be unaltered after the introduction of a new basic variable? Under what circumstances must the objective value decrease after the introduction of a new basic variable?

9.8.8. Let $\mathcal{K}$ denote the set of feasible solutions of an SLP. If $\mathcal{K}$ is nonempty and the LP is unbounded below, can $\mathcal{K}$ be a polytope?

PART 3

9.8.9. Prove: If all the input-output coefficients are nonpositive in row i of a canonical tableau, and $b > O$, then the SLP is infeasible.

9.8.10. Suppose the canonical tableau

Basic variables	x_1	x_2	x_3	x_4	x_5	x_6	x_7	$-z$	b
x_1	1	0	0	1	a_{15}	a_{16}	a_{17}	0	1
x_2	0	1	0	1	a_{25}	a_{25}	a_{26}	0	2
x_3	0	0	1	1	a_{35}	a_{36}	a_{37}	0	3
$-z$	0	0	0	0	$\bar{c}_5$	$\bar{c}_6$	$\bar{c}_7$	1	$-z_0$

terminates because the optimal stopping criterion is satisfied. Show that $\mathbf{x}_f = [0 \quad x_2 \quad x_3 \quad x_4 \quad 0 \quad 0 \quad 0]^T$ is an alternative optimal solution, and find the value of its entries.

9.8.11. Permute the entries in $\mathbf{b}$ of the tableau in Problem 9.8.10 so that $\mathbf{x}_f = [x_1 \quad x_2 \quad 0 \quad x_4 \quad 0 \quad 0 \quad 0]^{\mathrm{T}}$ is an optimal solution. What is z_0 and $\mathbf{x}_f$?

9.8.12. Prove: If $\mathbf{b} > \mathbf{0}$ in an SLP and $\overline{c}_s < 0$ with respect to some BFS, then the value of the objective function decreases when x_s enters the set of basic variables.

9.9 THE SIMPLEX METHOD: PHASE 1

Phase 2 of the simplex method requires that the tableau representing the system of equality constraints in nonnegative variables be in canonical form. This implies that we know a set of basic vectors. However, an initial tableau is not generally canonical, nor are we likely to know which variables are basic variables. Indeed, if the SLP is infeasible, there is no choice of basic variables that implies a feasible solution. We now show that we can both test feasibility and discover a feasible solution by use of the simplex method on a cleverly constructed auxiliary SLP related to the given program.

Suppose the *original* SLP is:

$$\text{minimize:} \qquad z(\mathbf{x}) = \mathbf{c}^{\mathrm{T}}\mathbf{x}$$

$$\text{subject to:} \qquad \mathbf{A}\mathbf{x} = \mathbf{b}, \ \mathbf{b} \geq \mathbf{0}, \ \mathbf{x} \geq \mathbf{0}$$

Define the phase 1 SLP as follows:

$$\text{minimize:} \qquad w = [\mathbf{0} \quad \mathbf{1}]\begin{bmatrix}\mathbf{x}\\ \mathbf{t}\end{bmatrix} = \mathbf{0}^{\mathrm{T}}\mathbf{x} + \mathbf{1}^{\mathrm{T}}\mathbf{t}$$

$$\text{subject to:} \qquad [\mathbf{A} \quad \mathbf{I}]\begin{bmatrix}\mathbf{x}\\ \mathbf{t}\end{bmatrix} = \mathbf{b} \geq \mathbf{0}; \qquad \mathbf{x} \geq \mathbf{0}, \ \mathbf{t} \geq \mathbf{0}$$

The tableau corresponding to the phase 1 SLP is given by

Basic variables	x_1	$\cdots$	x_n	t_1	t_2	$\cdots$	t_m	$-w$	$\mathbf{b}$
x_1	a_{11}	$\cdots$	a_{1n}	1	0	$\cdots$	0	0	b_1
x_2	a_{21}	$\cdots$	a_{2n}	0	1	$\cdots$	0	0	b_2
				$\vdots$					
x_m	a_{m1}	$\cdots$	a_{mn}	0	0	$\cdots$	1	0	b_m
$-w$	0	$\cdots$	0	1	1	$\cdots$	1	1	0

(9.9.1)

The vector $\mathbf{t}$ in the phase 1 SLP is called a *vector of artificial variables,* and w is called the *artificial objective function*. The connections between the original SLP and the corresponding phase 1 SLP are brought out in the next two results.

Lemma 9.1. *The phase* 1 SLP *is always feasible and has a nonnegative optimal objective value.*

Proof. The feasibility is obvious because $\mathbf{x} = \mathbf{0}$, $\mathbf{t} = \mathbf{b}$ is a feasible solution.

Thus the phase 1 problem is either unbounded below or has an optimal feasible solution. It cannot be unbounded below, however, because

$$w = \mathbf{1}^{\mathrm{T}}\mathbf{t} = t_1 + t_2 + \cdots + t_m \geq 0$$

shows that 0 is a "floor" to all values of w. Hence w is nonnegative. ■

Theorem 9.9.1. *An* SLP *is feasible if and only if the artificial objective function in the phase* 1 SLP *satisfies* $w_{\min} = 0$. *Moreover, if* $w = 0$ *for* $\hat{\mathbf{x}} \geq \mathbf{0}$ *and* $\mathbf{t} \geq \mathbf{0}$, *then* $\hat{\mathbf{x}}$ *is a feasible solution of the original* SLP.

Proof. By Lemma 9.1, the phase 1 SLP has an optimal solution for which $w_{\min} \geq 0$. First, suppose $w_{\min} = 0$. Then there exist $\bar{\mathbf{x}}$ and $\bar{\mathbf{t}}$ such that $w(\bar{\mathbf{x}}, \bar{\mathbf{t}}) \geq 0$, $\bar{\mathbf{x}} \geq \mathbf{0}$, $\bar{\mathbf{t}} = 0$, and $\mathbf{A}\bar{\mathbf{x}} + \mathbf{I}\bar{\mathbf{t}} = \mathbf{b}$. But the definition of w shows that $w = 0$ implies $\bar{\mathbf{t}} = \mathbf{0}$. Hence, it follows that $\mathbf{A}\bar{\mathbf{x}} = \mathbf{b}$; thus the tableau of Eq. 9.9.1 is feasible.

Conversely, suppose there exists a feasible solution of $\mathbf{Ax} = \mathbf{b}$, say $\hat{\mathbf{x}}$. Then $\mathbf{Ax} + \mathbf{It} = \mathbf{b}$ is solvable in nonnegative variables by choosing $\mathbf{t} = \mathbf{0}$ and $\mathbf{x} = \hat{\mathbf{x}}$. For these values of $\mathbf{t}$ and $\mathbf{x}$, $w(\hat{\mathbf{x}}, \mathbf{0}) = 0$. Since $w \geq 0$ must hold for every feasible solution of the phase 1 SLP, $w_{\min} = 0$. ■

Once a feasible solution is found, either from an application of the phase 1 technique or by inspection, it is always possible to compute a BFS by resorting to the method of the fundamental theorem (Theorem 9.6.1). It often happens, however, that when phase 1 terminates with $w = 0$, the resulting tableau is in canonical form with a BFS in the original variables. This phenomenon is illustrated in the concluding two examples of this section.

Example 9.9.1. Show that the following system is feasible:

$$\left.\begin{aligned} -x_1 - 2x_2 + 2x_3 + x_4 &= 3 \\ -x_1 - x_2 + x_3 + 3x_4 &= 1 \end{aligned}\right\} \qquad x_1 \geq 0,\ x_2 \geq 0,\ x_3 \geq 0,\ x_4 \geq 0$$

Remark. Note that this is not an SLP because there is no objective function. However, this omission is irrelevant, since the phase 1 SLP furnishes an artificial objective function.

Solution. Introduce artificial variables t_1 and t_2 and the artificial objective function $w = t_1 + t_2$. The initial tableau for the phase 1 SLP is given by

	x_1	x_2	x_3	x_4	t_1	t_2	**b**
t_1	−1	−2	2	1	1	0	3
t_2	−1	−1	1	3	0	1	1
$-w$	0	0	0	0	1	1	0

The steps in the row reductions are diagramed below. Note that the first step is pricing out the cost coefficients of t_1 and t_2 to convert the initial tableau into a canonical tableau:

$$\left[\begin{array}{cccccc|c} -1 & -2 & 2 & 1 & 1 & 0 & 3 \\ -1 & -1 & 1 & 3 & 0 & 1 & 1 \\ \hline 0 & 0 & 0 & 0 & 1 & 1 & 0 \end{array}\right] \rightarrow$$

$$\cdots \rightarrow \left[\begin{array}{cccccc|c} -1 & -2 & 2 & 1 & 1 & 0 & 3 \\ -1 & -1 & 1 & 3 & 0 & 1 & 1 \\ \hline 2 & 3 & -3 & -4 & 0 & 0 & -4 \end{array}\right]$$

There is a choice of entering variables because of the appearance of two negative relative cost coefficients. Select the third column.

$$\begin{array}{c} t_1 \\ t_2 \\ \\ \end{array} \left[\begin{array}{cccccc|c} -1 & -2 & 2 & 1 & 1 & 0 & 3 \\ -1 & -1 & \mathbf{1} & 3 & 0 & 1 & 1 \\ \hline 2 & 3 & -3 & -4 & 0 & 0 & -4 \end{array}\right] \begin{array}{c} \text{ratios} \\ 3/2 \\ 1 = \vartheta \\ \\ \end{array} \rightarrow$$

$$\cdots \rightarrow \begin{array}{c} t_1 \\ x_3 \\ \\ \end{array} \left[\begin{array}{cccccc|c} \mathbf{1} & 0 & 0 & -5 & 1 & -2 & 1 \\ -1 & -1 & 1 & 3 & 0 & 1 & 1 \\ \hline -1 & 0 & 0 & 5 & 0 & 3 & -1 \end{array}\right] \begin{array}{c} \text{ratios} \\ 1 = \vartheta \\ - \\ \\ \end{array} \rightarrow$$

$$\cdots \rightarrow \begin{array}{c} x_1 \\ x_3 \\ \\ \end{array} \left[\begin{array}{cccccc|c} 1 & 0 & 0 & -5 & 1 & -2 & 1 \\ 0 & -1 & 1 & -2 & 1 & -1 & 2 \\ \hline 0 & 0 & 0 & 0 & 1 & 1 & 0 \end{array}\right]$$

The last matrix in this diagram shows that $w_{\min} = 0$; hence the given system is feasible. Moreover, a BFS for the original system in nonnegative variables can be read directly from the last tableau: $x_1 = 1,\ x_3 = 2,\ x_2 = x_4 = 0$.

Example 9.9.2. Show that the following system is infeasible:

$$\left.\begin{array}{r} -x_1 - 2x_2 + 2x_3 + x_4 = 3 \\ x_1 - x_2 + x_3 + 3x_4 = 1 \end{array}\right\} \qquad x_1 \geq 0,\ x_2 \geq 0,\ x_3 \geq 0,\ x_4 \geq 0$$

Solution. The work in this problem is almost identical to that in Example 9.9.1. The cost coefficients of the artificial variables are priced out, and a pivot is selected from the input-output coefficients in the columns with negative relative cost coefficients:

$$\begin{array}{c} t_1 \\ t_2 \\ \\ \end{array} \left[\begin{array}{cccccc|c} -1 & -2 & 2 & 1 & 1 & 0 & 3 \\ -1 & -1 & 1 & 3 & 0 & 1 & 1 \\ \hline 0 & 0 & 0 & 0 & 1 & 1 & 0 \end{array}\right] \rightarrow$$

$$\cdots \rightarrow \left[\begin{array}{cccccc|c} -1 & -2 & 2 & 1 & 1 & 0 & 3 \\ -1 & -1 & \mathbf{1} & 3 & 0 & 1 & 1 \\ \hline 0 & 3 & -3 & -4 & 0 & 0 & -4 \end{array}\right] \begin{array}{c} \text{ratios} \\ 3/2 \\ 1 = \vartheta \\ \\ \end{array}$$

$$\rightarrow \begin{array}{c} t_1 \\ x_3 \\ \\ \end{array} \left[\begin{array}{cccccc|c} 1 & 0 & 0 & -5 & 1 & -2 & 1 \\ 1 & -1 & 1 & 3 & 0 & 1 & 1 \\ \hline 3 & 0 & 0 & 5 & 0 & 3 & -1 \end{array}\right]$$

The simplex method for the phase 1 problem terminates because the optimal stopping criterion is met. The optimum objective value is $w = -(-1) = 1$. By Theorem 9.9.1, the original problem is infeasible.

PROBLEMS

PART 1

9.9.1. Solve the LP

$$\begin{aligned} \text{minimize:} \quad & z(\mathbf{x}) = -x - y \\ \text{subject to:} \quad & 0 \leq x \leq 1 \\ & -1 \leq x + y \leq 1 \end{aligned}$$

9.9.2. Find an optimal BFS or show that this SLP is unbounded below:

Basic variables	x_1	x_2	x_3	x_4	x_5	**b**
x_3	3	2	1	0	0	2
x_4	1	1	0	1	0	1
x_5	1	2	0	0	1	2
$-z$	2	−2	0	0	0	0

9.9.3. Find the set of b for which the LP

$$\left.\begin{aligned} -x_1 - 2x_2 + 2x_3 + x_4 &= 3 \\ x_1 - x_2 + x_3 + 3x_4 &= b \end{aligned}\right\} \qquad x_1 \geq 0,\ x_2 \geq 0,\ x_3 \geq 0,\ x_4 \geq 0$$

is feasible by using phase 1.

9.9.4. Show that the following SLP is unbounded below:

$$\begin{aligned} \text{minimize:} \quad & z = -4x_3 + x_4 + 2x_5 + x_6 \\ \text{subject to:} \quad & \left.\begin{aligned} x_1 \qquad - x_3 + 3x_4 - 2x_5 + x_6 &= 3 \\ x_2 + 2x_3 + x_4 - x_5 - x_6 &= 4 \end{aligned}\right\} \qquad (x_1 \geq 0) \end{aligned}$$

9.9.5. Test the following system for feasibility using phase 1:

$$\left.\begin{aligned} x - y + z &= -2 \\ y - z &= 1 \end{aligned}\right\} \qquad x \geq 0,\ y \geq 0,\ z \geq 0$$

9.9.6. Solve the SLP

$$\begin{aligned} \text{minimize:} \quad & z = -x_1 - x_2 + x_3 \\ \text{subject to:} \quad & \left.\begin{aligned} x_1 - x_2 + x_3 + x_4 &= 2 \\ x_1 - 2x_2 - x_3 + 3x_4 &\geq 1 \\ 2x_1 + x_2 - 2x_3 - x_4 &= 4 \end{aligned}\right\} \qquad \begin{aligned} x_1 \geq 0, \quad & x_2 \geq 0, \\ x_3 \geq 0, \quad & x_4 \geq 0 \end{aligned} \end{aligned}$$

9.9.7. Test the following system for feasibility using phase 1:

$$\left.\begin{aligned} x - y + z &= 1 \\ 2x + y - z &= 0 \\ x \qquad + z &= 1 \end{aligned}\right\} \qquad x \geq 0,\ y \geq 0, z \geq 0$$

PART 2

9.9.8. Show that the constraints

$$\left.\begin{aligned} 0 \le x + y &\le 2 \\ x - y &= 1 \end{aligned}\right\} \qquad x \ge 0,\ y \ge 0$$

imply the constraint $1 \le x + 2y \le 5/2$.

9.9.9. If a_{ij} is the pivot in a step in the simplex algorithm, show that z is unaltered if either b_i or c_j are zero.

9.9.10. Show that $\mathbf{Ax} > \mathbf{b}$, $\mathbf{x} \ge \mathbf{0}$, is feasible if any of the following conditions is satisfied:

(*a*) $\mathbf{A}$ has a nonnegative column.

(*b*) $\mathbf{b} \le \mathbf{0}$

9.9.11. If a_{ij} is the pivot in a step in the simplex algorithm, show that x_i enters and x_j exits the set of basic variables.

PART 3

9.9.12. Show that the the following SLP has an optimal feasible solution and that $w_{\min} \ge 0$.

$$\begin{aligned} \text{minimize:} \quad & w(\mathbf{x},\ \mathbf{t}) = t \\ \text{subject to:} \quad & [\mathbf{I} \quad \mathbf{D} \quad -\mathbf{1}]\begin{bmatrix} \mathbf{x_B} \\ \mathbf{x_D} \\ t \end{bmatrix} = \mathbf{b}, \qquad \begin{bmatrix} \mathbf{x_B} \\ \mathbf{x_D} \\ t \end{bmatrix} \ge \mathbf{0} \end{aligned}$$

9.9.13. For the SLP in Problem 9.9.12 show that $w_{\min} = 0$ if and only if the optimal feasible solutions have $\mathbf{t} = \mathbf{0}$.

9.9.14. Use the results of Problems 9.9.12 and 9.9.13 to conclude that the SLP

$$\begin{aligned} \text{minimize:} \quad & z(\mathbf{x}) = \mathbf{c}^{\mathrm{T}}\mathbf{x} \\ \text{subject to:} \quad & [\mathbf{I} \quad \mathbf{D}]\mathbf{x} = \mathbf{b}, \qquad \mathbf{x} \ge \mathbf{0} \end{aligned}$$

is feasible if and only if $w_{\min} = 0$ for the SLP in Problem 9.9.12.

9.10 THE GEOMETRY OF THE SIMPLEX METHOD

The simplex method traces a path from one vertex to another along the edge of the convex polyhedron of feasible solutions of an SLP. Although we do not offer a proof of this assertion[1], it is not difficult to verify in special cases. Consider, for example, the subset $\mathcal{K}$ of $\mathcal{R}^2$, sketched in Fig. 9.11, which describes the polytope of feasible solutions of

$$\begin{aligned} -x_1 + \ x_2 &\le 1 \\ x_1 + \ x_2 &\le 5 \\ x_1 - 4x_2 &\le 0 \end{aligned} \qquad x_1 \ge 0,\ x_2 \ge 0 \tag{9.10.1}$$

[1]See Katta G. Murty, *Linear Programming*. New York: Wiley, 1983.

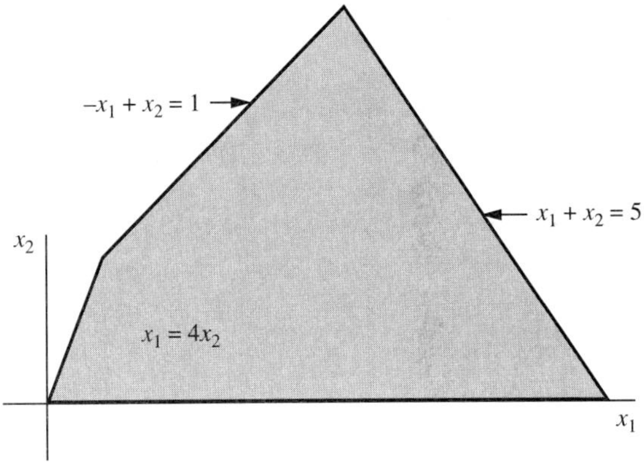

FIGURE 9-11
The polytope of feasible solutions of $-x_1 + x_2 \le 1$, $x_1 + x_2 \le 5$, $x_1 - 4x_2 \le 0$, $x_1 \ge 0$, $x_2 \ge 0$.

The addition of a slack for each inequality constraint and the trivial objective function $z(\mathbf{x}) = \mathbf{0}^T\mathbf{x}$ converts Eq. 9.10.1 into the SLP

$$\begin{aligned} \text{minimize:} \quad & z(\mathbf{x}, \mathbf{s}) = \mathbf{0}^T \begin{bmatrix} \mathbf{x} \\ \mathbf{s} \end{bmatrix} = 0, \qquad \mathbf{x} \ge \mathbf{0},\ \mathbf{s} \ge \mathbf{0} \\ \text{subject to:} \quad & -x_1 + x_2 + s_1 = 1 \\ & x_1 + x_2 + s_2 = 5 \\ & x_1 - 4x_2 + s_3 = 0 \end{aligned} \tag{9.10.2}$$

Example 9.10.1. Sketch the path in the (x_1, x_2) plane taken by the simplex algorithm applied to the SLP in Eq. 9.10.1.

Solution. The initial tableau corresponding to Eq. 9.10.2 is canonical:

Basic variables	x_1	x_2	s_1	s_2	s_3	**b**
s_1	-1	1	1	0	0	1
s_2	1	1	0	1	0	5
s_3	1	-4	0	0	1	0
$-z$	0	0	0	0	0	0

(Note that the SLP is in five nonnegative variables, but $\mathcal{K}$, the feasible solution set for the original LP, is a subset of two-dimensional-space.) Since the objective function is zero for all **x**, we can ignore the $-z$ row in performing the steps in the simplex method.

$$T_1 = \begin{matrix} s_1 \\ s_2 \\ s_3 \end{matrix}\left[\begin{array}{rrrrr|r} -1 & 1 & 1 & 0 & 0 & 1 \\ 1 & 1 & 0 & 1 & 0 & 5 \\ 1 & -4 & 0 & 0 & 1 & 0 \end{array}\right] \rightarrow$$

$$\cdots \rightarrow T_2 = \begin{matrix} s_1 \\ s_2 \\ x_1 \end{matrix}\left[\begin{array}{rrrrr|r} 0 & -3 & 1 & 0 & 1 & 1 \\ 0 & 5 & 0 & 1 & -1 & 5 \\ 1 & -4 & 0 & 0 & 1 & 0 \end{array}\right] \rightarrow$$

$$\cdots \rightarrow T_3 = \begin{matrix} s_1 \\ x_2 \\ x_1 \end{matrix}\left[\begin{array}{rrrrr|r} 0 & 0 & 1 & 3/5 & 2/5 & 4 \\ 0 & 1 & 0 & 1/5 & -1/5 & 1 \\ 1 & 0 & 0 & 4/5 & 1/5 & 4 \end{array}\right] \rightarrow$$

$$\cdots \rightarrow T_4 = \begin{matrix} s_3 \\ x_2 \\ x_1 \end{matrix}\left[\begin{array}{rrrrr|r} 0 & 0 & 5/2 & 3/2 & 1 & 10 \\ 0 & 1 & 1/2 & 1/2 & 0 & 3 \\ 1 & 0 & -1/2 & 1/2 & 0 & 2 \end{array}\right] \rightarrow$$

$$\cdots \rightarrow T_5 = \begin{matrix} s_3 \\ x_2 \\ s_2 \end{matrix}\left[\begin{array}{rrrrr|r} 0 & 0 & 4 & 0 & 1 & 4 \\ -1 & 1 & 1 & 0 & 0 & 1 \\ 2 & 0 & -1 & 1 & 0 & 4 \end{array}\right]$$

The BFSs implicit in each of the tableaux T_1 through T_5 correspond to vertices of $\mathcal{K}$. The connections are given in the following table.

Tableau	Basic Variables	BFS of SLP	Vertices in $\mathcal{K}$
T_1	s_1, s_2, s_3	$x_1 = [0 \;\; 0 \;\; 1 \;\; 5 \;\; 0]^T$	(0, 0)
T_2	s_1, s_2, x_1	$x_2 = [0 \;\; 0 \;\; 1 \;\; 5 \;\; 0]^T$	(0, 0)
T_3	s_1, x_2, x_1	$x_3 = [4 \;\; 1 \;\; 4 \;\; 0 \;\; 0]^T$	(4, 1)
T_4	s_3, x_2, x_1	$x_4 = [2 \;\; 3 \;\; 0 \;\; 0 \;\; 10]^T$	(2, 3)
T_5	s_3, x_2, x_2	$x_5 = [0 \;\; 1 \;\; 0 \;\; 4 \;\; 4]^T$	(0, 1)

The first two tableaux yield the same vertices in $\mathcal{K}$ and the same BFSs of the SLP, although the basic variables are different.

Figure 9.11 shows that the simplex algorithm traverses the edges of $\mathcal{K}$. This can be understood by considering the diagram displaying the steps in the algorithm that takes T_2 to T_3. The matrix of tableau T_2,

$$\left[\begin{array}{rrrrr|r} 0 & -3 & 1 & 0 & 1 & 1 \\ 0 & 5 & 0 & 1 & -1 & 5 \\ 1 & -4 & 0 & 0 & 1 & 0 \end{array}\right]$$

shows that the second column is a linear combination of columns 1, 3, and 4. Hence, $\mathbf{a} = [4 \;\; 1 \;\; 3 \;\; -5 \;\; 0]^{\mathrm{T}}$ is a solution of $\mathbf{Aa} = \mathbf{0}$. The BFS that is associated with T_2 is the vector $\mathbf{x}_2 = [0 \;\; 0 \;\; 1 \;\; 5 \;\; 0]^{\mathrm{T}}$. So

$$\mathbf{x}(\lambda) = \mathbf{x}_2 + \lambda \mathbf{y}_h = \begin{bmatrix} 0 \\ 0 \\ 1 \\ 5 \\ 0 \end{bmatrix} + \lambda \begin{bmatrix} 4 \\ 1 \\ 3 \\ -5 \\ 0 \end{bmatrix} \geq \mathbf{0} \tag{9.10.3}$$

is a feasible solution if and only if $0 \le \lambda \le 1$. Choosing $\lambda = 0$ gives $\mathbf{x}(0) = \mathbf{x}_2$, of course. If $\lambda = 1$, then $\mathbf{x}(1) = \mathbf{x}_3$. In terms of the points in the (x, y) plane, the vector $\mathbf{x}(\lambda)$ represents a line segment joining the vertex (0,0) to the vertex (4,1). Indeed, it is easy to verify that this line segment is precisely the line $4y = x$. Problems 9.10.1–9.10.3 of the following exercise set demonstrates that each step in the simplex method moves along an edge from one vertex of $\mathcal{H}$ to another, adjacent vertex.

The objective function $z = 0$ in Eq. 9.10.2 is a device introduced to convert Eq. 9.10.1 into an LP. Indeed, for such problems optimization is irrelevant, since every feasible solution is an optimal solution, and the simplex algorithm can be invoked without a cost coefficient row. In optimization problems with a nontrivial object function $z(\mathbf{x}) = \mathbf{c}^T\mathbf{x}$, $\mathbf{c} \ne \mathbf{0}$, account must be taken of the cost coefficients to ensure that the value of the objective function does not increase. The net effect of this condition is that the set of edges traversed by the simplex method is a subset of the edges available at each vertex for which $z(\mathbf{x})$ is monotone-nonincreasing.

Example 9.10.2. Find an optimal BFS for the LP given by the constraints in Eq. 9.10.1 with the nontrivial objective function: minimize $z(\mathbf{x}) = -x_2$.

Solution. The constraints are the same as in Example 9.10.1, but the effects of a nontrivial objective function are shown in the path taken by the simplex algorithm:

$$
\begin{array}{c|ccccc|c}
s_1 & -1 & 1 & 1 & 0 & 0 & 1 \\
s_2 & 1 & 1 & 0 & 1 & 0 & 5 \\
s_3 & 1 & -4 & 0 & 0 & 1 & 0 \\
\hline
-z & 0 & -1 & 0 & 0 & 0 & 0
\end{array}
\quad \rightarrow
$$

$$
\cdots \rightarrow \quad
\begin{array}{c|ccccc|c}
x_2 & -1 & 1 & 1 & 0 & 0 & 1 \\
s_2 & 2 & 0 & -1 & 1 & 0 & 4 \\
s_3 & -3 & 0 & 4 & 0 & 1 & 4 \\
\hline
-z & -1 & 0 & 1 & 0 & 0 & 1
\end{array}
\quad \rightarrow
$$

$$
\cdots \rightarrow \quad
\begin{array}{c|ccccc|c}
x_2 & 0 & 1 & \tfrac{1}{2} & \tfrac{1}{2} & 0 & 3 \\
x_1 & 1 & 0 & -\tfrac{1}{2} & \tfrac{1}{2} & 0 & 2 \\
s_3 & 0 & 0 & \tfrac{5}{2} & \tfrac{3}{2} & 1 & 10 \\
\hline
-z & 0 & 0 & \tfrac{1}{2} & \tfrac{1}{2} & 0 & 3
\end{array}
$$

Thus, an optimal solution is $\mathbf{x}_0 = [2 \;\; 3 \;\; 0 \;\; 0 \;\; 1 \;\; 0]^T$, which corresponds to the vertex (2,3). The path traced by the simplex method is given symbolically by $T_1 \rightarrow T_5 \rightarrow T_4$. Here z takes on the successively smaller values $0, -1, -3$.

The argument presented in Examples 9.10.1 and 9.10.2 to show that the simplex method is an "edge-traversing" algorithm depends on our ability to sketch the set of feasible solutions so that the terms *edge* and *vertex* can be interpreted geometrically. For those $\mathcal{H}$ in which a sketch is impossible, the proof requires algebraic definitions for *edge* and *vertex*. These definitions are beyond the scope of this text. Nonetheless, the following argument shows why the simplex method is a line-traversing algorithm from one boundary point of $\mathcal{H}$ to another. (It fails to establish that the line is an edge of $\mathcal{H}$ and the boundary point(s) is a vertex.) Consider the tableau

Basic variables	x_1	x_2	x_3	x_4	......	x_n	$-z$	**b**
x_1	1	0	0	a_{14}	...	*	0	b_1
x_2	0	1	0	a_{24}	...	*	0	b_2
x_3	0	0	1	a_{34}	...	*	0	b_3
$-z$	0	0	0	$\bar{c}_4$	...	*	1	*

As in the special case illustrated in Eq. 9.10.3, set $\lambda_+ = \vartheta = \min\{b_i/a_{i4}\}$ for all i such that $a_{i4} > 0$. Then $\mathbf{a} = [a_{14} \quad a_{24} \quad a_{34} \quad -1 \quad 0 \quad \ldots \quad 0]^{\mathrm{T}}$. Thus, for $0 \leq \lambda \leq \lambda_+$

$$\mathbf{x}(\lambda) = \begin{bmatrix} b_1 \\ b_2 \\ b_3 \\ 0 \\ \vdots \\ 0 \end{bmatrix} - \lambda \begin{bmatrix} a_{14} \\ a_{24} \\ a_{34} \\ -1 \\ \vdots \\ 0 \end{bmatrix} \geq \mathbf{0}$$

(Recall that the simplex method requires the computation of ϑ to determine the exiting variable.) Moreover, note that $\mathbf{x}(\lambda)$ is a BFS using x_4 and two of the previous basic variables x_1, x_2, x_3. The set of feasible vectors $\mathbf{x}(\lambda), 0 \leq \lambda \leq \vartheta$, is clearly a line segment. Thus, the simplex algorithm traverses along a line of feasible solutions.

PROBLEMS

PART 1

The next three problems refer to Example 9.10.1, the arrow diagram $T_1 \rightarrow T_2 \rightarrow \cdots \rightarrow T_5$, and Fig. 9.11.

9.10.1. Find the line segment $\mathbf{x}(\lambda)$ of feasible solutions that join the BFS $\mathbf{x}_3$ to $\mathbf{x}_4$, by finding $\mathbf{a}$ and $\lambda_+ = \vartheta$.

9.10.2. Repeat Problem 9.10.1, except use $\mathbf{x}_4$ and $\mathbf{x}_5$, and then $\mathbf{x}_1$ and $\mathbf{x}_5$.

9.10.3. Trace the path of the simplex algorithm in Fig. 9.11 if the objective function is $z(\mathbf{x}) = 2x_1 - x_2$.

9.10.4. Refer to Example 9.8.4. Assume that x_3, x_4, and x_5 are slacks and that x_1 and x_2 are the original variables. Sketch the set of feasible solutions in the (x_1, x_2) plane and trace the edge path of the simplex method. (See also Problem 9.10.5)

9.10.5. Show that the line of feasible solutions arising from the tableau in Eq. 9.8.4 and starting from (1,0) represents an unbounded edge of the set of feasible solutions of the LP in the original variables x_1 and x_2.

9.10.6. Sketch the set of feasible solutions for the LP given in Example 9.8.5. Sketch $\mathcal{K}$ in the (x,y) plane and trace the edge path taken by the simplex algorithm applied to the SLP equivalent to the original LP.

9.10.7. Repeat Problem 9.10.6 except the first variable to enter the basic set is x_2 instead of x_1.

PART 2

9.10.8. Refer to Example 9.10.1. Explain why we can move from tableau T_1 to T_5 in one step of the simplex algorithm but we cannot do the same for T_2 to T_5, although both T_1 and T_2 correspond to the same vertex.

9.10.9. Explain why the simplex method generates a line segment that begins at a boundary point of $\mathcal{K}$.

APPENDIX A

The following three tables provide a summary of three aspects of MATLAB relevant to the material in this text. The first table is a translation from text to MATLAB notation. The second table is a list of some of the .m files that are relevant to text material. The third table contains a variety of .m files written expressly for use with this text.

Translation from text to MATLAB

Text	MATLAB	Meaning
$\mathbf{A}^{\mathrm{H}}$	A'	Conjugate transpose of **A**
$\mathbf{A}^{\mathrm{T}}$	A.'	Transpose of **A**
$\mathbf{A}_{*j}$	A(:,j)	jth column of **A**
$\mathbf{A}_{i*}$	A(i,:)	ith row of **A**
a_{ij}	A(i,j)	The i, jth entry of **A**
$\mathbf{I}_n$	eye(n)	Identity matrix of size n
$\mathbf{O}_n$	zeros(n)	$n \times n$ matrix of 0s
$\mathbf{J}_n$	ones(n)	$n \times n$ matrix of 1s
$(0)_{m\times n}$	zeros(m,n)	$m \times n$ matrix of 0s
$\mathbf{J}_{m\times n}$	ones(m,n)	$m \times n$ matrix of 1s
$\mathbf{0}_n$	zeros(n,1)	$n \times 1$ vector of 0s
$\mathbf{1}_n$	ones(n,1)	$n \times 1$ vector of 1s
det(**A**)	det(A)	Determinant of **A**
$\mathbf{A}^{-1}$	inv(A)	Inverse of **A**
$\mathbf{A}^{-}$	pinv(A)	Pseudo-inverse of **A**
rref(**A**)	rref(A)	Reduced row echelon form of **A**
rank(**A**)	rank(A)	Rank of **A**

MATLAB functions

.mfile	Description
W = chol(A)	For positive definite A, W is upper triangular and W' * W = A.
W = compan(p)	For $p = [1 \quad p_1 \quad \cdots \quad p_{n-1}]$, W is a $n \times n$ companion matrix whose eigenvalues are the roots of $p(x) = x^n + p_1 x^{n-1} + \cdots + p_{n-1}$. [There are a variety of forms for the companion matrix. The one given by this function is related to the one in the text (denoted here by C) as follows: C = flipud(fliplr(W)). See mcompan.m.]
fliplr(A), flipud(A)	fliplr rotates A about a vertical axis drawn through the middle of A. flipud rotates A about a horizontal axis drawn through the middle of A.
[S,D] = eig(A)	Provides a matrix S whose columns are eigenvectors of A and a diagonal matrix D whose diagonal entries are its eigenvalues. If A is simple, inv(S) * A * S = D.
[L,U] = lu(A)	The LU factorization of A. L is a row-permuted lower triangular matrix, and U is upper triangular.
[Q,R] = qr(A)	The QR factorization of A. Q is an orthogonal matrix, and R is upper trapezoidal such that A = Q * R. (The exact natures of Q and R are highly conventionalized and are described in full in the MATLAB manual. This factorization does not generally agree with the QR factorization given in the text. See mqr.m.)
null(A)	An orthonormal basis for the null space of A.
orth(A)	An orthonormal basis for the column space of A.
v = poly(A)	The entries in the row vector v are the coefficients of the characteristic polynomial of A in order of descending power.
B = polyvalm(p,A)	If $p(x) = p_1 x^n + p_2 x^{n-1} + \cdots + p_{n+1}$ and p denotes the row vector $p = [p_1 \quad p_2 \quad \cdots \quad p_{n+1}]$, then polyvalm(p,A) returns B = p(A) = p_1 * A^n + p_2 * A^($n - 1$) + $\cdots$ + p_{n+1}*eye(A). That is, B = p(A).
[U,T] = schur(A)	If A is a real square matrix, U' * A * U = T, where U is unitary and T is upper triangular. If A has complex entries, schur(A) returns the complex schur form. (See text and MATLAB reference.)

Special functions

.mfile	Description
B = mc(A,n)	B is A rounded to n places.
W = mcirc(v)	If row vector v = $[b_1 \quad b_2 \quad \cdots \quad b_{n-1} \quad b_n]$, W = $$\begin{matrix} b_1 & b_2 & \cdots & b_{n-1} & b_n \\ b_n & b_1 & \cdots & b_{n-2} & b_{n-1} \\ \vdots & \vdots & & \vdots & \vdots \\ b_2 & b_3 & \cdots & b_n & b_1 \end{matrix}$$
[C,M] = mcol(A)	The matrix C contains the leading columns of A, and M is A with its nonleading columns set to zero.

(continued)

Special functions—cont'd.

.mfile	Description
W = mcompan(b)	If b is a row vector whose first entry is 1, then W is a companion matrix as defined in the text. (See W = compan(p) in the Table of MATLAB functions.)
[V,e,g] = meig(A)	For square matrices A, e is a column vector whose entries are the eigenvalues of A arranged in increasing order; V is a rectangular matrix whose columns are the corresponding linearly independent eigenvectors; g is a row vector whose entries are the geometric multiplicities of each eigenvalue. If A is simple, V has the property inv(V) * A * V = diag(e).
N = mnull(A)	N is a matrix whose columns are a basis for the null space of A. Unlike the output of null.m, the columns of N are not normalized.
[U,S] = morth(A)	The set of columns of U is an orthogonal basis for the column space of A, which is generally not an orthonormal basis. The matrix S is an upper triangular, nonsingular matrix with positive entries on its diagonal such that U * S is a submatrix of A whose columns are the leading columns of A. If A has full column rank, then A = U * S and A(:,k) = U * S(:,k) for each k. (See the corresponding file orth.m in the table of MATLAB functions.)
[Q,R] = mqr(A)	Q is an orthonormal matrix whose set of columns is a basis for the column space of A. R is an invertible, upper triangular matrix with positive entries on its diagonal. Q * R is a submatrix of A whose columns are the leading columns of If A has full column rank, then A = Q * R and A(:,k) = Q * R(:,k) for each k. If D = diag(diag(R)) then the outputs U and S of [U,S] = morth(A) are related to Q and R by U = Q * D and S = inv(D) * R. (See qr.m in the table of MATLAB functions.)
[PMAT,L,U,pvec] = mplu(A)	L is a lower triangular matrix, U is upper triangular, and PMAT is a permutation matrix such that PMAT * L * U = A. The vector pvec displays the permutations of rows of L that produce the permuted LU decomposition of A. (See the file lu.m in the table of MATLAB functions.)
R = mrow(A)	R = mcol(A.').'.
[R,S] = mrrf(A,b)	The matrix R has the same size as A, and S is a nonsingular matrix such that S * A = R. The matrix R is a generalization of the reduced row echelon form of A. If the entries in b are n distinct nonnegative integers, say b = [4, 1, 2], then the columns of A are temporarily reordered so that B = [A(:,4) A(:,1) A(:,2)]. The matrix rref(B) is found and then the columns of rref(B) are restored to their original positions. If b = [1:n] and n is the number of columns of A, then R = rref(A). b = [] is treated as b = [1:n].
X = msoln(A,B)	If AX = B is consistent, then msoln(A,B) returns a solution X. The matrix **A** need not be square. If the system is inconsistent, X = [].

APPENDIX B

The .m files presented in this appendix were written to facilitate the use of the text. They were designed to output answers that more closely resemble the results of hand computations than do the corresponding MATLAB functions.

There is a cost for this convenience. Little concern was taken to minimize round-off and truncation errors and computation time. (Indeed, for some of the functions, it takes quite some time to do rather simple matrix processing.) For these reasons, these functions should not be used for large-scale problems. In the context for which these programs were designed, the issues of round-off and truncation errors seldom arise. Moreover, the matrices used as examples and exercises in the text are never more than 5×5 and the answers can usually be expressed in terms of rationals and or quadratic surds of rationals. A further simplification is used rather extensively; most matrices are rounded by the file mc.m.

In a word, the functions presented here are educational programs, and their use should be reserved for this purpose.

BASIS

Description. If **A** is $m \times n$ with rank r, [C,M] = mcol.(A) returns **C**, a submatrix of **A**, such that $col(\mathbf{A}) = col(\mathbf{C})$ and **C** has full column rank. Hence, the columns of **C** are a basis for $col(\mathbf{A})$. The matrix **M** has the same size as **A** with the same leading columns. The nonleading columns of **A** are zero in **M**. This file calls mqr.m

Conventions.

[C,M] = mcol(A)

Usage. Finds a basis for $col(\mathbf{A})$ among the columns of **A**.

Example.

(1) Enter

$$\mathbf{A} = \begin{bmatrix} 1 & -1 & 1 & 2 \\ 1 & -1 & 1 & 2 \\ 1 & -1 & 0 & 1 \end{bmatrix}$$

[C,M] = mcol(A)

$$C = \quad \begin{matrix} 1 & 1 \\ 1 & 1 \\ 1 & 0 \end{matrix} \qquad M = \quad \begin{matrix} 1 & 0 & 1 & 0 \\ 1 & 0 & 1 & 0 \\ 1 & 0 & 0 & 0 \end{matrix}$$

CIRCULANTS

Description. The function W = mcirc(v) returns the circulant matrix **W** whose first row is the row vector v = $[b_1 \quad b_2 \quad \dots \quad b_{n-1} \quad b_n]$.

$$W = \quad \begin{matrix} b_1 & b_2 & \cdots & b_{n-1} & b_n \\ b_n & b_1 & \cdots & b_{n-2} & b_{n-1} \\ \vdots & \vdots & & \vdots & \vdots \\ b_2 & b_3 & \cdots & b_n & b_1 \end{matrix}$$

This file calls mc.m.

Conventions.

W = mcirc(v)

v is a row vector.

Usage. Generate the circulant matrix **W**.

Examples.

(1) Enter $\mathbf{v}^T = [1 \quad 2 \quad -1 \quad 0]$.

W = mcirc(v)

$$W = \quad \begin{matrix} 1 & 2 & -1 & 0 \\ 0 & 1 & 2 & -1 \\ -1 & 0 & 1 & 2 \\ 2 & -1 & 0 & 1 \end{matrix}$$

(2) Enter $\mathbf{v}^T = [0 \quad 1 \quad 0 \quad 0]$.

W = mcirc(v)

$$W = \quad \begin{matrix} 0 & 1 & 0 & 0 \\ 0 & 0 & 1 & 0 \\ 0 & 0 & 0 & 1 \\ 1 & 0 & 0 & 0 \end{matrix}$$

As a pre- or postmultiplier of **A**, **W** rotates the columns of **A** to the right with wrap-around. This is equivalent to rotating the rows of **A** upward.

COMPANION MATRIX

Description. The function C = mcompan(v) returns a companion matrix as defined in the text. Compare with C = compan(A).

Conventions.

C = mcompan(v)

v is a row vector whose first entry is 1.

Usage. Let $p(x) = x^n + v_1 x^{n-1} \cdots + v_n x + v_{n+1}$ and v = $[1 \quad v_1 \quad \cdots \quad v_{n+1}]$. Then C = mcompan(v) returns an $n \times n$ matrix whose characteristic polynomial is $c(\lambda) = p(-x)$. This file invokes compan.m.

Examples.

(1) Enter v = [1 0 0 − 1].

C = mcompan(v)

```
C =
     0  1  0
     0  0  1
     1  0  0
```

(2) v = [1 − 1 2 3]

C = mcompan(v)

```
C =
      1   0   0
      0   1   0
     -3  -2   1
```

CLEAN

Description. The function A = mc(A,n) returns **A** rounded so that all digits past 10^{-n} are cleared to zero.

Conventions.

A = mc(A,n)

Usage. Rounds **A** to n places.

Examples.

(1) Enter c = 0.00000000000023

c = mc(c,11)

```
c =
     0
```

EIGENVALUES AND EIGENVECTORS

Description. The function [V,e,g] = meig(A) returns a vector **e** whose entries are the eigenvalues of **A**, a rectangular matrix **V** whose columns are the corresponding linearly independent eigenvectors, and a row vector **g** whose entries are the geometric multiplicities of each eigenvalue. The eigenvalues are listed in order of increasing magnitude. If the eigenvalue λ is repeated k times, these k repeated eigenvalues are grouped consecutively in **e**. If **A** is simple, then **V** has the property inv(V)*A*V = diag(e). The eigenvectors are presented as columns of **V** in such a manner that consecutive columns provide a basis for the eigenspace corresponding to their eigenvalue. This file calls mcirc.m, mcol.m, mc.m and mrrf.m.

Conventions.
[V,e,g] = meig(A)

Usage. This function provides the eigenvalues, their algebraic and geometric multiplicities, and their corresponding eigenvectors.

Examples.
(1) Enter

$$\mathbf{A} = \begin{bmatrix} 2 & 1 & 1 \\ 0 & 3 & 1 \\ -2 & -1 & -1 \end{bmatrix}$$

[V,e,g] = meig(A)

```
V =
        1    1      e =                  g =
        1    1           0  2  2              1  1
       -3   -1
```

(2) Enter A = ones(3)

[V,e,g] = meig(A)

```
V =
       1    0   1      e =                g =
       0    1   1           0  0  3            2  1
      -1   -1   1
```

LU FACTORIZATION[1]

Description. The function [PMAT,L,U,pvec] = mplu(A) returns a lower triangular matrix **L**, an upper triangular matrix **U**, and a permutation matrix PMAT

[1]This program is the work of R. Moore of the University of Washington.

such that PMAT*L*U = A. If [LP,U] = lu(A) is called, LP is a permuted form of **L**, and **U** is the same for the two functions. The matrix LP satisfies LP*U = A and is related to **L** by PMAT*L = LP. The vector pvec displays the permutations of rows of **L** that produce LP.

Conventions.
[PMAT,L,U,pvec] = mplu(A)
pvec and PMAT are optional in calling mplu.m.

Usage. Displays the **LU** factorization of a row-permuted form of **A**.

Examples.
(1) Enter

$$\mathbf{A} = \begin{bmatrix} 1 & -1 & 1 \\ -1 & 1 & 1 \\ 1 & 1 & -1 \end{bmatrix}$$

[PMAT,L,U,pvec] = mplu(A)

```
PMAT =            L =              U =               pvec =
   1  0  0          1  0  0          1  -1   1          1
   0  0  1          1  1  0          0   2  -2          3
   0  1  0         -1  0  0          0   0   2          2
```

Note that PMAT*L*U = A.

NULL SPACE

Description. The function N = mnull(A) returns a matrix whose columns are a basis for *null*(**A**). If **A** has full column rank so that *null*(**A**) contains only **0**, N = [] is returned. This file calls mrrf.m.

Conventions.
N = mnull(A)

Usage. Find a basis for the solutions of **Ax** = **0**. A "general" solution to the consistent system **AX** = **B** is **Na** + $\mathbf{X}_p$, where $\mathbf{X}_p$ is a solution of **AX** = **B** and **a** is a vector of weights.

Examples.
(1) Enter

$$\mathbf{A} = \begin{bmatrix} 2 & 1 & 1 \\ 0 & 3 & 1 \\ -2 & -1 & -1 \end{bmatrix}$$

N = mnull(A)

N =

$$\begin{matrix} 1 \\ 1 \\ -3 \end{matrix}$$

(2) Enter $\mathbf{A} = [1 \quad 1 \quad 1]$

N = mnull(A)

N =

$$\begin{matrix} 1 & 0 \\ 0 & 1 \\ -1 & -1 \end{matrix}$$

(3) Enter $\mathbf{A} = [1 \quad 1 \quad 1]^{\mathrm{T}}$

N = mnull(A)

N =

[ ]

ORTHOGONAL BASIS

Description. The function [U,S] = morth(A) provides an orthogonal basis for $col(\mathbf{A})$, which is generally not an orthonormal basis. This basis is the set of columns of $\mathbf{U}$. The matrix $\mathbf{U}$ has r columns where r = rank($\mathbf{A}$). $\mathbf{S}$ is an upper triangular, nonsingular matrix with positive entries on its diagonal such that $\mathbf{US}$ is a submatrix of $\mathbf{A}$ whose columns are the leading columns of $\mathbf{A}$. If, in particular, $\mathbf{A}$ has full column rank, then $\mathbf{A} = \mathbf{US}$, and $\mathbf{A}_{*i} = \mathbf{US}_{*i}$ for each i. This function calls mcol.m, mqr.m, mc.m and msubqr.m.

Conventions.
[U,S] = morth(A)

Usage. If $\mathbf{A} = [\mathbf{a}_1 \quad \mathbf{a}_2 \quad \ldots \quad \mathbf{a}_k]$ and $\mathbf{A}_{*j}$ is the ith leading column of $\mathbf{A}$ for $1 \leq i \leq j \leq k$, then $\mathbf{A}_{*j} = \mathbf{US}_{*i}$ where $\mathbf{S}_{*i}$ is the ith column of $\mathbf{S}$. This function is closely related to [Q,R] = mqr(A). (See mqr.m.)

Examples.
(1) Enter A = ones(3)

[U,S] = morth(A)

U = S =

$$\begin{matrix} 1 \\ 1 \\ 1 \end{matrix} \qquad \begin{matrix} 1 \end{matrix}$$

(2) Enter

$$\mathbf{A} = \begin{bmatrix} 1 & -1 & 1 \\ -1 & 1 & 1 \\ 1 & 1 & -1 \end{bmatrix}$$

[U,S] = morth(A)

U =

1.0000	−.6667	1.0000
−1.0000	.6667	1.0000
1.0000	1.3333	0

S =

1	−.3333	−.3333
	1.0000	−.5000
	0	1.0000

QR FACTORIZATION

Description. The function [Q,R] = mqr(A) provides a **QR** factorization of **A**. The matrix **Q** has r columns, where r = rank(**A**), and is an orthonormal matrix. **R** is an upper triangular, nonsingular matrix with positive entries on its diagonal such that **QR** is a submatrix of **A** whose columns are the leading columns of **A**. If, in particular, **A** has full column rank, then $\mathbf{A} = \mathbf{QR}$ and $\mathbf{A}_{*i} = \mathbf{QR}_{*i}$ for each i. Set D = diag(diag(R)). Then the outputs **U** and **S** of [U,S] = morth(A) are related to **Q** and **R** by U = Q*D and S = inv(D)*R. This file calls msubqr.m and mc.m.

Conventions.
[Q,R] = mqr(A)

Usage. If $\mathbf{A} = [\mathbf{a}_1 \;\; \mathbf{a}_2 \;\; \ldots \;\; \mathbf{a}_k]$ and $\mathbf{A}_{*j}$ is the ith leading column of **A** for $1 \leq i \leq j \leq k$ then $\mathbf{A}_{*j} = \mathbf{QR}_{*i}$, where $\mathbf{R}_{*i}$ is the ith column of **R**. If **A** has full column rank so that its columns are linearly independent, then $i = j$ and the columns of **Q** provide the orthonormal vectors computed by the Gram-Schmidt method.

Examples.
(1) Enter A = ones(3)

[Q,R] mqr(A)

Q =

.5774
.5774
.5774

R =

1.7321

(2) Enter

$$\mathbf{A} = \begin{bmatrix} 1 & -1 & 1 \\ -1 & 1 & 1 \\ 1 & 1 & -1 \end{bmatrix}$$

[Q,R] mqr(A)

Q =

.5774	−.4082	.7071
−.5774	.4082	.7071
.5774	.8165	.0000

R =

1.7321	−.5774	−.5774
0	1.6330	−.8165
0	0	1.4142

REDUCED ROW FORM

Description. The function [R,S] = mrrf(A,b) returns a matrix **R** whose size is the same as **A** and a nonsingular matrix **S** such that **SA** = **R**. The matrix **R** is a generalization of the reduced row echelon form of **A**. If the entries in **b** are n distinct nonnegative integers, say **b** = [4, 1, 2], then the columns of **A** are temporarily reordered so that $\mathbf{B} = [\mathbf{A}_{*4} \quad \mathbf{A}_{*1} \quad \mathbf{A}_{*2} \quad \mathbf{A}_{*3} \quad \mathbf{A}_{*5} \quad \ldots \quad \mathbf{A}_{*n}]$. The matrix **B** is put in reduced row echelon form, $\mathbf{B}_R$, and then the columns of $\mathbf{B}_R$ are restored to their original positions. If b = [1 : n] and n is the number of columns of **A**, then R = rref(A). b = [] is treated as b = [1 : n]. This file calls mc.m.

Conventions.
[R,S] = mrrf(A,b)

The row vector **b** (which may be []) has distinct nonnegative integer entries. The null vector [] is treated as b = [1 : n], where n is the number of columns of **A**.

Usage. The reduced row forms and the nonsingular **S** are called by other .m files (such as msoln.m) and are used frequently in the simplex method.

Examples.
(1) Enter

$$\mathbf{A} = \begin{bmatrix} 1 & -1 & 1 & 0 \\ 1 & -1 & 1 & 0 \\ 0 & -1 & 1 & 1 \end{bmatrix}$$

[R,S] = mrrf(A,[])

R =

1	0	0	−1
0	1	−1	−1
0	0	0	0

S =

0	1	−1
0	0	−1
1	−1	0

(2) Enter

$$\mathbf{A} = \begin{bmatrix} 1 & -1 & 1 \\ 1 & 1 & 1 \\ 0 & 1 & 1 \end{bmatrix}, \qquad \mathbf{b} = [3 \quad 2 \quad 1]^{\mathrm{T}}$$

```
[R;S] = mrrf(A,b)
     R =                    S =
          0  0  1               0.5000  -0.5000  1
          0  1  0              -0.5000   0.5000  0
          1  0  0               0       -1       1
```

SOLUTION OF AX = B

Description. Provides a solution of **AX** = **B**. **A** need not be a square matrix. If the system is inconsistent, X = msoln(A,B) returns the null matrix []. This file calls mrrf.m, mcol.m and mc.m.

Conventions.
X = msoln(A,B)

Usage. Finds a solution of **AX** = **B**. Combined with mnull.m, this leads to a general solution of this system, $\mathbf{Na} + \mathbf{X}_p$, where **N** is a matrix whose columns are a basis for *null*(**A**), **a** is an arbitrary vector of weights, and $\mathbf{AX}_p = \mathbf{B}$.

Examples.
(1) Enter A = ones(3) and

$$B = \begin{bmatrix} 3 & 1 & 1 \\ 3 & 1 & 1 \\ 3 & 1 & 1 \end{bmatrix}$$

```
X = msoln(A,B)

     X =
          3  1  1
          0  0  0
          0  0  0
```

.MFiles

mc.m

```
function E = mc(A,n)
E = round(10^n*A)/10^n;
a = real(E); b = imag(E);
c = rem(a,1)/10^n; d = rem(b,1)/10^n; e = a + c; f = b + d;
g = round(10^n*e)/10^n; h = round(10^n*f)/10^n;
E = g + i*h;
```

mcirc.m

```
function W = mcirc(v)
[m,n] = size(v); B = zeros(n,n); A = eye(n);
B(:,1) = A(:,n); B(:,2:n) = A(:,1:n-1); v = v(:,n:-1:1);
```

```
C = polyvalm(v,B);
W = mc(C,12);
```

mcol.m

```
function [N,M] = mcol(A)
[m,n] = size(A); A = mc(A,12);
v = zeros(1,n); u = v; B = A; Z = zeros(A);
    if n > 1
        for k = 1:n,
        v(k) = rank(A(:,1:k));
        end
    u(1,2:n) = v(1,1:n-1); r = u-v;
    A(:,~r) = []; B(:,~r) = Z(:,~r);
    end
    if A == zeros(A), A = [];
    end
N = mc(A,12); M = mc(B,12);
```

mcompan.m

```
function C = mcompan(p)
B = compan(A); C = flipud(fliplr(A);
```

meig.m

```
function [V,e,g] = meig(A)
[V,D] = eig(A); e = diag(D); e = mc(e,4); V = mc(V,4);
[l,k] = sort(e); e = l; V = V(:,k); e = e';
[m,n] = size(e);
t = zeros(1,n); t(2) = 1; C = mcirc(t); x = abs(e-e*C);
y = x(1,:) > .001; y(1) = 1; v = find(y);
N = []; g = [];
[r,s] = size(v); w = [v,n + 1];
    for k = 1:s
        S = V(:,w(k):w(k + 1)-1); [a,b] = size(S); S = mrrf(S,'[])';
        N = [N,S]; g = [g,b];
    end
W = mcol(N); V = mc(W,4); g;
```

mnull.m

```
function N = mnull(A)
Q = null(A); N = mrrf(Q',[]);
N = N';
```

morth.m

```
function [U,S]= morth(A)
[Q,R] = mqr(A); D = diag(diag(R)); S = inv(D);
U = Q*D; S = S*R;
```

mplu.m

```
function [PMAT,L,U,pvec]=mplu(A)
s=size(A);
     if s(1)= =1;PMAT=[1];pvec=1;L=1;U=A;return,end
[SL,U]=lu(A);
pt1=(SL= =ones(s(1)))*diag(1:s(1));
pvec=max(pt1')';
PMAT=eye(s(1));PMAT=PMAT(pvec,:);
L = mc(PMAT,L,12); U = mc(U,12);
```

mqr.m

```
function [Q,R]= mqr(A)
[Q,R] = msubqr(A);
Q = mc(Q,12); R = mc(R,12);
```

mrow.m

```
function [N,M] = mrow(A)
[B,C] = mcol(A');
N = B'; M = C';
```

mrrf.m

```
function [R,S] = mrrf(A,b)
[m,n] = size(A);
B = A(:,b); C = A; C(:,b) = []; H = [B,C];
D = rref([H,eye(m)]); D = D(:,n + 1:m + n);
S = mc(D,12); R = mc(D*A,12);
```

msoln.m

```
function X = msoln(A,B)
[m,n] = size(A);
     if rank([A,B]) > rank(A), y = [];
     else
     [R,S] = mrrf(A,1:n); [B,C] = mcol(R); y = mc(C'*S*b);
     end
X = y;
```

msubqr.m

```
function [Q,R]= msubqr(A)
A = mcol(A); [Q,R] = qr(A);
tol = eps*norm(A,'fro'); d = abs(diag(R)) > tol; r = sum(d); r = r(1);
     if r > 0
     Q = Q(:,1:r); Q = -Q;
     else
     Q = [];
     end
R = Q'*A;
```

ANSWERS TO SELECTED ODD-NUMBERED PROBLEMS

CHAPTER 0

Section 0.2

PART 1

0.2.1. $\begin{bmatrix} 1 & 2 & 3 \\ 1 & 4 & 9 \\ 1 & 8 & 27 \end{bmatrix}$ **0.2.3.** $\begin{bmatrix} 1 & 1 & 1 \\ 2 & 2 & 2 \\ 3 & 3 & 3 \end{bmatrix}$ **0.2.5.** $\begin{bmatrix} 1 & 0 & 0 \\ 0 & 1 & 0 \\ 0 & 0 & 1 \end{bmatrix}, \begin{bmatrix} 1 & 0 & 0 & 0 \\ 0 & 1 & 0 & 0 \\ 0 & 0 & 1 & 0 \end{bmatrix}$

0.2.7. $\begin{bmatrix} 1 & -1 & 0 \\ 0 & 1 & -1 \\ 0 & 0 & 1 \end{bmatrix}, \begin{bmatrix} 1 & -1 & 0 & 0 \\ 0 & 1 & -1 & 0 \\ 0 & 0 & 1 & 1 \end{bmatrix}$

0.2.9. If **A** is upper triangular, then all the entries below the diagonal are zero. If **A** is lower triangular, then all the entries above the diagonal are zero. Hence, a matrix that is both upper and lower triangular has zeros off the diagonal and is therefore a diagonal matrix.

0.2.11. $\{0, 0\}$ for both matrices.

0.2.13. $\begin{bmatrix} * \\ 0 \\ \vdots \\ 0 \end{bmatrix}$, and any row matrix will do.

Section 0.3

PART 1

0.3.1. (*a*) $\begin{bmatrix} 1 & -2 & -4 \\ 1 & 1 & 6 \\ 0 & 0 & 1 \end{bmatrix}$, (*c*) $\begin{bmatrix} 2 & 1 & 0 \\ 1 & 2 & 6 \\ 0 & 6 & 0 \end{bmatrix}$, (*e*) $\begin{bmatrix} -1 & 2 & 4 \\ -1 & -1 & -6 \\ 0 & 0 & -1 \end{bmatrix}$

0.3.3. $\begin{bmatrix} 0 & 1 & \cdots & 1 \\ 1 & 0 & \cdots & 1 \\ \vdots & & & \\ 1 & 1 & \cdots & 0 \end{bmatrix}$, $\begin{bmatrix} 2-n & 1 & \cdots & 1 \\ 1 & 2-n & \cdots & 1 \\ \vdots & & & \\ 1 & 1 & \cdots & 2-n \end{bmatrix}$

Section 0.4

PART 1

0.4.1. (*a*) $\begin{bmatrix} x & -z \\ & 2y+2z \\ -x & +2y+2z \end{bmatrix}$, (*b*)$x^2 + 2y^2 + 2z^2 - 2xz + 4yz$

(*c*) $(x-z)^2 + (2y+2z)^2 + (-x+2y+2z)^2$

0.4.3. $[0 \quad -1 \quad -2]$, $[1 \quad 0 \quad -3]$, $[2 \quad 3 \quad 0]$, $\begin{bmatrix} 0 \\ 1 \\ 2 \end{bmatrix}$, $\begin{bmatrix} -1 \\ 0 \\ 3 \end{bmatrix}$, $\begin{bmatrix} -2 \\ -3 \\ 0 \end{bmatrix}$

0.4.5. $\dfrac{\sqrt{2}}{2}\begin{bmatrix} 1 \\ 1 \end{bmatrix}$

PART 2

0.4.7. $\mathbf{x} = [1 \quad i]$ **0.4.11.** $\mathbf{x} \cdot \mathbf{x}$ is a sum of real squares. $\mathbf{x} = [0 \quad i]$.

Section 0.5

PART 1

0.5.1. $\begin{bmatrix} 1 & 0 \\ 0 & 1 \end{bmatrix}$ **0.5.7.** 16

PART 2

0.5.15. If $\mathbf{AB} = \mathbf{BA}$. **0.5.17.** $\mathbf{A}^3 = \mathbf{A}^2\mathbf{A} = (\mathbf{AA})\mathbf{A} = \mathbf{A}(\mathbf{AA}) = \mathbf{AA}^2$.
$(\mathbf{AB})\mathbf{C} = \mathbf{A}(\mathbf{BC})$.

0.5.23. Yes: $(\mathbf{AB})^{\mathrm{T}} = (\mathbf{BA})^{\mathrm{T}}$ implies that $\mathbf{B}^{\mathrm{T}}\mathbf{A}^{\mathrm{T}} = \mathbf{A}^{\mathrm{T}}\mathbf{B}^{\mathrm{T}}$.

CHAPTER 1

Section 1.3

PART 1

1.3.1. Write diag$[a, b, c, d]$ for the matrix $\mathbf{A}$. Then $\mathbf{A}^{-1} = \text{diag}[a^{-1}, b^{-1}, c^{-1}, d^{-1}]$.
$\mathbf{B}^{-1} = \mathbf{B}$.

PART 2

1.3.5. $(\mathbf{SAS}^{-1})^{-1} = (\mathbf{S}^{-1})^{-1}\mathbf{A}^{-1}\mathbf{S}^{-1} = \mathbf{SA}^{-1}\mathbf{S}^{-1}$

1.3.7. $\mathbf{PM} = \begin{bmatrix} 1 & 0 & 0 & 0 \\ 0 & 1 & 0 & 0 \\ 0 & 0 & 0 & 1 \\ 0 & 0 & a & 0 \end{bmatrix}$, $\mathbf{PE} = \begin{bmatrix} 1 & 0 & 0 & 0 \\ 0 & 1 & 0 & 0 \\ 0 & 0 & 0 & 1 \\ b & 0 & 1 & 0 \end{bmatrix}$, $\mathbf{ME} = \begin{bmatrix} 1 & 0 & 0 & 0 \\ 0 & 1 & 0 & 0 \\ ab & 0 & a & 0 \\ 0 & 0 & 0 & 1 \end{bmatrix}$,

$\mathbf{MP} = \begin{bmatrix} 1 & 0 & 0 & 0 \\ 0 & 1 & 0 & 0 \\ 0 & 0 & 0 & a \\ 0 & 0 & 1 & 0 \end{bmatrix}$, $\mathbf{EP} = \begin{bmatrix} 1 & 0 & 0 & 0 \\ 0 & 1 & 0 & 0 \\ b & 0 & 0 & 1 \\ 0 & 0 & 1 & 0 \end{bmatrix}$, $\mathbf{EM} = \begin{bmatrix} 1 & 0 & 0 & 0 \\ 0 & 1 & 0 & 0 \\ b & 0 & a & 0 \\ 0 & 0 & 0 & 1 \end{bmatrix}$;

$(\mathbf{PM})^{-1} = \begin{bmatrix} 1 & 0 & 0 & 0 \\ 0 & 1 & 0 & 0 \\ 0 & 0 & 0 & a^{-1} \\ 0 & 0 & 1 & 0 \end{bmatrix}$, $(\mathbf{PE})^{-1} = \begin{bmatrix} 1 & 0 & 0 & 0 \\ 0 & 1 & 0 & 0 \\ -b & 0 & 0 & 1 \\ 0 & 0 & 1 & 0 \end{bmatrix}$,

$(\mathbf{ME})^{-1} = \begin{bmatrix} 1 & 0 & 0 & 0 \\ 0 & 1 & 0 & 0 \\ -b & 0 & a^{-1} & 0 \\ 0 & 0 & 0 & 1 \end{bmatrix}$, $(\mathbf{MP})^{-1} = \begin{bmatrix} 1 & 0 & 0 & 0 \\ 0 & 1 & 0 & 0 \\ 0 & 0 & 0 & 1 \\ 0 & 0 & a^{-1} & 0 \end{bmatrix}$,

$(\mathbf{EP})^{-1} = \begin{bmatrix} 1 & 0 & 0 & 0 \\ 0 & 1 & 0 & 0 \\ 0 & 0 & 0 & 1 \\ -b & 0 & 1 & 0 \end{bmatrix}$, $(\mathbf{EM})^{-1} = \begin{bmatrix} 1 & 0 & 0 & 0 \\ 0 & 1 & 0 & 0 \\ -ba^{-1} & 0 & a^{-1} & 0 \\ 0 & 0 & 0 & 1 \end{bmatrix}$

Section 1.4

PART 1

1.4.1. $[1]$; $\mathbf{I}_2$, $\begin{bmatrix} 1 & 0 \\ a & 1 \end{bmatrix}$, $\begin{bmatrix} 1 & a \\ 0 & 1 \end{bmatrix}$, $\begin{bmatrix} 0 & 1 \\ 1 & 0 \end{bmatrix}$, $\begin{bmatrix} a & 0 \\ 0 & 1 \end{bmatrix}$, $\begin{bmatrix} 1 & 0 \\ 0 & a \end{bmatrix}$, $a \neq 0$

1.4.3. (*a*) $\begin{bmatrix} 1 & 0 & 0 & 0 \\ 0 & 1 & 0 & 0 \\ 2 & 0 & 1 & 0 \\ 0 & 0 & 0 & 1 \end{bmatrix}$ (*b*) $\begin{bmatrix} 0 & 0 & 0 & 1 \\ 0 & 1 & 0 & 0 \\ 0 & 0 & 1 & 0 \\ 1 & 0 & 0 & 0 \end{bmatrix}$ (*c*) $\begin{bmatrix} -4 & 0 & 0 & 0 \\ 0 & 1 & 0 & 0 \\ 0 & 0 & 1 & 0 \\ 0 & 0 & 0 & 1 \end{bmatrix}$

(*d*) $\begin{bmatrix} 1 & 0 & -2 & 0 \\ 0 & 1 & 0 & 0 \\ 0 & 0 & 1 & 0 \\ 0 & 0 & 0 & 1 \end{bmatrix}$

1.4.5. $\mathbf{P}_1 = \begin{bmatrix} 0 & 0 & 0 & 1 \\ 0 & 1 & 0 & 0 \\ 0 & 0 & 1 & 0 \\ 1 & 0 & 0 & 0 \end{bmatrix}$, $\mathbf{P}_2 = \begin{bmatrix} 1 & 0 & 0 & 0 \\ 0 & 0 & 1 & 0 \\ 0 & 1 & 0 & 0 \\ 0 & 0 & 0 & 1 \end{bmatrix}$

PART 2

1.4.9. Yes, because **IA** = **A**

1.4.11. **A** → **B** and **B** → **C** by hypothesis. Then **A** → **B** → **C**.

1.4.13. Consider $\mathbf{A}_i$ and $\mathbf{A}_j$ with $i < j$. Delete from the original diagram the arrows and matrices to the left of $\mathbf{A}_i$ and to the right of $\mathbf{A}_j$.

1.4.15. Multiply row i by $1/\alpha$.

1.4.17.

$$\mathbf{1r}^{\mathrm{T}} = \begin{bmatrix} r_1 & r_2 & \cdots & r_n \\ r_1 & r_2 & \cdots & r_n \\ \vdots & \vdots & & \vdots \\ r_1 & r_2 & \cdots & r_n \end{bmatrix} \to \cdots \to \begin{bmatrix} r_1 & r_2 & \cdots & r_n \\ 0 & 0 & \cdots & 0 \\ \vdots & \vdots & & \vdots \\ 0 & 0 & \cdots & 0 \end{bmatrix}$$

1.4.19.

$$\mathbf{S} = \frac{1}{4}\begin{bmatrix} 0 & 2 & -2 \\ 0 & 1 & -3 \\ 4 & -5 & 7 \end{bmatrix}, \qquad \mathbf{T} = \begin{bmatrix} 2 & 1 & 1 \\ 3 & -2 & 0 \\ 1 & -2 & 0 \end{bmatrix}$$

Section 1.5

PART 1

1.5.1. $\mathbf{P}^{-1} = \mathbf{P}$; $\quad \mathbf{M}^{-1} = \begin{bmatrix} a^{-1} & 0 & 0 \\ 0 & 1 & 0 \\ 0 & 0 & 1 \end{bmatrix}$; $\quad \mathbf{E}^{-1} = \begin{bmatrix} 1 & 0 & 0 \\ 0 & 1 & 0 \\ -\alpha & 0 & 1 \end{bmatrix}$

1.5.3. (*a*) $\begin{bmatrix} 0 & 1 & 0 \\ 1 & 0 & 0 \\ 0 & 0 & 1 \end{bmatrix} \begin{bmatrix} 1 & 0 & 0 \\ 0 & 1 & 0 \\ -1 & 0 & 1 \end{bmatrix}$

(*b*) $\begin{bmatrix} 1 & 0 & 0 \\ 0 & 1 & 0 \\ 0 & 0 & \gamma \end{bmatrix} \begin{bmatrix} 1 & 0 & 0 \\ 0 & \beta & 0 \\ 0 & 0 & 1 \end{bmatrix} \begin{bmatrix} \alpha & 0 & 0 \\ 0 & 1 & 0 \\ 0 & 0 & 1 \end{bmatrix} \begin{bmatrix} 0 & 0 & 1 \\ 0 & 1 & 0 \\ 1 & 0 & 0 \end{bmatrix}$

(*c*) $\begin{bmatrix} 1 & 0 \\ -1 & 1 \end{bmatrix} \begin{bmatrix} 1 & -2 \\ 0 & 1 \end{bmatrix} \begin{bmatrix} 1 & 0 \\ 0 & -1 \end{bmatrix}$

1.5.5. $\mathbf{A}^{-1} = \begin{bmatrix} -1 & 0 & -1 \\ -1 & 1 & 0 \\ 1 & -1 & 1 \end{bmatrix}$

PART 2

1.5.7. Either all three matrices are nonsingular or, if either **A** or **B** is singular, so is **C**. If **C** is singular, then either **A** or **B** or both are singular.

Section 1.6

PART 1

1.6.1. (*a*) a; (*b*) 1; (*c*) 0; (*d*) 1; (*e*) −20; (*f*) 1

PART 2

1.6.3. Since $1 = \det(\mathbf{I}) = \det(\mathbf{AA}^{-1}) = \det(\mathbf{A})\det(\mathbf{A}^{-1})$, $\det(\mathbf{A}^{-1}) = \det(\mathbf{A})^{-1}$.

1.6.5. $\det(\mathbf{S}^{-1}\mathbf{AS}) = \det(\mathbf{S}^{-1})\det(\mathbf{A})\det(\mathbf{S}) = \det(\mathbf{S}^{-1})\det(\mathbf{S})\det(\mathbf{A}) = \det(\mathbf{A})$.

Section 1.7

PART 1

1.7.7. By Theorem 1.7.1, $\mathbf{II}^+ = \det(\mathbf{I})\mathbf{I} = \mathbf{I}$. Hence, $\mathbf{I}^+ = \mathbf{I}^{-1} = \mathbf{I}$.

PART 2

1.7.9.

$$\det\begin{bmatrix} a & a & \cdots & a & a \\ b & a & \cdots & a & a \\ 0 & b & \cdots & a & a \\ \vdots & \vdots & & \vdots & \vdots \\ 0 & 0 & \cdots & b & a \end{bmatrix} = a \cdot \det\begin{bmatrix} 1 & 1 & \cdots & 1 & 1 \\ b & a & \cdots & a & a \\ 0 & b & \cdots & a & a \\ \vdots & \vdots & & \vdots & \vdots \\ 0 & 0 & \cdots & b & a \end{bmatrix}$$

$$= a \cdot \det\begin{bmatrix} 1 & 1 & \cdots & 1 & 1 \\ 0 & a-b & \cdots & * & * \\ 0 & 0 & \cdots & * & * \\ \vdots & \vdots & & \vdots & \vdots \\ 0 & 0 & \cdots & 0 & a-b \end{bmatrix}$$

$$= a(a-b)^n.$$

1.7.11.

$$\det\begin{bmatrix} 0 & a & \cdots & a & a \\ a & 0 & \cdots & a & a \\ a & a & \cdots & a & a \\ \vdots & \vdots & & \vdots & \vdots \\ a & a & \cdots & a & b \end{bmatrix} = a^{n-1} \cdot \det\begin{bmatrix} 0 & 1 & \cdots & 1 & 1 \\ 1 & 0 & \cdots & 1 & 1 \\ 1 & 1 & \cdots & 1 & 1 \\ \vdots & \vdots & & \vdots & \vdots \\ a & a & \cdots & a & b \end{bmatrix}$$

$$= a^{n-1} \cdot \det\begin{bmatrix} 0 & 1 & \cdots & 1 & 1 \\ 1 & -1 & \cdots & 0 & 0 \\ 1 & 0 & \cdots & 0 & 0 \\ \vdots & \vdots & & \vdots & \vdots \\ a & 0 & \cdots & 0 & b-a \end{bmatrix}$$

$$= a^{n-1} \cdot \det\begin{bmatrix} n-2 & 1 & \cdots & 1 & 1 \\ 0 & -1 & \cdots & 0 & 0 \\ 0 & 0 & \cdots & 0 & 0 \\ \vdots & \vdots & & \vdots & \vdots \\ a & 0 & \cdots & 0 & b-a \end{bmatrix}$$

$$= a^{n-1}\Big((n-2)(-1)^{n-2}(b-a) + (-1)^{n-1}a\Big)$$

$$= (-a)^{n-1}\Big((n-1)(a-b) - a + 2b\Big).$$

CHAPTER 2

Section 2.2

PART 1

2.2.1. (*a*) 1 (*c*) Each column
(*e*) The columns of **I** (*g*) 1 and 2

2.2.3. (*b*), (*d*), and (*e*) are in rref. (*a*) $\text{rref}(\mathbf{1}\mathbf{1}^{\mathrm{T}}) = \mathbf{e}_1\mathbf{1}^{\mathrm{T}}$ (*c*) [1]

2.2.7. All matrices are in rref.

2.2.9. $\mathbf{e}_i, i > 1$ has a zero in its first row.

PART 2

2.2.11. The rref of $\mathbf{A}, \mathbf{A}_r$, is upper triangular. If $\mathbf{A}_r$ has a nonleading column, then a diagonal entry of $\mathbf{A}_r$ would be zero. This implies that $\det(\mathbf{A}_r) = 0$ and hence that $\mathbf{A}_r$ is singular.

2.2.13. Suppose $\mathbf{A} \to \cdots \to \mathbf{B}$, and $\mathbf{A}_r$ and $\mathbf{B}_r$ are the rrefs of **A** and **B**. Then $\mathbf{B} \to \cdots \to \mathbf{B}_r$. Thus, $\mathbf{A} \to \cdots \to \mathbf{B} \to \cdots \to \mathbf{B}_r$. Since $\mathbf{B}_r$ is in rref, it is the rref of $\mathbf{A}_r$ by Theorem 2.2.1.

2.2.15. No. Consider

$$\left[\begin{array}{c:c} 1 & 1 \\ 0 & 1 \end{array}\right]$$

Yes, for then the columns of **B** are irrelevant.

2.2.17. $\text{rref}(\mathbf{J}_n) = \mathbf{e}_1\mathbf{1}^{\mathrm{T}}$.

Section 2.3

PART 1

2.3.1. (*a*) $\begin{bmatrix} -1 \\ 0 \\ 2 \\ 1 \end{bmatrix}$ (*b*) $\begin{bmatrix} 1 \\ 1 \\ 1 \\ 0 \end{bmatrix}$ (*c*) $\frac{1}{2}\begin{bmatrix} 0 \\ 3 \\ -1 \end{bmatrix}$ (*d*) $\begin{bmatrix} -1 \\ 0 \\ 0 \\ 0 \\ 0 \\ 2 \end{bmatrix}$

2.3.3. $b + c = 0$, so

$$\mathbf{b} = \begin{bmatrix} a \\ b \\ -b \end{bmatrix}$$

where a and b are arbitrary.

PART 2

2.3.5. $\mathbf{A}(k\mathbf{x}_h + \mathbf{x}_f) = k\mathbf{A}\mathbf{x}_h + \mathbf{A}\mathbf{x}_f = k\mathbf{0} + \mathbf{b} = \mathbf{b}$

2.3.7. $\mathbf{A}(a\mathbf{x}_1 + b\mathbf{x}_2) = a\mathbf{A}\mathbf{x}_1 + b\mathbf{A}\mathbf{x}_2 = (a + b)\mathbf{b} = \mathbf{b}$, if and only if $a + b = 1$

Section 2.4

PART 1

2.4.1. (*a*) $\frac{1}{2}\begin{bmatrix} -3 \\ 3 \\ 2 \end{bmatrix}$ (*b*) $\begin{bmatrix} -1 \\ 1 \\ 1 \end{bmatrix}$ (*c*) $\frac{1}{2}\begin{bmatrix} -1 \\ 0 \\ 1 \end{bmatrix}$

2.4.3. (*a*) $\begin{bmatrix} 2 & -2t \\ -1 & +\ t \\ t & \end{bmatrix}$ (*b*) $\begin{bmatrix} 1 & -2t \\ -1 & +\ t \\ t & \end{bmatrix}$

Section 2.5

PART 1

2.5.1. (*a*) $\mathbf{L} = \begin{bmatrix} 1 & 0 \\ 1 & 1 \end{bmatrix}$, $\mathbf{U} = \begin{bmatrix} 1 & a \\ 0 & b-a \end{bmatrix}$ (*b*) $\mathbf{L} = \begin{bmatrix} 1 & 0 \\ c & 1 \end{bmatrix}$, $\mathbf{U} = \begin{bmatrix} 1 & a \\ 0 & b-ca \end{bmatrix}$

2.5.3. $k = 1$ and $\mathbf{P}_1 = \begin{bmatrix} 0 & 0 & 1 \\ 0 & 1 & 0 \\ 1 & 0 & 0 \end{bmatrix}$

Section 2.6

PART 1

2.6.1. (*a*) $2\begin{bmatrix} 1 \\ 0 \\ 1 \end{bmatrix} - \begin{bmatrix} 1 \\ 1 \\ -1 \end{bmatrix} + \begin{bmatrix} -1 \\ 1 \\ -3 \end{bmatrix} = \mathbf{0}$ (*b*) and (*c*) are linearly independent.

2.6.3. (*a*) and (*c*) are linearly independent.

(*b*) $2\begin{bmatrix} -1 \\ 0 \\ 0 \\ 1 \end{bmatrix} + \begin{bmatrix} 2 \\ -1 \\ 1 \\ 1 \end{bmatrix} - \begin{bmatrix} 0 \\ -1 \\ 1 \\ 3 \end{bmatrix} = \mathbf{0}$

2.6.5. $\begin{bmatrix} 1 \\ 1 \\ 2 \\ -1 \end{bmatrix} + \begin{bmatrix} 1 \\ 0 \\ 1 \\ 1 \end{bmatrix} + \begin{bmatrix} -1 \\ 1 \\ 0 \\ 0 \end{bmatrix} - \begin{bmatrix} 1 \\ 2 \\ 3 \\ 0 \end{bmatrix} = \mathbf{0}$

2.6.7. $\begin{bmatrix} 1 \\ 2 \\ 3 \\ 0 \end{bmatrix} - \begin{bmatrix} 1 \\ 1 \\ 2 \\ -1 \end{bmatrix} - \begin{bmatrix} 1 \\ 0 \\ 1 \\ 1 \end{bmatrix} - \begin{bmatrix} -1 \\ 1 \\ 0 \\ 0 \end{bmatrix} = \mathbf{0}$

PART 2

2.6.9. Suppose $a_1\mathbf{x}_1 + a_2\mathbf{x}_2 + a_3\mathbf{x}_3 = \mathbf{0}$ for some $\{a_1, a_2, a_3\}$ not all zero. Then $a_1\mathbf{x}_1 + a_2\mathbf{x}_2 + a_3\mathbf{x}_3 + 0\mathbf{x}_4 = \mathbf{0}$ is a dependency relationship.

2.6.11. If $\mathbf{x}_1 \neq \mathbf{0}$, then $a\mathbf{x} = \mathbf{0}$ implies that $a = 0$.
2.6.13. If $\mathbf{x}_0 = a_1\mathbf{x}_1 + a_2\mathbf{x}_2 + \cdots + a_k\mathbf{x}_k$, then $-\mathbf{x}_0 + a_1\mathbf{x}_1 + a_2\mathbf{x}_2 + \cdots + a_k\mathbf{x}_k = \mathbf{0}$ is a dependency relationship.
2.6.15. $a_1\mathbf{S}\mathbf{x}_1 + a_2\mathbf{S}\mathbf{x}_2 + a_3\mathbf{S}\mathbf{x}_3 + a_4\mathbf{S}\mathbf{x}_4 = \mathbf{S}(a_1\mathbf{x}_1 + a_2\mathbf{x}_2 + a_3\mathbf{x}_3 + a_4\mathbf{x}_4) = \mathbf{0}$ if and only if $a_1\mathbf{x}_1 + a_2\mathbf{x}_2 + a_3\mathbf{x}_3 + a_4\mathbf{x}_4 = \mathbf{0}$. Since $\{\mathbf{x}_1, \mathbf{x}_2, \mathbf{x}_3, \mathbf{x}_4\}$ is linearly independent, $a_1\mathbf{x}_1 + a_2\mathbf{x}_2 + a_3\mathbf{x}_3 + a_4\mathbf{x}_4 = \mathbf{0}$ if and only if $a_i = 0$ for all i.
2.6.17. There exist a_1 and a_2 not both zero such that $a_1\mathbf{x}_1 + a_2\mathbf{x}_2 = \mathbf{0}$. Hence, $a_1\mathbf{x}_1 = a_2\mathbf{x}_2$. Divide by the scalar that is not zero.

Section 2.7

PART 1

2.7.1. (*a*) 1 (*c*) n (*e*) n (*g*) 2 (*i*) 1
2.7.3. (*a*) 1 (*b*) 0 (*c*) 1 (*d*) 1 (*e*) 1
2.7.5. (*a*) 4 (*b*) 3 (*c*) 3 (*d*) 2
2.7.7. Adjoining an extra column increases the rank by at most 1.

PART 2

2.7.11. $\text{Rank}(\mathbf{A}^T) = \text{rank}(\mathbf{A}) = \text{rank}(\mathbf{B}) = \text{rank}(\mathbf{B}^T)$
2.7.13. (*a*) n (*b*) $n - 1$

2.7.15. (*a*) $\mathbf{A} = \begin{bmatrix} 1 & 0 & 0 \\ 0 & 0 & 0 \\ 0 & 0 & 0 \end{bmatrix}$, $\mathbf{B} = \begin{bmatrix} 0 & 0 & 0 \\ 0 & 1 & 0 \\ 0 & 0 & 0 \end{bmatrix}$ (*b*) $\mathbf{A} = \begin{bmatrix} 1 & 0 & 0 \\ 0 & 0 & 0 \\ 0 & 0 & 0 \end{bmatrix}$, $\mathbf{B} = \begin{bmatrix} 1 & 0 & 0 \\ 0 & 0 & 0 \\ 0 & 0 & 0 \end{bmatrix}$

(*c*) $\mathbf{A} = \begin{bmatrix} 0 & 1 & 0 \\ 0 & 0 & 0 \\ 0 & 0 & 0 \end{bmatrix}$, $\mathbf{B} = \begin{bmatrix} 1 & 0 & 0 \\ 0 & 1 & 0 \\ 0 & 0 & 0 \end{bmatrix}$ (*d*) $\mathbf{A} = \begin{bmatrix} 0 & 1 & 0 \\ 0 & 0 & 0 \\ 0 & 0 & 0 \end{bmatrix}$, $\mathbf{B} = \begin{bmatrix} 1 & 0 & 0 \\ 0 & 0 & 0 \\ 0 & 0 & 0 \end{bmatrix}$

(*e*) $\mathbf{A} = \begin{bmatrix} 0 & 1 & 0 \\ 0 & 0 & 0 \\ 0 & 0 & 0 \end{bmatrix}$, $\mathbf{B} = \begin{bmatrix} 0 & 1 & 0 \\ 0 & 0 & 0 \\ 0 & 0 & 0 \end{bmatrix}$ (*f*) $\mathbf{A} = \begin{bmatrix} 0 & 1 & 0 \\ 0 & 0 & 0 \\ 0 & 0 & 0 \end{bmatrix}$, $\mathbf{B} = \begin{bmatrix} 0 & 0 & 0 \\ 0 & 0 & 0 \\ 0 & 0 & 0 \end{bmatrix}$

CHAPTER 3

Section 3.2

PART 1

3.2.1. All vector spaces contain $\mathbf{0}$. The set of solutions does not.

3.2.3. (*a*) $\left\{\begin{bmatrix} 1 \\ 2 \\ -1 \\ 0 \end{bmatrix}\right\}$ (*b*) $\left\{\begin{bmatrix} 1 \\ -1 \\ 0 \\ 0 \end{bmatrix}\right\}$

3.2.5. The sum of two vectors in this set may not be in the set.

PART 2

3.2.7. Yes. For example, assume $\mathbf{x}_1$ is a linear combination of $\mathbf{x}_2$ and $\mathbf{x}_3$.

3.2.9. No. Suppose $\mathbf{x} \neq \mathbf{0}$ is a member of this set. Then $-\mathbf{x}$ is not.

3.2.11. Suppose $\mathbf{x}$ and $\mathbf{y} \in \mathcal{V} \cap \mathcal{W}$. Then $\mathbf{x}$ and $\mathbf{y} \in \mathcal{V}$ and $\mathcal{W}$. Hence, $a\mathbf{x} + b\mathbf{y} \in \mathcal{V}$ and $\mathcal{W}$, and hence $a\mathbf{x} + b\mathbf{y} \in \mathcal{V} \cap \mathcal{W}$.

Section 3.3

PART 1

3.3.1. All three sets are linearly independent. (*a*) The dimension is 2. (*b*), (*c*) The dimensions are 3.

3.3.3. (*a*) $\left\{\begin{bmatrix} 1 \\ 2 \\ -1 \\ 0 \end{bmatrix}\right\}$, dimension is 1. (*b*) $\left\{\begin{bmatrix} 1 \\ -1 \\ 0 \\ 0 \end{bmatrix}\right\}$, dimension is 1.

(*c*) $\left\{\begin{bmatrix} 1 \\ 1 \\ 1 \end{bmatrix}, \begin{bmatrix} -1 \\ 0 \\ 0 \end{bmatrix}\right\}$, dimension is 2.

PART 2

3.3.5. 0, 1, and 2.

3.3.7. Let $\{\mathbf{x}, \mathbf{y}\}$ be a basis for $\mathcal{S}$. If $\mathbf{z} \notin span\{\mathbf{x}, \mathbf{y}\}$ and $\mathbf{z} \in \mathcal{R}^2$, then $\{\mathbf{x}, \mathbf{y}, \mathbf{z}\}$ is a set of three linearly independent vectors in $\mathcal{R}^2$, contradicting Theorem 3.3.1.

Section 3.4

PART 1

3.4.1. (*a*) 2 (*b*) 3 (*c*) 3

3.4.3. (*a*) The rows and columns are bases for the row and column spaces. The common dimension is 4. (*b*) The columns are linearly independent, and so are rows 1, 2, 4. The common dimension is 3. (*c*) The first four columns are linearly independent, and so are all the rows. The common dimension is 4. (*d*) The first three columns and rows 1, 2, and 4 are linearly independent sets. The common dimension is 3.

3.4.5. n

PART 2

3.4.7. Suppose $\mathbf{A}$ is $m \times n$. Then rank($\mathbf{A}$) $= m$. Hence, $col(\mathbf{A}) = \mathcal{R}^m$. Thus, every column of $\mathbf{B}$ is in the span of the columns of $\mathbf{A}$.

3.4.9.
$$\left\{\begin{bmatrix} -(n-1) \\ 1 \\ 1 \\ \vdots \\ 1 \end{bmatrix}, \begin{bmatrix} 1 \\ -(n-1) \\ 1 \\ \vdots \\ 1 \end{bmatrix}, \ldots, \begin{bmatrix} 1 \\ 1 \\ 1 \\ \vdots \\ -(n-1) \end{bmatrix}\right\}$$

Section 3.5

PART 1

3.5.1. (*a*) $\left\{\begin{bmatrix}1\\0\\0\\-1\end{bmatrix}, \begin{bmatrix}0\\1\\0\\-1\end{bmatrix}, \begin{bmatrix}0\\0\\1\\1\end{bmatrix}\right\}$ (*b*) $\left\{\begin{bmatrix}1\\0\\0\\-1\end{bmatrix}, \begin{bmatrix}0\\1\\1\\0\end{bmatrix}\right\}$ (*c*) $\left\{\begin{bmatrix}1\\0\\2\\1\end{bmatrix}, \begin{bmatrix}0\\1\\2\\1\end{bmatrix}\right\}$

3.5.3. (*a*) $\left\{\begin{bmatrix}1\\-1\\0\\\vdots\\0\end{bmatrix}, \begin{bmatrix}1\\0\\-1\\\vdots\\0\end{bmatrix}, \ldots, \begin{bmatrix}1\\0\\0\\0\\0\\-1\end{bmatrix}\right\}$ (*b*) $\left\{\begin{bmatrix}u_2\\-1\\0\\\vdots\\0\end{bmatrix}, \begin{bmatrix}u_3\\0\\-1\\\vdots\\0\end{bmatrix}, \ldots, \begin{bmatrix}u_n\\0\\0\\\vdots\\-1\end{bmatrix}\right\}$

3.5.5. (*a*) $\left\{\begin{bmatrix}1\\0\\0\\-1\end{bmatrix}, \begin{bmatrix}0\\1\\0\\-1\end{bmatrix}, \begin{bmatrix}0\\0\\1\\-1\end{bmatrix}\right\}$ (*b*) $\left\{\begin{bmatrix}1\\0\\-1\end{bmatrix}, \begin{bmatrix}0\\1\\0\end{bmatrix}\right\}$ (*c*) $\left\{\begin{bmatrix}a\\-1\\0\end{bmatrix}, \begin{bmatrix}b\\0\\-1\end{bmatrix}\right\}$

3.5.7. (*a*) $\begin{bmatrix}1 & 0 & -1 & 0\\0 & 1 & 0 & 0\\0 & 0 & 0 & 1\end{bmatrix}$ (*b*), (*c*) $\begin{bmatrix}1 & 0 & -1 & 0\\0 & 1 & 0 & -1\end{bmatrix}$ (*d*) $[1 \quad -1 \quad -1 \quad 1]$

PART 2

3.5.9. By Corollary 2 of Theorem 3.4.1 rank(**A**) $=$ dim(*col*(**A**)) $= n$. By Theorem 3.5.2, dim(*null*(**A**)) $= \eta = r - n = 0$.

3.9.11. By Theorem 2.3.1, the solution sets of $\mathbf{Ax} = \mathbf{b}$ and $\mathbf{Bx} = \mathbf{c}$ are identical if $[\mathbf{A} \quad \mathbf{b}] \to \cdots \to [\mathbf{B} \quad \mathbf{c}]$. If **A** is row equivalent to **B**, then $\mathbf{A} \to \cdots \to \mathbf{B}$, and this implies $[\mathbf{A} \quad \mathbf{0}] \to \cdots \to [\mathbf{B} \quad \mathbf{0}]$. Hence, the solution sets of $\mathbf{Ax} = \mathbf{0}$, and $\mathbf{Bx} = \mathbf{0}$ are the same. But these are the null spaces of **A** and **B**.

Section 3.6

PART 1

3.6.1. (*a*) $a_1\begin{bmatrix}1\\0\\0\\-1\end{bmatrix} + a_2\begin{bmatrix}0\\1\\0\\-1\end{bmatrix} + a_3\begin{bmatrix}0\\0\\1\\1\end{bmatrix} + \begin{bmatrix}1\\0\\0\\0\end{bmatrix}$ (*b*) $a_1\begin{bmatrix}1\\0\\-1\\0\end{bmatrix} + a_2\begin{bmatrix}0\\1\\1\\0\end{bmatrix} + \begin{bmatrix}0\\1\\0\\1\end{bmatrix}$

3.6.3. (*a*) $a_1\begin{bmatrix}1\\0\\1\end{bmatrix} + \begin{bmatrix}1\\1\\0\end{bmatrix}$ (*b*) $a_1\begin{bmatrix}3\\-2\\1\end{bmatrix} + \begin{bmatrix}3\\-2\\0\end{bmatrix}$

3.6.5. Only the matrix of Problem 3.6.3(*b*) has full column rank. All matrices have full row rank.

3.6.7. (*a*) $\frac{1}{2}\begin{bmatrix} 1 \\ -1 \\ 2 \end{bmatrix}$ (*b*) $a_1\begin{bmatrix} 1 \\ -2 \\ -1 \\ 0 \end{bmatrix}$ (*c*) $a_1\begin{bmatrix} 2 \\ 1 \\ -1 \\ 0 \\ 0 \end{bmatrix} + a_2\begin{bmatrix} 0 \\ 0 \\ 0 \\ 1 \\ -1 \end{bmatrix} + \begin{bmatrix} 0 \\ -1 \\ 0 \\ -2 \\ 0 \end{bmatrix}$.

3.6.9. (*a*) $\begin{bmatrix} 1 \\ 1 \\ 0 \end{bmatrix}$ (*b*) $\begin{bmatrix} 0 \\ 2 \\ 0 \end{bmatrix}$

PART 2

3.6.11. Since **A** has full row rank, rank([**A** **b**]) $= m$ for all **b**.

3.6.13. Since **A** has full column rank and $m > r$, the rank of [**A** **b**] depends on **b**. However, $\eta = n - r = 0$, so $\mathbf{Ax} = \mathbf{0}$ has only the trivial solution by Theorem 3.5.2. By Theorem 3.6.2, $\mathbf{Ax} = \mathbf{b}$ has a unique solution if it is consistent.

3.6.15. We have $\mathbf{A}(\alpha\mathbf{x}_1 + \beta\mathbf{x}_2) = \alpha\mathbf{A}\mathbf{x}_1 + \beta\mathbf{A}\mathbf{x}_2 = \alpha\mathbf{b} + \beta\mathbf{b} = (\alpha + \beta)\mathbf{b} = \mathbf{b}$. Since $\mathbf{b} \neq \mathbf{0}, \alpha + \beta = 1$.

Section 3.7

PART 1

3.7.1. (*b*) $\begin{bmatrix} -1 \\ 1 \\ 1 \end{bmatrix} + \alpha\begin{bmatrix} 1 \\ 0 \\ -2 \end{bmatrix}$; $z + 2x = -1, y = 1$

(*d*) $\begin{bmatrix} 1 \\ 1 \\ 1 \\ 1 \end{bmatrix} + \alpha\begin{bmatrix} 1 \\ 0 \\ -1 \\ 1 \end{bmatrix}$; $x = t = 2 - z, y = 1$

3.7.3. $\begin{bmatrix} 0 \\ 1 \\ 1 \end{bmatrix} + \alpha\begin{bmatrix} 4 \\ -1 \\ 0 \end{bmatrix}$; $z = 1, y = 1 - x/4$

3.7.5. (*c*) $\begin{bmatrix} 1 \\ 0 \\ 0 \\ 1 \end{bmatrix} + \alpha\begin{bmatrix} -1 \\ 1 \\ 0 \\ 0 \end{bmatrix} + \beta\begin{bmatrix} -1 \\ 0 \\ 1 \\ 0 \end{bmatrix}$; $t = 1$ and $x + y + z = 1$

3.7.7. (*a*) $x = 1 + 2z = 1 + 2y + 2t$ (*b*) $x + y = 0, t = 3z + 1$

3.7.9. $x = 1, y + z + t = 3$

3.7.11. $\begin{bmatrix} 1 \\ 0 \\ 1 \end{bmatrix} + \alpha\begin{bmatrix} 1 \\ 0 \\ 3 \end{bmatrix} + \beta\begin{bmatrix} 1 \\ 1 \\ 1 \end{bmatrix}$ **3.7.13.** $\begin{bmatrix} 1 & 2 & 3 & 4 \end{bmatrix}\begin{bmatrix} x \\ y \\ z \\ t \end{bmatrix} = 4$

3.7.15. The two translates are parallel to the original vector space and are therefore parallel to each other. Hence, they are identical if they contain a point in common.

3.7.17. $\frac{1}{2}\begin{bmatrix}3\\2\\0\\1\end{bmatrix} + \alpha\begin{bmatrix}-1\\0\\0\\2\end{bmatrix} + \beta\begin{bmatrix}3\\2\\-2\\0\end{bmatrix}$

3.7.19. By Eq. 3.7.13,

$$[1 \quad 1]\begin{bmatrix}1 & -1\\0 & 1\end{bmatrix}\begin{bmatrix}x\\y\end{bmatrix} = x = 1$$

Hence, the hyperplane is the line $x = 1$.

3.7.21. By Eq. 3.7.13,

$$[1 \quad 1]\frac{1}{3}\begin{bmatrix}1 & -2\\1 & 1\end{bmatrix}\begin{bmatrix}x\\y\end{bmatrix} = 1$$

implies $2x - y = 3$. Hence, the line $2x - y = 3$ is the hyperplane.

PART 2

3.7.25. (*a*) $\begin{bmatrix}1\\-1\\0\\1\end{bmatrix} + \alpha\begin{bmatrix}0\\0\\1\\1\end{bmatrix}$ (*b*) $\begin{bmatrix}1\\-1\\0\\0\end{bmatrix} + \alpha\begin{bmatrix}0\\1\\0\\0\end{bmatrix} + \beta\begin{bmatrix}0\\0\\0\\1\end{bmatrix}$

(*c*) $\begin{bmatrix}1\\0\\0\\0\end{bmatrix} + \alpha\begin{bmatrix}0\\1\\0\\0\end{bmatrix} + \beta\begin{bmatrix}0\\0\\1\\0\end{bmatrix} + \gamma\begin{bmatrix}0\\0\\0\\1\end{bmatrix}$

Section 3.8

PART 1

3.8.1. The columns of

$$\mathbf{S} = \begin{bmatrix}1 & 0 & 0\\1 & 1 & 0\\1 & 1 & -1\end{bmatrix}$$

are the coordinate vectors of $\mathbf{w}_i$, $i = 1, 2, 3$, relative to $\mathcal{V}$.

3.8.3. The columns of

$$\mathbf{S} = \begin{bmatrix}1 & 1 & 1\\0 & 1 & -1\\0 & 0 & -1\end{bmatrix}$$

are the coordinate vectors of $\mathbf{w}_i$, $i = 1, 2, 3$, relative to $\mathcal{V}$.

3.8.5. Relative to the basis $\mathcal{V}$,

$$\mathbf{x}_V = \begin{bmatrix}1\\2\\2\\-3\end{bmatrix}, \qquad \mathbf{y}_V = \begin{bmatrix}2\\1\\0\\1\end{bmatrix}$$

The matrix whose columns are the coordinate vectors of $\mathbf{e}_1, \mathbf{e}_2, \mathbf{e}_3, \mathbf{e}_4$ relative to $\mathscr{V}$ are the columns of

$$\mathbf{S} = \begin{bmatrix} 1 & 0 & 0 & 0 \\ -1 & 1 & 0 & 0 \\ 0 & 1 & -1 & 0 \\ 1 & 0 & 1 & 1 \end{bmatrix}$$

Set $\mathbf{B} = \mathbf{S}^{-1}\mathbf{AS}$. Then $\mathbf{y}_V = \mathbf{B}\mathbf{x}_V$.

PART 2

3.8.7. $\mathbf{W} = \mathbf{I}$, so that Eq. 3.8.3 leads to $\mathbf{S}^{-1} = \mathbf{V}$, and from Eq. 3.8.5, $\mathbf{x}_E = \mathbf{V}\mathbf{x}_V = \mathbf{x}$.

CHAPTER 4

Section 4.2

PART 1

4.2.1. (*a*) 1 (*b*) $\sqrt{n}$ (*c*) $|a|$ (*d*) $|\Sigma x_i|$ (*e*) $\sqrt{3}$ (*f*) 1
4.2.3. (*a*) 0 (*b*) 0 (*c*) 1

PART 2

4.2.9. Yes. $\langle \mathbf{x},\mathbf{y}+\mathbf{z}\rangle = \langle \mathbf{x},\mathbf{y}\rangle + \langle \mathbf{x},\mathbf{z}\rangle = 0$
4.2.11. and 4.2.13. $(\mathbf{uu}^{\mathrm{T}})^2 = (\mathbf{uu}^{\mathrm{T}})(\mathbf{uu}^{\mathrm{T}}) = \mathbf{u}(\mathbf{u}^{\mathrm{T}}\mathbf{u})\mathbf{u}^{\mathrm{T}} = \|\mathbf{u}\|^2\mathbf{uu}^{\mathrm{T}}$

Section 4.3

PART 1

4.3.5. $\left\{ \frac{1}{\sqrt{3}}\begin{bmatrix} 1 \\ 1 \\ 1 \end{bmatrix}, \frac{1}{\sqrt{2}}\begin{bmatrix} 1 \\ 0 \\ -1 \end{bmatrix}, \frac{1}{\sqrt{6}}\begin{bmatrix} 1 \\ -2 \\ 1 \end{bmatrix} \right\}$

4.3.9. (*a*) 0 (*b*) $\mathbf{q}_1$ (*c*) $\frac{1}{4}\begin{bmatrix} 1 \\ 1 \\ 1 \\ 1 \end{bmatrix} + \frac{1}{4}\begin{bmatrix} 1 \\ -1 \\ -1 \\ 1 \end{bmatrix} - \frac{1}{4}\begin{bmatrix} -1 \\ 1 \\ -1 \\ 1 \end{bmatrix} = \frac{1}{4}\begin{bmatrix} 3 \\ -1 \\ 1 \\ 1 \end{bmatrix}$

(*d*) $\frac{1}{4}\begin{bmatrix} 1 \\ 1 \\ 1 \\ 1 \end{bmatrix} - \frac{1}{4}\begin{bmatrix} 1 \\ -1 \\ -1 \\ 1 \end{bmatrix} + \frac{1}{4}\begin{bmatrix} -1 \\ 1 \\ -1 \\ 1 \end{bmatrix} = \frac{1}{4}\begin{bmatrix} -1 \\ 3 \\ 1 \\ 1 \end{bmatrix}$

(*e*) $\frac{1}{4}\begin{bmatrix} 1 \\ 1 \\ 1 \\ 1 \end{bmatrix} - \frac{1}{4}\begin{bmatrix} 1 \\ -1 \\ -1 \\ 1 \end{bmatrix} - \frac{1}{4}\begin{bmatrix} -1 \\ 1 \\ -1 \\ 1 \end{bmatrix} = \frac{1}{4}\begin{bmatrix} 1 \\ 1 \\ 3 \\ -1 \end{bmatrix}$

PART 2

4.3.13. $\|\mathbf{q}_1 - \mathbf{q}_2\|^2 = \|\mathbf{q}_1\|^2 + \|\mathbf{q}_2\|^2 + 2\langle \mathbf{q}_1, \mathbf{q}_2\rangle = 1 + 1 + 0 = 2$

4.3.15. $\|\mathbf{u}_1 + \mathbf{v}_2\|^2 - \|\mathbf{u}_1 - \mathbf{v}_2\|^2 = 2\langle \mathbf{u}, \mathbf{v}\rangle$

4.3.17. Since

$$\mathbf{Q}^{\mathrm{T}}\mathbf{b} = \begin{bmatrix} \langle \mathbf{q}_1, \mathbf{b}\rangle \\ \langle \mathbf{q}_2, \mathbf{b}\rangle \\ \vdots \\ \langle \mathbf{q}_k, \mathbf{b}\rangle \end{bmatrix}, \ \mathbf{Q}(\mathbf{Q}^{\mathrm{T}}\mathbf{b}) = \langle \mathbf{b}, \mathbf{q}_1\rangle \mathbf{q} + \langle \mathbf{b}, \mathbf{q}_2\rangle \mathbf{q} + \cdots + \langle \mathbf{b}, \mathbf{q}_k\rangle \mathbf{q} = \mathbf{b}_{\perp}.$$

Section 4.4

PART 1

4.4.1. $\mathbf{Q} = \frac{1}{3}\begin{bmatrix} -2 & 1 & 2 \\ 1 & -2 & 2 \\ 2 & 2 & 1 \end{bmatrix}$

4.4.3. $(\mathbf{I} - \mathbf{J}_4/2)^{\mathrm{T}}(\mathbf{I} - \mathbf{J}_4/2) = \mathbf{I} - \mathbf{J}_4 + \mathbf{J}_4^2/4 = \mathbf{I} - \mathbf{J}_4 + \mathbf{J}_4 = \mathbf{I}.$

4.4.5. (*a*) $\begin{bmatrix} 0 & 1 & 0 & 0 \\ 1 & 0 & 0 & 0 \\ 0 & 0 & 0 & 1 \\ 0 & 0 & 1 & 0 \end{bmatrix}$ (*b*) $\frac{1}{2}\begin{bmatrix} -1 & 1 & -1 & -1 \\ 1 & -1 & -1 & -1 \\ -1 & -1 & -1 & 1 \\ -1 & -1 & 1 & -1 \end{bmatrix}$ (*c*) $\begin{bmatrix} -1 & 0 & 0 & 0 \\ 0 & -1 & 0 & 0 \\ 0 & 0 & -1 & 0 \\ 0 & 0 & 0 & -1 \end{bmatrix}$

(*d*) $\begin{bmatrix} -1 & 0 & 0 & 0 \\ 0 & 1 & 0 & 0 \\ 0 & 0 & 1 & 0 \\ 0 & 0 & 0 & 1 \end{bmatrix}$ (*e*) -1 (*f*) -1

PART 2

4.4.7. Since $a^2 + b^2 = 1$, $|a| \le 1$ and $|b| \le 1$, and hence there exists a ϑ such that $a = \cos\vartheta$. Then $b = \sqrt{1 - \cos^2\vartheta} = \sin\vartheta$.

Section 4.5

PART 1

4.5.1. $\left\{\frac{1}{\sqrt{3}}\begin{bmatrix} 1 \\ 1 \\ 1 \end{bmatrix}, \frac{1}{\sqrt{6}}\begin{bmatrix} 1 \\ 1 \\ -2 \end{bmatrix}, \frac{1}{\sqrt{2}}\begin{bmatrix} 1 \\ -1 \\ 0 \end{bmatrix}\right\}$

4.5.3. $\left\{\frac{1}{\sqrt{2}}\begin{bmatrix} 1 \\ 1 \\ 0 \end{bmatrix}, \begin{bmatrix} 0 \\ 0 \\ 1 \end{bmatrix}, \frac{1}{\sqrt{2}}\begin{bmatrix} 1 \\ -1 \\ 0 \end{bmatrix}\right\}$

4.5.5. $\left\{\begin{bmatrix} 1 \\ 0 \\ 0 \end{bmatrix}, \begin{bmatrix} 0 \\ 1 \\ 0 \end{bmatrix}, \begin{bmatrix} 0 \\ 0 \\ 1 \end{bmatrix}\right\}$

4.5.7. For Problems 4.5.1 and 4.5.3,

$$\frac{1}{2}\begin{bmatrix} -1 \\ -1 \\ 2 \end{bmatrix}$$

For Problem 4.5.4,

$$\frac{1}{2}\begin{bmatrix} 2 \\ -1 \\ -1 \end{bmatrix}$$

Section 4.6

PART 1

4.6.1. (*a*) $\mathbf{Q} = \frac{1}{\sqrt{2}}\begin{bmatrix} 1 & 1 \\ -1 & 1 \end{bmatrix}$, $\mathbf{R} = \frac{1}{\sqrt{2}}\begin{bmatrix} 2 & -1 \\ 0 & 1 \end{bmatrix}$

(*b*) $\mathbf{Q} = \begin{bmatrix} 0 & 1 \\ 1 & 0 \end{bmatrix}$, $\mathbf{R} = \begin{bmatrix} 1 & -1 \\ 0 & 1 \end{bmatrix}$ (*c*) $\mathbf{Q} = \frac{1}{\sqrt{2}}\begin{bmatrix} 1 & -1 \\ 1 & 1 \end{bmatrix}$, $\mathbf{R} = \frac{1}{\sqrt{2}}\begin{bmatrix} 2 & 3 \\ 0 & 1 \end{bmatrix}$

4.6.3. $\mathbf{Q} = \frac{1}{\sqrt{2}}\begin{bmatrix} 1 & -1 & 0 \\ 1 & 1 & 0 \\ 0 & 0 & \sqrt{2} \end{bmatrix}$, $\mathbf{R} = \frac{1}{\sqrt{2}}\begin{bmatrix} 2 & -1 & 2 \\ 0 & 1 & 0 \\ 0 & 0 & \sqrt{2} \end{bmatrix}$

PART 2

4.6.5. From $\mathbf{A} = \mathbf{QR}$ it follows that $\mathbf{A}^T\mathbf{A} = \mathbf{R}^T\mathbf{Q}^T\mathbf{QR} = \mathbf{R}^T\mathbf{R}$ since $\mathbf{Q}^T\mathbf{Q} = \mathbf{I}$.
4.6.7. If $\mathbf{Q}$ is orthogonal, then $\mathbf{Q} = \mathbf{QI}$ is its **QR** factorization.
4.6.9. If $\mathbf{D}$ is a diagonal matrix, then $\mathbf{D} = \mathbf{ID}$ is its **QR** factorization.

Section 4.7

PART 1

4.7.1. (*a*) *span* $\left\{\begin{bmatrix} 1 \\ 0 \\ 0 \\ 1 \end{bmatrix}, \begin{bmatrix} 0 \\ 1 \\ 0 \\ 1 \end{bmatrix}, \begin{bmatrix} 0 \\ 0 \\ 1 \\ 0 \end{bmatrix}\right\}$ (*c*) *span* $\left\{\begin{bmatrix} 1 \\ -1 \\ 1 \\ 0 \end{bmatrix}, \begin{bmatrix} 2 \\ -1 \\ 0 \\ 1 \end{bmatrix}\right\}$ (*c*) *span* $\left\{\begin{bmatrix} 1 \\ -1 \\ 1 \\ 0 \end{bmatrix}\right\}$

4.7.3. *span* $\left\{\begin{bmatrix} 0 \\ 1 \\ 0 \\ 0 \end{bmatrix}, \begin{bmatrix} 1 \\ 0 \\ 1 \\ -1 \end{bmatrix}\right\}$ **4.7.5.** $\begin{bmatrix} -1 \\ 1 \\ 0 \end{bmatrix} + a\begin{bmatrix} 0 \\ -1 \\ 1 \end{bmatrix} + b\begin{bmatrix} 1 \\ 0 \\ 0 \end{bmatrix}$, or $y = 1 - z$.

PART 2

4.7.9. Consider $\mathcal{R}^3$ and $\mathcal{V} = span\{\mathbf{e}_1, \mathbf{e}_2\}$. Then $\mathcal{S}$ is not a vector space because $\mathbf{1}_3$ and $\mathbf{e}_1 + \mathbf{e}_2$ belong to $\mathcal{S}$ but $\mathbf{1}_3 - (\mathbf{e}_1 + \mathbf{e}_2)$ does not.

Section 4.8

PART 1

4.8.1. $\frac{1}{2}\begin{bmatrix} 1 \\ 0 \\ 0 \\ 1 \end{bmatrix}$ **4.8.3.** $\frac{1}{2}\begin{bmatrix} 1 \\ -1 \\ 0 \\ 1 \end{bmatrix}$

4.8.5. $\mathbf{O}_3$, $\mathbf{I}_3$, and $\mathbf{P} = \begin{bmatrix} a & \pm(a - a^2)^{1/2} \\ \pm(a - a^2)^{1/2} & 1 - a \end{bmatrix}$, $|a| \leq 1$

4.8.7. $\begin{bmatrix} 1 & 0 & 0 \\ 0 & 0 & 0 \\ 0 & 0 & 1 \end{bmatrix}$ **4.8.9.** $\mathbf{J}_3/3$

PART 2

4.8.11. No, because it is not always the case that $(\mathbf{P}_1\mathbf{P}_2)^2 = \mathbf{P}_1\mathbf{P}_2\mathbf{P}_1\mathbf{P}_2 = \mathbf{P}_1\mathbf{P}_2$. However, if $\mathbf{P}_1\mathbf{P}_2 = \mathbf{P}_2\mathbf{P}_1$, then $\mathbf{P}_1\mathbf{P}_2\mathbf{P}_1\mathbf{P}_2 = \mathbf{P}_1\mathbf{P}_1\mathbf{P}_2\mathbf{P}_2 = \mathbf{P}_1^2\mathbf{P}_2^2 = \mathbf{P}_1\mathbf{P}_2$.
4.8.13. Let $\mathbf{Q} = 2\mathbf{P} - \mathbf{I}$. Then $\mathbf{Q}^T\mathbf{Q} = 4\mathbf{P}^2 - 4\mathbf{P} + \mathbf{I} = \mathbf{I}$. Now use Theorem 4.4.1.
4.8.15. If $\mathbf{Q}$ is orthogonal and a projector, then $\mathbf{Q}^2 = \mathbf{Q}$ implies $\mathbf{Q} = \mathbf{I}$.
4.8.17. From Example 4.7.3(*b*), $(null(\mathbf{P}))^\perp = col(\mathbf{P})$ since $\mathbf{P}^T = \mathbf{P}$. However, by Theorem 4.8.2, $col(\mathbf{P}) = (col(\mathbf{I} - \mathbf{P}))^\perp$. Hence, $(null(\mathbf{P}))^\perp = (col(\mathbf{I} - \mathbf{P}))^\perp$. By Example 4.7.3(*d*), $(col(\mathbf{I} - \mathbf{P}))^\perp = null(\mathbf{I} - \mathbf{P})$. Note that we use $(\mathcal{V}^\perp)^\perp = \mathcal{V}$ and $(\mathbf{I} - \mathbf{P})^T = \mathbf{I} - \mathbf{P}$.
4.8.19. Set $\mathbf{R} = 2\mathbf{P} - \mathbf{I}$. Then

$$\mathbf{R} = \frac{1}{9}\begin{bmatrix} 1 & 0 & 4 \\ 0 & 1 & 4 \\ 4 & 4 & 7 \end{bmatrix} \quad \text{and} \quad \mathbf{Rb} = \frac{1}{9}\begin{bmatrix} 5 \\ -4 \\ 11 \end{bmatrix}$$

Section 4.9

PART 1

4.9.1. The normal equations are

$$\begin{bmatrix} 6 & 0 \\ 0 & 2 \end{bmatrix}\mathbf{x} = \begin{bmatrix} 2 \\ 0 \end{bmatrix}$$

4.9.3. The normal equations are

$$\begin{bmatrix} 6 & 0 \\ 0 & 2 \end{bmatrix}\mathbf{x} = \begin{bmatrix} 3 \\ 1 \end{bmatrix}$$

4.9.5. $span\left\{\begin{bmatrix} 1 \\ 1 \\ 1 \end{bmatrix}\right\}$

4.9.7. The line through (1,1,1) is perpendicular to the plane $x + y + z = 0$ because

$$\mathbf{P} = \frac{1}{3}\begin{bmatrix} 2 & -1 & -1 \\ -1 & 2 & -1 \\ -1 & -1 & 2 \end{bmatrix}\begin{bmatrix} 1 \\ 1 \\ 1 \end{bmatrix} = 0$$

Hence, the distance is $\|\mathbf{b}\| = \sqrt{3}$.

4.9.9. $\left\{\frac{1}{2}\begin{bmatrix} 1 \\ 1 \\ 1 \\ 1 \end{bmatrix}, \frac{1}{2\sqrt{5}}\begin{bmatrix} -3 \\ -1 \\ 1 \\ 3 \end{bmatrix}\right\}$

4.9.11. $\mathbf{P} = \mathbf{J}_3/3$, and

$$\frac{\mathbf{I} - \mathbf{J}_3}{3} = \frac{1}{3}\begin{bmatrix} 2 & -1 & -1 \\ -1 & 2 & -1 \\ -1 & -1 & 2 \end{bmatrix}$$

But

$$\frac{1}{3}\begin{bmatrix} 2 & -1 & -1 \\ -1 & 2 & -1 \\ -1 & -1 & 2 \end{bmatrix}\begin{bmatrix} a \\ b \\ c \end{bmatrix} = \begin{bmatrix} x \\ y \\ z \end{bmatrix}$$

implies that $x = 2a - b - c$, $y = -a + 2b - c$, $z = -a - b + 2c$. Hence, the plane is $x + y + z = 0$, and the normal line is $x = y = z$.

PART 2

4.9.13. $\mathbf{x} = [b_1 \quad b_2 \quad \cdots \quad b_k]^{\mathrm{T}}$. $\mathbf{x}_m = \mathbf{x}$. $r_m^2 = b_{k+1}^2 + b_{k+2}^2 + \cdots + b_n^2$.

4.9.15. Let $\mathbf{P} = \mathbf{A}(\mathbf{A}\mathbf{A}^{\mathrm{T}})^{-1}\mathbf{A}^{\mathrm{T}}$. $\mathbf{P}^2 = (\mathbf{A}(\mathbf{A}\mathbf{A}^{\mathrm{T}})^{-1}\mathbf{A}^{\mathrm{T}})^2 = \mathbf{A}(\mathbf{A}\mathbf{A}^{\mathrm{T}})^{-1}\mathbf{A}^{\mathrm{T}}\mathbf{A}(\mathbf{A}\mathbf{A}^{\mathrm{T}})^{-1}\mathbf{A}^{\mathrm{T}} = \mathbf{A}(\mathbf{A}\mathbf{A}^{\mathrm{T}})^{-1}\mathbf{A}^{\mathrm{T}}$ shows that $\mathbf{P}^2 = \mathbf{P}$. $\mathbf{P}$ is symmetric.

Section 4.10

PART 1

4.10.5. $L = 11.3916 + 0.698t$

PART 2

4.10.7. $\overline{\mathbf{X}} = \mathbf{1}^{\mathrm{T}}\mathbf{x}$, $\overline{\mathbf{Y}} = \mathbf{1}^{\mathrm{T}}\mathbf{y}$, $\hat{s}_x = (\mathbf{x} \cdot \mathbf{x} - \mathbf{1}^{\mathrm{T}}\mathbf{x})/n$, $\hat{s}_y = (\mathbf{y} \cdot \mathbf{y} - \mathbf{1}^{\mathrm{T}}\mathbf{y})/n$, $\hat{s}_{xy} = \mathbf{x} \cdot \mathbf{y}/n - (\mathbf{1}^{\mathrm{T}}\mathbf{x})(\mathbf{1}^{\mathrm{T}}\mathbf{y})/n^2$.

4.10.9. $a = \overline{w}$.

CHAPTER 5

Section 5.2

PART 1

5.2.1. (*a*) 5 (*b*) −5 (*c*) 4 (*d*) −3 (*e*) 3 (*f*) −1
(*g*) $5 - 12i$ (*h*) $i/2$ (*i*) 1/2 (*j*) 3/2

5.2.5. $c_2 = 3$, $c_1 = 5$, $c_0 = 3$

Section 5.3

PART 1

5.3.1. (*a*) $\lambda^2 = 0$, $\rho = 0$
(*b*) $\lambda^2 - 2\lambda\cos\tau + 1 = 0$, $\lambda = \cos\tau \pm i\sin\tau$, $\rho = 1$
(*c*) $\lambda^2 - a^2 = 0$, $\rho = |a|$
(*d*) $\lambda^2 + a^2 = 0$, $\rho = |a|$

5.3.3. (*a*), (*b*), (*c*) $(\lambda - 1)^3 = 0$, $\rho = 1$

5.3.5. (*a*) $\lambda^2 - 2 = 0$, $\rho = \sqrt{2}$
(*b*) $\lambda^2 = 0$, $\rho = 0$
(*c*) $\lambda^2 + a^2 = 0$, $\rho = |a|$
(*d*) $\lambda^2 - a^2 = 0$, $\rho = |a|$

5.3.7. $(\lambda + 1)^2(\lambda - 5)^2 = 0$, $\rho = 5$

5.3.9. (a) $(\lambda - 1)^2(\lambda + 2) = 0$, $\rho = 2$ (b) $(\lambda + 1)^2(\lambda + 4) = 0$, $\rho = 4$
(c) $(\lambda - 4)(\lambda + 2)^2 = 0$, $\rho = 4$ (d) $(\lambda - 1)(1\,^2 2\,4\lambda - 1)\,^2 = 0$,
$\lambda_1 = 1$, $\lambda_2 = 2 + \sqrt{5}$, $\lambda_3 = 2 - \sqrt{5}$ $\rho = 2 + \sqrt{5}$
(e) $(\lambda + 1)^2(\lambda - 5) = 0$, $\rho = 5$ (g) $\lambda(\lambda^2 + 4) = 0$, $\rho = 2$

5.3.11. (a) $(\lambda - 1)(\lambda^2 - 1) = 0$, $\rho = 1$
(b) $\lambda^3 - 1 = 0$, $\lambda_1 = 1$, $\lambda_{2,3} = (-1 \pm \sqrt{3}i)/2$, $\rho = 1$
(c) $\lambda(\lambda - 2)(\lambda - 1) = 0$, $\rho = 2$

PART 2

5.3.13. The set of eigenvalues of

$$\begin{bmatrix} A & O \\ O & B \end{bmatrix}$$

is the union of the sets of eigenvalues of **A** and **B**.

5.3.19. All three parts are necessary and sufficient conditions that there be a nontrivial
solution of $\mathbf{Ax} = \lambda\mathbf{x}$.

Section 5.4

PART 1

5.4.1. (a) $\left\{ \begin{bmatrix} 1 \\ 1 \end{bmatrix} \right\}$ (b), (d) $\left\{ \begin{bmatrix} 1 \\ -i \end{bmatrix}, \begin{bmatrix} 1 \\ i \end{bmatrix} \right\}$ (c) $\left\{ \begin{bmatrix} 1 \\ -1 \end{bmatrix}, \begin{bmatrix} 1 \\ 1 \end{bmatrix} \right\}$

5.4.3. (a) $\left\{ \begin{bmatrix} 1 \\ 0 \\ 0 \end{bmatrix} \right\}$ (b) $\left\{ \begin{bmatrix} 1 \\ 0 \\ 0 \end{bmatrix}, \begin{bmatrix} 0 \\ 1 \\ 0 \end{bmatrix} \right\}$ (c) $\left\{ \begin{bmatrix} 1 \\ 0 \\ 0 \end{bmatrix}, \begin{bmatrix} 0 \\ 1 \\ 0 \end{bmatrix}, \begin{bmatrix} 0 \\ 0 \\ 1 \end{bmatrix} \right\}$

5.4.5. (a) $\left\{ \begin{bmatrix} i \\ -1 + \sqrt{2} \end{bmatrix}, \begin{bmatrix} i \\ -1 - \sqrt{2} \end{bmatrix} \right\}$ (b) $\left\{ \begin{bmatrix} 1 \\ i \end{bmatrix} \right\}$ (c) $\left\{ \begin{bmatrix} 1 \\ 1 \end{bmatrix}, \begin{bmatrix} 1 \\ -1 \end{bmatrix} \right\}$

(d) $\left\{ \begin{bmatrix} 1 \\ -i \end{bmatrix}, \begin{bmatrix} 1 \\ i \end{bmatrix} \right\}$

5.4.7. $\left\{ \begin{bmatrix} 1 \\ 0 \\ -1 \\ 0 \end{bmatrix}, \begin{bmatrix} 0 \\ 1 \\ 0 \\ -1 \end{bmatrix}, \begin{bmatrix} 1 \\ 0 \\ 1 \\ 0 \end{bmatrix}, \begin{bmatrix} 0 \\ 1 \\ 0 \\ 1 \end{bmatrix} \right\}$

5.4.9. $\lambda_{1,2} = -1 \pm i$. $\left\{ \begin{bmatrix} 1 \\ -1 - i \end{bmatrix}, \begin{bmatrix} 1 \\ -1 - i \end{bmatrix} \right\}$

PART 2

5.4.11. $(\mathbf{uv}^T)\mathbf{u} = \mathbf{u}(\mathbf{v}^T\mathbf{u}) = \langle \mathbf{v}, \mathbf{u} \rangle \mathbf{u}$ shows that $(\langle \mathbf{v}, \mathbf{u} \rangle, \mathbf{u})$ is an eigenpair. $(0, \mathbf{u})$ is an
eigenpair provided that $\langle \mathbf{v}, \mathbf{u} \rangle = 0$.

Section 5.5

PART 1

5.5.1. (*a*) $\lambda = 0, a(0) = 2, g(0) = 1$ (*b*) $\lambda_{1,2} = \cos\tau \pm i \sin\tau$
$a(\lambda_{1,2}) = g(\lambda_{1,2}) = 1$
(*c*) For $a \neq 0$, $\lambda_{1,2} = \pm a$, $a(\lambda_{1,2}) = g(\lambda_{1,2}) = 1$
(*d*) For $a \neq 0$, $\lambda_{1,2} = \pm ia, a(\lambda_{1,2}) = g(\lambda_{1,2}) = 1$

5.5.3. (*a*) $\lambda = 1$, $a(1) = 3$, $g(1) = 3$ (*b*) $\lambda = 1$, $a(1) = 3$, $g(1) = 2$
(*c*) $\lambda = 1$, $a(1) = 3$, $g(1) = 1$

5.5.5. (*a*) $\lambda_{1,2} = \pm\sqrt{2}$, $a(\lambda_{1,2}) = g(\lambda_{1,2}) = 1$ (*b*) $\lambda = 0$, $a(0) = g(0) = 1$
(*c*) For $a \neq 0$, $\lambda_{1,2} = \pm ia$, $a(\lambda_{1,2}) = g(\lambda_{1,2}) = 1$

5.5.7. $\lambda_{1,2} = -1$, $\lambda_{3,4} = 5$, $a(\lambda_{1,2}) = g(\lambda_{1,2}) = 1$

5.5.9. (*a*) 1 (*b*) n (*c*) 3

5.5.11. (*a*) $\lambda^2(\lambda - 2(a - b))(\lambda - 2(a + b))$
(*b*), (*c*) Set $c = (a - b)(1 + i)$. Then $\lambda(\lambda - 2(a + b))(\lambda - c)(\lambda - \overline{c})$.

PART 2

5.5.13. $\begin{bmatrix} -1 & 0 & 0 & 0 & 0 \\ 0 & -1 & 0 & 0 & 0 \\ 0 & 0 & 2 & 0 & 0 \\ 0 & 0 & 0 & 0 & 0 \\ 0 & 0 & 0 & 0 & 0 \end{bmatrix}$

Section 5.6

PART 1

5.6.1. $\mathcal{E}(1) = span\left\{\begin{bmatrix} 1 \\ 0 \\ 0 \end{bmatrix}\right\}$, $\mathcal{E}(-1) = span\left\{\begin{bmatrix} -2 \\ 0 \\ 1 \end{bmatrix}\right\}$, $\mathcal{E}(2) = span\left\{\begin{bmatrix} 14 \\ 3 \\ 2 \end{bmatrix}\right\}$

5.6.3. $\mathcal{E}(2) = span\left\{\begin{bmatrix} 1 \\ 0 \\ 0 \end{bmatrix}\right\}$, $\mathcal{E}(-2) = span\left\{\begin{bmatrix} -2 \\ 0 \\ 1 \end{bmatrix}\right\}$, $\mathcal{E}(4) = span\left\{\begin{bmatrix} 14 \\ 3 \\ 2 \end{bmatrix}\right\}$

$\mathcal{E}(2) = span\left\{\begin{bmatrix} 1 \\ 0 \\ 0 \end{bmatrix}\right\}$, $\mathcal{E}(0) = span\left\{\begin{bmatrix} -2 \\ 0 \\ 1 \end{bmatrix}\right\}$, $\mathcal{E}(3) = span\left\{\begin{bmatrix} 14 \\ 3 \\ 2 \end{bmatrix}\right\}$;

5.6.5. $\mathcal{E}(1) = span\left\{\begin{bmatrix} 1 \\ 0 \\ 0 \end{bmatrix}, \begin{bmatrix} 0 \\ 1 \\ 0 \end{bmatrix}, \begin{bmatrix} 0 \\ 0 \\ 1 \end{bmatrix}\right\}$

PART 2

5.6.9. Since $n\mathbf{K}_{n+1} + \mathbf{I}_{n+1} = \mathbf{J}_{n+1}$, $\mathbf{K}_{n+1} = (\mathbf{J}_{n+1} - \mathbf{I}_{n+1})/n$, and therefore the eigenvalues of $\mathbf{K}_{n+1}$ are $\{-1/n, -1/n, \ldots, -1/n, (n - 1)/n\}$.

Section 5.7

PART 1

5.7.1. (*a*) $\left\{\begin{bmatrix}1\\0\\0\end{bmatrix}, \begin{bmatrix}1\\ \beta-\alpha\\0\end{bmatrix}, \begin{bmatrix}1-\beta+\gamma\\ \gamma-\alpha\\ (\gamma-\alpha)(\gamma-\beta)\end{bmatrix}\right\}$ (*b*) $\left\{\begin{bmatrix}1\\0\\0\end{bmatrix}, \begin{bmatrix}0\\1\\0\end{bmatrix}, \begin{bmatrix}1\\1\\ \gamma-\alpha\end{bmatrix}\right\}$

(*c*) $\left\{\begin{bmatrix}-1\\1\\0\end{bmatrix}, \begin{bmatrix}-1\\1\\1\end{bmatrix}, \begin{bmatrix}0\\1\\1\end{bmatrix}\right\}$ (*d*) $\{\mathbf{e}_1, \mathbf{e}_2, \ldots, \mathbf{e}_m\}$ (*e*) $\{\mathbf{e}_1, \mathbf{e}_2, \ldots, \mathbf{e}_n\}$

(*f*) $\left\{\begin{bmatrix}1\\0\\0\end{bmatrix}, \begin{bmatrix}0\\1\\0\end{bmatrix}, \begin{bmatrix}0\\0\\1\end{bmatrix}\right\}$ (*g*) $\left\{\begin{bmatrix}1\\1\end{bmatrix}, \begin{bmatrix}1\\-1\end{bmatrix}\right\}$ (*h*) $\left\{\begin{bmatrix}1\\-i\end{bmatrix}, \begin{bmatrix}1\\i\end{bmatrix}\right\}$

5.7.3. (*a*) $\mathbf{S} = \begin{bmatrix}1 & 1 & 0\\ -1 & 1 & 0\\ 0 & 0 & 1\end{bmatrix}, \quad \mathbf{S}^{-1} = \frac{1}{2}\begin{bmatrix}1 & 1 & 0\\ 1 & -1 & 0\\ 0 & 0 & 2\end{bmatrix}$

(*b*) Set $\omega = (-1+\sqrt{3}i)/2$

Then

$$\mathbf{S} = \begin{bmatrix}\omega^2 & \omega & 1\\ \omega & \omega^2 & 1\\ 1 & 1 & 1\end{bmatrix}, \quad \mathbf{S}^{-1} = \begin{bmatrix}\omega & \omega^2 & 1\\ \omega^2 & \omega & 1\\ 1 & 1 & 1\end{bmatrix}/3$$

(*c*) $\mathbf{S} = \mathbf{S}^{-1} = \mathbf{I}$

5.7.5. (*a*) $a(\alpha) = 3,\ g(\alpha) = 1$ (*b*) $a(\alpha) = 3,\ g(\alpha) = 2$
(*c*) $a(3/2) = 2,\ g(3/2) = 1$ (*d*) $a(0) = 2,\ g(0) = 1$
(*e*) $a(\alpha) = 2,\ g(\alpha) = 1$

5.7.7. $\begin{bmatrix}0 & 1\\ 0 & 0\end{bmatrix}$

5.7.9. (*a*) $\begin{bmatrix}2 & 0 & -15/7\\ 0 & 2 & 2/7\\ 0 & 0 & 3\end{bmatrix}$ (*b*) $\begin{bmatrix}2 & 0 & 0\\ 0 & 3 & 1\\ 0 & 0 & 2\end{bmatrix}$ (*c*) $\begin{bmatrix}2 & 0 & -1\\ 0 & 2 & -1\\ 0 & 0 & 3\end{bmatrix}$

5.7.11. (*c*)

PART 2

5.7.15. The matrix

$$\mathbf{A} = \begin{bmatrix}1 & 1\\ 0 & -1\end{bmatrix}$$

is simple, but

$$\begin{bmatrix}1 & 0\\ 0 & -1\end{bmatrix}\mathbf{A} = \begin{bmatrix}1 & 1\\ 0 & 1\end{bmatrix}$$

is defective. Also, the matrix

$$\mathbf{A} = \begin{bmatrix}1 & 1\\ 0 & 1\end{bmatrix}$$

is defective, but

$$\begin{bmatrix} 1 & -1 \\ 0 & 1 \end{bmatrix} \mathbf{A} = \begin{bmatrix} 1 & 0 \\ 0 & 1 \end{bmatrix}$$

is simple.

5.7.17. $a(r) = 3$, but $g(r) = 1$.

5.7.19. The eigenpairs are

$$\left(1, \begin{bmatrix} 3 \\ 2 \\ 1 \end{bmatrix}\right), \quad \left(-1, \begin{bmatrix} 1 \\ 0 \\ 1 \end{bmatrix}\right), \quad \left(1 - s, \begin{bmatrix} s^2 - 3s + 3 \\ 2 - s \\ 1 \end{bmatrix}\right)$$

$\mathbf{D}(s)$ is simple if $s \neq 2$ or 0. However, $\mathbf{D}(0)$ and $\mathbf{D}(2)$ are defective.

5.7.23. $\lambda_1 = d, \lambda_2 = a - b, \lambda_3 = a + d$. (*a*) $a(d) = 2$, but $g(d) = 1$. (*b*)$a(d) = 2$, and $g(d) = 2$.

$$\mathbf{S} = \begin{bmatrix} 1 & 0 & b \\ 0 & 1 & c \\ -1 & 0 & b \end{bmatrix}$$

Section 5.8

PART 1

5.8.3. $\begin{bmatrix} 0 & 1 \\ 1 & 0 \end{bmatrix}$

PART 2

5.8.5. $\mathbf{S}^{-1}\mathbf{AS} = \mathbf{B}$ implies $(\mathbf{S}^{-1}\mathbf{AS})^{-1} = \mathbf{B}^{-1}$. **5.8.9.** $\mathbf{B}(\mathbf{AB})\mathbf{B}^{-1} = \mathbf{BA}$.

5.8.11. $\mathbf{S}^{-1}\mathbf{AS} = \mathbf{M}$ implies $(\mathbf{S}^{-1}\mathbf{AS})^2 = \mathbf{S}^{-1}\mathbf{A}^2\mathbf{S} = \mathbf{M}^2 = \mathbf{M}$. Hence, $\mathbf{S}^{-1}\mathbf{AS} = \mathbf{S}^{-1}\mathbf{A}^2\mathbf{S}$, and thus $\mathbf{A} = \mathbf{A}^2$.

Section 5.9

PART 1

5.9.1. (*c*) The eigenvalues are $1, \omega = \cos 2\pi/3 + i \sin 2\pi/3, \omega^2 = \overline{\omega}$. The corresponding eigenvectors are

$$\begin{bmatrix} 1 \\ 1 \\ 1 \end{bmatrix}, \begin{bmatrix} \omega \\ \omega^2 \\ 1 \end{bmatrix}, \begin{bmatrix} \omega^2 \\ \omega \\ 1 \end{bmatrix}$$

PART 2

5.9.5. Since $\mathbf{J}_n = \mathbf{I} + \mathbf{C}_n + \mathbf{C}_n^2 + \cdots + \mathbf{C}_n^{n-1}$, the eigenvalues of $\mathbf{J}_n$ are

$$1 + \omega^k + (\omega^k)^2 + \cdots + (\omega^k)^{n-1} = \frac{1 - (\omega^k)^n}{1 - \omega^k} = 0$$

for $k = 1, 2, \ldots, n - 1$. If $k = n$, then $1 + \omega^k + (\omega^k)^2 + \cdots + (\omega^k)^{n-1} = n$. One set of eigenvectors is given by Eq. 5.9.8.

Section 5.10

PART 1

5.10.1. (*a*) $\mathbf{x}_k = \mathbf{0}$ for all $k > 0$ (*b*) $\mathbf{x}_k = \frac{-2}{3}(3)^k\begin{bmatrix} 2 \\ -1 \end{bmatrix}$ for all $k > 0$

(*c*) $\mathbf{x}_k = \frac{-1}{3}(3)^k\begin{bmatrix} 2 \\ -1 \end{bmatrix}$ for all $k > 0$ (*d*) $\mathbf{x}_k = \frac{1}{3}(3)^k\begin{bmatrix} 2 \\ -1 \end{bmatrix}$ for all $k > 0$.

5.10.3. (*a*) $\mathbf{x}_k = (6)^k\begin{bmatrix} 1 \\ 1 \\ 1 \end{bmatrix} - \frac{1}{2}(2)^k\begin{bmatrix} 1 \\ 2 \\ 3 \end{bmatrix} + \frac{1}{2}(4)^k\begin{bmatrix} 1 \\ 0 \\ 1 \end{bmatrix}$ for all $k > 0$

(*b*) $\mathbf{x}_k = (6)^k\begin{bmatrix} 1 \\ 1 \\ 1 \end{bmatrix} - (4)^k\begin{bmatrix} 1 \\ 0 \\ 1 \end{bmatrix}$ for all $k > 0$

(*c*) $\mathbf{x}_k = (6)^k\begin{bmatrix} 1 \\ 1 \\ 1 \end{bmatrix} + \frac{1}{2}(2)^k\begin{bmatrix} 1 \\ 2 \\ 3 \end{bmatrix} + \frac{1}{2}(4)^k\begin{bmatrix} 1 \\ 0 \\ 1 \end{bmatrix}$ for all $k > 0$

5.10.5. (*a*) $\mathbf{x}_k = \begin{bmatrix} 1 \\ 1 \\ 1 \end{bmatrix}$ (*b*) $\mathbf{x}_k = (-i/2)(2i)^k\begin{bmatrix} 0 \\ i \\ -1 \end{bmatrix} + (i/2)(-2i)^k\begin{bmatrix} 0 \\ -i \\ -1 \end{bmatrix}$

(*c*) $\mathbf{x}_k = \left(\frac{-1}{2}\right)(2i)^k\begin{bmatrix} 0 \\ i \\ -1 \end{bmatrix} + \left(\frac{1}{2}\right)(-2i)^k\begin{bmatrix} 0 \\ -i \\ -1 \end{bmatrix}$

5.10.7. (*a*) $\mathbf{x}_k = \begin{bmatrix} 1 \\ 0 \\ 0 \end{bmatrix}$ (*b*) $\mathbf{x}_k = (2)^k\begin{bmatrix} 0 \\ 1 \\ 1 \end{bmatrix} + (-2)^k\begin{bmatrix} 0 \\ 1 \\ -1 \end{bmatrix}$

(*c*) $\mathbf{x}_k = (2)^k\begin{bmatrix} 0 \\ 1 \\ 1 \end{bmatrix} - (-2)^k\begin{bmatrix} 0 \\ 1 \\ -1 \end{bmatrix}$

5.10.9. (*a*) $\mathbf{x}_k = (-1)^k\begin{bmatrix} 1 \\ 1 \\ 1 \end{bmatrix} + (2)^k\begin{bmatrix} 1 \\ 0 \\ 1 \end{bmatrix} + \begin{bmatrix} 1 \\ 1 \\ 0 \end{bmatrix}$

(*b*) $\mathbf{x}_k = (-1)^k\begin{bmatrix} 1 \\ 1 \\ 1 \end{bmatrix} + (2)^k\begin{bmatrix} 1 \\ 0 \\ 1 \end{bmatrix}$

(*c*) $\mathbf{x}_k = (-1)^k\begin{bmatrix} 1 \\ 1 \\ 1 \end{bmatrix} - (2)^k\begin{bmatrix} 1 \\ 0 \\ 1 \end{bmatrix}$

5.10.11. $\mathbf{x}_k = (-1)^k\frac{2}{3}\begin{bmatrix} 1 \\ -1 \\ 0 \end{bmatrix} - (-1)^k\frac{1}{3}\begin{bmatrix} 1 \\ 0 \\ -1 \end{bmatrix} + (2)^k\frac{2}{3}\begin{bmatrix} 1 \\ 1 \\ 1 \end{bmatrix}$

Section 5.11

PART 1

5.11.1. (*a*) $\mathbf{x}(t) = \begin{bmatrix} 1 \\ 1 \end{bmatrix}, \quad t \geq 0$ (*b*) $\mathbf{x}(t) = -\dfrac{2}{3} e^{3t} \begin{bmatrix} 2 \\ -1 \end{bmatrix} + \dfrac{1}{3} \begin{bmatrix} 1 \\ 1 \end{bmatrix}, \quad t \geq 0$

(*c*) $\mathbf{x}(t) = -\dfrac{e^{3t}}{3} \begin{bmatrix} 2 \\ -1 \end{bmatrix} + \dfrac{2}{3} \begin{bmatrix} 1 \\ 1 \end{bmatrix}, \quad t \geq 0$ (*d*) $\mathbf{x}(t) = \dfrac{e^{3t}}{3} \begin{bmatrix} 2 \\ -1 \end{bmatrix} + \dfrac{1}{3} \begin{bmatrix} 1 \\ 1 \end{bmatrix}, \quad t \geq 0$

5.11.3. (*a*) $\mathbf{x}(t) = e^{6t} \begin{bmatrix} 1 \\ 1 \\ 1 \end{bmatrix} - \dfrac{1}{2} e^{2t} \begin{bmatrix} 1 \\ 2 \\ 3 \end{bmatrix} + \dfrac{1}{2} e^{4t} \begin{bmatrix} 1 \\ 0 \\ 1 \end{bmatrix}, \quad t \geq 0$

(*b*) $\mathbf{x}(t) = e^{6t} \begin{bmatrix} 1 \\ 1 \\ 1 \end{bmatrix} - e^{4t} \begin{bmatrix} 1 \\ 0 \\ 1 \end{bmatrix}, \quad t \geq 0$

(*c*) $\mathbf{x}(t) = e^{6t} \begin{bmatrix} 1 \\ 1 \\ 1 \end{bmatrix} + e^{2t} \begin{bmatrix} 1 \\ 2 \\ 3 \end{bmatrix} + \dfrac{1}{2} e^{4t} \begin{bmatrix} 1 \\ 0 \\ 1 \end{bmatrix}, \quad t \geq 0$

5.11.5. (*a*) $\mathbf{x}(t) = \begin{bmatrix} 1 \\ 1 \\ 1 \end{bmatrix}, \quad t \geq 0$

(*b*) $\mathbf{x}(t) = \left(\dfrac{-i}{2}\right) e^{2it} \begin{bmatrix} 0 \\ i \\ -1 \end{bmatrix} + \left(\dfrac{i}{2}\right) e^{-2it} \begin{bmatrix} 0 \\ -i \\ -1 \end{bmatrix} = \begin{bmatrix} 0 \\ \cos 2t \\ -\sin 2t \end{bmatrix}, \quad t \geq 0$

(*c*) $\mathbf{x}(t) = \left(\dfrac{-1}{2}\right) e^{2it} \begin{bmatrix} 0 \\ i \\ -1 \end{bmatrix} - \left(\dfrac{1}{2}\right) e^{-2it} \begin{bmatrix} 0 \\ -i \\ -1 \end{bmatrix} = \begin{bmatrix} 0 \\ \sin 2t \\ \cos 2t \end{bmatrix}, \quad t \geq 0$

5.11.7. (*a*) $\mathbf{x}(t) = \begin{bmatrix} 1 \\ 0 \\ 0 \end{bmatrix} \quad t \geq 0$ (*b*) $\mathbf{x}(t) = \dfrac{e^{2t}}{2} \begin{bmatrix} 0 \\ 1 \\ 1 \end{bmatrix} + \dfrac{e^{-2t}}{2} \begin{bmatrix} 0 \\ 1 \\ -1 \end{bmatrix}, \quad t \geq 0$

(*c*) $\mathbf{x}(t) = \dfrac{e^{2t}}{2} \begin{bmatrix} 0 \\ 1 \\ 1 \end{bmatrix} - \dfrac{e^{-2t}}{2} \begin{bmatrix} 0 \\ 1 \\ 1 \end{bmatrix}, \quad t \geq 0$

5.11.9. (*a*) $\mathbf{x}(t) = e^{-t} \begin{bmatrix} 1 \\ 1 \\ 1 \end{bmatrix} + e^{2t} \begin{bmatrix} 1 \\ 0 \\ 1 \end{bmatrix} + e^{t} \begin{bmatrix} 1 \\ 1 \\ 0 \end{bmatrix}$ (*b*) $\mathbf{x}(t) = e^{-t} \begin{bmatrix} 1 \\ 1 \\ 1 \end{bmatrix} + e^{2t} \begin{bmatrix} 1 \\ 0 \\ 1 \end{bmatrix}$

(*c*) $\mathbf{x}(t) = e^{-t} \begin{bmatrix} 1 \\ 1 \\ 1 \end{bmatrix} - e^{2t} \begin{bmatrix} 1 \\ 0 \\ 1 \end{bmatrix}$

5.11.11. $\mathbf{x}(t) = e^{-t} \dfrac{2}{3} \begin{bmatrix} 1 \\ -1 \\ 0 \end{bmatrix} - e^{-t} \dfrac{1}{3} \begin{bmatrix} 1 \\ 0 \\ -1 \end{bmatrix} + e^{2t} \dfrac{2}{3} \begin{bmatrix} 1 \\ 1 \\ 1 \end{bmatrix}$

PART 2

5.11.13. $\mathrm{Re}(\mathbf{x}') = \left(\mathrm{Re}(\mathbf{x})'\right) = \mathrm{Re}(\mathbf{A}\mathbf{x}) = \mathbf{A}\mathrm{Re}(\mathbf{x})$

5.11.15. $\mathrm{Re}(\mathbf{x}(t)) = \mathrm{Re}\left(e^t(\cos t + i \sin t)\begin{bmatrix} 1 \\ i \end{bmatrix}\right) = e^t\begin{bmatrix} \cos t \\ -\sin t \end{bmatrix}$ and

$\mathrm{Im}(\mathbf{x}(t)) = \mathrm{Im}\left(e^t(\cos t + i \sin t)\begin{bmatrix} 1 \\ i \end{bmatrix}\right) = e^t\begin{bmatrix} \sin t \\ \cos t \end{bmatrix}$

Hence

$$\mathbf{x}(t) = e^t\begin{bmatrix} \cos t \\ -\sin t \end{bmatrix} + e^t\begin{bmatrix} \sin t \\ \cos t \end{bmatrix}$$

is the real solution.

5.11.17. $\mathbf{y} = \begin{bmatrix} -1 \\ 1 \end{bmatrix}$

Section 5.12

PART 1

5.12.1. This is the example worked in Section 5.12.1 with $a = 1$ and $b = 0$. Hence, using these values in Eq. 5.10.11:

$$y_n = \frac{1}{\sqrt{5}}\left(\frac{1+\sqrt{5}}{2}\right)^{n+1} - \frac{1}{\sqrt{5}}\left(\frac{1-\sqrt{5}}{2}\right)^{n+1}$$

5.12.3. $\mathbf{y}_n = \begin{bmatrix} 0 & 1 \\ 1 & 0 \end{bmatrix}\mathbf{y}_{n-1}, \mathbf{y}_0 = \begin{bmatrix} 1 \\ 0 \end{bmatrix}$. $\left(1, \begin{bmatrix} 1 \\ 1 \end{bmatrix}\right)$, and $\left(-1, \begin{bmatrix} 1 \\ -1 \end{bmatrix}\right)$. Therefore,

$$\mathbf{y}_n = \frac{1}{2}(1)^k\begin{bmatrix} 1 \\ 1 \end{bmatrix} + \frac{1}{2}(-1)^k\begin{bmatrix} 1 \\ -1 \end{bmatrix}$$

and hence $y_n = (1 + (-1)^k)/2$.

5.12.5. $\mathbf{y}'(t) = \begin{bmatrix} 0 & 1 \\ 1 & 0 \end{bmatrix}\mathbf{y}(t), \mathbf{y}(0) = \begin{bmatrix} 1 \\ 0 \end{bmatrix}$. $\left(1, \begin{bmatrix} 1 \\ 1 \end{bmatrix}\right)$ and $\left(0, \begin{bmatrix} 1 \\ 0 \end{bmatrix}\right)$. Therefore, $\mathbf{y}(t) = \begin{bmatrix} 1 \\ 0 \end{bmatrix}$ and hence $y(t) = 1$.

5.12.7. $\mathbf{y}'(t) = \begin{bmatrix} 0 & 1 \\ 1 & 0 \end{bmatrix}\mathbf{y}(t), \mathbf{y}(0) = \begin{bmatrix} 0 \\ 1 \end{bmatrix}$. $\left(1, \begin{bmatrix} 1 \\ 1 \end{bmatrix}\right)$ and $\left(-1, \begin{bmatrix} 1 \\ -1 \end{bmatrix}\right)$. Therefore,

$$\mathbf{y}(t) = \frac{1}{2}e^t\begin{bmatrix} 1 \\ 1 \end{bmatrix} - \frac{1}{2}e^{-t}\begin{bmatrix} 1 \\ -1 \end{bmatrix}$$

and hence $y(t) = (e^t - e^{-t})/2$.

5.12.9. $\begin{bmatrix} 0 & 1 & 0 & 0 & 0 \\ 0 & 0 & 1 & 0 & 0 \\ 0 & 0 & 0 & 1 & 0 \\ 0 & 0 & 0 & 0 & 1 \\ 0 & 0 & 1 & -3 & 3 \end{bmatrix}$

PART 2

5.12.11. (*a*) $\mathbf{y}'(t) = \begin{bmatrix} 0 & 1 & \cdots & 0 & 0 \\ 0 & 0 & \cdots & 0 & 0 \\ \vdots & \vdots & & \vdots & \vdots \\ 1 & 1 & \cdots & 1 & 1 \end{bmatrix} \mathbf{y}(t)$

(*b*) $\mathbf{y}_n(t) = \begin{bmatrix} 0 & 1 & \cdots & 0 & 0 \\ 0 & 0 & & 0 & 0 \\ \vdots & \vdots & & \vdots & \vdots \\ 1 & 1 & \cdots & 1 & 1 \end{bmatrix} \mathbf{y}_{n-1}(t)$

5.12.13. By Theorem 5.12.1, the geometric multiplicity of each eigenvalue is 1, and therefore $\sum g(\lambda_k)$ equals the number of distinct eigenvalues. By Corollary 1 of Theorem 5.7.2, $\sum g(\lambda_k) = n$ is necessary and sufficient for a matrix to be simple. Thus, a companion matrix is simple if and only if it has exactly n distinct eigenvalues.

CHAPTER 6

Section 6.1

PART 1

6.1.1. (*a*) $\sqrt{2}$ (*b*) 2 (*c*) $\sqrt{7}$

PART 2

6.1.5. $\mathbf{y}_1 = [1 \quad 0 \quad 1]^{\mathrm{T}}, \mathbf{y}_2 = [-i \quad -2 \quad i]^{\mathrm{T}}$

6.1.9. $\langle \mathbf{Ax}, \mathbf{y} \rangle = (\mathbf{Ax})^{\mathrm{H}}\mathbf{y} = \mathbf{x}^{\mathrm{H}}(\mathbf{A}^{\mathrm{H}}\mathbf{y}) = \langle \mathbf{x}, \mathbf{A}^{\mathrm{H}}\mathbf{y} \rangle$

6.1.11. $\mathbf{V}^{\mathrm{H}}\mathbf{V} = \mathbf{V}\mathbf{V}^{\mathrm{H}} = \mathbf{I}$

6.1.13. $\det(\mathbf{A}^{\mathrm{H}}) = \sum \pm \overline{a_{1*}a_{2*}\cdots a_{n*}} = \sum \pm \overline{a_{1*}}\,\overline{a_{2*}}\cdots\overline{a_{n*}} = \overline{\det(\mathbf{A})}$

Section 6.2

PART 1

6.2.5. $\begin{bmatrix} 0 & i & 0 \\ i & 0 & 0 \\ 0 & 0 & 1 \end{bmatrix}$

PART 2

6.2.7. $\gamma^2 + \delta^2 = 1$

6.2.9. $(\mathbf{U}^{-1})^{\mathrm{H}}\mathbf{U}^{-1} = (\mathbf{U}^{\mathrm{H}})^{-1}(\mathbf{U}^{-1}) = (\mathbf{U}\mathbf{U}^{\mathrm{H}})^{-1} = \mathbf{I}$

6.2.11. Follows by choosing $\mathbf{V} = \mathbf{U}$ in Example 6.2.1(*a*) and then by induction.

Section 6.3

PART 1

6.3.11. (*a*) $\mathbf{U} = \frac{\sqrt{5}}{5}\begin{bmatrix} -1 & 2 \\ 1 & -1 \end{bmatrix}, \mathbf{T} = \begin{bmatrix} 2 & 5 \\ 0 & 2 \end{bmatrix}$ (*b*) $\mathbf{U} = \frac{\sqrt{2}}{2}\begin{bmatrix} 1 & 1 \\ -1 & 1 \end{bmatrix}, \mathbf{T} = \begin{bmatrix} 0 & 0 \\ 0 & 2 \end{bmatrix}$

(*c*) $\mathbf{U} = \frac{\sqrt{2}}{2}\begin{bmatrix} 1 & i \\ i & 1 \end{bmatrix}, \mathbf{T} = \begin{bmatrix} i & 0 \\ 0 & -i \end{bmatrix}$ (*d*) $\mathbf{U} = \frac{\sqrt{2}}{2}\begin{bmatrix} 1 & 1 \\ -1 & 1 \end{bmatrix}, \mathbf{T} = \begin{bmatrix} -1 & 0 \\ 0 & 1 \end{bmatrix}$

PART 2

6.3.13. $(\mathbf{Q}^{-1}\mathbf{A}\mathbf{Q})^{\mathrm{T}} = \mathbf{T}$ and $\mathbf{Q}^{\mathrm{T}}\mathbf{A}\mathbf{Q} = \mathbf{T}(\mathbf{Q}^{\mathrm{T}}\mathbf{A}\mathbf{Q})^{\mathrm{T}} = \mathbf{Q}^{\mathrm{T}}\mathbf{A}\mathbf{Q} = \mathbf{T}$ implies that the upper triangular matrix $\mathbf{T}$ is symmetric. Thus, $\mathbf{T}$ is diagonal.

Section 6.4

PART 1

6.4.1. (*a*) $\left(-1, \begin{bmatrix} 1 \\ i \end{bmatrix}\right), \left(1, \begin{bmatrix} i \\ 1 \end{bmatrix}\right)$, and $\rho = \sqrt{2}$

(*b*) $\left(2i, \begin{bmatrix} 3 \\ -i \end{bmatrix}\right), \left(-2i, \begin{bmatrix} -i \\ 1 \end{bmatrix}\right)$, and $\rho = \sqrt{10}$

(*c*) $\left(2i, \begin{bmatrix} 2 \\ -i \end{bmatrix}\right), \left(-2i, \begin{bmatrix} -i \\ 2 \end{bmatrix}\right)$, and $\rho = \sqrt{5}$

6.4.3. $\overline{\det(\mathbf{A})} = \det(\overline{\mathbf{A}}) = \det(\overline{\mathbf{A}}^{\mathrm{T}}) = \det(\mathbf{A}^{\mathrm{H}}) = \det(\mathbf{A})$

6.4.5. There exists an orthogonal matrix $\mathbf{Q}$ such that $\mathbf{Q}^{-1}\mathbf{A}\mathbf{Q} = \mathbf{O}$.

6.4.9. $(\mathbf{A}^{\mathrm{T}})^{\mathrm{H}} = (\mathbf{A}^{\mathrm{H}})^{\mathrm{T}} = \mathbf{A}^{\mathrm{T}}$

6.4.11. $(k\mathbf{A})^{\mathrm{H}} = \overline{k}\mathbf{A}^{\mathrm{H}} = -\overline{k}\mathbf{A} = k\mathbf{A}$ if and only if $-k = \overline{k}$, that is, if and only if $\mathrm{Re}(k) = 0$. Hence, k is imaginary.

6.4.13. $(k\mathbf{A})^{\mathrm{H}} = \overline{k}\mathbf{A}^{\mathrm{H}} = \overline{k}\mathbf{A} = k\mathbf{A}$ if and only if $k = \overline{k}$, that is, if and only if k is real.

PART 2

6.4.15. (*a*) $\frac{1}{10}\begin{bmatrix} 4 & 2 & 2 \\ 2 & 10 & -5 \\ 2 & -5 & 10 \end{bmatrix}$ (*b*) $\frac{1}{2}\begin{bmatrix} 2 & 0 & 0 \\ 0 & 3 & -1 \\ 0 & -1 & 3 \end{bmatrix}$ (*c*) $\lambda_1\mathbf{I}$

(*d*) $\frac{1}{3}\begin{bmatrix} 2+3\lambda & 1 & 1 \\ 1 & 3\lambda-1 & 2 \\ 1 & 2 & 3\lambda-1 \end{bmatrix} = \frac{1}{3}\begin{bmatrix} 2 & 1 & 1 \\ 1 & -1 & 2 \\ 1 & 2 & -1 \end{bmatrix} + \lambda\mathbf{I}$

6.4.19. If $\mathbf{U} = (i\mathbf{I} - \mathbf{H})(i\mathbf{I} + \mathbf{H})^{-1}$, then $\mathbf{U}^{\mathrm{H}} = (-i\mathbf{I} - \mathbf{H})(-i\mathbf{I} + \mathbf{H})^{-1}$. Hence,

$$\begin{aligned} \mathbf{U}^{\mathrm{H}}\mathbf{U} &= (-i\mathbf{I} - \mathbf{H})(-i\mathbf{I} + \mathbf{H})^{-1}(i\mathbf{I} - \mathbf{H})(i\mathbf{I} + \mathbf{H})^{-1} \\ &= (-i\mathbf{I} - \mathbf{H})(i\mathbf{I} - \mathbf{H})(-i\mathbf{I} + \mathbf{H})^{-1}(i\mathbf{I} + \mathbf{H})^{-1} = (\mathbf{I} + \mathbf{H}^2)(\mathbf{I} + \mathbf{H}^2)^{-1} = \mathbf{I} \end{aligned}$$

Section 6.5

PART 1

6.5.1. Let $\omega = \cos(2\pi/3) + i\sin(2\pi/3)$. Then

$$\mathbf{U} = \frac{\sqrt{3}}{3}\begin{bmatrix} 1 & 1 & 3 \\ 1 & \omega & \omega^2 \\ 1 & \omega^2 & \omega \end{bmatrix}$$

6.5.7. No.

PART 2

6.5.9. $(\mathbf{U}^{\mathrm{H}}\mathbf{A}\mathbf{U})^{\mathrm{H}}(\mathbf{U}^{\mathrm{H}}\mathbf{A}\mathbf{U}) = \mathbf{U}^{\mathrm{H}}\mathbf{A}^{\mathrm{H}}\mathbf{A}\mathbf{U} = \mathbf{U}^{\mathrm{H}}\mathbf{A}\mathbf{A}^{\mathrm{H}}\mathbf{U} = \mathbf{U}^{\mathrm{H}}\mathbf{A}\mathbf{U}\mathbf{U}^{\mathrm{H}}\mathbf{A}^{\mathrm{H}}\mathbf{U} = (\mathbf{U}^{\mathrm{H}}\mathbf{A}\mathbf{U})(\mathbf{U}^{\mathrm{H}}\mathbf{A}^{\mathrm{H}}\mathbf{U})$

6.5.11. By the symmetry of the definition.

6.5.15. If either $\mathbf{u}$ or $\mathbf{v}$ is zero, then $\mathbf{u}\mathbf{v}^{\mathrm{H}} = \mathbf{O}$ and the result is trivial. So assume that neither $\mathbf{u}$ or $\mathbf{v}$ is zero. Now $\mathbf{u}\mathbf{v}^{\mathrm{H}}$ is normal if and only if $(\mathbf{u}\mathbf{v}^{\mathrm{H}})^{\mathrm{H}}\mathbf{u}\mathbf{v}^{\mathrm{H}} = \mathbf{u}\mathbf{v}^{\mathrm{H}}(\mathbf{u}\mathbf{v}^{\mathrm{H}})^{\mathrm{H}}$. But this simplifies to $\|\mathbf{v}\|^2\mathbf{u}\mathbf{u}^{\mathrm{H}} = \|\mathbf{u}\|^2\mathbf{v}\mathbf{v}^{\mathrm{H}}$. Postmultiply by $\mathbf{u}$ to obtain $\|\mathbf{v}\|^2\|\mathbf{u}\|^2\mathbf{u} = \|\mathbf{u}\|^2\langle\mathbf{v},\mathbf{u}\rangle\mathbf{v}$, from which it follows that $\|\mathbf{v}\|^2\mathbf{u} = \langle\mathbf{v},\mathbf{u}\rangle\mathbf{v}$. Hence, $\mathbf{u}$ is proportional to $\mathbf{v}$. Thus, if $\mathbf{u}\mathbf{v}^{\mathrm{H}}$ is normal, there is some k such that $\mathbf{v} = k\mathbf{u}$. Conversely, if $\mathbf{v} = k\mathbf{u}$ then $\mathbf{u}\mathbf{v}^{\mathrm{H}} = \bar{k}\mathbf{u}\mathbf{u}^{\mathrm{H}}$, which is normal.

6.5.17. Use Example 6.5.6.

Section 6.6

PART 1

6.6.1. $(3, \mathbf{1}_3)$ **6.6.3.** $(1, \mathbf{1}_3)$ **6.6.5.** $\left(0, \begin{bmatrix} a \\ -b \end{bmatrix}\right), \left(a^2 + b^2, \begin{bmatrix} b \\ a \end{bmatrix}\right)$

Section 6.7

PART 2

6.7.3. No. No.

CHAPTER 7

Section 7.1

PART 1

7.1.1. $\mathbf{G} = \frac{1}{2}\begin{bmatrix} -1 & 9 \\ 1 & -1 \end{bmatrix}$, $\lambda = 1, -2$.

7.1.3. If $\mathbf{x} \in \mathcal{S}$ then $\mathbf{x}_1 = \mathbf{A}\mathbf{x} \in \mathcal{S}$, and hence $\mathbf{x}_2 = \mathbf{A}\mathbf{x}_1 = \mathbf{A}^2\mathbf{x} \in \mathcal{S}$. So, in this notation, $\alpha\mathbf{x}_k + \beta\mathbf{x}_m \in \mathcal{S}$.

Section 7.2

PART 2

7.2.3. Since $\mathbf{A}$ is $r \times 2r$ and rank($\mathbf{A}$) is r, $\mathbf{N}$ is $2r \times r$. Hence, $\mathbf{AN} = \mathbf{O}_r$, $\mathbf{AN}$ is simple, and rank($\mathbf{AN}$) $= 0$. On the other hand, $\mathbf{NA}$ is $2r \times 2r$. If $\mathbf{NA} = \mathbf{O}_{2r}$, then $\mathbf{A}^T\mathbf{N}^T = \mathbf{O}$ shows that $null(\mathbf{A}^T)$ is r-dimensional. However, $\mathbf{A}^T$ has r columns. Hence, $r = r + \text{rank}(\mathbf{A}^T) = r + r$, a contradiction. So $\mathbf{A}^T\mathbf{N}^T \neq \mathbf{O}$, and hence rank($\mathbf{A}^T\mathbf{N}^T$) > 0. By Theorem 7.2.4, $\mathbf{NA}$ is defective.

Section 7.3

PART 1

7.3.1. $s_i = a_{ii} = k$ implies $s_{\min} = k$. Also $|\det(k\mathbf{I})| = k^n$.
7.3.3. Use Corollary 1 of Theorem 7.3.1., (*a*) $r_i = 9$, so $\rho \leq 9$. (*c*) $\rho \leq n$. (*d*) $\rho \leq 2$. (*e*) $\rho \leq r_{\max} = r_i = |\sin\vartheta| + |\cos\vartheta| \leq \sqrt{2}$.

PART 2

7.3.7. By Corollary 1 of Theorem 7.3.1, $|\lambda| \leq r_{\max}$. However $|\lambda_1\lambda_2\cdots\lambda_n| = |\det(\mathbf{A})|$. Hence, $|\det(\mathbf{A})| \leq r_{\max}^n$.
7.3.11. The tridiagonal matrix is nonsingular if $|d| \leq 2|e|$.

Section 7.4

PART 1

7.4.1. (*a*), (*b*) $\sqrt{1+\sin^2\tau}$ (*c*) $\sqrt{3}$ (*d*) $|a|$.
7.4.3. $\|\mathbf{A}/M\|^2 = M^{-2}\|\mathbf{A}\|^2 = 1$

PART 2

7.4.7. $\|\mathbf{D}^{-1}\mathbf{AD}\|^2 = \sum a^{2(i-j)}a_{ij}^2$
7.4.9. $\|\mathbf{P}\| = \|\mathbf{P}^2\| \leq \|\mathbf{P}\|^2$, so that $1 \leq \|\mathbf{P}\|$ **7.4.11.** $\begin{bmatrix} 1 & 1 \\ 0 & 2 \end{bmatrix}$

Section 7.5

PART 1

7.5.1. (*a*) $\mathbf{A}_\infty = \mathbf{A}^k = \mathbf{A}$. (*b*) $\mathbf{A}_\infty = \mathbf{A}^k = \mathbf{O}, k > 0$ (*c*) $\mathbf{A}_\infty = \mathbf{A}^k = \mathbf{A}$
(*d*) $\mathbf{A}_\infty$ does not exist. $\mathbf{A}^k = \begin{bmatrix} 1 & k \\ 0 & 1 \end{bmatrix}$

(*e*) $\mathbf{A}_\infty = \mathbf{O}$. $\mathbf{A}^k = \dfrac{1}{2^k}\begin{bmatrix} 1 & 2k \\ 0 & 1 \end{bmatrix}$

(*f*), (*g*). $\mathbf{A}_\infty$ does not exist. $\mathbf{A}^{2m} = \mathbf{I}$, $\mathbf{A}^{2m+1} = \mathbf{A}$.
7.5.3. (*a*) $\mathbf{A}_\infty$ does not exist. $\mathbf{A}^{2m} = \mathbf{I}$, $\mathbf{A}^{2m+1} = \mathbf{A}$.
(*b*) $\text{diag}(a, b, c, d, e)^k = \text{diag}(a^k, b^k, c^k, d^k, e^k)$. Hence, $\mathbf{A}_\infty$ exists if and only

if each entry is 1 or has magnitude less than 1. Thus, $\mathbf{A}_\infty = \text{diag}(\delta_1, \delta_2, \ldots, \delta_5)$, where $\delta_i = 1$ or 0.

7.5.5. $\mathbf{A}^{2m} = \mathbf{I}, \mathbf{A}^{2m+1} = \mathbf{A}$; hence, $(\mathbf{A}^{2m}\mathbf{C}) = \mathbf{C}, (\mathbf{A}^{2m+1}\mathbf{C}) = \mathbf{AC} \neq \mathbf{C}$.

Section 7.6

PART 1

7.6.1. (*a*), (*b*) In both cases the eigenvalues are 1, 0 and the limits exist by Theorem 7.6.1. In (*a*) $\mathbf{S} = \mathbf{I}, \mathbf{C} = [0]$, so $\mathbf{A}_\infty = \mathbf{A}$. In (*b*), $\mathbf{S} = \begin{bmatrix} 1 & 1 \\ 1 & -1 \end{bmatrix}$, $\mathbf{T} = [0]$, and

$\mathbf{C} = [1]$, so $\mathbf{A}_\infty = \mathbf{S}\begin{bmatrix} 1 & 0 \\ 0 & 0 \end{bmatrix}\mathbf{S}^{-1} = \begin{bmatrix} 1 & 1 \\ 0 & 0 \end{bmatrix} = \mathbf{A}$

(*c*) The limit fails to exist because $a(1) = 2$ but $g(1) = 1$.

(*d*), (*e*) The limit fails to exist because there is an eigenvalue -1.

7.6.3. The limit fails to exist because there is an eigenvalue -1.

7.6.5. $\mathbf{A}^m = \mathbf{I} + m\mathbf{A}$. Hence, $t_{ij}^{(m)} = m$.

PART 2

7.6.7. Since $C\binom{m}{k}$ is a polynomial of degree k in m, $t_{ij}^{(m)}$ is a polynomial of degree 1 or more. But polynomials are unbounded as $m \to \infty$.

Section 7.7

PART 1

7.7.1.

$$\mathbf{T} = \begin{bmatrix} a & 1-b \\ 1-a & b \end{bmatrix}$$

The eigenvalues of $\mathbf{T}$ are 1 and $a + b - 1$. But $a + b - 1 = 1$ if and only if $a = b = 1$. But then $\mathbf{T} = \mathbf{I}$.

7.7.3. $\mathbf{1}^\mathrm{T}\mathbf{AB} = \mathbf{1}^\mathrm{T}\mathbf{B} = \mathbf{1}^\mathrm{T}$.

7.7.5. The sum of all the columns and rows is $S - a_{11} + a_{12} \cdots + a_{1n}$. Hence, $\mathbf{A} = \mathbf{W}_n/S$ and $\mathbf{A}^\mathrm{T}$ are regular transition matrices. Moreover, by Theorem 7.7.8, $\mathbf{A}_\infty = \mathbf{p}\mathbf{1}^\mathrm{T}$, where $\mathbf{p}$ is a stationary vector of $\mathbf{A}$. However, $\mathbf{A1} = \mathbf{1}$ so that $\mathbf{p} = \mathbf{1}/n$. Hence, $\mathbf{A}_\infty = \mathbf{11}^\mathrm{T}/n = \mathbf{J}/n$.

7.7.7. All the eigenvalues of $\mathbf{Q}$ have modulus 1. By Theorem 7.7.2 all the eigenvalues with modulus 1 of a transition matrix are 1. Hence, all the eigenvalues of $\mathbf{Q}$ are 1. Since $\mathbf{Q}$ is simple, $\mathbf{S}^{-1}\mathbf{QS} = \mathbf{I}$, and hence $\mathbf{Q} = \mathbf{I}$.

PART 2

7.7.13. $\rho(\mathbf{B}) = (2/3)^{1/2}$

CHAPTER 8

Section 8.2

PART 1

8.2.1. (*a*) $\begin{bmatrix} 0 & \frac{1}{2} & \frac{1}{2} \\ \frac{1}{2} & 1 & 0 \\ \frac{1}{2} & 0 & 0 \end{bmatrix}$ (*b*) $\begin{bmatrix} 1 & 0 \\ 0 & 1 \end{bmatrix}$ (*c*) $\begin{bmatrix} 0 & \frac{1}{2} \\ \frac{1}{2} & 0 \end{bmatrix}$

8.2.3. 4

PART 2

8.2.5. $\begin{bmatrix} -1 & i \\ i & 1 \end{bmatrix}$

8.2.7. Choose $\mathbf{A} = \mathbf{I}$; then $k = 1$ is necessary. Clearly, it is also sufficient.

8.2.9. From $\mathbf{S}^{\mathrm{T}}\mathbf{A}\mathbf{S} = \mathbf{B}$ it follows that $\mathbf{S}^{-1}\mathbf{A}^{-1}\mathbf{S}^{\mathrm{T}} = \mathbf{B}^{-1}$

Section 8.3

PART 1

8.3.1. (*a*) $(x_1 + x_2/2 + x_3/2)^2 - (x_2 + x_3)^2/4 + 0x_3^2$
(*b*) $(x_1 + x_2/2)^2 - x_2^2/4 + 2x_3^2$ (*c*) $(x_1 + x_3)^2 + x_2^2 - x_3^2$

8.3.3. (*a*) $\begin{bmatrix} 1 & 0 \\ 0 & -1 \end{bmatrix}$ (*b*) $\begin{bmatrix} 1 & 0 & 0 \\ 0 & 1 & 0 \\ 0 & 0 & 0 \end{bmatrix}$ (*c*) $\begin{bmatrix} 2 & 0 & 0 \\ 0 & 1 & 0 \\ 0 & 0 & -\frac{1}{2} \end{bmatrix}$

Section 8.4

PART 2

8.4.7. Suppose $\mathbf{S}^{\mathrm{T}}\mathbf{A}\mathbf{S} = \mathbf{B}$ and $\mathbf{x}^{\mathrm{T}}\mathbf{A}\mathbf{x} < \mathbf{0}$ and $\mathbf{y}^{\mathrm{T}}\mathbf{A}\mathbf{y} > \mathbf{0}$. Since $\mathbf{S}$ is nonsingular, set $\mathbf{u} = \mathbf{S}^{-1}\mathbf{x}$ and $\mathbf{v} = \mathbf{S}^{-1}\mathbf{y}$. Then $\mathbf{u}^{\mathrm{T}}\mathbf{B}\mathbf{u} = (\mathbf{S}^{-1}\mathbf{x})^{\mathrm{T}}\mathbf{B}\mathbf{S}^{-1}\mathbf{x} = \mathbf{x}^{\mathrm{T}}\mathbf{S}^{-\mathrm{T}}\mathbf{B}\mathbf{S}^{-1}\mathbf{x} = \mathbf{x}^{\mathrm{T}}\mathbf{A}\mathbf{x} < \mathbf{0}$. Similarly, $\mathbf{v}^{\mathrm{T}}\mathbf{B}\mathbf{v} = (\mathbf{S}^{-1}\mathbf{y})^{\mathrm{T}}\mathbf{B}\mathbf{S}^{-1}\mathbf{y} = \mathbf{y}^{\mathrm{T}}\mathbf{S}^{-\mathrm{T}}\mathbf{B}\mathbf{S}^{-1}\mathbf{y} = \mathbf{y}^{\mathrm{T}}\mathbf{A}\mathbf{y} > \mathbf{0}$.

8.4.9. Since $\mathbf{Q}^{-1} = \mathbf{Q}^{\mathrm{T}}, \mathbf{Q}^{-1}\mathbf{A}\mathbf{Q}$ is congruent to $\mathbf{A}$.

8.4.11. Each eigenvalue of $\mathbf{M}$ is either $+1$ or -1. Hence, if $\mathbf{M}$ is positive semidefinite, all the eigenvalues are $+1$, and because $\mathbf{M}$ is simple, this implies that $\mathbf{M} = \mathbf{I}$. If $\mathbf{M} \neq \pm\mathbf{I}$, there is at least one eigenvalue that is $+1$ and one that is -1. Hence, $\mathbf{M}$ is indefinite and nonsingular.

Section 8.5

PART 1

8.5.1. $\det(\mathrm{A}_3) = -162$, so $\mathbf{A}$ is not positive definite. Since $-\mathbf{A}$ is clearly not positive definite, $\mathbf{A}$ must be indefinite.

8.5.3. (*a*) $\begin{bmatrix} 2 & 3 & -2 \\ 3 & 6 & -2 \\ -2 & -2 & 3 \end{bmatrix} \rightarrow \begin{bmatrix} 2 & 3 & -2 \\ 0 & -3/2 & 1 \\ -2 & -2 & 3 \end{bmatrix}$

Hence, $\det(\mathbf{A}_2) < 0$, so **A** is not positive definite.

(*b*) $\begin{bmatrix} 6 & 1 & -4 \\ 1 & 2 & 0 \\ -4 & 0 & 3 \end{bmatrix} \rightarrow \begin{bmatrix} 6 & 1 & 4 \\ 0 & 11/6 & 2/3 \\ 0 & 2/3 & 1/3 \end{bmatrix} \rightarrow \begin{bmatrix} 6 & 1 & -4 \\ 0 & 11/6 & 2/3 \\ 0 & 0 & 1/11 \end{bmatrix}$

Hence, **A** is positive definite.

PART 2

8.5.5. If **A** is 2×2 then $\det(\mathbf{A}_1) = a_{11} > 0$, and $\det(\mathbf{A}) > 0$ is the condition of Theorem 8.5.2. Also, if **A** is 3×3, then $\det(\mathbf{A}_2) = a_{11} > 0$, $\det(\mathbf{A}_2) = a_{11}a_{22} - a_{12}a_{21} > 0$, and $\det(\mathbf{A}) > 0$ is the condition of Theorem 8.5.2.

Section 8.6

PART 1

8.6.1. All are hyperbolas.

8.6.3. (*a*) $\mathbf{x} = [0 - 1]$ and $\mathbf{H} = \begin{bmatrix} 1 & 1 \\ 1 & 0 \end{bmatrix}$. Hence, **H** is indefinite, and **x** is a saddle point.

(*b*) There are no extreme points.

Section 8.7

PART 1

8.7.1. $\mathbf{M}^{1/2} = \begin{bmatrix} 2 & 1 \\ 1 & 2 \end{bmatrix}, \mathbf{M}^{-1/2} = \frac{1}{3}\begin{bmatrix} 2 & -1 \\ -1 & 2 \end{bmatrix}$ **8.7.3.** $\mathbf{T} = \frac{\sqrt{2}}{6}\begin{bmatrix} 1 & 1 \\ -3 & 3 \end{bmatrix}$

8.7.5. $\det(\mathbf{S}_1) = k_1 + k_2 > 0$, $\det(\mathbf{S}_2) = k_1k_2 + k_1k_3 + k_2k_3 > 0$, and $\det(\mathbf{S}_3) = k_1k_2k_3$.

PART 2

8.7.7. $\mathbf{M}^{1/2}$ is symmetric, and since it is positive definite it is not singular. Hence, $\mathbf{M}^{1/2}\mathbf{A}\mathbf{M}^{1/2} = (\mathbf{M}^{1/2})^H\mathbf{A}\mathbf{M}^{1/2}$.

Section 8.8

PART 1

8.8.1. (*a*) $r = 3, p = 2, q = 1$ (*b*) $r = 2, p = 1, q = 0$
(*c*) $r = 2, p = 2, q = 2$

8.8.3. (*a*) $r = 4, p = 2, q = 0$

8.8.5. $p = n - r, q = n - r$

Section 8.9

PART 1

8.9.1. Let $\mathbf{x} = [x_1 x_2 \cdots x_n]^T$. There is one singular value $s = \|\mathbf{x}\|$. $\mathbf{V} = [1], \mathbf{U} = [\mathbf{x}/\|\mathbf{x}\|^2 \ \ \mathbf{u}_2 \ \ \mathbf{u}_n]$, where $\{\mathbf{u}_2 \ \ \mathbf{u}_n\}$ is any orthonormal basis for $null(\mathbf{x}\mathbf{x}^H)$.

8.9.3. Since $\mathbf{Q}^T\mathbf{Q} = \mathbf{Q}\mathbf{Q}^T = \mathbf{I}_2$, $s_1 = s_2 = 1$ and $\mathbf{V} = \mathbf{U} = \mathbf{I}_2$.

PART 2

8.9.5. $\det(\mathbf{S}) = |\det(\mathbf{U}^H\mathbf{A}\mathbf{V})| = |\det(\mathbf{U}^H)| \cdot |\det(\mathbf{A})| \cdot |\det(\mathbf{V})| = |\det(\mathbf{A})|$. But $\det(\mathbf{S})$ is the product of the singular values.

8.9.7. $|\alpha|\sigma$ are the singular values of $\alpha\mathbf{A}$.

8.9.9. $(\mathbf{QA})^H(\mathbf{QA}) = \mathbf{A}^H\mathbf{Q}^H\mathbf{Q}\mathbf{A} = \mathbf{A}^H\mathbf{A}$.

8.9.11. $\mathbf{Q}^H\mathbf{Q} = \mathbf{Q}^T\mathbf{Q} = \mathbf{I}$. Hence, the singular values of $\mathbf{Q}$ are all 1, and the singular vectors (right and left) may be chosen as $\{\mathbf{e}_1, \mathbf{e}_2, \ldots, \mathbf{e}_n\}$.

8.9.13. Suppose $\mathbf{W}^H\mathbf{A}\mathbf{W} = \mathbf{B}, \mathbf{B}^H\mathbf{B} = (\mathbf{W}^H\mathbf{A}^H\mathbf{W})(\mathbf{W}^H\mathbf{A}\mathbf{W}) = \mathbf{W}^H\mathbf{A}^H\mathbf{A}\mathbf{W}$. So $\mathbf{B}^H\mathbf{B}$ is unitarily similar to $\mathbf{A}^T\mathbf{A}$, and hence they have the same eigenvalues.

Section 8.10

PART 1

8.10.1. $\mathbf{U} = \mathbf{V} = \begin{bmatrix} ½ & 0 & 0 & \sqrt{3}/2 \\ ½ & 0 & \sqrt{6}/3 & -\sqrt{3}/6 \\ ½ & -\sqrt{2}/2 & -\sqrt{6}/6 & -\sqrt{3}/6 \\ ½ & \sqrt{2}/2 & -\sqrt{6}/6 & -\sqrt{3}/6 \end{bmatrix}, \quad \mathbf{S} = \begin{bmatrix} 3 & 0 & 0 & 0 \\ 0 & 1 & 0 & 0 \\ 0 & 0 & 1 & 0 \\ 0 & 0 & 0 & 1 \end{bmatrix}$

8.10.3. For any real symmetric matrix $\mathbf{A}$, there exists an orthogonal matrix $\mathbf{Q}$ such that $\mathbf{Q}^T\mathbf{A}\mathbf{Q} = \Lambda$, where $\Lambda = \operatorname{diag}(\lambda_1, \cdots, \lambda_r, 0, \cdots, 0)$ and λ_i is real. Hence, the SVD of $\mathbf{A}$ is given by $\mathbf{Q}^T\mathbf{A}\mathbf{Q} = \operatorname{diag}(|\lambda_1|, \cdots, |\lambda_r|, 0, \cdots, 0)$.

PART 2

8.10.5. $\mathbf{V}^H\mathbf{A}^{-1}\mathbf{U} = \mathbf{S}^{-1}$.

Section 8.11

PART 1

8.11.1. All the properties listed for the p-inverse follow from the identities

$$\mathbf{S}^-\mathbf{S} = \begin{bmatrix} \mathbf{I} & \mathbf{O} \\ \mathbf{O} & \mathbf{O} \end{bmatrix} \quad \text{and} \quad \mathbf{S}\mathbf{S}^- = \begin{bmatrix} \mathbf{I} & \mathbf{O} \\ \mathbf{O} & \mathbf{O} \end{bmatrix}$$

8.11.11. Use Example 8.11.4 with $\mathbf{u} = \mathbf{1}_m$ and $\mathbf{v} = \mathbf{1}_n$. Then $\mathbf{J}^-_{m\times m} = \mathbf{J}_{n\times m}/mn$.

8.11.13. If $\mathbf{A}$ is normal, so are $\mathbf{A}^k$ for each positive integer k, and hence, there exist unitary matrices $\mathbf{U}^H$ and $\mathbf{V}$ such that $\mathbf{U}^H\mathbf{A}^k\mathbf{U} = \Lambda^k$. By Example 8.11.3 $(\mathbf{U}^H\mathbf{A}^k\mathbf{U})^- = \mathbf{V}(\mathbf{A}^k)^-\mathbf{U} = (\Lambda^k)^- = (\Lambda^-)^k$ because Λ is a diagonal matrix. However $(\Lambda^-)^k = (\mathbf{U}^H\mathbf{A}^-\mathbf{V})^k = \mathbf{U}^H(\mathbf{A}^-)^{k-}\mathbf{V}$. Hence, $\mathbf{U}^H(\mathbf{A}^k)^-\mathbf{V} = \mathbf{U}^H(\mathbf{A}^-)^k\mathbf{V}$, which implies that $(\mathbf{A}^k)^- = (\mathbf{A}^-)^k$.

PART 2

8.11.17. By Eq. 8.11.4 $\mathbf{A}^- = \mathbf{V}\mathbf{S}^-\mathbf{U}^H$ where $\mathbf{A}, \mathbf{V}, \mathbf{S}^-$ and $\mathbf{U}$ are square matrices. Hence, $(\mathbf{A}^-)^T = (\mathbf{V}^H)^T\mathbf{S}^{-T}\mathbf{U}^T = (\mathbf{V}^T)^H\mathbf{S}^-(\mathbf{U}^T)$ since $\mathbf{S}^-$ is diagonal. However, $\mathbf{A} = (\mathbf{A}^-)^- = \mathbf{U}(\mathbf{S}^-)^-\mathbf{V}^H = \mathbf{U}\mathbf{S}\mathbf{V}^H$ by Example 8.11.3. Hence $\mathbf{A}^T = (\mathbf{V}^T)^H\mathbf{S}(\mathbf{U}^T)$, and therefore $(\mathbf{A}^T)^- = (\mathbf{U}^T)^H\mathbf{S}^-(\mathbf{U}^T) = (\mathbf{A}^-)^T$.

8.11.19. From $\mathbf{U}^H\mathbf{A}\mathbf{U} = \mathbf{B}$ it follows that $(\mathbf{U}^H\mathbf{A}\mathbf{U})^- = \mathbf{U}^H\mathbf{A}^-\mathbf{U} = \mathbf{B}^-$ by Example 8.11.3.

8.11.21. $\mathbf{A}^-\mathbf{A}(\mathbf{A}^-\mathbf{B}) = (\mathbf{A}^-\mathbf{A}\mathbf{A}^-)\mathbf{B} = \mathbf{A}^-\mathbf{B}$

CHAPTER 9

Section 9.2

PART 1

9.2.1. (*a*) The line segment joining the points (1,2) and (−1,0). (*b*) The triangle whose vertices are the points (1,2) (−1,0), and (1,−1). (*d*) The square whose vertices are the points (1,0) (−1,0) (0,−1), and (0,1).

9.2.3. The points above and on the line $y = 1$ to the left and on the line $y > 2x - 1$.

PART 2

9.2.5. If $\mathcal{S}$ is a vector space, $\mathbf{x} \in \mathcal{S}$ and $\mathbf{y} \in \mathcal{S}$ implies $\alpha\mathbf{x}+\beta\mathbf{y} \in \mathcal{S}$. Hence, $\alpha\mathbf{x}+\beta\mathbf{y} \in \mathcal{S}$ if $\alpha + \beta = 1$.

9.2.7. In the definition, $\mathbf{x} = \mathbf{y} \in \mathcal{S}$ implies $\alpha\mathbf{x} + \beta\mathbf{y} = (\alpha + \beta)\mathbf{x} = \mathbf{x} \in \mathcal{S}$.

Section 9.3

PART 1

9.3.1. Set $x_1 = x + 2$ and $x_2 = y + 1$. Then $x_1 + s_1 = 5$, $x_2 + s_2 = 2$, in nonnegative variables.

9.3.3. Define the slack s by $x + y - s = 1$. There are no constraints since y is unrestricted. For any nonnegative x and s, $x + y - s = 1$ determines y.

9.3.5. Define the slacks s_1 and s_2 by $x + y - s_1 = -2$, $x + y - s_2 = 2$. Then $s_1 + s_2 = 4$, in nonnegative variables. x and y are recovered from either $x + y - s_1 = -2$ or $x + y - s_2 = 2$.

9.3.7. Set $x_1 = x$. Then, in nonnegative variables, $-x_1 + y + z = 1$ and $-x_1 + y = 2$.

9.3.9. The inequalities $x \geq -1$ and $y \geq -1$ are subsumed in the nonnegative restrictions on x and y. Define the slack s_1 by $z + s_1 = 1$ and s_2 by $x + y + z + s_2 = 2$. Then these equations in nonnegative variables constitute the standard form.

PART 2

9.3.11. $\mathbf{x} \geq \mathbf{0}$

9.3.13. $[\mathbf{A} \quad -\mathbf{I}]\begin{bmatrix}\mathbf{x}\\ \mathbf{s}\end{bmatrix} = \mathbf{Ax} - \mathbf{Is} = \mathbf{b}, x \geq \mathbf{0}, \mathbf{s} \geq \mathbf{0}.$

9.3.15. $\mathbf{Ax} = \mathbf{b}, \mathbf{Dx} - \mathbf{Is} = \mathbf{d}$. So

$$\begin{bmatrix}\mathbf{O} & \mathbf{A}\\ \mathbf{D} & -\mathbf{I}\end{bmatrix}\begin{bmatrix}\mathbf{x}\\ \mathbf{s}\end{bmatrix} = \begin{bmatrix}\mathbf{b}\\ \mathbf{d}\end{bmatrix}$$

Section 9.4

PART 1

9.4.1. $\{(1,1), (3,-1)\}$ **9.4.3.** $\{(0,1)\}$ **9.4.5.** None.
9.4.7. $\{(0,-2,3)\}$ **9.4.9.** $\{(0,3), (3,0)\}$.

PART 2

9.4.11. Set $x_1 = -x$ and introduce slacks $s_1 \geq 0$ and $s \geq 0$. Eliminate y, which is unrestricted. This leaves $s_1 - s_2 = 4$, in nonnegative variables. Finally, for every $x \leq 0$ and $s_1 \geq 0$, $s_1 - s_2 = 4$ and $y = -4 + s_1 - x$.

9.4.13. In nonnegative variables, $x + y + s_1 = 3, -x - y - s = 1$.

9.4.15. The set of feasible solutions are the points on the line $y = -2x + 4$ in the first quadrant. The BFSs are (0,4) and (2,0).

Section 9.5

PART 1

9.5.1. $\mathbf{x} + \lambda\mathbf{a} = \begin{bmatrix}1\\1\\0\\1\\1\end{bmatrix} + \lambda\begin{bmatrix}-1\\0\\0\\0\\1\end{bmatrix}, -1 \leq \lambda \leq 1$ **9.5.3.** There are no **a**.

PART 2

9.5.7. (*a*) $\mathbf{x}_1$ in an interior point of $\mathcal{H}$. (*b*) $\mathbf{x}_3$ is on the boundary but not on a vertex of $\mathcal{H}$. (*c*) $\mathbf{x}_3$ is on a vertex of $\mathcal{H}$.

9.5.9.

$$\mathbf{x}(\lambda) = \begin{bmatrix}\tfrac{1}{2}\\2\\\tfrac{1}{2}\end{bmatrix} + \lambda\begin{bmatrix}1\\0\\-1\end{bmatrix} \geq 0$$

implies that $\frac{-1}{2} \leq \lambda \leq \frac{1}{2}$. Then

$$\mathbf{x}(\tfrac{1}{2}) = \begin{bmatrix}1\\2\\0\end{bmatrix}$$

and we find

$$\mathbf{x}(\lambda) = \begin{bmatrix} 1 \\ 2 \\ 0 \end{bmatrix} + \lambda \begin{bmatrix} 1 \\ -1 \\ 0 \end{bmatrix} \geq 0$$

Hence $-1 \leq \lambda \leq 2$. Then

$$\mathbf{x}(2) = \begin{bmatrix} 3 \\ 0 \\ 0 \end{bmatrix}$$

Section 9.6

PART 1

9.6.1. (*a*) The BFSs are $\mathbf{x}_k = 3\mathbf{e}_k$, for $k = 1, 2, 3$. So $\min z(\mathbf{x}) = 3$, and each BFS is optimal. No.

9.6.3. (*a*) The BFSs are $\mathbf{x}_k = 3\mathbf{e}_k$, for $k = 1, 2$. So $\min z(\mathbf{x}) = 3$, and each BFS is optimal. No.

9.6.5. There are two optimal solutions, both arising from Theorem 9.6.1. They follow from

$$\mathbf{x}_0(\lambda) = \begin{bmatrix} 2 \\ 1 \\ 1 \end{bmatrix} + \lambda \begin{bmatrix} 1 \\ -2 \\ 1 \end{bmatrix} \geq 0$$

Then $-1 \leq \lambda \leq \frac{1}{2}$. So

$$\mathbf{x}_0(-1) = \begin{bmatrix} 1 \\ 3 \\ 0 \end{bmatrix} \quad \text{and} \quad \mathbf{x}_0(\tfrac{1}{2}) = \begin{bmatrix} \frac{5}{2} \\ 0 \\ \frac{3}{2} \end{bmatrix}$$

and $\min(z(\mathbf{x}) = 4$.

PART 2

9.6.7. $z(\mathbf{x}_1 + \lambda\mathbf{a}) = z(\mathbf{x}_1) + \lambda z(\mathbf{a})$. But $\lambda z(\mathbf{a}) < 0$ for all $\lambda > 0$. Hence, $z(\mathbf{x}_1 + \lambda\mathbf{a}) \to -\infty$ as $\lambda \to \infty$.

Section 9.7

PART 1

9.7.1. (*a*)
$$\left[\begin{array}{ccccc|c} 1 & 0 & 0 & -\frac{1}{2} & 1 & 2 \\ 0 & 1 & 0 & \frac{1}{2} & 0 & 1 \\ 0 & 0 & 1 & \frac{1}{2} & 1 & 5 \\ \hline 0 & 0 & 0 & -3 & 0 & -17 \end{array}\right]$$

(*c*)
$$\left[\begin{array}{ccccc|c} 1 & 0 & -1 & -1 & 0 & -3 \\ 0 & 1 & 0 & \frac{1}{2} & 0 & 1 \\ 0 & 0 & 1 & \frac{1}{2} & 1 & 5 \\ \hline 0 & 0 & 0 & 0 & 0 & -17 \end{array}\right]$$

(e) $\left[\begin{array}{ccccc:c} 0 & 2 & 0 & 1 & 0 & 2 \\ 1 & 2 & -1 & 0 & 0 & -1 \\ 0 & -1 & 1 & 0 & 1 & 4 \\ \hdashline 0 & 0 & 0 & 0 & 0 & -17 \end{array}\right]$

9.7.3. $\left[\begin{array}{cccc:c} 2 & -1 & 1 & 0 & 1 \\ 0 & 1 & 0 & 1 & 2 \\ \hdashline 1 & 1 & 0 & 0 & 0 \end{array}\right]$ The variables are x, y, s_1, s_2.

PART 2

9.7.5. $b_i > 1$.

Section 9.8

PART 1

9.8.1. x_4 leaves. The tableau is canonical after the cost coefficients have been updated. No; $\overline{c_1} = -3$.

9.8.3. The tableau is canonical after the cost coefficients have been updated. No; $\overline{c}_2 = -3$.

9.8.5. If the basic variables are x_2, x_1, x_5, then column 4 exhibits the unboundedness criterion.

PART 2

9.8.7. $b_i = 0, b_i > 0$.

Section 9.9

PART 1

9.9.1. Introduce three slacks, and then eliminate the unrestricted variable y. The resulting SLP has the optimal solution $x = 1, y = 0$, and $z = -1$.

9.9.3. The problem is feasible for all $b \geq 9$. Set $x_i = 0, i \neq 4, x_4 = 3$.

9.9.5. Infeasible. The phase 1 problem has $\min w = 1$ when y enters the set of basic variables.

9.9.7. Infeasible. The phase 1 problem has $\min w = -1$ when the artificial variable exits the set of basic variables.

PART 2

9.9.9. For the given set of constraints, minimize $z = x + 2y$. Then $\min z = 1$. Hence, $1 \leq x + 2y$. Next, maximize $z = -x - 2y$. Then $\max z = 5/2$ and hence $-x - 2y \leq -5/2$. Thus, $x + 2y \geq 5/2$.

9.9.11. Suppose $\mathbf{A}_{*i}$ is a column with positive entries. Then if $x_j = 0$ for all $j \neq i$, $\mathbf{Ax} = \mathbf{A}_{*i}x_i \geq b$ can always be satisfied for $x_i \geq \max\{b_k/a_{ki}\}$, the maximum taken over all nonnegative b_k. If $b \leq 0$, then $x = 0$ suffices.

Section 9.10

PART 1

9.10.1. $\mathbf{x} + (\lambda) = \mathbf{x} + \lambda\mathbf{a} = \begin{bmatrix} 4 \\ 1 \\ 4 \\ 0 \\ 0 \end{bmatrix} + \lambda \begin{bmatrix} -1 \\ 1 \\ -2 \\ 5 \\ 0 \end{bmatrix}, 0 \leq \lambda \leq 2$. Then $\mathbf{x}(2) = \begin{bmatrix} 2 \\ 3 \\ 0 \\ 10 \\ 0 \end{bmatrix}$.

9.10.3. $T_1 \rightarrow T_5$. The optimal stopping condition is met, and $\min z = -1$.

9.10.5. $\mathbf{x}(\lambda) = \begin{bmatrix} 1 \\ 0 \end{bmatrix} + \lambda \begin{bmatrix} 2 \\ 1 \end{bmatrix}$. Hence, the line of feasible solutions is $x_1 = 1 + 2x_2$ for $x_1 \geq 1$ and $x_2 \geq 0$.

INDEX

D

E

F